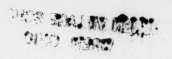

HOUSE DOCUMENT NUMBER 480

80TH CONGRESS FIRST SESSION

19  48

The Yearbook of Agriculture

Grass

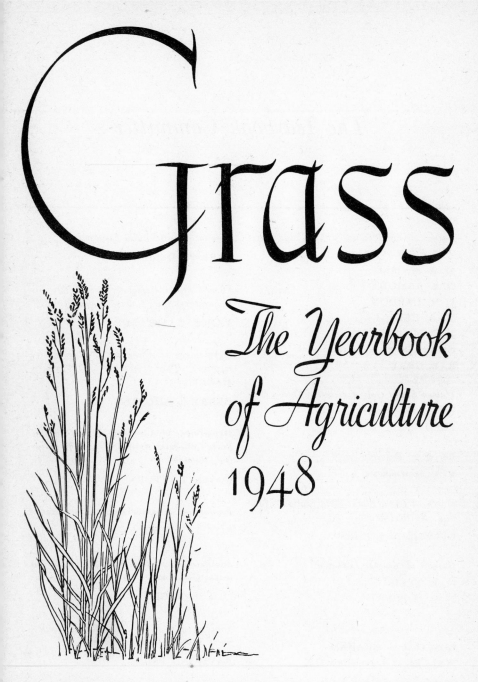

The Yearbook of Agriculture 1948

UNITED STATES DEPARTMENT OF AGRICULTURE

U. S. GOVERNMENT PRINTING OFFICE · · · WASHINGTON 1948

The Yearbook Committee

Bureau of Plant Industry, Soils, and Agricultural Engineering

M. A. McCALL
O. S. AAMODT
P. V. CARDON
M. A. HEIN
J. K. McCLARREN
CHARLES E. KELLOGG
R. B. GRAY

United States Golf Association Green Section

FRED V. GRAU

Bureau of Dairy Industry

R. E. HODGSON

Northern Great Plains Field Station, Mandan, North Dakota

GEORGE A. ROGLER

Bureau of Animal Industry

N. R. ELLIS
H. C. McPHEE

Soil Conservation Service

EDWARD H. GRAHAM
WALTER C. LOWDERMILK

Forest Service

W. R. CHAPLINE
WILLIAM A. DAYTON

Bureau of Agricultural Economics

CARL P. HEISIG

United States Regional Pasture Research Laboratory, State College, Pennsylvania

VANCE G. SPRAGUE

Department of Agronomy, College of Agriculture, The University of Wisconsin, Madison

HENRY L. AHLGREN

Department of Agronomy, North Carolina State College of Agriculture and Engineering, Raleigh

ROY L. LOVVORN

Production and Marketing Administration

ROY J. JORDRE

Southern Great Plains Field Station, Woodward, Oklahoma

D. A. SAVAGE

Southwestern Forest and Range Experiment Station, Tucson, Arizona

RAYMOND PRICE

Oregon Agricultural Experiment Station, Corvallis, Oregon

H. A. SCHOTH

ALFRED STEFFERUD, *Office of Information, Editor*

iv

Foreword

A happy sign in this troubled year is the conviction held by many people that the time is now and the chance is here to plan for a more secure agriculture in the United States.

In conferences and meetings in the past twelvemonth I have encountered this conviction and sensed its force as I have traveled the length and breadth of the country. I have encountered it, stronger than ever before, on Capitol Hill and in rural communities where men and women have gathered to consider present urgency and future uncertainty.

They apply different words to the goal they mean to reach. Some call it a balanced agriculture or permanence in farming. Some call it stability or continued abundance. Others think of it as converting agriculture from a wartime to a peacetime basis.

But whatever the words, they express a common idea—the goal of security. To the farmer, security means year-to-year and generation-to-generation assurance that he can use his land as it should be used, free from fear of boom or bust; that he will have a fair market for the products of his soil and toil; that he will get the amenities that he earns; that he can serve community and country.

And many of the people with whom I have talked look upon grassland as the foundation of security in agriculture. They believe in grass, and so do I, in the way we believe in the practice of conservation, or in good farming, or prosperity, or cooperation. For grass is all those things; it is not just a crop. Grassland agriculture is a good way to farm and to live, the best way I know of to use and improve soil, the very thing on which our life and civilization rest.

Through the foods that come from it, grass can give us better health. It is our alliance with nature. It is a tool against floods and a guardian of the water supplies of cities.

It is a source of strength as we face that time when we shall give less emphasis to commodities likely to produce surpluses and instead direct more attention to practices designed to sustain the productivity of our soils. Indeed, because we now produce a great deal more than before the war, we are to that extent placing an extraordinary burden on the land. Our land resources will be better used when we can turn more to grass and livestock farming.

Grass has other important values, as told in this Yearbook. I pass over them now, except one which is seldom mentioned but which I think of often as I travel and see the beauty of our country. I am particularly conscious of it now, as I write these lines in May of 1948, when spring brings out again her mantle of green and I am preparing to leave the Secretaryship of Agriculture.

That use is the use of beauty itself.

Grass can make beautiful the hillsides, schoolyards, roadsides, farmsteads; in doing so it brings greater utility and efficiency.

Beauty also brings serenity, and serenity is a quality we and the troubled world need.

CLINTON P. ANDERSON.

The Editor's Preface

The men and the women who wrote this book are agronomists, economists, farmers, teachers, military men, students of nutrition, husbandmen, foresters, entomologists, agrostologists, engineers, workers in conservation, and ecologists. They are experts in many different disciplines. They represent all sections of the United States and many points of view. They plead no selfish case, therefore, when they agree that grassland agriculture is the most important single element in American farming today.

This book is the first word, so to speak, on the subject of grass, legumes, and the associated herbage, for, regardless of its importance, grass has been a comparatively neglected matter-of-course. We hope it will not be the last word, because there is still much to be learned about subjects so diverse and plants so versatile.

It has many articles on how farmers, ranchers, poultrymen, livestock raisers, dairymen, and the conservationists can grow and use grasses and legumes. And because those plants are so basic to farming and living, discussions of them must include a great deal about soils, geography, agricultural history, economics and marketing, genetics, public programs, and natural resources.

It is therefore a book for city people as well as for farmers. It contains information on grass for lawns, parks, roadsides, playgrounds, and so on, but more than that, it is about a subject of concern to everyone, wherever he lives or whatever he does for a living.

We hope the reader will read the whole book, but we have organized it so that if need be he can use only the chapters that pertain to his problems and still get an idea of the kinds, values, and adaptation of grass.

The four parts progress from the general aspects of the subject to the more specific.

First is an examination of grass as it applies to people anywhere. The emphasis is on livestock and soils and conservation.

Next is a study of grass as it is used in the regions of the United States, the emphasis being on varieties and uses.

The third part is a handbook that considers the nature and identification of the most important and most useful grasses, legumes, and associated plants.

Finally comes a section of tables, charts, lists of plant names, recommendations of seedings and mixtures, references to further reading, and the index. The material has been put together there for economy and con-

vii

venience; for many farmers and students the last part will be the most valuable of the entire volume.

Grateful acknowledgment is made of the help given by the Division of Typography and Design of the Government Printing Office on the format of the book.

Louis H. Anderson, of the Office of Information, helped in many mechanical details involved in the transferring of hundreds of thousands of typewritten words into type.

Miss Leta Hughey, of Forest Service, and Mrs. Agnes Chase, of the Smithsonian Institution, made a number of the drawings of plants. Joseph H. Stevenson and Wynne Johnson, of the Office of Information, drew the charts and maps.

Most of the photographs in color are by Herrin F. Culver and Hermann Postlethwaite, of Soil Conservation Service. Others are by Bob Branstead, John W. Busch, A. F. Hollowell, Richard Mawhinney, Anne Ware, Nicholas Webster, and Dale L. Swartz, of Soil Conservation Service; Wilfred J. Mead and Otis H. Greeson, of the Bureau of Plant Industry, Soils, and Agricultural Engineering; Leland J. Prater, of Forest Service, and Irene H. Stuckey, of the Rhode Island Agricultural Experiment Station. Many of the black-and-white photographs were taken by Wilfred J. Mead and Otis H. Greeson.

The photographs in color are modern counterparts of colored illustrations used in Yearbooks fifty years and more ago. They are used to show aspects of the subject that cannot be done in black-and-white pictures and to underscore again that our land and its beauty and capacity are something to be cherished and cared for.

We plan to devote the 1949 Yearbook of Agriculture to an allied and equally important subject—trees and forests.

On the Yearbook staff are Margaret V. Loyd, assistant to the editor, and Berenice A. Zander.

ALFRED STEFFERUD.

Contents

Grass in the Nation's Life

A PERMANENT AGRICULTURE

SOIL · GRASS · CONSERVATION

FORAGE FOR LIVESTOCK

Grass in the Ten Regions

THE NORTHERN GREAT PLAINS

THE SOUTHERN GREAT PLAINS

THE MOUNTAIN REGION

THE PACIFIC COAST STATES

Grass in a Plant Round-up

Grass in Charts and Tables

Grass in the Nation's Life

And I will send grass in thy fields for thy cattle that thou mayest eat and be full.

DEUTERONOMY 11:15

A Permanent Agriculture

OUR AIM: AN INTRODUCTION

P. V. CARDON

OUR GOAL is permanency in agriculture — an agriculture that is stable and secure for farm and farmer, consistent in prices and earnings; an agriculture that can satisfy indefinitely all our needs of food, fiber, and shelter in keeping with the living standards we set. Everybody has a stake in a permanent agriculture.

It is attainable—but only through the wise application of our expanding knowledge about the use of land, capital, and labor in production and distribution. It does not deny full use of the land to any generation of owners. It does require that each generation, in its turn, observe land-use practices that insure sustained production.

Perhaps no farmer has yet developed a permanent agriculture even within his own fences. It is still a goal to be achieved by communities, districts, or regions. No nation has it; no group of nations has done more than to recognize hazily the need for permanency in agriculture and to consider general ways of cooperating to meet that need.

Yet permanency in agriculture is a goal to be sought always by all people, everywhere. It was never more clearly recognized than during the past sad decade. To lose sight of it is to invite the specter of tragic want—the end product of soil depletion.

So, in the wake of war and in the glow of our unprecedented production, this country looks to the future and considers again the land and its management—this time, as never before, in terms of grass. For around grass, farmers can organize general crop production so as to promote efficient practices that lead to permanency in agriculture.

Grass, as a family (*Gramineae*), includes the great food crops, wheat, rice, corn, sugarcane, sorghum, millet, barley, oats. It also includes the many species of sod crops which provide the cured forage or pasturage for all types of farm animals.

But grass in the concept of grassland agriculture is not limited to the grasses; it embraces also their common associates of the legume family (*Leguminosae*)—the clovers, lespedezas, alfalfas, and many others.

Grassland agriculture is a commonly accepted term in most European countries and is coming into wider use elsewhere. Grassland conferences have been conducted the past quarter century in different countries of Europe, and several met in the United States in 1939 and 1940. Renewed interest in such conferences here and abroad followed the end of the Second World War. There have been four International Grassland Congresses. The fifth is scheduled for 1949 in Holland.

A decade ago I noted America's trend toward a grassland agriculture. The war modified that trend to accommodate emergency crop requirements, but its general direction continued. Today it is even more pronounced because experience has shown that good grass can enhance efficiency of production at the same time that it tends to insure permanency in agriculture. Recognition of the intrinsic value of grass itself—of grass as a farm crop it pays to grow—has elevated it to a plane that more and more people have come to appreciate.

Grassland agriculture does not mean necessarily extensive agriculture. In some areas it is very intensive—as much so as vegetable farming.

Inseparably linked to livestock production, grassland agriculture under good management may equal or increase the production of digestible nutrients to the acre and reduce materially the labor needed to grow and utilize a given amount of those nutrients. It may also lower significantly the cost of supplying the protein—often bought as concentrates—required for high levels of animal nutrition. Grassland agriculture envisions the use of grasses and legumes alone or in combination or rotation according to systems of management best suited to land use under various environments, with ample provision for root crops, leafy vegetables, fruits, fibers, forests, and specialty crops as needed.

Thus grassland agriculture differs from other types of farming chiefly with respect to the emphasis placed on grasses and legumes. They are dominant in a flexible pattern designed to conserve the land and its productivity but at the same time keep it adjustable to emergency needs.

To be fully effective, grassland agriculture, like agriculture by any other name, is subject to modification by the sweeping influence of social and economic change. It cannot deny or ignore the effects of varying systems of land tenure, the requirements of sound credit, the impact of shifts in national policies, or the political trends resulting from these and other factors that affect the lives of people on the land. But conceived and advanced as nearly as possible in harmony with known physical and biological principles, grassland agriculture better than any other type of agriculture will continue in the face of economic and social change to conserve the land and insure a food supply of the desired quantity, variety, and quality.

Soil and climate in the various sections determine the intensity of grassland farming that is most likely to prove satisfactory, and even they must be considered in terms of more specific physical, biological, and managerial factors that govern species, cultural and grazing practices, and the place of grass in the cropping system. Thus grass in Aroostook County in Maine may be of different composition and managed differently from grass in Pointe Coupee Parish in Louisiana. So also grassland agriculture in Tama County in Iowa may differ widely from that of Woodward County in Oklahoma, and both may differ from that of Cache County in Utah, Snohomish County in Washington, or the Salt River Valley of Arizona.

But regardless of variation in the degree of intensity of the grassland farming suited to different regions, underlying principles to be observed are much the same everywhere. Those principles relate to the productive capacity of the soil—the factors that conduce to its deterioration on the one hand, or its improvement on the other—and to the control of factors that soil management can exert.

What the soil will produce or may be made to produce this year or next is of immediate importance in terms of current food supply and demand. How the soil may be used to insure sustained production is of continuing importance to national welfare. How to use his soil for his immediate purposes and yet keep it usable indefinitely is the user's responsibility and trust.

Knowledge of his soil and of what

he can do with it prompts the farmer to design or adopt management practices that make for high yield at low unit cost, with minimum reduction in the productive capacity of the soil which is his heritage.

Productive capacity, defined by R. M. Salter and his associates in Ohio as "the inherent potential capacity of a soil to produce," depends upon infixed characteristics that can be modified only slowly; major changes may require several years. But productive capacity is responsive to management. A high productive capacity with good management approximates the ultimate, but even high productive capacity responds poorly to poor management. And a low productive capacity can be made to respond surprisingly to good management.

The farmer makes his arable soil from the natural soil. His cultural practices may increase its productivity or decrease it. Large areas of soil in western Europe and the eastern part of the United States, for example, are more productive now after years of careful mixed farming than the original acid, leached soils under the natural forest. On the other hand, many soils are poorer by use, especially the dark-colored soils developed under natural grassland.

A primary factor is the reduction of organic matter and nutrient elements. Organic matter is reduced through microbiological activities, which are stimulated by the aeration incident to cultivation. For that reason, organic matter in soil under intertilled crops is lost at a higher rate than in the same soil under crops requiring less tillage.

Contained in the soil organic matter is nitrogen, an important nutrient element. A loss of nitrogen, therefore, accompanies the destruction of organic matter. An example: The loss of nitrogen in various cropped soils in Ohio in 50 to 75 years averaged 35 percent of the nitrogen present in comparable virgin soils.

Along with the decline in organic matter and nitrogen, tilth declines.

Loss of tilth (which is most apparent on heavier soils, but is present also in lighter soils) is principally a physical phenomenon involving the proportion of solid material to pore space in a given volume of soil. Since pore space may be filled with air or water or occupied by roots, a fair proportion of it is essential to crop growth in any soil. The proportion of pore space declines with the loss of organic matter, and there is a larger proportion of solid matter, so that the soil becomes heavier and tighter and—in consequence—less productive and more susceptible to erosion.

Since deterioration of productive capacity in soil accompanies loss of organic matter and nutrient elements, it follows that deterioration might be halted and the soil-improvement forces stimulated through the addition of organic matter and nutrient elements to the soil.

The addition of the organic matter takes place to some extent with incorporation of roots and crop residues into the soil. This is true even with intertilled crops but to a lesser extent than with sod crops. The application of barnyard manure and the plowing under of green-manure crops are ways of supplementing organic matter in roots and crop residues.

The addition of organic matter restores nutrient elements in some measure to the soil but seldom in sufficient quantities to retain productive capacity. Even the nitrogen in organic matter usually must be supplemented, as is the case with phosphorus, potash, and other mineral elements—hence the importance of adding fertilizers.

Lime also is important. Its value in correcting acidity is reflected in larger crops or in making possible the production of a wider selection of crops. Larger and more varied crops provide more residues for return to the soil.

Fortunately, factors of soil improvement are better understood today than ever before, and they will be still better understood as science continues to advance. An understanding of them enables farmers to remain on the land and plan hopefully for permanency—instead of moving, like the old tribesmen, to other land when the old is worn out. The farmer of today can, in fact, eat his cake and have it, too. He can offset, and on some soils more than offset, factors of soil deterioration by factors of improvement, and make the most of all of them. Some of the factors of deterioration are beneficial, if utilized—microbiological activity in breaking down the organic matter, for example. The aim is not to stop such activity but to take advantage of it.

To accomplish the balance between these forces, the farmer has many aids and practices: Crop rotation, barnyard manure, green-manure crops, fertilizers, lime, contouring, strip cropping, and other devices. And for inclusion with all of these—as a part of them, in fact—he has grass.

Crop rotation, he knows, entails practices that tend to utilize activities destructive of organic matter, to take advantage of the presence in the soil of the microbiological life involved, to supply additional organic matter to replace what is destroyed, and, by the varying root actions of different crops in the rotation, to preserve tilth and curb erosion.

The effectiveness of the rotation in these respects is increased by supplemental practices: The addition at one or another place in the rotation of barnyard manure, green manure, nitrogenous or mineral fertilizers, and lime. Where the land is sloping, contouring may be advisable, or strip cropping, or terracing—each of which may be accomplished to enhance the value of the other practices. And, to repeat, all these practices are most effective when applied with grass, including deeply rooted legumes.

Take grass in the rotation—grass-legume mixtures or legumes alone. There grass becomes a farm crop—a crop with a lofty purpose and a high value. More than any other crop, it provides organic matter for return to the soil and, being a sod crop, exerts

on the soil none of the adverse influences of intertilled crops. It harbors and nurtures beneficial organisms, as nitrogen-fixing bacteria on various legumes; its innumerable roots pervade the soil and aid in preserving its tilth. Grass is green manure, or it is forage which comes back to the land as barnyard manure. Grass responds productively to fertilizers, thereby providing organic matter and nitrogen in greater abundance. Lime makes possible better legumes, which in turn make better forage and, in the long run, better land.

On sloping lands, for controlling soil erosion, grass is indispensable. Besides all its values in the cropping system, it has the unique value of simplifying the maintenance of contours, terraces, and watercourses.

Grass is important in uses other than those common to the farm—important for the same reason, namely, the preservation of balance in the productive capacity of the land.

There is the broad use of grass in the protection of watersheds, for instance, as insurance against destructive floods. On watersheds which mostly are rough and wooded, grass holds the soil in place, and slows the washing runoff of rain and melted snow. The tendency to deterioration is present on the watershed as on all other lands, although normally it is not so pronounced. Under good grass the tendency is minimized; but where grass is abused or destroyed the tendency is accelerated and the difficulty of applying counter practices is greatly increased.

The same may be said of less rugged lands, as in the Great Plains, where in certain areas destruction of the natural grass cover has subjected land to excessive wind erosion and dust storms.

To balance the forces that tend to lower the productive capacity of still other land not in farm use, highway engineers pay increasing attention to soil types and practices that help maintain suitable grass covers on highway shoulders and the slopes of cuts and fills. Railroad construction engineers and maintenance-of-way crews seek grass covers for similar purposes. The high value of grass as a covering for airfields has become generally recognized. The grass in parks and cemeteries, on ball fields and other recreational grounds has, besides an esthetic value, much the same soil-saving purpose as grass on the farm.

To be most successful, grassland agriculture looks not only to the uses and purposes we have been considering, but to improving grass and using it to still better advantage—through breeding and the use of improved species, alone or in seeding mixtures; cultural practices, including amending the soil to promote herbage growth best suited to its specific purpose; grazing practices to keep the desired species in good vigor; and the adoption of better harvesting and storage techniques.

We need no longer speculate about such attainments. Some farmers in almost every county today are producing better grass by employing just such methods and modifying them to suit their own situations of climate, soil, and farm practice.

But many farmers are not producing as good grass as they could, and more educational work is required to bring about widespread application of grass-improvement practices.

Of equal importance is the development of a more general understanding of the superior nutritional value of good grass and of ways in which this value can be preserved for use in livestock feeding.

Thus far I have discussed grassland agriculture as if it were a simple remedy for land-management problems generally. But grassland agriculture is not simple. On the contrary, it is so complex as to command a high type of managerial ability if it is to prove successful in any given situation. The grassland farmer is required not only to decide upon the place grass is to have in his cropping system; he has to manage grass in relation to other crops and to livestock. Much information drawn from experience and experiment is available to him, but not

enough. More research is needed to develop understanding of the basic problems he encounters and more study of local adaptation of principles and their incorporation in farm practice.

This is true even on the broad sweep of grassland that is the great western ranges, and on watersheds generally. It is true in even greater degree as the intensity of farming increases.

But the complexities of grassland agriculture are surmountable and need not impede the more general spread of grassland agriculture in this country. Many farmers have made decisions relative to grassland agriculture and are far advanced in its practice. Moreover, experience in other countries, including western Europe, Great Britain, New Zealand, and Australia, points to the feasibility of grassland farming under such a wide variety of conditions that its feasibility in appropriate form in all parts of the United States seems to be a fact.

And it is a fact that everyone has a stake in this goal of permanency.

THE AUTHOR««   *P. V. Cardon,* *who is now special assistant to the* *Chief of the Bureau of Plant Industry,* *Soils, and Agricultural Engineering,* *has been engaged in agricultural re-* *search since 1910. His work has in-* *cluded investigations of dry farming* *and irrigation in the Intermountain* *and Pacific Coast States, studies of cot-* *ton throughout the South, and the* *directorship of the Utah Agricultural* *Experiment Station. As head of the* *Division of Forage Crops and Diseases* *in the Department, beginning in 1935,* *he organized an enlarged grass breed-* *ing and improvement program. In* *1937 he was chairman of the United* *States delegation to the Fourth Inter-* *national Grassland Congress in Great* *Britain, and studied grassland practice* *in many of the European countries. In* *1945 he became Administrator of the* *Agricultural Research Administration;* *for reasons of health, he transferred* *back to the Bureau where he began* *his career.*

IN PRAISE OF BLUE GRASS

JOHN JAMES INGALLS (1833–1900)

JOHN JAMES INGALLS *was Senator from Kansas from 1873 to 1891. An address of his, printed in the* Kansas Magazine *in 1872 and here reprinted in part because copies of it are hard to get, contains a passage that is quoted often. He was an eloquent man but not a scientist.*

ATTRACTED by the bland softness of an afternoon in my primeval winter in Kansas, I rode southward through the dense forest that then covered the bluffs of the North Fork of Wildcat. The ground was sodden with the ooze of melting snow. The dripping trees were as motionless as granite. The last year's leaves, tenacious lingerers, loath to leave the scene of their brief bravery, adhered to the gray boughs like fragile bronze. There were no visible indications of life, but the broad, wintry landscape was flooded with that indescribable splendor that never was on sea or shore—a purple and silken softness, that half veiled, half disclosed the alien horizon, the vast curves of the remote river, the transient architecture of the clouds, and filled the responsive soul with a vague tumult of emotions, pensive and pathetic, in which regret and hope contended for the mastery. The dead and silent globe, with all its hidden kingdoms, seemed swimming like a bubble, suspended in an ethereal solution of amethyst and silver, compounded of the exhaling whiteness of the snow, the descending glory of the sky. A tropical atmosphere brooded upon an arctic scene, creating the strange spectacle of summer in winter, June in January, peculiar to Kansas, which unseen cannot be imagined, but once seen can never be forgotten. A sudden descent into the sheltered valley revealed an unexpected crescent of dazzling verdure, glittering like a meadow in early spring, unreal as

an incantation, surprising as the sea to the soldiers of Xenophon as they stood upon the shore and shouted "Thalatta!" It was BLUE GRASS, unknown in Eden, the final triumph of nature, reserved to compensate her favorite offspring in the new Paradise of Kansas for the loss of the old upon the banks of the Tigris and Euphrates.

Next in importance to the divine profusion of water, light, and air, those three great physical facts which render existence possible, may be reckoned the universal beneficence of grass. Exaggerated by tropical heats and vapors to the gigantic cane congested with its saccharine secretion, or dwarfed by polar rigors to the fibrous hair of northern solitudes, embracing between these extremes the maize with its resolute pennons, the rice plant of southern swamps, the wheat, rye, barley, oats, and other cereals, no less than the humbler verdure of hill-side, pasture, and prairie in the temperate zone, grass is the most widely distributed of all vegetable beings, and is at once the type of our life and the emblem of our mortality. Lying in the sunshine among the buttercups and dandelions of May, scarcely higher in intelligence than the minute tenants of that mimic wilderness, our earliest recollections are of grass; and when the fitful fever is ended, and the foolish wrangle of the market and forum is closed, grass heals over the scar which our descent into the bosom of the earth has made, and the carpet of the infant becomes the blanket of the dead.

As he reflected upon the brevity of human life, grass has been the favorite symbol of the moralist, the chosen theme of the philosopher. "All flesh is grass," said the prophet; "My days are as the grass," sighed the troubled patriarch; and the pensive Nebuchadnezar, in his penitential mood, exceeded even these, and, as the sacred historian informs us, did eat grass like an ox.

Grass is the forgiveness of nature— her constant benediction. Fields trampled with battle, saturated with blood, torn with the ruts of cannon, grow green again with grass, and carnage is forgotten. Streets abandoned by traffic become grass-grown like rural lanes, and are obliterated. Forests decay, harvests perish, flowers vanish, but grass is immortal. Beleaguered by the sullen hosts of winter, it withdraws into the impregnable fortress of its subterranean vitality, and emerges upon the first solicitation of spring. Sown by the winds, by wandering birds, propagated by the subtle horticulture of the elements which are its ministers and servants, it softens the rude outline of the world. Its tenacious fibres hold the earth in its place, and prevent its soluble components from washing into the wasting sea. It invades the solitude of deserts, climbs the inaccessible slopes and forbidding pinnacles of mountains, modifies climates, and determines the history, character, and destiny of nations. Unobstrusive and patient, it has immortal vigor and aggression. Banished from the thoroughfare and the field, it bides its time to return, and when vigilance is relaxed, or the dynasty has perished, it silently resumes the throne from which it has been expelled, but which it never abdicates. It bears no blazonry or bloom to charm the senses with fragrance or splendor, but its homely hue is more enchanting than the lily or the rose. It yields no fruit in earth or air, and yet should its harvest fail for a single year, famine would depopulate the world.

One grass differs from another grass in glory. One is vulgar and another patrician. There are grades in its vegetable nobility. Some varieties are useful. Some are beautiful. Others combine utility and ornament. The sour, reedy herbage of swamps is baseborn. Timothy is a valuable servant. Redtop and clover are a degree higher in the social scale. But the king of them all, with genuine blood royal, is BLUE GRASS. Why it is called blue, save that it is most vividly and intensely green, is inexplicable, but had its unknown priest baptized it with all the hues of the prism, he would not have changed its hereditary title to imperial superiority over all its humbler kin.

Taine, in his incomparable History of English Literature, has well said that the body of man in every country is deeply rooted in the soil of nature. He might properly have declared that men were wholly rooted in the soil, and that the character of nations, like that of forests, tubers, and grains, is entirely determined by the climate and soil in which they germinate. Dogmas grow like potatoes. Creeds and carrots, catechisms and cabbages, tenets and turnips, religions and rutabagas, governments and grasses, all depend upon the dew point and the thermal range. Give the philosopher a handful of soil, the mean annual temperature and rainfall, and his analysis would enable him to predict with absolute certainty the characteristics of the nation.

Calvinism transplanted to the plains of the Ganges would perish of inanition. Webster is as much an indigenous product of New England as its granite and its pines. Napoleon was possible only in France; Cromwell in England; Christ, and the splendid invention of immortality, alone in Palestine. Moral causes and qualities exert influences far beyond their nativity, and ideas are transplanted and exported to meet the temporary requirements of the tastes or necessities of man; as we see exotic palms in the conservatories of Chatsworth, russet apples at Surinam, and oranges in Atchison. But there is no growth: nothing but change of location. The phenomena of politics exhibit the operations of the same law. . . .

The direct agency upon which all these conditions depend, and through which these forces operate, is food. Temperature, humidity, soil, sunlight, electricity, vital force, express themselves primarily in vegetable existence that furnishes the basis of that animal life which yields sustenance to the human race. What a man, a community, a nation can do, think, suffer, imagine or achieve depends upon what it eats.

*   *   *

The primary form of food is grass. Grass feeds the ox: the ox nourishes man: man dies and goes to grass again; and so the tide of life, with everlasting repetition, in continuous circles, moves endlessly on and upward, and in more senses than one, all flesh is grass. But all flesh is not bluegrass. If it were, the devil's occupation would be gone.

THE MEEK THAT INHERIT THE EARTH

AGNES CHASE

OF ALL PLANTS the grasses are the most important to man. All our breadstuffs—corn, wheat, oats, rye, barley—and rice and sugarcane are grasses. Bamboos are grasses, and so are the Kentucky bluegrass and creeping bent of our lawns, the timothy and redtop of our meadows.

If such different-looking plants as bamboo, corn, and timothy are all grasses, what is it that characterizes a grass? It is the structure of the plant.

All grasses have stems with solid joints and two-ranked leaves, one at each joint. The leaves consist of two parts, the sheath, which fits around the stem like a split tube, and the blade, which commonly is long and narrow. No other plant family has just this structure. Clover and alfalfa, built on a very different plan, are not grasses. The seed heads of grasses are still more distinctive. The minute flowers are borne on tiny branchlets, often several crowded together, always two-ranked, like the leaves.

The grasses specialize in simplification; only rarely do they have non-essentials.

Being wind-pollinated, their flowers need no gay colors, no fragrance, no honey to attract insects. The flower consists of a single pistil with one ovule, two styles, each with a feathery stigma, and three (rarely one or six) stamens. Only three, or two, delicate little scales (lodicules) remain of the floral envelope, the calyx and corolla, of other flowers. These minute flowers are borne singly or two to many together in spikelets, which are really little flowering branches. The hypothetical flower-bearing branchlet is never elongated, as shown in figure 3 for the sake of comparison. The palea is immediately above the lemma, and the flower immediately above the palea. The axis of the spikelet (rachilla) is jointed as is the culm of a grass, and the lemmas (specialized leaves reduced to a blade-like sheath) are two-ranked as are the leaves.

The flowers have to do with perpetuating the species. Most grasses flower every year. But some perennials, which spread by specialized underground stems (rhizomes or rootstocks), may cover extensive areas, especially in salt or brackish marshes, without flowering regularly; bamboos flower mostly at intervals of a few to many years.

The root, stem, and leaves constitute the vegetative part of the plant, and are concerned with the life of the individual plant.

In grasses the vegetative parts are more uniform and characteristic than in most other families. If one has the stem and leaves of a plant, he can decide readily whether or not it is a grass. The only plants that may reasonably be mistaken for grasses are the sedges—the culms are not jointed and are commonly three-sided, and the leaves are always three-ranked.

In grasses, specialization takes place mostly in the spikelet. By its vegetative characters a given plant is shown to be a grass, but it is the spikelets and their arrangement which indicate the kind

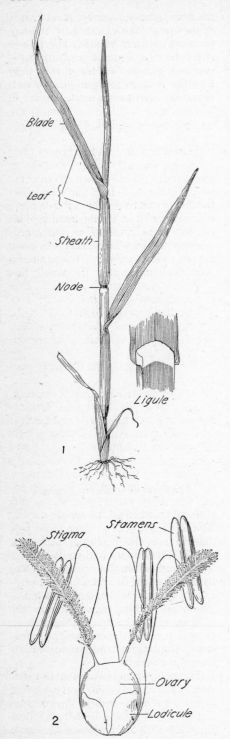

Blade

Leaf

Sheath

Node

Ligule

1

Stigma

Stamens

Ovary

Lodicule

2

of grass it is. The spikelet of cheat or chess (figure 5) is shown as seen naturally, the two glumes at the base, the florets (lemma, palea, and enclosed flower together) borne on opposite sides of the jointed rachilla, and the flower concealed. The palea with two nerves, its back to the rachilla, subtends and usually surrounds the flower. The glumes bear no flowers and are without paleas. This simple fundamental floral structure is subject to all manner of modification, but every organ found in the most highly specialized spikelet is to be interpreted as an elaboration or reduction of some part of this structure. The floret is the unit of the spikelet; the spikelet is the unit of the inflorescence.

The spikelets of wheat (figure 6) are sessile, that is, borne directly (without pedicel) on opposite sides of a stout axis, being placed flatwise against it; those of Italian ryegrass (figure 7) are borne in like manner but are placed edgewise to the axis.

In wild oats (figure 8), the glumes are enlarged and the fertile florets are but two, with an additional sterile one. The lemmas bear a stout twisted bristle (awn) from the back near the base. In timothy (figure 9), the spikelet has but one floret, which is enclosed in a pair of rigid-pointed glumes. In bluejoint (figure 10), the one floret is surrounded by long silky hairs at the base and the lemma bears a slender awn from the back, and a segment of the rachilla is produced beyond the base of the palea, suggesting that this spikelet is derived from a form with more than one floret. In the needlegrasses, the lemma bears a stout twisted awn from the summit (figure 11), and in three-awn grasses the awn is divided into three branches (figure 12).

In all grasses mentioned so far the structure is simple and all florets in a spikelet are alike. In some groups single spikelets may contain two very different kinds of florets, at least one perfect (that is, enclosing a flower having

[Opposite: The parts of a young shoot; (2) The flower of a grass plant.]

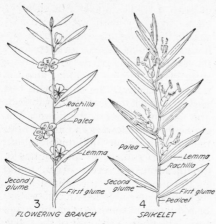

Diagram of leafy flowering branch, the flowers and bracts arranged as are those in grasses. Figure 4: Diagram of grass spikelets for comparison.

falograss is dominant over vast areas of the Great Plains from the Canadian border to central Mexico. The foliage cures on the ground and furnishes yearlong grazing. Its tough sod, held together by interlacing stolons, or runners, was used by the early settlers in making their sod houses. There were no dust bowls while buffalograss held the soil.

The millets and their relatives form a group characterized by spikelets which fall entire and which are dorsally compressed. They have one perfect floret and below this a sterile floret represented by a sterile lemma. This sterile lemma and the second glume are similar; in some earlier works on grasses these have been referred to as a pair of glumes, and the small first

stamens and pistil, and perfecting a grain) and one or more reduced sterile florets. The grama grasses (*Bouteloua*) have spikelets of this kind (figure 13). In this and allied genera the spikelets are borne in spikes; that is, sessile, as in wheat (figure 6), but all on one side of the rachis, not on opposite sides as in wheat. (The axis of a single spike or of a branching panicle is termed *axis;* that of a secondary spike or raceme is termed *rachis.*)

In grama grasses, of which there are 17 very valuable forage grasses in this country, the lemmas of the sterile florets are greatly altered (figure 13, *C, D*). The fertile and sterile florets fall together, the sterile with their long hairs and awns serving to disperse the seed. Bermuda-grass, goosegrass, the cordgrasses, and Rhodesgrass are familiar examples of this group.

The most curious is buffalograss, in which the male (staminate) and female (pistillate) spikelets are usually borne on separate plants and are so different in appearance as to suggest no relationship (figure 14). The hardened second glumes, grown together at their bases on a short, hardened rachis, form little hard white heads which are borne near the ground, much overtopped by the leaves. Buf-

The floret of needlegrass (*Stipa*).

glume was called an "accessory valve." The fertile floret is hardened and permanently encloses the grain which germinates within it and sends its rootlet through a thin place in the back of the lemma and its shoot out the summit between the lemma and palea. These are shown (figure 15) in the spikelet of broomcorn millet. Witchgrass, a weed of the cornfields, switchgrass, Guineagrass, and many others have this structure.

The genus *Panicum,* with 160 species, is the largest one in the United States. In true millets, introduced from the Old World, and their native allies, the spikelets are much like those

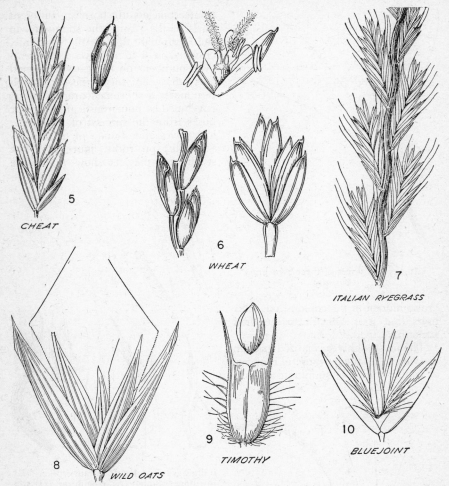

5 CHEAT

6 WHEAT

7 ITALIAN RYEGRASS

8 WILD OATS

9 TIMOTHY

10 BLUEJOINT

Spikelet of cheat; floret showing palea and rachilla segment. Figure 6: Spikelet of wheat with segment of axis; three segments of spike, showing arrangement of spikelets, flat against the axis; spikelet open.   7: Part of spike of Italian ryegrass, showing arrangement of spikelets, edge to the rachis. 8: Spikelet of wild oats. 9: Spikelet of timothy, floret above.   10: Glumes and floret of bluejoint.

of *Panicum* but are surrounded by bristles, which are sterile, reduced branches of a contracted panicle. A further specialization of sterile branches is seen in the sandbur. Here the bristles grow together into a sort of spiny cup which contains from 2 to 5 spikelets (figure 16). The grains of the sandbur germinate within the spikelets and send out rootlets and shoots between the spines.

In the *Sorghum* tribe the spikelets fall entire as in *Panicum* and its group, but here it is the glumes which are hardened and enclose the entire floret. The spikelets are in pairs at each node of a jointed rachis—one is sessile and perfect and the other pedicellate and usually sterile; the pair fall together with the rachis-segment and pedicel. Bluestem of the prairies (figure 17) and broomsedge of the Southeast show this arrangement. In sorghum the racemes of spikelets are reduced to a few segments and are borne in a panicle.

In sugarcane and plumegrass both spikelets of the pair are perfect. They

Glumes and floret of three-awn grass (Aristida).

tillate spikelets are borne in different parts of the plant—the staminate, in the terminal tassel; the pistillate, crowded in 8 to 16 rows (always an even number) on a greatly thickened axis (the cob), forms the ear, which terminates a shortened branch and is enveloped by numerous leafy bracts or husks from the summit of which the long styles and stigmas of the flowers (the silk) protrude (figure 18). The staminate spikelets show much the

are so hidden in the copious long silky hairs that it is difficult to see their structure.

The most highly specialized grass in the world and the most useful is maize, or Indian corn. The staminate and pis-

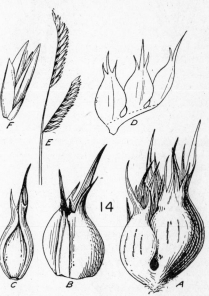

Buffalograss: (*A*), Pistillate spike; (*B*), pistillate spikelet; (*C*), ripe floret; (*D*), diagram of pistillate spike; (*E*), staminate spike; (*F*), staminate spikelet.

same structure as those of bluestem and sorghum, and the pistillate are exceptional only in their arrangement on the axis, standing at right angles to it. Rarely in grasses does the grain protrude beyond the glumes as it does in maize, but it also occurs in pearlmillet and in the native *Diarrhena*.

Grasses have been so successful in the struggle for existence that they have a wider range than any other plant family; they occupy all parts of the earth and exceed any other in the number of individuals. They reach the limits of vegetation (except for lichens and algae) in the polar regions and on

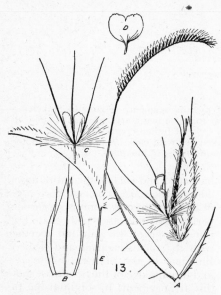

Grama grass: (*A*), Glumes and fertile floret, sterile florets attached; (*B*), lemma of fertile floret displayed; (*C*), (*D*), lemmas of first and second sterile florets; (*E*), spikes showing arrangement of spikelets.

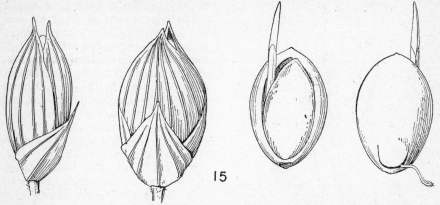

15

Broomcorn millet: Side and back view of spikelet; two views of germinating grain.

mountaintops. They endure both cold and torrid desert conditions, form the main part of the vegetation of vast prairies, plains, savannas, and steppes of both hemispheres, and occupy great stretches of marsh and tidal flats, where they are building up the land. Bamboos, the largest of grasses, form extensive forests and dense jungles.

Mostly low in stature and relatively inconspicuous, grasses attract but little attention—but they are the meek that inherit the earth. They form the third largest family of flowering plants, exceeded in number of species only by the aster family and the orchids. But in the number of individual plants, grasses far outnumber all others and have a wider range than any other family of flowering plants.

Grasses owe their dominance to their ability to make a living under all conditions where flowering plants can live at all and to their usually abundant seed crop and its wide dispersal. The seeds are carried far and wide by the wind. Some years ago entomologists exposed insect traps from an airplane to learn how high insects were carried by air currents. Numerous grass seeds found in the traps were given to me. The flat hairy spikelets of Vaseygrass were captured at a height of 4,000 feet. This grass was introduced into Louisiana from South America some sixty years ago and is now spontaneous from Virginia to southern California. Seeds,

such as those of the common reed, the plumegrasses, most of the beardgrasses, and many others which are surrounded by long hairs, fly like thistledown.

Many grasses are adapted to dispersal by animals; such seeds as those of needlegrasses and three-awn grasses (figures 11 and 12), and others with needlelike bases attach themselves to the hair or fur of animals or the clothing of man. In the sandbur (figure 16), barbed spines serve the same purpose. The needle-point seeds, especially the florets of some weedy annual bromes and the spikelets of wild barleys, are harmful to grazing animals—the barbed points work into the mouth parts, nostrils, and eyes and cause serious injury. The barbed spears of needlegrasses and of some others catch in the wool of sheep, and the awns, twisting and untwisting in dew and sunshine, drive the barbed point through the wool into the skin.

Grasses have spread over continents and across the seas by the agency of man, often unintentionally. Guineagrass, Bermuda-grass, and molassesgrass (in the Tropics) are common wherever slaves were unloaded in the Americas. These African grasses, which were used for bedding for slaves and as feed for such animals as were carried, were unloaded with the slaves and ballast, and soon took possession of suitable areas. Grasses spread along old trade routes and have come in as impurities

16

Branch of sandbur; spikelet, enlarged.

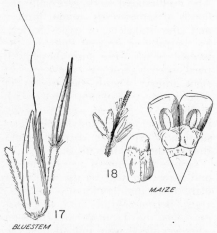

18

MAIZE

17

BLUESTEM

Pair of spikelets of bluestem with rachis segment and pedicel.   Figure 18: Maize or Indian corn: Pair of pistillate spikelets attached to rachis (cob), the mature grains much exceeding the glumes, second glume and embryo side of grain showing; single pistillate spikelet soon after flowering, the stigmas fallen; 2 pairs of staminate spikelets on fragment of rachis (tassel).

in imported seeds. Seeds of a strange millet were found in 1932 by seed analysts in millet imported from China. It proved to be *Setaria faberi,* an annual related to green foxtail (wild millets are called foxtails or bristlegrasses in this country). By 1947 it was found from New York to North Carolina and west to Missouri and Nebraska.

One of the cordgrasses, *Spartina pectinata,* has filled up vast stretches of marshland in the Middle West, converting it into rich black prairie. But eons before that, during the Miocene, when our Great Plains were being uplifted, the common reed must have stretched across the continent. Dr. A. P. Dachnowski, peat specialist for many years in the Department of Agriculture, found that the peat deposits throughout the Mississippi Valley and west to the Rockies are composed largely of the remains of this reed. Since this is a circumpolar species, it is probable that the flat lands of Finland, northern Russia, and Siberia were built up by this grass.

Along the north Atlantic coast and at the southern end of Lake Michigan are great hills of sand piled up by wind and wave. Unless held by vegetation, these sand dunes travel inland, a thin layer of the upper, driest sand blowing up the windward and sliding down the leeward side. The dune thus advances a few inches to a few feet in a year.

Grasses with strong rhizomes flourish on these windswept sands and serve to hold them. The principal species is beachgrass. The sand-laden winds are checked by the clumps of beachgrass and drop their sand; this raises the level of the dune about the grass, which is able to grow upward indefinitely, rooting at the buried nodes. A related European species, *Ammophila arenaria,* is planted extensively in northern Europe to hold the drifting sand along the coast. Along the Baltic, in Denmark, the Netherlands, and along the French coast of the Bay of Biscay, a great line of barrier dunes protects the land behind them. Trees are planted in the lee of the dunes, but they can not endure the severe conditions of the seaward side. The dunes are constantly guarded and, if a break occurs, tufts of grass are planted to hold the barrier.

Our cordgrasses have for ages been building meadowland on mud flats and tidal estuaries in the Gulf of St. Lawrence, Chesapeake Bay, San Francisco Bay, and the lesser inlets. These grasses thrive in the soft mud, submerged at high tide; their stout rhizomes form a firm network ever pushing seaward on the shallows of the Continental Shelf. The coarse grass impedes the oncoming waves, causing the water to drop its silt; thus the grass protects the shore while building up the floor until it becomes marshmeadow and, finally, dry land; at that time the cordgrass dies out and leaves the land ready for cultivation. Much of tidewater Virginia was built up by the cordgrasses.

Smooth cordgrass, which ventures farther into the water than other species, extends its land building from Newfoundland to Texas (figure 19). A few years ago when oysters were being transplanted from the Atlantic to the Pacific coast, this grass was accidentally, but fortunately, introduced with them. By 1945 it formed a flourishing colony at Willapa Refuge in Pacific County, southwest Washington.

A striking example of land building is going on today on a gigantic scale along the English Channel and the North Sea. The traveler on a ship entering Southampton today will see vast green meadows stretching into the sea. Two generations ago these were bare mud flats. *Spartina townsendii* (called ricegrass by the English), nearly related to our smooth cordgrass, was first observed on the Southampton salt marshes in 1870; it now occupies the tidal flats for 150 miles.

"These bottomless muds, though they stood empty of vegetation probably for thousands of years," F. W. Oliver wrote, "found no plant capable of solving the problems of invasion and establishment till *Spartina townsendii* came and made light of the task."

19

Smooth cordgrass (*Spartina alterniflora*): Base of plant showing rhizomes; inflorescense; spikelet, enlarged.

THE AUTHOR ≪ *Agnes Chase is research associate in grasses in the Department of Botany, United States National Museum, Smithsonian Institution. She retired from the Department of Agriculture in 1939 after serving as agrostologist for 36 years, and in 1946 relinquished her duties as custodian of grasses in the National Museum in Washington.*

Mrs. Chase is the author of numerous articles and books on grasses of North and South America, among them First Book of Grasses, and has been engaged in revising Hitchcock's Manual of Grasses of the United States. She has done considerable field work in Puerto Rico and South American countries and has studied in England and on the Continent.

THE SETTLEMENT OF GRASSLANDS

EVERETT E. EDWARDS

THE AGRICULTURAL settlement of the United States took nearly three centuries and involved two processes—horizontal movements of pioneer conditions across the continent and vertical movements of improvements within every community.

Quickenings and some lags occurred within the two processes. Old and new systems of farming and crop rotations might exist side by side for a considerable time. Grassland generally tended to be the marginal part of every farm, and its integration into a farming system was slow. To the average farmer, grass was only grass. While some kinds were eventually recognized as better than others for livestock, the general recognition of the place of the various grasses and forage plants in rotations, soil improvement, and animal nutrition came slowly and relatively late.

In considering the place of grasses in the farming of the Thirteen English Colonies that became the United States, we should recall two basic background situations. One is the state of the farming that was familiar to the folk who colonized the North Atlantic seaboard. The second is the state of the forage resources that they found where they settled.

Another point: In the history of grasslands settlement in the United States, several factors make careful historical delineations and generalizations difficult. Grass was generally such a taken-for-granted item that it was not commented upon in historical records unless something went amiss with the supply. In the records also, and especially in the seventeenth and eighteenth centuries, the terminology used for grasses was vague and overlapping—a grass might be known by one name in one part of the country and by quite a different one in another; or two distinct grasses might be known by the same name in different localities. Although agriculturists have long recognized the prime importance of an abundant supply of nutritious forage plants for the successful raising of livestock, the early colonists of the seventeenth century were not keenly cognizant of this fact. They came from an England whose agriculture was primitive. Arable and pasture land were still regarded as permanently separate. The introduction of a rotation of crops, founded on the field cultivation of roots and clover usually attributed to Sir Richard Weston, did not take place until after the first settlements in America were made, and popularization of improved methods of farming and of better livestock was still more than a century and a half away.

The vegetation of North America at the time of European colonization was strikingly deficient in forage plants suitable for livestock. The American Indians had made phenomenal progress in the domestication and development of economic plants, but they had used these for human food. They had no herbivorous domestic animals and had, therefore, no occasion to give attention to forage plants.

The first pastures in the English colonies were the natural openings or clearings in the lowlands along the banks of streams and the woods where the underbrush had been burned by the Indians for hunting. In these places the colonists found two native forage plants, the wild-rye and the broomstraw. The first was common along the Atlantic coast from Virginia northward, and the second was dominant in the Middle Colonies and in parts of New England.

These grasses grew high and thick, and the early commentators wrote enthusiastically about them. The cattle ate them freely during the summer, but shortly came the realization that it was practically impossible to make enough hay of these grasses to carry the cattle through the winter. The fact was that the proportion of roughage to nutrient made them of little value as hay.

The attention the early settlers gave to the coarse reeds and sedges of the fresh- and salt-water marshes emphasizes the lack of good pasture and hay in the first half of the seventeenth century. If droughts reduced the forage, whole herds might be lost. Sometimes cattle were slaughtered to keep them from starvation, and there was always this danger as long as the livestock had to depend on native grasses.

It was not long, however, before the grasses of England appeared in the Colonies. On shipboard the animals were fed the forage provided for them, and when they were landed the ships were cleared of litter and manure. The grasses thus introduced spread rapidly and in a few generations came to be regarded as indigenous. In 1665 English grass, a term which regularly included bluegrass and white clover, was noted in a report on Rhode Island. In 1679, a visitor on Long Island saw fields of clover in bloom "which diffused a sweet odor in the air for a great distance."

Long before this time some of the seeding was intentional. In 1685 William Penn described an experiment in sowing English grass and noted that one of his colonists had sowed "great and small clover." As the seed used for these intentional sowings was unwinnowed chaff from hay stacks, the resulting pastures included an abundance of Old World weeds.

In view of the state of knowledge concerning livestock husbandry and the scarcity of labor, the first colonists turned their livestock loose on the unoccupied lands adjacent to their holdings as a matter of course and depended on the natural vegetation to carry them at all seasons. The realization that the rigorous winters of the more northern latitudes dictated shelters and supplies of fodder came slowly. As a system of mixed farming prevailed in all the earliest settlements, the protection of growing crops from the depredations of livestock was a prime necessity. Enclosures or fences of some kind were obviously needed, but fencing would have taken more labor than could be spared from clearing land, providing shelter, and cultivating crops. Out of this situation emerged several forms or stages of range husbandry which, generally speaking, were repeated again and again during the course of the American westward movement.

In New England and in the localities developed by New Englanders in New York and northern New Jersey, the method of community settlement made possible a system of common pasturage. The duties of the community cowherd who went through the village street every morning sounding his horn and gathering the livestock were set forth repeatedly in the ancient town records.

If the farmers of the community had enough sheep to justify segregation they were handled separately by a shepherd during the grazing season. Swine were especially troublesome and became the subject of more legislation than any other single agricultural matter. Circumstances soon compelled the registering of livestock brands and earmarks with the town authorities.

The Dutch of New Netherland had common pastures, and the practice was recognized legally when the colony was taken over by the English. In the Middle Colonies, where settlements were made by individuals without group cooperation at first, each farmer had to handle his own livestock. Farther south the same situation prevailed.

In the Southern Colonies the abundance of open range, even though poorly provided with grasses, discouraged the planting of artificial grasses. The straw of wheat, rice, and other small grains was used for roughage, and Virginia farmers sometimes pastured growing wheat. The soils of the Coastal Plain would have needed special fertilization for the growing of the ordinary meadow and pasture grasses and the extreme heat of the summers would also have hindered their extensive introduction.

On the frontier of the Southern Colonies a range-cattle industry developed—which was an eighteenth-century counterpart of the later industry on the Great Plains. Even at the close of the seventeenth century, herds of wild cattle and horses ranged on the western edge of the Virginia settlements. These animals were hunted by the planters, driven into pens, and branded as needed. Cattle raisers, learning from the fur traders about the rich pea-vine pastures of the uplands, pushed into the Piedmont. Sometimes they drove their herds from range to range; sometimes they established permanent ranges around the cowpens that they erected. The cattle were marketed in Charleston and later even driven to Baltimore, Philadelphia, or New York. Sometimes the cattle were sold to Delaware farmers for fattening. By the middle of the eighteenth century the outbreak of diseases necessitated colonial regulation of the cattle drives.

By the eighteenth century the problem of adequate pasturage on farms became accentuated. The supply of grasses in the woods and unenclosed meadows did not keep pace with the increase in livestock.

Pehr Kalm, the famous Swedish botanist who visited the Colonies in the middle of the century, noted that the pastures of the older settlements in Pennsylvania and New Jersey were failing because they were overstocked and the annual grasses could not ripen and reseed themselves. Because of the persistence of the practice of burning the woods, the timber forage declined. The lands, worn out from overtillage and then abandoned to a weed fallow, made poor pasture. Perhaps half of the average farm was a vast pasture largely overrun with sour grass, briers, and bushes. The farmers continued to cut their hay chiefly from the natural meadows and the marshes. Large quantities of coarse hay, chiefly *Carex*, were gathered, but as the livestock numbers increased the sources became increasingly unreliable.

Some time before 1750 the German farmers of Pennsylvania began to irrigate natural meadows. The streams flowing through the meadows were diverted along the hillsides and the water distributed by lateral ditches over the lowlands. The procedure often took much labor, but the increased hay crops apparently justified the expense. Farms with a large acreage capable of irrigation were highly valued. A few localities in New England also developed what was called "watered meadows." In the years 1745 to 1760 many of the salt marshes along the Delaware River were drained with dikes and tide gates and the land seeded to grain and then to clover or other English grasses.

A step of significance for the livestock industry was the creation of so-called artificial meadows. The seeding of tilled uplands with tame grasses as a substitute for weed fallow provided the farm stock with a very necessary and better supply of forage. The procedure was an important step forward in crop management.

In the eighteenth century such sowings increased, and selected seed began to be substituted for haymow sweepings. In 1749 Kalm saw fields of red clover near New York, and a decade later another observer found Pennsylvania farmers sowing clover seed "after they have harrowed in their wheat to make the crop stronger." The culture of clover, however, did not become widespread until after the American Revolution. By the beginning of the nineteenth century the advantage of using cultivated grasses on uplands as the source of hay had won recognition, and there was less reliance on natural meadows in the older and more settled parts of the country. Even the Pennsylvania-German farmers no longer valued irrigated meadows.

Timothy was the first grass cultivated in America to attract much attention. It was supposedly found growing near Portsmouth, in New Hampshire, about 1700 by a man named John Herd, and as its cultivation spread through New England it came to be known appropriately as Herd's grass. Seed was taken to New York, Maryland, Virginia, and North Carolina by one Timothy Hanson, and there the plant was called timothy. Although long assumed to be indigenous in America, it is now recognized as an Old World plant that grew naturally in England, where it was called cats-tail grass. The cultivation of timothy spread through New England and the Middle Colonies during the eighteenth century. Its dominance as a hay plant in the United States today is a tribute to the shrewdness of the colonists who first recognized its value.

Different kinds of grasses had been tried in the Colonial South.

In 1635 the prospective settlers of Maryland were urged to bring a "good store of Claver grasse seede, to make good meadow."

In 1735 the settlers at Frederica, in Georgia, planted lucerne, and a few years later Eliza Lucas began experimental plantings of it in South Carolina. George Washington tried lucerne at Mount Vernon in the 1760's but the soil was not suitable.

Thomas Jefferson, in his *Notes on the State of Virginia,* published in 1785, stated: "Our grasses are Lucerne, St. Foin, Burnet, Timothy, ray [rye], and orchard grass; red, white and yellow clover; greenswerd, blue grass, and crab grass." The fact that Jefferson listed these grasses does not mean, however, that they were widely cultivated even in Virginia.

Before the American Revolution the growing scarcity of open range led some of the more enterprising planters of Maryland and Virginia to introduce timothy and clover and to give attention to watered meadows. But even in the 1790's foreign travelers noted the backwardness of the meadows in these States as compared with those to the north. In the Carolinas and Georgia even less attention was paid to artificial pastures and meadows. No wild grass was mowed for hay. The livestock shifted for themselves at all seasons.

The data of the first agricultural census delineate the Northeastern States as the main hay-producing area in 1839. Except where wheat dominated in western New York and Pennsylvania, hay was the staple. To the west of Ohio the cultivation of grasses and clover was still unimportant, and the hay harvested was largely native grasses. In the older settled East increased use was being made of clover and of gypsum, lime, and manure.

The growth of towns and cities necessitated stage, livery, and private stables. Until the advent of the motorcar and truck in the twentieth century, these stables were an ever-growing market for hay. As early as 1837 Essex County, in Massachusetts, supplied more than a thousand tons to the Boston market, and the average price was about $16 a ton.

In the older communities of the Atlantic seaboard, market opportunities influenced the management of grasslands increasingly as the nineteenth century progressed. Localities that could specialize in beef fattening or dairying improved their upland mowing lands by sowing clover and other grasses and even permanent meadows might be manured occasionally. Arable fields were regularly laid down to grass after two or three grain crops and then mowed or pastured for several years.

The pasturage afforded by the natural openings west of the Alleghenies was richer than that of the Atlantic seaboard. The wild-rye and *Andropogons* grew more luxuriantly. The first settlers also found bluegrass and white clover, and their presence there in advance of settlement gave rise to the belief that they were indigenous. The cane along the banks of the rivers was used as forage for livestock. There were also two indigenous species, buffalograss and buffalo-clover, which were unknown east of the Alleghenies. The first of these was a coarse grass with a broad leaf. It belonged to the same family as the famous buffalograss of the Great Plains. The latter was a native clover.

The pioneer farmers who began to push westward across the Alleghenies during and following the American Revolution were confronted with the same task of carving out farms from the heavy timber just as their ancestors had done in the Atlantic Coastal Plain. Although the natural openings or treeless meadows were more numerous and extensive west of the Alleghenies, they were neglected except for pasturage. Nearly two centuries of the woodland farming had developed techniques which the pioneers did not abandon until confronted with the true prairies of Illinois. The farm seekers had come to select their soils on the basis of the kind of forest growth that covered them. It was reasonable to believe that land which grew only grass was not valuable.

In the Ohio River Valley the natural openings became the starting point of another extensive range-cattle industry. As early as 1805 George and Felix Renick of Ohio drove a herd of range cattle overland to Baltimore, where they cleared a profit of more than $30 a head. Their success led to other similar drives, and shortly the marketing of range cattle in the East became the main source of cash income for many western farmers of that time. The cattle were started eastward in the early spring. Each night the herds were halted at drove stands, where food and shelter were provided for both the drovers and their charges.

By 1840 the farmers of the Ohio Valley had taken on the fattening of their own cattle with corn, and this development became concentrated in a zone bounded on the north by the 40° parallel and on the south by the 36° parallel. The Scioto Valley and the bluegrass region of Kentucky were centers of corn feeding, and many of the leaders in the enterprise were former Virginians who had known of similar methods on the banks of the Potomac in the days of Washington. Eventually these feeders reached out to the prairies of Illinois, Iowa, and Missouri for additional stock. In the absence of large-scale refrigeration, the eastern cattle drivers continued until the coming of railroads.

By 1840 the westward movement was confronted with the true prairies of what came to be known as the Middle West. Many of the small prairies of Ohio and Indiana adjacent to rivers and timber had already been occupied, and the prairies of Stark County, Ohio, had become a leading wheat center. The oak openings and the small prairies of Michigan, Indiana, Wisconsin, Illinois, and Missouri then were being settled.

But the pioneers hesitated on the edge of the large prairies with their seemingly endless expanse of thick grass. There was a sense of vastness about them that seemed overpowering, an impression of a greatness that could not be subdued. Indeed, some contended that they would not be brought under cultivation for centuries.

There were many reasons for this hesitation on the edge of the prairies.

There was the lore of woodland farming that associated certain types of soil with specific stands of timber. Besides, forests were of great importance in the pioneer economy. They sheltered the game that constituted a chief source of meat, and they supplied logs for cabins, stock shelters, fuel, fences, furniture, and tools. They offered protection from winds and storms that open prairies did not give.

In addition to the lack of timber, the prairies did not provide a proper water supply until wells were dug. In some places the land of the prairies was low and swampy and needed to be drained before cultivation. Fever and ague attacked the settlers who tried these parts.

Another reason for avoiding the prairies was the desire to be near the watercourses that provided avenues of transportation. Trails into the prairies were practically impassable in the spring because of the deep mud.

It was soon demonstrated that the cast-iron plows brought from the East would not scour when used to break the prairie sod. Large plows with wooden moldboards plated with iron strips would turn furrows, but it took as many as six yoke of oxen to pull them. The process of prairie breaking cost less per acre than woodland in terms of manual labor but far more in terms of animal power.

Necessity eventually forced the conquest of the prairies. By the 1840's the land east of the Mississippi River that provided the favorite combination of timber and small clearings was occupied by settlers or held by speculators. Latecomers had to try the prairies or go farther west.

The development of the steel plow provided a satisfactory means of turning over the sod. The building of railroads across the prairie region connected the farmers with better markets and brought them fuel and building material. The advent of the reaper pointed to the day when the farmers would prefer the open, level prairies with their glaciated soils for extensive grain production.

As the cost of timber for the traditional types of fences became almost prohibitive, resort was made to sod fences, smooth wire, and Osage-orange hedges, but the problem of fences on the prairies remained essentially unsolved until the invention of barbed wire in 1874—a simple thing, but one of great significance.

The problems of prairie settlement were not peculiar to the Middle West. They were much accentuated on the Great Plains, where the uncertainties of rainfall were an additional factor. Similar problems arose on the pampas of Argentina, the grassy steppes of Siberia, and even on the grasslands of North Manchuria when the Chinese migrated there this century.

The systematic occupation of semiarid California was begun by the Spaniards in 1769. To this end they used three institutions—the presidio or military establishment, the pueblo or colonial settlement, and the mission. Of these the last became by far the most significant agriculturally. Although the friars introduced the crops and fruits and irrigation practices of their Mediterranean homeland, the natural grasses and related vegetation were sufficient to support cattle raising as the dominant occupation during the Spanish-Mexican period, 1769–1848, and even into the 1860's, when droughts ended it as a distinctive industry.

Migratory sheep raising recovered from the droughts, reached its peak in 1874, and then began to decline. Except in isolated areas livestock husbandry became a subsidiary part of the specialized agriculture which came to dominate the California scene.

By 1850 the westward-moving frontier of agricultural settlement had reached the eastern edge of the Great Plains, where it halted for nearly two decades. Mounted on horses, the Plains Indians were a much more effective barrier to the advance of the white men than the native population to the eastward had been. For two and a half centuries the Plains Indians maintained themselves against the Spaniards, English, French, Mexicans, Texans, and Americans, despite missionaries, whiskey, diseases, gunpowder, and lead.

Besides, it was generally believed that this region was unfit for white settlement. The geographers of the day pictured large portions of it as the Great American Desert. In addition, the rush to the gold fields in 1849 and the years immediately following made California the great objective of those moving west. The Great Plains and the Rocky Mountain region became merely a long, tedious, and hazardous roadway to the Pacific coast. The basic reason, however, for the halt of the frontier at approximately the eastern edge of the Great Plains was that it, by virtue of its climate, challenged the accepted methods of agricultural conquest.

The vegetation of the Great Plains was strikingly different from that of the United States to the eastward. The level land from the ninety-eighth meridian westward was practically tree-less. The characteristic natural vegeta-tion was grass and desert shrub, ranged according to the rainfall in generally north-to-south belts. In the low plains, like the prairies to the eastward, the grass was tall, luxuriant, and deep-rooted. To the west, on the High Plains, the grass was short but the sur-face sodded. Farther west the grass grew in tufts or bunches because the rainfall was too scanty to support con-tinuous growth. In the arid intermoun-tain region beyond, creosotebush was characteristic in the south, sagebrush in the north, and greasewood in the salt-desert areas.

The main short grasses were the grama, galleta, buffalo, and mesquite. Although not continuous, the grama grass extended through Colorado, New Mexico, Arizona, and Utah, especially in the higher valleys and plateaus. The galleta grass was found in New Mex-ico, Arizona, and Utah. The buffalo-grass thrived from the Panhandle of Texas to South Dakota. Mesquite grass grew where there was summer rainfall in western Texas, southern New Mex-ico, and Arizona.

Largely because of its natural vege-tation the Great Plains became the scene of a range-cattle industry which far exceeded in scale and results any of its predecessors in American history. The building of the Union Pacific Rail-road brought hunters who supplied the construction crews with buffalo meat, and its completion in 1869 let in addi-tional throngs which eliminated the buffalo and left the grasses of the plains unused.

During the years of the Civil War a vast reserve of range cattle had grown up on the Texas plains. The growth of population in the East and the ad-vance of the railroads into the Great Plains provided both a market and a means for shipping these cattle. This combination of circumstances enabled the range-cattle industry to dominate the Great Plains from the late sixties to the late eighties. A less-publicized but comparably important cattle busi-ness overflowed from the interior of the Oregon Country during 1875–85.

Starting from their breeding grounds in lower Texas, great herds of cattle were driven northward to Abilene and other shipping points in Kansas. Later, herds were pushed into Nebraska, the Dakotas, and Montana, first to provide meat for Indian reservations and mili-tary posts and later to raise cattle for eastern markets. Incident to this busi-ness, trial-and-error experimentation developed standard procedures for trail management, the round-ups, and so on, which contributed so much romance and color to American his-tory through western stories, movies, and folklore. The grass supply of the vast range of the Great Plains seemed unlimited, and the region was regarded as a permanent paradise for cattlemen.

About 1880 the boom element began to enter this cattle industry. Companies financed chiefly with outside, generally European, capital entered the business. The number of cattle increased rapidly, and soon the range was fully stocked. The land was still largely public domain, unfenced and unclaimed, except for extralegal holdings of the ranchers. Without regulated grazing, the supply of tall grass was soon ex-hausted, leaving only buffalograss and grama grass, and shortly these also were threatened in many places.

The lack of adequate provision for winter feed spelled widespread and terrific disaster when the unusually severe winter of 1886–87 came. The decreased grass supply of the summer range, due to the prolonged drought of 1886–95, brought further losses to the cattle companies, and the inroads of homesteaders on the range con-tributed other difficulties. Because of these circumstances, large-scale cattle ranching was gradually replaced by smaller operations.

The range-cattle industry eventu-ally found farming invading its do-main from both the east and west. The railroads had made the development of the industry possible; they also brought in homesteaders and other land seekers who disrupted the range and forced the cattlemen to shift to a ranch basis. The uncertainties of the business, especially the water supply and the problem of winter forage, had long since demonstrated the value of permanent headquarters.

With the decline of gold production in California, the miners turned eastward to the unoccupied valleys and mountain ranges. Their rush into the region of Colorado laid the basis for permanent settlement there. The corresponding occupation of Nevada, Arizona, New Mexico, western Montana, Idaho, and eastern Washington took place during the decade of the Civil War. The need for food supplies for the mining camps led to the beginning of agriculture in the favored parts of the intermountain valleys.

The farmers from the East who pushed into the Great Plains brought with them the eastern ways of farming, but the fact that this was a region with less than 20 inches of rainfall a year foredoomed them to failure except in favored localities and years. In the end the farmers had to develop new methods and crops adapted to the region. In some places irrigation was the permanent solution. In others dry farming became important for the first time in the United States, and as a method it also had to pass through stages of adaptation and experimentation as regards tillage methods, machinery, crops, and rotations.

As long as the grass of the public domain was the main reliance for the grazing of stock, whether cattle, sheep, or horses, no thought was given by their owners to range conservation. The prevailing principle was first come, first served. Besides, the stockmen were unaware of the rudiments of forage growth and requirements of plants. Shortly the indigenous forage plants were being gnawed to the roots and so weakened that they gave place to worthless weeds and annuals or even only dust heaps. The shrubs along the streams were devoured and the meadows dried out, thus giving freshets a chance to tear gashes in the sod and soil. This destruction, which took place both on the open plains and in the intermountain ranges, was accentuated in periods of drought.

The inevitable disasters resulting from the unbridled competition of the stockmen for the grass of the public domain were anticipated in the 1870's by Maj. J. W. Powell and a few other scientists.

Powell strongly urged classification of the remaining public lands and development of a scientific system of survey and disposal for each of the classes defined. The Public Land Commission, authorized by Congress in 1879, investigated the whole land system and proposed general reforms.

In the early 1880's there was a marked quickening of public interest in the conservation of the Nation's remaining natural resources. The attempts to reform the land system during President Cleveland's first administration met with only temporary success. The Federal Government remained committed to the principle of homesteads adopted in 1862 as the main means of developing the West. To this end various supplementary acts, which by their nature acknowledged that the homestead policy was not suitable for the region to which it applied, were passed. Even in 1916, when the Stock-Raising Homestead Act was enacted, Congress clung to the homestead principle at the same time that it belatedly acknowledged the destiny of much of the land in the West.

Not until the end of the nineteenth century was the necessity for regulating grazing on the public domain generally conceded by stockmen. At a national meeting in Denver in 1898 two divergent proposals were considered. One called for the ceding of the remaining public lands to the States, and this idea continued to have its advocates as late as President Hoover's administration, when it was embraced as the official objective of the executive branch of the Government. The other proposal at Denver urged that the Federal Government lease the public lands for grazing. Being better able to adjust to varying conditions, the sheep interests opposed all suggestions, but many of the cattlemen ultimately favored some form of control similar to that which the Forest Service was gradually working out for the management of the grazing ranges within the national forests. By this system stockmen were issued annual permits to graze a specified number of livestock on a range deemed big enough to support them.

The ultimate solution of the problem was provided by the Taylor Grazing Act of 1934, which undertook "To stop injury to the public grazing lands by preventing overgrazing and soil deterioration; to provide for their orderly use, improvement, and development; to stabilize the livestock industry dependent upon the public range. . . ." To effect these ends, 142,000,000 acres of the public lands were to be organized into grazing districts under the control of the Department of the Interior. It was also given broad powers to develop water power, to carry on soil-erosion control, and to provide for the disposal of land not needed for the grazing districts.

The history of grasslands settlement in the United States reveals definite patterns of utilization that were largely determined by the relationship between the supply of grassland and population.

In most newly settled communities the livestock were turned loose to graze on such grasses and other palatable vegetation as they could find in the natural clearings and woods. While in this stage, the owners of the livestock might be engaged in clearing their first fields for corn and garden crops, but there was nothing even approximating systematic crop farming. Communities settled by group action might hire one or more herders to watch their livestock.

The second stage emerged when the keeping of large numbers of stock by semiherding methods was combined with the production of crops. In this stage, and sometimes also in the first, the crops rather than the livestock were enclosed with fences of some sort.

The third stage began to develop when the grass on the range became scarce, and the raising of livestock had to be integrated with general farming. With the introduction of this stage, the first steps toward systematic animal husbandry were taken. In some communities, especially in plantation districts and other staple-producing areas, the raising of stock became subordinate to the production of staples and was continued largely for domestic needs. In other communities, notably in the Corn Belt as it moved westward to its present location, livestock continued to have an important place and most of the crops were marketed in the form of animals ready for slaughter. Cattle also gained a dominant place in communities that specialized in dairying.

In this third stage consideration had to be given to grassland, regardless of what the livestock were kept for, because they had to have pasture of some sort during the grazing season and hay for the winter. The farmers might depend on enclosed natural grassland, either clear or cut-over, for considerable time. In the end, however, they had to integrate the grassland with the rest of the farming system. They might try to improve the natural meadows by cursory seeding to tame grasses, by manuring, or even by irrigation.

The nature of the open-range stage of grassland utilization ultimately necessitated not only community but colony-wide and State-wide regulations of various sorts. The depredations of wild animals and Indians led to the hiring of herders and similar safeguards. Most communities also burned the range in order to get a seemingly luxuriant spring growth of grass, regardless of injuries to the soil. The supply of grass also led to regulations as to who could utilize the range. To facilitate identification and to thwart stealing, extensive legislation concerning branding and earmarks became necessary. In the early development of farming communities the relatively small acreage in crops led to the requirement that the crops rather than the range be fenced, but as communities became well settled this practice was usually reversed. Even in the colonial period, this situation with regard to fencing resulted in fence wars.

The limitations and failures of the grass supply led to range wars between ranchers or groups of ranchers and also between cattlemen and sheepmen. Incident to such clashes, associations were formed which, among other things, divided the range into zones of priority for the various herds. Each rancher had to give attention to the water supply needed for his herds. A group of buildings to use as headquarters for the range operations was also necessary. Probably the earliest record in United States history of such headquarters is a court judgment on the Eastern Shore of Virginia in 1634 which refers to the "cowpens" of that time. Except in the southern latitudes, the problem of winter feed shortly pressed for attention. At first this was usually met by making hay of the natural grass. Later fields of tame grasses, legumes, or fodder plants were developed for the purpose. In the end the operations were shifted from the open range on the public domain to ranches on privately owned land. In other words, the range industry became a ranch industry.

Sooner or later individuals who wished to develop farms invaded the domain of the range industry. The result was friction and conflict until one or the other way of life prevailed. The interests of the rancher and the nester clashed inevitably not only along the Atlantic coast in the seventeenth century but in the Great Plains as late as the early twentieth century. Ultimately the issue was usually resolved according to the economic returns from the land. Farming of some sort prevailed in the humid regions and also in semiarid regions where irrigation and dryland methods could be used. In the semiarid regions ranching as the most profitable occupation continued on private holdings and on public grazing districts where geographical factors gave it the necessary advantage.

THE AUTHOR««‑ *Everett E. Edwards, a native of Minnesota and a graduate of Carleton College and Harvard University, has been engaged in research on the history of agriculture since 1927. Mr. Edwards is senior agricultural historian in the Bureau of Agricultural Economics.*

A BILLION ACRES OF GRASSLANDS

H. H. WOOTEN, C. P. BARNES

THE GRASSLANDS, hay lands, and forested range lands of the entire United States cover more than a billion acres, nearly 60 percent of the total land area. They furnish about half of the feed for all livestock. Two-thirds of this land is privately owned. The rest, mainly in the dry and mountainous parts of the Western States, is publicly owned. More than half of the farms and ranches of the country depend largely on grassland for feed.

Originally about 700 million acres in the United States were covered with grass, usually mixed with other herbaceous plants. Nearly 250 million acres of that grassland have been plowed up and used for crops or for pasture in rotation with crops, including about 10 million acres of irrigated land.

The grasslands of the central prairies formed the largest body of highly productive soils in America; they have been converted almost entirely to cropland. Semiarid, desert vegetation characterized about 400 million acres, of

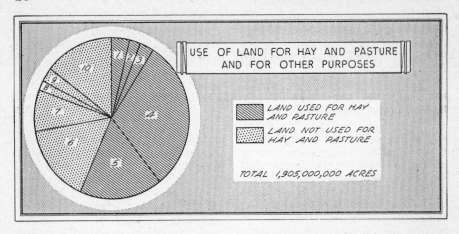

LAND USED FOR HAY AND PASTURE

	Million acres	Percent
1. Hay	74	3.9
2. Cropland used for pasture	48	2.4
3. Other plowable pasture	61	3.3
4. Other nonforested pasture and grazing (chiefly nonarable)	598	31.3
5. Woodland and forest pasture	345	18.1
Total land used for hay and pasture	1,126	59.0

LAND NOT USED FOR HAY AND PASTURE

	Million acres	Percent
6. Woodland and forest not pastured	257	13.5
7. Urban, service, and other land areas	149	8.0
8. Farmsteads, farm roads, etc,	44	2.3
9. Crop failure, idle and fallow	50	2.6
10. Grain, fiber, vegetables, fruit, and other crops	279	14.6
Total land not used for hay and pasture	779	41.0

Grand total — 1,905 million acres in 1945

which about 12 million acres have been reclaimed by irrigation.

Forests (not including semiarid woodland like pinyon, juniper, mesquite, and chaparral) originally covered about 800 million acres; about 350 million acres have been cleared at one time or another for agriculture, of which probably more than 50 million acres have reverted to forest cover and about 25 million acres have been converted to other uses. More than half of the present area of forest and cut-over land is pastured.

The country has probably more than 175 million acres of improved pasture on fair to good land, some of which compares favorably with cropland in productivity, but most grazing lands

are arid or rough, uncultivated, unfertilized, and relatively poor land as compared with cropland.

Pasture and grazing lands, excluding hay land but including forested land that is pastured, cover considerably more than half the area of continental United States—approximately 1,052 million acres—about 513 million acres in the West, 242 million acres on the Great Plains, 116 million acres in the North, and 181 million acres in the South. About 707 million acres are open pasture and 345 million acres forest or woodland pasture.

Only about 10 percent of the pasture land, 100 to 110 million acres, is suitable for regular cultivation in its present condition. The rest generally is too dry, rough, wet, or steep or too high in elevation for field crops, although some of it could be made fit for tillage by irrigation, drainage, clearing, or better management.

Approximately 683 million acres, or two-thirds of the pasture and grazing lands, is privately owned. Of the other 369 million acres, about 304 million acres is federally owned. The rest belongs to States and counties.

The principal native grazing lands are in the West and lower South. Those in the West are predominantly grasslands or desert shrub lands too dry for arable farming, although an important part is mountain woodland, moist enough for trees but generally too rough for cultivation. Those of the South are principally forested grazing lands, wet prairie, and marsh.

The western and Great Plains pasture and grazing lands occupy approximately 755 million acres. They form the largest and most important grazing area in the Nation.

The six Great Plains States include a grassland area of about 242 million acres, approximately 30 percent of the western grazing land. Here grazing is primarily of native short grasses, principally grama grass and buffalograss, although tall grasses predominate toward the eastern margin of the area and on deep, sandy soils. The only extensive area of native grazing land remaining in the humid, tall-grass, prairie region is the Flint Hills, in eastern Kansas.

Formerly much of the western Great Plains was used for grazing all year. Subdivision of land into farms and ranches, and fencing have now reduced the grazing area open to stockmen in many sections until it has generally become necessary to shorten the grazing season and substitute more winter feed. Weather conditions, deterioration of grass cover, and lack of brush for shelter also have induced a shift from yearlong grazing. The Great Plains grazing lands are mainly in privately owned ranches.

The six northern Mountain and In-

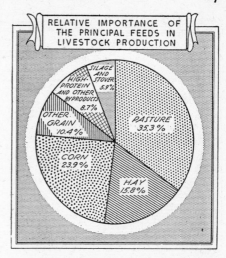

RELATIVE IMPORTANCE OF THE PRINCIPAL FEEDS IN LIVESTOCK PRODUCTION

termountain States contain approximately 295 million acres of grazing land. Much of it is covered with forest or sparse woodland, although open, grassy "parks" and sage-covered basins are numerous in the forested areas. Grass is the principal type of forage. The higher mountains furnish from 3 to 6 months of grazing in summer. Cattle and sheep are driven from these summer ranges to the lower valleys in winter, where they are grazed or fed forage produced mainly under irrigation. Some intermediate elevations afford grazing during most of the year, but the forage is generally not sufficient to carry the animals more than 6 to 8 months without a change of pasture. A large part of the mountain grazing lands is in public ownership.

The southwestern arid division of the western grazing lands occupies about 125 million acres of grazing land, mainly in Arizona and New Mexico. The dominant vegetation is desert shrub—sagebrush, shadscale, creosotebush, greasewood, mesquite, and many others. Some are not palatable and are not grazed, but others, like winterfat or mesquite, are grazed or browsed. Associated desert grasses furnish some of the grazing. Much of this arid range is used in winter, when the summer ranges are snow-covered. Some of the Mohave Desert region of Arizona and

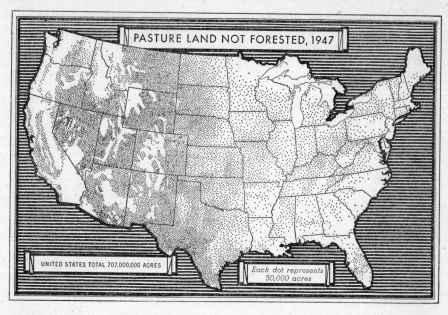

The general location of the 707 million acres of nonforested pasture land is indicated; approximately 10 percent of this land is suitable for regular cultivation as it stands.

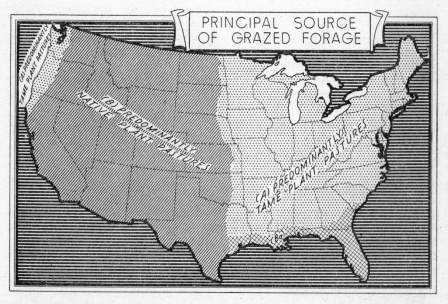

Although native forage plants may furnish most of the feed in Region (Ba), tame grasses and grazed crops have increasing importance and may furnish more feed in some areas.

southern California is practically un-usable for livestock because of lack of water. Most of this arid division of the western grazing lands is in public ownership.

The Pacific Coast States have nearly 100 million acres of grazing land, open and forested. The range of forage types is remarkably wide. Humid pastures in farms in the Northwest contain about 5 million acres. Irrigated pastures in all the Western States cover about 2 million acres, much of it in the Pacific Coast States.

In all four divisions of the western grazing lands, about 590 million acres may be classed as semiarid and arid range, an area nearly equal to the national acreage used for crops and humid pasture combined. It is an area of relatively low carrying capacity. Even if cropland were pushed virtually to its physical limits, there would still be almost 500 million acres left for grazing in this region.

Because of the low capacity, large acreages are required for an economic operating unit. In western Texas many ranches have 20,000 or more acres; in Arizona and New Mexico many have 30,000 to 40,000 acres. Many ranchers graze their animals under permit over large acreages of public land and national forests.

Even though the carrying capacity is often low, the western grazing lands are excellent for grazing because many of the grasses and other plants are nutritious; some of them cure on the ground and make winter feed.

The other important region of native grazing extends from central Texas to North Carolina.

It consists primarily of the southern pineland, but includes also the oak forests of eastern Texas and Oklahoma, the hardwood region of the southern Mississippi Delta, and extensive, poorly drained prairies or marshlands along the Gulf coast in Texas and Louisiana and in central and southern Florida.

A great variety of native plants, including wiregrasses, bluestem or broomsedge grasses, panicums, reeds, and browse plants furnish grazing. Carpetgrass has spread also into the woods in many places. The acreage of improved tame pasture is increasing.

Within the Southern States is 180 million acres or more of uncultivated forage-producing land available for grazing use. Besides the grazing in open woods and natural prairies, there is much grazing of cut-over tracts and abandoned fields that have not been restocked fully with timber.

Grazing in the north-central and northeastern sections is mainly of tame plants in improved farm pastures; there is some grazing of abandoned cultivated farm fields and farm woods. About 116 million acres of pasture is in the region. The humid part of the Pacific Northwest is another region where improved tame pastures afford a large share of the grazing.

In these humid areas, pastures are predominantly grasses and legumes, introduced from abroad. Pastures in these parts of the country generally have been made by preparing the land and seeding it to one or more of the introduced plants, some of which (such as bluegrass and white clover) spread naturally to favorable open or cleared land and are regarded by some as wild or native plants. Of improved tame pastures in 1945, about 130 million acres was permanent pasture and 48 million acres rotation pasture. Between 5 million and 7 million acres of this rotation pasture produced a harvested crop that year besides the pasture.

In some places an acre of pasture furnishes all the roughage a dairy cow or steer can eat the whole year. In other places a steer cannot get enough to eat from 50 acres. The main geographic differences that explain this disparity have to do with long seasons, plenty of moisture, and fertile soil. That is why the most productive pastures are in mild humid regions like the Mississippi Delta, on alluvial soils along the coast of Oregon and Washington, or in the mild-climate regions where irrigation is practiced.

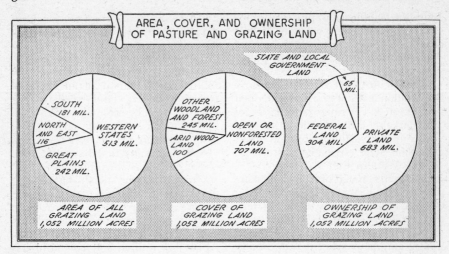

AREA, COVER, AND OWNERSHIP
OF PASTURE AND GRAZING LAND

About one-fourth of western pasture and grazing land is forested; the larger part of this is arid woodland and open areas within forests. About 70 percent of the southern grazing land is cut-over woodland and abandoned brush-grown fields. More pastures in the North Central and Northeastern States are improved than in the South and West.

Another item, besides the fertility of soils, is their capacity to supply moisture. Steep soils, however fertile, are not the best pasture soils because so much of the water that falls on them runs off instead of entering the soil. That is why the Blue Ridge of North Carolina and Georgia does not afford a large amount of grazing per acre, even though the climate is well suited to pasture. A favorable climate and fertilization can offset the effect of infertile soils in making good pasture if the soils have good moisture-supplying capacity. The soils of the Southeast, for example, generally do not make good pasture unless they are fertilized. When they are fertilized, seeded to good grasses and legumes, and properly grazed, the long grazing season provides as much forage per acre as many of our colder regions where the soils are more fertile. Where the soils do not hold enough water for the grass, however, an acre of pasture will produce little forage even though the climate favors grazing. For example, the deep sands of the Carolina sand hills and those of central Florida are so porous they do not hold and sup-

ply enough moisture for good pasture.

Generally speaking, the lands giving the greatest amount of grazing per acre are not the ones used most for grazing. This is because such lands are also the most productive for cultivated crops, whereas dry and steeply sloping lands can be grazed but are not suited to cultivated crops.

There are broad differences in the productivity of improved tame pasture in the different regions. They reflect principally rainfall, length of pasture season, and productivity of soil. By productivity of soil we mean not merely its fertility but its ability to produce, which depends also on its capacity for taking in and supplying moisture.

Unimproved native pastures on the whole have a much lower carrying capacity than improved tame pastures. Some of our most productive improved pastures will carry two cows or steers on an acre for a grazing season 8 months long. Native grazing land that will sustain a cow on less than 8 acres is rare. The increase in carrying capacity from pasture improvement is greatest on productive soils where moisture is abundant and available.

The harvested acreage of all hay is around 75 million acres a year. Of the hay acreage, about 60 million acres is tame hay and 15 million acres wild or natural grass hay. The acreage of tame hay has increased in the past few decades from 50 million acres to 60 million acres. About 8 million acres of the increase occurred between 1915 and 1924. From 1925 to 1939 severe droughts brought a moderate decrease; by 1940 the acreage reached the 60-million-acre level, where it has stayed since.

In the 1920's nearly 60 percent of the tame hay acreage was in clover and timothy. Now clover and timothy represent but a third of the tame hay, while legumes reported separately total about 50 percent of all hay. Wild hay has declined from 16 to 11 percent.

Higher yielding, more nutritious, and better adapted legume forages are replacing timothy, bluegrass, white clover, and other grasses and legumes that under certain conditions do not yield well. Recently there has been a trend, however, toward growing legumes in mixture with new and improved grasses. Despite an increase in the number of dairy cows and beef cattle, the number of roughage-consuming animal units is now only slightly higher than in the early 1920's—about 75 million in 1940–44—as compared with 74 million roughage-consuming animal units in 1920–24, because of the decline in numbers of horses and mules. The quantity of hay available per unit, however, excluding horses and mules, is about one-third greater.

Higher yields made it possible for us to produce all the hay we needed and still use about 6 million fewer acres for hay than would have been required if yields had been no higher than in 1925–29. Of even greater importance were the changes in quality. If the composition of all hay had not improved from 1925 to 1944, nearly 18 million more acres would have been needed to provide the same amount of digestible feed nutrients. The shift to higher yield-ing types of hay contributed to the wartime food output by making acres available for other food crops.

The acreage in pasture, grazing, and hay declined about 5 percent, or 64 million acres, from 1910 to 1945. In all, about 35 to 40 million acres was developed for crops; the rest was changed to various other uses. Of this reduction, nearly all was open land or nonforested grazing land in the Western States. Pastured woodland increased in part to make up for the decrease in open grazing land. Tame hay, mostly legumes, increased 10 million acres. Because of the drop in the wild hay acreage, the net increase in acreage of all hay was only 6 million acres.

Open or nonforested pasture covers 529 million acres, and hay 74 million acres on farms. Altogether 603 million acres of hay and open pasture is in farms. Woodland pasture in farms covers 95 million acres. Thus, 698 million acres of pasture and hay land are in farms, or 62 percent of the total pasture, grazing, and hay land acreage.

Agricultural census data indicate that more than 200 million acres of open pasture and grazing land in farms were leased in 1945 by tenants and part owners. Pasture and grazing land make up nearly half of the farm land rented. A large proportion of the grazing land rented is by part owners in the Western States. In addition to rented land, much larger acreages are used under grazing permits. With the rented acreage of 200 million and the approximate 300 million acres used by permit, farmers and ranchers graze their livestock on 500 million acres or more of private and public land that they do not own.

In 1940 on farms operated by tenants, not including part owners, more than half of the open pasture was on farms rented for cash, at least in part, and the remainder on farms rented on shares. Frequently the pasture is rented for cash on the same farms where the cropland is rented for a share of the crop. Consequently, the rental values

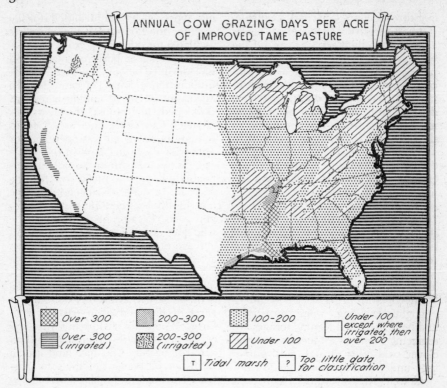

Long seasons, sufficient moisture, and fertile soils explain differences in cow grazing days per acre of pasture land. The most productive pastures are in mild humid regions on alluvial soils of the Pacific coast area and in irrigated regions of mild climate.

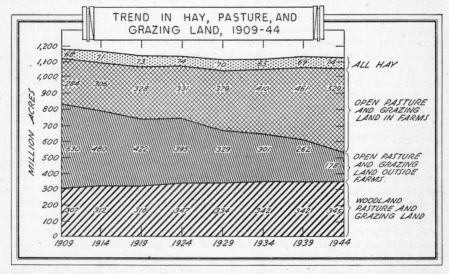

From 1909 to 1944, hay, pasture, and grazing acreages declined about 64 million acres, largely because of development of the land for other uses. Open pasture and grazing land declined about 107 million acres and woodland pasture increased 38 million acres.

for pasture usually fluctuate less than those of cropland.

An estimated 60 million acres of the open pasture reported in farms and ranches was publicly owned land under State or Federal administration, leased or used by farmers under individual permits and allotments, and about 40 million acres was Indian lands. A large part of the State land is leased to individual livestock operators.

One of the most noticeable changes in reported ownership of grassland since 1910 has resulted from reporting as in farms and ranches nearly all the open or nonforested privately owned grazing land, along with a considerable acreage of publicly owned land. This is due to the development of new farms and ranches in the Western States and to the leasing by farmers of tracts of State and Federal land, which is then reported as being in farms, whereas formerly such land was not considered in farms. Much of the Indian land also is now reported by the Census Bureau as in farms and ranches.

Comparatively few livestock operators in the Western States own all of the range land required by their livestock. Use of leased land or of grazing permits in connection with one's own land is common throughout the West. Tenure and control of grazing land vary widely from that of the stockman who owns no land to that of the operator who owns a home ranch and all necessary range land. In between are many combinations of ownership, leases, permits, and unauthorized use. The most common type of tenure is that of an operator who owns some farm and range land, leases some of both from private owners, and uses public lands under permit at certain seasons.

State land is important in several States. Ten Western States have substantial acreages, ranging from 1 to 10 million acres each. The operators of these lands pay rentals to the States. For example, on the 11 million acres of State-owned grazing lands in New Mexico are hundreds of ranches. Grazing leases there are limited to a term of 5 years but may be renewed.

About 428 million acres of grazing land is outside of farms. Of such lands, 178 million acres is open or nonforested and 250 million acres is woodland and forest. Practically all of the 178 million acres is publicly administered, although most of it is used by private farmers and ranchers. Of the forested land grazed outside farms, about 100 million acres is publicly owned and administered by Federal, State, or local governments. Nearly all grazing land outside farms is used by private parties under a grazing-permit system. Payments are based on the number, kind, and age of livestock grazed. Local farmers, with only a few head of livestock for home farm use, are permitted free grazing under certain conditions. The commercial livestock man, however, pays for the grazing on public land.

In parts of the lower South and in the Ozarks, privately owned land on which there are no restrictions against grazing is "free" range. Here free range areas include mostly timbered nonfarm lands, but also some farm lands that are not fenced. Farmers in free range areas normally fence only the fields used for cultivated crops and depend almost entirely on the unfenced land for pasture, particularly from April through October. In several Southern and border States a relatively large percentage of the total unimproved land area is subject to free grazing.

The free range areas, which are determined by an elimination process, include areas where livestock laws or stock law improvement districts do not prohibit livestock from running at large. Areas in which free grazing is prohibited are known generally as closed range.

Under the homestead laws and the various other means of disposing of the public lands (such as the railroad grants) approximately 385 million acres, or more than 50 percent, of the western range land passed into private ownership. By various processes, States and counties acquired about 65 million acres of grazing land.

In contrast to the laws which encouraged the passing of public lands to private ownership were the various Federal reservation acts. Under these acts the remaining unappropriated lands were set aside for public use in national forests, grazing districts, and reclamation and other reservations. These public reservations, together with lands bought by the Federal Government in recent years, include some 304 million acres useful for grazing.

Of the federally administered grazing land, including Indian lands, about 202 million acres is open or nonforested grazing land and 102 million acres woodland and forest. Multiple-use values are found especially in the forested parts of the federally owned or administered lands where lands serve not only for timber production but also for grazing, recreation, wildlife, and watershed protection.

Of the federally administered grazing land, nearly half is in grazing districts. More than one-fourth is in national forests and about 15 percent in Indian landholdings. Altogether, more than 20 million head of livestock are grazed part of the year on Federal and Indian lands under Government administration.

THE AUTHORS ≪ *H. H. Wooten is principal agricultural economist, land utilization studies, Division of Land Economics, Bureau of Agricultural Economics.*

C. P. Barnes is chief analyst, soil uses and productivity, Division of Soil Survey, Bureau of Plant Industry, Soils, and Agricultural Engineering.

THE HELP THE GOVERNMENT OFFERS

NEIL W. JOHNSON, CHARLES W. LOOMER

IN EVERY State, in every county, on every farm in the United States men and women are constantly at work to extend their knowledge of grasslands.

The workers are the farmers and ranchers, whose questions about grass reflect their growing interest in it; State and Federal research scientists, who try to find the answers to the questions; and the persons in public and private agencies, who administer educational, financial, and other programs that have been established to improve grazing uses and to encourage the adoption of improved practices on public and private grasslands.

Several Government agencies carry on many types of research on problems related to farm grasslands, often in cooperation with State agricultural experiment stations.

The research worker seeks to know how each grass and hay crop is adapted to a wide range of soil and climatic conditions, what its growth habits are in different localities, how it propagates itself, how palatable it is to various kinds of livestock, what its nutritive values are, how well it stands up under grazing, how many tons of hay it will yield, how many head of livestock it will carry when pastured, how to establish and maintain a grass cover. Knowing these things, he can help answer the intensely practical questions that farmers ask.

A whole series of studies tries to determine the losses of dry matter and feed nutrients during harvesting and storage. They inquire into changes in chemical composition and in color and leafiness of forage, and into the labor and machinery requirements for putting up the crop by different methods. Comparative feeding experiments are conducted to determine the value of each roughage for meat and milk production, its effect on the vitamin A content of milk, and on other nutritive properties of livestock products.

Related studies are made on how to fit the forage crop into a rotation and what effect it will have on the yield of subsequent crops. Other research is concerned with the effect of grass on soil properties. A growing appreciation of the value of legumes has given importance to investigations into the production of legume seed. Studies are made of the influence of environment, variety, and disease, and the effect of both beneficial and destructive insects. Special attention is given to the development of varieties and methods of management that will produce more satisfactory and reliable yields of seed.

Our Government, in cooperation with State agricultural experiment stations, also carries on intensive research in soil and water conservation, in which grass is an effective tool. There is progressive need to know just what combination of practices best suits each location under widely different conditions of soils and climate. Much of the work with the experiment stations is on a plot basis, and countless types of experiments are conducted under controlled conditions. The more promising experiments are carried to field trials and then to the final stage of testing under farm conditions. Only after results have been verified thus is a practice recommended for wide adoption.

In 29 conservation nurseries, agencies of the Department cooperate with State workers in testing the possibilities of native and introduced grasses, shrubs, and trees. Typical is the nursery at Pullman, Wash., where 500 to 1,000 varieties have been tested each year for the past 10 years. Seeds of the improved strains of soil-conserving crops are produced in volume at the nurseries and distributed to farmers. Work is carried on to determine the best methods of producing and processing legume seeds; this knowledge is made available to farmers, who can produce crops of seed for their own use or for sale.

In studies in more than 30 States, various sod crops have been introduced into farming systems for one or more years to determine the soil-building and soil-conserving values of different crop rotations. So, farmers are generally able to select from a number of tested systems the one that best fits their own needs.

Pasture renovation is studied intensively in all parts of the country. Attention is directed to the grasses that are best suited to pastures under different conditions of soil and climate, to methods of getting good stands, pasture management, and restoration of overgrazed pastures. Where water removal is a problem, special studies have been made to determine the suitability of different grasses for the construction of grassed waterways.

In scores of places a comprehensive program of economic research is conducted to evaluate developments associated with improvements in kinds and quality of forage and in breeding, feeding, and care of forage-consuming livestock. Methods of harvesting hay that reduce labor and preserve the quality of the crop are tested for their effects on the farmer's pocketbook. The economic implications of advances in the control of internal parasites, the elimination of insect pests of livestock, of the breeding of new types of livestock better adapted to southern climates, and of the extension of farm refrigeration by the use of cheap power are studied. Attention is also given to the current organization and the operation of farms, the amounts of capital required to make desirable adjustments, the market outlets for livestock products, income possibilities, and to long-time stability under new systems of farming. These analyses are designed to help the agricultural economy keep pace with changing physical developments and to reduce the costly trial-and-error experiments farmers have so often had to make for themselves.

The Government sometimes develops special programs to speed the correction of long-standing abuses.

Reconnaissance surveys in the early 1930's, for instance, gave a rough idea of the extent and rapidity of soil depletion and indicated where restorative work was urgently needed. Problem areas were outlined, technical staffs assembled, research and educational programs initiated, demonstration areas established, and aid given individual farmers and ranchers for carrying out conservation practices.

Now about 7 out of every 10 farms in the United States, and more than 5 out of every 10 acres of farm land are within soil conservation districts in the 48 States. The farmer-managed districts are organized under State laws and are empowered to deal with the Secretary of Agriculture in obtaining various kinds of technical assistance for conserving the agricultural plant. Heavy equipment may be loaned to build terraces, assistance given to establish contour lines, planting materials supplied, advice offered regarding the most effective combinations of erosion-control practices, or aid given in developing annual and long-time farm plans.

The fields in which soil technicians operate are many and varied. They group soil types according to adaptability to various crops and methods of land management. They help farmers use both vegetative and mechanical measures to solve conservation problems. Methods of handling farm wood lots are demonstrated, and farmers are helped to develop a sustained yield of forest products. Farmers come to a better understanding of water in its relation to land, whether the problem is one of excess supply or of deficiency.

As part of a program that has been operating since 1936, through locally elected county and community committees in every county, Congress made more than a quarter of a billion dollars available to farmers and ranchers to encourage agricultural conservation practices in 1946. Forty-one percent of this sum was spent to lime soils and fertilize pastures, hay lands, and cover crops. More than 14 million

acres were limed, about 20 million acres had applications of phosphates, and more than 6 million acres were treated with potash in the 1946 program. Farmers were given purchase orders for these materials and the Government furnished part of the cost of carrying out the practices.

Next to the program for improving soil fertility was that of erosion-control practices. Payments in 1946 were made for such practices as terracing a million and a half acres of cropland, contour farming more than 10 million acres, strip farming more than 6 million acres, and using special measures to protect from erosion the 14 million acres of summer fallow. Conservation funds were used to encourage the use of green manure and cover crops to protect soil from water and wind erosion, to restore plant food to the soil and to improve its texture. The latter program covered more than 18 million acres in 1946 and is especially important in East Central, North Central, and Southern States. Other conservation payments were used for practices designed to improve range and pasture lands.

In the 1946 appropriation for conservation, Congress provided special funds to encourage the harvesting of legume and grass seeds, many types of which have been in short supply. Payments were also made for control of perennial noxious weeds, improving or maintaining a stand of forest trees, clearance of land, and other miscellaneous conservation practices. The emphasis on these conservation practices varies widely from county to county. Local committees of farmers and technical workers determine from year to year the combination of practices they consider the most effective for conservation of soil and water resources in the locality and those for which payments will be offered.

Since 1933 the conversion from row crops to grassland agriculture has been particularly emphasized in the seven States of the Tennessee Valley. The shift to grass, livestock, and dairying is part of a larger program for water control and better use of resources. The principal instruments in this conversion are new phosphate fertilizers produced in the area, which in cooperation with Federal and State extension services have been tested and demonstrated on approximately 30,000 farms. The influence of this regional program extends beyond the Tennessee Valley, since nearly 6,000 test demonstration farms are scattered throughout 26 other States.

In a 10-year period, the total hay acreage of the 125 counties in the Tennessee watershed increased 136,000 acres, or 8 percent. Alfalfa accounted for 73,000 acres of this increase, expanding 226 percent from the 1934 acreage. In 15 counties in northern Alabama applications of phosphates and lime have made possible extension of improved pasture of from 10,001 to 111,214 acres in 10 years; perennial legumes have increased from 2,312 to 61,477 acres; and winter legumes from 79,930 to 288,392 acres. The production of legume seed increased similarly.

The results of this program have gone beyond increased acreages and yields. An improved grassland agriculture has been developed through good land use and soil, water, and crop management in which phosphate fertilizer has played an important part. Livestock enterprises have been added, together with necessary additions to power, machinery, and equipment. This has been accompanied by increases in the skill, knowledge, and judgment of the farmer and his family and by development of many kinds of cooperative community action.

Scientific interest in range lands goes back to journals of botanists attached to the Lewis and Clark expedition and to other military explorations shortly after the turn of the nineteenth century. Over the years, scientists of the United States Department of Agriculture have added to the growing fund of knowledge on how to use our native forage-producing lands— brush and grazed forest as well as true

untimbered range. At present, the work is centered in a group of regional departmental experiment stations in cooperation with the various State agricultural experiment stations.

Underlying all range research must be an intimate knowledge of range plants—their identification, habits of growth, life cycles, forage values, resistance to drought and grazing, soil-building and soil-binding properties, and their values in watershed control. Department agencies cooperating with the United States National Museum have built up the world's largest herbarium of range plants. Work continues in assembling and classification of specimens as well as in the publication of findings.

Research on grazing management seeks to develop the principles and practices of good husbandry of range land. These include grazing at the proper season of the year, grazing the kind of livestock best adapted to the range, balancing numbers of livestock with the forage-producing capacity, and encouraging uniform grazing and preventing localized damage to the range through better distribution of livestock watering places and salt. Poisonous plants are identified, methods are devised for their eradication, and grazing systems are worked out to reduce losses.

In cooperation with State agricultural experiment stations, livestock are placed on experimental ranges, and studies are made of the rates of stocking that permit most efficient use of the forage supply under varying climatic conditions. Death losses, calf and lamb crops, net turn-off of beef and mutton, fleece weights, and other data are recorded year by year and related to maintenance and improvement of the range as a means of increasing the net income. Feed concentrates and pastures needed to supplement range grazing are investigated. Studies are made of soil texture, structure, and fertility in relation to the erosion problem on range land, to the water-holding capacity of the grass cover, and to

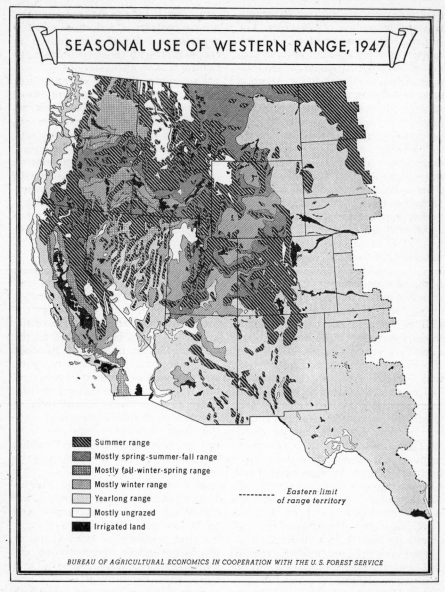

SEASONAL USE OF WESTERN RANGE, 1947

Summer range
Mostly spring-summer-fall range
Mostly fall-winter-spring range
Mostly winter range
Yearlong range
Mostly ungrazed
Irrigated land

Eastern limit of range territory

BUREAU OF AGRICULTURAL ECONOMICS IN COOPERATION WITH THE U. S. FOREST SERVICE

its ability to recover after periods of depletion. Most of this work has been concentrated in the 17 Western States, but in 1940 it was extended to the South and Southeast, especially to forest ranges in the Coastal Plain.

Research in revegetation aims to find good species and planting methods to speed the rehabilitation of depleted ranges and those mistakenly plowed

and later abandoned, which are characteristically slow in developing a desirable perennial grass cover.

Numerous attempts have been made to adapt cultivated forage plants to range use, but these have succeeded only under the most favorable conditions. A more fertile field has been that of studying the growth habits of plants native to the range, both in this country and abroad, and the conditions under which they can be reseeded. Attention is given to plants that can restore or increase the range forage and to those that aid in watershed protection. The work involves selection of superior strains and improvement through breeding. Studies of how to evaluate sites on which reseeding is needed and justified are basic to the program. In recent years the work has been reinforced in its western locations and extended into the South and Southeast.

We have learned through the years that loss of life and property through floods frequently may be traced to unwise use of ranges and forests many miles from the scene of the worst damage. The water supply of cities may fail and crops dependent on irrigation wither for the same reasons. So-called natural disasters are thus seen to be but the delayed results of the acts of man. Engineers design scientific upstream controls, and these have proved effective, but only at costs that need not have been incurred if abuse of natural resources had not occurred in the first place.

Studies of range and forest watersheds are the medium through which we come to understand these relationships. Investigations are made of the influence of cover afforded by different types and amounts of vegetation on soils, run-off, percolation, and storage of water for irrigation, power, and domestic use. Then the rates of stocking that can be sustained without impairing the water-holding and soil-binding functions of the vegetative cover are determined. Torrential rains in some areas of long-standing abuse have caused the surface of whole hillsides to descend upon fertile farm lands on the valley floor. Range research has devised the means of preventing recurrence of such damage, but the methods are costly. Emphasis accordingly is placed on using the range in ways that will maintain or improve rather than destroy its many values.

Prairie dogs, ground squirrels, and other rodents can seriously affect the supply of range forage available to livestock so much that rodent control is an important activity in many range areas. Elk and deer make their demands on the supply of native grasses. Coyotes, cougars, and other predators must be kept in check to prevent serious losses to flocks and herds. Research in this field studies the life cycle of the animals, their habits of feeding and breeding, the diseases and insect pests to which they are susceptible, and methods for their extermination or control.

Economic problems confront the researcher in nearly all the fields previously described. What does it cost to control range rodents and predators by different methods? Will the benefits exceed the costs? How many dollars can we afford to invest in restoration of depleted range lands? How should these costs be distributed between private users of the range and public beneficiaries of the work? What are the costs and returns from various processes of brush removal or of artificial revegetation of the range? What system of range management results in the greatest margin of profit to the rancher over the long pull?

Closely allied to these considerations of the costs and returns from various practices are the economic questions that confront the producer of cattle and sheep in the organization and operation of his ranch enterprise. The business side of ranch operation and the profitable marketing of range-livestock products are broad fields of economic research in which the Department of Agriculture engages, usually in cooperation with the land-grant colleges in States where range-livestock production is important.

For the private stockman, the importance of public land programs comes from the fact that Uncle Sam owns a great deal of the land used in private ranch and livestock operations. The Federal Government owns approximately 458 million acres of land in the United States, most of it in the 17 range States of the West. Less than

1 percent of this area is classed as cropland, and most of that is located in Indian reservations. Approximately 9 percent is classified as barren land, absolute desert, sand dunes, brushland, swampland, marshes, and other types of wasteland useful only for recreation, wildlife, and watershed protection. About 40 percent is forested or wooded land, largely administered as national forests and national parks and located in both Eastern and Western States. The remainder—approximately half of all Federal land—is untimbered range land, principally in the arid and semiarid regions of the West.

Grazing is an important use on about 304 million acres of Federal land. Taylor grazing districts, Indian reservations, and other lands administered by the Department of the Interior account for 204 million acres. The Department of Agriculture administers about 158 million acres of national forest land, exclusive of that in Alaska and Puerto Rico. Of this area about 83 million acres is used for grazing. Other Federal lands used for grazing account for an additional 17 million acres. In other words, about two-thirds of all Federal land in the continental United States contributes to livestock production and is used by stockmen and ranchers in connection with their private livestock operations. The area so used is roughly equivalent to the combined land area of Montana, Wyoming, Idaho, Oregon, and Washington. The public land programs, accordingly, play a dominant role in the range-livestock industry of the West.

A distinction must be made between public lands devoted exclusively to a public use and those used wholly or partly for private uses like grazing. The national parks and monuments, for example, are administered primarily for the preservation of scenery, wildlife, and natural historic objects. All other uses, including grazing, are restricted in accordance with the purpose for which the withdrawals were made. The unreserved public grazing lands and the Federal lands in grazing districts and national forests, on the other hand, are administered for conservation, improvement, and development of range watershed resources; orderly grazing by livestock and wildlife; stabilization of the livestock industry; and equitable distribution of grazing privileges.

The most important sources of grazing privileges are found in three types of public land: (1) The unreserved public grazing land and the Federal land in grazing districts administered under the provisions of the Taylor Grazing Act; (2) more than half of the total area of national forests, and (3) submarginal lands acquired for land use adjustments under the Federal soil conservation program. In most respects, the management objectives for these different lands are similar. They are designed to promote sustained yields of range forage, and they incorporate the findings of the many range-research activities described above.

Grazing privileges on Federal land are generally granted in the form of permits which authorize livestock operators to graze a certain number of livestock for a prescribed period. The fees paid by the individual operators are based on an animal-unit-month charge. Grazing permits often grant grazing privileges in common pasture areas used by two or more stockmen, although in many areas permits are given in individual allotments. Privileges are distributed among individual applicants on the basis of their qualifications; factors usually considered are priority of use, dependence on Federal range, and ability to provide sufficient feed and forage to care for permitted livestock during the period it is off the Federal range.

In the national forests and in the Taylor grazing districts, local groups of stockmen act in an advisory capacity with regard to allocation of grazing privileges and details of administration. In the submarginal land purchase projects, grazing privileges are granted to cooperative grazing associations and to soil conservation districts. These groups, in turn, grant privileges to individual operators within the districts.

The Federal land agencies are charged with the responsibility of conserving and improving forage and watershed resources on public lands. Grazing privileges are restricted to a long-time grazing capacity as determined by careful range surveys. Although grazing is thus restricted in areas subject to overgrazing, the total amount of available forage is increased by programs designed to improve livestock distribution and range use. Among these may be listed development of such stockwater facilities as dams, wells, dugouts, and tanks; construction of corrals, fences, and access roads; rodent eradication; and fire protection organization to control range and brush fires.

On deteriorated range, major emphasis is given to reseeding and restoration of perennial grass cover. A newly developed method for sowing grass seed from airplanes was tried in 1946. The seed is enclosed with plant food in small clay pellets, which protect the seed when it is first sown and give it a start when the rains come. The method may prove effective in reseeding some areas of semiarid range land.

Our Government also encourages conservation on privately owned range lands. Ranchers in soil conservation and grass conservation districts are given technical and other assistance in developing and carrying out management plans designed to prevent soil erosion and achieve a better balance between range forage and nonrange feed supplies. Such assistance has been extended to ranchers on nearly 50 million acres of privately owned range lands, largely in the 17 Western States. Moderate rates of stocking, together with supplemental conservation practices, offer a means of controlling erosion and increasing production.

In the practice-payment program of the Government, assistance is offered in supplying conservation materials such as fertilizer, lime, plants, and seeds, or in the form of direct payment of a part of the cost of performing certain practices. After consulting with agricultural workers in the land-grant colleges and with technicians in other agencies, local county committees select the practices that have greatest application to the conservation needs of the county and, working with the State conservation committee, they determine rates of payment for these practices.

Nearly 40 million dollars of conservation credits were earned by participating ranchers in 1946 for carrying out various range and pasture practices. Practices for which payments were made in 1946 included construction of dams and reservoirs, deferred grazing to permit natural reseeding, eradication of destructive plants, development of springs and seeps, rodent control, and establishment and maintenance of fireguards.

To carry the benefits of research and action programs to people wherever they live, the Government conducts extension and educational activities, mostly through local committees of farmers and ranchers. The purpose is to make available the findings of technical and scientific research, outline the steps that farmers and ranchers can take on their own farms and ranches, and show how they can participate in and benefit by the various Government action programs.

Every effort is made to gear the extension program to the needs of the community. National and State extension organizations exist for the purpose of throwing the full weight of governmental and private support behind the program, but local committees and the county agricultural agents working together determine lines of local action.

In Nebraska, for instance, after the drought of 1934, the State outlined a pasture-forage-livestock program designed to promote well-balanced diversified farming, with particular attention to the maintenance of soil fertility, feed reserves, and quality livestock. It was decided that the program should stress improvements in pastures, forage and feed grains, livestock management, control of animal and crop disease, pest control, weed control, and windbreaks. Within this framework, the counties select the lines of the work to be advanced year by year in their individual county programs. Individual farmers are given advice and assistance with the specific problems that are of greatest interest to them.

Basically, the extension program is carried on by the dissemination of information and by the exchange of ideas and experiences between cooperating farmers and ranchers. Individual operators, by means of bulletins and circulars, discussion groups, moving pictures, and talks by agricultural experts, are given the latest information regarding their problems of farm and ranch operation. They are encouraged to try new methods and keep records by which their neighbors can profit from the experiment. By means of tours and discussion groups, other farmers are kept informed of the results. By demonstration, farm and ranch operators can see in their own neighborhoods what progress is being made in the solution of their problems.

One of the most important aspects of the extension programs is the opportunity for concerted action by Federal, State, and private organizations. County agricultural agents are joint employees of the State extension services and the Federal Government, and the research and extension facilities of Federal and State Governments are available to the local program. With experiment and demonstration activities organized at the local level, the extension program is also closely related to the Government programs of greatest local interest.

In the Tennessee Valley, for instance, the Government furnishes fertilizer for the program described earlier in this article. In the range country, several Government agencies cooperate in emphasizing range management and improvement. Private as well as public organizations cooperate in these educational activities. Private corpora-

tions, for instance, may provide supplies for farm demonstration projects. Meetings, tours, and discussions are frequently sponsored by chambers of commerce and other civic organizations.

Research often points the way to adjustments farmers need to make for increased incomes under stable systems of farming. Farmers may be powerless to make these changes, however, because of lack of capital for the initial investment and for living expenses during the adjustment period. Shifts from cash-crop farming to greater emphasis on forage and livestock production are particularly of this type. Funds may be needed for application of lime and fertilizer to improve stands of legume hays and pasture, hay harvesting equipment may be needed, and the operator may have to make investments in livestock, together with buildings and equipment to care for them. Several years may elapse before these adjustments are reflected in increased income.

Farmers and stockmen obtain most of the credit required to finance the acquisition, operation, and improvement of farms by borrowing from individuals, commercial banks, life insurance companies, and other private agencies. Federal Reserve banks are authorized within certain limitations to discount agricultural loans submitted to them by State and national banks that are members of the Federal Reserve System. Two Department of Agriculture agencies also serve as suppliers of credit. One of these agencies supervises a Nation-wide system of credit for farmers, stockmen, and their cooperatives who can qualify for credit on the usual business basis. The other agency, by close supervision of the farm and home operation, makes loans to low-income farmers who are unable to obtain credit from other sources. Loans are usually made for the operation or purchase of a farm, and as such affect the entire farm business, including forage and livestock production.

Cooperative credit on a sound basis is available on terms and at rates of interest adapted to the needs of the individual farmer, stockman, or cooperative. Long-term loans secured by first mortgages on farms or ranches are available from the 12 Federal land banks. Such loans are made through local cooperative national farm loan associations and are based on the normal agricultural value of the land, including improvements thereon.

Short-term or production credit is available through local production credit associations. Farmer borrowers are shareholders in the associations, which are organized on a cooperative basis. The associations obtain their loan funds by discounting farmers' notes with the 12 Federal intermediate credit banks. These banks also discount agricultural paper for State and national banks, privately capitalized agricultural and livestock credit corporations, and other similar institutions.

Farmers' cooperatives may obtain loans suited to their needs from the 13 banks for cooperatives. The borrowing cooperatives are required to be shareholders in the banks, which may obtain needed loan funds by rediscounting notes with the Federal intermediate credit banks or by borrowing from other sources.

Loans supervised by the Department are designed to offer credit to operators who cannot ordinarily furnish security for other types of loans. The supervised loans are of three types—those for farm ownership, those for production and subsistence, and those for water facilities. The farm-ownership loan enables the borrower to acquire and improve a farm or to buy additional land to make a more efficient family-sized unit. This loan may include funds for land development such as fencing, clearing, terracing, draining and irrigation systems, development of permanent pasture, wood lots and orchards, and the application of soil amendments and fertilizers not normally applied each year. Production and subsistence loans enable the borrower to purchase machinery, livestock, farm supplies such

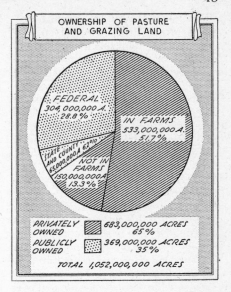

OWNERSHIP OF PASTURE AND GRAZING LAND

FEDERAL 304,000,000 A. 28.8%

IN FARMS 533,000,000 A. 51.7%

STATE AND COUNTY 65,000,000 A. 6.2%

NOT IN FARMS 150,000,000 A. 13.3%

PRIVATELY OWNED — 683,000,000 ACRES 65%

PUBLICLY OWNED — 369,000,000 ACRES 35%

TOTAL 1,052,000,000 ACRES

as feed, seed, fertilizer, and family subsistence needed to carry out the annual farm program.

Water-facility loans, available to farmers in the 17 Western States, are frequently used to enable the borrower to diversify and stabilize an otherwise risky farm program by developing pastures and forage crops and feeding livestock. The installation of a water facility on the range may encourage proper distribution of grazing and thereby promote the conservation and production of natural grasses. The best use of grazing privileges on national forests or the public domain may be promoted by an irrigation facility installed on a nearby unit to develop a winter feed base for stock carried on the forests in the summer.

All three types of supervised loans as a rule are based on farm and home plans developed by the borrower in consultation with the agency's local supervisor. These plans represent the kind of program the borrower expects to follow in the years to come and are of value as a guide to farm operations. They also assist in determining the soundness of the loans. Any farmer who obtains one or more of these supervised loans is entitled to receive advice and guidance from the local supervisor about any phase of his farming program. Most of the advice given concerning the establishment and care of pastures or hayfields is based upon recommendations of the Department, State agricultural colleges, and experiment stations. Hence the programs of other agencies relating to grassland agriculture are further drawn upon in the farm planning and supervisory phases of this loan program.

THE AUTHORS ⋘ *Neil W. Johnson, assistant head of the Division of Farm Management and Costs, Bureau of Agricultural Economics, grew up on an irrigated farm in the State of Washington. Trained at Washington State College and Harvard University, he has devoted more than 24 years to re-*

search in agricultural economics. He is the author of numerous bulletins and articles in the field of farm management, many dealing with problems of western agriculture.

Charles W. Loomer, formerly acting head of the land policy section, Division of Land Economics, Bureau of Agricultural Economics, is now associate professor of agricultural economics in the University of Wisconsin. Dr. Loomer has written a number of bulletins and articles on problems of land management in the Great Plains.

[*A directory of Federal agencies whose work includes activities pertaining to grasslands and a list of State agricultural experiment stations are given at the end of the book.*]

Soil · Grass · Conservation

ENVIRONMENT OF NATURAL GRASSLAND

C. P. BARNES

THE FOUR great plant formations of the land surface of the earth are forest, grassland, desert shrub, and tundra. Grasslands are believed to include about a fourth of the area occupied by these types of vegetation and about a fifth of the land surface of the globe.

These four formations reflect chiefly climate. Generally speaking, humid lands are woodlands and dry lands are desert shrub or waste; the grasslands lie between these climatic extremes in zones of intermediate moisture supply. There are many important exceptions to this generalization: Lack of moisture does not explain the marshlands, and some kinds of trees grow even in desert climates, like the Joshua tree of the Mohave Desert. Actually, grasslands will stand greater extremes of environment than forest—not only greater aridity but greater cold—and will grow in wetter places.

Grass is usually first to invade shallow water, and the marshlands thus created may exist for centuries until the accumulating organic remains of the grasses and the sediment lodging in them create an environment where trees can live. Grassland extends into the frigid zones above the timber line on high mountains, forming alpine meadows. Grass will stand soils with more soluble salts than forest, even

though the mangrove tree can grow with its roots in sea water at high tide.

Near the transition zones between the major plant formations, soils may offset the effect of climate and tip the scales in favor of forest, grass, or desert shrub, although the climate might lead us to expect a different formation. In some places we find natural grassland not because forest would not grow there but because the forest has not had time enough or opportunity to invade and occupy them. In Manitoba and Saskatchewan and on Kodiak Island, for example, forest has advanced considerably into grassland during the past century.

Once the land is covered with vigorous turf grasses, it is hard for forest to gain an entry; the tiny tree seedling must compete with the grass for moisture and light. Conversely, grass advances with great difficulty into dense forest, even though it might grow perfectly well were the forest cleared away. Quite often a plant formation dominates in the transition zones until some accident or slight change in environment gives the competing formation opportunity to invade.

The grassland formation tends to dominate when the upper layers of the soil are moist during a considerable part of the year but the deeper layers are too dry for such deep-rooted plants

45

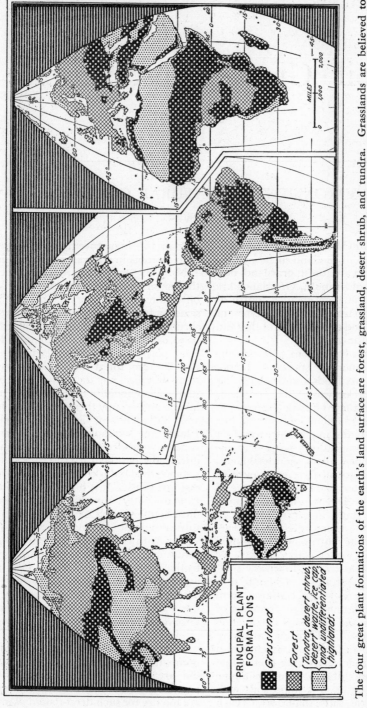

The four great plant formations of the earth's land surface are forest, grassland, desert shrub, and tundra. Grasslands are believed to include about one-fourth of the area occupied by these types of vegetation and about one-fifth of the earth's land surface. These four formations reflect chiefly climate. As a rule, humid lands are woodlands and dry lands are desert shrub or waste; the grasslands lie between these climatic extremes in zones of intermediate moisture supply. There are, however, many important exceptions to this generalization.

as trees. The soil moisture, therefore, rather than total rainfall, governs the distribution of grasslands. Deep sandy soils that allow moisture to penetrate deeply may support trees in a region that is generally grassland, while adjoining fine-textured soils that allow water to run off or evaporate from the surface before it can penetrate will be grass-covered.

Three broad kinds of grassed lands are recognized: The short-grass land, sometimes called steppe; the tall-grass land, or prairie; and savanna. Each has many variations. The first and third make up the great bulk of the earth's grasslands.

Short-grass lands characterize a large part of the subhumid lands of the Temperate Zone. The largest and best known are the Great Plains of North America and the steppes of Eurasia. The rainfall of the short-grass lands keeps the upper soil layers moist during the warm season in most years, sufficient to support the shallow-rooted short grasses.

The rainfall is not enough to moisten the soil down to the ground water; hence, a permanent dry layer lies beneath the moist layer. The depth of the moist surface layer varies with the rainfall and the soil. Near the humid border of the short-grass land, several years of above-normal rainfall may encourage tall grasses and convert the short-grass land to tall. Sandy soils that permit water to penetrate and moisten a deeper layer of soil will often bear tall grasses in a short-grass region. The western part of the Nebraska sand hills is a good example.

Rainfall in the short-grass lands fluctuates enormously from year to year. Years occur when the rainfall is no greater than might be expected in the desert, and so do years when it equals that in the humid forested regions. Evaporation is rapid in the warm season because of much wind and high temperatures. Farming must be adjusted to these conditions. Land is kept fallow in alternate years to accumulate enough soil moisture for good crops.

Some of the feed produced in the moist years must be stored for use in dry ones to come. Incomes must likewise be husbanded. The soils of the short-grass areas tend to be fertile, but the rainfall in most years is not enough to allow the full potentialities of the fertile soils to be realized. Fertilizers, as a rule, do not produce substantial increases in crop yield because moisture rather than fertility usually limits production. Limestone is seldom needed since the short-grass lands exist under climates where lime accumulates in the soil, instead of leaching out.

Prairie

Tall-grass land or prairie is found where soil moisture is deeper than in short-grass lands. Prairies are found mainly in three parts of the world—in Central North America, the Argentine Pampa and nearby Uruguay and Brazil, and European Russia. In each, the prairies lie along the moister edge of the short-grass lands. A great many small bodies of prairie exist, but altogether prairies cover far less of the earth than the short-grass lands or savannas.

Toward its drier margin, prairie occupies soils where a dry layer intervenes between moist surface and ground water. Toward its moister margin it extends into the region of soils that are moist down to the ground water. In fact, in the United States and in Argentina, prairies extend onto soils where the water table reaches the surface. Thus prairies occupy both humid and subhumid lands. In the United States particularly, prairies extend into the humid region where trees grow perfectly well when planted.

Why prairies should be found in such a climate has long been a matter of speculation. Given prairie to start with, it is not hard to imagine that the dense, vigorous grass, with the help of fire, could have kept trees from invading. A good prairie fire would destroy any tree seedlings that might have come up, with no permanent injury to

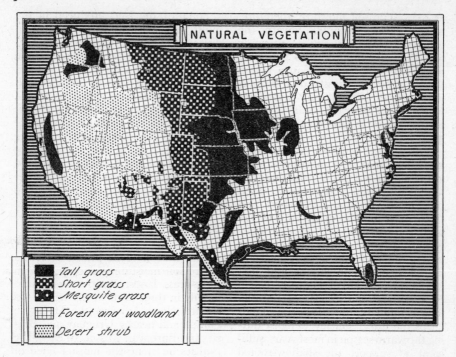

NATURAL VEGETATION

Tall grass
Short grass
Mesquite grass
Forest and woodland
Desert shrub

Short-grass lands characterize a large part of the subhumid lands of the Temperate Zone. The rainfall of the short-grass lands keeps the upper soil layers moist during the warm season in most years, enough to support the shallow-rooted short grasses. Near the humid border of the short-grass land, several years of above-normal rainfall may encourage tall grasses and convert short-grass land to tall. Rainfall fluctuates enormously—years occur when rainfall is no greater than might be expected in the desert, and so do years when it equals that in the humid forested regions. Tall-grass land or prairie is found where soil moisture is deeper than in short-grass lands.

the grass. There is some evidence that the central prairie region has somewhat more dry years and perhaps less actual moisture than the forested regions adjoining it.

But this fact obviously cannot explain the absence of trees in the wet swales that, before they were drained, covered a great acreage in northern Illinois and northern Iowa. These wet places in the prairies were grass-covered, while in the forested parts of Indiana and Ohio some of the correspondingly wet places had become timbered. It seems possible, then, that forest might in time have occupied the humid prairie, if the white man had not intervened.

Some prairies are found in humid

climates where soils have developed from chalk, marl, or other highly calcareous material. The Black Prairies of Texas and Alabama are examples. Most trees seem to be less tolerant of salts, including calcium carbonate, than grasses are. This may explain these humid, calcareous prairies, the soils of which are known as Rendzinas.

Some tall-grass prairies are marsh-lands. Some of these wet prairies, as I have noted, occur within general prairie regions; others occur in forested or in desert regions. Some, like the Everglades, occur in fresh water; others, like the tidal marshes, grow in salt water. Marshlands generally occur in environments too wet for most trees—yet mangrove woodlands grow with roots submerged by sea water. The most we can say by way of general explanation of marshland is that tree species tolerant enough of the soil and moisture conditions of the particular marshland to compete with grasses have not existed near enough to invade the marsh. This can be said about any grassland near the transition zone between woodland and grassland.

The humid prairies combine high soil fertility with adequate moisture for high yields of crops. They have contributed a great deal to the impressive agricultural productivity of the United States and Argentina.

Savannas are the great grasslands of the Tropics. In extent they greatly exceed the tall-grass prairies of the Temperate Zone and nearly, if not fully, equal the short-grass areas. They cover more of Africa than any other plant formation, and occupy a great area in the interior of Brazil.

Measured by total annual rainfall, the climate of the savannas might seem to be humid, but little rain falls in 3 to 8 months in winter. That dry period, plus the high temperature and evaporation typical of the Tropics, hinders the development of forests.

Characteristic of the savannas are scattered trees that usually are small and scrubby and grow singly or in groups. The vegetation is dominantly grass, however. Where the rainfall is greater or where the soils collect and hold more moisture, the trees grow close enough to form woodland. In some areas the grasses are tall, in others short, corresponding to zones of greater or less moisture. They generally do not form sods as in the prairies and short grasslands. During the dry period they become dormant and dry out and the scattered trees lose their leaves. Fires burn over much of the grassland in this period and hinder the spread of woodland.

Soils of the savannas are generally far less fertile than those of the prairies and short grasslands. A very small part has been put into cultivation. Under good husbandry, with adequate fertilization, an enormous area of this grassland can be brought into production when food needs of the world require it. Crops must be adjusted to the dry period—but that, of course, is no longer than the winter dormant period in much of the Temperate Zone. Much research will be needed before modern methods of farming suited to this region can be widely practiced.

THE AUTHOR⋘ *C. P. Barnes is chief analyst in the Division of Soil Survey, Bureau of Plant Industry, Soils, and Agricultural Engineering, at Beltsville, Md. He has worked on problems of soil uses and productivity in the Department of Agriculture since 1929.*

GRASS AND THE SOIL

CHARLES E. KELLOGG

THE GREAT variety and complexity of the country scene appeals to most people whether they are professional naturalists or not. Each rural landscape has its own set of characteristics. Any one may be just a little different from the thousands of others, or very unlike any of them. Through science modern man tries to understand these landscapes—to unravel their many interlocking relationships—in order to discover principles that can be used to guide the great producing powers of nature to his own ends.

But the job is so big that scientists have had to divide it among them. Thus botanists, geologists, foresters, climatologists, horticulturists, agronomists, soil scientists, farmers, and others are each concerned with some part of the whole. Yet at some stages in scientific work the facts and principles discovered in these specific lines of inquiry must be brought together if principles of prediction value in the real world are to be developed. That is, plants growing in even the simplest farm, or garden, or forest are subject to all the influences of the environment acting together and they contribute to this environment as well.

Nothing illustrates this complexity better than grass. In some landscapes tall, luxuriant grasses grow naturally and help make black soils that are naturally productive for cultivated plants. The invasion of such landscapes by forest degrades these soils—they lose part of their great producing potential for crops. And this may happen quickly—not in terms of a man's lifetime perhaps, but in 200 years or so.

Yet in other places more productive soils are found under forest than under grass. Here invasion of the soil by grasses degrades it rapidly, within the period of one man's life or much less.

These are two extremes. But often it is by looking at the extremes that we discover principles of great importance to the soils between them, where differences are not so easily seen.

The Soil

Suppose we look at the soil itself. What is it? First of all, it is the natural medium in which plants grow. It is a mixture of mineral matter and organic matter, some of which is living. Things are being added to it and taken away from it. The soil on the very surface is not like that just beneath it; in fact, the soils in most places consist of a series of unlike layers, one over the other, each from a few inches to several feet in depth.

Then, too, the surface is gradually changing. Some soils are slowly being eroded, bit by bit, so that all the layers move down. To each layer a bit of the one beneath is being changed and added to its lower side as it loses its upper part by erosion or to another layer above it. Finally, new fresh minerals from the rock beneath are incorporated into the lower part of the lowest layer of the soil.

Other soils, of course, receive additions to the top instead of to the bottom. Along great rivers silty alluvium settles out of the water over the soil. Dust settles from the air—perhaps just a little; often a great deal. Volcanoes add ash or cinders to soils, sometimes lowering their productivity for crop plants but more often increasing it.

When water enters the soil, air is forced out of the pore spaces. Then as the soil dries, air returns. In this process gasses like carbon dioxide escape and others like ammonia enter the soil to be absorbed.

The entering water, either as rain or irrigation water, brings soluble materials with it too—usually just a little, but sometimes a great deal. The excess water beyond what the soil can hold seeps out into deep drainage and carries soluble materials away.

Then, of course, plants are growing on the soil, extracting nutrients, and producing organic matter from these soil nutrients and those from the air and water. Depending on the kind of vegetation, the total organic matter may be a ton or so per acre up to several hundred tons. Thus, in the living organic matter the soil has a great storehouse of nutrients. When the plants and animals die, the remains serve as food for micro-organisms. As it decomposes, the nutrients in it are made available to new plants.

Thus a soil changes between day and night, from season to season, and over long periods of geological time.

Yet soils are not quite so difficult to understand as this recital might suggest because many of the processes go together. Ignoring for the moment man's interference, a soil—an individual set of soil characteristics that we call a soil type—results from a particular combination of five genetic factors—climate, vegetation, parent rock, relief, and time. Thus soils are not distributed promiscuously over the earth, but in an orderly discoverable geographic pattern. A given set of the five genetic factors everywhere produces the same set of soil characteristics—the same soil type.

But to these natural types of soil must be added the changes caused by use—often drastic changes for better or for worse, in terms of crop production. That is, many soils developed originally under forest in the humid temperate regions have been made ever so much more productive by careful husbandry, including the growing of grasses, the use of lime and manures, and improved drainage for hundreds of years. Other soils have been deprived of their essential cover of grass or trees and exposed directly to the sun, wind, and water, with serious degradation by erosion, blowing, burning of organic matter, and loss of structure.

Soil scientists have been and are now attempting to discover precisely what types of soil exist in the world, where they are, and how they respond to that whole group of practices we call "husbandry."

One cannot understand a soil by looking simply at one or two of its characteristics. Slope, depth, texture, color, structure, chemical composition, and many more must be seen in combination. Not only that, a soil must be seen in relation to those around it. A soil is three-dimensional. It occupies discreet areas of the earth. Around each area are boundary lines that separate it from the other soil types with different sets of soil characteristics. These boundary lines come in places where there is a change in one or more of the five genetic factors.

So a soil is a solid, the upper surface of which is the surface of the land. The lower surface is defined by the lower limits of biological forces, and the sides are the boundaries with other soil types. One cannot take a soil into the laboratory any more than he can a mountain or a river; but one may take samples of rock, water, or soil into the laboratory for important investigations to determine some of the characteristics of mountains, rivers, or soils. Even further, a soil is a landscape with a characteristic climate and vegetation. Thus plants and soils are essential parts of one whole, each influencing the other and both reacting to the climate.

Soil Productivity

A central problem of inquiry in soil science is soil productivity for various crops, grasses, and trees and how to increase it or maintain it efficiently. The two principal aspects of soil productivity are its structure, or tilth, and its fertility, or content and balance of available plant nutrients.

Let us consider the fertility. Commonly, soil scientists attempt to express the amounts of nutrients available to plants in terms of "pounds per acre" of available phosphorus, potassium, calcium, and so on. These figures permit the comparison of soils only in the narrow sense, not as landscapes.

Suppose, for example, that we compare the black grassland soils (Chernozem) of eastern North Dakota with the light-colored forested soils of northern Michigan (Podzol). We shall see at once that the content of available plant nutrients is considerably higher in the Chernozem than in the Podzol. But to compare the total plant nutrients in, and available to, the biological cycles of the natural untouched landscapes, we shall need to add to the amount in the acre of soil that in the living matter—in the trunks, branches, and leaves of the trees, in the animals, and in the other plants and microorganisms. This additional amount will be large for the forest and relatively low for the grasses. Of course, the nutrients tied up in living matter are not subject to much leaching—not until the material dies and begins to decompose. It is mainly the material in the soil that is subject to leaching. Thus, of this total, more will be subject to leaching under grass than under forest.

Generally, the percentage of mineral plant nutrients in the organic remains from grass is higher than in those from forest. Thus more organic acids result from the decomposition of forest litter, even though the total of minerals supplied is somewhat greater. Per ton of dry matter produced, grasses return to the soil more bases, like calcium, potassium, and so on, than trees, other conditions being comparable; and, with nearly equivalent synthesis of organic matter, grasses produce more humus—black, stable organic matter—because of their chemical nature and their dense, fibrous root systems.

Then because of the relatively drier climate, the Chernozem soil is much less subject to leaching than the Podzol. Grass, side by side with forest in the moist Podzol region, holds less against leaching than the forest; grass side by side with forest at the boundary between the Chernozem and Podzol zones gives a darker soil, higher in organic matter and plant nutrients, than forest. The dark, fertile, granular surface soil is deeper under the grass and more suitable for crop plants than that under forest from the same rock material.

Thus, the figures selected for a comparison of an acre of Chernozem with an acre of Podzol vary greatly, depending upon whether we think only of the soil in a narrow sense or of the total landscape, including soils and plants together. In both scientific and practical work, both sets of comparisons are needed.

If the light-colored Podzols are fertilized, it is possible to have soil fertile for grass, despite the leaching. If this grass cover is maintained, the cultivated soil itself then takes on some of the physical and biological characteristics of the Chernozem of the black grasslands. But if we do not make up for the greater leaching in the Podzol landscape by the proper use of lime and fertilizers, the pastures and meadows are likely to be poor—indeed, not only poor, but the soil may actually become less fertile under the grass than under the forest. (Young alluvial soils or others too young to have received normal leaching are exceptions.)

In practice a farmer on the Podzol soils, let us say in New England, will produce pasture more efficiently by using lime and fertilizer on a small area to develop a soil approaching the less-leached Chernozem in fertility than to use a far larger area for untreated pasture. That is, a hundred acres of untreated pasture will, ordinarily, give less return in the Podzol landscape than the same area with 20 acres of well-treated pasture and 80 acres of forest, to say nothing of the fact that the long-time productivity of the soil will be better.

In this comparison both landscapes have a cold season when the ground is frozen. Let us look at the contrasting relationships between grass (savanna) and soil, and forest and soil in the humid Tropics with only a short dry season. In these comparisons it must be clear that reference to "grass" or "forest" includes all the plants, animals, and micro-organisms associated with them, not simply the trees and grasses themselves.

First of all, leaching under the heavy rainfall in equatorial regions is very severe. At high temperatures all chemical reactions are accelerated. (Generally the speed of chemical reactions doubles with each rise of $18°$ F.) Thus at any moment the (unfertilized) soil is low in all available plant nutrients (again except for very young soils like those on fresh alluvium or volcanic ejecta). The deep-rooted trees of the tropical rain forest draw nutrients from a great volume of soil. A large amount of these nutrients is collected and stored in the great tree trunks, in the branches and leaves of trees and other plants, and in micro-organisms and animals. At equilibrium, a small amount continually returns to the soil surface as the plants drop their leaves, and some is returned on or near the surface as the other living matter dies. And the amount lost by leaching balances the gains from new minerals and from the atmosphere. But the total amount of nutrients collected in the savanna is relatively small.

Thus, if we compare equal areas of

the two landscapes under the same climate, one with a cover of tropical rain forest and the other with a cover of savanna, we shall find an enormous amount of material held by the living plants and not subject to leaching under the forest, and only a small amount held by the plants in the savanna with the rest subject to leaching. And, of course, that which is subject to leaching is leached out of the soil. Matters are made worse by fire. Whereas the tropical forest does not burn unless it is cut and made to burn, the savanna burns like gasoline-soaked rags when dry and so usually burns in the dry season. Moreover, tropical soils are relatively low in their capacity to absorb plant nutrients. Thus, a large part of the ash from burning the savanna is lost with the first heavy rains.

In such landscapes, then, we find the most productive soils, other things being equal, under the forest—the reverse of our comparison at the boundary between Chernozem and Podzol. In the Chernozem region where leaching is low and temperatures are relatively low, grass acts as a great soil builder and conserver of plant nutrients. In the hot humid Tropics, grass has the reverse effect and becomes a degrader of soil.

After cutting the luxuriant forest, crops may be grown in rotations and mixtures for periods of 2 to 7 years— sometimes even longer—depending upon local soil conditions. But it is necessary for forest to return to this soil again before the nutrient supply built up under the forest has been seriously depleted. Otherwise, the savanna will come into the cleared land and injure the soil for both trees and crops. After 10 to 15 years of forest growth, the land may again be devoted to a rotation of crops.

Soil Structure

Soils productive for crops are permeable to roots, water, and air. The productive soil has the individual grains grouped into aggregates so there are pore spaces for passage. Generally speaking, tillage by itself tends to destroy structure, tends to break up the soil crumbs and granules, and causes the clay particles to "run together" into masses. This effect of tillage varies enormously with different soil types and within one soil type, according to moisture conditions at the time of tillage and other cultural practices. In fact, a few soils become too granular with tillage so that contacts between roots and soil particles are too few for the proper transfer of water and the nutrients.

Even though tillage has the effect of injuring soil structure—scarcely at all with some soil types and a great deal with others—it often cannot be eliminated. Soil structure must be good in the lower layers as well as in the upper ones. Since an active population of micro-organisms is essential for good structure in most soils, organic materials and fertilizers must be added to many soils to make them productive for crops and grasses, and added not only to the surface, but also to the subsoils. This may require deep plowing or chiseling to get the materials into the lower layers so that roots may go deeply.

The exposure of many soils to the hot sun injures structure by decreasing the micro-population, hastening the decomposition of organic matter, and causing a hard crust at the surface. Excess erosion, beyond that normal for the soil, may remove surface layers with good crumb structure and expose lower layers with poor structure. In fact, this type of injury by erosion is, generally, far more important than the nutrient losses from erosion.

Vigorous, close-growing, deep-rooted vegetation is the best builder of soil structure. Generally, the deep-rooted legumes and grasses are best for cultivated soil, provided, and only provided, that proper varieties are grown with adequate fertilization or manuring as needed on the individual soil type. But a well-growing forest produces better soil structure than poorly growing grasses. The best structure of all is produced under tall grasses in subhumid regions, as in Chernozem. Where leaching is low, organic matter and nutrients are conserved, and a deep fibrous root system develops. In areas of high leaching, like the humid Tropics, where the forest grows much better than grasses and conserves the nutrients, forest is superior to grass in developing and maintaining good soil structure.

In temperate regions, like most of the United States and Europe, the growing of vigorous stands of the deep-rooted grasses and legumes is generally the most effective way to develop soil structure, provided the soil is properly fertilized, as needed, in depth as well as in the surface. Of course, in the humid parts of the country soil structure can be maintained under a stand of forest also. But it is usually more efficient in the United States to work out a cropping system that does not require the periodic use of forest for the regeneration of soils for cropping.

The Place of Grass

Grass is the natural cover of many soil types throughout the world. It is the natural cover of the Chernozem—the famous black soils of subhumid temperate regions. But we must not conclude that grass is everywhere a conserving cover or that it always improves the soil. In moist regions where there is a great deal of leaching, the forest is generally a more conserving natural cover because it gathers a large body of plant nutrients, holds them in living forms, and gradually returns them to the soil.

In hot humid regions it is especially difficult to have good grass and productive soil together—one must make up through practice the great ability of the forest to shade the soil and keep it cool, to maintain structure, and to conserve plant nutrients against the strong forces of leaching. Unless management practices can offset these changes in environment, grasses will not grow well and the soils will deteriorate.

The same principle holds in all humid regions, like the eastern part of the United States, where the natural cover is forest, except for young soils that have not been leached importantly, even though the contrast may not appear to be so great as in the Tropics. Grass can often be established and maintained in naturally forested regions simply by seeding and by fire, mowing, or cutting to keep out the young shrubs and trees. But under such conditions, without fertilizers or manures, most pastures and meadows will be poor and the soils will deteriorate, perhaps rapidly, perhaps slowly.

Farmers really should make a clear decision between grass or forest. Although wild grass is a good soil-building cover in semiarid and subhumid regions if protected against overgrazing, it usually is not in humid regions except for relatively unleached soils. Wild, uncared for, frequently burned grassland in humid regions produces little. The soil is made more productive and yields more if forested.

Thus grass cannot be classified definitely as "soil-conserving" or "soil-depleting"; it may be one or the other on the same farm, on the same soil type, depending on cultural practices.

Except for young alluvial soils, most soils in the United States must be periodically devoted to the grasses and grasslike plants to remain productive for crop plants. Thus proper liming and fertilization for deep-rooted legumes, alone or in mixtures with grass, are the first steps for either production or soil conservation on millions of American farms. The amount of lime and the kinds of fertilizers vary from soil to soil but emphasis needs to be given phosphates, potash, and boron, roughly in that order, although each field has its individual needs for these and other nutrients according to the soil type and previous management.

For the efficient production of grasses—efficient in terms of quality, yield, and good effects on the long-time productivity of the soil—practices must be used to maintain within the soil conditions similar to those in the natural Chernozem. This means abundant plant nutrients and good structure for considerable depth. Such a deep layer of fertile soil with good structure often needs to be made by the farmer from the natural soil. An individual set of practices to this end will be required in each individual landscape.

With the proper practices, grasses can be grown efficiently in most parts of the world, but not everywhere. One of the great problems of agricultural science is to learn how to make these practices more efficient and especially how to adapt them more precisely to the individual soil types. Then too, we need to discover practices for growing good grass efficiently on those soils for which we have as yet no satisfactory methods.

THE AUTHOR≪≪≪≪ *Charles E. Kellogg is chief of the Division of Soil Survey in the Bureau of Plant Industry, Soils, and Agricultural Engineering. Before joining the Department in 1934, he taught soil science and did research in that subject at Michigan State College, the University of Wisconsin, and the North Dakota Agricultural College. He is a graduate of Michigan State College. Dr. Kellogg has written and lectured widely on soil science and general agriculture.*

HOW SOILS DEVELOP UNDER GRASS

JAMES THORP

RELATIONSHIPS between grassland soils and their dominantly grassy cover are close and complex. The soils owe many of their properties to the kinds of vegetation they support; the kinds and qualities of grasses and associated plants depend considerably upon the characteristics of the soil.

Native dense stands of tall grasses in the United States usually have produced thick, dark-colored soils, high in fertility and suitable for growing many economic crop plants, especially members of the grass and legume families.

Less luxuriant grasses in drier areas have produced lighter colored soils with less organic matter and nitrogen, but frequently with more mineral plant nutrients than those of tall-grass regions. The variety of adapted crops on these soils is narrower, and yields are limited by the lower rainfall, except where crops are irrigated.

In the *Atlas of American Agriculture,* 1936, H. L. Shantz said this about the location and conditions in the United States under which grasslands develop: "Lying between the western and eastern forest belts, and extending from Canada on the north to Mexico on the south, is the great grassland area, broken only by river courses and occasional buttes or low mountains.

"Grasslands characterize areas in which trees have failed to develop, either because of unfavorable soil conditions, poor drainage and aeration, intense cold and wind, deficient moisture supply, or repeated fires. Grasses of one kind or another are admirably suited to withstand conditions of excess moisture, excess drought, and fires which would destroy tree growth."

Important smaller areas of grassland in this country occur also on the Coastal Plain of Alabama and Mississippi, in north-central Oregon and southeastern Washington, in the Central Valley of California, and in hundreds of narrow strips along the mountains and basins from the eastern limit of the Rocky Mountains to the Pacific coast.

The type of grass and the density of cover—both important to soil formation—are determined by the interaction of many factors. For example, rank water-loving grasses and sedges and other grasslike plants grow in poorly drained areas and contribute enormous quantities of organic matter to soils of marshy and semimarshy lands. Wiesenboden [1] (wet meadow soils) and Half Bog soils develop in these situations.

The well-drained black Prairie and Chernozem soils have thick covers of sod-forming tall-grass associations. Heavy, dark, grayish-brown clay soils like the Pierre clay developed from Pierre shale of South Dakota and northwestern Nebraska seem to provide conditions where western wheatgrass is best able to survive as the dominant grass. Shantz's map of the grasslands of the United States, in the *Atlas of American Agriculture,* shows an area of western wheatgrass coextensive with a large area of Pierre clay soil. On very sandy soils, as in the sand hills of Nebraska, are associations of sand sage and sand reedgrass with bluestem grass. Farther south, as in sandy soils of Texas, a low scrubby growth of shinnery oak is associated with bunchgrasses.

Blue grama appears to be the dominant grass of medium-textured soils in the zone of Brown soils from Colorado to the Canadian line, while mixed grama and buffalograss are widely distributed in the dry parts of the Chestnut and Reddish Chestnut and the Reddish-Brown soils zones. Red Desert soils and some areas of Reddish-Brown soils in New Mexico and western Texas are dominated by black grama grass, associated with other grasses and desert shrub.

The formation of grassland soils involves the accumulation of mineral

----

[1] Throughout the text of this paper references are made to great soil groups, as Prairie, Chernozem, Wiesenboden, Chestnut soils, Brown soils, etc. These are described by C. F. Marbut in the *Atlas of American Agriculture,* 1936, and redefined and (in part) renamed in the chapter on soil classification in the *Yearbook of Agriculture 1938.* Prairie soils, for example, do not include all grassland soils but are restricted in the United States largely to the Corn Belt.

soil materials, the invasion of these materials by grass, and the accumulation of organic matter and development of soil structure.

Mineral soil materials accumulate through the direct chemical and physical weathering of rocks and through the deposition of broken and chemically weathered rock fragments (sand, silt, clay, and gravel) by streams, lakes, glaciers, wind, and down-slope gravitational movement. A very rough estimate is that one-third to one-fourth of the soil materials of the natural grasslands in the United States are the products of direct weathering of rocks of greatly varying composition and hardness. The remaining materials have been deposited by streams and the other agencies I have listed.

The larger areas of grassland soil materials, developed directly through the weathering of rock, came from soft rocks that either were weathered easily to form soil or were already soft enough in their original state to be penetrated easily by the fibrous roots of grasses. The great area of Pierre shale in South Dakota, Colorado, and Nebraska, and the still larger areas of tertiary shales, silt-stones, and soft sandstones of Montana, North Dakota, Wyoming, Colorado, and Utah are good examples.

The extensive loess (wind-blown dust) deposits of the Great Plains east of the Rockies and of the Palouse region of Oregon and Washington are ideal for the growth of grass. Loess is a uniform unstratified mixture of silt, very fine sand, and clay. It varies in thickness from a few inches to more than 100 feet in the United States. Probably loess is the most extensive single kind of parent material of grassland soils in the world as a whole.

Glacial deposits composed of clay, sand, silt, and stone fragments of many kinds are parent materials of thousands of square miles of grassland soils of the northern Great Plains of the United States and of the Great Plains of Canada. Possibly wind-laid and water-laid sands are third in importance. For example, the grassy sand hills of Nebraska are only slightly smaller in area than all of the cultivated land of Japan, and very large areas of aeolian sands occur in Kansas, Colorado, Wyoming, Oklahoma, Texas, Oregon, and Washington.

Stream alluvium and lake sediments of medium to clayey textures also are important, especially along the large river valleys and mountain fronts.

Where climatic conditions are favorable, grass invades areas of freshly deposited soil materials very soon after they are first exposed. If accumulation of sediments or weathered rock materials is slow, grasses become well established and begin immediately the work of soil building. Roots spread through the soil and sooner or later die, providing organic, humus-forming waste.

Indeed, where the accumulation is slow, soil formation can almost keep pace with weathering and deposition, and upper soil layers rapidly take on a dark color. Where accumulation of soil material is rapid, as is true of some sedimentary deposits, vegetation has relatively little effect on soil development until accumulation slows down or stops. Plants are covered before they can contribute much to the soil.

Abundant geologic evidence in large areas of grassland in the United States shows not only that the stream sediments and wind-laid dust (loess) and sand are extensive, but also that many of them accumulated so rapidly that soil formation did not advance appreciably until the deposits were almost complete. Furthermore, buried remnants of soils, in some places one above another, show that the history of soil formation has been repeated many times. Waves of catastrophic erosion have advanced across the land, destroying strongly developed soils and concurrently building up new deposits of alluvium, loess, or sand. Local accumulation of sediments has been so rapid that soil formation could not keep pace, and soil development has been delayed until the rapid erosion and deposition have abated.

Even now, the opposing processes of erosion and deposition are working in the grasslands of the United States. In the Badlands of South Dakota, Wyoming, and Montana, for example, catastrophic erosion is rapidly eating away the cliffs of soft bedrock and dumping sediments indiscriminately on the lowlands and along the stream courses. After the first big wave of deposition has subsided, grasses and other plants take root quickly on smooth land below the Badland cliffs and a new cycle of soil formation begins on the fresh deposits. High grasslands behind the cliffs, meanwhile, are undermined and destroyed.

When grasses and other herbaceous plants secure a foothold, the soil materials are held in place by a network of roots. Old roots die and new ones take their places. Dead roots are attacked by bacteria, microscopic animals, and fungi, and mineral and organic nutrients are made available to living plants. Under the climatic and biotic conditions of grasslands, part of the root material, as well as part of the annual crop of grass tops, remain to form dark-colored, finely divided organic matter (humus) in the soil, and a larger part is absorbed by other plants or dissipated into the air as gas or into the soil water and carried away.

Organic material in grassland soils, then, includes living and dead plant parts, living and dead organisms, and humus. The decay of grass roots and leaves and the formation of humus so improve the fertility, physical condition, and moisture-holding capacity of the soil that more luxuriant grasses will survive as time goes on. Light-colored soils, shallow to the underlying parent soil material, which are characteristic of the first stages of development, are thickened and darkened gradually with the improvement of the grassy cover. The end point of this process varies with the moisture supply.

As soon as vegetation is established, many kinds of animals take up their abode in the soil to take advantage of the food provided by plants or to prey

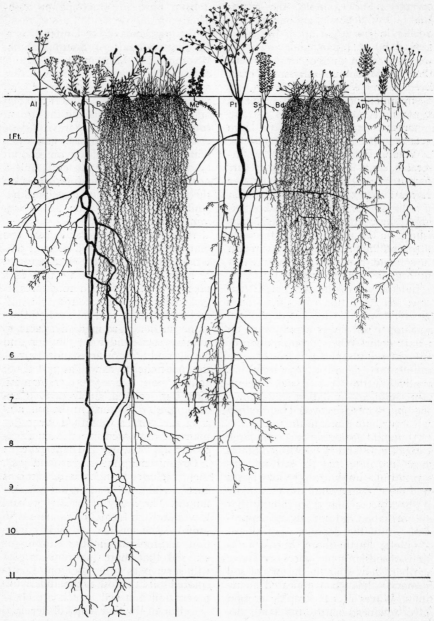

Roots of different grassland plants draw their moisture from different soil layers. Some native plants extend their roots to depths of 20 or more feet. Drawing made at Hays, Kans., before the great drought, by J. E. Weaver and F. W. Albertson (Ecol. Monographs, volume 13, p. 100).   *Al,* narrow-leafed 4-o'clock, *Allionia linearis; Kg,* prairie false boneset, *Kuhnia gultinosa; Bg,* blue grama, *Bouteloua gracilis; Mc,* globemallow, *Malvastrum coccineum; Pt,* a legume, *Psoralea tenuiflora; Ss, Sideranthus spinulosis; Bd,* buffalograss, *Buchloe dactyloides; Ap,* western ragweed, *Ambrosia psilostachya;* and *Lj,* skeleton weed, *Lygodesmia juncea.*

on one another. Insects (especially ants), millipedes, earthworms, gophers, prairie dogs, and many other animals live interdependent lives in the soil. Their burrowing operations stir the soil, mix it with fresh minerals, kill some roots, and hasten the process of humification. The soil becomes a community of teeming activity.

Organic matter in grassland soils acts as a sponge to absorb rain water, as a home and as food for the microscopic plants and animals that prepare the soil for the use of higher plants, and as a water reservoir to supply plants with needed moisture and to cushion them against drought. Much of the all-essential nitrogen is stored in the organic material waiting to be made available by micro-organisms for the use of higher plants.

Field studies of grassland soils that range in age from a few years to a probable age of many thousand years indicate that organic matter accumulates somewhat slowly during the first few years until a good relationship for the formation of organic matter is reached among the microscopic plants and animals, the higher plants, and the higher animals that live in the soil. Following the establishment of this favorable relationship, the rate of accumulation increases rapidly for many years and more slowly after that. In medium-textured soil materials of well-balanced mineral composition, it is thought that the maximum content of organic matter will be attained in several hundred years.

Ultimately some rough balance is reached between the rate of accumulation and destruction of humus and between types of grasses and forbs present and the degree of their luxuriance. The level at which this rough balance is struck depends on the texture, porosity, and plant-nutrient content of the soil material and on the amount of easily available moisture received, absorbed, and retained by the soil for use of plants. This balance is a dynamic one, subject to minor fluctuations, and probably is maintained un-

der natural conditions for a few thousand years.

During periods of greater-than-normal humidity, the grasses are more luxuriant and contribute more organic material to the soil; leaching goes to a greater depth than in dry years, and some of the soluble compounds are carried out in subsoil water. In most grasslands, both wind and water erosion are reduced during years of abundant rainfall because the luxuriant vegetation can better hold the soil in place.

During dry periods, grass cover may be largely destroyed if the droughts are prolonged, and contribution of organic matter to the soil may be stopped temporarily. Erosion by wind and water becomes active during or immediately following these dry periods, and organic matter is lost that took years and years for accumulation.

Grasses have a profound effect on the structure of soil. Organic matter from the decomposition of grassroots and leaves helps to hold clay, silt, and sand particles together to form structure particles or aggregates of various shapes, sizes, and degrees of firmness. Generally the upper layers of grassland soils, where roots are most abundant, attain an extraordinary degree of granulation in which the structure particles take the form of firm granules or porous crumbs ranging from less than one-thirty-second of an inch to a half inch in diameter. Some of these aggregates, especially those containing more than about 30 percent clay, are firm and hold their size and shape even with rough handling; others, especially those containing much sand and silt and little clay, are soft, porous, and unstable. The development of granular structure makes the clayey soils of grasslands crumbly and friable and almost as easily tilled as sandy soils.

In all but the very sandy soils, the structure particles of subsoil layers (roughly, the layers lying between 10 and 30 inches below the surface) usually are coarser, more angular, and firmer than those of the upper soil layers, partly because many of them are more clayey and partly because they contain less organic matter.

Some of these structure particles are angular and blocky, others are more or less rounded and nut-shaped, and still others take the form of small prisms. They have less organic matter than the surface layers and usually are held together by thin films composed of jelly-like clay mixed with organic matter. Probably the shape, size, and arrangement of the subsoil structure particles are related partly to shrinking and swelling caused by changes in moisture conditions, and partly to the wedging action of roots that penetrate deep into the soil in search of moisture.

Once the pattern of soil structure is established, many of the grass roots work their way into minute crevices where they expand with growth and press the structure particles into a still firmer consistence. Where clayey soils swell and shrink greatly with changes in moisture, roots are sometimes unable to expand in the normal way and so take on flattened shapes. Some roots do not confine themselves to the crevices but pierce the structure particles and so tend to make them more porous or to break them into smaller units.

Although soils are considered to reach equilibrium with their environment, it is probable that soils of the grasslands gradually change with time. Mineral plant nutrients are removed slowly in solution from subhumid grasslands (Prairie and Chernozem soils). The clay content of the soils is gradually increased by chemical processes, and is concentrated in subsoil horizons where it impedes water movement in the soil and makes soil water less quickly available to plants. In other words, a slow deterioration sets in as soils become older.

In a few places natural erosion and soil formation seem to have reached a balance that keeps the soils fertile and productive for a long time. Generally, however, it appears that soils are either improving gradually through the slow accumulation of organic matter and fresh sediments, or are deteriorating slowly with the aging process. Plowing and cultivating the soil may either increase the rate of improvement or hasten deterioration. Good husbandry improves the land for man's use and raises the level of fertility and productivity. On the other hand, because the nutrient requirements of cultivated plants are different from those of the native grasses, nutrient deficiencies may be expected to develop. In Illinois, Iowa, and eastern Nebraska and Kansas, for example, farmers are already beginning to obtain benefit from the use of superphosphate on some of the older soils.

A large proportion of the Chernozem, Chestnut, Reddish Chestnut, Brown, and Reddish-Brown soils of the Great Plains and of the Pacific Northwest probably had been in a state of temporary dynamic equilibrium for a few thousand years when the region was invaded by white colonists. Most of the Chernozem and Reddish Chestnut soils and a smaller proportion of the others have been plowed and planted for two or three generations, and it cannot be denied that much of the soil has deteriorated under this regime. Some of the organic matter has been lost by wind erosion, some has been oxidized, and some has been washed away. And crops also have made serious inroads on the supply of easily available plant nutrients. Soil management practices are now in a state of slow evolution that we hope will eventually correct a bad situation.

Development of Soils

The dark-colored Prairie and Chernozem soils, with the associated Wiesenboden (dark-colored wet meadow soils) and Planosols (soils with claypan), show the maximum effects of true grasses and other grasslike plants on soil formation. These soils occur in subhumid and dry-subhumid areas where climatic conditions are generally better suited to the growth of grasses than to forest, but where moisture is sufficient to support a dense growth of grass. In the Prairie soils zone, forests will spread over the grasslands fairly readily if young trees are protected from fire until they are well established. Trees can also be made to grow on medium- to sandy-textured soils in the Chernozem soils zone, and even in drier areas, with still greater care; but it is doubtful whether any extensive forest could establish itself on these soils with or without the aid of man. Only on steep north- or east-facing slopes and along stream valleys do forests obtain a permanent foothold in zones of Chernozem and Chestnut soils.

Parent materials of Chernozem and Prairie soils are developed from a very wide variety of rocks, loess, aeolian sand, and alluvium, but loess, glacial drift, alluvium, and soft sedimentary rocks comprise the greater part. Most of the parent materials are calcareous (contain carbonate of lime) or have been in the recent geologic past.

Typical soils of these groups are all well drained, either because of moderate slopes or because substrata are porous and permeable to water and have suitable natural outlets to remove excess water. The land surface ranges from level to gently sloping. Soils of other groups occur on the steep slopes and in wet depressions.

Prairie and Chernozem soils support a natural cover of tall prairie grasses dominated by a few species, with a minor constituent of legumes and other shrubby perennial and annual plants that are not true grasses. Under virgin conditions the original tall-grass cover formed a dense sod at the surface of Prairie soils, but the cover was less complete in the drier parts of the Chernozem soils zone where bunchgrass associations are the rule.

While Prairie and Chernozem soils have in common dark colors, much organic matter, and similar structure, they differ in one important respect: Prairie soils generally are acid in reaction and have lost most of their original carbonate of lime through leaching. Rainfall provides enough moisture nearly every year to pass entirely through the profile. Chernozem soils generally are neutral or slightly alkaline in reaction and typically have a horizon, or layer, of subsoil enriched with carbonate of lime. This horizon is developed because rain water frequently is insufficient to pass entirely through the soil. Percolating water usually reaches only a few feet into the subsoil, where it gradually evaporates into the soil air or is picked up by grass roots and carried back to the surface and transpired through the leaves. Soluble material like carbonate of lime is thus carried to the subsoil and left behind when the water is dissipated.

It is generally true on the Great Plains of the United States and Canada that grassland soils in the cool regions have more organic matter than those in the warmer regions. Soils in subhumid grassland areas of Texas generally have less organic matter than those in areas of southern Manitoba and North Dakota where effective soil moisture is comparable.

After an exhaustive study of the nitrogen and organic matter of hundreds of soils in the United States, Hans Jenny, in *Research Bulletin No. 152* of the Missouri Agricultural Experiment Station, drew a number of conclusions regarding the accumulation of soil organic matter in relation to climate. Among them are:

1. Within regions of equivalent effective moisture, the nitrogen and organic matter contents of soils of medium textures increase 2 to 3 times with every 18° F. fall in average annual temperature, from south to north in the United States. The statement holds for both forested and grassland soils.

2. Within regions of equal average annual temperatures, the nitrogen and organic matter content of grassland soils increases with increasing humidity. The rate of increase is greater in the cool northern regions than in the warmer southern regions. This conclusion does not hold for forested soils.

3. From data available to Jenny at the time his bulletin was written in

1930, he felt that climate and vegetation were more significant to the accumulation of nitrogen in loamy soils than topography, parent material, or age of the soil.

Those who have studied the grass roots in the Great Plains tell us that different kinds of grasses and associated herbaceous plants distribute their roots in different layers of the soil. Some species have concentrated their roots in the uppermost layer where they depend on moisture from rains which penetrate the soil only to a relatively shallow depth. Other plants draw their water from intermediate layers. Still others reach down to obtain water from the deep layers of the parent material and even from the ground water, many feet below the surface. Most of the deepest-rooted plants of the prairies are perennial herbaceous or shrubby plants (known technically as forbs) that grow in close association with the grasses. In times of protracted drought, many of these plants survive while some of the grasses with shallower roots die.

Prairie and Chernozem soils have deep, nearly black surface soils with well-developed granular or crumb structure and much organic matter. Fertility is high. The dark surface layers, under natural conditions, are matted with grass roots to depths of 1 or 2 feet, and many grass roots penetrate to depths of 5 to 8 feet.

J. E. Weaver and others estimated that 60 percent of the underground parts of little bluestem grass on Lancaster loam in Nebraska were in the top 6 inches of soil and that 68 percent of underground parts of big bluestem grass were in the top 6 inches of Wabash clay loam.

S. B. Shively and Dr. Weaver report that the top 6 inches of Prairie soils in western Iowa and eastern Nebraska contain from about 4.5 to about 2.6 tons of underground plant parts (dry weight) per acre, and Chernozems from 2.34 to 2.6 tons per acre in Nebraska and Kansas. Big bluestem produced a larger amount of under-

ground plant parts than little bluestem in the same region. In the same soil, the dark humified organic matter ranges from about 25 to about 40 tons in the top 6 inches of soil on each acre.

Analyses of Prairie and Chernozem soils in North Dakota, Manitoba, and Saskatchewan show that the weights of humified organic matter are considerably greater in the northern parts of the Plains and range from about 40 to possibly 100 tons an acre in the top 6 inches of Manitoba and Saskatchewan soils. In warmer southern areas, total weights of humified organic matter to the acre of the dark-colored Reddish-Prairie and Rendzina soils average considerably less than in Nebraska—roughly 10 to 20 tons in the top 6 inches of soil, on the basis of very limited information.

C. C. Nikiforoff estimates totals of from 120 to 240 tons of humus an acre in Chernozem soils of the United States. His maximum figure is for the entire profile of Chernozems with exceptionally thick dark surface soils.

Dr. Weaver and Ellen Zink have estimated the rate at which roots of various perennial grasses die in the soil under various conditions. The estimates were based on periodic examination of a large number of roots banded with soft tin strips. They found that big bluestem lost 19 percent of its original coarse roots in 3 years, little bluestem and porcupinegrass each 90 percent, blue grama 55 percent, and side-oats grama 86 percent.

All the losses were gradual, and replacements doubtless were made by the plants, but it is interesting that even the relatively long-lived big bluestem roots are able annually to contribute about 312 to 540 pounds of raw organic matter an acre to the top 6 inches of soils in western Iowa and eastern Nebraska and Kansas, assuming pure stands of this grass. This would mean that from about 520 to 900 pounds per acre of raw organic matter is added annually to the entire soil profile.

L. E. Andrew and H. F. Rhoades analyzed a sample of soil developed in calcareous glacial till thrown out from a railroad cut in Lancaster County, Nebr., 75 years ago. Organic matter is most concentrated in the topmost 2 inches of soil, which contains 4.3 percent. Possibly part of this organic matter came from wind-blown dust. The average for the top 6 inches is about 2.9 percent. Assuming that 0.4 percent of the material deposited with the recent dust or present in the original material was organic material, it seems safe to estimate that organic material accumulated in the last 75 years comprises 2.5 percent of the top 6 inches of soil. Assuming further a volume weight of about 1.1 for this layer, the total estimated weight of dry organic matter per acre to 6 inches is about 18.7 tons. At a uniform rate of accumulation, this would be 500 pounds a year. The figure seems high and suggests that organic accumulation might reach its maximum for the region within as little as 200 or 300 years. With a diminishing rate of accumulation, the period might be somewhat longer. The development of a clayey subsoil would take considerably longer, perhaps a few thousand years.

Traveling from east to west across the Great Plains, from subhumid to semiarid or arid climates, one can observe a gradual decrease in the darkness and thickness of the surface soil. The horizon of carbonate of lime lies at shallower depths than in Chernozem soils and is proportionally thicker on soils of equal age and like parent material. These changes correspond directly with the decrease in the height and concentration of grasses on the soil, as well as with the decrease in effective moisture.

Virgin areas of dark grayish-brown Chestnut and dark-brown Reddish Chestnut soils occur under a mixed cover of tall, medium-height, and short grasses, with a considerably less dense cover on the ground. Moisture is not sufficient in the zone of Chestnut and Reddish Chestnut soil to support the luxuriant growth of tall grasses characteristic of the Prairie

and Chernozem zones. The Chestnut-soils zone grades imperceptibly into the zone of Brown soils, and the Reddish Chestnut into the Reddish-Brown soils, where short grasses are dominant and shrubby plants characteristic of still drier regions fairly common.

The Sierozem (gray-earth) soils are in a still drier climate with a dominant cover of sagebrush and only a sparse growth of short grasses. This zone is not very distinct and is considered to be just a little more moist than true Desert and a little drier than the zone of Brown soils. The break between Sierozem soils and Desert soils is approximately the break between the complex of sparse short grass and sagebrush and the zone where desert shrub plants, like creosotebush, shadscale, or white bur-sage are dominant, and grass is almost nonexistent.

Soils in semiarid regions generally are not covered completely by grass. Bare spots are subject to erosion by wind and water and to beating by the occasional torrential rains. The wind removes fine soil from the bare spots, deposits some of it in adjacent grassy patches, and carries the rest greater distances to form dust deposits, frequently in Chernozem and Prairie soils zones. The ultimate result is that the surface of the land in semiarid regions has a peculiar micro-relief with minute basins a few inches deep interspersed between grassy mounds a few inches high. Where soils contain pebbles or rock fragments, these are left behind to form a cover or pavement that protects the soil from further wind erosion.

One or more groups of soils within each soil zone have peculiar properties that set them apart from soils considered "normal" for that zone. Usually one or more horizons of each of these soils is overdeveloped and in marked contrast to the normal soil. These are called intrazonal (within-zone) soils. Planosols of the Prairie and Chernozem soils zones, and claypan soils (some of which are known technically as Solonetz and solodized-Solonetz) of drier regions are intrazonal soils characterized by grassy vegetation. The most extremely developed of the Planosols have very thin surface horizons of dark-colored material rich in organic matter. Beneath the thin dark horizon is light-colored, friable, platy material, several inches thick, with little organic matter, and usually moderately to strongly acid in reaction. Beneath is a strongly developed clayey horizon, or claypan.

While the claypan may appear to be practically impervious, it is easy to demonstrate that grass roots will pierce it if nutrients and moisture are there to attract them. E. G. Fitzpatrick, formerly soil scientist of the Division of Soil Survey in the Department of Agriculture, once made root counts in a claypan soil of Oklahoma. He found more roots in the claypan layer than in the friable silty leached soil immediately above it.

Furthermore, dry weather so shrinks and cracks many of the claypans that water penetrates them readily following dry weather. Grass roots work their way between the blocky- and prismatic-structured particles into deeper layers of the subsoil in search of moisture, and some of the roots actually pierce the dense blocks and prisms of clay. Such penetration tends to lessen the undesirable physical conditions of the soil. Shrinking and expanding of the clay blocks with changes in moisture have the effect of flattening the roots, but this process does not kill them except where extreme shrinkage in dry weather breaks them asunder. Only in soils with subsoil horizons very low in plant nutrients and moisture do the roots fail to penetrate the claypans. But roots generally encounter considerably more difficulty in penetrating claypans than friable soil layers.

All gradations of claypan soils exist from those in which there is a well-developed gray layer like the one described to one in which there is only a thin sprinkling of light-gray silt on the aggregates at the top of the claypan subsoils. Under like climate, the claypan soils with only the beginnings of a gray layer have a more dense grassy vegetation than those in which the gray layer has become well developed. The development of a thick gray layer above the claypan usually is interpreted as evidence of soil deterioration.

Morphology of solodized-Solonetz soils of the drier regions resembles that of Planosols. Most solodized-Solonetz soils have a less dense grass cover than most Planosols. Many of them have innumerable small bare spots where wind erosion has removed the surface horizon and has exposed the intractable clay subsoil. These "scab spots" or "slick spots" are abundant in areas of imperfectly drained soils of the semiarid plains from southern Texas to northern Saskatchewan and Alberta, and in the drier grasslands of California and the Pacific Northwest.

A peculiar group of intrazonal soils known as Rendzinas occurs in regions ranging from subhumid climates where Chernozems are normal to humid climates where leached, strongly acid, light-colored forest soils are dominant. These soils are covered largely with grass and other herbaceous plants and have dark-colored, thick surface layers much like those of the Chernozems. They are developed in soft calcareous clays, marls, and chalk deposits (soft powdery limestone), all of which contain much soft carbonate of lime. It seems that the excessive amount of easily available lime carbonate and the clayey texture of the parent material encouraged the growth of grasses at the expense of forests. Only where soils of this kind have been exposed for a long time to leaching without erosion do the soils become acid and the forests invade the grasslands. The Houston soils of the "blackland prairies" of Texas, Mississippi, and Alabama are good examples. These soils are generally more fertile than the associated strongly acid forested sandy soils.

The Rendzinas in scattered belts of the Southern States from central Texas to Alabama are nearly black in color, but they contain less organic matter on the whole than Chernozems and

Prairie soils of similar colors in the North Central States. It is generally thought that the higher temperatures of the South accompanied by greater activity of bacteria keep the organic material of the soils at a somewhat lower percentage than in grassland soils of the cooler Northern States.

Azonal soils are those which are so young that they have not yet developed distinct soil horizons. The group includes soils with only the beginnings of organic accumulation in the upper layers where grass roots are abundant. Many of these soils are younger than 100 years. The development of older ones has been retarded by rapid geologic erosion on steep slopes or accumulation of sediments on flood plains.

J. E. Weaver and F. W. Albertson have demonstrated the harmful effects on the soil brought about by the invasion of the bluestem prairie by western wheatgrass during and immediately after the great drought of the mid-1930's. Western wheatgrass lacks the dense mass of fine leaves characteristic of the bluestems and so permits the beating rains to destroy the soft crumblike soil aggregates at the surface. The soil runs together and prevents rapid penetration of water. As a result, the soil absorbs less of the rain water, runoff is promoted, and erosion is accelerated. In this way drought conditions are maintained longer than would be expected otherwise.

Forested Soils and Deserts

While it is altogether possible that the total percentage of living and dead organic matter of soils of many forested areas is equal to or greater than that of the Chernozem and Prairie soils, the organic matter of most forest soils is not quite so dark-colored as that of the grasslands and is distributed through greater thicknesses of soil materials.

Probably, also, the ratio of humified soil organic matter to roots in most forest soils is less than in the grasslands. Generally speaking, the majority of forest soils of the United States are

light-colored except for a very thin layer immediately under the decaying leaves of the forest. The important exceptions to this are in the Brown forest soil and a few areas of forested Rendzinas, which have dark-colored surface soils not greatly different in superficial appearance from the Chernozem.

The usual explanation for this difference between the black soils of the Prairie and Chernozem zone and the light-colored soils of the forested areas is that the organic matter of the grassland soils is developed largely through the decay in place of myriads of grass roots rather evenly distributed through the soil, and secondarily by the decomposition of grass tops which die back annually. Every year a certain proportion of grass roots, varying with species, and all of the tops, decay and become mixed with the soil. Part of the material disappears as gas, part of it seeps away in ground water solutions, and part of it remains behind in the form of dark-colored, fairly stable, organic matter. The amount of grass roots thus contributed annually to the soil decreases with decreasing rainfall westward across the Plains. Certain roots of grasslike plants like those of the sedge commonly called black root decay so slowly that their contribution to humified soil organic matter is very little, indeed. It is possible to identify the roots of this sedge in Brown soils of the Great Plains many years after the plants have been killed by plowing.

The differences in the amount of organic matter between the dark-colored grassland and light-colored forested soils is ascribed partly to the fact that forest soils are generally more acid in reaction than grassland soils. The "mild" or nonacid humus of grasslands is more stable than the relatively soluble acid humus of forests. Part of this difference may be due to the fact that the molds (fungi) are more active in the organic matter of forest soils than bacteria, whereas the reverse is true in most grasslands.

Grasses will survive better than forest trees in subhumid and semiarid regions in soils of clayey textures, so that we find many areas of grasslands in heavy clayey soils surrounded by forests on soils of medium to sandy texture. Examples of this may be seen in Texas, where the forested Cross Timbers areas are interspersed with grass-covered Rendzina soils. Furthermore, grassland parks have persisted within areas of forests where subsoils are very droughty, as on some of the gravelly and sandy outwash deposits of northern Indiana and southern Michigan.

Deserts of the United States generally are not grassy, although certain species of grasses are able to survive in some regions commonly called desert. Even in the Yuma Desert of Arizona where rainfall averages less than 5 inches a year, bunchgrasses can be found on certain sandy soils.

None of the desert plants can support a dense growth of fine roots in upper soil layers for any long period of time and so provide enough organic matter to darken the soil appreciably. Furthermore, vegetation in the desert nowhere covers the soil sufficiently to prevent erosion by wind and water. Fine-textured soil materials are removed by the wind or washed away by the occasional rains. Sand is heaped up by the wind around clumps of brush or cactus and silty materials are carried farther to be deposited in denser vegetation around the desert border. Where soil materials contain coarse rock fragments, these are left behind to form a "desert pavement" which helps to check further erosion. As a net result, desert soils contain less organic matter than soils of grasslands.

Medium-textured Desert soils with well-balanced mineral nutrients can become just as productive under irrigation as grassland soils of similar texture, but this can be achieved only after the organic material and nitrogen content have been built up through good agricultural practices.

THE AUTHOR≪← *James Thorp, a native of Pennsylvania and a graduate of Earlham College, has been engaged in research on soils since 1921 in the United States, the West Indies, China, and Japan. Mr. Thorp, principal soil scientist in the Bureau of Plant Industry, Soils, and Agricultural Engineering, is principal soil correlator for the Great Plains, with headquarters at the University of Nebraska.*

THE TOOLS OF FLOOD CONTROL

HUGH H. BENNETT

FLOOD CONTROL begins where the rains fall and runoff originates. Flood control ends only when that runoff has safely reached the ocean.

The work, then, of preventing floods (which annually cost citizens of the United States 250 million dollars in crops, equipment, and other property damage) does not consist only of installing major engineering works along the main channelways of our trunk streams. It consists also of treating the land surface in such a way as to obtain maximum infiltration consistent with proper use of land for crops, pasture, forest, and other purposes. It covers the orderly disposal of runoff from fields, pastures, and woodlands through stabilized waterways and the temporary detention of runoff in small upland storage basins and temporary pools where practicable. It requires, too, the control of the erosional debris—silt—that shoals waterways, fills ditches, and reduces the capacity of flood-control reservoirs.

Sometimes it involves the improvement and maintenance of minor stream channels. In many watersheds large detention reservoirs are required at critical locations to hold back excess floodwaters that would otherwise overflow important urban and agricultural areas. Levees, revetments, floodwalls, floodways, cut-offs, and other channel improvements are required for control operations on many major streams and their principal tributaries, such as are not contemplated in the operations to be carried on by the Department of Agriculture. It is a big project.

Since 1936 the Department of Agriculture has been specifically authorized by Congress (in the Omnibus Flood Control Bill—Public No. 738, 74th Congress, June 22, 1936, as amended and supplemented) to share with the Department of the Army responsibilities in flood control. These departments are now working together on the problem, although progress was curtailed considerably during the war.

The Soil Conservation Service and the Forest Service have been designated by the Secretary of Agriculture as the agencies to carry out the Department's responsibilities in flood control. This phase of the work has to do chiefly with the retardation of runoff, increase in the absorption of rainfall, and control of erosion over that part of watersheds lying back from the channels of main streams.

The original Soil Conservation Act (Public No. 46, 74th Congress), by which the Soil Conservation Service was set up in the Department of Agriculture in 1935, declared it to be the policy of Congress "to provide for the control and prevention of soil erosion and thereby to preserve natural resources, control floods, prevent impairment of reservoirs, and maintain the navigability of rivers and harbors. . . ."

Flood-control work, however, was not set up as a separate part of the coordinated program of soil and water conservation carried on by the Soil Conservation Service under that act. In many watersheds physical conditions are exceptionally favorable for reducing flood damage by increasing infiltration of rainfall into the soil. In other areas, especially where the soils are thin or impervious and the slopes prevailingly steep, conditions for water absorption are not so favorable, and extra water-retardation measures are needed over and above those required for the normal protection of croplands from erosion. Small retention dams installed in headwater drainageways and gullies, contour furrowing, water spreading, and intensive vegetative treatment of steep areas and shallow soils are among the extra structures and measures used under these conditions.

Various other measures needed for the control and prevention of erosion and reduction of sedimentation supplement the more strictly flood-control types of work. There is no conflict between these big engineering operations and the soil and water conservation work of the Department of Agriculture.

No one measure can be expected to give the maximum possible protection to any considerable part of a watershed. Certainly, no single treatment can give adequate protection to all parts of a normal watershed.

Take, for example, the case of a major flood-control reservoir. It may give complete protection to the valley for some distance downstream for all floods except those of extra severity, such as may be expected less frequently. Why, then, would watershed treatment be necessary, as well as the flood-control reservoir, in solving the flood problems of such a drainage area?

The answer is, first, that watershed treatment usually is necessary to reduce flood damage along the smaller tributary valleys above the influence of the reservoir. Damage along these small tributary valleys in the aggregate often exceeds the damage done along the main stream that carries the collected drainage of the entire watershed.

Secondly, watershed treatment is by far the best way to reduce the sediment load of streams, and thereby assure longer life to reservoirs, while keeping the channels in best condition for proper flowage. Moreover, as I pointed out, upstream work, by storing more of the rainfall in the soil and retarding runoff, supplements the effectiveness of the control operations downstream.

There is only one way to stop erosion and maintain land in a permanently productive condition, and that way is to treat the different parcels of land according to the individual needs and capabilities.

Land varies greatly from place to place. Often there are extreme differences between adjoining fields or parts of fields. The soil may be different— or the slope, the degree of erosion, the amount of rainfall it is subjected to, the availability of plant nutrients, or other factors. An acre of land may differ from the next in just one of these ways, in several, or in all of them.

The soil conservationist has at his command many different types of control measures for handling different types of problems. The steeper, less productive lands, for example, may be earmarked for a permanent cover of grass or trees. Trees may be planted where grass is not paying out or is failing to hold the soil. Gullied areas may be turned into grass-covered waterways, farm sanctuaries for wildlife, or valuable pastures of kudzu.

The perennial lespedezas and kudzu have wrought profound changes in the use of much severely sheet-eroded and gullied land in many parts of the Southern States. Lands that a little while ago were considered too poor, too steep, or too erodible to farm— even some areas so gullied they could not be used for anything—are now providing excellent grazing with these valuable crops. And these crops are holding and improving the soil, retarding runoff, reducing the effects of silting, and increasing yields.

Grass—especially the sod-forming kinds—is a powerful weapon for holding rainfall where it hits the ground. It is therefore one of the best means known for preventing erosion. One often sees clear or nearly clear water flowing out of a well-grassed area after a heavy rain. On the contrary, clear water is never seen flowing off unprotected, cultivated slopes. It is always

muddy. And the mud consists of soil washed out of the field.

Thousands of measurements have been made at the 10 erosion research stations established since 1930 by the Department of Agriculture. Both soil and water losses have been measured from standardized plots on different types of land used for various crops, including grass, legumes, trees, and shrubs.

From clean-tilled crops, grown at the 10 older stations, the average soil loss over a period ranging from 6 to 11 years amounted to 42.10 tons an acre annually, and the water loss ranged from 2.50 to 40.32 percent of the rainfall. In contrast, from the same kind of land on the same stations, the corresponding losses from grassed fields were only 0.08 of a ton of soil an acre, and from 0.05 to 8.1 percent of the rainfall. Expressed differently, the soil loss from clean tillage was 526 times as much as that from the same kind of land under grass, and the greatest loss of water from the clean-cultivated fields exceeded the corresponding water loss from grass by five times.

The greatest effectiveness of grass in holding soil and storing water in the ground measured at these stations was at Temple, Tex. There, from black, waxy clay of the Texas blackland, 20.58 tons of soil an acre (the 11-year average) were lost where corn was grown, along with 13.6 percent of the rainfall. From Bermuda-grass grown on the same kind of land, receiving the same rainfall (an average of 32.74 inches), the soil loss was only 0.02 of a ton an acre; the water loss was 0.05 percent of the precipitation. In other words, soil lost from corn was 1,029 times greater and the water loss 272 times greater than the corresponding losses from a cover of grass.

Many thousands of additional measurements have confirmed the effectiveness of grass in holding back water— storing it in the reservoir of the soil. Seldom has there been an exception to this water-conserving effect of grass. Offhand, I can think of none at all.

Soil conservation is based largely on the control of runoff from rain and snow. This control of runoff (through the use of such practical measures as terracing, contouring, strip cropping, utilization of crop residues as a protective surface mulch, and retirement of steep, erodible land from clean cultivation to grass or trees) results in the storage of much of the rainfall which otherwise would run off into neighboring streams to increase flood flows.

The result has been a marked reduction of flood heights on many small streams in many parts of the country.

For example, the South Palouse River for many years had practically ceased to flow during late summer; in late winter or spring, when the snow was suddenly melted by chinook winds or when there was a heavy rain, the river used to flood Pullman, Wash., nearly every year. Then the Soil Conservation Service carried out considerable work on various critical portions of the watershed.

Among other items was the planting of approximately 10,000 acres of steep, cultivated land to grass and grass-legume mixtures. In 1946, for the ninth consecutive year, the South Palouse River had maintained a lively flow throughout the summer and the banks of the stream at Pullman had not been overflowed. Much of the water that formerly ran off to develop floods and to carry away vast quantities of productive soil now goes into the ground to increase crop yields, bring a former perennial stream back to continuous flow, revive numerous local springs, and reduce the flooding.

What happened at the Soil and Water Conservation Experiment Station about 6 miles west of Zanesville, Ohio, on soil typical of eastern Ohio, southwestern Pennsylvania, and West Virginia, is illustrative of how grass fits splendidly into the flood control program. The station has been operated for about 13 years by the Soil Conservation Service, in cooperation with the Ohio Agricultural Experiment Station. I give a few of the results.

The annual loss of soil from typical land on this experimental farm where corn was grown continuously has amounted to 94.6 tons an acre; the accompanying loss of rainfall as immediate runoff has amounted to 42.4 percent of all the rain and snow that fell on the land. But on precisely the same kind of land on the same farm the corresponding losses from soil devoted to grass have been only 0.02 ton of soil an acre annually (1/4730th as much as under continuous corn), and about 4.8 percent of the rainfall as runoff (1/9th as much as under continuous corn). Rotations, contouring, terracing, and other measures have also greatly reduced losses of both soil and water at this station.

In January 1937, when 11 inches of rain fell, coming in heavy downpours, 94.7 percent of the total precipitation was lost as immediate runoff from a severely eroded cornfield on the farm, but only 25.8 percent of this same precipitation was lost from grassland and about 31.5 percent from woodland on the farm. So, with 94 percent of all this terrific downpour charging into the Ohio River by way of the local drainage system, together with similar heavy discharges of accelerated runoff from unprotected land on hundreds of other similar watersheds, the Ohio River broke over its banks in a flood of great destructive force, a flood that exceeded in height all previous records.

One of the most effective ways to build up the content of organic matter in the soil is to grow grass on it. The effect of organic matter thus added to the soil, plus the tendency of grass hair-roots to develop a grain structure, is to bring about a marked improvement in the granularity of soil.

Granular soils are much more open natured and spongy than compact or dense soils. This condition of openness aids the infiltration of rain water and the circulation of soil moisture and air within the soil. Granularity means larger pore space; larger pore spaces mean more effective channelways for water movement.

Loss of organic matter, on the other hand, means a reduction of the pore space, greater density, and reduced soil capacity for proper drainage and moisture circulation. Some of the clay soils on the very flat clay lands in the lake-laid area of northern Ohio have lost granularity as the result of continuous row cropping to such a degree that farmers are now putting in additional tile drains in that locality between the old tile drains that formerly were adequate for high production. As an indication of increased density of the soil resulting from depletion of organic matter, by constant oxidation through continuous cultivation, mostly to corn and oats, it has been found possible to put 81.7 pounds of soil into a cubic-foot measure of the same type of soil that formerly was filled with 65.5 pounds of the same soil type just across the road. The altered pore space was a reduction from 60.3 percent in the virgin soil to 50.5 percent in the cultivated soil, and the organic matter content reduction for the corresponding conditions was from 66 to 44.7 tons per acre. The remaining pores were small and less effective as water channels.

In the 1,839 soil conservation districts that were being assisted by the Soil Conservation Service, 536,000 active conservation plans had been completed on January 1, 1948. These individual farm and ranch plans covered about 148 million acres, of which 36 percent (53 million acres) were used for cultivated crops at the time of planning. The plans revealed that only 31 percent, or 46 million acres, were suitable for cultivation.

Because of the steepness of slope, droughtiness, susceptibility to erosion, low content of plant nutrients, shallow soil, stoniness, or other unfavorable soil condition, more than 7 million acres have been found to be much more suitable for close-growing vegetation, like grass and legumes, than for row crops or small grain.

I believe that such a shifting from water- and soil-wasting practices, extended to all farms and ranches of the country, will in itself be a substantial contribution toward flood control.

THE AUTHOR≪≪ *Hugh H. Bennett has been Chief of the Soil Conservation Service since April 1935. He was Director of the Soil Erosion Service from 1933 to 1935.*

GRASSES THAT FIX SAND DUNES

CHARLES J. WHITFIELD, ROBERT L. BROWN

SAND DUNES have been a problem for centuries. The earliest modern reference to dune control was in 1316 in Germany. Laws limiting the use of dune lands have been enacted in nearly every country. The best estimate as to the area of the earth covered by sand dunes is 3,200,000,000 acres—nearly twice the total area and seven times the agricultural land area of the United States.

Sand dunes in the United States, not including those in deserts, occupy an area one-tenth as large as the area of agricultural land. These dunes are found along the coasts, bordering the Great Lakes, and in practically all of the inland States.

Permanent control of active sand dunes can be accomplished only by establishing on them a vegetative cover, either by natural succession or by seeding. Mechanical structures stop sand movement only temporarily.

Grasses have a major role in the fixation of sand dunes, but only a few grasses are widespread and important on these sandy areas. For example, on the Pacific and Atlantic coasts and on the shores of the Great Lakes, beach-grasses grow either as native or naturalized plants. Dune-control work during the past 200 years in this country has established the value of both American beachgrass and European beachgrass on these coastal areas and for inland dunes.

Purple beachpea, a legume native on the Pacific and Atlantic coasts and along the Great Lakes, has been used successfully in mixtures that give permanent cover on the dunes.

In the Middle West and the Great Plains States, switchgrass, big bluestem, sand bluestem, Indiangrass, and giant sandreed grass are outstanding. Sand blowout grass, sandreed grass, and yellow lyme grass were among those listed as important dune-control plants in the 1894 and 1898 Yearbooks of Agriculture. These are found to be less effective, however, than switchgrass, big bluestem, giant sandreed grass, and Indiangrass for permanent fixation.

Among grasses that assume considerable local importance are side-oats grama, sea-oats, sand lovegrass, weeping lovegrass, iceplant, and a strain of mammoth wild-rye.

Indian ricegrass and sand dropseed are well adapted to sand-dune conditions. They are primary invaders into temporarily controlled dunes but tend to disappear when competition becomes great, so that areas of sand often are left unprotected.

Most of the active sand dunes in the United States are caused by man's abuse of the protective vegetative cover. The goal in dune control is the reestablishment of a dense, permanent cover of vegetation. The cover may be herbaceous (grasses and legumes) or woody (shrubs and trees). These types are not easily or quickly established on infertile eroding sands subject to high-velocity winds. Provisions must be made for stilling the sand and for the orderly building up of the fertility and organic matter in the surface until vegetation of permanent types can be planted. Permanent fixation of dunes has been efficiently accomplished in recent years in a number of localities.

Coastal sand-dune control in the cool temperate regions is illustrated by the Warrenton Dune Control Project at the mouth of the Columbia River in Oregon. Encroaching dunes were menacing agricultural lands, forts, military reservations, highways, towns, and resort homes valued in all at many millions of dollars. The dunes were also threatening to impede annually the movement of nearly $300,-000,000 worth of ocean-going commerce moving at the mouth of the Columbia directly in the path of the encroaching dunes.

Dune-control work was started in July 1935. The men in charge first studied the factors they believed contributed to the continuance of active dunes by destroying vegetative cover: Fire, grazing by livestock, construction of roads and buildings, cultivation of sandy soils, and so on. They also investigated the jetties at the mouth of the river that alter the ocean currents, because they cause scouring of the ocean bottom and wash sand shoreward to cause dunes faster than vegetation can stabilize them. The causes determined, work was started to establish a permanent plant cover according to the needs of the land.

In most cases permanent cover was obtained in only two stages after the source of incoming sand had been controlled by mechanical devices or by vegetation. The first stage required sand-stilling plants. The final stage was the seeding or planting of permanent vegetation—grasses and legumes or woody plants.

American beachgrass, European beachgrass, and American dunegrass were used effectively for the first stage of control. The first has been outstanding because it spreads by vigorous rhizomes and can persist longer than the other species.

The first year, fertilizer applications that provided 40 pounds of nitrogen an acre insured a better sand-stilling cover and made possible early seeding of the permanent cover. Seedings of permanent species were usually made at the end of the first growing season where beachgrass plantings had been fertilized. Such seedings could not be made before the end of the second or third year without this fertilization.

Native species were good for use in the permanent stage of control, but they were expensive and scarce. On the basis of several trials, the following combination of native and commercially available species was selected and used for final control: Tall fescue, Clatsop red fescue (a strain developed on the job from native stands), common ryegrass, purple beachpea, and hairy vetch. The vetch was the key to successful establishment of grasses; the beachpea provided the long-lived legume in the mixture.

As in the first-stage plantings, a fertilizer application at seeding time assured success with permanent seedings if the vetch was included. An application of 300 pounds an acre of ammonium phosphate (16–20–0) gave best results. Seedings without vetch failed. The vetch provided protection against wind and intense light, protected the more slowly developing species, and supplied organic matter. Seedings were made in the early fall in the mild climatic conditions that exist on the west coast. Stabilization progressed rapidly, and the shifting dunes were tied down with vegetation.

The plantings are being maintained to assure permanent dune fixation and give protection to farm, military, and other properties to the leeward.

Similar work has been done on the dune areas of Michigan, New York, and Massachusetts, and at other points along the Pacific and Atlantic coasts; slight variations in planting and management from those at Warrenton were due to differences in proposed uses of the land, type of sand, climate, and plants used.

Sand-dune control in the Great Plains area is typified by the Dalhart Sand Dune Stabilization Project in the Panhandle of Texas, and the Caddoa Sand Dune Stabilization Project in southeastern Colorado.

In 1936 studies were started near Dalhart to determine ways and means of stabilizing and utilizing sand-dune areas in the Southern Great Plains. The method developed for dune fixation included five steps: Controlling the critical or contributing area; deep listing between and around the dunes to catch the dune sand; breaking down crests and lowering the dunes to a point where they could be planted; establishing temporary control on the loose drifting sands by planting cover crops, mulching, and aiding the development of a weed cover; finally, seeding the area for permanent control.

The principal method of temporary control was planting sorghum as a cover crop for grass establishment. Three types were outstanding—Sudangrass, broomcorn, and Black Amber cane. Western wheatgrass drilled with a 12-inch, spaced-row grass drill on 20-inch spaced rows of broomcorn made a perfect stand. Seedings of a mixture of blue grama, side-oats grama, sand dropseed, and sand bluestem on 20-inch spaced rows of cane (which volunteered heavily) produced a good stand.

The first work at Dalhart to establish grass for dune fixation was with mulch. Hay of giant sandreed grass with viable seed in the heads was spread over a dune. A good stand was obtained.

Sand bluestem, Indiangrass, switchgrass, Canada wild-rye, and western wheatgrass were found to be most effective in reducing wind velocity at the surface and binding the soil with root growth. Weeping lovegrass, which produced heavy forage when planted alone, did not hold up well in mixtures.

In southeastern Colorado, near Caddoa, permanent sand-dune stabilization eliminated the need of rerouting a transcontinental railroad across the Arkansas River. The problem was one of controlling hundreds of acres of loose, sandy material in a region of low rainfall. The dunes were leveled and shaped with a bulldozer to conform as nearly as possible to the undulating topography of the surrounding terrain. The dune areas were then seeded to mixtures of grasses with a double coulter disk-type drill. Switchgrass, sand bluestem, big bluestem, sand dropseed, side-oats grama, little bluestem, sand blowout grass, giant sandreed grass, sandreed grass, Canada wild-rye, blue grama, and western wheatgrass were among the grasses seeded on these dunes.

Following the seeding, a 2-inch straw mulch was applied and rolled with a weighted subsurface packer to hold the straw in place. The mulch tended to reduce the evaporation of surface moisture, lower the soil temperature, and protect the young grass plants from the sweeping action of the surface sand.

The tall grasses—big bluestem, sand bluestem, giant sandreed grass, sand dropseed, and side-oats grama—were the best for stabilizing these sandy soils. They were more effective than the short grasses because their height cut down wind action and produced more mulch for the protection of the soil. Giant sandreed grass was further effective because of its ability to spread by rhizomes.

As a result of construction activities on the Tooele Ordnance Depot area in Utah and on the Umatilla Ordnance Depot area in Oregon, sand dunes of small size, but hazardous to efficient operation of these depots, were developing. A large part of a 21,000-acre area was affected. With the destruction of the native vegetation, the loose, sandy soils began to shift so severely that it was impossible to stabilize them by natural reseeding alone. A survey was made, and control by vegetation, rather than mechanical methods, was initiated at great savings of public funds.

On the more favorable areas, where there was some protection, the blowouts were seeded to a mixture of sand dropseed, Indian ricegrass, and crested wheatgrass in Utah and bulbous bluegrass and crested wheatgrass in Oregon. Where the dunes to be controlled were unprotected and small seedlings could not be established without protection, a crop of cereal rye at the rate of 30 pounds an acre was drilled to establish a covering in which perennial vegetation could be seeded. On the most severe sites on active dune areas a mulch of straw and manure was disked into the land before seeding. The same mixture that was used on the more protected areas was then used for permanent stabilization on the Oregon site, where annual precipitation is only 10 inches. At Tooele, where the annual precipitation is 13 inches, a mixture of sand dropseed, Indian ricegrass, crested wheatgrass, and western wheatgrass was used.

The control of coastal sand dunes in warm temperate regions having summer rainfall is illustrated by the Gulf coast dunes in Kenedy County, Tex. Active dunes are found in many parts of the Gulf coast; the most extensive are in Kenedy County, where it is estimated there are more than 100,000 acres of dunes. Some of the important factors that prevent natural vegetative stabilization of these dunes are overgrazing, failure to control small blowouts, erratic precipitation and periods of drought, and large rodent and insect populations. Natural vegetative succession when allowed to develop has effectively stabilized dunes in this locality.

In the early stages of succession, such plants as dune paspalum, camphorweed, and sandbur are found. These are followed by perennials such as witchgrass and purple lovegrass, both rhizomatous plants; signalgrass; and others. Stabilization is assured when subclimax species, such as seacoast bluestem, crinkle-awn, fingergrass, and false-gama replace the initial invaders. Grasses such as switchgrass, big bluestem, and Indiangrass, which are of the climax vegetation on these and similar soils throughout much of the Great Plains and Middle West, may eventually become established if the area is well managed and is lightly grazed.

Artificial stabilization of these dunes has been by mulching with straw or other organic material and either encouraging native vegetation or seeding to subclimax grasses.

The principles of dune fixation are the same throughout the country, but the materials used to attain the goal will vary in different sections. First, incoming sand on any area must be stopped at or near its source by vegetation or mechanical operations. Second, the dune area must be returned to its original topography or to the topography of surrounding areas, either in the preparation for planting or in planting by selection of plants that will conform to topographic surroundings. Third, initial sand-stilling cover must be placed on the active dune area. This may be done by planting sand-stilling species such as European or American beachgrass, or mammoth wild-rye, or by mulches. Fourth, perennial vegetation such as sand bluestem, purple beachpea, crested wheatgrass, giant sandreed grass, red fescue, and switchgrass must be seeded to insure rapid development of permanent dune control. Fifth, extreme care is always necessary in the management of the areas.

THE AUTHORS≪ *Charles J. Whitfield has degrees from Iowa State Teachers College, the University of Nebraska, and the University of Chicago. Since 1926 he has carried on ecological studies, including investigations of grasses and other vegetation in relation to the control of sand dunes. Since 1937 Dr. Whitfield has been with the Soil Conservation Service as project supervisor of the Amarillo Conservation Experiment Station in Texas. His primary interest has been wind erosion investigations.*

Robert L. Brown is a native of Montana and a graduate of Oregon State College. He joined the Soil Conservation Service in 1934 and has worked on the control of eroding sand dunes and as a technical consultant on dune-control problems. He has visited all major sand dune areas in the United States to study their causes and methods of control. Mr. Brown is assistant chief of the Regional Nursery Division, Soil Conservation Service, Portland, Oreg.

Simon E. Wolff, Clifton Etter, Glenn W. Eaton, Jr., Albert F. Dodge, Dr. A. L. Patrick, A. D. Slavin, and Victor A. Surface of the Soil Conservation Service supplied some of the details given in this article.

[See also: The Meek that Inherit the Earth, by Agnes Chase, page 8; Data on the Seed and Culture of Common Grasses and Legumes, in the section, Grass in Charts and Tables.]

Forage for Livestock

PLUS AND MINUS: AN OVER-ALL VIEW

N. R. ELLIS, L. A. MOORE, M. A. HEIN

ALL CLASSES of domestic animals are alike in that they eat forage in some form. They differ, though, in the extent of their use of grass and such crops. Dog foods may contain small amounts of alfalfa leaf meal; poultry diets include forage meals to supply vitamins, minerals, and proteins, and increasing emphasis is placed on pasturage for poultry flocks; swine consume much more herbage; and horses, goats, sheep, and dairy and beef cattle sometimes get all their feed from forage.

This difference rests on differences in their digestive systems and ability to handle the bulky forages, which have a relatively high content of celluloses, lignins, and other carbohydrate materials that are not readily attacked by the enzymes of the digestive tract. Micro-organisms in the digestive tracts of cattle, sheep, goats, and horses secrete enzymes that can break down celluloses, but the lignins seem to be left relatively untouched.

Also, quite apart from the matter of bulkiness, the cell walls in the plants resist digestion, and so affect the ability of swine and poultry, for example, to make full use of the proteins, fats, minerals, and even the vitamin factors within the cells. In other words, horses, cattle, and sheep have special advantages in utilization of forages not shared by single-stomach animals such as swine.

The first need of animal life is for heat and energy, and the central chemical element is carbon. Carbon occurs in starches, sugars, and other carbohydrates, fats and oils, proteins, and even in plant pigments and the vitamin compounds. Depending on the animal's digestive capacity, the forages are therefore prime sources of energy by which to maintain life, grow, secrete milk, perform work, and reproduce.

Protein is next. Growing animals, which are building their muscular structure, need more protein than mature, resting animals. Likewise the growth of wool, the formation of milk, and the development of the fetus call for a relatively high intake of protein. These varying requirements for protein (which cut across the varying percentages of proteins in forages) produce a situation in which the animal may sometimes fail to eat sufficient forage to obtain enough protein to meet the requirements. In such a case retardation must result, whether it be production of wool or of the muscle structure.

Proteins are complex substances that are built up from amino acids. The twenty-odd amino acids are the channels through which food protein

75

passes in the body in the transformation to the proteins formed by the animal and built into muscular framework, milk, eggs, wool, hair. About 10 of the amino acids known to science are essential to man, and probably to poultry and swine. Apparently the micro-organisms that grow in the rumen of cattle and sheep can build up these essential amino acids to the benefit of the host. Accordingly, the amino-acid make-up or quality of the protein in forages is not highly important to cattle and sheep. Poultry and swine, although quality of protein is important to them, do not subsist on forage to such an extent as to make the matter of much importance.

The mineral elements generally considered essential to animal life include calcium, phosphorus, magnesium, sodium, chlorine, iodine, iron, copper, manganese, sulfur, zinc, potassium, and cobalt. The actual needs of the several classes of farm animals for a number of the elements have not been demonstrated for a certainty, however, because of their occurrence in animal tissues and in feeds in very small amounts.

The content of the more common minerals in the body can be illustrated by data on steers. Expressed as percentages of the fat-free body, the approximate figures are: Calcium, 1.33; phosphorus, 0.74; potassium, 0.19; sodium, 0.16; sulfur, 0.15; chlorine, 0.11; magnesium, 0.41; iron, 0.013.

From the standpoint of forages and their supply of these eight mineral elements, the principal concern in animal feeding is in calcium, phosphorus, sodium, and chlorine. Skeletal growth depends largely on an adequate supply of calcium and phosphorus. Sodium and chlorine, which together form common salt, are constituent parts of body tissues and fluids. Iron, cobalt, and copper are generally associated because of their roles in blood formation. Iodine is needed in the normal functioning of the thyroid gland. Other than the needs of poultry for manganese, little is known about the functions and requirements for manganese and zinc in other livestock. On the other hand, too much of certain substances—selenium and fluorine, for instance, can have harmful effects.

Even greater extremes exist in the requirements of different classes of animals for particular vitamins. Problems also arise from the differences in the disappearance of the vitamins in successive stages of ripening of the forage and in the ways the harvested crop is preserved and stored.

Only two vitamins, A and D, are known to be required by cattle, sheep, and goats. For horses, it appears that riboflavin and pantothenic acid need to be added to the list. For swine, thiamine, nicotinic acid, pyridoxine, and choline are certainly needed. The list for poultry must also include biotin, vitamin E, and vitamin K. These differences, as they concern the so-called vitamin-B-complex factors, are related largely or entirely to the activities of the micro-organisms in the digestive tracts of animals.

General Feeding Values

It follows from the long history of the reliance of different livestock on grassland crops for their food supply that forages in general must supply these necessary feed nutrients. In the unraveling of the details about individual items, it has become evident that the exceptions to this generalization account for much of the failure to obtain best performance in our livestock. In many parts of the world in many ages, people have learned to avoid troubles with their flocks by moving them from one area to another. Restrictions of feed supplies in one way or another have brought about conditions conducive to many of the nutritional deficiencies that confront us today. In the main, grassland crops do supply those nutrients that animals require—within the limits, of course, to which different kinds of livestock are naturally adapted to utilize forage.

The energy supply on which life so

heavily depends can be obtained readily enough from forages, providing a few conditions are met. These include an adequate supply, reasonable palatability and digestibility, and adequate quality. A cow that has to search over 40 acres of range for a few pounds of grass may not be able to obtain the needed energy to maintain weight. Likewise, consumption of 30 pounds of dry forage of low digestibility may not support life so well as 15 pounds of a highly digestible forage.

This difference in feeding value is determined markedly by seasonal and climatic factors. Furthermore, it is often more accentuated on ranges than in pastures. The growth of most range grasses in the South, for example, revives early in the spring, and the plants grow and mature comparatively rapidly. The peak in their feeding value is passed even by the beginning of summer. In the drier sections of the West, somewhat similar conditions exist with slower rates of growth and later maturity in the northern zones. Thus a wide difference in feeding value may exist on a given range at different times of the year.

On the average, cattle and sheep can digest and assimilate approximately 60 pounds of feed nutrients for every 100 pounds of dry matter in forages. In other words, 100 pounds of dry matter yield about 60 pounds of total digestible nutrients.

Some variations from this figure are of interest. For example, young plant growth generally yields more than older, more mature growth. Pasturage generally yields 3 or 4 pounds above the 60-pound average; hays and silages yield 2 or 3 pounds less. The approximate equality of hays and silages and the near 10-percent superiority of tender green material in total digestible nutrients is borne out, in the usual case, in actual production of livestock and livestock products.

A 600-pound steer that gains an average of 1.4 pounds daily needs about 8.5 pounds of total digestible nutrients. In terms of timothy hay with a dry-matter content of 90 percent, this is 16.3 pounds. On pasture, the steer must eat nearly 67 pounds when the dry matter is as low as 20 percent.

That is not to say, however, that wide differences in available energy or total digestible nutrients do not occur within classes of forages, whether pasture, silage, or hay. The studies of E. W. Crampton and others in eastern Canada give evidence that the digestibility of the dry matter of pasture herbage may drop from a high value of 80 percent in the early spring to 60 percent and less in midsummer. Significant changes occur in chemical composition, of course.

But Dr. Crampton's work, which discloses the lack of positive and high correlations between the data on composition and digestibility, shows that we cannot trust ordinary data on chemical composition as indices of digestibility and (still more important) of feeding value. From the practical, economic standpoint, the results emphasize the great need for further studies to find some constitutent that can be determined chemically and that can give more reliable information on the digestibility of forages.

These studies on composition and feeding values suggest, however, that increasing the ratio of leaves to stems may be associated fairly well with increasing the digestibility. Possibly not enough attention has been given to the usefulness of forages with a maximum leaf content. We have realized for some time that leafy hays were much more valuable than those with a high content of stems. Much of this advantage has been attributed to the content of protein, minerals, and vitamins. Typical figures on the digestible nutrients of alfalfa leaves (dry-matter basis) may reach or surpass 65 percent and for alfalfa stems may fall to 46 percent or less. It thus appears that available energy may be the more important factor in many instances.

It has been estimated that forages supply approximately 60 percent of the protein consumed by livestock. Of that amount, pasturage and range supplies about two thirds; hays, silages, and other harvested forages supply the other third. The other 40 percent of protein consumed is obtained from the concentrate feeds.

Protein Supply in Forages

A point of great importance is the deficit between the protein an animal actually consumes and the amount it needs for most efficient production. Taken all in all, the estimated deficit is an imposing figure, but it is actually only about 10 percent of the total requirement. This interesting situation suggests the potentialities of forages in cutting down this country-wide deficit. The possibilities are greatest in the case of cattle, sheep, goats, and horses and least with poultry and swine.

Despite the large contribution made by forages as a group in furnishing protein, grasslands do not always supply the needed amounts to livestock. Grasses as a class generally contain adequate amounts during the early growing period, but the proportion declines as plants mature. The proteins in forages also vary considerably in digestibility. Average figures obtained in tests with cattle show 63 percent digestibility for the protein in green grasses, 75 percent in green legumes, 54 percent in grass silages, 66 percent in legume silages, 52 percent in grass hays, and 67 percent in legume hays. Later articles also treat this subject.

Using the example of a 600-pound steer with a requirement of 0.9 pound of digestible protein, we can estimate that 1.73 pounds of original grass hay protein must be consumed to meet the daily needs. In terms of timothy hay, 23 pounds may be required, compared to the 16.3 pounds calculated to meet the energy requirement. For a legume hay the situation is reversed, however. The same is true for pasture grasses where the amount needed for energy is more than sufficient to supply the protein. Indeed, young grasses may supply a considerable surplus of protein not only through high content in the dry matter but also through higher digestibility. Admixture of legumes, of course, accentuates the situation.

On pastures and ranges after the forages have matured or have passed into the dormant stage and weathering has leached out some of the nutrients, livestock often need supplementary protein feeds especially where legumes are absent. On Southern forest range, the protein and likewise the phosphorus content is adequate during the spring months but goes down during early summer. Accordingly, the most profitable use from the new growth is obtained during the spring. During much of the rest of the year, protein supplements can be used to advantage. Fortunately, cottonseed cake not only supplies protein but phosphorus as well. Sometimes supplementary pastures that contain grasses with different growth habits can be used to lessen or remove the needs for protein concentrates. In some places, legume silages and hays are used to good advantage as supplements, or the livestock are removed from the pasture or range and fed entirely on harvested crops.

Mineral Supply

The forages generally can meet the full needs of animals for the necessary mineral elements. Possible exceptions are sodium and chlorine. As with proteins, however, unhappy combinations of high demands of particular animals and low yields from some forages may be serious deterrents to maximum performance of the animal. For example, a low calcium content in a native range may lead to poor skeletal development with weak, easily broken bones or simply to a retardation in growth as a whole. Instances of low calcium content in forages are not common. The situation in the Southern forest range may be cited, however, where a moderate deficiency often exists during the winter months.

Recent research work has brought out the interesting situation of regionalized deficiencies and excesses of minerals in the forages (and other crops as well) that are due to soil and other closely related environmental factors. Thus certain areas of low feed phosphorus content predispose cattle and sheep to phosphorus deficiency. Other areas are associated with iodine, iron, copper, or cobalt starvation, as the case may be.

Under the leadership of the United States Plant, Soil, and Nutrition Laboratory in Ithaca, N. Y., this information on regional aspects of mineral nutrition has been brought up to date. Phosphorus deficiency is common in the Pacific Northwest and the Rocky Mountain States and the area extends eastward to northern Michigan. It is also common along the Gulf coast and in the Appalachian Mountain area. The States bordering on the Great Lakes and extending westward through the Northern Great Plains and Intermountain States are recognized as deficient in iodine in varying degrees.

A deficiency of calcium, as we said, is the exception rather than the rule in the forages of continental United States. Iron, copper, and cobalt deficiencies occur at various places in the Atlantic Coastal Plain. Investigators in Florida have given the subject special attention. Cobalt is low in forages grown in certain districts of New Hampshire, Wisconsin, and Michigan. Selenium excesses occur in various places in the Northern Great Plains and Rocky Mountain States. In many instances these abnormal areas are relatively small. Much remains to be done in determining the relation of forage composition to animal health and the mapping of the entire country as to its importance in animal feeding. But one should not get the idea that the country as a whole or forages as a class offer any special hazard to livestock farmers. On the whole, forages, especially where there is variety in species composition, provide the mineral elements needed by most livestock most of the time.

In connection with species, compo-sition, and the desirability of using grass mixtures, a recent contribution from the Plant, Soil, and Nutrition Laboratory in Ithaca illustrates some of the characteristic differences which can be expected to occur in mineral content of different grasses. Analyses for phosphorus, cobalt, manganese, and copper on 17 species of grasses grown under similar conditions on the same kind of soil showed a marked trend for certain ones to be high and others low in this group of mineral elements. Kentucky bluegrass was in the high group, Dallisgrass, orchardgrass, Johnsongrass, and redtop were in the intermediate class, and timothy was in the low class.

Vitamin Supply

Green forages in the form of pasturage provide a very reliable source of the known vitamins with the possible exception of vitamin D. Since this factor is supplied through sunshine, animals on pasture are not likely to suffer any shortage. Carotene is so abundant in succulent green grass that as little as a pound of Kentucky bluegrass will supply the requirements of a 600-pound steer.

The main difficulty arises when the forage matures and becomes brown and weathered. A point may be reached in late winter when a full feed of this dry and weathered grass does not supply sufficient carotene for cattle and sheep. The better hays while they deteriorate progressively are fully adequate for a year and sometimes more. Hays, along with silages, provide the most dependable source of vitamin A for fattening cattle and sheep in the feed lot. Some feeders have tended to rely too much on yellow corn and too little on reasonable-quality forage, with resulting cases of vitamin A deficiency in their cattle.

Forages supply significant amounts of the various B vitamins in livestock rations. They are not so important to cattle and sheep as to swine and poultry because of the apparent synthesis either in the body tissues or in the rumen by micro-organisms. Recent evidence appears to show that calves do need certain factors, biotin for one, in their feed supply, and forages, especially pasture, certainly supplement the milk supply for suckling calves.

The thiamine content of the dry matter in green grass or well-cured hay is equivalent to that in cereal grains and legume seeds. The riboflavin content is definitely higher and nearly equal to that in milk byproducts.

The nicotinic acid content is comparable to that in seeds and milk byproducts. Pantothenic acid, like riboflavin, is higher in forages. The tocopherols (vitamin E) are also abundant in green forages. Other known vitamins and other unidentified nutrient factors are likewise present.

Many of these factors decline in content as the plants mature or are partially destroyed during the making of hay. Nevertheless, ordinary hay is generally a valuable and dependable source of such factors as riboflavin, thiamine, and nicotinic acid.

Classes of Forages

The livestock man has appreciated some of the differences as reflected in feeding value for many years. From the standpoint of energy or over-all feed value, grasses and legumes yield up their constituents about equally well. In other words, an animal obtains about as many pounds of total digestible nutrients from 100 pounds of grass as from legume.

There is a considerable difference in protein, however, as already mentioned. The protein content of legumes is normally the higher and more digestible thus making this class of forage much the more valuable from the standpoint of protein. The composition of the proteins with respect to amounts of essential amino acids has not been studied in much detail as yet. The available data do not suggest much difference between grasses and legumes. As compared to corn, the forages appear to have the advantage in content of arginine, lysine, and tryptophane, at least.

The legumes have another advantage in their relatively high content of calcium. The forbs are often well supplied with calcium also. There is not much choice between the several classes of plants with respect to phosphorus. There are some individual species of both grasses and legumes which appear to possess the power to take up and build into their cellular structure more of certain specific elements than do others. The diverse nature of grass and legume species offers many points of contrast fully as important within the class as between. Especially important are the contrasts in plants growing in cool versus hot weather and dry versus humid climate.

THE AUTHORS«« *N. R. Ellis is in charge of the section of animal nutrition investigations of the Bureau of Animal Industry. He has been with this Bureau since 1920 and has conducted researches in a wide field of problems dealing with the nutrition of swine, cattle, and other stock.*

L. A. Moore is in charge of the section of dairy cattle nutrition of the Bureau of Dairy Industry. He was formerly associated with the Michigan State College and later with Maryland University. His contributions on the nutrition of dairy cows, especially with respect to vitamin A deficiency, have been outstanding.

M. A. Hein is an agronomist in charge of grass and pasture work in the Bureau of Plant Industry, Soils, and Agricultural Engineering. He joined the Department of Agriculture in 1928, the year he received his master's degree in agronomy from the University of Illinois. Since entering the Department he has been extensively engaged in experimental work on adaptation studies, breeding for improvement, cultural practices, and other factors relating to the production of native and introduced grasses for hay, pasture, and silage.

SOILS, CROPS, MINERALS, ANIMALS

C. F. HUFFMAN, N. R. ELLIS, L. A. MOORE

OF ALL the nutrients that livestock get from forages, the mineral elements depend most directly on the soil and climate.

The energy-yielding nutrients are built up by the aid of carbon dioxide breathed in by the plant leaf structure. Even some of the protein originates from synthesis by bacteria growing in nodules on the roots of legumes, which gather nitrogen (a constituent of protein and of living matter) from the air.

Thus we see why animal life is so dependent on soil and climate when it comes to the mineral elements. The constant leaching by rains and the removal of the elements by plants, by grazing animals, and by harvesting impoverish the soil of these needed minerals. Another aspect and example of this close relationship of soils, crops, minerals, and animals is that certain toxic minerals present in the soil in excessive amounts are taken up by plants and in turn exert poisoning effects on the animals that eat the plants. This point was mentioned in the preceding discussion and is amplified here; also mentioned earlier were the mineral elements of greatest importance in livestock feeding, among them phosphorus.

Cows particularly need phosphorus, which is a part of the protoplasm of all living cells and occurs in rather large amounts in nervous tissue, bones, and milk. When they do not get the needed element, their appetite lags and milk production drops sharply. In many sections of the United States, pastures, ranges, and hay crops are low in phosphorus because the soil has a low phosphorus content, or it lacks available phosphorus, or climate (like too little rainfall) is unfavorable. It is an example of regional deficiency of certain minerals too acute to support efficient production in farm animals that consume much roughage.

Phosphorus deficiency in cattle may

be associated with a depraved appetite (pica), a craving for things not ordinarily classed as food, such as bones, wood, hair, and putrid flesh. Depraved appetite is of little diagnostic value because it is also manifested in cobalt deficiency and many known and unknown conditions. The outstanding symptom of too little phosphorus is a lack of appetite for food: The animal starves amid plenty. Milk production, in the case of milking cows, and body weight drop markedly. Eventually animals become emaciated.

A long-continued phosphorus deficiency may result in erosion of the cartilage at the ends of the bones and the animals may walk with difficulty. When the intake of calcium and phosphorus is low, their continued withdrawal weakens bones and makes them easily fractured. When the calcium intake is more than adequate and the phosphorus content of the ration is low, the breaking strength of the long bones remains normal.

Since depraved appetite is not a reliable index of phosphorus deficiency and a lack of appetite may be due to many other conditions, the positive diagnosis of phosphorus deficiency is difficult. Chemical analyses of the blood and the feed may give the answer, but such a service is not often available.

The best way to determine phosphorus deficiency on the farm is to feed a phosphorus supplement. If the animals improve in appetite then lack of phosphorus can be considered the cause of the trouble. Calves under a year of age seldom show phosphorus deficiency. If the cows in a herd show a lack of appetite while the heifers under 1 year of age have normal appetites, then a phosphorus deficiency among the cows is indicated.

The lack has not been observed among dairy cattle that get liberal amounts of roughage when the herbage contains 0.18 percent or more of phosphorus on the air-dry basis even when corn was the only supplement. Growing beef cattle appear to grow normally when the phosphorus content of the roughage tops 0.13 percent.

For the forage crops, enough phosphate fertilizer should be used to give maximum crop yields and to increase the phosphorus content if it is low. Under some conditions plants take up too little phosphorus to supply the needs of the animals. The positive method of assuring plenty of phosphorus for livestock is to allow them free access to a mixture of one-third special steamed bonemeal and two-thirds salt. Defluorinated phosphate may be used in place of bonemeal. Phosphorus can also be supplied by reasonable amounts of wheat bran, wheat middlings, or cottonseed meal.

Cobalt

Another example of regionalized deficiency is cobalt, a silvery metal of the iron-cobalt-nickel triad. Ruminants, especially cattle, have failed to thrive in some districts and often have died although they were fed seemingly good rations. This "wasting disease" has occurred in the United States for more than a century; in 1935 investigations of the condition among sheep and cattle in New Zealand and Australia resulted in the discovery of the role of cobalt in nutrition. Since then the use of a tiny amount of cobalt as a supplement to the ration of affected cows and sheep has produced dramatic recoveries. It is hard to understand how so little can do so much and so quickly. Many farms where cattle and sheep farming had never been productive are profitable livestock farms today.

As with phosphorus, the commonest symptom of too little cobalt is a lack of appetite—but many other abnormalities put livestock off their feed and the diagnosis of the disorder often involves chemical and biological tests plus feeding trials to establish fully the part that a specific element plays.

Cobalt deficiency, limited to ruminants, has been called a variety of names—"salt sick" in Florida, "neck ail" in Massachusetts, "Grand Traverse" or "Lake Shore Disease" in Michigan, "Burton-ail" in New Hampshire, and many other names in different parts of the world.

Sheep are more susceptible to it than cattle; young animals suffer more than mature animals of the same species. Apparently cobalt works through the rumen, because only ruminants appear to need the element and the injection of cobalt into the blood stream does not give so good results as feeding by mouth.

The symptoms of cobalt deficiency in sheep and cattle are a loss of appetite and emaciation; finally death from starvation despite plenty of other good nutrients. In sheep the wool is weak and easily broken. Cattle, especially calves, frequently show depraved appetite and many chew wood, hair, bones, tin cans, and similar objects.

Anemia is usually present in sheep and cattle in cases of long standing, but is of little help in diagnosing the trouble. In cattle the symptoms are the same as those of phosphorus deficiency. The difference can be determined from blood-phosphorus analysis, but usually this is out of the question. Heifers from 6 months to 1 year old are more likely to suffer from a lack of cobalt than mature cows. Consequently, if some of the heifers show a lack of appetite for feed and the milking cows are eating satisfactorily, then cobalt deficiency is indicated. The best methods of determining cobalt deficiency is to feed cobalt. If the appetite of the animals returns in 3 to 7 days, the ration is deficient in cobalt. If appetite has not improved within 10 days, the trouble is not cobalt, but something else.

Extensive investigations in Australia showed that the cobalt content of pasture generally varies with the amount in the soil. The cobalt content of pastures apparently tends to increase in late fall and early winter when growth is retarded, and to go down in the spring and summer when growth is at its maximum. Several studies show the effect of adding cobalt compounds to the land on the cobalt content of the herbage. As little as 4 ounces of cobalt chloride to the acre resulted in healthy pastures for a period of 2 years. Usually, however, 2 pounds of cobalt sulfate are applied per acre. Apparently plants take up more cobalt when cobaltized superphosphate is used.

The most satisfactory method of administering cobalt to cattle and sheep is to mix ½ to 1 ounce of either cobalt chloride or cobalt sulfate with 100 pounds of salt. Cobalt carbonate is sometimes used, but the amounts added to salt should be ¼ to ½ ounce per 100 pounds. When young milk-fed calves develop cobalt deficiency, an ounce of cobalt sulfate or cobalt chloride dissolved in a gallon of water and fed at the rate of a teaspoonful of the solution per calf per day is effective.

Calcium and Magnesium

Large roughage-consuming animals seldom suffer from a lack of calcium in the ration. The calcium content of forage plants depends largely on the species. Legumes are excellent sources of the element; nonlegumes, however, may not contain enough calcium for heavy-milking cows. Both calcium and phosphorus decline as the plant matures. During drought, the calcium increases and the phosphorus decreases. There are not very many areas in the United States where cattle, especially milking cows, and also sheep and horses may need a calcium supplement. Generally the lack of legumes and exclusive use of mature grasses, either as grazing or a hay crop, is an important factor. The lack of sufficient calcium results in withdrawal of calcium from the bones and its secretion in the milk of milking cows.

In areas where a calcium supplement may be needed, free access to a mixture of one-third calcium carbonate and two-thirds salt is a good way to supplement the ration. The calcium carbonate may be ground limestone, high-grade marl, or ground oyster shell. Bonemeal or defluorinated phosphate, which are also excellent sources of phosphorus, may be used in place of calcium carbonate. The most practical answer in many sections is to introduce a legume into the pasture and hay-crop mixtures.

Too little magnesium is comparatively rare among farm animals on pasture or when liberal amounts of roughages are fed, even though variations in magnesium content (that are due to species of plant and soil characteristics) are found among forage crops. But there occurs a condition sometimes referred to as "grass tetany" that does not appear to be associated with low magnesium content of the ration, although the addition of magnesium supplements cures it. In this condition there is a disturbed magnesium metabolism in which the blood plasma magnesium drops, followed by various degrees of excitability. In mild cases, the eyelids, ears, or various muscles may twitch. In the extreme form the animal goes into a violent convulsion and dies. The blood magnesium shows a seasonal drop, which usually hits bottom during March, April, and May.

When the symptoms of low blood magnesium are first noticed, it is necessary to start feeding magnesium compounds immediately. In the case of sheep and calves, one ounce of magnesium sulfate (epsom salts) should be given each day. Heifers and cows should receive 2 and 4 ounces a day, respectively. Treatment with magnesium sulfate should be discontinued after a week. Magnesium carbonate in the form of a high-grade, finely ground dolomite may be used in place of magnesium sulfate in one-half the amounts.

Iodine

Enlargement of the thyroid gland (goiter) is a common sign of iodine deficiency in livestock. It can be prevented or cured by feeding iodized salt. Three hundred pounds of such salt ordinarily contains the equivalent of approximately an ounce of potassium iodide stabilized to prevent loss of iodine. Thyroid enlargements in calves is sometimes referred to as "big neck." Although some of the goitered calves are dead at birth or die shortly after birth, most of them will live and do well. In those cases the enlargements recede, and the animals appear normal within a reasonable period.

A sign of iodine deficiency in sheep is evidenced by the birth of lambs that are dead or dying. Scanty wool and myxedema (water swelling) are frequently found in lambs with large goiters. In the few lambs that survive the goiter usually disappears within a month.

Symptoms of iodine deficiency in the newborn foal are difficult to diagnose because the only manifestation is extreme weakness. Foals seldom show a visible goiter, but enlargement of the thyroid gland can be observed at post mortem. In iodine deficiency the foal is born at full term, but so weak that it cannot stand; its appearance is dull, and it usually dies in 12 to 48 hours.

The loss of young because of lack of iodine in the dam's ration during gestation is greater among swine than among any other class of livestock. Goiter in pigs is termed "hairless pigs" because the pigs are almost hairless at birth. The pigs markedly affected may seem unusually fat. The skin of the head, neck, shoulders, and down over the thorax is thickened, pulpy, and of a watery nature (edematous). The thyroid gland appears normal.

The association of goiter and iodine deficiency with the area bordering on the Great Lakes and extending westward to the Rocky Mountains has become widely accepted. In that region considerable variation exists, however. Sandy soils are usually much poorer in iodine than clay soils. In general, the iodine in acid soils appears to be more readily available to plants than the iodine in alkaline soils. Several investigators have shown that the iodine content of plants can be increased by adding iodine to the soil and as a general rule soils rich in humus are rich in iodine also. Greater amounts of iodine are absorbed by plants when accompanied by the application of manure. There is some evidence that the application of potassium iodide along with superphosphate is the most effective from the standpoint of availability of iodine to the plant.

Copper

Cattle, sheep, and foals may get too little copper. The symptoms in cattle and sheep appear to vary in different parts of the world. In some places it is manifested in sheep by a wasting disease, swayback in lambs, and stringy wool in sheep of all ages. Breeding ewes are often anemic and show diarrhea. Swayback may affect lambs from birth to 3 months of age. They become unthrifty, walk stiffly, and show retarded growth. When driven, the lambs develop ataxia. Anemia, although commonly present in subacute cases, is not always present. The appetite for feed is normal. Post mortem findings show characteristic lesions of the spinal cord.

The most noticeable symptom of copper deficiency in cattle observed in southwestern Australia is "sudden death" or "falling disease." This disease is associated with a change in the heart muscle. The clinical symptoms are loss of condition, rough hair, and evidence of anemia. Depraved appetite is common. Diarrhea is not always a symptom of copper deficiency. Suppression of the heat period and temporary sterility in cows is attributed to a lack of copper. Calves stand on their toes and show stunted growth.

Copper deficiency in cattle in Holland, Scotland, New Zealand, and Florida is characterized by diarrhea. A change in the color of the hair coat in cattle has also been attributed to a lack of copper. Not all affected cattle are anemic. In some sections of the world the symptoms of copper deficiency occur in cattle even though the forage fed contains a normal amount of the element. Since the herbage is low in molybdenum, the cause remains obscure.

Copper deficiency in foals is characterized by unthriftiness and in more severe cases by pronounced stiffness of the limbs and enlargement of the joints. Affected animals frequently stand up on their toes, apparently as a result of contraction of the tendons. This condition may be apparent at birth or it may develop within the succeeding 6 months.

Copper deficiency in sheep and cattle may occur with a normal hemoglobin. This suggests that copper plays a role in the nutrition of these animals other than its classical one of stimulating iron in hemoglobin building.

Low copper content of plants is usually due to copper deficiency in the soil. There is some evidence that the copper in pastures during seasons of luxuriant growth is reduced. The heavy application of copper sulfate to high-lime soils has failed to increase the copper content of pasture; plants, therefore, cannot take up copper efficiently from alkaline soils.

The best treatment for livestock suffering from copper deficiency due to low content in the pasture and hay crops lies in two alternatives. The first is to apply 5 pounds of copper sulfate per acre of forage. The second is to mix 1 ounce of copper sulfate with 100 pounds of salt; the mixture can be self-fed to the livestock.

Iron and Manganese

In the past, cobalt and copper deficiencies among livestock have been successfully treated with iron compounds. The success was not necessarily due to the iron, however, but to cobalt and copper that were present as impurities. There is little evidence that sheep and cattle suffer from an iron deficiency; apparently pasture and hay crops give them enough of the element. Young pigs farrowed in clean quarters in winter may suffer from anemia due to a lack of iron and probably copper.

At times the manganese content of pasture grasses and hay crops may fall below the optimum standards. There is no correlation, though, between the manganese in soils and in plants grown on them. The element may not be present in an available form, notably in alkaline soils. Furthermore there is no convincing evidence that livestock other than poultry suffer from manganese deficiency under farm conditions.

Selenium and Molybdenum

Selenium and molybdenum are of interest because under certain conditions plants take up enough of them to be poisonous to animals. Selenium reaches toxic levels only in soils that are derived from cretaceous shales in semiarid climates. Investigations indicate that selenium may exist in several forms in the soil, but it is readily available to plants in the form of selenates.

Certain plants contribute indirectly to selenium poisoning because they can take up selenium, which is unavailable to ordinary forage plants, and convert it into an available form. When selenium is combined with iron it is less available to plants. Irrigation drainage water removes appreciable amounts of selenium from the soil, and plants grow there with low selenium content. But that is not the case when the water used for irrigation contains selenium.

High selenium content of forage plants is injurious to cattle, sheep, horses, pigs, and chickens, and is responsible for two types of symptoms referred to as "alkali disease" and "blind staggers."

"Alkali disease," the chronic type, is characterized by dullness and lack of vitality, depraved appetite, rough coat in horses and cattle, loss of hair from the mane and tail of horses and from the switch of cattle, soreness and sloughing of the hoofs, and stiffness of the joints. Selenium passes into the milk of selenized animals to the extent that the suckling young are very often affected.

In "blind staggers," the acute type,

the animal tends to wander from the herd, its vision appears to be affected, and it manifests a depraved appetite for bones and metal objects. In the final stage there is almost complete blindness and varying degrees of paralysis. The animal salivates freely, grates its teeth, and grunts. Death is due to respiratory failure. Anemia is common to both types of selenium poisoning. No simple, practical solution to the selenium poisoning problem has been developed so far.

The molybdenum content of herbage depends on the molybdenum in the soil and whether the soil is acid or alkaline. The more alkaline the soil, the greater the amount of this element that is taken up by plants. Certain plant species seem to take up more molybdenum than others.

Molybdenum poisoning has recently been reported among cattle in the United States. Symptoms are severe diarrhea, loss of weight, and a change in color of the hair—Holstein-Friesians change from black to a mouse gray, Herefords to a rusty orange, Guernseys and Red Devons to a muddy yellow, and black cattle become rusty. Anemia is usually manifested. The average death loss is about 80 percent. Young cattle are more susceptible than older ones; dairy cattle are more susceptible

than beef cattle. Sheep are rarely affected. Horses and swine are believed to be resistant.

Feeding copper sulfate in solution is effective in treating molybdenum poisoning. The dosage for heifers is 1 gram a day and for cows 2 grams a day, both as a cure and a preventive. The reasons for the benefits from the use of copper sulfate are not known. Possibly the effect of molybdenum in producing diarrhea and its counteraction by copper may affect the bacteria in the digestive tract.

THE AUTHORS≪≪≪   *C. F. Huffman is research professor of dairying in Michigan State College, School of Agriculture. His principal contributions have been in the field of mineral nutrition of cattle and the nutritive value of roughage crops for milk production. For outstanding research relating to the nutrition of dairy cattle, Dr. Huffman received the Borden Award in 1937.*

N. R. Ellis, since 1920, has studied fat, protein, minerals, and vitamins in the nutrition of swine, sheep, goats, beef cattle, horses, and poultry.

L. A. Moore in 1943 received the Borden Award from the American Dairy Science Association for his research on the feeding of dairy cattle.

GRASSLAND CROPS AS FEED FOR HORSES

I. P. EARLE

THE HORSE is a product of the grasslands and grass is therefore his natural feed.

Only after he had ventured away from the forest, where he was accustomed to living on the twigs of shrubs and trees, and became adapted to living on the grass of the plains did the horse develop from the dog-sized creature that was his progenitor to the princely animal that he is today.

The small wild horse of Asia and the so-called wild, or feral, horse of

our western plains still live entirely on grass. Often they refuse, when captured, to change their dietary habits to include any form of concentrate feeds. Only in the process of domestication has the horse been induced to adapt himself also to diets that may include all kinds of feeds supplied (according to the fancy of the feeder or the exigencies of circumstances) in the form of grains, seeds, roots, and tubers; animal products such as milk, meat, eggs, and bonemeal; byproducts of the mill, brewery, and distillery; cannery wastes and cull fruits; seaweeds, fish meal, and some fish oils. Even wood pulp and treated sawdust have been tried.

Such feeds have been used to replace varying proportions of the natural grass ration, sometimes because of convenience and availability and sometimes because of economy in utilizing materials that perhaps otherwise would be wasted—but oftener because a substitution of other feeds for part of an all-grass ration makes for better development and more efficient use of the horse.

The grassland crops, pasture herbages and cured hays, and fodder and straw constitute most of that class of feeds commonly called roughages.

No one feed is as complete a ration for the horse as good pasture grass, or good grass or legume hay of the current season's crop. But rations composed of roughages alone are usually less efficient than rations made up of combinations of roughage feeds and concentrate feeds, especially for horses at work and for the growing young. Nevertheless, the roughage feeds have special functions in the equine ration apart from their value as sources of energy and protein. They are important sources of the vitamins and minerals that are associated with green leaves, and they serve further to satisfy whatever may be the needs of the horse for bulk.

The green leaves of growing pasture plants are rich sources of carotene, which is converted into vitamin A in the animal body. But when green pasture is not available, the ordinary horse ration is often deficient in vitamin A activity because of the use of poor or old hay. In a study of the minimum carotene and vitamin A requirements of the horse, a group of investigators in California produced symptoms of acute vitamin A deficiency, in which the symptoms were night blindness, rough coat, reproductive failure, respiratory difficulties, and, eventually, death.

But one of the more commonly observed symptoms of a subacute vitamin A deficiency occurring spontaneously from the use of carotene-deficient rations is faulty hoof development. Some observers believe that vitamin A deficiency also constitutes one factor in the production of many of the common unsoundnesses of horses, for example, stringhalt, roaring, ring bones, side bones, arthritis, and navicular disease. Others have associated vitamin A deficiency with respiratory infections and with the occurrence of urinary calculi. The poor condition seen frequently in horses kept for long periods on restricted diets has often been attributed to vitamin A deficiency and has been reported to be relieved by injecting or feeding vitamin A in some form.

The minimum daily requirement of the mature horse has been estimated at about 2.0 to 2.4 micrograms of vitamin A or 9 to 14 micrograms of carotene per pound of body weight. Thus, to assure freedom from symptoms of vitamin A deficiency, the daily ration of the 1,000-pound horse should provide at least 15 milligrams of carotene, an amount that can easily be supplied by one-half pound of fresh, young, pasture grass, or by a similar quantity of carrots; by 1 pound of average No. 1 alfalfa hay or 2 pounds of average No. 1 timothy hay; by one-fourth pound of dehydrated alfalfa leaf meal, or by 1 to 3 pounds of silage. Four or five times that allowance should be made for breeding animals. A still more generous allowance is advisable for growing colts.

Animals on pasture depend on the action of the sun's rays on their skin for the manufacture of their own vitamin D because green pasture plants have practically no vitamin D activity, either fresh or as silage. When cut for hay, however, the forage achieves a vitamin D potency during exposure to the sun while curing. Artificially dried hay is high in carotene but quite low in vitamin D. With the exception of the sun-cured hays, the common horse feeds are lacking in this factor.

Information regarding the vitamin D requirements of horses at different ages and the interrelation of this vitamin with the horse's utilization of calcium and phosphorus is badly needed. The sun-cured hays usually supply adequate amounts for the adult animal, but the requirements of the young, growing animal are considerably greater than those of the adult. Unless the young animal has access to ample sunshine, he may be deficient in the vitamin D needed for normal calcification of growing bone. In this case he will probably show some of the manifestations of rickets. Supplementary vitamin D can be supplied in the form of one of the readily available vitamin D concentrates.

The recent investigations concerning the B vitamin requirements of the horse have indicated that riboflavin and possibly pantothenic acid also are required preformed in the horse ration. The investigators have concluded that the riboflavin requirements of the horse are of the same order as those of man; that is, about 20 micrograms daily per pound of body weight. The forage feeds are generally much richer in riboflavin than the grains. In order to provide 20 milligrams (which is the probable daily requirement of a 1,000-pound horse) from oats or barley, 33 pounds of grain would be required—but this same amount of the vitamin can be obtained from about 2½ pounds of good sun-cured alfalfa hay or 5 pounds of average timothy hay.

Some research carried out in the Veterinary Research Laboratory of the United States Army has directed attention to an apparent relation between riboflavin deficiency and the occurrence of periodic ophthalmia. The workers reported that daily doses of 40 milligrams per horse prevented the development of the condition although it was not effective as a cure.

Feeds such as the grains and the protein concentrates may be depended upon generally to supply ample phosphorus in the horse ration, but the forages are the important sources of calcium and of many of the so-called trace minerals. The forages, if they are grown on good soil, may also supply adequate phosphorus for the horse, but if they are produced on phosphorus-deficient soil they are usually too low in phosphorus for safe use as the sole source of supply.

Aside from the necessity of providing extra salt and of using iodized salt in the goitrous sections where there is a known iodine deficiency in the soil, the problem of satisfying the mineral requirements of the horse becomes— as far as practical feeding is concerned—a matter of supplying adequate amounts of calcium and phosphorus. The requirements for these elements are greatest during the first year and a half, when bone is being developed at the greatest rate, and during pregnancy and lactation in the mare.

It is important that calcium and phosphorus be supplied not only in quantities sufficient to meet the requirements, but also in a desirable ratio, preferably one to two times as much calcium as phosphorus. Deficiencies in either or both calcium and phosphorus will result in poor development of the young animal and in skeletal abnormalities in both young and mature horses. It has been roughly estimated that the calcium and phosphorus requirements of the growing colt, after weaning, can be met by a ration that contains as much as 0.20 percent of each of these elements.

Even when the calcium level of the ration is itself sufficient, however, if the phosphorus is much in excess of the calcium, the calcium is not well utilized and there may be an effect of a calcium deficiency. The result is a tendency to skeletal disorders more marked in growing animals but operating also in the mature ones. The disturbance in mineral metabolism, occurring as a result either of an unbalanced calcium-phosphorus ratio or of a combination of this with vitamin deficiencies, may be manifested as stiffness, shifting lameness, or stumbling gait, and, in extreme cases, by marked bone deformities that are characteristic of "big head."

An excess of phosphorus may occur when large amounts of the phosphorus-rich grains and of protein supplements are used. In the forages, calcium usually exceeds the phosphorus. As a rule the legumes are richer in calcium than the grasses. For that reason the legume hays are even more useful than grass hays in balancing the calcium-phosphorus ratio of a high-grain ration.

Besides their value as sources of vitamins and minerals, the roughage feeds are also important in the horse ration because they supply a certain amount of bulk, which seems to be needed for normal physiological processes. Because roughage feeds under usual conditions have always been cheaper and more plentiful than the grains or other concentrate feeds, and because the horse can utilize large amounts of forages, there has been more interest in knowing the maximum amount of roughage that can be used efficiently than in investigating the minimum amount that is required.

But both the bulk and weight of the usual amounts of roughage feeds that must be supplied to horses according to current practice are limiting factors in the economy of using horses where feeds must be transported long distances and where storage space is at a premium. The point is especially true of horses in the armed forces.

An investigation into the minimum amount of roughage required by horses for the efficient utilization of the entire ration under various conditions of activity was undertaken at the Agricultural Research Center at Beltsville in the interest of suitable concentrated rations for army horses. The investigation included studies of the minimum hay requirements of ponies and of farm work horses under conditions both of idleness and of work.

Our results indicated that ponies apparently differ little from horses in their roughage requirements; a ration made up of concentrate feeds alone, even though fortified with vitamins and minerals, is unsatisfactory without the addition of some roughage; the requirements for roughage can apparently be met satisfactorily by rations supplying hay at levels as low as 0.2 percent of body weight; the rations which supplied hay at levels of from 0.2 percent to 0.6 percent of body weight were better utilized than the control ration which supplied hay at a level of 1 percent of body weight.

The roughage content of the ration is closely related to the efficiency of utilization of the nutrients therein. That fact was brought out strongly in studies of the digestibility of low-roughage rations. The increases in the digestibility coefficients of the protein, fat, and nitrogen-free extract of the ration as a whole, which occurred with the decrease in the hay level, indicated the better utilization of the component feeds.

The results suggest that roughage feeds—beyond the amounts needed to satisfy whatever physiological requirement there may be for roughage as bulk—may serve to lower the efficiency of utilization of the rest of the ration.

From further studies of the roughage requirements of pony mares during pregnancy and lactation, it appears that the requirements for bulk are somewhat greater during pregnancy.

Under an experimental regimen it is possible to maintain horses, either idle or at work, without any pasture and on extremely low levels of cured hay by fortifying the ration with the minerals and vitamins that are recognized as being needed by horses. Under special conditions, where the use of concentrated rations of minimum bulk and weight will increase the usefulness of the horse, we think it is practical to feed rations having a very small proportion of roughage, but under ordinary conditions the margin of safety offered by the use of green pastures and more generous amounts of good hay is to be preferred.

It is a common observation that horses that regularly get green feed seem to have fewer of the ailments that are apt to plague the animals on dry feed. Even if pasture is available for only a few weeks of the year, it still has a role as a conditioner and tonic when used for short periods. Young pasture herbage grown on fertile soil seems to have properties beyond those ordinarily determined by analysis.

Good pasture alone may be used as the entire ration for breeding stock and growing colts, but if the maximum rate of growth is desired in the latter, pasture usually must be supplemented with other feeds. Studies made at the United States Range Livestock Experiment Station in Montana of the growth of young stock, which were kept from 1 to 3 years of age on western range without supplementary feed, have illustrated the effect of such a procedure in delaying maturity and in stunting skeletal development.

Other studies made at the agricultural experiment stations of Missouri and Michigan on the effects on growth of draft colts of limiting the grain ration but allowing unlimited roughage have shown that such limitations as were practiced slowed up maturity and growth rate but had a less marked effect on the skeletal development.

One can maintain idle horses on rations consisting largely or wholly of roughages, either fresh or cured, but as sources of energy for the production of work such feeds are much less efficient than the concentrate feeds. The more severe the work the less efficiently can the roughages be utilized.

On the basis of determinations made on horses, it has been estimated that 1½ pounds of hay is worth about as much as 1 pound of oats as a source of energy for the maintenance of idle animals, but for the production of work 2½ to 3½ pounds of hay is worth only as much as 1 pound of oats. Thus, even when hay is cheap, it is not economical when used as too large a part of the ration of the working horse.

The balanced horse ration depends largely on the roughage feeds for the necessary vitamins and minerals as well as for needed bulk. The amount of roughage necessary to supply the horse's requirements for the first two factors is highly variable and depends on the kind and quality of the product used. The smallest amount that will meet the requirements for minerals and vitamins will also probably meet the requirements for bulk.

THE AUTHOR ≪≪← *I. P. Earle, a Mississippian and a graduate of Vanderbilt University, is an associate biochemist in the Bureau of Animal Industry. Dr. Earle is stationed at the Agricultural Research Center at Beltsville, where she is engaged in research in animal nutrition.*

THE VITAL 10 PERCENT FOR POULTRY

H. R. BIRD

OF THE COMMON species of domestic poultry, only geese do well on a diet that is largely grass. Chickens, turkeys, and ducks require grains and other concentrates, and the proportion of grass that they can utilize effectively is small. But the economic importance of the grass in such diets is not small. In the nutrition of chickens, turkeys, and ducks, grass may be looked upon as home-grown vitamins, particularly vitamin A and riboflavin. If grass is not available, other sources of the vitamins must be bought.

Investigators disagree as to the amount of grain and mash feed that can be saved by providing pasture for chickens. Some have found no saving at all; others reported that growing birds or laying hens that had good pasture ate 5 to 20 percent less grain and mash than did birds confined on bare ground or on wire. The results were obtained without limiting the quantity of concentrate feed that was available to the chickens.

It is probably safe to estimate that under favorable conditions 10 percent of the dry matter of the diet of chickens on good pasture is furnished by the pasture.

So much for quantity, but what about the quality of this 10 percent? It furnishes one-eighth of the protein needed by growing chickens (more than 8 weeks old) and by laying hens. It furnishes about one-tenth of the calcium required by growing chickens and about one-twentieth of that required by laying hens, and about one-eighth of the manganese needed by laying hens if their eggs are to be used for hatching. These figures would justify some interest in pasture grass as a feed for chickens, but, as I said, its chief importance lies in its vitamin content.

The vitamins most likely to be lacking in poultry diets are vitamins A and D and riboflavin. Ten percent of grass in the diet would furnish several times the quantity of vitamin A needed by growing chickens and laying hens. It would furnish all the riboflavin needed by growing chickens or by hens whose eggs were not to be hatched and three-fourths of the riboflavin required by breeding birds. It would not supply vitamin D, but the sunshine to which birds on pasture are exposed would furnish enough of this vitamin for growing or laying chickens.

Turkeys are better grazers than chickens, but if they are given free choice of mash, grain, and good pasture, grass makes up about the same proportion of the diet as it does in the case of chickens. Savings of mash and grain feed ranging from 3 to 19 percent have been reported as a result of providing good pasture. As in the case of chickens, the dry matter of pasture grass as 10 percent of the diet would provide all the vitamin A and riboflavin needed by growing turkeys; sunshine would supply enough vitamin D.

The diet of growing ducks frequently contains 10 percent of cut green feed, and the diet of mature birds may contain as much as 25 percent. The dry matter supplied by these quantities would amount to 2 or 3 percent and 5 or 6 percent of the diet, respectively.

For geese, grass is a complete diet during most of the life cycle. Young goslings require some grain during the first 3 weeks of life, and some grain is required by breeders during the period of egg production, but otherwise good pasture is all that is needed.

The best crop or combination of crops for poultry pasture is the one that provides the greatest quantity of succulent, actively growing material during the greatest part of the year. It has been reported that chickens, when given free choice, prefer oats to other grasses, and that they prefer cereal grasses to alfalfa. Such differences in palatability may be kept in mind in selecting a pasture crop, but only as a secondary factor.

Among the commonly used pasture crops, palatability depends less on species than on stage of growth. As plants approach maturity their fiber content increases, and they become less palatable to chickens and less digestible. So it is recommended that the crops that continue to grow after cutting be cut often lest they go beyond the stage of early succulent growth.

Chickens are not proficient as grazing animals. When they are placed on pasture they are likely to destroy the vegetation completely in a small area around the house and neglect the more distant parts of their range. For that reason, and also from the standpoint of disease control, it is well to use movable houses or range shelters.

When birds are reared on sod range, the danger from disease will be reduced if the range is divided into two parts, one part of which is used one year and the other the next year. If movable houses or shelters are used, as many as 800 to 1,000 chickens or 200 turkeys per acre can be reared on annual pastures. Good permanent pasture should support 300 growing chickens or 200 laying hens or 100 growing turkeys to the acre.

Shade is important to birds on range. If natural shade is not available, it is well to provide some other shelter from the sun at locations where the chickens are fed and watered. It has been suggested that a crop like Sudangrass may be drilled in rows 24 to 30 inches apart and that alternate rows may be cut occasionally to provide a continuous source of succulent green feed, while the remaining rows are permitted to grow tall to provide shade.

Chickens can be induced to graze more extensively by limiting the quantity of mash and grain. A saving of as much as 22 percent of the concentrate feed by this method has been reported. The practice is not recommended for laying hens because any limitation of their intake of concentrate feed is likely to reduce the rate and efficiency of egg production. There are several methods of restricting the quantity of mash and grain supplied to growing birds on pasture, and if the restriction is not too severe, growth and maturity will not be affected. For example, at the New York (Cornell) Agricultural Experiment Station, allowing pullets to have access to grain and mash only in the afternoon stimulated their consumption of grass without interfering with their development. Experiments at the Delaware Agricultural Experiment Station indicated that limitation of the mash and grain intake of pullets on range to 75 percent of the quantity that would be eaten if the birds were permitted free choice was too severe a restriction and retarded growth.

Mash Formulas

Besides effecting some saving in the quantity of mash and grain fed, good pasture also permits the use of simplified, economical mash formulas.

Research at the Ohio Agricultural Experiment Station demonstrated that a mash for growing pullets on pasture could be simplified by omitting all protein and vitamin supplements, leaving a mash consisting of 90 parts of ground corn, 6 parts of bonemeal, and 2 parts each of oystershell, granite grit, and salt. Pullets were pastured on Ladino clover at the rate of 250 to the acre and fed this mash and whole corn, beginning in one experiment at 5 weeks and in another at 8 weeks of age. In both cases they grew as rapidly and efficiently as did birds fed mashes containing meat scrap and soybean oil meal.

Similar results were obtained at the New York station with pullets that were placed on Kentucky bluegrass and Ladino clover pasture when 8 weeks old and given a mash composed of ground wheat plus 4 percent of dicalcium phosphate and 1 percent each of ground limestone and iodized salt.

Attempts at the Michigan and New Jersey stations to rear pullets on pasture and grain, without mash, resulted in serious limitation of growth and were unsuccessful. Mineral supplements were not provided as they were in the Ohio and Cornell experiments.

The New York experiments showed that the consumption of grass was increased just as effectively by feeding a simplified mash as by limiting the quantity of mash fed. Earlier experiments in Great Britain and Canada led to the same conclusion, but in those studies the diets were inadequate for good growth even when supplemented with pasture.

It is not as easy to demonstrate a saving of feed by the use of pasture in the case of laying hens as in the case of growing birds, although it was found at the Kentucky Agricultural Experiment Station that spring bluegrass pasture permitted a 20-percent saving in mash consumption. Mature bluegrass pasture permitted no saving.

We have read several reports of a beneficial effect of pasture upon egg production and hatchability. But it has also been well established that laying mashes can be devised which, when fed to confined birds, will support egg production and hatchability at high levels that cannot be raised by supplying fresh green feed.

Pastures make it possible to reduce the quantity of alfalfa leaf meal and other vitamin supplements in laying and breeding mashes, as well as in growing mashes. Range is less important to laying birds because the heaviest egg production and most extensive hatching of eggs occur at a time of year when much of the country is without pasture and because hens on pasture produce eggs with deep yellow-orange yolks rather than the pale yolks that some markets demand. It also has been said that pasture favors the production of "grass eggs" with olive-colored yolks; in experiments at the Kansas Agricultural Experiment Station, however, that condition was not produced by feeding freshly chopped oatgrass or high-quality silage. It was produced by feeding one sample of oatgrass silage of poor quality.

Except for yolk color, the interior quality of eggs is not affected by the consumption of green feed.

Feed for Confined Chickens

In recent years, raising and keeping large numbers of chickens and turkeys in close confinement without access to range has directed attention to methods of supplying green feed under such conditions. By far the most important sources of the nutrients of green feed are alfalfa meal and leaf meal. Alfalfa meal contains, by definition, not more than 33 percent of crude fiber; leaf meal, which is cut at an earlier stage of growth, contains not more than 18 percent. Of the known nutrients supplied by these materials, the most important are, first, carotene and related compounds, which are converted by poultry into vitamin A, and, second, riboflavin. Unfortunately the carotene content of these materials varies from about 5 to about 300 micrograms per gram, depending on stage of growth at cutting and methods of processing and storage. To be of value in poultry feeds, alfalfa products should contain at least 50 (preferably 100) micrograms of carotene per gram.

Besides supplying carotenoids and riboflavin, these products also contain an unknown factor of particular value in helping to maintain high hatchability.

Almost all of the commercial poultry mashes contain some alfalfa meal or leaf meal, usually at a level between 3 and 10 percent of the mash. If these alfalfa products are of satisfactory quality, there is little reason for including more than 5 percent in a mash for chickens, especially as there is some evidence that, when fed at high levels, they are unpalatable to chickens, and that their high fiber content reduces efficiency of feed utilization. On the other hand, as much as 35 percent of alfalfa meal has been included in mash for growing turkeys with good results.

The usefulness of dried meals other than alfalfa in poultry mashes has been investigated. Satisfactory results have been obtained with Sudangrass meal, dehydrated immature oatgrass meal, dehydrated clover and perennial grasses, kudzu meal and leaf meal, and cowpea hay meal.

Although favorable results have been obtained in several experiments with grass and legume silages, the feeding of silage to poultry has not been widely practiced. Mature chickens or growing chickens more than 6 weeks old will consume 2 to 4 ounces of fresh silage per bird per day, but they may also consume as much concentrate feed as do birds without silage.

Tests at the New Jersey and Kansas Agricultural Experiment Stations showed that young chickens fed a mash that was deficient in riboflavin and probably in other vitamins ate enough grass silage to stimulate their growth but not enough to prevent symptoms of riboflavin deficiency. In those experiments, the addition of silage did not improve a good starting and growing mash nor did it improve a good laying diet. Reference has been made to the undesirable color of egg yolks that results from feeding silage of poor quality.

Satisfactory silage for poultry has been prepared from immature oatgrass, alfalfa, red clover, lespedeza sericea, mixed lawn grasses, and a mixture of white clover, alfalfa, and grasses. Either molasses or dilute mineral acid may be used as an aid to preservation.

THE AUTHOR≪ *H. R. Bird got his doctor's degree in biochemistry from the University of Wisconsin in 1938. He was associate professor of poultry nutrition at the University of Maryland from 1938 until 1944, when he became senior biochemist in charge of poultry nutrition investigations in the Bureau of Animal Industry.*

SHEEP, GOATS, AND GRASSLANDS

C. E. HOLSCHER, D. A. SPENCER

SHEEP and goats are grazing animals by nature. For the 50 million sheep and 4 million goats in the United States vast areas of cultivated crops, farm pastures, and range must be provided. In the range country, which lies west of the one hundredth meridian, roughly 70 percent of the sheep and 80 percent of the goats are produced.

Ordinarily, ranges are relatively large areas, privately or publicly owned or controlled, and mostly in semiarid and forested districts. Range forage usually is a mixture of native grasses, legumes, sedges, rushes, other grasslike plants, weeds, and, sometimes, woody plants. Pasture management usually aims to maintain maximum production of young palatable growth of tame grasses and legumes; on ranges such a practice is all but impossible because drier conditions limit regrowth after grazing.

Harvested crops, distinct from range and pasture, are usually stored against the time when ranges and pastures cannot be used. Usually, harvested crops supplement ranges and pastures and play a part in all the many different kinds of sheep operations, in which time of lambing and locality are big factors. For example: Lambing dates range from October in southern California to May in many parts of the range area; in southwestern Idaho, lambing in January and February is common.

Early lambing is done in sheds where ample protection from severe weather can be given to the newborn lambs. Late lambing is done on the range—a more economical system but one that usually results in a larger portion of the lambs being sold as feeders. In areas where lambs are produced on farm pastures, early lambing prevails. Flocks are usually small and the necessary attention and care can be given to early lambing.

Lambing in sheds makes it necessary to feed ewes hay and other supplements. Range-lambing operations as a rule do not produce a high proportion of fat lambs. Consequently many lambs are put in the feed lot on a ration of concentrates and hay for further fattening. Fattening on the farm may be on grass or harvested crops or both. Range operations are different from sheep raising in other sections—in the North Central States, Kentucky, Tennessee, Virginia, and West Virginia, where sheep raising also is a sizable enterprise.

As for goats, they are found in all parts of the country, too. Texas produces maybe 70 percent of all goats raised in the United States, but there are many in New Mexico, Arizona, California, Oregon, Missouri, Arkansas, and Oklahoma. The greatest concentration of goats is on the Edwards Plateau of Texas, where, as elsewhere, they are grazed on the range.

There are many milk goats in the Southwest also, and many in the farm-pasture areas of the Middle West and the East. They are handled much like milk cows, but they can live where milk cows cannot. Angora goats on the western range are usually herded, much like sheep, but where pastures are available they may also be turned loose to range for themselves. Milk goats may be fed harvested crops during much of the year, but particularly when pasture grasses are not growing. Angora goats are fed harvested crops only in case of shortage of pasture or range forage or during severe weather.

In the range country tremendous variations in topography (elevations range from near sea level to 12,000 feet or more), climate (precipitation ranges from 5 inches annually on some desert areas to 50 inches in the higher mountains, and frost-free periods extend from a few weeks to 230 days), and soils cause great variations in the type and amount of forage.

Grasses, weeds or forbs, and browse or woody plants all are part of the diet of sheep and goats. Sheep prefer weeds and finer grasses, but during the fall and winter they graze considerably on browse plants. Goats, however, are mainly browse eaters, although they graze many of the green, succulent grasses and weeds. During lambing and kidding the finer, juicier plants are important in keeping up the milk supply of the nursing ewes and does.

In the East, the Middle West, the Ozarks, and the Pacific Coast States goats often are used to clear pastures of undesirable brush. Sheep sometimes are used to clear pastures of weeds. But where sheep and goat operations are on a permanent basis, care must be taken not to overuse the type of forage most desirable for the animals produced. An overgrazed sheep range in a few years can change from one producing numerous weeds and fine grasses to one producing only coarse grasses and brush.

Similarly, the browse plants so essential in goat operations can be quickly eliminated by too heavy grazing. The grazing capacities of most of the range types are considerably below their potential because of overgrazing and other mismanagement. We can do a great deal to improve them.

The Range Types

Ten broad range types occur in the West and, in addition, the forest ranges of the South and Southeast. They differ in grazing capacity because of the amount and composition of the vegetation, variations in rainfall, productivity of the soil, and so on. Grazing capacity varies more or less directly with the effective precipitation unless overgrazing or another abuse reduces the productivity. Sheep use parts of every major forage type found in the West. Some sheep and goats also graze on the forest ranges of the South, but much of the sheep and goat production in that area is on farm pastures. Goats are generally found on the drier, browse-producing ranges.

The grazing capacities of the various types are: Tall grass, 0.5 acre per sheep and goat month, not used much by goats; short grass, 0.8 acre, used very little by goats except in Texas and New Mexico; Pacific bunchgrass, 0.9 acre, used very little by goats; semidesert grass, 1.1 acres, extensively used by sheep and goats (Edwards Plateau is in this type); sagebrush grass, 1.8 acres, excellent spring-fall range for sheep, but used little by goats; southern desert shrub, 2.3 acres, chiefly sheep range but grazed by goats also; salt desert shrub, 3.6 acres, used mainly as winter range for sheep, but used little by goats; pinyon-juniper, 1.7 acres, used a great deal by sheep and considerably by goats; woodland chaparral, 2.0 acres, usually valuable as goat range and in California it is also grazed by cattle and sheep; and open forest, 1.6 acres, valuable as summer range for sheep.

The mountain brush and aspen subtypes are valuable as goat ranges. Goats use cut-over lands extensively in Oregon and Missouri.

In almost every region (except perhaps the short-grass Plains) there is a seasonal movement, particularly of sheep. Goats are often ranged close to the home ranch, although even there the spring, summer, fall, and winter ranges are usually separated.

The usual pattern in the Mountain West is to graze sheep on the sagebrush-grass type in the spring, progressing toward the higher country as the range becomes ready for grazing. By the time the open forest or high-altitude range is ready for grazing, the sheep have migrated to it. They spend their summers there and return over the sagebrush-grass ranges in the fall.

Forage on the spring range is made up of the finer grasses and palatable weeds: Arrowleaf balsamroot, penstemons, lupines, tapertip hawksbeard, bluebunch wheatgrass, Sandberg bluegrass, Nevada bluegrass, and needlegrass. In the fall the same grasses are used to some extent, but much browse is included in the diet. This includes bitterbrush, big sagebrush, threetip sagebrush, and rabbitbrush. In a mild autumn far less use is made of the browse species than when the weather is cold and snow is on the ground.

Summer range is used to attain growth and fill on the lambs. The forage remains green most of the season and lambs ordinarily gain rapidly. Much of this type of range is in the open-forest type on national forest lands. Some of the important forage species on the high ranges are bluegrasses, bromes, wheatgrasses, fescues, wild carrot, sweet-anise, wild geranium, sedges, alpine timothy, dandelion, cinquefoil, and groundsel. Browse plants eaten on the open-forest ranges include mountain-mahogany, snowberry, ceanothus, serviceberry, and bitterbrush.

Wintering of sheep and goats differs in the various parts of the western range country more than other seasonal operations. Much of the winter range is included in the broad type called the salt-desert shrub. Precipitation is irregular, and forage production varies as much as 300 percent between good and poor years. These ranges must be used in winter because of lack of stock water at other seasons. Winter snows provide some water, but even in winter snow water is undependable. Some operators find it profitable to haul water to the sheep.

The principal plants of the salt-desert shrub type are Indian ricegrass, galleta, winterfat, shadscale, saltbush, black sagebrush, bud sagebrush, and rabbitbrush. Many are shrubs high in protein and make the desert excellent winter range if there is plenty of good water.

Livestock without winter range must winter in feed yards, chiefly on alfalfa hay and some grain.

In much of the short-grass region, sheep are wintered on the range. Winter range is somewhat rougher than the range used for summer. The main winter forage species—bluestem wheatgrass, needle-and-thread grass, big sagebrush, silver sagebrush, false-tarragon sagebrush, and cudweed sagebrush—retain considerable nutritive value and provide good winter grazing. Grazing on the range forage is more economical than wintering in feed yards if ample forage is available, deficiencies are offset by supplemental feeding, and extra care is given the flocks in bad weather.

The Essential Nutrients

Good goat management requires that weeds and grasses be present on the range when the kids are small. Since goats are primarily browsing animals, considerable brush should be available at all seasons, especially on the winter ranges. The Edwards Plateau is of the semidesert-grass type. The principal species found in that type are Rothrock grama, black grama, curly-mesquite, and such thorny shrubs and dwarfed trees as mesquite, mimosa, catclaw, hackberries, creosotebush, jojoba, ceanothus, and low-growing live oaks.

For the most part, range forage provides the minerals, proteins, and vitamins essential for growth and maintenance of strong, healthy sheep and goats. Chemical analyses show that the protein content of growing range plants equals or exceeds that of good alfalfa hay. Harvested directly and used immediately by the grazing animals, range forage supplies the vitamins often lost in the storage of harvested crops.

During fall and winter the nutritive value of standing herbage drops markedly because of leaching, drain of materials back into the roots, and increase of fiber and lignin. The food values of browse plants, however, remain high through most of the year, particularly the protein and sugars. Hence, sheep and goats on browse range need less supplemental feeding than those on grass ranges. The soils of some ranges lack essential elements, and the deficiency is passed on through the forage to the animals. Much of Montana east of the Continental Divide and the Coastal Plain of Texas, for example, are wanting in phosphorus. Southeastern Montana and North Dakota are deficient in iodine. Other parts of the country may be low in other essential elements. The deficiencies must be corrected by supplementing the regular diet with feeds high in the missing elements.

Alfalfa hay is one of the best sources of minerals, vitamins, and protein, provided the area on which it grows has no deficiencies. Alfalfa hay is an especially good source of vitamin A and calcium. Sodium and chlorine are supplied by common salt. Iodized salt provides iodine. Phosphorus can be provided by feeding bonemeal along with salt. Ordinarily vitamins and protein can be best provided by feeding green forages. Therefore hay must be properly cut and cured so that a maximum of these elements is retained in the stored roughage.

In any range operation supplemental feeding is sometimes necessary. Plenty of supplemental feeds to carry flocks through emergencies, like droughts, have to be kept on hand.

In some localities, supplemental feeding during the winter is common; snow covers the ranges and forage is not available, or range is insufficient for winter use. Many operators feed grain to their animals before breeding to insure a greater lamb or kid crop and again before lambing or kidding to insure a good supply of milk for the suckling animals. Ranchmen on the short-grass Plains resort to supplemental feeding only in case of drought or severe weather. On the desert-shrub areas few supplements are fed except when snow is deep. The Southwestern ranges are used yearlong, but droughts often make supplements necessary.

Supplemental feeding is, of course, more costly than is harvesting of forage by grazing animals. The wise operator tries to stock his range so that he has ample forage even in years of drought. By such management, he maintains his animals in better condition and safeguards the high productivity of his range.

Alfalfa hay is the most common supplement used on the range, especially where the animals receive no other feed or forage. In some cases, animals may have access to range, but the forage lacks the necessary nutrients to keep the animals thrifty. Then the use of a more concentrated feed is wise. Roughage is obtained from the range forage, but the essential nutrients are obtained from the concentrates. The most common types of concentrates are cottonseed cake or meal or soybean or grain pellets.

Farm Pastures

Pastures for sheep and goats in farming regions include permanent and temporary (or supplemental) grazing areas. Permanent pastures often occupy steep, rough or stony lands, farm wood lots, orchards, fields of low fertility, and erodible areas. Hay meadows, stubblefields, and areas suitable for growing crops of annual forage plants normally fit into the grazing program as temporary or supplemental pastures. These are also useful during dry periods or when permanent pastures are resting and least available.

Kentucky bluegrass is the most common forage for permanent pastures in the upper Mississippi Valley and eastward. Timothy furnishes good early pasture, but after it heads out sheep and goats do not relish it. Farther south, redtop is a good permanent pasture plant; in the Southern States Bermuda-grass is valuable.

The clovers and alfalfa furnish abundant permanent pasture, but in grazing them care must be exercised to prevent bloat. The trouble from bloat differs widely in various sections, so in using these legumes one should be guided by the experience in his locality. Mixtures of clover and alfalfa with timothy or other grasses furnish pastures safer from bloat than legumes alone. Such mixed pastures provide better feed, especially for lambs and kids, than bluegrass or timothy. In Southern States, lespedeza may be used to good advantage as a pasture legume. It is good for soil and animal.

Winter rye furnishes the earliest spring grazing for temporary pastures in the Northern States. It may be grown also for fall grazing. Farther south, winter wheat and winter oats are good temporary grazing crops during the colder months. Oats and peas, oats and vetch, and soybeans make excellent temporary pasture. Rape is widely used as pasture for sheep, especially in midsummer as a supplement when permanent pastures are scanty. It may also be used for goats.

Rape may cause bloat, but the danger is reduced by a combination of oats and rape. It is well to avoid grazing rape, especially with lambs and kids, when it is wet or immature, for it may cause young animals to scour.

Kale provides good winter and spring pastures in the mild climate of the Pacific coast. Kohlrabi, cabbage, turnips, and rutabagas may be useful for grazing in the fall.

Good bluegrass pastures in regions to which they are well adapted have a higher grazing capacity for sheep and goats than other types of pasture. Normally, however, bluegrass becomes dry in midsummer and takes a rest, so that it needs to be supplemented with temporary pastures.

In tests at Beltsville the Bureau of Animal Industry found that a bluegrass pasture furnished 821 ewe-days of grazing per acre; soybeans furnished 465 ewe-days; and a mixture of barley and winter oats, 348 ewe-days. Other useful temporary pastures tested there included oats and rape; wheat and rye; wheat, rye, and barley; and winter oats alone, but they produced less grazing forage per acre than soybeans and the mixture of barley and winter oats.

The grazing capacity of different pastures varies greatly, depending on fertility, rainfall, length of growing season, and grazing management, but the numbers of ewe-days of grazing per acre here reported may be taken as the capacities to be expected from moderate grazing by sheep and goats.

Good farm pastures furnish minerals, proteins, and vitamins that animals need for normal growth and health. This is particularly true of pasture forages when they are growing and their protein content is at its peak. In dry seasons or in the fall and winter when the forages are scanty and not growing, the animals may need supplementary protein-rich feeds, such as daily allowances of one-fourth to one-half pound per sheep of cottonseed meal or cake.

Minerals like salt, calcium, phosphorus, and iodine, and the highly essential vitamin A may be furnished sheep and goats on pastures in the ways we listed for furnishing them on the range.

Under normal conditions on farms well managed for the production of sheep and goats, supplemental feeding on pastures will be confined largely to periods of drought or to early spring and late fall. Even then, efficient operators try to guard against scarcity of pasture forage by providing supplemental pasture crops, but under some conditions that may be impossible. So, it is safest to be prepared to feed hay and grain if necessary.

If the forages available on sparse pastures are nonleguminous plants, low in protein, it is desirable to feed cottonseed, linseed, or soybean meal or cake. If the pasture forage is extremely scarce, it may pay to feed alfalfa, clover, soybean, or lespedeza hay. If the sparse pasture is of legumes, the grain supplement may be corn, or corn and oats in equal parts by weight. Daily allowances of feed for supplementing pastures vary with the degree of scarcity of pasture forage, but as a rule one-third to one-half pound of concentrates should be enough for a ewe or doe

as a daily allowance where the pasture forage can supply their roughage.

THE AUTHORS ⫸ *C. E. Holscher is a graduate of Iowa State College and has been engaged in range research work with the Forest Service since 1937. He is a forest ecologist and is range-research project leader at the United States Sheep Experiment Station at Dubois, Idaho.*

D. A. Spencer is a graduate of Michigan State College. He is a senior animal husbandman in charge of sheep and goat husbandry investigations in the Bureau of Animal Industry and is stationed at the Agricultural Research Center at Beltsville.

THE USE OF FORAGE IN FEEDING HOGS

JOHN H. ZELLER

PORK can be produced on good, clean hog pastures with 15 to 50 percent less concentrates than dry-lot feeding requires, depending on the method of management. Good legume pastures may replace one-half the protein supplement ordinarily fed in dry-lot rations, besides minerals, vitamins, and other essential food elements. Pigs on pasture usually gain faster and reach the market several weeks earlier than pigs fed balanced rations in dry lot.

Sanitation is easier when hogs are on a rotation-pasture system, and the danger of parasitic infestation is lessened. More runty pigs are found under dry-lot feeding conditions than with pasture-fed pigs. Hogs on pasture help to maintain soil fertility by scattering the manure over the land; as much as 75 percent of the fertilizing value of feeds fed to hogs on pasture may be recovered and returned to the land. Another advantage of pastures for swine is the saving of labor.

Despite those advantages, though, it will not do to think that that is all there is to it. Hogs have a limited digestive capacity; their stomachs cannot

utilize the large amounts of forage that cattle, horses, and sheep do. Even the best pastures generally provide little more than a maintenance ration for swine—for economical production, hogs must be fed a certain amount of concentrate feed in addition to pasture. The basic point regarding the pastures is one of quality, then, not one of quantity.

I think of seven essentials of good pasture crops for swine production, regardless of locality. They must be adapted to the soil and climatic conditions under which they are grown. They must be grown at small expense. They must provide abundant growth for a short pasture period, or consistent growth over a long period. They must be palatable and succulent so as to be readily consumed, and rich in protein, vitamin, and mineral nutrients. They must have a good carrying capacity over the grazing period.

Four types of pastures are used in swine production: Permanent, rotation, and temporary pastures, and grain crops to be hogged down. Many successful hog growers combine two or more types to furnish the maximum grazing facilities, with planned rest periods for the pastures.

Permanent pasture plants most generally used are perennials like bluegrass, white clover, Bermuda-grass, carpetgrass, and Dallisgrass. Permanent hog pastures can be utilized over a long grazing season. They usually furnish the most nutrients, though, during the spring and fall growing periods, and have a dormant period during July and August.

Rotation pastures may include alfalfa, red clover, Ladino, sweetclover, alsike, orchardgrass, bromegrass, lespedeza, and others. These pastures grow rather consistently and can be utilized at any time during the growing season until other crops are ready to graze.

The temporary or annual pastures, which are seeded each year and supplement or replace permanent pastures, fit well into a swine sanitation program. Under the McLean County system, for instance, hogs are raised on clean pastures, the land having been plowed and planted since it was used previously by hogs. Temporary pastures include crops like rape, soybeans, cowpeas, Sudangrass, rye, oats, wheat, barley, Italian ryegrass, and field peas. The rate of seeding temporary pastures should be heavier than that for grain crops so as to get a denser sod, which provides more pasture than hogs can keep closely grazed and therefore lessens the danger of parasites. Frequently the pastures, after providing succulent grazing, will produce a grain crop that can be harvested.

Hogged-down crops include corn, sorghums, sweetpotatoes, peanuts, and small grain. A good practice is to have a pasture crop in a field next to a hogging-down crop so hogs will have access to both fields. Frequently soybeans or a similar crop is seeded at the last cultivation of corn so that the two crops can be grazed in the same field.

The proper use of the different types of pastures requires careful planning so as to have the hogs on each pasture get the most nutrients at the proper time and not handicap the carrying capacity of the pasture later.

Alfalfa makes one of the best legume pastures for swine. It is high in nutrients, provides a long grazing period, and gives an efficient substitute for the high-priced protein supplements. Alfalfa is rated 100 percent as a basis for comparison with other crops in value in pork production. If it is not grazed too closely, the crop will grow enough to be cut for hay and yield 1 or 2 tons of hay an acre in addition to the grazing.

Red clover, properly grazed, rates next to alfalfa in feeding value and economy as a forage for hogs. It is a high-yielding forage, but it should not be grazed too early in the season before growth starts. It fits well into crop rotation systems. On some soils it often excels alfalfa.

Rape, though not a legume, compares favorably in nutrients with both alfalfa and red clover. In all-around value, it is on a par with the clovers for hogs. Besides its long grazing season, it has a high carrying capacity. The Dwarf Essex variety is more palatable to hogs than other varieties. The crop may be seeded any time during the growing season; it grows quickly. It is often sown in combination with oats, barley, or oats and field peas.

Sweetclover is valuable as a soil builder and high in nutrients and is a large yielder of forage or hay. Best results are obtained when hogs graze the crop the first year, as growth in the second and third years is coarser and less palatable.

Bluegrass furnishes excellent grazing for hogs in early spring, fall, and early winter. It is a permanent grass that can be utilized on lands unfit for other crops. The crop becomes dry and unpalatable in midsummer.

Soybeans, a popular temporary crop for hogs, are planted about the time corn is planted. They furnish excellent green forage in midsummer. When the crop matures, it can be hogged down.

Oats may be seeded in early spring

for an early forage. Oats and field peas are often seeded together.

Sudangrass furnishes green grazing in the hot, dry months. The grazing period is short, but the crop has a heavy carrying capacity.

Winter rye sown early in the autumn furnishes late-fall and winter grazing. It is also a good spring grazing crop for sows and litters in the Corn Belt. The crop should be heavily grazed; otherwise it soon becomes coarse and of little value.

Mixed grass pastures are becoming popular in many districts. They make succulent forage available at almost any season, depending on the plants used. Ladino clover, a legume of high protein content, is used in many such mixtures. Alfalfa, Ladino clover, alsike, bromegrass and orchardgrass are often used in one mixture.

The research worker is always on the alert to test new pasture grasses to determine their value in livestock production. An example is the use of cheatgrass, once considered a weed, as an early-spring pasture for grazing sows and litters. The unnamed variety used at Beltsville originated from seeds collected in Maryland by Dr. W. B. Kemp, of the Maryland Agricultural Experiment Station, and developed as an excellent crop for the prevention of soil erosion. In the tests at the Agricultural Research Center, cheatgrass pasture was palatable to hogs and furnished a longer grazing period than either rye, barley, or wheat pastures.

Results of tests at various experiment stations show the value of hogging off crops. Corn, soybeans, small grains, peanuts, sweetpotatoes, sorghums, and such crops fit well into such a system. The chief advantages of the system are that it saves labor costs of harvesting the crop, increases soil fertility, aids in swine sanitation, and lowers cost of pork production. Year-round grazing systems of green and mature crops are the basis of increased hog production in Georgia, South Carolina, Florida, and other Southern States.

The use of ground legume hay or meal in the winter ration has become an established practice in many herds. Feeding sun-cured or dehydrated hay is an excellent way to supply the nutrients found in pasturage. The dry legume forages are particularly valuable in speeding up gains in dry-lot feeding: They supply health-giving nutrients that might otherwise be lacking.

A series of experiments over 6 years at Beltsville were aimed to find out the most efficient levels at which sun-cured legume-hay meals could be fed to pigs from weaning to a market weight of 225 pounds. The hays tested were alfalfa, soybean, and sericea lespedeza. The hay meals were fed at 0-, 5-, 10-, 15-, and 20-percent levels. Somewhat more rapid gains were had on the 5- and 10-percent levels. Up to the 10-percent level the ground hay effected an appreciable saving of concentrates. Leafy soybean hay, cut in the early bloom stage, ranked ahead of No. 2 alfalfa hay; sericea lespedeza was the least valuable. Thus, we found home-grown legume crops can be utilized in swine feeding with a saving in the purchase of protein feeds needed to help balance home-grown grains.

Other tests were conducted with spring- and fall-farrowed pigs at Beltsville to compare the value of dehydrated legume hay meals in the rations of feeder pigs from weights of approximately 62 to 125 pounds. Dehydrated soybean, kudzu, sericea, and alfalfa hay meals, and a sun-cured alfalfa hay meal were fed at 10 percent of the total ration; a check group received no hay meal. The pigs fed the dehydrated alfalfa hay meal made approximately 9 percent faster gains, with a saving of 10 percent of feed over those receiving the sun-cured hay. Dehydrated kudzu and soybean meals gave results about equal to those of the sun-cured alfalfa meal. The pigs receiving the dehydrated sericea hay meal made the slowest and most expensive gain.

The value of alfalfa hay in the ration of brood sows was demonstrated by investigators at the Wisconsin Agricultural Experiment Station. Sows that received only 5 percent of alfalfa hay in the ration during gestation raised only half as many pigs to weaning age as other sows that were fed 15 percent of alfalfa. The pigs from sows receiving the lower level of alfalfa hay were much lighter in weight at weaning. Growing and fattening pigs made the cheapest gains from 53 to 200 pounds in weight when alfalfa made up 10 percent and 15 percent of the ration fed in dry lot. Feed costs at the 20- and 5-percent levels were more costly per 100 pounds of gain. Many farmers, besides putting 10 or 15 percent of ground hay or meal in the mixed ration, make legume hays available in racks so that sows can eat all they want.

Young grass silage preserved with concentrated whey can be used successfully as a supplement in the winter ration of growing and fattening pigs. At Beltsville we tested the value of such silage with 4 lots of 10 pigs each. A standard ration plus supplements was fed from weights of approximately 65 to 225 pounds. One lot received ground alfalfa hay at a 5-percent level; the second lot, corn silage; the third, concentrated whey-grass silage; and the fourth, concentrated whey-grass silage and 2 pounds of concentrated whey per 100 pounds of live weight. The corn silage and whey-treated grass silage made up 13.6 percent of the ration. The pigs gained at the rate of 1.83, 1.48, 1.78, and 1.81 pounds each daily, and required 357, 422, 411, and 398 pounds of feed, respectively, on the rations in the order given.

This test demonstrates that green forage can be processed in periods of plenty and fed to advantage in off seasons to help balance the ration with home-grown feeds. It also suggests the possibilities of other ways of preparing silages for use in hog feeding.

Young grass is nature's contribution to healthy livestock nutrition. Green forage crops provide succulent grazing for brood sows during the gestation and suckling periods, as well as for growing and fattening pigs. A system of green forage crops should be worked out that provides green grazing for hogs for as much of the year as possible.

Experimental results at the Missouri Agricultural Experiment Station show that sows fed good rations in dry lot farrowed pigs that were not so healthy or thrifty as pigs from sows fed similar rations on good pasture. A noticeable improvement in health occurred when fresh growing forage was given the unthrifty pigs. The results show the importance of pastures for brood sows.

Brood sows during the gestation period can obtain a large percentage of the nutrients needed on good pasture. The better legume swine pastures may replace most of the protein supplement and 40–50 percent of the grain concentrate for bred sows. Only about three-fourths of a pound of corn, or its equivalent, in addition to a small amount of tankage or skim milk, is needed daily per 100 pounds live weight of sow to produce one-half to 1 pound of gain per day during gestation, depending upon her condition at breeding time. Proteins of animal origin such as tankage, fish meal, or skim milk are effective in supplementing plant proteins and should be included in the rations of brood sows, even when they are on pasture.

Many swine growers have sows farrow their litters on pasture. Others farrow the litters in central houses and move them to a clean pasture in a week or 10 days. The use of good pasture simplifies feeding and helps to increase the milk flow of the sow. The most satisfactory method of feeding is to allow both the sow and pigs access to a self-feeder. Grain, a protein supplement, and a mineral mixture may be made available in separate compartments of the feeder, and the sow and litter allowed to balance their own ration. A mixed ration, balanced with respect to energy values, protein, and minerals, is often fed free choice. In addition, pigs should have access to high-protein feeds in a creep, including an animal protein feed such as tankage, fish meal, or skim milk.

The amount of grain to feed to growing and fattening pigs on pasture is important for economical production. The two methods generally used are full feeding of concentrates on pasture for early marketing, and growing on limited feeding of concentrates on pasture followed by full feeding for late marketing. The former method usually gets early spring pigs on the market during the pasture-growing season, at a good market price, ahead of the general run of hogs. There is also less labor, risk, and carrying cost. The latter method requires feeding over a longer period, more labor, and greater risks; marketing is later and at a lower price. A summary of the results of the two methods of feeding at the Indiana Agricultural Experiment Station showed that the full-feeding method returned the greater profit between feed cost and market price of hogs in 5 out of 6 years.

Hog pastures should be tightly fenced to confine pigs of all ages. The most satisfactory hog fence is wire, 39 inches high with 9 bars, 6 inches between stays, and No. 9-gauge wire throughout. Two strands of barbwire above the 39-inch fencing provides a fence to turn stock of all kinds. A strand of barbwire at ground level will keep small pigs from digging holes under the fence.

Three other points need emphasis.

A hog lives close to the ground. He has a tough snout, and it is natural for him to root, especially when the ground is soft. Putting a ring in his snout will keep him from rooting holes or tearing up the sod. The ringing operation should be done carefully to prevent infection. Hogs that are furnished a well-balanced ration with adequate minerals are less likely to root than those on a mineral-deficient ration.

Shelter in the form of movable colony houses or open-front houses exposed to the south should be provided for protection against cold, rain, and high winds. Shade should be provided in all hog pastures if natural shade is not available. Temporary shade can be provided cheaply by using poles, brush, and straw. If shade is not furnished, hogs will root holes in the soil to obtain moist earth to cool their bodies.

Clean, fresh water is essential at all times if hogs are to gain rapidly and economically. Water may be furnished naturally by streams or springs in the pasture or be provided in water fountains or troughs. Mud wallows or ponds should be avoided. If a hog wallow is necessary for comfort, a movable wallow built on skids can be provided and dragged from pasture to pasture.

THE AUTHOR «« *John H. Zeller is in charge of swine investigations in the Bureau of Animal Industry. He has been in swine research work in Washington and at the Agricultural Research Center at Beltsville continuously since 1917. Mr. Zeller is a graduate of Pennsylvania State College and George Washington University.*

GRASS FOR THE PRODUCTION OF BEEF

W. H. BLACK, D. A. SAVAGE

BEEF CATTLE lead all classes of American livestock in the consumption of grass and grassland crops. They utilize about one-third of the permanent pastures, three-fourths of the range areas, and a high percentage of the harvested crops. Grass usually represents the principal and cheapest feed of beef cattle. Pastures can be regarded as a costly source of feed only on highly productive farm land, but their use in rotation with cultivated crops on such land is certain to continue and be expanded as a sound practice.

About 12 billion pounds of dressed beef and veal was produced in the

United States in 1947 through the conversion of grassland crops into meat by cattle. The quantity of forage required to produce this huge output of meat is indicated by the average daily requirement of beef cattle. An average beef animal consumes at least 50 pounds of green or succulent forage daily in humid locations and probably about half that quantity in drier areas.

Our experiments near Jeanerette, La., in 1939, 1940, and 1941 in which pastures were grazed to maintain the weight of steers indicated a carrying capacity of more than 1,800 pounds of animal weight an acre. The seasonal yield from clippings was 27,403 pounds of fresh forage an acre. That was 43 percent greater than the consumption by comparable steers that were kept in a dry lot and fed fresh clippings from a similar pasture so as to maintain their weight at the same level. The dry-lot steers ate about 50 pounds of fresh forage daily per 1,000 pounds of live weight. This quantity of vegetation contained 13.02 pounds of dry matter and provided 1.17 pounds of digestible protein and 8.77 pounds of digestible nutrients. These values are within the range of theoretical requirements for the maintenance of 1,000-pound mature beef animals, plus 25 percent for the "activity" factor.

A study of grazing capacity, conducted by S. E. Clarke and associates, of the Canadian Department of Agriculture, has indicated that about 25 pounds of the native grass of southern Alberta, Saskatchewan, and Manitoba is required to make a pound of beef and leave sufficient growth as carry-over. The grasses of southern Canada are more nutritious and contain less moisture than the more succulent grasses of humid areas. The native grasses in the Great Plains of the United States are likewise superior in year-long nutritive qualities to those of humid areas, according to results of analytical and grazing work reported by D. A. Savage and V. G. Heller.

Grasses furnish almost the entire feed supply of beef cattle for at least half the year in most areas and for the entire year in some.

In the Great Plains and other parts of the West, breeding herds are maintained on grass and fed only a limited quantity of protein-rich supplements during periods of drought or snow. The native bluestem grasses of the Flint Hills of Kansas and of the Osage region of Oklahoma are noted for their fattening qualities. Thousands of fat cattle from those areas are slaughtered annually.

The Mineral Point section of southwestern Wisconsin and the Appalachian region enjoyed a similar reputation for many years. In recent times, however, the trend there has been toward the production of farm crops. The fattening of steers on grass alone is giving way to the production of beef on grass and harvested crops supplemented with concentrates. The fattening of aged steers is being replaced by breeding herds, the creep-feeding of calves, and the fattening of yearlings and 2-year-olds on grass and concentrated supplements.

Blue grama is the most valuable and widely distributed native grass in the Great Plains. It occurs from the Peace River of Canada to Mexico and represents about a 50–50 mixture with buffalograss from southeastern Montana southward through the Plains. These two famous short grasses, with their comparatively high feed value at all stages of growth, give to the Great Plains region its enviable reputation as the home of feeder cattle—the Nation's leading area for the yearlong grazing of beef cattle.

Many other desirable native grasses add greatly to the value of the region for grazing purposes. Chief among these in the Northern Great Plains is western wheatgrass. This cool-weather grass helpfully lengthens the green grazing season in the short-grass region and often produces more total feed than the true short grasses. It is well established from the Dakotas to the Pacific Northwest and from northern Alberta to central Colorado and

Kansas, with some occurrence in Texas and Oklahoma. It is found in nearly all upland pastures of the Northern Great Plains, but is most abundant on lowlands and on heavy upland soils. Flats subject to flooding are frequently occupied by western wheatgrass to the almost total exclusion of other grasses; they have furnished excellent hay and winter pasture for beef cattle since the country was first settled.

Western wheatgrass provides highly palatable grazing in the spring and fall in the Northern Great Plains and throughout most of the fall, winter, and spring months when reseeded in parts of the Southern Great Plains. The grass is not so palatable as the short grasses in the cured stage of growth but is eaten readily when other grasses are not available. It does not recover rapidly from close early grazing but, when allowed to complete its growth, it ranks among the leading forage-yielding grasses of the region.

Carrying Capacity

Moderation in stocking native range has shown outstanding advantages in all degree-of-grazing tests conducted throughout the West. In most instances total gains per acre have favored the heavier rates of stocking, but the fallacy of heavy grazing has been consistently demonstrated in greatly reduced gains per head, lowered market value of the cattle produced, and decreased vigor of the vegetation.

About 7 acres of native range represented the proper carrying capacity for a 2-year-old steer for a 5-month grazing season at Mandan, N. Dak., according to experiments conducted by J. T. Sarvis between 1916 and 1935. This rate was the only degree of continuous grazing that produced the highest gain per acre without sacrificing gain per head, length of grazing season, or vigor of vegetation. It was shown that 20 to 25 percent of the annual forage production must be left standing at the close of the season in order to protect the range from vegetative injury. The 7-acre rate returned 12.9 pounds more steer gain per acre than the 10-acre rate, produced almost the same gain per head, and maintained the vigor and desirable composition of the vegetation. Heavier rates of stocking—3 and 5 acres per head—returned more gain per acre for the 20-year period, but produced much less gain per head and badly damaged the desirable vegetation.

Similar results were recorded by George A. Rogler for the yearling steers grazed on the same pastures at four rates of stocking during the next 8-year period, 1936–43. He also found that yearlings consume about 30 percent less forage than 2-year-olds.

The Department's experiments at Ardmore, S. Dak., from 1919 to 1930 showed that the native vegetation, consisting mostly of western wheatgrass, blue grama, and buffalograss, is not damaged by cattle if grazing is delayed until the middle of May and the pasture is stocked so that the cattle make fair gains during the growing season. Some loss in fall weight of cattle did not reflect injury to the range nor loss in carrying capacity. The more intensively grazed pastures produced greater seasonal gain per acre than those less intensively used. None of the rates abused the vegetation, and 10 acres per head was considered the optimum carrying capacity of the range.

Cooperative grazing experiments conducted with a breeding herd on native range at Miles City, Mont., showed that heavy, moderate, and light rates of stocking—23.1, 30.5, and 38.8 acres per head—were negligible in their effect on the vegetation but pronounced in their influence on the production of beef cattle. Conservative grazing, as represented by the average for moderate and light rates of stocking, showed increases of 6 percent in percentage of calf crop, 28 pounds in weaning weight per calf, 45 pounds in weight of calf per cow, and 98 pounds in weight of cow, when compared with the heavy-grazing rate.

In contrast with the results recorded at Miles City, three degrees of continuous yearlong grazing and two degrees of continuous summer grazing of native range near Woodward, Okla., (where the Southern Great Plains Field Station is located), were much more evident in their effect on the vegetation than on cattle gains during the 5-year period 1941–46. In yearlong grazing rates of 6.6, 9.8, and 12.9 acres per yearling steer, the heavier rate produced average annual gains of 25 pounds per head less and 22 pounds per acre more than the average of the two more conservative rates of stocking. The detrimental effect of overgrazing on the vegetation was increasingly evident throughout the 5 years, but the experiment had to be continued into the sixth year before heavy grazing caused sufficient reduction in gain per head to result in less gain per acre than was obtained from the moderate rate. More total gain was produced with fewer cattle during the winter of 1946–47.

Other sets of pastures were grazed only from April to October on both a continuous and rotational basis at the overgrazed rate of 4.1 acres per yearling and the moderate rate of 6.0 acres per head. In these comparisons, the heavier rate reduced average gain per head to the extent of 35 pounds and seriously damaged the vegetation but caused a 15-pound increase in gain per acre. These results also showed that the optimum carrying capacity of non-mowed native range in the vicinity of Woodward was 10 acres per steer on a yearlong basis and 6 acres for the growing season.

Deferred-and-rotation grazing has shown no advantage over continuous grazing of sufficient magnitude to justify the extra expense involved in fencing and water development in the Great Plains. This rotation system consists of moving the cattle from one part of a pasture to another at intervals during the growing season of the vegetation. Its original purpose was to enable seeds produced by deferment one year to become established before grazing occurred the next year. However, natural reseeding of range plants rarely occurs extensively in the dense perennial grass cover of the Great Plains. Therefore, in order to be superior to continuous grazing, this rotation system must increase the vigor of the deferred plants by a greater margin than is required to offset their heavier use when grazed.

In the long-time grazing studies conducted near Mandan, N. Dak., continuous grazing at the moderate rate of 7 acres per head resulted in significantly higher gains than were obtained from deferred-and-rotation grazing at heavier rates. The results, as reported by Sarvis in 1941 and Rogler in 1944, showed conclusively that the deferred-and-rotation system of grazing was detrimental to yearling gains and had no advantage for 2-year-olds unless it was compared with continuous grazing at abusively heavy rates of stocking.

Alternate grazing of native range at Ardmore, S. Dak., showed slight advantages over the continuous grazing in gains per steer and per acre, but differences were not significant nor sufficient to offset the extra costs.

Continuous grazing of native range from April to October through the 5-year period 1942–46 gave consistently higher gains of yearling steers and left the grass in better condition than deferred-and-rotation grazing, under both heavy and moderate rates of stocking near Woodward. These results may be explained partly by the inability of yearlings to make maximum use of the coarser and more mature forage on deferred parts of the range. Another explanation lies in the successive decreases in nutritive qualities of the vegetation during the growing season. The cattle on continuously grazed range have free access to all of the forage when it is highest in food value, while the cattle on rotation pastures are restricted in acreage at any given time.

In contrast with the somewhat negative results usually obtained from the deferred-and-rotation system of grazing, the exclusion of livestock from native range for the entire growing season, thus deferring the use of the forage until fall or winter, has greatly improved the vegetation at Woodward. This desirable practice greatly increases the vigor of grass, permits natural reseeding, and provides a satisfactory reserve of winter forage. The winter gains on deferred summer range were 10 pounds per head heavier than on continuously grazed range. The deferred range was greatly improved by the summer rest period and supported twice as many cattle as the continuous range during the winter.

The grazing value of sagebrush-infested ranges at Woodward has been doubled by mowing the brush in June for two successive years and keeping livestock off the range during the growing season of those years. The sagebrush roots have the least stored food in June and can be controlled best by mowing at that time. Much of the sagebrush was eradicated and the remainder effectively controlled by these treatments. Steer-gain advantages the first two winters following the summers of mowing and deferment, were sufficient to defray the cost of the treatment. During the next 4 years (1943–46), the summer gain advantages from the original mowings were clear profit and consisted of a 60-percent increase in carrying capacity, 48.5 pounds more gain per head, and 42.4 pounds more gain per acre, or nearly double that of nonmowed land. In another set of pastures, mowing increased the yearlong carrying capacity 70 percent and yearlong gains 36.1 pounds per head and 35.7 pounds per acre.

Winter Planes of Nutrition

Many 2-year-old feeder cattle are produced in the Great Plains for fattening in the Corn Belt and elsewhere. A 3-year experiment at the Miles City station showed that summer range is best utilized by steers wintered on a relatively low plane of nutrition. The three groups wintered at different levels showed no significant difference in weight at the close of the second summer grazing season when they were approximately 2½ years old. Their average final weights were 1,068, 1,036, and 1,031 pounds per head, respectively, for the heavy, moderate, and light wintering levels.

The steers carried on the low wintering level made 94 percent of their total gain on summer range, as compared with 85 percent for the medium-plane steers, and 74 percent for those wintered at the high plane. These results show that if steer calves are to be developed into 2-year-old feeder steers by the use of native summer range they should be wintered so as to gain 25 to 50 pounds each during their first winter and kept in a thrifty condition on a plane slightly above maintenance during their second winter.

Similar results have been obtained in the production of feeder yearlings, a common practice in the Great Plains. Several investigations have shown that the heavier the winter gains of calves, the lighter are the summer gains of the same animals as yearlings, but the heavier winter-gaining cattle usually make the greatest yearlong gain. Heavy winter gains are highly desirable when economically made, but the cost of the extra winter feed required often reduces the net returns on a yearlong basis.

In wintering calves on prairie hay and summering them on grass, E. M. Brouse, of the Nebraska substation at Valentine, found that the combined winter and summer gain was most profitable when the winter supplements were adjusted to produce from 0.75 to 1.0 pound daily gain per head. A half pound of cottonseed cake fed daily as a winter supplement gave 61 percent as much yearlong gain as 1 pound. Feeding 0.75 pound of cottonseed cake as a winter supplement resulted in 77 percent as much combined winter and summer gain as feeding 1 pound. Feeding more than 1 pound of cottonseed cake per head daily during the winter was not profitable unless the calves were marketed in the spring or mid-summer.

L. C. Aicher, of Hays, Kans., conducted a 3-year test to determine the effect of four different planes of winter nutrition on winter gains, summer gains on grass, and yearlong gains of both heifers and steers wintered as calves and summered as yearlings. In addition to a full winter feed of sorghum silage, one lot each of steers and heifers received a daily ration of 4 pounds of grain and 1 pound of cottonseed cake; another lot, 2 pounds of grain and 1 pound of cake; a third lot, 1 pound of cake; and the fourth lot, no supplements.

In these tests the winter gains increased in direct proportion to the increase in the level of the plane of nutrition of the different lots during the winter phase, but subsequent gains on grass decreased. The winter gains and summer-grazing gains did not entirely equalize each other. Lots that made the heaviest winter gains made the heaviest yearlong gains. Net returns on a yearlong basis should be the determining factor in deciding upon the amount of feed to use during the winter. The first, second, and third heaviest winter-fed lots of steers produced yearlong gain advantages of 99, 65, and 40 pounds per head, respectively, over the lightest winter-fed lot. These advantages were obtained only at an additional cost of $14.28, $9.17, and $4.06 per head.

Reseeded Pastures

Reseeded pastures have shown outstanding advantages over virgin native range at many places in the Plains.

In cooperative grazing tests at Woodward, steer calves well wintered on a reseeded pasture of western wheatgrass produced 62 pounds more gain per head during the winter than comparable steers grazed continuously on native range. The well-wintered steers, when rotated to native range during the summer, made 6.7 pounds less gain per head during the summer but 55.5 pounds more for the entire year than

the cattle grazed continuously on native range. These results show the value of heavy winter gains when produced economically through the use of a cool-weather grass. The superiority of the reseeded western wheatgrass pasture is further indicated by the 45-percent saving it afforded in the use of cottonseed cake.

In further tests at Woodward, two lots of steer calves were grazed on reseeded western wheatgrass at the rate of 2.5 acres each during the winter. One lot received no cottonseed cake, except 9 pounds during a blizzard, and the other lot received 135 pounds of cake each. These were compared with similar lots grazed on native range at the rate of 11.4 acres per head annually and fed 135 and 270 pounds of cottonseed cake each during the winter. The cake-fed lot on western wheatgrass gained 102.5 pounds each and the "noncaked" lot gained 83.5 pounds, as compared with 57.5 pounds and 16.6 pounds, respectively, for heavily and lightly caked lots on native range.

In one case the western wheatgrass increased the winter gain per head about 80 percent and saved half of the protein requirement of native range.

In the other comparison the western wheatgrass increased the gain per head about 50 percent and saved nearly all of the cottonseed cake. Western wheatgrass is not adapted to yearlong grazing in the Southern Great Plains but makes an excellent pasture to graze during the cooler months of the year in rotation with native range in summer.

Four other reseeded pastures at Woodward were moderately grazed continuously throughout the year in comparison with native range. Every reseeded pasture supported many more cattle and produced greater total gains than the native range.

A reseeded field of native sand lovegrass carried 186 steers per section of land, produced 400.5 pounds of gain per head, and yielded 120.3 pounds of gain per acre, or three times that of moderately grazed native range.

A reseeded mixture of native grasses,

consisting of blue grama, side-oats grama, western wheatgrass, and Texas bluegrass, produced nearly one and a half times as much gain per acre as the native range. Weeping lovegrass produced 15.5 pounds less gain per head than native range but supported more cattle and, therefore, yielded two and a third as much gain per acre. The gain per acre on reseeded buffalo-grass was nearly one and three-fourths that on native range.

The Texas Agricultural Experiment Station reports that reseeded pastures produced heavier gains on yearling steers than did native range. A re-seeded pasture, consisting mostly of blue grama and western wheatgrass, produced average gains of 310 pounds per steer for 213 days, as compared with 241 pounds steer gain for cattle grazing a native range consisting prin-cipally of blue grama and buffalograss. The principal advantage of the re-seeded pastures was due to the presence of cool-weather species that produced good gains early and late in the season. The native short grasses had barely started growth by April 1, when west-ern wheatgrass was ready to be grazed.

Crested wheatgrass is rapidly replac-ing smooth bromegrass in cultivated pastures in the Northern Great Plains, where it is used widely as an early grazing plant in rotation with native range later in the season. About a mil-lion acres of abandoned cropland have been reseeded to crested wheatgrass and fully utilized by livestock in Mon-tana alone.

Crested wheatgrass pastures have produced greater total gains per steer and per acre than either native grass or smooth bromegrass pasture at Moc-casin, Mont., since 1934, according to R. M. Williams and A. H. Post. Crested wheatgrass furnished grazing about 3 weeks earlier in the spring than native grass and 2 weeks earlier than brome-grass. Ten-year average-weight gains per animal were 239, 207, and 233 pounds, respectively, with the crested wheatgrass, native grass, and brome-grass, and the annual weight gains per

acre were 78.6, 36.9, and 54.4 pounds, respectively. These results indicate a decided advantage for crested wheat-grass, as measured by earlier grazing, longer grazing season, higher carrying capacity, and greater beef production. Bromegrass was intermediate between crested wheatgrass and native grass in most respects.

Similar results have been obtained at Mandan. Smooth bromegrass pro-vided much early season grazing from 1921 to 1934, when it was killed by drought. Crested wheatgrass, grazed in the spring and early summer in com-bination with native range for the re-mainder of the season, provided a longer grazing season, and produced more beef on fewer acres than did the native range alone or crested wheat-grass alone. Cattle gain well on crested wheatgrass early in the season but make small gains after it is mature.

Experiments at Ardmore showed that crested wheatgrass and western wheatgrass had similar value in pro-ducing gains on 2-year-old cattle, but the introduced grass supported more cattle and produced 41 pounds more gain per acre.

Grass-Fattened Cattle

Comparatively few areas in the United States now produce highly fin-ished beef on grass alone, but creditable strictly grass-fattened beef comes from the Appalachian region, the Flint Hills of Kansas, the sand hills of Ne-braska, the Osage country of northern Oklahoma, and other sections of the Great Plains. Thousands of grass-fat steers and greater numbers of feeder cattle are marketed annually from those areas. Most of the feeder cattle are sent to the Corn Belt for fattening. Large numbers of 2-year-old steers are sent into the Flint Hills and Osage country from Texas in the early spring for strictly grass fattening; most of these cattle move to packing plants in the Middle West by midsummer.

Kling L. Anderson, of Kansas, re-ports that the bluestem pastures of the

Flint Hills region and their counterpart in the Osage country are among the finest native pastures for the summer fattening of beef cattle. A large part of this pasture land is grazed by "transient cattle" from the southwestern ranges which are shipped to market with stop-overs en route to fatten on the bluestem.

The pastures are stocked rather lightly to permit good gains. Bluestem pastures deferred until late June have been able to carry beef cattle at the rate of 1.7 acres per animal unit for the remainder of the growing season, while adjoining pastures required 4 acres per head when grazed from May 1. The 17-year average annual production of beef per acre was 55 pounds for the deferred areas and 34.8 pounds for the season-long pastures.

This deferred system, however, is not adapted to the grazing of transient cattle as the established plan is to graze early and get the cattle off to market in midseason. In 1947, bluestem pastures in Kansas and Oklahoma were stocked at an average rate of from 4.25 to 7 acres for 2-year-old steers and cows, and from 3.5 to 5.5 acres for younger cattle, with the cost averaging about $11.50 for the 2-year-old steers and cows and $8 for the young cattle.

A noticeable recent trend in many grass areas (except the strictly range areas) is to supplement grass with concentrates. Fattening cattle on grass usually requires only about one-half the quantity of grain or other concentrates that strictly dry-lot fattening requires. The practice of supplementing the grass with grain for production of grass-grain finished steers is well suited to areas where most of the land is in grass, with a limited acreage devoted to grain production.

Numerous experiments have shown that the quality and quantity of beef can be increased materially by feeding concentrates to steers on grass. The summer gain of yearling steers on native range near Woodward was increased by a 2-year average margin of 41.3 pounds each by feeding a daily

ration of a pound of cottonseed cake in late summer after the grasses had declined in nutritive qualities. This increase in gain represented a substantial profit from the supplement.

Feeding 2 pounds of the concentrate to comparable cattle during the same period resulted in profitable returns one year but not the next. Heavy use of cottonseed cake also increased the winter gains of steer calves. Calves fed a total of 270 pounds of 41-percent cottonseed cake during the 147-day winter grazing season of 1946–47 gained 57.5 pounds per head, as compared with only 16.6 pounds for comparable steers similarly grazed and fed half as much cake.

Feeding a grain supplement materially increased steer gains on native range at Ardmore. Two-year-old steers fed a ration of about 10.5 pounds of grain gained 296 pounds each in approximately 125 days, as against 238 pounds for steers fed about 10 pounds per head daily for the last 69 days (after being on the summer range for 56 days), and 182 pounds for similar steers grazing the range without supplemental feed. There was no significant difference in carcass grade between the supplement-fed groups. The feeding of a limited quantity of grain made it possible to market slaughter cattle instead of feeders and to do so profitably.

Two-year-old steers fed a ration of 4.43 pounds of cottonseed cake and half a pound of molasses on bluestem pastures gained 7.2 ounces a day more than comparable steers grazed on grass alone, according to a 3-year test by men at the Oklahoma Agricultural Experiment Station. The dressing percentages and carcass grades of the cattle fed concentrates were considerably higher than those for the cattle on a strictly grass diet.

Cooperative experiments in West Virginia showed increased gain, finish, dressing percentage, and profitable returns from the use of grain in fattening steers on Kentucky bluegrass pastures. The 3-year average gains were increased 37 percent and the sales price more than 10 percent by the grain supplements. The daily grain consumption, 7.5 pounds per head for 125 days, represented less than half that required for 2½- and 3-year-old steers when fattened in a dry lot. Therefore the pasture replaced more than half the grain and all the roughage required for dry-lot fattening. Higher dressing yields and fatter, more attractive carcasses were obtained by supplementing the grass with a limited grain ration.

In later experiments at the same station over a 3-year period, the feeding of concentrates to 2-year-old steers throughout a grazing season of 135 days produced only 23 pounds more gain per head than when concentrates were fed during the last 79 days of the grazing season, and 75 pounds more than when no concentrates were fed. The continuous feeding of concentrates, however, did not improve the carcass grade over that of steers carried on grass alone for the first 56 days of the grazing season and fed concentrates the last 79 days. The results do not justify feeding concentrates as a supplement in the early part of the grazing season (May–June) when the grass is most nutritious. The groups fed concentrates yielded significantly more dressed beef than the ones on grass only.

Still further experiments by W. H. Black and C. V. Wilson showed that steers and heifers that have been well wintered can be put into good marketable condition at about 16 months of age if given concentrates as a supplement to good bluegrass pasture for about 100 days during the first half of the grazing season.

Legumes for Beef

Legumes are important in beef production.

White clover furnishes much grazing in the Gulf Coast region. White clover and grass mixtures furnish satisfactory grazing in the East, Southeast, and Middle West. Experiments over 10 years, conducted in Georgia by J. L. Stephens, showed that the carrying capacity of white clover, in combination with carpetgrass, Dallisgrass, and lespedeza, was greatly increased when properly fertilized. This pasture mixture, when treated annually with 6–12–6 fertilizer, supported nearly 1.5 steers per acre and produced 320 pounds of live-weight gain per steer from about April 1 to November 15. Another pasture containing the same combination of grasses but treated with an application of 6–12–0 fertilizer supported the same number of cattle yet produced only 290 pounds of gain per head, showing the need for potash. The same pasture mixture, when treated with nitrogen alone, supported about 14 percent fewer cattle and produced less than half the gain of the pasture that received complete fertilizer.

White clover does its best in cool weather. In the South and Southeast it starts growth in September and October and usually continues through the winter and spring. It usually matures in hot weather and produces little grazing from then until fall, hence the importance of using it in a mixture to furnish grazing from early spring until fall.

In experiments conducted over a 4-year period by R. S. Glasscock and associates at the Florida Agricultural Experiment Station, in which yearling steers grazed improved pastures, a white clover-carpetgrass pasture produced 619 pounds of steer gain per acre annually, as compared with 219 pounds for steers on a carpetgrass-lespedeza pasture, 198 pounds for steers grazing on a fertilized carpetgrass pasture, and 75 pounds for steers on unfertilized carpetgrass.

The grazing of alfalfa and clover unmixed has not been popular in the United States, largely because of the danger from bloat. The risk is less when cattle have access to dry roughage before or while grazing legumes.

Alfalfa-grass mixtures have been used satisfactorily for beef production in various sections. In the Pacific Northwest, M. E. Ensminger and associates found that a grass-alfalfa mixture produced nearly three times as much beef per acre as pure grass pastures of smooth bromegrass and crested wheatgrass. The alfalfa with smooth bromegrass produced 225 pounds of beef per acre in 87 days, as compared with 84 pounds in 80 days for smooth bromegrass alone. Alfalfa with crested wheatgrass produced 218 pounds of steer gain in 87 days, as compared with 90 pounds of gain in 85 days from crested wheatgrass alone. The grass-alfalfa mixtures were ready to graze somewhat earlier in the spring, and the rate of increase of available forage was higher than from the pure grass pastures. The average carrying capacity of the mixtures was 4.28 steer-months per acre, as compared with 1.62 for the pure grass pastures.

Smooth bromegrass-alfalfa mixtures are recommended by the Kansas Agricultural Experiment Station as a means of lengthening the grazing season. A combination of tame pastures of this kind and native range permits grazing from April 1 through October, as each type can be grazed when it is most productive and protected when it is most susceptible to injury by grazing. Yield, carrying capacity, and efficiency of use are thus enhanced.

Studies by the Indiana Agricultural Experiment Station showed that a birdsfoot trefoil and bluegrass mixture under rotation grazing produced an average of about 250 pounds of cattle gains a year over a 2-year period, as compared with about 225 pounds for an alfalfa-timothy mixture and about 190 pounds for a Ladino clover-bromegrass mixture. These mixtures surpassed a permanent bluegrass pasture, which produced only 160 pounds of steer gain per acre. The pasture mixtures furnished more uniform grazing throughout the season than bluegrass, which is productive early and late in the season but not in midsummer.

Annual lespedeza is particularly valuable for grazing from midsummer until late fall, when many grasses are least productive. It serves well as a sup-

plementary grazing crop to Kentucky bluegrass, furnishing in normal seasons very satisfactory grazing in midsummer, when bluegrass is usually at its lowest carrying capacity.

Lespedeza is used extensively in many grass mixtures in the Southeastern States. Cooperative experiments conducted in Missouri showed that, by supplementing bluegrass pastures during the middle of July to about October 1 with a 40-percent increase in acreage consisting wholly of Korean lespedeza, steer gains per acre were increased 59 percent over those on a rotation-grazed pasture and 68 percent over those on a continuously grazed pasture.

Supplemental grazing of lespedeza made possible the most efficient use of the bluegrass in the permanent pasture during the period of maximum productivity when the grass was most palatable and nutritious.

J. L. Stephens reports that lespedeza will usually furnish excellent grazing in pasture mixtures for 3 to 4 years in Georgia. After that time it is likely to be crowded out by carpetgrass or other sod-forming grass.

Pastures containing lespedeza under annual fertilization in Georgia have produced 10-year average steer gains in excess of 300 pounds per acre.

Kudzu has been found to be quite useful for beef cattle in the Piedmont and Coastal sections of the Southeastern States. It has furnished temporary grazing for an average of 68 days a year since 1935 at the Alabama Agricultural Experiment Station when stocked at the rate of 1.25 animal units an acre. At the same station, kudzu has yielded more than 2 tons of hay per acre annually for 20 years. For 11 years it furnished grazing at the Georgia Coastal Plain Experiment Station from about May 7 to October 28 when stocked at the rate of 3.2 cows per 3 acres and produced 232 pounds liveweight gain per acre. The only other upland pasture to surpass this was Tift Bermuda-grass, which, when stocked at an average rate of 7.3 cows to 6 acres

(April 7 to October 23), produced 251 pounds cattle gain per acre. Numerous experiments have shown that kudzu hay compares favorably with other legume hays of comparable grade when fed so as to supply the roughage in either fattening or wintering beef cattle rations.

Sericea lespedeza has not proved to be a satisfactory grazing crop for beef cattle, but has some value as hay in wintering rations. Investigators are in general agreement that it can best be used to control soil erosion and to improve or correct soil acidity.

Creep Feeding on Grass

The development of earlier maturing beef cattle, plus the ability of younger cattle to make more economical use of grain, has resulted in the production of marketable beef from calves at weaning time. This is accomplished by the creep feeding of grain to nursing calves while on pasture.

Three years of experiments at the Sni-a-Bar Farm in Missouri showed that grain-fed calves could be made to weigh about 100 pounds more at weaning time than similar calves fed no grain. The grain-fed calves were usually fat enough for slaughter when weaned at 8 months of age.

Suckling calves fed shelled corn alone for 140 days consumed less feed per 100 pounds of gain than similar calves fed either a mixture of 8 parts of corn by weight and 1 part of cottonseed meal, or a mixture of shelled corn 2 parts and oats 1 part. The calves fed the corn and cottonseed meal, however, made greater gains, were fatter, and brought 50 cents per 100 pounds more at weaning time than the other groups. The increased gains and market value of the calves fed shelled corn and cottonseed meal more than offset their greater feed costs.

Later experiments indicated that ground corn or an alfalfa-molasses supplement produced no material benefits.

Pasturing cows and fattening their calves by creep feeding is usually a satisfactory method of beef production under farm conditions, but has not been satisfactory under range conditions where the herd is compelled to graze large areas and where there are several watering places. Range calves do not consume sufficient feed from a creep to improve their condition materially. But creep-fed range calves are not such a drain on their dams; hence the cows can carry more flesh and have greater fertility.

How best to winter beef cattle is an important problem of cattlemen in the range country and in most other beef-production areas.

The most widely used methods in the range country are wintering on the range (with and without supplemental feed) and in the dry lot (on roughage and a limited quantity of concentrates). But the tendency to reserve range or pastures for winter grazing is rapidly increasing.

Winter Pasture and Range

In the Southwest and the Southern States, particularly along the coasts, thousands of cattle have always had to depend upon range the year around. Heavy death losses occur, and the surviving cattle are usually in poor condition. It is difficult to improve many of these ranges by introducing better grasses or growing supplementary feed, especially during the winter. The most practical solution consists of feeding concentrates, usually in the form of protein-rich feeds, a practice that has been used in the Great Plains for years.

The Oklahoma Agricultural Experiment Station conducted supplemental-feeding experiments with some range cows for 4 years. One group of 20 cows was carried on the range year-long and fed cottonseed cake on the range for 5 months in winter. A similar group summer-grazed 7 months and was fed prairie hay and cottonseed meal in the dry lot for the winter season of 5 months. The results of the last year, 1945–46, are like those of the

757150°—48——9

first 3 years and show that cows wintered on bluestem grass and fed 2.97 pounds of cottonseed cake each daily gained 13 pounds for the winter period, compared to 71 pounds for similar cows wintered in the dry lot and fed 20.36 pounds of prairie hay and 1.32 pounds of cottonseed cake each daily. Both groups received a mineral mixture of equal parts by weight of salt, steamed bonemeal, and ground limestone. Wintering on the range with a supplement of cottonseed cake was slightly more economical. Feeding 1 ton of prairie hay saved 158 pounds of cottonseed cake and about 1 acre of grass in maintaining the commercial cow herd.

Experiments at Miles City showed that in 3 years out of 5 it was possible to keep breeding cows on the range all winter. One group of cows kept on the range through the winter got no supplemental feed. Another lot was fed 91 pounds of cottonseed cake per head for 156 days in winter. The cake-fed cows made a winter gain of 23 pounds per head; those on range alone lost about 11 pounds.

These results indicate that the use of cottonseed cake for breeding cows should be limited to seasons in which winter range conditions are severe and that a pound of cake fed as a supplement to the range can replace approximately 10 pounds of hay fed in the feed lot.

From 1 to 2 pounds of cottonseed cake a head daily or its equivalent in grain or hay will usually carry breeding cows or growing stock 1 year old or older through the winter in a satisfactory condition if they have access to reasonably good range.

Some experiments have been made to ascertain the possibility of supplementing the winter range with urea, a synthetic compound, as a source of protein. The results show that urea may be used to replace a part of the protein in the rations of ruminants. Approximately 1 pound of urea and 6 pounds of grain are required to replace 7 pounds of a 41-percent protein

feed. The feeder must take care to mix the urea well into the ration, and the feed must not contain more than 3 percent of urea, because excessive amounts may damage the kidneys and cause death.

Wintering cattle has been more of a problem in the southeastern Coastal Plains than in most other areas—especially in cut-over pine lands where the vegetation is low in food value. Millions of acres of forest range in the Southeast are used for grazing, but the returns are not in line with those of some other areas. Cattle losses have been particularly heavy in winter; many of the surviving cows are so thin in the spring that they fail to breed. Like all problems, however, this one can be solved.

In Georgia, feeding a small amount of cottonseed meal or peanut meal to breeding cows experimentally prevented severe losses in weight in fall and early winter. Dry cows on native range that were fed a protein supplement at the rate of 1 to 2 pounds each daily from October to February usually lost only a little weight during that period. But among cows that were left on the range in the fall in poor flesh and were not fed supplements until February 1, death losses were heavy.

It is practical to hold breeding cows on forest range all year by feeding protein meal from about October 15 to March 15. It is advisable, however, to confine the cattle to unburned range during the feeding period to allow sufficient forage growth on burned areas. Although the cows lose heavily in body weight, they appear to be strong and thrifty and produce calf crops equal to those obtained when harvested roughage is used.

The grazing of reeds or switch cane by beef cattle is becoming a general practice in the South Atlantic States; in the Coastal districts millions of acres of such forage make up about one-third of the forest grazing land and furnish nearly half of the native forage.

Calves averaging 395 pounds in weight at 8 months were produced by a breeding herd that had grazed reeds in eastern North Carolina during the summers of 1942–44. Near Wenona, N. C., about 4 acres of good reed pasture was required per cow from about May 15 to November 15, while in other localities up to 12 acres was needed. Reeds furnish some forage in winter, but a greater acreage is required per animal because the reeds are dormant in midwinter.

In many places grain crops are grazed in late fall, winter, and early spring. In the East and Southeast, rye, barley, oats, and wheat are used rather extensively for the purpose.

In the Southern Great Plains where the grazing of wheat pastures in the fall and early winter is becoming a common practice, producers occasionally incur heavy death losses because of a condition known as wheat poisoning, or grass tetany. Early symptoms of the ailment are rapid breathing and irritability. The losses are most frequent in pregnant cows and in cattle being transported from wheat pastures to other areas. Investigators attribute the malady to a diet high in protein, low in calcium, and deficient in magnesium, or to some other unexplained upset in metabolism. Access to dry roughage before and during the grazing of wheat is said to reduce the trouble.

The Texas Agricultural Experiment Station reports that steer calves grazed on wheat, with access to native range, from December 12, 1944, to April 23, 1945, gained 247 pounds each, as against 138 pounds for similar calves on range supplemented with 1 pound of cottonseed cake.

At Tifton, Ga., B. L. Southwell found that pastures of rye, wheat, and oats furnished more and better winter feed for steers than the mature growth of other grazing or harvested crops.

Choice of varieties also was found to be important. Abruzzi rye and rust-proof oats furnished grazing at the rate of 4 steers per acre from January 3 to April 3 and produced 277 pounds of gain per acre, compared with 230

pounds of gain from the more commonly used Vicland oats and Sanford wheat.

Grazing cornstalks and velvetbeans is a satisfactory method of wintering beef cows in the Southeast, where those crops usually furnish grazing from early November to mid-February.

At the Mississippi Agricultural Experiment Station, pastures of oats alone or oats with either wild winter peas or crimson clover furnished satisfactory grazing for beef calves from January 23 to May 15. The average daily gains of 1.5 pounds to more than 1.75 pounds compared favorably with dry-lot gains of well-wintered calves. An acre of oats pasture produced 234 pounds of live-weight gain; the addition of wild peas reduced the gain by a margin of 28 pounds; crimson clover increased the gain 64 pounds. Marketing the oats, peas, and clover as beef is a cheap way to harvest them, and the returns per calf compare well with the value of the crops in harvested form.

Roughages for Wintering

Wintering cattle on harvested roughages with restricted amounts of concentrates is necessarily a common practice where pastures or ranges are limited. Hay, silage, fodder, stover, and straw are the principal roughages used. They usually are supplemented with a small quantity of protein meal or grain. When good-quality legume hay—notably alfalfa—is available, little if any other feed is required.

Workers at the Ohio Agricultural Experiment Station found that alfalfa hay was slightly superior to clover hay or soybean hay for growing heifers when the hays were fed liberally and in conjunction with corn. No other proteins were required to grow and develop choice heifers from these feeds.

Men at the Washington Agricultural Experiment Station found that a daily winter gain of 1 pound per head was necessary to keep heavy calves in a thrifty growing condition. This they achieved by feeding about 13.5 pounds of alfalfa hay or by replacing about one-third of the hay with an equal weight of grain.

Heifers wintered on western wheatgrass hay and alfalfa hay at Miles City produced essentially the same gain over a 3-year period but consumed 12 percent more alfalfa.

Workers at Ardmore concluded that crested wheatgrass hay has much the same value as western wheatgrass hay for wintering yearling and 2-year-old cattle, although the animals gained 44 pounds each on the crested wheatgrass hay and only 25 pounds on native hay.

Daily gains of 1 pound per head were obtained at Moccasin, Mont., from wintering steers with a daily ration of about 21 pounds of crested wheatgrass and 1 pound of cottonseed meal-molasses-beet pulp pellets. Feeding 4 pounds less hay and 2 pounds more supplement was not considered necessary to insure continued growth of long yearlings. A further test at Moccasin indicated that crested wheatgrass hay, when cut before the bloom stage, was slightly superior to native grass hay for wintering steer calves.

Native hay is an important resource in the livestock economy in the eastern part of the Great Plains; in Nebraska alone there are about 2½ million acres of native hay lands.

Experiments at the Nebraska Agricultural Experiment Station, in which hays from early, midseason, and late cuttings were fed to wintering calves as the sole ration and with supplements of 0.5 and 1 pound of soybean meal, showed that as the maturity of the grass increased, the consumption of hay decreased and the feed required for 100 pounds of gain increased. The early cut hay contained the most protein and phosphorus, but those elements decreased as the grass matured.

The daily feeding of half a pound of soybean meal per head increased the consumption of the hay, more than doubled the gain, and greatly reduced the hay required per unit of gain. The addition of 1 pound of soybean meal to the hay ration resulted in a still further increase in gains and in a further saving of prairie hay per unit of gain. In other tests 1 ton of silage was replaced by 13 pounds of soybean meal and 1,026 pounds of July-cut hay.

Other experiments in the Nebraska sand hills near Valentine showed that calves wintered on prairie hay alone did not consume sufficient hay to meet their protein requirements. An average hay ration of 10.6 pounds for a winter period of 170 days produced an average winter gain per calf of 25 pounds. When prairie hay was supplemented with a protein concentrate, the hay consumption went up as much as 25 percent. Feeding up to 1 pound of cottonseed cake per head daily was considered a profitable practice. The experiments showed that the subsequent summer gains of yearlings were in inverse proportion to the previous winter gains.

Experiments in Nebraska, Kansas, and West Virginia disclosed that the combined winter-summer gains are most profitable when the ration for calves is adjusted so as to produce from 0.75 to 1.0 pound daily gain during the winter period.

Full use of roughage and grass makes for the most economical beef production in the Southern Great Plains.

Experiments at the Kansas station showed that about 3 pounds of silage equals 1 pound of prairie hay in satisfying the requirements of steers for roughage. No advantage came from feeding dry roughage with silage. Further tests showed that steers on a heavy silage ration of about 50 pounds, with 1 pound of cottonseed meal, made the greatest winter gain and the smallest summer gain per steer. Steers wintered on a ration of about 17 pounds of prairie hay with 1 pound of cottonseed meal made the least winter gain and most in the summer. A group wintered on about 31 pounds of silage and 7 pounds of prairie hay was intermediate in winter and summer gains. In total yearlong gains the strictly silage group had a slight advantage over the hay group, even though the silage-fed cattle gained only 47 percent as much during the summer as the group wintered on prairie hay.

Generally speaking, it is usually desirable therefore to get the greatest percentage of the total gain on grass by not too liberal feeding in winter.

Research workers at the Illinois Agricultural Experiment Station compared alfalfa silage and alfalfa and oats silage with corn silage as roughages in fattening rations for 2-year-old steers and for wintering beef calves. About 22 pounds of these silages, with a full feed of concentrates, gave similar feeding values.

A further comparison showed the corn silage to be slightly more palatable to calves, but the gain advantage was not significant.

Husbandmen at the Pennsylvania station reported that alfalfa silage containing 50 pounds of molasses per ton had no advantage over corn silage for fattening steers.

Sugarcane fed as a chopped roughage has been satisfactory for wintering beef cattle in the South and Southeast. Cooperative experiments at Tifton, Ga., showed that cows fed about 24 pounds of chopped sugarcane and 2 pounds of a protein meal gained an average of 20 pounds each, as compared with a loss of 61 pounds for cows wintered on the range with the same quantity of protein meal. The large yields of sugarcane and its relatively low cost make it highly suitable for wintering breeding cattle in the Southeast, where supplying winter feed is the producers' biggest problem.

Many roughages are more completely utilized by beef cattle in the form of silage than as fodders or stovers, and usually an acre can produce more edible feed in the form of silage than in any other. At the Nebraska Agricultural Experiment Station it was learned that corn silage produced 15.5 percent more gain per acre than ground corn fodder (when fed to calves) and was easier to handle.

Corn fodder is not an economical feed because of the waste in the coarse stalks. But a ration of 14.04 pounds of ground corn fodder and 2.41 pounds of alfalfa hay produced about the same gain in an average period of 143 days as 32.4 pounds of corn silage similarly supplemented with alfalfa hay. A ton of the silage costs about half as much as the ground fodder.

Roughages are most useful in wintering rations for beef cattle; they are needed also to supply bulk in fattening rations. Almost any type of roughage can be used for the purpose—the source is less important than quantity.

The extent to which roughages should be used in beef fattening rations should be governed largely by the relative availability of roughages and concentrates. Cattlemen usually make more profitable gains from the greater use of roughages, but often they find that the slightly higher production costs they incur by the liberal use of concentrates are offset by the improvement in the quality of the beef.

Cooperative experiments in North Carolina showed that of three groups of steers given hay free choice, the one on a full feed of grain made a daily gain of 1.62 pounds per head for 156 days; another fed two-thirds as much grain gained 1.32 pounds; and the third group, fed one-third of a full feeding of grain, gained only 0.92 pound. The full-fed steers produced the greatest gain and finish but showed no significant advantage in dressing percentage and carcass grade over the intermediate group.

Deficiencies in Rations

Nutritional disorders in cattle usually are associated with too little protein, minerals, and vitamins.

Vegetation is usually well fortified with protein in the early growing season, but it decreases with maturity. The protein content also has a close relationship to rainfall. In humid climates where the vegetation is kept in a growing stage, beef production is not often affected adversely by a lack of protein. In drier areas the reverse is often true.

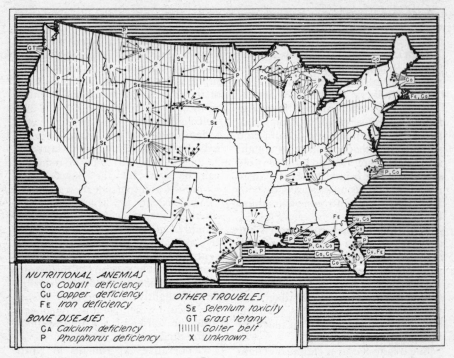

NUTRITIONAL ANEMIAS
Co *Cobalt deficiency*
Cu *Copper deficiency*
Fe *Iron deficiency*

BONE DISEASES
Ca *Calcium deficiency*
P *Phosphorus deficiency*

OTHER TROUBLES
Se *Selenium toxicity*
GT *Grass tetany*
|||||| *Goiter belt*
X *Unknown*

Areas having mineral deficiencies. In the Northern and Central Great Plains, selenium poisoning sometimes happens because of excess amounts of this mineral in the soil.

The feeding of protein concentrates as supplements to the vegetation is generally the most satisfactory method of correcting this deficiency.

Of the minerals, a lack of phosphorus has been of most concern to beef producers. The vegetation in many localities between southern Canada and the Gulf of Mexico and along the eastern seaboard is low in phosphorus. The nutritional disorders that result are usually recognized by bone chewing. Other evidences are depraved appetite, stiffness in the forequarters, emaciation, low fertility in breeding cattle, a low percentage of calves, impaired skeletal development, and loss of weight.

According to findings in cooperative experiments in Texas conducted by the Bureau of Animal Industry, the Texas Agricultural Experiment Station, and the King Ranch, phosphorus deficiencies can be corrected and prevented by feeding phosphorus supplements, such as bonemeal and disodium phosphates. The deficiencies were prevented when the products were hand-fed to supply about 6.5 grams of phosphorus per head daily to dry cows and about twice that amount to lactating cows. Bonemeal can be fed satisfactorily with a self-feeder. Phosphorus can also be fed easily by dissolving the phosphate in drinking water. Another effective way is to fertilize the land with triple superphosphate. All cattle fed phosphorus by direct feeding or through the grazing of fertilized pastures produced larger calf crops than did the control cows.

All the supplement-fed cows that weaned calves averaged 1,044 pounds at the end of their second calf-crop year, compared to 833 pounds for the control cows. The fertilized pasture was stocked at the rate of one cow to 10 acres, a rate that was 50 percent higher than for the other pastures. On the basis of weaning weights of the calves for the first two calf crops, the fertilized area produced about 32,000 pounds of calf weight per 640 acres annually, as against about 17,500 pounds for the pasture grazed by the control group of cows.

The cows fed bonemeal in a self-feeder and disodium phosphate in the water on pastures stocked at the same rate as the control pasture (15 acres per cow) produced about 20,800 pounds and 21,500 pounds of calf weight, respectively. For a 4-year average (1942–46) cows eating bonemeal from a self-feeder consumed an average daily intake of approximately 7.75 grams of phosphorus, compared to 8.6 grams for the cows getting phosphorus from drinking water treated with disodium phosphate.

These experiments indicate that the production of beef can be increased materially on the phosphorus-deficient ranges if phosphorus is supplied by practical methods.

In the Southern Great Plains, where grain sorghums are used extensively in fattening rations for steers, considerable trouble has been experienced in the formation of calculi in the urinary tract. Large calculi frequently become lodged in the urethra and cause death.

Tests by the Department of Agriculture and the Texas station at Big Spring indicate that the supplemental feeding of phosphorus reduces the occurrence of calculi. The first tests showed that 7 ounces of bonemeal fed each animal in the day's ration tended to check the calculi formation. Later tests in 1946 and 1947 disclosed that when phosphorus was supplied in the form of phosphoric acid (75 percent strength) at the rate of 52 cubic centimeters per head daily, there was also a marked tendency toward the control of the calculi. The phosphoric acid appeared also to add to the palatability of the ration.

Vitamin A is commonly deficient in beef cattle rations that contain large quantities of nonlegume roughages. The usual symptoms of the deficiency are blindness, convulsions, stiffness, edema, and rapid breathing in hot weather; extreme cases may terminate in death. Experiments at Beltsville indicated that fattening steers should have a daily allowance of at least 1.35 milligrams of carotene per 100 pounds by body weight and that a heavy ration of yellow corn and oat straw did not furnish the necessary carotene. Additional carotene in the form of green leafy hay of alfalfa or another legume, good silage, or fish oil should be supplied.

Vitamin A deficiencies are troublesome in the South, where supplements other than cottonseed products are limited. Experiments at Spur, Tex., by the Bureau of Animal Industry and the Texas Agricultural Experiment Station, have shown that cattle coming off the range in the fall have low carotene storage in their bodies, particularly in dry years. These cattle, when placed in the feed lot and fed cottonseed products and sorghum grain, soon show vitamin A deficiency. From 2,000 to 2,500 micrograms of carotene is required in rations for yearling cattle to prevent vitamin A deficiency. Good-quality sorghum silage fed liberally or 1 to 2 pounds of green alfalfa hay should supply the necessary carotene.

THE AUTHORS «« W. H. Black, *a native of Iowa and a graduate of Iowa State College, farmed in northwestern Iowa until 1918, when he was asked by the United States Department of Agriculture to assist in the war beef-production program. Mr. Black is senior animal husbandman in charge of beef and dual-purpose cattle investigations for the Department.*

D. A. Savage has been engaged in research on grass since his graduation from Montana State College in 1924. He is senior agronomist in the Bureau of Plant Industry, Soils, and Agricultural Engineering, and is stationed at the United States Southern Great Plains Field Station at Woodward.

[See pages 135, 212, and 256 for related articles on this subject.]

DAIRY CATTLE MUST HAVE GOOD FORAGE

L. A. MOORE

THE DAIRY COW is built to handle large quantities of roughage. She has a rumen or paunch that holds 2 or 3 bushels of ingested material and acts much like a fermentation vat in digesting the fibrous parts and other constituents of forage crops. She is highly efficient therefore in converting them into products that humans eat.

Harvested forages usually are the cheapest source of nutrients for dairy cattle during the winter feeding season. For the most economical production of milk under average conditions, 75 to 80 percent of the nutrients fed them should come from roughage. In the past much more attention has been paid to the quality and kind of materials going into the concentrate part of the ration than into the roughage part. Yet good forage is more necessary than concentrates to the health and reproduction of dairy cattle. Cattle cannot long survive and reproduce on a poor forage even though the best quality of grain ration may be fed at the same time. The reason is that roughages contain minerals and vitamins that dairy cattle need and that concentrates normally do not supply.

Harvested forages usually are crops stored as hays or silages. Corn and sorghum are commonly made into silage in most dairy areas, although in some sections they may be preserved as fodder. More recently, considerable tonnages of the forage crops have been stored as silages, and farmers in some sections now are keenly interested in methods of barn-drying hays. Needless to say, stage of maturity, conditions of curing, soil, and other such items materially affect the feeding value of any harvested forage. In general, crops harvested at an early stage of maturity and under conditions that prevent loss of leaves have the highest feeding value. Farmers therefore are looking for methods of preserving forages that prevent losses due to bad weather and other conditions and that can produce roughage of high quality.

In this connection the question arises as to the relative feeding values of forages produced by the different methods. Their adaptability to various feeding situations, the supplemental effects of one kind with another, and their uses along with other types of feed are all points to be considered.

Roughages contain vitamins A and D, which (except a small amount of vitamin A in yellow corn) are absent in grain. Every effort should be made to preserve those vitamins in roughage and to produce roughages that contain enough of them.

Forages that are considered high in quality (that is, green and leafy) generally contain the most carotene. The cow converts this substance into vitamin A. Roughages harvested under poor weather conditions or stored improperly may contain too little carotene to keep the cow healthy. If cows are fed poor hay or silage (or even if they are fed good forage in insufficient amounts) they give birth to weak, blind, and dead calves. They also retain the placental membranes.

Do forages that are harvested as grass silage contain enough vitamin D? In experiments at Beltsville, wilted alfalfa silage contained sufficient vitamin D for growing male calves when it was fed at the usual level of roughage feeding. It seems doubtful that there is need for vitamin D supplementation where wilted alfalfa silage is fed, especially where the herd is exposed to a few hours of sunshine each day.

The feeding of good quality forages is also important in maintaining a high vitamin A content of milk and butter in winter. While cows are on winter feeds, the vitamin A content of milk usually drops to 50 percent of the amount present in milk during the pasture season. The vitamin A content of milk in winter cannot be maintained at the summer level even when the best quality of field-cured hay is fed, but grass silage usually is sufficiently high in carotene to maintain the vitamin A content of milk at almost the summer level.

These qualities of roughages are therefore important to cattle and to the consumer of dairy products; they can be retained if the producer takes advantage of every means available to preserve forages. Good quality roughage fed in liberal quantities will supply sufficient vitamins A and D for cattle without need for further supplementation under usual farm conditions and should improve the vitamin quality of the milk produced.

Because of difficulties encountered in field curing, especially the first crop of hay, and the attendant field losses, a considerably greater portion of hay crops has been made into silages during the past few years, particularly in the humid sections of the country. These silages are made by adding molasses or some preservative at the time of ensiling or by wilting the crop slightly and using no preservative. The comparative feeding value of crops harvested as field cured hay or silage has not been studied thoroughly.

In tests at Beltsville by the Bureau of Dairy Industry, wilted alfalfa silage was shown to be as high or higher in feeding value than hay harvested from the same field and field-cured.

Several similar comparisons at Beltsville have shown that the experimental results obtained depend largely on the quality of the field-cured hay fed. If the field-cured hay is of excellent quality, it will be almost equal in feeding value to wilted silage on the dry-matter basis, but if the field-cured hay is of only fair quality the wilted silage will produce more milk.

In a comparative trial at the Virginia Agricultural Experiment Station, clover made into molasses silage produced 10 percent more milk than when the crop was made into hay from the same field. In trials at the Upper Peninsula Experiment Station at Chat-

ham, Mich., in which two groups of cows were used in a double reversal trial, alfalfa from the same field was put up as hay and as molasses silage. The cows fed field-cured hay consumed 30 pounds a day as the sole roughage; cows fed molasses-alfalfa silage consumed 87 pounds a day as the sole roughage. Ground barley was fed as a grain. During the time the cows were on the alfalfa silage they consumed a little less total digestible nutrients a day but out-produced the cows on hay.

These experiments indicate that grass silage (meaning, here, the crops put into a silo regardless of whether they are legumes or grass) is at least equal to hay in feeding value. In cases where the quality of the hay may be low because of poor curing conditions, silage made at the same time and from the same crop may be definitely superior.

During the past 10 years scientists and dairymen have thought and said much about the relative quantities of dry matter that cows will consume in the form of hay or grass silage.

In an experiment at the Dairy Field Experiment Station at Huntley, Mont., the Bureau of Dairy Industry fed grass hay as the sole ration to one group of four Holstein cows. The hay was cut at an immature stage from an irrigated area. A similar crop of grass, put up as silage with slight wilting, was fed to a similar group of three cows. The average dry-matter content of the silage was 33.3 percent. In both cases somewhat more hay or silage was fed than was consumed in order to obtain a proper measure of the cows' appetites. The cows fed the immature cut hay as the sole ration consumed somewhat more dry matter in the form of hay than the cows fed the grass silage made from a comparable crop. The quantities of grass silage eaten each day were large—one cow consumed daily 123 pounds of grass silage in her third month of lactation.

At Beltsville, the Bureau of Dairy Industry measured the comparative consumption of dry matter by similar groups of cows fed alfalfa hay or wilted alfalfa silage along with a concentrate ration. They were fed as much alfalfa hay or wilted alfalfa silage as they would consume. Grain comprised the rest of the ration. Ten cows that were fed alfalfa silage with a dry-matter content of 55 consumed 23.9 pounds of dry matter as silage and 22.8 pounds of dry matter as hay. Eight cows that got alfalfa silage with a dry-matter content of 62 consumed 25.6 pounds as silage and 24.0 pounds of dry matter as hay.

Although the dry-matter content of the wilted silages fed is somewhat high for silage of this class, as much dry matter was consumed in the form of silage as in the form of hay.

Workers at the Maryland Agricultural Experiment Station conducted two feeding trials involving 10 cows in each of 2 lots. They found that corn silage was more palatable than soybean-millet-molasses silage. The cows refused 1 pound of corn silage a day while they refused 2.56 pounds of soybean-millet silage fed on the same dry-matter basis. The rest of the ration consisted of grain and alfalfa hay.

At the Indiana Agricultural Experiment Station, alfalfa-bromegrass silage was as palatable as corn silage after the cows became accustomed to the grass silage. The rest of the ration consisted of grain and alfalfa hay.

At the New Jersey Agricultural Experiment Station, timothy silages made with molasses and ground barley were found less palatable than corn silage.

Milking cows at the Virginia Agricultural Experiment Station consumed as much dry matter in the form of molasses-clover silage as they did of clover hay made from the same field.

Some difficulty may be experienced in inducing cows to eat grass silage unless they have been accustomed to it as calves. At the West Virginia station it was noted that cows that had never received corn silage refused it at first and had to be starved into eating it for a short period.

Our experiments at Beltsville have shown that cows will eat more of grass silage that has been wilted than of one put up in a more moist condition. The general consensus would suggest that cows will consume enough wilted grass silages to maintain good production.

Dairymen agree that cows on an all-grass silage ration have a craving for some other form of roughage. Likewise cows that get only alfalfa hay or timothy hay as the sole roughage crave some other form of roughage. In practice it would seem wise to feed some hay along with a grass silage as roughage. This fits in well with the harvesting program because the best practice is to put the first crop of forage up as silage and to make the second or third crops into field-cured hay.

The greater emphasis on soil conservation has led to a tendency in some hilly areas to cut the use of row crops and to increase the use of grassland crops, even though corn will usually produce more total digestible nutrients per acre under most conditions. The substitution of hay crops for corn has raised the question of the relative feeding value of grass silage and corn silage.

At the Indiana Agricultural Experiment Station, molasses-alfalfa-bromegrass silage was compared in feeding value with corn silage in two trials in which two groups of five cows each were used in each trial. The silages were fed at the rate of 3 pounds per 100 pounds of body weight. The cows also received a limited quantity of alfalfa hay and a grain mixture. The cows on the alfalfa-brome silage produced slightly more milk but did not gain so much in body weight.

At the Maryland station, soybean-millet-molasses silage was compared with corn silage in two double reversal feeding trials with 16 and 20 cows, respectively. In addition, 1 pound of alfalfa hay per 100 pounds body weight was fed along with a grain mixture. The silages were fed at the rate of 3 pounds per 100 pounds body weight. There was no significant difference in milk production between the groups of cows although those on corn silage maintained live weight better.

At the New Jersey station one group of control cows was fed corn silage, alfalfa hay, and grain. A second group was fed molasses-timothy silage in place of corn silage; a third got ground barley-timothy silage instead of corn silage. There was essentially no difference in the production efficiency of the first two groups. The cows in the third group did not produce so efficiently as the other two groups. In tests covering 2 years, there appeared to be a loss of about 30 percent of the nutrients in the ground barley in the silage, probably due to fermentation.

I assume from these few results and others I have not cited that grass silage can be used to replace corn silage satisfactorily in the ration of dairy cattle. Where grass silage replaces corn silage (especially if the grass silage contains legumes), the protein portion of the grain mixture could be reduced because it would have a higher protein content than the corn silage.

The increased number of barn hay driers or barn finishers on farms has aroused considerable interest in the comparative feeding value of hays harvested as field-cured in comparison to hay that is barn-dried. Some work in this connection has been in progress at Beltsville for 2 years. The two crops were harvested simultaneously from the same field and fed to cows in reversal trials. The average of the 2 years' results are shown in the table at the top of the next page.

It should be kept in mind that the field-cured hay used in this experiment was put up under ideal conditions— barn-cured hay might produce more milk if the field-cured hay were put up in bad weather and therefore poor.

In somewhat similar experiments conducted at the New York Agricultural Experiment Station at Cornell University, a mixture of grasses and legumes were barn-dried, field-cured, and baled with a windrow baler, and field-cured and stored in a long condition. The cows produced 30.0 pounds of 4-percent fat-corrected milk on barn-cured hay; 29.3 pounds on field-cured baled hay; and 28.9 pounds on field-cured long hay in trials involving 15 cows fed each of the 3 hays for 3 periods of 6 weeks each. The palatability of the hays, as judged by the pounds consumed daily, were: Field-cured long, 33.5 pounds; barn-cured, 32.7; and field-cured baled, 30.8.

There does not appear to be any great advantage in the feeding value of barn-cured hay over a good quality of field-cured hay. Further work is needed on the comparative feeding value of barn-cured hay and field-cured hay, especially under adverse weather conditions. However, field losses under field-curing conditions are probably always greater, especially with legumes, than where hay is dried in the barn. Although the feeding values of the two hays do not differ materially, data at Beltsville show that about 9 percent more milk could be produced with barn-cured hay than with a like acreage of field-cured hay.

Enough feeding research has been carried on with artificially dehydrated forage to indicate its high feeding value. Because the crop may be dried immediately after it is cut, it can be harvested at an immature stage when it is high in protein. Thus artificially dried forage can compete with concentrates as a source of protein.

Work at the Vermont Agricultural Experiment Station indicated an increased production from cows when artificially dried young grass replaced field-cured hay in their ration. It also indicated that the digestible nutrients in artificially dried grass were at least equal to those in concentrate mixtures for milk production. Workers at that station have reported a high digestible protein and total digestible nutrient value for different kinds of forages cut and artificially dried when immature.

The United States Department of Agriculture found that Jersey heifers made better than average growth on artificially dried roughage alone. Later, when these heifers freshened, they pro-

Item	Field-cured hay	Barn-cured hay
Feed dry matter consumed per day:		
Alfalfa silage or hay............................pounds..	17.7	17.6
Corn silage...do....	4.8	4.7
Concentrates......................................do....	9.1	9.1
Total...do....	31.6	31.4
Milk production 4 percent fat content milk:		
Average per day....................................do....	34	33.6
30-day decline.................................percent..	6.6	7.8
Live weight:		
Average...pounds..	1,120.7	1,111.8
Daily gain..do....	.21	.01
Feed consumed per 100 pounds 4 percent fat content milk:		
Alfalfa dry matter................................do....	52.2	52.4
Total dry matter..................................do....	92.9	-93.5

Daily Quantities of Milk of Specified Butterfat Tests to be Expected from Cows Under Recommended Feeding Schedule of Concentrates

[Daily roughage: 1½ pounds of hay and 3 pounds silage per 100 pounds live weight]

Milk test (percent butterfat)	Milk daily from cows of indicated pound weight—				Extra concentrates needed to produce each additional 5 pounds of milk daily
	700	1,000	1,200	1,400	
	Pounds	*Pounds*	*Pounds*	*Pounds*	*Pounds*
3.0......................	12	18	22	25	2.0
4.0......................	10	15	19	22	2.2
5.0......................	9	13	17	19	2.5
6.0......................	8	12	14	17	2.8

Value of Wilted-Alfalfa Silage and Field-Cured Alfalfa Hay for Milk Production [1]

Experimental roughage in the ration	Cows	Average production of 4 percent f. c. m.[2]	Average daily gain in weight	Average daily consumption of dry matter in—			Total	Total dry-matter consumption per 100 lb. 4 percent f. c. m.[2]
				Silage or hay	Corn silage	Concentrates		
	Number	*Pounds*	*Pound*	*Pounds*	*Pounds*	*Pounds*	*Pounds*	*Pounds*
Wilted-alfalfa silage........	6	32.8	0.47	17.2	4.9	8.4	30.5	92.9
Field-cured alfalfa hay......	6	31.8	.40	17.5	4.9	8.6	31.0	97.4

[1] Silage and hays from same crop and fields harvested at the same time. (Fourth Experiment, 1945-46.)   [2] F. c. m.=fat content of milk.

duced well on an all-roughage ration of this type and consumed an average of 28.6 pounds a day, or 3.4 pounds per 100 pounds of body weight.

Other work indicates that young grass that was artificially dehydrated and fed as a substitute for concentrates produced milk efficiently.

Because forages are the cheapest source of nutrients for dairy cattle, it is essential that cattle consume as much of them as possible.

The experiments I have cited show that cows apparently have no particular preference for any one kind of forage. However, experiments conducted several years ago by our Bureau demonstrated that cows would consume more dry matter when two kinds of hay were fed than when one kind was fed. And experiments now in progress indicate that growing heifers will consume considerably more forage when they get several kinds than when only one kind is fed. As a matter of fact, good gains are being made by heifers past 10 months of age on roughage alone without grain when several kinds of forages are being fed. I conclude, then, that dairy cattle will consume more hay made from mixtures (such as brome seeded with alfalfa) than they will hay from unmixed stands.

To get the best results in terms of milk production, harvested forages are usually fed in combination with concentrates. In some of the western irrigated areas during the periods when milk is low in price, however, cows are fed nothing but alfalfa hay. Under these conditions the good cows do not produce at their maximum. On the other hand, the poor milkers may be stimulated but little to higher levels of milk production by grain feeding. Good cows generally will produce 60 to 70 percent as much milk on alfalfa alone as with supplementary grain.

In experimental work carried out by the Bureau of Dairy Industry, exceptionally good cows in 24 lactations produced 10,702 pounds of milk and 376 pounds of butterfat in a year on hay of high quality. This is superior production on roughage alone, but it should be remembered that the cows and the hay were far above average. In the fifth month the cows consumed an average of 44 pounds of alfalfa a day. On full feed, including grain, the cows produced 15,342 pounds of milk and 538 pounds of butterfat for the year.

Many experiments at other stations, where alfalfa hay was the sole feed, have given similar results.

The fact that dairy cows do not produce a maximum quantity of milk on roughage alone is not entirely due to a low intake of total digestible nutrients.

Experimental work at the Michigan and Oregon stations has shown that when fresh cows are placed on an all-forage ration their milk production goes down rapidly after 6 weeks to 2 months, but if a quantity of the total digestible nutrients fed as hay is replaced then by a similar quantity of total digestible nutrients fed as corn, milk production will increase materially. However, when nutrients in the form of starch or sugar were substituted for hay nutrients under similar circumstances there was no increase in production—an indication that the increased production resulting from feeding corn can not be attributed to the energy furnished by the corn but is probably due to some unknown nutrient contained in the corn that makes it possible for the nutrients in the hay to express their full feeding value.

The results from Michigan show that corn, wheat, oats, and barley contain the nutrient necessary for the proper utilization of hay nutrients. Similar work at the Oregon station demonstrated that ground soybeans, dried molasses, beet pulp, animal protein feeds, oats, peanut meal, and wheat middlings contain the necessary nutrient. It is probable also that forages in the immature stage may contain some of the nutrient, but further work is necessary to establish the conditions of maturity, harvesting, and so on that affect the presence or absence of the vital substance. It is therefore necessary to feed some concentrates in order to obtain the full feed value of harvested forages.

The grains and protein concentrates necessary to make up a grain mixture to be fed with harvested forage depends upon a great many factors, such as cost, type, and the quality of harvested forage to be fed.

The protein content of the concentrate mixture should vary somewhat with the type of forage. For instance, a lower-protein mixture can be fed with legumes than with the grasses.

But probably this point has been overemphasized in the past; perhaps the most important point is to get a sufficient total digestible nutrient intake into the milking cow. It is also probable that the recommendations for the protein content of concentrate mixtures have been too high.

More protein is fed to cows in the concentrate mixtures in some sections of the country, especially the East, than is necessary. Of course, where the relative costs of protein and carbohydrate feeds are practically the same, little attention needs to be given to minimum levels of protein in the concentrate mixture. Usually, however, the protein feeds cost more than the carbohydrate feeds so that some attention must be given to minimum levels of protein in the concentrate mixture for economical milk production.

In experiments at Beltsville, a group of cows fed a roughage ration of No. 1 timothy at the rate of 10 to 12 pounds, alfalfa at 3 to 4 pounds, and corn silage at 15 pounds per 1,000 pounds of body weight produced just as well on a concentrate ration of only 11 percent protein as a similar group that got an 18-percent protein-concentrate ration.

If the roughage part of the ration contains all good quality legumes (such as alfalfa hay or alfalfa silage with a small allowance of dry hay), little protein concentrate needs to be mixed with the cereal grains produced on the farm. A concentrate containing 10 to 11 percent protein should be ample.

If corn silage is fed and the rest of the roughage ration consists primarily of legumes, 10 to 12 percent of protein should be ample. If the ration is mostly grass hays of good quality, a ration containing 12 to 14 percent of protein should be ample. If corn silage is fed with grass hays, 14 to 16 percent of protein will satisfy the requirements. Where the roughages are of poor quality—if they have lost leaves and are leached—16 to 18 percent will meet the needs.

Which constituents should one use in making up a grain mixture? In the past, grain mixtures of many different items have been made. More recent experiments have shown that a large number of ingredients is not essential for good average production. Concentrate mixtures containing one or two home-grown grains, along with a protein concentrate, are adequate. Bran or other feeds often are added to feeds for dairy cattle in order to add bulk to the ration, but under ordinary conditions one need not pay too much attention to the matter of bulk.

If it is necessary to purchase grains to make up a concentrate mixture, it is most economical to purchase the grain in which the total of the digestible nutrients is the cheapest. Likewise, with protein concentrates it is most economical to purchase the feed in which a pound of protein can be bought most cheaply.

The amount of grain one should feed to cows depends on their level of production. The high-producing cows usually are fed more grain than the low producers. Low producers will sometimes consume enough roughage to meet their nutrient requirements.

THE AUTHOR ⋘ L. A. Moore is in charge of the section of dairy cattle nutrition of the Bureau of Dairy Industry. Before joining the Department of Agriculture in 1945 he was associated with the dairy departments of Michigan State College and Maryland University. For outstanding research relating to the nutrition of dairy cows, Dr. Moore received the Borden Award in 1943.

The Use and Value of Pastures

PASTURES ON THE DAIRY FARM

R. E. WAGNER, J. B. SHEPHERD

PASTURES have as many names as they have uses. We classify them here to indicate their scope and versatility, to show how any farmer who is prone to regard his pasture as just another piece of ground can extend its use and value.

Permanent pastures are the ones that are covered with perennial or self-seeding annual plants and are kept for grazing indefinitely. They seldom are plowed or cultivated. The terms tame pastures, improved pastures, or plowable pastures, as used in the census reports, are those planted or covered with domesticated or other pasture plants; the names often are applied also to many pastures that are classified as permanent pastures.

Permanent or natural pastures comprise a rather large percentage of the pasture area on many dairy farms. Although some dairymen could better utilize more of their permanent pasture area for rotation or supplementary pastures, the importance of the permanent pasture is great enough in its own right.

Nearly every farm has some land not suitable for cultivation and better left in permanent pastures. Much of such turf is thin, weedy, low in productivity, and otherwise run-down. Top dressing with phosphate and potash and sometimes nitrogen is one method of improvement. The amount of feed produced following such treatment is ordinarily greatly increased, but unfortunately the response sometimes is slow; while fertilization eventually may change the prevalence of the various species, the immediate benefits are manifested only in the species present, which usually lack the more nutritious, heat- and drought-tolerant grasses and legumes. Consequently, most of the increased production derived from top dressing permanent pastures results in increased spring grazing with little improvement in midsummer production.

Tests in Michigan have shown that the production of forage in permanent bluegrass pastures can be increased approximately 100 percent during May, June, and September by spring applications of complete fertilizers at the rate of 500 pounds to the acre. During July and August, however, the grass growing on the fertilized areas actually showed drought injury several days earlier than did the grass on the unfertilized pastures, and the growth on the fertilized areas during the drought period was no greater than on the unfertilized.

Ordinarily, the permanent pastures should be used only for grazing, because the species usually present are not well adapted by growth habit to ease of harvesting for hay or silage.

Rotation pastures are established

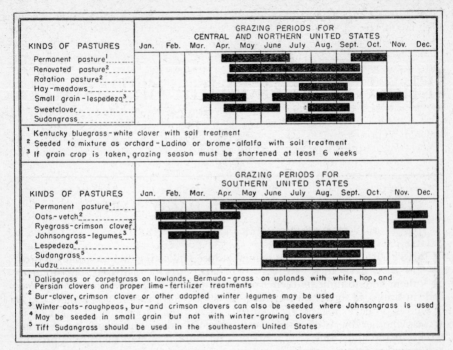

Kinds of pastures and seasons of best production. Renovated pastures are not usually classified separately but their place in the dairy pasture programs warrant recognition.

on the better cultivated cropland and are a part of the regular crop rotation. They are planted to quick-growing grasses and legumes that make rapid growth for hay or grazing. These pastures are usually higher in production throughout the growing season than permanent pastures.

Rotation pastures are recommended for most dairy farms. A suggested rotation consists of 1 year of row crops, 1 year of small grain, and 2 or 3 years of pasture combined with hay or silage. Rotation pastures are especially productive in summer because they are seeded with nutritious, tall-growing, drought-tolerant species. These mixtures for the North usually contain such combinations as bromegrass-alfalfa, orchardgrass-Ladino clover, and (on poorly drained soils) reed canarygrass-Ladino clover.

At Montrose, Pa., in 1942, 1943, and 1944, rotation pastures, grazed all season with milk cows, produced 51 percent more total digestible nutrients to the acre before July 15 and 113 percent more after that date than was produced by permanent pastures of about average carrying capacity. Men who made a survey in southeastern Minnesota determined on a basis of farmers' estimates that 1 acre of crop-rotation pasture equals 1.5 acre of previously cropped and permanent pastures, or 2.6 acres of wooded pasture.

Rotation grazing, where the animals are allowed to graze for a time and then moved to another area, is a desirable practice—at least in theory. The pasture just grazed is allowed to recover. Seasonal conditions and type of pasture are important considerations in judging the value of such grazing. Rotation grazing of permanent pastures has given slightly higher production in some localities. Results have shown an increase of 10 to 15 percent in production over continuous grazing in some instances. It is questionable if this will pay for additional fencing and other costs required.

With rotation or renovated pastures planted to the rapid-growing grasses and legumes such as brome-alfalfa, or orchardgrass-Ladino clover, rotation grazing is necessary. Not only is a greater production obtained but the stands of the desirable pasture plants are maintained over a longer period. Also more pastures of higher quality are obtained in summer.

Rotation pastures go a long way toward easing the midsummer feed shortage if they are properly handled. They can be used to extend the ends of the pasture season and will furnish considerable reserve feed of high quality in the form of hay or silage besides.

Irrigated pastures are figuring more and more prominently in the dairy-pasture programs of the West. They also merit consideration in other sections for supplementing natural rainfall in midseason when ample water supplies are available for irrigation. Such pastures are especially valuable in increasing summer production and are generally more economical than harvested feed or feed purchased to maintain summer milk flow. With an adequate water supply, proper fertilization, and adapted mixtures, herbage can be kept growing vigorously, and hence palatable and nutritious. Furthermore, irrigation may help maintain the more desirable species in the pasture sward.

Records obtained from 1936 to 1940 by the California Agricultural Extension Service in conducting studies of the management of irrigated pasture, revealed that pasturage from irrigated pastures is usually more expensive than from natural range, but is a cheaper source of nutrients than most other livestock feeds. The records showed that hay containing 50 percent of total digestible nutrients would have to be obtainable at from $3.80 to $7.50 a ton to be as cheap a source of feed as irrigated pastures.

Workers in California have reported that of the 300,000 acres of irrigated pastures in that State, about 100,000 acres are used for beef cattle. They

reported that no innovation in the livestock business has done so much to relieve the stress on overburdened ranges and uniform quality of meat animals. Under that type of management, 100 acres of irrigated pastures properly managed will carry as many animals during 6 to 7 months of the summer as 1,000 acres of range will support the other 5 to 6 months.

Renovated pastures, so named because the methods of establishment and management differ from those used in rotation or permanent pastures, recently have come into use. The object of renovation is to increase the production of run-down permanent pastures by disking or other cultivation, applications of lime and fertilizer, and seeding rapid-growing and good grasses and legumes without subjecting the land to cropping. The last point is especially important on erodible lands. Renovation also shortens the time that land will be out-of-the-pasture system.

The actual methods used in developing a renovated pasture depend on local conditions, but good results require that one subdue existing vegetation to prevent competition with new seedings; incorporate lime, manure, and fertilizer into the soil; seed rapid-growing grasses and legumes; and observe proper grazing management and subsequent fertilizer treatments to maintain the stand and growth of the seeded species.

Wisconsin was among the first to apply the principle and promote its use on a widespread scale. H. L. Ahlgren and his co-workers at the University of Wisconsin learned from a series of investigations that renovated pastures on slopes ranging from 15 percent to 35 percent produced as much as five and one-half times as much dry matter an acre as similarly situated but untreated pastures in the year after seeding. The second year, the renovated areas produced approximately twice that of the untreated pastures. Similar results, but perhaps less striking in some cases, were obtained in Pennsylvania, Iowa, West Virginia, other States

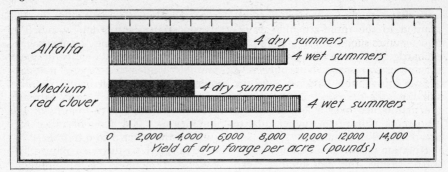

in the bluegrass area, and at Beltsville.

The advantages of renovated pastures are several. Total production is greatly increased, and the distribution of the seasonal production is superior. The quality of the forage is improved by the introduction of the nutritious grasses and legumes and by fertilization. Renovation allows for an ideal seedbed, with an abundance of organic matter in the surface—an aid in establishing the seeded species and preventing erosion.

The process of renovation is a system of conversion from run-down pastures directly to improved pastures without the serious hazards of erosion and with a minimum of loss in production during the year of seeding. Of particular importance is the fact that in the year of renovation the area involved is out of production in the spring during peak pasture growth, when the farmer ordinarily has more pasture than he can handle efficiently anyway. These areas then usually will furnish grazing when it is most needed later in the season after permanent pastures start their decline in production. Renovated pastures will continue to show improvement for at least 2 or 3 years.

The job of renovation is not a difficult or costly one and is admirably adapted to a dairy pasture program, since the work and labor involved come during slack periods in the fall and early spring. Thorough working of the sod is important and often the key to success in renovation. The other steps in the process, namely, liming, fertilizing, and seeding, are handled in much the same manner as for cultivated pastures.

Some of the more important tall-growing species commonly seeded in renovated pastures include Ladino clover, red clover, alfalfa, bromegrass, and orchardgrass. To meet certain conditions, birdsfoot trefoil, sweetclover, alsike clover, lespedeza, tall fescue and meadow fescue, reed canarygrass, and tall oatgrass are sometimes used.

Supplemental or temporary pastures include several types. The second growth of a harvested hay meadow, if grazed, may be called aftermath pasture. Perennial legumes such as kudzu and others in the South are used to supplement the permanent and annual pastures. Harvested fields of small grains and corn are often used as supplementary pastures. These are sometimes referred to as stubble pastures.

Some dairymen depend upon annual supplementary pastures to help meet feed needs during midsummer, when more grazing is needed than is available from permanent, renovation, or rotation pastures, or when winter-killing or other hazards have damaged areas intended for grazing. Sudangrass is one of the best and most common crops used for the purpose. Small grains, soybeans, sweetclover, and millet are also often used as supplementary pastures. Grazing the aftermath or second growth from meadow and hay fields is often practiced in midsummer where the need exists.

In the South, supplementary pastures have become such an integral part of the year-round grazing program that it might be incorrect to call them that; actually, farmers depend on so-called supplementary pastures for grazing in nearly all seasons.

Small grains, particularly oats, or ryegrass in combination with such legumes as crimson clover, vetch, and winter peas, are becoming increasingly popular as·winter pasture. A popular winter-summer combination is oats and annual lespedeza. The oats may be grazed off completely or harvested for grain. Sudangrass, Johnsongrass, and kudzu are used for summer grazing. The use of various of these supplementary crops along with permanent pastures of Dallisgrass or carpetgrass on the lowlands and Bermuda-grass with white, Persian, and hop clovers on the uplands, will go far toward meeting the grazing needs of Southern dairymen.

Temporary or annual pastures are used for grazing during a short period, not more than one crop season. The cereal crops such as wheat, oats, and rye, or Sudangrass, soybeans, and pearl-millet are examples of the annual crops that are rather widely used on these pastures.

Native, wild, or natural pastures are areas covered with native plants useful for grazing. When they cover an extensive area they are generally referred to as range pastures. Also included in this classification are shrub or brush pastures, which are covered mainly with shrubs or browse plants; woodland pastures, on which grass or other forage plants grow among trees; and finaly, the stump or cut-over pastures, on land where the forest has been removed.

Regardless of the type of pasture, the objective in a sound, economical, and well-balanced pasture program should be to maintain enough pasture of high quality adequately to supply the cow herd at all times during the grazing season.

A successful dairy enterprise is built around an adequate, efficient, and well-balanced forage program. Keeping the year. Thereafter, care should be taken to prevent too intensive utilization.

is as important in dairying as in any other industry. The place of pastures in meeting this ideal is exemplified in a study made of dairy farms in New York in 1936. On them, the cost of pasture was only 4 percent of the total cost of milk production, although the cows were pastured 149 days of the year. Of the 154 man-hours a year required to take care of each cow, 45 were required during the pasture season and 109 during the winter season. A more recent study made for the year that ended April 30, 1946, showed the cost of pasture to be only 3 percent of the total milk production cost.

Three points are paramount in the proper management of pastures on dairy farms.

The plants should be used when they are at their peak in nutritive value.

The highest possible carrying capacity should be obtained and kept.

The stand and balance of legumes and grasses should be maintained throughout the pasture season.

Many experiments have established that the nutritive composition of forage, whether used for pasture, hay, or silage, varies widely according to its stage of development. Immature forage is a highly digestible and nutritious animal food, but as the plants mature their percentage of protein and vitamins decreases and crude fiber increases rather rapidly. Management of pastures, therefore, must allow for their use when they are most palatable and nutritious; if that cannot be done to advantage by grazing, a part of the pasture can be cut for hay or silage.

Permanent pastures should be fully utilized in spring when the grasses on them are in their most nutritious form. Relatively heavy utilization in the spring also will encourage the growth of legumes.

Renovation, rotation, and irrigated pastures are much alike in management. A successful pasture first must become well established, which means only moderate grazing during the first year. Thereafter, care should be taken to prevent too intensive utilization.

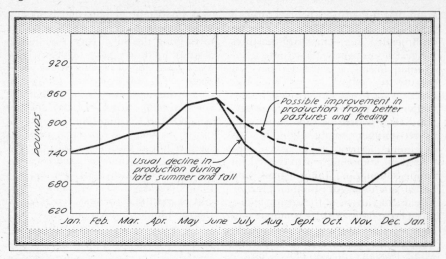

Average monthly production of milk cows by months for the year. Milk flow closely follows seasonal production of pastures; the midsummer slump in quantity and quality of forage is critical and the extension of both ends of the grazing season is important.

Grazing too closely should be avoided during dry periods, late in the fall, and too early in the spring.

The grazing season depends largely upon the length of the growing season and the type of pasture. Too often the grazing season is extended at the expense of the pasture and livestock production of both. Permanent pastures made up of turf-forming grasses such as Kentucky bluegrass or Bermuda-grass-white clover can withstand heavy and rather intensive use without injury to the stand, providing the plant food requirements are maintained, but rotation or renovated pastures, as bromegrass-alfalfa or orchardgrass-Ladino, must be protected from grazing early in the spring or late in the fall if satisfactory stands continue. For this reason an improved permanent pasture, along with annual or supplementary pasture, can be used to good advantage in protecting the rotation or renovated pastures. Fortunately permanent pastures or selected annual crops can be grown that are most productive at early and late seasons.

Although forage should be utilized in a relatively immature stage in order to obtain the most nutritious feed, the plants comprising the pasture should be given due consideration at all times.

Most species, particularly of the taller growing types, will not withstand continuous, heavy utilization. They must be given periodic opportunities to recover. Too heavy utilization may reduce yields, weaken many of the more desirable species, and permit weeds and undesirable species to enter.

The maintenance of a balance of legumes and grasses in a mixture is influenced to a considerable extent by grazing management. In most regions the legume generally dictates the grazing management since it must be favored to persist in mixed seedings. In general, the competitive ability of a plant in mixture depends upon its height and density. No two species of plants are equal in their competitive abilities at all times of the year. Thus grazing must be managed to favor the least aggressive species in pasture mixtures; that means subduing the more aggressive species by grazing or clipping at the time of their strongest growth.

Differentials in species competition at different times are tremendously important in relation to the seasonal succession of species and, hence, to season-long grazing. For instance, if the orchardgrass of a Ladino clover-or-chardgrass mixture is allowed to reach full height, particularly in the spring, the clover that normally comes on later tends to be weakened and suppressed.

Mowing to control brush and weeds has increased yields as much as 50 to 60 percent. The quality of forage is materially benefited by such a practice. Clipping pastures to remove mature herbage is desirable if high quality herbage is desired. On the other hand, this surplus growth can be utilized to a good advantage by dry stock and light feeder cattle that would otherwise require harvested roughage. Under such conditions mowing may not be practical or economical since this type of pasturage contains ample feed to supply the grazing animals with necessary requirements for maintenance.

Under intensive pasture production it is necessary to give particular attention to cultural practices such as mowing and spreading of droppings to insure maximum production of high quality pasturage. With more extensive types of pasture operations it may not be economical to devote as much attention to mowing or cultivation.

Nearly all soils in the humid sections of the United States are deficient in calcium, phosphorus, potassium, and nitrogen. Adequate fertilization of all areas containing desirable pasture species should be given high priority in the dairy pasture program. Most irrigated pastures of the drier sections are highly productive, which means that the drain upon soil resources is heavy. While in some few cases irrigated soils have not responded to fertilizers, the majority require proper fertilization for maximum and most efficient production.

Commercial fertilizers are generally relied upon to furnish the plant food to pastures. Although barnyard manure is ordinarily used on cropland its value for use on pastures should not be overlooked. Local soil and climatic conditions will not allow specific recommendations for lime and fertilizers to be applied generally. It is wise to determine such needs first by soil tests.

Plant competition can be materially influenced by fertilizers. Heavy applications of nitrogen favor the growth of grasses at the expense of the legume in mixtures, whereas phosphorus and potassium encourage the growth of legumes. Nitrogen fertilizers are seldom used on mixtures of grasses and legumes except in small amounts on new seedings.

The use of manure, lime, and fertilizers, where needed, is an essential in any good pasture-management program. Considerable improvement can be made by top dressing many permanent pastures. This will encourage the growth of the more desirable pasture plants and increase the nutritive value of the forage. For the best success the soil-improvement program must be a part of the grassland system. Data obtained from seven Southern States indicate that for each pound of plant food used production was increased equal to 4 pounds of milk or one-half pound in live-weight gain.

In Iowa the recommendation has been made that "pasture management is no substitute for pasture improvement with lime, fertilizers, etc., but rather a supplement to improvement."

The experimental pasture program at Beltsville has effectively furnished grazing throughout the pasture season and has provided reserve feeds in the form of silage and hay. Rotation, renovation, and permanent pastures are included. A 5-year rotation consisting of corn, wheat, and pasture (3 years) is employed. Five fields are maintained, so that in any year one of the fields is in corn, another in wheat, and the other three in first-, second-, and third-year pasture. The first-year pasture is grazed rotationally throughout the season. From the second-year pasture at least the first crop and sometimes the first two crops, depending upon the need for pasture, are taken for hay or silage and the aftermath is grazed. The third-year pasture is grazed early for a few days before the permanent pasture is ready, followed by the removal of a crop of hay and then rotationally grazed during the rest of the season.

The order of grazing consists first of all of a few days of early spring grazing on the third-year pasture, from there to the permanent pasture and first-year rotation pasture. The first crops of the renovated pastures are either grazed or removed for hay or silage. As the permanent pasture drops in production, the second- and third-year rotation pastures and the renovated pastures are ordinarily ready for grazing.

Pastures utilized in this or a similar manner would seem to have rather widespread application and could be made a sound and economical farm pasture and forage program.

Supplemental Feeding

The need for supplemental feeding of dairy cows on pasture should be kept at a minimum by adopting a program that will provide a continuous and adequate supply of nutrients through high-quality pasturage. Cows on good pasture will eat about as much roughage as they can well handle.

It may be advisable to feed some supplemental grain to the high-producing cows. In general, cows producing less than a pound of butterfat a day will receive the nutrients they require from good pasture and thus will need no supplemental feeding. Pastures vary so much in quality and quantity at different periods of the year that no fixed rule for supplementary feeding throughout the season can be established. The farmer must be guided by the condition of his pastures, his cows, and the flow of milk.

Extension dairymen in some States are recommending that dry hay be kept before dairy cows at all times on the theory that if the pasture is adequate they will eat very little and if it is not adequate they will require additional feed. Furthermore cattle provided with plenty of supplementary hay are not apt to graze scanty pastures too closely. Cattle grazing on a luxuriant growth of young and tender pasturage will also eat considerable quantities of hay, and for maximum milk production should probably be given access to it. Such supplementation adds very little to costs and is wise economy.

When it is necessary to feed supplemental hay or grain because of pasture shortages, costs of production rise rapidly. These costs should be checked by the most efficient and economical manner, which generally means revamping the pasture program to meet the needs of the animals at all times.

In many sections of the range country pasturage can be held in reserve for maintaining livestock during the fall and winter seasons. The same is true to a lesser extent in the bluegrass sections of the Middle West and Appalachian region. Many of our native grasses such as buffalograss and blue grama grass under deferred grazing will provide winter maintenance of livestock in good condition with a minimum of supplemental concentrates. Successful livestock men have reserve pastures for feeder or light cattle. The methods of grazing management are determining factors in the value of pasture.

THE AUTHORS≪≪≪ *R. E. Wagner is an associate agronomist in the Bureau of Plant Industry, Soils, and Agricultural Engineering. He is a graduate of the Kansas State College and the University of Wisconsin. Currently he is engaged in research on the culture, production, utilization, and improvement of grass and pasture crops.*

J. B. Shepherd is a dairy husbandman, in charge of pasture and forage investigations in the Division of Nutrition and Physiology of the Bureau of Dairy Industry. He is a graduate of the University of Nebraska and since 1917 has been engaged in research having to do with dairy production, pastures, forage, and grass silage and its utilization as feed.

THE MANAGEMENT OF GRAZING

E. MARION BROWN

THE MOST difficult problem to be solved in the management of grazing arises from the seasonal differences in the rate at which pasture plants grow. I give a few examples.

Measurements of the seasonal growth of pasture grasses and mixtures in Maryland and Missouri showed that more than half of the total annual yield occurred during the first one-third, and more than two-thirds of the total occurred during the first half of the growing season.

No one crop or seed mixture yet tried in Connecticut supplies uniform grazing, and it becomes increasingly difficult to provide any pasturage there from June 15 to November 1.

In some years all of the annual gain made by beef steers on winter clover-Bermuda-grass mixtures in Arkansas had been made by July; in every year most of the annual gain had been made by that date.

Because winter legume-Bermuda-grass-Dallisgrass pastures in Mississippi have peaks of production in spring and fall, the number of animals adequately carried in spring would overgraze the same pasture in the summer period of lessened production.

The productivity of mixed grasses and winter clovers increased rapidly in the Black Belt of Alabama from late March to May, remained high through May, declined during June, remained low through July, rose to and remained at a moderate rate during August and September, and then declined to the March level by the end of October.

So, whether the grazing season is 5 months long, as it is in Maine, or 12 months long, as it might be in Florida, the problem is to provide good pasturage throughout this season.

Saving part of the spring growth for summer and fall grazing is not the solution, because of the poor quality of mature grass. Chemical analyses, combined in some instances with feeding trials, have shown that some pasture grasses (such as bromegrass) deteriorate less in quality than others but that all of them are less palatable, less digestible, and less nutritious when mature than when young, vegetative, and actively growing.

When, therefore, hay of the desired quality cannot be made from surplus growth, the size of the pasture and herd should be adjusted to herbage growth during spring, and temporary pastures should be used to supplement permanent pastures summer and fall.

Heavy grazing of Kentucky bluegrass and associated legumes in Missouri from mid-April to early July and again during September and October produced large acre yields of beef but weakened the grass. Close defoliation during the cool periods of spring and fall prevented the synthesis of sufficient carbohydrates to satisfy plant requirements for current growth and for the storage of organic food reserves.

The use of Korean lespedeza for supplementary pasture from July 10 to September 1 increased live-weight gains during the summer, but resting the permanent pasture at that time had little beneficial effect on the bluegrass.

Kentucky bluegrass will benefit from undergrazing or rest both during the cool period of spring, when two-thirds of the total forage is produced, and that of autumn, when less than one-fifth of the total top growth occurs.

Supplemented grazing, whereby the permanent pasture was grazed to capacity from mid-April to early July and at a greatly reduced rate from early July to mid-September, and then rested from mid-September to late November was tried in Missouri from 1941 to 1944. The pasture sward, consisting of Kentucky bluegrass, Korean lespedeza, and volunteer white clover, improved steadily under this grazing schedule and in 1944 produced 250 pounds of beef-cattle gain an acre, as compared with 199 pounds obtained from the season-long grazing of a comparable pasture. Furthermore, the September-October growth was available in the supplemented-grazing pasture for winter feed.

Korean lespedeza grown with wheat, winter barley, or spring oats, each harvested for grain, supplied summer pasture from July 10 to September 30. The average live-weight gain made on this supplementary pasture from 1940 to 1944 by beef steers was 103 pounds an acre.

Feed costs can be reduced and injury to permanent and rotation pastures from too early grazing can be avoided by the use of supplementary pastures in the spring. Rye provides pasture earlier than any other crop. In the middle latitudes, Missouri to Virginia, rye is ready to be pastured a month earlier than permanent or rotation pastures, but in the northern tier of States not more than 2 weeks of early grazing can be gained.

Winter oats, barley, wheat, and rye supply both winter and early-spring pasture in the Cotton Belt. Only light intermittent grazing can be expected from them before February in the northern part of this region, but beef steers gained 139 pounds per head and 190 pounds an acre in northern Florida on winter oats pastured continuously from December 20 to April 20. Ryegrass, crimson clover, bur-clover, vetch, and roughpea, in pure stand, with one of the above cereals, or in Johnsongrass sod also are used for winter and early-spring grazing in the Southern States.

Summer is a period of low productivity for permanent and rotation pastures from Canada to the Gulf coast, and eastward from western Minnesota and eastern Texas, the area to which the management practices discussed here apply and which, although it is large and diverse in soils and climate, has several common problems of pasture management. North of the region within which annual lespedezas can be grown successfully, Sudangrass is the standard supplementary pasture crop from early July to late September. Japanese-millet, second-growth meadow, oats or barley planted as companion crops, and reed canarygrass also can be pastured during summer. From northern Missouri and Maryland to the South, the annual lespedezas fill this gap exceedingly well. Sudangrass, pearlmillet and cattail millet, Johnsongrass, kudzu, and soybeans are also used.

Autumn is a favorable period for root growth and for the storage of carbohydrate reserves by Kentucky bluegrass and other cool-weather perennial grasses. Protection from grazing during this period increases the vigor and prolongs the life of the grass with a minimum waste of forage, for only a small fraction of the annual top growth occurs after mid-September, and this growth can be pastured off after mid-November without harm to the grass.

Annual lespedezas and Sudangrass supply grazing until the end of September. Early-sown rye, winter barley, or oats and first-year sweetclover are usually ready to be pastured by early October. The fall growth in the permanent or rotation pastures can and should be pastured off after frosts in November.

Rotation Grazing

Farm animals never eat pasture herbage down to a uniform height unless compelled by being confined to an area so small that it is pastured out completely within a few days. Without this restriction, spot grazing occurs and the grass first refused is eaten only after livestock have failed to obtain a fill from vegetation shortened by previous grazing. Overgrazing and undergrazing within the same enclosure are the result.

Rotation grazing, whereby the pasture is fenced into two to eight separate enclosures of equal size to be grazed alternately, has been devised to reduce uneven grazing. If there are enough of these enclosures, the herbage can be pastured down quickly to the desired level as soon as it has grown to a height suitable for grazing. Between brief periods of intensive grazing, the sward is protected from defoliation and trampling.

During the spring period of flush growth, individual fields not needed then for pasture can be withheld from grazing and the forage in them harvested for hay or grass silage. Later these fields are pastured in turn, thereby lengthening the rest periods for all enclosures as herbage growth slows up. This practice reduces but usually does not eliminate the need for summer supplementary pasture.

A further refinement of rotation grazing is to divide the dairy herd, so that producing cows have first access to new growth and dry cows and young stock finish pasturing out each enclosure after the producing cows have been moved to another field.

Each grazing period lasts from 3 to 7 days for each group of a split herd or from 1 to 2 weeks for an undivided herd or flock; and the intervening rest periods will last from 2 to 4 weeks, depending on the number of enclosures, the kind of pasture, and the weather.

Even when rotation grazing is practiced, tall grass will accumulate near droppings. If each field is mowed a day or two before the animals are to be removed, most of this previously avoided grass will be eaten after having been moved by the mower a short distance from the excrement around which it grew.

Rotation grazing has been advocated for improved permanent pastures in Maine, Connecticut, Rhode Island, New York, Ohio, Illinois, and Wisconsin; for rotation pastures of bromegrass and alfalfa or Ladino clover in Wisconsin and Indiana; and for Sudangrass in Ohio and Georgia. But in each of the experiments in which rotation grazing has been compared with uncontrolled grazing in Maryland, Michigan, Wisconsin, Missouri, and Washington, the increase in production has been too small to justify the added expense of fencing and water supply, unless these could be provided at moderate cost and unless the pasture was high in yield and quality. Rotation grazing may be necessary to maintain in pastures such crops as alfalfa and Ladino clover, although it was found to have no advantage for the pasturing of bromegrass and alfalfa in Michigan.

The Hohenheim system of pasture management provides for grazing rotationally from four to nine fields and for heavy applications of nitrogenous fertilizers to the grass at regular intervals during the growing season. Although yields of dairy products obtained per acre under this system of management have been large, cost has been correspondingly high, so that the increased production has been profitable in some trials and unprofitable in others. Although widely publicized in this country following its use in Germany during the First World War, the Hohenheim system has never been used extensively and it is not now generally recommended, although it might have a limited usefulness under certain conditions.

Time to Graze

Deferred grazing is defined as delaying grazing for a part of the growing season to permit sufficient top growth to maintain the vigor of pasture plants. The nutritive quality of bromegrass declines little and its carrying capacity is greatly increased by delaying grazing until the grass is 10 inches high. The destructive effect of early clipping or grazing on alfalfa and its high nutritive quality even when in bloom are well known. Deferred grazing is a good practice for bromegrass and alfalfa and other mixtures that have similar habits of growth.

Many other pasture grasses deteriorate in quality with advancing maturity much faster than bromegrass, and low-growing legumes, such as white clover and annual lespedezas, may be suppressed by the vigorous early growth of ungrazed grass.

Deferring the pasturing of winter clovers too long in the South, on the other hand, may reduce greatly the growth of associated Bermuda-grass or Dallisgrass. The net effect of early grazing on the pasture sward may therefore be beneficial even though the vigor of the more aggressive early-growing component is somewhat reduced.

In Connecticut, cattle gained more than twice as much when grazing began May 5 as when it began June 10, although the yield of herbage was larger under delayed grazing. Deferring the grazing of bluegrass from 2 to 4 weeks after mid-April reduced cattle gains by 13 percent in Missouri. Although livestock should never be turned on pastures before the vegetation has made sufficient growth to permit them to obtain a fill readily, a longer delay in grazing is justified only when the herbage consists of erect, tall crops that are highly sensitive to pasturing when small.

A common recommendation is that grazing begin when the vegetation is 3 to 4 inches tall. Permanent pastures in the northern tier of States are usually ready for grazing by May 15. Renovated permanent pastures or rotation pastures of bromegrass and Ladino clover or alfalfa are ready a few days earlier in Wisconsin.

Farther south, central Missouri to Maryland, livestock can be turned on permanent pastures in mid-April. From Arkansas and North Carolina to the South, pastures that contain winter legumes are ready to be grazed by late March.

Grazing Intensity

Overgrazing should be avoided because livestock cannot obtain enough nutrients to support profitable production if the vegetation is too short, and because certain valuable pasture plants may be destroyed.

Since, however, most pastures pro-duce two-thirds of their herbage during April to July, since this vegetation deteriorates in nutritive quality and palatability if not eaten as it grows, and since rank growth tends to suppress low-growing legumes, most pastures should be grazed during periods of flush growth to the minimum height that will permit adequate daily consumption of pasturage by the grazing animals. This is not overgrazing except for mixtures of hay-type grasses and legumes.

Pasture herbage can be consumed most rapidly and easily from a dense stand of grasses and legumes about 4 inches tall. A cow must have favorable grazing conditions in order to consume the quantity of green herbage required for maximum production during the 8 hours of each day that she is willing to spend grazing.

Beef steers averaged 287 pounds of gain per steer and 145 pounds of gain per acre on a permanent pasture at Beltsville that was stocked at the rate of one steer to 2 acres, as compared with 195 pounds of gain per steer and per acre when the rate of stocking was doubled. Both groups of steers gained equally well from April to July. The unsatisfactory gains made after June on the heavily grazed pasture is not sufficient reason for understocking during spring and early summer if land is available for the production of supplementary pastures for summer and early fall grazing.

The need to leave enough leaf surface to manufacture the carbohydrates required to sustain current and future growth of pasture plants is recognized, but the level of carbohydrates that is best for the grass may not be best for the pasture. Close grazing in May has been found to increase the growth of volunteer white clover, and later in the season the grass benefited more from this increase in clover than it had been injured earlier by close grazing.

The specific height to which the vegetation should be eaten down depends on the crops which constitute the pasture. The opinion has been expressed that the average height of bluegrass and volunteer white clover should be one-half inch after being grazed and mowed in rotation. It is now generally believed that these and similar pasture species should not be grazed shorter than 1 to 2 inches. Two inches has been recommended as the minimum to which pastures containing Ladino clover should be grazed in Connecticut and pastures containing Bermuda-grass in Georgia.

Under skillfully managed rotation grazing, grass 3 to 4 inches tall can be quickly pastured down to a desired height. Without such management, grazing is never uniform except on a badly overgrazed pasture. Intensity of grazing on the average pasture is indicated by the comparative size of grazed and ungrazed areas. If more than 25 percent of the total area remains ungrazed by June, the pasture is understocked, but if less than 10 percent of the area remains ungrazed, overgrazing will probably occur before supplementary pastures are ready in July.

Hay-type grasses and legumes will not withstand close grazing. It is recommended in Wisconsin that Ladino clover be pastured not shorter than 4 to 5 inches. Still more lenient grazing is required for bromegrass and alfalfa, the management of which is governed by the requirements of alfalfa. In order to maintain a well-balanced mixture of alfalfa and bromegrass through three or four seasons in Michigan, it is considered advisable to maintain a growth 8 to 10 inches tall during May and June, and not less than 4 inches high during the summer.

Special Management

Managed grazing is not only the means by which pasture herbage is used efficiently, but it may also be the means by which other improvement practices are applied.

Most low-growing legumes are favored in their association with competing grasses by grazing practices that utilize most efficiently the available herbage. But when sweetclover, red clover, or alfalfa is used to renovate pastures, grazing must be adjusted to the requirements of the seedlings.

Severe grazing of the grass during the fall preceding and the spring of seeding sweetclover reduces competition which the grass offers the clover. As sweetclover seedlings are more sensitive to grazing than to competition, pasturing ends as soon as they become tall enough to be bitten off and is not resumed until July, when the clover has attained a height of 12 to 18 inches. Moderate grazing during July and August is permissible, but stock should be kept off from the first of September until freezing weather.

During the second year, pasturing begins in the renovated pasture as soon as the sweetclover attains 6 to 8 inches, and, until the clover begins to set seed, continues with an intensity that utilizes most of the grass and leaves 8 to 10 inches of leafy sweetclover stubble when the cattle are taken off in early July. After the sweetclover has matured seed, grazing is resumed and is continued throughout late summer and fall with an intensity that will not only utilize all available herbage but will also weaken the grass, thereby reducing the competition offered clover seedlings next spring.

Much grass is wasted and low production often results from the grazing schedule required for the establishment of sweetclover and similar legumes in grass sod. The beneficial effect of legumes that require inefficient grazing for their establishment must be great and lasting to justify their use.

THE AUTHOR ⋘ *E. Marion Brown, a graduate of the University of Missouri, has been engaged in research on grass since 1931. Dr. Brown is an agronomist in the Bureau of Plant Industry, Soils, and Agricultural Engineering and professor of fields crops at the University of Missouri.*

[See also: Articles on pastures in the Northeast, and on hay and grass silage.]

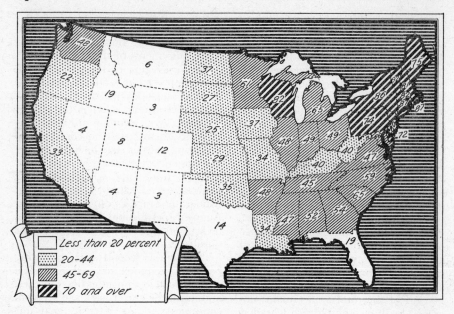

Pasture: Percentage of total units consumed in each State by dairy cattle in 1941–42.

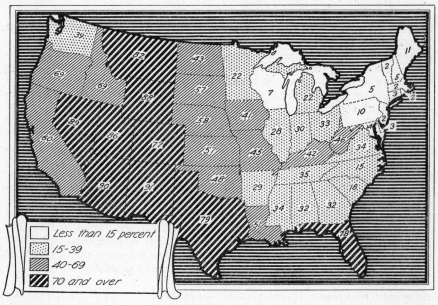

Pasture: Percentage of total consumed by beef cattle and sheep, by States, 1941–42.

MANAGEMENT OF IRRIGATED PASTURES

D. W. THORNE

VIRGIN desert lands lack most of the characteristics of productivity associated with the forest and prairie regions. The sparse plant cover varies from bunchgrasses to desert shrubs. The soil is commonly light in color and often is coated with a hard crust. Low rainfall makes the growth of even quickly maturing crops hazardous without supplemental water. But despite discouraging appearances, millions of acres of such land in the United States have become highly productive through the development of irrigation agriculture in the past 100 years, in the short span since Horace Greeley wrote in 1859 after traveling across the northern part of what was then called the Great American Desert: "I fear it is doomed to perpetual barrenness. . . . This land of desolation seems, therefore, utterly irredeemable."

The principal problems of soil management in this western irrigated region result partly from the inherent characteristics of virgin desert soils and partly from the relationships between these soils and the water applied during irrigation.

Because of low rainfall and limited plant growth, desert soils are naturally low in organic matter and nitrogen; sometimes they have only a tenth as much of these essential soil ingredients as a good virgin prairie soil. Because most of the rainfall on desert soils has been used by plants or evaporated, there has been little leaching of the soluble products formed from rock weathering. Consequently, desert soils usually contain large quantities of calcium, magnesium, potassium, sodium, carbonates, sulfates, and often chlorides; sometimes, in fact, the accumulations of such materials is so concentrated as to limit plant growth. But although many nutrients are present, the soils, when placed under irrigation, often lack enough phosphorus and nitrogen for maximum crop yields.

Irrigation water, which converts the soil environment from desert conditions to humid conditions, stimulates plant growth, increases the quantity of organic matter added to the soils, stimulates microbial activity, and brings many mineral constituents of the soils into solution.

If the water is low in salt and drainage is good, the soil gradually changes from a desert to a humid type. In Arizona, a Red Desert soil increased in nitrogen from 0.052 percent in the virgin state to 0.076 percent after cropping under irrigation in a lysimeter for 12 years. Studies on the changes in irrigated soils in New Mexico indicate a gradual leaching of calcium carbonate from surface soils to lower horizons.

On irrigated lands, less grass has been grown in rotation systems than its value for soil fertility and immediate income justifies because farmers have not been educated to irrigated pastures and have been using unirrigated range lands and low, wet areas for grazing.

The principal, special soil-management problems in pasture production under irrigation include land preparation for planting, irrigation, drainage, fertilization, and salt control.

Irrigation farming requires more thorough land preparation than other types of agriculture.

The land must be leveled to permit uniform application of water; otherwise either the low spots will receive excessive water or the high soil areas will not receive enough. Leveling permits a better job of irrigation, reduces the labor required in getting water over the land, and often helps control erosion. It is usually necessary when new land is brought under irrigation. Virgin desert soils are commonly hummocky and otherwise uneven in surface topography. Land that has been farmed for some time is also often not sufficiently level for efficient irrigation.

Modern machinery has greatly lowered the costs of leveling land and has improved the quality of work done.

Irrigated pastures have about the same seasonal total water need as alfalfa, but require smaller, more frequent applications. Water moves over sodded land more slowly than over similar land in alfalfa or grains; it also penetrates much more rapidly. Consequently, large heads of water commonly are needed on pastures to obtain quick coverage and uniform distribution in the root zone. The distance between head ditches should likewise be less for pastures than for other crops.

On uniform slopes of 3 percent or less, border irrigation is usually recommended, but frequently flooding from field ditches is the accepted method because of uneven topography. Soils covered by irrigation water tend to form hard crusts under the rapid drying conditions of an arid climate. Since furrows or corrugations limit the soil surface covered with water, the use of corrugations is common in establishing pastures on heavy soils regardless of subsequent procedures. After grass is established, the corrugations fill in rather quickly unless they are frequently cleaned out. In some areas, particularly where only supplementary irrigation is needed and where topography is rolling or the soil highly permeable, sprinkling is used for pasture irrigation. Sprinkling permits a uniform water application on rolling land and highly permeable soils, and greatly reduces runoff.

Low-lying lands in irrigated areas, which frequently are waterlogged, are commonly used for pasture. Exceptionally high water tables and water standing on the surface for long periods kill many of the more desirable species of grass and legumes. They are replaced with sedges and weeds of comparatively low palatibility. Some pasture plants, as reed canarygrass and strawberry clover, endure such wet conditions, but quality and quantity of pasture are generally greatly increased by drainage. Wet lands used only for pasture often can be economically improved by short, open drains to remove excess surface water. Deeper open or tile drains are more expensive, but they increase the productivity of pastures and the number of plant species that will grow.

Because the soils of arid regions are generally low in nitrogen and available phosphorus, fertilizers for pastures in irrigated regions often include one or both of these elements. Enough potassium is present in most irrigated soils to meet plant needs. Current soil-management programs cause deficits in the soil-potassium balance, however, so that instances of potassium deficiencies can be increasingly expected. Some fields of Ladino clover in California have been reported to respond to potash fertilizers.

Lack of nitrogen in irrigated pastures can be handled in part by planting legumes in mixtures. Most of the soils contain lime or are neutral in reaction and are favorable for growth of legumes. In mixed pastures more economical results are often had from phosphate fertilizers than from nitrogen. Superphosphate fertilizers have generally given better results in arid regions than other types of phosphate. Ground rock phosphate, colloidal phosphate, and basic slag have low availability on alkaline calcareous soils.

Combinations of nitrogen and phosphate fertilizers or of farm manure and phosphate have generally given higher pasture yields than phosphate alone. Both nitrogen and phosphate fertilizers are usually applied to establish pastures in late fall or early spring. Phosphate is commonly worked into the seedbed by plowing under, drilling, or by broadcasting and disking or harrowing into the soil. Farm manure is usually applied on established pastures in winter or early spring.

Large acreages of irrigated lands contain too much soluble salts for good crop growth. Grass is commonly grown on them, but often the forage produced is much lower in yield and quality than could be produced with improved plant species and improved soil-management practices.

The most satisfactory solution to the salt problem in soils is to establish drains and wash out the excess soluble materials by repeated heavy irrigations. In many areas the complete reclamation of salty soils is not feasible, however, because of factors like impermeable subsoils, poor drainage outlets, or inadequate or low-quality irrigation water. Salty soils are commonly divided into two groups: Saline soils that contain 0.2 percent or more of soluble salts and whose pH is below 8.5, and alkali soils that have a pH above 8.5 and 15 percent or more of the exchange capacity occupied with adsorbed sodium. The alkali soils frequently contain caustic salts such as sodium carbonate.

Procedures for obtaining maximum plant growth on saline soils are based on the fact that plant growth decreases as the salt concentration in the soil solution increases. If salt concentration is expressed on the basis of osmotic pressure, the various neutral salts exert similar effects on numerous plants.

The injurious effects of the salts are caused more by a limiting of the availability of soil water to plants than by direct toxic effects. Under highly saline conditions the osmotic concentration of the soil solution may be so high that plants suffer for lack of water on soils that actually seem to have plenty of moisture.

The problem is further complicated by the rapid movement of soluble materials toward the soil surface in a drying soil, so that they are concentrated in the root zone. Frequent light irrigations encourage this type of salt accumulation and injure the plant roots. Good pasture production on saline soils requires keeping the soil moderately moist with relatively heavy irrigations rather than light irrigations at more frequent intervals.

Alkali soils are commonly highly impermeable because of the effects of adsorbed sodium on clay. These soils are also frequently too alkaline in reaction for most plants. Chemical treatment with gypsum to furnish soluble calcium, or with sulfur to increase the solubility of calcium in soil lime, promotes the replacement of exchangeable sodium with calcium if drainage is provided to leach away the soluble materials. Laboratory analyses are needed as a basis for detailed recommendations for treating alkali soil.

Many grasses have a high tolerance of saline and alkali soil conditions. They are, consequently, well adapted for planting during reclamation of salty soils and also for giving maximum returns on low-quality salty lands that cannot be reclaimed. Rhodesgrass and Bermuda-grass are well adapted to irrigated saline soils in warmer regions. In the more northern States, smooth bromegrass, tall oatgrass, and western wheatgrass have all yielded well in the presence of high salt concentrations.

Mixed grass and legume pastures are admirably adapted for the improvement of desert soils for irrigation agriculture. If properly managed, they rapidly increase the content of organic matter and nitrogen. Furthermore, the distinctive effects of grass in promoting a water-stable granular structure in soils is especially important under irrigation. Soils recently plowed out of pasture are more permeable, have better aeration, and are less susceptible to crusting than similar soils that have been producing either small grain or intertilled crops. Recognition of these advantages is leading to increased use of pastures in regular crop rotations in many irrigated areas.

THE AUTHOR «« *D. W. Thorne has been engaged in teaching and research since 1936, at Iowa State College, the University of Wisconsin, Agricultural and Mechanical College of Texas, and Utah State Agricultural College. During the past 8 years his research has been on problems related to the fertility of irrigated soils. Dr. Thorne is professor of agronomy and head of the agronomy department at Utah State Agricultural College.*

GRASS IN NATURAL FORESTED AREAS

RICHARD BRADFIELD

THE CLIMATE of the humid forested area differs from that of the natural grassland areas in the western part of the United States in several important respects. The average rainfall is higher and is better distributed throughout the year. Droughts are not so frequent, they do not last so long, and they are not so severe. The average humidity is higher and the average temperature in summer is lower.

As a result of these differences in humidity and temperature and some differences in wind movement, the amount of evaporation in the growing period is less in the forested area than it is in the natural grassland regions. Taken as a whole, the climate of the forested regions is better suited for the growth of grass than that of the natural grassland areas.

With good management, higher yields of grass can be obtained in the humid regions than in the natural grassland regions. The grassland area is characterized by short periods which are very favorable for the growth of grass, followed by periods in which the growth of the grass practically ceases. As a result, growth takes place in these areas for a much smaller proportion of the growing season.

Soils are also greatly influenced by climate. Forests and associated climatic factors tend to produce soils that are not so well adapted to grasses naturally as soils of the prairies.

There are two principal reasons for this. First, soils of the forested region do not as a rule contain so high a reserve of organic matter as prairie soils. The organic matter in forest soils is contributed largely by leaves that fall upon the surface. It is mixed to a limited extent with mineral soil material underneath by soil fauna. Because of its superficial position, a high proportion of the litter in forest soils may be lost by burning when the soil is cleared. Most of that remaining is concentrated in a relatively shallow surface layer. A high proportion of the organic matter in prairie soils is contributed by grass roots and as a result it is diffused through 2 to 4 feet of soil. Because of this difference in distribution, organic matter of forest soils is more quickly oxidized by soil micro-organisms than that of prairie soil when put under cultivation. Many such soils, when first cultivated, were cropped heavily to the most profitable cash crop of the region—corn, cotton, tobacco. The fertility from decomposition of the accumulated organic matter was rapidly exhausted; crop yields soon declined; erosion was accelerated. The poorer farms were soon abandoned and many of them still are in that state.

The second reason that forest soils are not so well adapted to grasses as prairie soils is that the nutrients essential for the vigorous growth of grass are leached from soils of the humid region to a greater extent than from the soils of the prairie region. Because of the higher average rainfall, lower average summer temperature, and higher humidity, less water evaporates at the surface or is transpired by the grass and more of it percolates through the soil each year.

Studies made at several locations indicate that frequently from 25 percent to more than 50 percent of the total rainfall percolates through the soil. These percolating waters, enriched by carbon dioxide from the soil air and by other acids produced by the decomposition of plant and animal residues in the surface soil, dissolve large quantities of certain minerals required for the growth of grasslands and carry them beyond the reach of crop roots.

The amounts of some of the more important of these minerals removed from two soils that differ widely in natural productivity, Dunkirk silty clay loam and Volusia silt loam, are given in the table.

Average Annual Loss of Nutrients by Percolation Through Bare and Cropped Soils
[Cornell lysimeters, Ithaca, N. Y.   Average of 10 and 15 years, respectively]

Soil condition	Pounds to the acre a year					
	N	P_2O_5	K_2O	CaO	MgO	SO_3
Dunkirk silty clay loam:						
Bare	69. 0	Trace	86. 8	557. 2	104. 4	132. 5
Rotation	7. 8	Trace	69. 1	332. 0	73. 2	108. 5
Grass	2. 5	Trace	74. 5	364. 0	83. 1	111. 1
Volusia silt loam:						
Bare	43. 0	Trace	77. 3	452. 6	68. 3	88. 5
Rotation	6. 6	Trace	68. 9	350. 5	45. 7	82. 0

The Volusia silt loam referred to in the table is a very acid soil of very low natural productivity; the Dunkirk silty clay loam is a fairly productive soil that is acid in the surface but contains free calcium carbonate in the subsoil.

The absolute amounts of the various minerals that will be removed by percolating waters each year will vary widely, depending upon the nature of the soil, the amount and distribution of the rainfall, the nature of the vegetative cover, and several other factors.

In spite of all of these complicating factors, however, several general statements can be made with reference to the soils of the humid region. In all such studies, calcium is the predominating constituent in the leachate. Magnesium and potassium are usually present in fairly large quantities, but usually in much smaller quantities than calcium. As a result of this removal of basic elements in relatively large quantities each year, the soils become increasingly acid. In large areas in the forested region, this leaching of bases has proceeded so far, and the soils have become so acid, that certain desirable species of grassland crops cannot be grown without replacing some of these leached elements. This is usually done by the use of limestone and in many cases potash as well.

Most of the nitrogen lost is in the form of nitrates. It is also interesting to note that where the soil is covered with grass the loss of nitrogen in the leachings is very small—because grass has the ability to absorb nitrates from the soil about as fast as they are formed. This is important when we consider the treatment of grass with nitrogenous fertilizers. In general, such nitrogen is used very efficiently by grass.

Another important lesson to be learned from the table is that but little phosphorus is lost from the soil by leaching. In no case has more than a trace (usually less than a part per million) of phosphorus been found in the leachings from soils, even though they had been fertilized rather liberally with phosphatic fertilizers. The reason is that soils have an enormous capacity for fixing soluble phosphates. A part, at least, of the phosphate added to such soils, while not readily soluble in water, is nevertheless available to plants. Because of the small loss by leaching and the fact that added phosphates do retain a certain degree of availability for long periods, it is possible to add sufficient phosphate to the soil at the time of seeding grass to last for at least 5 or 6 years. Such applications usually give better results than more frequent top dressings.

While all soils of the humid region are subject to more or less leaching of the type I have described, their capacity to support a good cover of grasses today varies widely. This variation is due partly to differences in the original soils and partly to differences in the type of management they have received since they have been under cultivation.

One way in which we obtain valuable information regarding the soil conditions that are favorable for the production of certain types of grasses and legumes is to study the soils upon which the various types of grasses and legumes seem to predominate in old pastures and meadows.

In West Virginia

An interesting study of this type was made by W. H. Pierre and his colleagues in West Virginia a few years ago. West Virginia is near the center of this area, and the results of the study are rather typical of what might be observed in many other places in the humid regions of the United States. In the poorer pastures of the area, plants like povertygrass, broomsedge, and weeds made up 50 percent or more of the total ground cover. An average of about one-fourth of the surface of such pastures was bare; only about 25 percent was occupied by the more desirable species of pasture plants. The cover of the more productive pastures was made up of Kentucky and Canada bluegrass, timothy, orchardgrass, white clover, and hop clover, with small percentages of the undesirable species. The study of the soils that produce these different types of pasture indicated that, in general, the soils that produced the higher proportion of undesirable pasture species were higher in acidity and lower in exchangeable calcium and the available phosphoric acid than the other soils.

If the pH value of the soil were 5.8 or above and an adequate supply of available phosphoric acid were present, it generally supported a good stand of Kentucky bluegrass and white clover. (pH refers to the degree of acidity or alkalinity of the soil. pH 7.0 indicates neutrality, higher values alkalinity, and lower values acidity.)

Eighty percent of the soils in the area studied were found to need lime in order to grow the desirable species of pasture plants satisfactorily. Of the soils having less than 10 pounds of readily available phosphorus as measured by Emil Truog's test, only 20 percent had a cover consisting of more than 50 percent of desirable species, while of the soils containing more than 20 pounds of readily available phosphorus, 72 percent carried a cover of the desirable species, Kentucky bluegrass and white clover.

This study indicates rather clearly that the first requirement of the soils of the area for growing desirable species of forage grasses and legumes is a more adequate supply of lime. A close second need in many parts of the area is for additional amounts of available phosphoric acid. In certain sections, the need for phosphorus is more acute than the need for more lime.

With these facts in mind, let us now approach the problem from a somewhat different point of view.

Nitrogen

Grasslands are used primarily to produce beef, mutton, and various products derived from milk. In most sections, and under most economic conditions, grass is the cheapest source of total digestible nutrients for these animals and by far the cheapest source of digestible protein. Consequently, the amount of digestible protein that an acre of grassland will produce each year is a fairly satisfactory criterion of its potential value to the farmer.

The amounts of nitrogen required to produce maximum yields of forage grasses and legumes is quite large. Even in the northern half of the region, where the growing period of grasses is only 5 or 6 months, as much as 200 to 300 pounds of nitrogen is frequently found in the harvested portions of the crop. This is almost twice as much as is commonly considered necessary to produce 100 bushels of corn. As a result of this great importance of nitrogen in hay and pasture, one of the first problems confronting the farmer interested in growing high yields of grasses and legumes is to find a fully satisfactory source of nitrogen.

As stated, grass uses available nitrogen in the soil efficiently. Very little is lost in the drainage water under most conditions. Recoveries of from 60 to more than 90 percent of the soluble nitrogen added as a commercial fertilizer as protein in the harvested crop are commonly obtained.

In the case of pastures, where the livestock consume the grass on the spot and return about 65 to 70 percent of nitrogen in the herbage to the soil in the form of excreta, thus recirculating the added nitrogen and using it for two, three, or, at times, four cycles of growth during the season, an apparent recovery exceeding 100 percent is commonly observed and apparent recoveries of as much as 125 percent are readily conceivable.

With such high efficiency possible under conditions of good management, the farmer is then confronted with the problem of how he can most economically supply the large quantities of nitrogen needed. The question is crucial because it determines largely the type of soil management required. The two alternatives available to the farmer are: First, to grow the nitrogen required, taking it from the free supply in the atmosphere by means of leguminous crops; or, second, to purchase it from the fertilizer manufacturer who fixes the atmospheric nitrogen in a chemical plant. Doubtless many conditions exist under which each of these alternatives is to be preferred and there are numerous other conditions under which a combination of the two sources is to be preferred.

Let us consider first the conditions under which it would be advisable to rely in part or wholly on legumes to supply the nitrogen needed in pasture and meadow.

For most types of livestock, a combination of grasses and legumes is desirable in both pasture herbage and hay. In most cases, such mixtures are actually preferred to covers made up exclusively of grasses. In many sections of the area, legumes are available, which with proper management are capable of producing satisfactory feed and of persisting long enough in the grass-legume mixture to contribute enough to the mixture to justify the expenses involved in their establishment and maintenance. Under such circumstances, the farmer will usually find it to his advantage to try to keep a satisfactory proportion of legumes in both meadow and pasture. This is by far the more common situation in the area.

But under a limited number of conditions the legume program is not feasible. Some farmers object to having any large quantity of legumes in their hay or pasture mixtures. Also, there are certain sections of the country that have fairly satisfactory forage grasses available to them but in which satisfactory legumes for growing with these grasses have not yet been found. In other situations, a very high proportion of the farm must be kept in grass; consequently, it is not feasible to plow up the grassland occasionally and reseed. Under such circumstances, unless legumes can be maintained in the sward indefinitely, such farmers prefer to use the more persistent grass cover and to purchase their nitrogen from the fertilizer dealer.

Requirements

If soil conditions are suitable for their growth, legumes as a rule are quicker to establish than the common forage grasses, but are more difficult to maintain. Consequently, when it is advisable to maintain a high proportion of legumes in the grassland mixture for several years, the management practices should be built around the legume, for if the legume can be maintained, the grass species can usually be depended upon to take care of themselves.

The requirements of legumes and grasses of the type desired in both pastures and meadows, while they have much in common, vary in certain important respects.

In the first place, legumes are usually more sensitive than grasses to acid conditions in the soil. As a general rule, therefore, the soil should be limed to a somewhat higher level if legumes are to be grown than would be necessary if grasses were being grown alone. The various species of forage legumes differ rather widely among themselves. Alfalfa, for example, has a much higher requirement than Ladino clover, and some of the newer pasture legumes, like birdsfoot trefoil, can grow quite satisfactorily at lime levels somewhat lower than those required for Ladino clover.

Much more potash is required for the luxuriant growth of legumes than for the grasses. The lime and phosphorus required for legumes can usually be supplied at seeding time in sufficient quantity to last for 5 or 6 years. Potash must be supplied in smaller, more frequent doses. In many cases, annual applications are necessary. A shortage of potash in the soil can usually be detected by studying the leaves of the legume in midsummer. If potash is seriously deficient, brown spots can often be observed on the margins of the leaves.

As long as a satisfactory proportion of legumes (usually 20 percent or more) can be maintained in the stand, fairly satisfactory yields can be obtained with grass-legume mixtures without the use of any additional nitrogen. This does not mean that it will not be profitable at times to use some commercial nitrogen on grass-legume mixtures. If the soil is very deficient in organic matter, the application of a little commercial nitrogen at planting time will frequently be beneficial. In many locations where it is desirable to encourage early spring growth for early pasturing, an application of nitrogen before growth starts in the spring will frequently be profitable.

Properly managed, however, a good legume-grass combination can produce herbage containing from 200 to 300 pounds of nitrogen without the use of any commercial nitrogen.

The management of grassland, in which the cover is made up almost exclusively of various species of grasses, is similar to that described above for mixtures of legumes and grasses in that it is highly important to have satisfactory reserves of both lime and phosphorus present in the soil. The level of these two elements does not need to be quite so high, in most cases, as would be advisable in the case of legumes. Potash fertilization is not so important and only in cases of very potash-deficient soils does it become a problem of much significance.

The biggest fertilizer problem in this case is that of maintaining an adequate supply of nitrogen. Nitrogen is the most expensive fertilizer element to buy in the commercial form. As I said, grasses utilize it very efficiently, but the response from nitrogen is usually very quick and of rather short duration. In most sections of the humid region, the effect of a spring application of nitrogen will practically disappear by midseason, and a second application will be necessary if the grass is to be kept growing well. If maximum yields are desired and rainfall is plentiful, even three or four top dressings with nitrogenous fertilizers each season will be necessary. Such practices are usually rather expensive, but under certain circumstances it is cheaper to provide feed in this way than to purchase it in the form of concentrates and under certain circumstances than to grow legumes.

Taking the area as a whole, however, a combination of practices is probably best, depending upon legumes to furnish the bulk of the nitrogen but using some supplemental commercial nitrogen to stimulate growth at critical seasons and in case of the sudden failure of the legumes.

In much of the area, grasses are grown in rotation with other crops. In such situations, it is found that an old grass sod, while of excellent physical structure, is frequently deficient in readily available nitrogen. J. A. Bizzell found at Cornell University that an average of 26 bushels more corn was produced following a 1-year-old clover-timothy sod than was produced following a 2-year sod, the second-year sod being practically pure timothy. This would seem to be an argument for shorter leys, in which the sod is plowed up while it still contains a high proportion of legumes instead of waiting until the grasses have used up the nitrogen fixed by the legume.

In conclusion, a word about the importance of grassland in soil management. Grassland farming is an almost indispensable tool in developing good systems of soil management. Land in grass does not erode. Areas or countries that have or can work out a profitable system of farming involving a high percentage of productive grassland seldom, if ever, have a serious soil conservation problem.

THE AUTHOR«« *Richard Bradfield, a native of Ohio and a graduate of Ohio State University, has been engaged in soil research since 1920. He has been associated successively with the University of Missouri, Ohio State University, and Cornell University. He is now head of the department of agronomy at Cornell University.*

SOIL MANAGEMENT ON FARM PASTURES

HORACE J. HARPER

THE KIND of soil management to use in establishing or improving pastures and meadows on farms in the natural grassland area depends primarily on climatic environment and character of the soil.

The average annual rainfall varies from 40 inches in the eastern part of the tall-grass country to less than 15 inches in the western part of the short-grass region. A high proportion of the prairie soils that developed under the influence of a humid climate are acid and are low in available phosphorus. Acid, low-phosphate soils occur frequently also in the eastern part of the Reddish Prairie soil region. On many of them fertilizer and lime are needed.

Acid soils seldom occur in the northern part of the subhumid portion or in the semiarid portion of the natural grass-land area. Chernozem, Chestnut, Reddish Chestnut, and Brown soils found there usually are high in available plant nutrients. Consequently methods for pasture improvement will be limited to tillage requirements for reseeding cultivated land and procedures that increase the efficiency of rainfall.

Soils in the eastern part of the natural grassland area are higher in organic matter and nitrogen than similar soils farther west in the same latitude. Temperature, however, has a greater influence than rainfall on the quantity of organic matter in the natural grassland area.

Soils in the northern part of the area contain two to three times as much organic matter and nitrogen as soils of similar texture in the southern part. The organic matter content of southern grassland soils is relatively low, except in the blackland areas (Rendzina soils), where a high content of clay and lime has provided a favorable environment for the accumulation of organic matter.

A high proportion of the pastures in the humid and subhumid part of the areas are on shallow soil or on slopes too steep to cultivate. Much of the cultivated land has been damaged by erosion, and soils that were originally deep are now too shallow for cultivation. A grass cover can be established on them but yields will be poor unless fertility can be improved. Several grasses will grow on them, but the forage is usually low in protein and deficient in available phosphorus. Where a grass-legume mixture cannot be readily established, pasture improvement is a slow process, especially on low-nitrogen soils.

The response of grasses to soil improvement practices on shallow soils depends largely on the porosity of subsurface layers. Occasionally subsoils are too sandy to hold water. On such soils and on shallow soils with impervious subsoils, plant growth will be restricted by lack of moisture even in a humid climate. Increased income will not be sufficient to pay the cost of soil improvement on this type of land. On deeper soils, pasture improvement can be an important factor in increasing farm income.

Different parts of a pasture may respond differently to the same type of soil management. A soil survey will indicate areas where the physical character of the land may or may not be favorable for more intensive use.

Disking or shallow plowing is a part of the treatment needed to establish native or introduced grasses on formerly cultivated land or on low-producing pastures that do not respond quickly to controlled grazing. The forage-producing capacity of the sod-bound pastures composed principally of Kentucky bluegrass, bromegrass, or Bermuda-grass can be increased by early spring tillage. Spring plowing also stimulates forage production in Johnsongrass pastures where rootstock vigor has been decreased by soil packing. Stirring the soil hastens the decay of organic matter and indirectly provides more nitrogen and other nutrients for plant growth.

Low-producing Kentucky bluegrass pastures in the northeastern part of the natural grassland area can be improved by a combination of tillage, liming, fertilization, and reseeding to adapted legumes or maybe timothy and bromegrass. Plowing these pastures about 3 inches deep in late fall will destroy many of the bluegrass plants and provide a more favorable condition for the development of introduced grasses and legumes. Renovating and reseeding a southern Iowa pasture increased beef production 35 pounds an acre over untreated land. This treatment plus lime increased production 85 pounds per acre.

In Oklahoma and Texas many low-producing weedy pastures east of the 30-inch rainfall belt should be plowed and planted to Bermuda-grass, lespedeza, and hop clover. In the lower rainfall areas, cool season grasses, such as weeping lovegrass, should be planted on a firm seedbed in the southern part and crested or western wheatgrass in the northern part of the natural grassland area to lengthen the grazing season.

Pasture renovation is needed also to obtain more rapid benefits from the application of limestone. Limestone applied on the surface of a pasture sod dissolves very slowly and maximum benefit is not obtained for several years. When lime is applied to a pasture that has been stirred 3 or 4 inches deep by disking or shallow plowing, it can be thoroughly mixed with the surface soil by double disking. Phosphate or mixed fertilizer can also be applied more effectively on a loose soil.

Pasture land on long slopes may be damaged by gully erosion when the vegetative cover is destroyed by disking or plowing and torrential rainfall occurs before a grass cover can be reestablished. Narrow terrace ridges constructed at 8-foot or 10-foot vertical intervals, with a variable grade of 0.1 to 0.3 percent fall per 100 feet, can be used to intercept runoff and prevent soil loss in areas where danger from soil erosion is likely.

Legumes are the key to pasture and meadow improvement where climatic conditions are favorable for their growth. Soils must contain more lime for alfalfa and sweetclover to grow successfully in a grass mixture, than for clover. A neutral soil also provides a more favorable condition for the release of plant nutrients locked up in the soil organic matter as a result of a more rapid growth of soil microorganisms. Although the addition of lime to an acid soil may increase the liberation of plant nutrients from the decay of soil organic matter, the residues produced from an increased growth of a legume-grass mixture will return more organic matter and nitrogen to the soil than would have been returned on unlimed land. Legumes will also replace losses of nitrogen that may occur as a result of increased biological activity when lime is applied to acid pasture land containing no legumes.

Lime must also be applied to replace calcium removed from pasture soils by the leaching effect of rainfall and to neutralize the acids produced when protein in soil organic matter or legume residue decays. If lime is not applied, acid-sensitive legumes eventually will disappear, and growth of acid-tolerant legumes will be poor. However, many natural grassland soils are high in lime content and can continue to produce excellent yields of legumes for a long time before forage production will be seriously reduced by soil acidity or calcium deficiency.

Sweetclover has the highest lime requirement of the legumes normally planted in pasture mixtures. This crop will produce maximum yields in neutral to slightly alkaline soils. Data published in Ohio Agricultural Experiment Station Bulletin 588 show that alfalfa and red, mammoth, and alsike clovers produce maximum yields in a neutral soil, and higher yields in slightly alkaline soils than in moderately acid soil.

Experimental studies at different locations over the Prairie soil area show that the white clover will grow very well in slightly acid soil when other conditions such as drought do not limit plant development. Many winter legumes, such as big and little hop clover, bur-clover, black medic, and Persian clover, will make an excellent growth on slightly acid soil; but lime must be applied to produce maximum yields on moderately acid or strongly acid soil. Big and little hop clover will grow on poorer land than other winter legumes, partly because of their lower potassium requirement.

Common lespedeza is more acid tolerant than Korean lespedeza. Maximum yields of Korean lespedeza will usually not be obtained on moderate to strongly acid soils unless lime is applied.

Soils low in available phosphorus should be fertilized with superphosphate to provide more favorable conditions for the growth of a legume-grass mixture on pasture land where the physical character of the soil is favorable for deep moisture penetration and root development. The phosphorus content of legume crops is frequently 25 to 50 percent higher than that of native grasses. Many grasses will make a good growth on low-phosphate soils where legumes will fail. Alfalfa has a higher soil phosphorus requirement than red, alsike, or white clovers, or sweetclover.

Korean lespedeza is less responsive to phosphate fertilization than winter legumes. Maximum growth occurs during summer months when a considerable quantity of organic phosphate is released by the decay of soil organic matter. Because of this condition and also because of summer drought which frequently limits the growth of lespedeza, response from phosphate fertilization is quite variable. Lespedeza can feed on relatively insoluble forms of mineral phosphate in the soil. However, the phosphorus content of forage produced on very poor soils is frequently below minimum requirements for the growth of livestock.

Recent studies at the Southeast Pasture-Fertility Research Station near Coalgate, Okla., indicate that the fertilizer cost of a pasture improvement program can be reduced and the efficiency of fertilization increased by drilling superphosphate in 14-inch rows. The legume seeds were dropped on the soil above the fertilized zone in this experiment. Ryegrass was planted between the fertilized rows because the phosphorus requirement of this crop is much lower than that of hop, Persian, and white clovers, and black medic. Less fixation of phosphorus will occur on many soils when the fertilizer is drilled in 14-inch rows as compared with a similar quantity of fertilizer applied broadcast.

Rock phosphate drilled in rows 14 or 16 inches apart at the rate of 150 pounds an acre between drill rows of spring oats has produced excellent yields of sweetclover on phosphorus-deficient soils where lime has been applied to correct soil acidity. The quantity of sweetclover seed can also be reduced by scattering it on the surface of the soil above the fertilized zone. A good temporary pasture can be produced on cultivated land at a relatively low cost for phosphate fertilizer. A modification of this procedure is needed in areas where crop response from soil-improving factors may be low because of limited rainfall. A larger area of soil must be provided under such conditions to supply the moisture needed for the survival of legume seedlings. Width of soil between plants rather than depth may be the important limiting factor under many conditions.

Young soils make up a high percentage of the pastures in the natural grassland area. They are usually high in available potassium, except on areas of deeply leached sandy land. The availability of soil potassium frequently declines as soil acidity increases. However, the available potassium is more closely related to clay content than to acidity. Moderately acid or strongly acid surface soils in the southern prairie area are frequently quite deficient in available potassium but the subsoils usually contain a good supply because they are high in clay content. This condition commonly occurs in Planosols. The Parsons series is a good example of this soil group.

Potassium is not removed from pasture land when livestock or livestock products are sold; consequently the potassium requirement to maintain a vigorous grass-legume mixture should not be as great on pastures after the initial need is supplied, as it is on land where hay crops are harvested. Hays, such as lespedeza and alfalfa, contain from 30 to 90 pounds of potassium per ton. The application of a high potash fertilizer, or barnyard manure which contains about 8 pounds of potassium per ton, will be an important factor in maintaining hay yields on land where the available potassium is low. The manure, an excellent pasture fertilizer, is best applied at the beginning of the growing season.

Increased forage production from either small grain or Sudangrass can be obtained in that part of the natural grassland area where a legume, such as sweetclover, can be grown in the rotation. A complete fertilizer, such as 5–10–5, drilled in the row at the time small grain is planted, will stimulate early growth of a fall-planted crop and also increase spring growth. The difference between fertilized and unfertilized, fall-planted small grain will be greater as the time interval between seedbed preparation following harvest and the planting of small grain is reduced.

Native grasses have been replaced on a high percentage of the meadows in the Corn Belt by alfalfa, timothy, and red, mammoth, and alsike clovers. The use of lime, barnyard manure, and phosphate, or a mixed fertilizer will greatly increase the yield of these crops on acid, mineral-deficient soil. The nitrogen and available mineral content of soils in the northern part of the natural grassland area is high. Native or introduced grasses in this area will continue to produce maximum yields, which are usually limited by seasonal rainfall, for a long time before lack of soil fertility limits hay production.

Fertilizer studies over a 17-year period on an area of native grassland on the Oklahoma Agricultural Experiment Station farm at Stillwater indicate that a profitable increase in the yield of prairie hay has not been obtained under average conditions on a slightly acid Reddish Prairie soil from the application of nitrogen with or without mixed fertilizers. Superphosphate increased the phosphorus content of the hay but did not increase yields.

The quantity of nitrogen, phosphorus, and calcium removed from soil when prairie hay is harvested is low, as compared with legume crops. Nitrogen added to the soil each year in the rain and by nitrogen-fixing bacteria will supply a considerable portion of the nitrogen removed by the hay. Eventually phosphorus and/or potash will limit production. The phosphorus content of little bluestem will decline to 0.03 percent before any appreciable decrease in yields will occur.

Some reports indicate that cattle will eat hay from an area where superphosphate has been applied to low-phosphate soil in preference to hay from an adjacent area of unfertilized land. More experimental data is needed to show whether it is more profitable to supply phosphate fertilizer to increase the phosphorus content of the forage on low-phosporus soils or to supplement a low-phosphorus forage with a salt-bonemeal mixture.

The protein and mineral content of prairie hay can be improved in the southern part of the Prairie soil area by planting legumes such as Kobe or Korean lespedeza each year. Prairie hay is cut before these legumes mature seed, consequently they must be reseeded each spring. If a legume could be introduced into a native meadow by fertilization, the increase in the protein and mineral content of the hay might be worth more than the cost of the fertilizer even if total yields were not increased.

Nitrogen fertilizers will increase the quantity of seed produced by grasses such as bluestem, brome, and weeping lovegrass. The production of weeping lovegrass has been increased 300 percent by the use of ammonium nitrate alone or by an application of ammonium phosphate on soils low in organic matter and available phosphorus.

Some tillage is needed to reestablish grasses on many cultivated soils in the subhumid and semiarid portion of the natural grassland area. Weeds and unpalatable grasses are frequently present on soils where cultivated crops have not been planted for several years. These plants should be destroyed to provide more available soil moisture for the growth of grass seedlings. Summer fallow in the northern part of the area will destroy weeds and grass and will increase the supply of subsoil moisture. It will also produce a firm seedbed which is favorable for the germination and early growth of plants.

A good seedbed for small grain is too loose for grasses and young legumes. Grass seeds are small and should be planted about $\frac{1}{4}$ to $\frac{1}{2}$ inch deep in a firm, moist seedbed to survive. Packing a loose seedbed with a roller is important where land is plowed or stirred only a short time before the grasses are planted.

Soil blowing will occur on a high percentage of the cultivated land in the Great Plains area when the land is not protected during the winter and early spring by crop residues. Subsurface tillage is an effective method of controlling weed growth during the summer; and crop residues left on the surface protect young seedlings from high wind velocities and soil movement.

In the southern part of the Great Plains area a recommended procedure for establishing pasture grasses on old cultivated fields is to plow the land and drill sorghum in rows 8 or 10 inches apart. The sorghum should be cut before seed matures, and the residue left on the land to protect the soil from wind erosion. Grass seed is drilled in the sorghum residue the following spring without stirring the soil. Weed growth following sorghum provides less competition for the young grass seedlings because of a reduced availability of soil nitrogen under such conditions.

Good stands of fall-planted alfalfa have been obtained at the Nebraska Agricultural Experiment Station when small grain stubble is tilled with sweeps after harvest to control weeds and a rotary hoe is operated in reverse to pack the seedbed before the alfalfa seed is planted.

The problem of stirring pasture soils to conserve water and improve the growth of grass has been studied at Spur, Tex. Yields of buffalograss were three times as high over a 5-year period where a native buffalograss pasture was cultivated shallow with a lister as compared with grassland which was not listed. Stirring the soil not only increased the supply of available soil nitrogen, which stimulated the growth of the grass, but it also increased the

utilization of rainfall because the lister furrows had been made carefully on the contour.

THE AUTHOR≪≪ *Horace J. Harper has been professor of soils in the Oklahoma Agricultural and Mechanical College since 1925. He is a graduate of Iowa State College and received his doctor's degree from the University of Wisconsin. Dr. Harper is the author of many research papers in the field of soil morphology, soil chemistry, soil fertility, and soil conservation.*

PASTURE IN A CONSERVATION FARM PLAN

HARRY H. GARDNER, JOHN P. JONES

A FARM conservation plan is based on three factors: The land, the farm organization, and the farmer.

The land must be used properly to prevent loss of soil by erosion and loss of production by soil deterioration. The farm organization must be considered because crop and pasture programs, livestock, equipment, buildings, and supplies affect the farm income. The farmer's desires and abilities limit the use of land and the economic returns.

Two farm conservation plans are cited to illustrate how proper land use is determined, the development of crop and pasture systems, and the use of soil conservation measures.

One of the farms selected as an example is a dairy farm in a Northeastern State. The other is a grain farm at the edge of the Corn Belt.

The dairy farm had 20 acres in corn, 6 acres in truck crops, 17 acres in grain, and 43 acres of meadow, approximately a 2–1–3 rotation—that is, 2 acres of cultivated crops to 1 acre of grain and 3 acres of meadow. Such a rotation can be considered satisfactory for maintaining the productivity of the cropland if all the manure is saved and returned to the land. But the 25 acres of permanent pasture on the farm and 41 acres of woodland did not produce

enough pasture throughout the year for a herd of 32 cows and 5 heifers. Pasture—any forage crop harvested by grazing—is the cheapest feed for dairy cows, and the farm conservation plan should usually provide all the green forage needed.

Despite this requirement, the first adjustment in pasture practice was to take the livestock out of the 41-acre woodland. That reduced the number of acres of grazing but made little difference in the amount of feed since woodland produces very little palatable forage for dairy cows. Grazing the woodland harms the land and the trees; the trampling of the cattle interferes with the accumulation of litter, which helps prevent erosion; the cattle also graze on new growth and thus prevent young trees from developing; the older trees do not grow so rapidly as where the woods are protected.

The problem then was to work out a plan for cropland and pasture that would provide the needed green forage and grain and hay. Of course, there is always more than one way to do it, and no standard formula can be followed on all farms, but it is logical to make an inventory of land, livestock, feed requirements, farm buildings, available help, and all pertinent items.

On the basis of a soil conservation survey, the land on this farm was placed in four classes, depending on suitability for a specific use. Much of the land is cropland suitable for corn and other grain if proper soil-saving practices are used—Classes II and III in the Use Capability Classes that are designated by the Soil Conservation Service.[1] (Plan A, page 156.)

There seemed to be little justification for changing the number of dairy cows on the farm if enough feed could be grown. Barn facilities were adequate, and sufficient help available. It did seem advisable to increase the number of young stock from 5 to 8 in order to maintain a dairy herd of 32 cows.

On the Land Use Map three fields, numbered 6, 8, and 12 (of 10, 17, and 32 acres, respectively) were laid out for crops because they are fertile and suitable for cultivation. Much of the land is level (from 1- to 3-percent slopes), but some slopes are fairly steep (8 percent or a little more). More than half of the original topsoil still remains. Erosion has not yet been severe. (Plan A, page 157.)

A 4-year rotation of corn-grain-meadow-meadow with strip cropping is adapted to this field arrangement and should provide ample protection against erosion. Fields 6 and 8 (27 acres in all) are used as one field unit; field 12 (32 acres) is used as the second field unit. Since the fields are strip-cropped—that is, the crops are grown in strips or bands on the contour—alternate strips of corn and first-year meadow are in one field unit and alternate strips of grain and second-year meadow are in the other field unit every year. This meadow is used for hay, although the oats and second-year meadow in one field unit or a part of it may be pastured, if the farmer desires to do so.

Fields 3, 4, 7, and 11 (32 acres) are planned for meadows to be used for hay and grazing. Because of the slope of the land, the amount of erosion, and the soil conditions, these fields are better adapted for forage than for grain crops. Five acres formerly used as permanent pasture were shifted to this land use because the soil is productive enough for more intensive use. This change in use does not increase the erosion hazard on this class of land.

Twenty acres, in fields 2, 5, and 10, were maintained in permanent pasture. Such an arrangement of pasture fields—that is, the four hay-pasture fields and the three permanent-pasture fields—permits rotation grazing and the separation of young stock and dry cows from the milking herd. These 52 acres should produce about 160 pasture-days. In some years that may not be quite enough for the entire herd, so the grazing management must be well planned and supervised. Rotation grazing should be practiced on all the pastures.

The 20 acres of bluegrass can nor-

[1] The land-capability classes are:

Class I. Good, level land, well-drained, subject to little erosion. May be cultivated safely with good soil-management practices.

Class II. Good land, moderately steep, subject to some erosion. Requires simple, soil-conservation practices such as contouring, cover crops, and water management for safe cultivation.

Class III. Moderately good land, subject to severe erosion. Can be cultivated safely with intensive treatments such as terracing, water-control operations, strip cropping, and cover crops in rotation.

Class IV. Fairly good land, subject to damaging erosion if cultivated on slopes. Best suited to complete cover of grasses and legumes for pasture and hay, but may be cultivated occasionally. This is the crucial type of land for soil conservation. If given no care, it will rapidly fall into one of the classes not suited to any cultivation. With adequate conservation practices it can be maintained as productive land.

Class V. Land nearly level but not suited for cultivation. Best used with grass cover for grazing or for growing trees.

Class VI. Land requiring complete cover of grass or trees. Suited only to grazing or forestry under careful management.

Class VII. Land requiring complete cover for safety. Requires extreme care in management, even for grazing or forestry.

Class VIII. Rugged land, usually steep and stony, too dry, too wet, or severely eroded. May be suited to wildlife, recreation, or watershed protection.

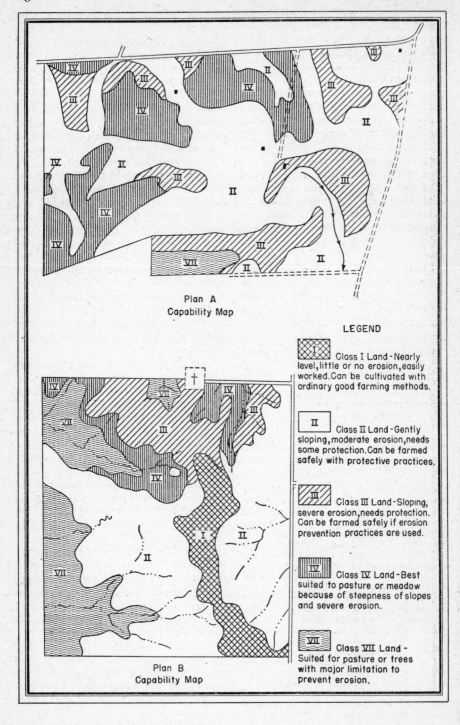

Plan A
Capability Map

LEGEND

Class I Land - Nearly level, little or no erosion, easily worked. Can be cultivated with ordinary good farming methods.

Class II Land - Gently sloping, moderate erosion, needs some protection. Can be farmed safely with protective practices.

Class III Land - Sloping, severe erosion, needs protection. Can be farmed safely if erosion prevention practices are used.

Class IV Land - Best suited to pasture or meadow because of steepness of slopes and severe erosion.

Class VII Land - Suited for pasture or trees with major limitation to prevent erosion.

Plan B
Capability Map

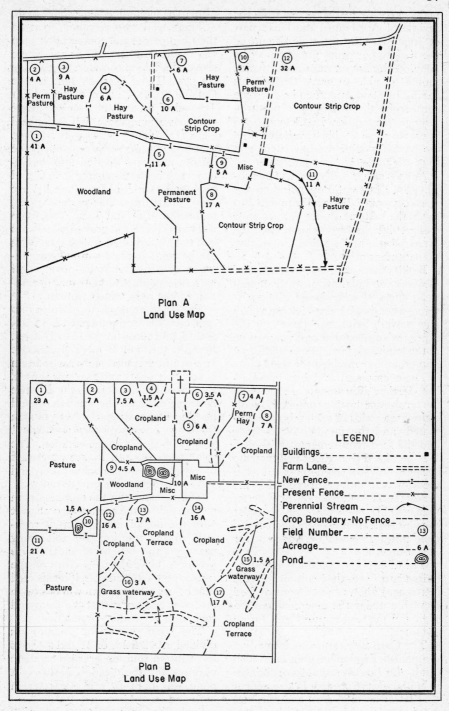

Plan A
Land Use Map

LEGEND

Buildings	▪
Farm Lane	=====
New Fence	—I—
Present Fence	—x—
Perennial Stream	⌒→
Crop Boundary - No Fence	-----
Field Number	⑬
Acreage	6 A
Pond	◎

Plan B
Land Use Map

mally carry all the dairy cows from the middle of April until the latter part of June. To vary the time of cutting the hay, some spring grazing may be done on the hay-pasture fields, which should be able to carry the animals during July and August and, with some help from the bluegrass pastures, through September. In October considerable grazing will be available from the hayfields after the hay is cut and from the barley in the rotations.

Any plan that is devised will be subject to adjustment, depending on the season. To make these adjustments and to get the best return, the farmer must observe his pastures closely and be prepared to make shifts in grazing management promptly.

Besides these adjustments, 3 acres of meadow were planned near the homestead (field 9) to be used for hog pasture—a total of 55 acres for use as hay and pasture. Also, two horses on the farm are not pastured and may not be in the long-time farm plan, so only hay and grain are provided for them.

These cropland and hay and pasture acreage adjustments are shown in the farm-organization summary. In addition, the yields of each crop are estimated, and the number of livestock and the feed requirements are shown. It is predicted that yields will increase because only the land most suited is used for corn and grain crops and the meadow and pasture land will be better managed. It is estimated that under the new plan an acre of treated permanent pasture should be sufficient for one animal unit.

The table of feed production and requirements (at the bottom of the next page) shows the amount of feed available under the new conservation plan and the feed requirements for all livestock.

The Corn Belt farm was formerly a grain farm. Erosion has gone on at such a fast rate, however, that some changes in land use were needed. It was evident that fewer acres of corn and oats and more meadow should be grown if erosion was to be reduced and crop yields

were to be maintained on a stable basis.

There were two cropping areas on the farm before the conservation plan was made. One area of 37 acres where erosion had done considerable damage is Class III and Class IV land on the Capability Map. (Plan B, page 156.) The other area of 68.5 acres, where erosion was moderate, is Class I and Class II, but deep gullies were starting.

When the farm was replanned, the smaller area was divided into four 7-acre crop fields, numbered 2, 3, 5, and 8 on the Land Use Map (Plan B, page 157), and three hay-pasture fields, numbered 4, 6, and 7, where erosion was most severe and grassed waterways had to be established. These crop fields can be contour-tilled with a 4-year rotation of corn-grain-meadow-meadow with reasonable assurance that the erosion will be reduced to a minimum.

The larger area was also divided into four crop fields, numbered 12, 13, 14, and 17, and consisting of 16 or 17 acres. Because this soil is more productive and can be terraced, a 4-year rotation of corn-corn-oats-and-meadow is used. By shortening the slope to the distance between terraces, the soil loss should be practically stopped, even though there are 2 years of corn and only 1 year of meadow in the rotation. The small fields, 15 and 16, are waterways that will be maintained in meadow and serve as outlets to the terrace system.

These changes in the cropping plan greatly reduce the acreage of corn. But with the use of meadow crops regularly in the rotation, the soil-saving practices, the benefit of the manure produced by feeding the crops on the farm, and the treatments, it is expected that nearly as much corn will be grown on fewer acres and that the farm will remain in permanent production.

The large permanent pasture was divided into 2 fields of 21 and 23 acres to facilitate rotation grazing on these pastures and the meadow pastures. A pond was built to provide water in both permanent pastures.

Such adjustments in the cropping system and permanent pasture make

Farm Organization Summary

CROPS AND FEED

Kind	Before		Planned	
	Acres	Yield	Acres	Yield
Corn-grain..........................	13	650 bushels.....	8	480 bushels.
Corn-silage........................	7	80 tons.......	6	90 tons.
Oats..............................	11	440 bushels....	....	
Barley............................	6	210 bushels.....	15	750 bushels.
Clover-grass hay...................	31	40 tons......	30	60 tons.
Alfalfa............................	12	30 tons.......	....	
Truck.............................	6	....	....	
Permanent pasture.................	25	....	20	
Hay pasture.......................	......	....	35	20 tons.
Woods pastured...................	41	....	....	
Woods not pastured................	......	....	41	
Home site.........................	5	....	2	
Total......................	157	....	157	

LIVESTOCK

Kind	Before	Planned	
	Number	Number	Animal units
Horses...	2	2	2
Dairy cows...	32	32	32
Dairy yearlings.....................................	5	8	4
Hogs..	22	22	2
Poultry..	100	100	1

FEED REQUIREMENTS

Kind	Grain	Hay	Pasture
	Bushels	Tons	Acres
Horses......................................	60	4. 5	....
Dairy cows...................................	800	80. 0	48
Dairy yearlings...............................	100	8. 0	6
Hogs..	160	....	3
Poultry......................................	75	....	....
Total...................................	1, 195	92. 5	57

Balance of Feed Production and Requirements

Item	Grain—corn equivalent	Roughage—hay equivalent	Pasture
	Bushels	Tons	Acres
Feed available (new plan)	1, 080	110. 0	55
Feed required................................	1, 195	92. 5	57
Difference..............................	−115	+17. 5	−2

it advisable to produce some beef and pork on roughage. In the past the grain was fed to cattle and hogs in dry lots or sold on the market.

With the addition of more than 30 acres of rotation pasture and increased production from the original permanent pasture by treatment and improved management, it is estimated that 50 beef calves can be grown and put in marketable condition each year. They can be purchased in the fall whenever the price is right. The permanent pasture fields, the cornstalk fields after the corn is picked, and the meadow fields to be plowed the following year for corn are available for grazing as long as weather permits. These should be utilized each year as long as the calves continue to gain in weight.

Legume hay, oats, and corn are available to keep calves growing during the winter. As soon as pasture is ready in the spring, rotation grazing starts, using both permanent pasture and meadow as conditions warrant. Greater gains can be obtained when grain is fed in addition to pasture. This can continue until June or July, as long as there is sufficient pasture. The farmer then has a choice of feeding corn in dry lot for 10 to 20 days and selling the cattle in good condition, or feeding them 60 to 90 days and selling them in prime condition.

Besides the beef enterprise, at least 100 pigs could be raised and fattened. Rye grown in the rotation on the small fields for spring and fall use and the 2 years of alfalfa-bromegrass meadow should produce a long grazing season for brood sows and pigs. Forty acres of corn will provide all the grain needed for both beef and pork production.

The location of the buildings, the lane leading in from the highway, the two ponds and the woods behind the buildings, the large pasture across the back of the entire farm, and the two cropping areas, one on each side of the building, make an ideal farm arrangement. All crop fields and the two permanent pasture fields are accessible to either machinery or livestock. Water is easily available from any field. Electric fence may be used when it is necessary to restrict livestock to certain areas.

Thus, on both farms, the land has been put to its proper use: The farm organization was adapted to the capability of the land and the desire of the farmer. The land is protected from erosion by water- and soil-saving practices; provisions are made for improving its productivity. The net income is increased by higher yields and by providing and utilizing the proper feeds in adequate amounts for the greatest production.

THE AUTHORS «« *Harry H. Gardner was reared on a farm in western South Dakota. For 12 years after he was graduated from South Dakota State College, he taught, served as county agent, farmed, and did graduate work at Oregon State College. For 20 years he has worked in the Midwest, 12 of those years in the Soil Conservation Service. Since 1938 he has been regional agronomist in the eight States of the Upper Mississippi Region, with headquarters at Milwaukee, Wis.*

John P. Jones holds degrees in agronomy and plant physiology from the University of Maryland and Cornell University. He was research agronomist at the Massachusetts Agricultural Experiment Station for 7 years and did commercial research work in agronomy for 5 years before he joined the Soil Conservation Service in 1935. He is the regional conservator and agronomist for the Northeastern Region.

Storage of Forage

PRINCIPLES OF MAKING HAY

R. E. HODGSON, R. E. DAVIS, W. H. HOSTERMAN, T. E. HIENTON

THERE ARE two ways to harvest and store forage crops: Making them into silage or drying them.

There are two ways to dry them—naturally (field curing, that is) and artificially.

Artificial drying generally is done in the United States also in one of two ways, barn finishing or dehydration.

In barn finishing, a practice that has received a great amount of attention recently, the forage is partly dried in the field; then it is placed in a mow, and natural or heated air is forced through the forage to complete the drying.

In artificial dehydration the forage is taken from the field as soon as it is cut (in some instances it is allowed to wilt), chopped, and passed through a suitably constructed chamber where it comes in contact with heated air, which rapidly evaporates the moisture in it. The length of time the forage is in contact with the hot air varies from a few minutes to a half hour, depending on the temperature in the drier.

The underlying principle of drying—the evaporation of water from the surface of the forage and its removal by the surrounding air—is the same for both natural and artificial dehydration. The rate of drying depends on the amount of water in the forage, the temperature and humidity of the surrounding air, the rate the moisture-laden air is moved, and the kind of forage and texture of the plant.

Conditions that favor the most rapid removal of moisture generally produce a dried product most nearly resembling the original crop in appearance and in composition and feeding value. Thus artificial drying generally produces forage of higher feeding value than natural drying, and losses of nutrients are also somewhat smaller.

But the introduction of artificial aids to replace the natural drying generally adds to the costs. The relative advantages of such aids, therefore, must be weighed against the costs in individual situations.

In drying forage by natural or artificial means or a combination of both, the primary concern should be to conserve the maximum quantity of dry matter and of feed nutrients in the crop at the least cost.

The mere evaporation of enough moisture from forage so that it will keep in storage should not greatly change the composition of the dry matter or its feeding value. In fact, in feeding tests in which dairy cows were fed forage that was dried by natural methods under ideal conditions or forage that was artificially dehydrated immediately after it was cut, the cows

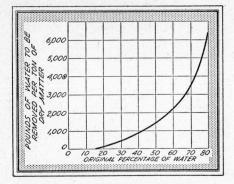

consumed as much dry matter and produced as much milk on either kind of dried forage as they did when they were fed green forage of the same mixture and stage of maturity.

Conditions are seldom ideal for drying when the farmer has forage ready to be harvested. Weather is uncertain and facilities are limited on farms in most of all the major hay-producing areas, so that there are important losses of dry matter and nutrients in drying the forage.

Some of the losses in quality generally are obvious enough—the loss of leaves, color, and aroma, and changes in the physical condition and palatability of the feed. The latter characteristics, which constitute what is called quality in hay, reflect other losses, such as losses of dry matter, total digestible nutrients, and carotene.

The losses in nutrients are not so easily recognized as the losses in leaves, color, and aroma; from the feeder's standpoint, however, they are of great significance. Producers of hay need to become much more quality-conscious; that is, they need to learn that certain quality characteristics in the dried product indicate that relatively small losses occurred in making it and that it therefore has a high feeding value for the animals that consume it.

We can define high-quality hay as weed-free forage that was dried under such conditions that there was no loss of leaves from handling, no deterioration in dry matter and nutrients from various causes, no mold develop-

ment, and no loss of the natural green color and sweetness of the original crop. Under normal curing conditions, however, losses will occur, but these losses should be kept to a minimum.

Freshly cut forage contains about 75 to 80 percent moisture. Under most conditions of natural drying the moisture content must be reduced from 20 to 25 percent or below for storage in the mow, in order to avoid serious deterioration in quality, loss of nutrients from fermentation, and danger of spontaneous combustion.

The accompanying chart shows how much moisture must be evaporated from forage of varying moisture contents for each ton of hay having a moisture content of 15 percent. The permissible moisture content for safe storage without heating varies somewhat according to how the forage is stored. If it is chopped it must be drier than if it is stored long, and the finer it is cut the drier it must be. Also, hay that is baled from the field for storage must be drier than hay stored long, and the tighter the bale the drier the hay must be. In undercured hay mold and dust might develop.

When the barn-finishing method is used, the hay can be taken from the field when it has considerably more moisture, but drying must be continued until the forage on the top of the mow averages 20 percent or less. It is generally preferable to bring chopped hay or baled hay to the barn finisher at a lower moisture content than long hay. When barn-drying installations permit the use of heated air, however, differences in moisture content are not so important.

The moisture content at which forage should be taken in for completing the drying on the barn finisher will vary considerably. Under ideal conditions, when everything is considered, it probably is best to leave the forage in the field as long as is possible without permitting much leaf shatter. We need much more information on this point; the best recommendation now is that the moisture content of the crop should be between 35 and 40 percent when it is taken from the field.

When weather conditions do not permit leaving the forage in the field long enough to reduce the moisture content that much, it may be brought in earlier, but when this is done it will take longer to complete drying on the drier and the barn losses may be higher. The barn-finishing method makes it possible, however, to get the crop off the field, in case of threatening rain, with a moisture content at which the hay would become musty and moldy and might burn by spontaneous combustion in regular storage.

Forage that is to be artificially dehydrated is generally hauled to the drier immediately after it is cut. This is important in the production of high-carotene feeds, such as alfalfa leaf meal, but for drying forage for cattle feed it appears that considerable saving can be made in the cost of drying by allowing it to wilt in the field several hours before it is gathered. From the chart it is evident that when forage is wilted from 75 to 60 percent moisture in the field, only about half as much water must be evaporated by artificial means for each ton of forage of 15 percent moisture content as when it is not wilted. This saving in drying costs may well outweigh the small losses in dry matter and in quality of the forage that might result from leaving it in the field a few hours after cutting. However, the rate of drying is reduced as the moisture content is lowered.

During the interval from cutting until the forage is dry enough to keep in storage, a progression of events promotes losses and deterioration of the quality and feeding value of the forage. These field losses generally originate from three sources: Respiration and fermentation (chemical and bacteriological), mechanical damage, and weather damage. The amount of destruction caused by the three factors varies according to conditions and determines the amount of field losses. Field operations should be managed to keep these factors to a minimum.

Freshly cut forage is living material. The plant cells continue to respire, and plant enzymes continue active for some time after the crop is cut. In addition, micro-organisms naturally contained in the forage continue activity as long as air is present and there is sufficient moisture. These fermentation processes affect principally the soluble carbohydrate fractions and the carotene. If drying is prolonged, however, important losses in dry matter and protein may also occur. Losses amounting to 5 to 15 percent of the total crop have been found to occur from so-called field fermentation losses.

The methods of handling the forage in the field should be designed to promote the most rapid evaporation of moisture so that these losses may be kept to a minimum. The new types of equipment developed for handling forage in the field tend to keep fermentation losses low. Moisture evaporates faster from the leaves than from the stems when the crop is lying in the swath, and this condition promotes serious shattering of the leaves when the hay is handled. Besides, the color and carotene decrease more rapidly when forage is exposed in the swath. It is highly important to conserve the leaves since they contain in alfalfa about 70 percent of the protein and 90 percent of the carotene of the entire plant.

Work at the Nebraska Agricultural Experiment Station and elsewhere has shown that the best way to handle forage in the field is to allow it to lie in the swath for only 1 to 3 hours and then pick it up into medium-sized windrows with a side-delivery rake or a dump rake. The side-delivery rake rolls the forage off the ground, protecting the leaves so that they dry at a rate more nearly the same as the stems. When the partly cured forage must lie out overnight, it is often advisable to give the windrow a half turn with the side-delivery rake the next day after the surface is dried off but before the leaves shatter. Cocking has been used advantageously in areas where drying

Losses of Dry Matter and Protein in Alfalfa Made by Field Curing and Barn Finishing [1]

Item	Field curing			Barn finishing		
	Field losses	Storage losses	Total losses	Field losses	Storage losses	Total losses
Dry matter:	*Percent*	*Percent*	*Percent*	*Percent*	*Percent*	*Percent*
First-cutting alfalfa—1945.........	21	5	26	16	[2] 1	17
Second-cutting alfalfa—1945......	17	4	21	13	8	21
Protein:						
First-cutting alfalfa—1945.........	31	2	33	26	[2] 1	27
Second-cutting alfalfa—1945......	29	1	30	16	10	26

[1] Adapted from Bureau of Dairy Industry, BDIM–Inf–43. 1946.
[2] Heated air was used in this installation to complete drying.

The Relative Feeding Values of Normal Hay and of Hay That Has Heated in the Stack [1]

Item	Normal hay	Brown hay	Black hay
Digestibility percentages:			
Dry matter.................................	60	41	27
Protein....................................	67	16	3
Fiber......................................	41	36	14
Ether extract..............................	25	33	42
Nitrogen-free extract.......................	72	59	53
Calculated digestible nutrients:			
Protein....................................	14. 4	3. 4	. 6
Total......................................	55. 8	37. 7	23. 4
Palatability: Pounds eaten for 1,000 pounds weight....	20	15	10

[1] Adapted from Bechtel et al., Journal of Dairy Science. 1945.

Comparative Feeding Value of Forage Made by Field Curing and Artificial Drying [1]

Kind of forage	Digestible protein		Total digestible nutrients	
	Field-cured hay	Artificially dried hay	Field-cured hay	Artificially dried hay
	Percent	*Percent*	*Percent*	*Percent*
Alfalfa (1st cut).....................	10. 9	10. 3	56. 4	60. 0
Alfalfa (2d cut)......................	14. 7	13. 8	57. 1	60. 2
Clover...............................	8. 2	8. 0	63. 3	61. 8
Timothy (early cut)..................	4. 8	4. 6	66. 4	65. 8

[1] Adapted from Vermont Agricultural Experiment Station Bulletin 494. 1942.

must be carried on for several days, but this practice increases the cost.

A new development that is being observed with interest by researchers is the crushing of the stems as the forage is being cut. In this operation forage passes from the cutting bar through spring-tension-controlled rollers, which gently crush the stems. The advocates of this idea state that the moisture is evaporated from the crushed stems at about the same rate as from the leaves and that the total drying period, therefore, is cut almost in half. This process needs further testing under different conditions of hay making.

Mechanical losses vary considerably, depending on the method of handling the forage and the type of equipment used. The shedding of leaves is the most serious loss because they contain most of the feed nutrients. Leaves generally do not shatter to any great extent when the forage contains 35 to 40 percent or more of moisture. Therefore, forage for artificial dehydration and for barn finishing can be handled without serious loss of leaves in the field. The problem of leaf shatter, of course, is much more serious with legumes than with grasses or with mixtures of grasses and legumes.

Hay that is drier than it need be for safe storage is very susceptible to leaf shattering, and such hay usually is graded lower in quality because of lack of leaves. Field baling may also promote leaf shattering since, if the forage is dried sufficiently to prevent mold development, it is dry enough to allow easy leaf shedding. Field-dried forage should be handled as little as possible and with as few machines as possible. Experiments in Kansas, England, and Switzerland indicate that mechanical losses from curing hay in the field total as much as 10 percent of the crop.

Leaching and bleaching also cause losses when forage is dried in the field. Rain falling on partly dried forage produces losses that result from shattering of the leaves and from the leaching of soluble nutrients from the forage. Various workers have shown that hay that has been rained on is lower in protein, nitrogen-free extract, and carotene and higher in crude fiber than hay not rained on. Rain promotes mold development and this also contributes to nutrient loss and lowered feeding value. Excessive exposure of forage to the sun increases its vitamin D value but causes a decrease in color and carotene content.

Field-cured hay generally will sweat after it is stored. If it is undercured, it will heat in the mow and this heating produces losses in dry matter and feeding value. Frequently such hay will lose 5 to 15 percent of its dry matter and nutrients while in storage. If heating is excessive in the mow, brown and black areas of charred and burnt hay may develop and, as is all too frequently the case, heating may continue until spontaneous combustion occurs and the hay and storage barn are burned. Brown and black hay appears to be palatable to livestock, but numerous investigations have shown that this type of hay has a decidedly lowered feeding value.

Experiments in this country do not indicate that the addition of salt or another chemical substance, supposed to aid in keeping hay from heating in the mow, will prevent hay from heating or increase or preserve its feeding value.

When partly dried forage is placed on a barn hay finisher, it is still wet enough to allow rapid fermentation to take place. Air moving through the mass of hay carries with it the moisture evaporated from the forage. The temperature of the air will govern how much moisture it will pick up. Heated air will pick up more moisture than unheated air, and drying will be hastened if the air is heated before it enters the drier. The heat created by fermentation may also increase the temperature of the air and thereby increase its water-holding capacity. It is important to spread the forage evenly over the drying system and to have the same degree of packing throughout. The air will then flow evenly through the for-

Losses From Field Cured and Artificially Dried Forage During Making and Storage [1]

Crop and method of drying	Dry matter	Protein	Fiber	Ether extract	N-free extract	Ash
	Per-cent	Per-cent	Per-cent	Per-cent	Per-cent	Per-cent
Sun curing:						
Alfalfa (1st cut)	23. 6	29. 4	7. 1	41. 0	30. 8	20. 5
Alfalfa (2d cut)	13. 4	20. 7	3. 9	37. 7	10. 7	25. 2
Clover	36. 1	39. 8	29. 5	52. 6	37. 7	39. 2
Timothy (early cut)	8. 6	11. 2	2. 0	14. 4	10. 0	22. 1
Average	20. 4	24. 3	10. 6	36. 4	22. 3	26. 7
Artificial drying:						
Alfalfa (1st cut)	3. 2	14. 4	+7. 4	+4. 1	4. 4	12. 4
Alfalfa (2d cut)	6. 8	13. 4	8. 2	+10. 1	. 1	17. 8
Clover	2. 8	14. 7	+. 6	2. 6	. 4	5. 6
Timothy (early cut)	6. 9	4. 1	9. 2	+12. 0	7. 0	6. 3
Average	4. 9	11. 7	2. 4	+5. 9	3. 0	10. 4

[1] Adapted from Vermont Agricultural Experiment Station Bulletin 494. 1942.

age and the hay will dry thoroughly in all parts of the mow. The hay dries from the bottom up, and when the top layer is dry enough to prevent heating, the lower layers are even drier.

The drying should be completed as rapidly as possible to retard fermentation. The longer fermentation takes place the greater the losses of dry matter and nutrients because optimum temperature and moisture conditions are present for microbiological activity.

Tests were conducted by the Department of Agriculture with hay that contained from 40 to 45 percent of moisture when it was put in the drier. It took about 13 days to dry the hay to a point where it would keep. During this time there was a loss of about 9.3 percent dry matter, 11.2 percent protein, and 78.2 percent carotene. These losses appear to be rather typical for this method of drying, when unheated air is used. Considerably better preservation was accomplished, however, and in a much shorter time, when heated air was used.

Other tests indicate that better preservation of dry matter and nutrients is obtained with forage stored in a chopped condition when it is dried in the field to a relatively low moisture content before it is put on the barn drier. Various workers have successfully dried baled forage on barn finish-

ers. Here again, getting the forage as dry as possible in the field and using heated air in the barn finisher have proved advantageous.

Much of the hay made by the barn-finishing method is greener, leafier, and generally of a better grade than similar hay made by field curing. This is particularly true of hay in which no mold has developed during drying.

The development of mold in hay made in a hay drier is very common. It is not clear how much this affects its feeding value but moldiness does indicate that fermentation losses have occurred. An important advantage of the barn-finishing method is that it makes it possible to get the crop off the field sooner, in case of threatening weather, and to save large amounts of feed nutrients that would be lost by field curing during extended wet spells. The best information to date is that the forage should be allowed to dry in the field as much as possible, without running the risk of damage from rain or inclement weather or excessive leaf shatter from too much drying before it is stored on the mow finisher to complete drying.

The most popular type of artificial forage dehydrator in use in this country is one that uses a high initial heat (1,200° to 1,400° F.), which is usually produced from fuel oil. The forage is

Changes in Carotene Content of Alfalfa Harvested by Field Curing and Barn Finishing [1]

When sample was taken	Carotene content (dry basis)	
	Field curing	Barn finishing
	mcg. per gram	mcg. per gram
When cut..............	297	308
When put on drier.....	....	122
When dry (13 days later)...................	....	29
When stored..........	49	....
When stored 30 days...	26	....
When fed.............	12	22

[1] Adapted from Bureau of Dairy Industry, BDIM-Inf-43. 1946.

usually chopped before entering the drier. The forage and heated air are in contact in the drying chamber for only a few minutes. The temperature of the air at the exhaust end of the machine seldom is over 300°.

Experimental results show that forage dried under such conditions has a normal composition and feeding value. There is no danger of affecting the feeding value as long as the forage is removed from the heated air as soon as it is dry. The appearance of burning on the leafy portions of the forage indicates that the temperature is too high or that the forage is overdried.

Experiments in drying grass showed that the digestibility of the protein and calcium was severely affected when it took 2 to 5 minutes to evaporate the moisture and the exhaust air temperature was 400°. It is not necessary to operate at such high temperatures, however, to dry forage efficiently.

Under average conditions the gross loss of dry matter from artificial dehydration varies from 5 to 7.5 percent. This loss must be charged to the costs of drying. Costs of artificial drying have been so great that its use has been limited to large-scale operations and to specialty products, such as alfalfa meals

of high carotene content which are used in the feeding of poultry and swine.

Artificial dehydration produces feed of high carotene and riboflavin content, if the crop is dried soon after it is cut. Dehydrating the forage preserves the carotene effectively, although dehydrated forage like other dried forage undergoes carotene loss in storage during warm weather. The dry matter and other nutrients keep very well in storage when the forage is properly dehydrated artificially.

THE AUTHORS ≪ *R. E. Hodgson is assistant chief of the Bureau of Dairy Industry. During 1942–43 he conducted a survey of dairying in seven Latin-American countries; in 1939 he received the Borden Award for outstanding research in dairy production. Dr. Hodgson is a graduate of the University of Wisconsin.*

R. E. Davis is a nutritionist in the Bureau of Animal Industry. He has been engaged in research in the nutrition of farm animals since 1931. Much of his research has been directed toward determining the vitamin A requirements of cattle and the carbohydrate components of feedstuffs. Dr. Davis is a graduate of Wilmington College and Ohio State University.

W. H. Hosterman, marketing specialist in the Grain Branch of Production and Marketing Administration, is in charge of hay standardization and inspection. He has been associated with this work since 1933 and in charge since 1940. Mr. Hosterman is a graduate of Pennsylvania State and Michigan State Colleges.

T. E. Hienton is in charge of the Division of Farm Electrification, Bureau of Plant Industry, Soils, and Agricultural Engineering. From 1925 to 1941 Mr. Hienton was in charge of farm electrification investigations at Purdue University, where he conducted research on development of farm electrical equipment. He holds degrees from Ohio State University and Iowa State College.

EQUIPMENT FOR MAKING HAY

R. B. GRAY

OF THE MANY methods of putting up hay, no one way now seems to be the best for all farms. The choice depends on items like the kind and amount of hay to be harvested, the use to be made of it, the conditions under which it is grown, the distance between the field and the place where it is stored or processed, and the availability of power, labor, and equipment.

This discussion deals with the types of equipment available, my aim being to help a farmer select the tools that will best meet his particular needs.

Regardless of method of harvesting, the grass must first be cut, and except in small patches where a scythe is sometimes used, the operation is performed by the mower, the familiar machine that needs little description beyond a mention of sizes and types.

Probably the smallest grass mower cuts a 4½-foot swath. It is pulled by one horse and can cut about 6 acres in a 10-hour day. At the other extreme is the tractor mower, which cuts a 7-foot swath and can cover about 25 acres a day at about 4 miles an hour. Intermediate are the 5-foot and 6-foot sizes, the smaller one generally pulled by two horses and the larger by two horses or a small tractor. Sometimes a 7-foot mower is pulled by three horses.

Tractor mowers are of four general types. The ground-driven trailer type can be used singly, in series with one or more, or as a trailer behind a power take-off driven mower. The drawbar-attached mower is driven through a power take-off. A third kind is driven by a power take-off that is rear-attached but mounted on one or two wheels. The fourth is driven by power take-off mounted amidships in front of the drive wheels.

Like all power-driven machinery, these mowers have safety features to prevent damage in case a stone or another obstruction is encountered (the safety release) or when the cutter bar becomes clogged (the slip clutch). Another attachment holds the cutter bar at uniform height up to 12 inches for cutting in rocky fields. For cutting lespedeza, special guards with 1½-inch spacing are available. The ordinary spacing is 3 inches.

Often, with a field grass chopper, the green crop is cut and chopped for silage as it stands in the field. This machine is operated by the tractor power take-off and is a combination of a mower (which is provided with a reel to whisk the material back onto a conveyor) and a chopping box (which is fed by this conveyor), from which the chopped material is blown into a trailing truck or wagon. The material, transported to a silo, is blown into it by means of a power-driven combination screw conveyor and blower. When it is placed directly into the silo, the chopped grass has a rather high moisture content, so that some sort of preservative sometimes is added. If the material is allowed to wilt in the field and lose 10 to 20 percent of its moisture before ensiling, however, no preservative is needed.

Should it be desired to mow-finish the crop—dry it in the mow—it is mowed, wilted a few hours to a moisture content of about 50 percent, windrowed, loaded, and hauled to a mow fitted for the purpose.

Sometimes it is expedient to chop cured hay and place it in the mow. This may be done by a field hay chopper, which differs from the green-crop chopper in that a pick-up cylinder replaces the cutter bar. The dried hay is thereby picked up and is caused to pass into the chopping box; from there it is delivered by means of a blower and spout into the trailing truck. It is then transported to a blower and blown into the mow. Sometimes the whole hay when cured is taken from the windrow, chopped by a stationary hay chopper, and blown into the mow.

It should be pointed out that chopped cured hay packs down as it is blown into the mow with a density two to three times greater than that of whole hay. One has to be careful therefore to see that the structure can stand the load.

After the hay or grass is cut in swaths it is generally concentrated in long, narrow windrows to facilitate later handling. Windrowing is done with a dump rake (which is 8 to 14 feet wide and generally pulled by horses or a small tractor) or by a side-delivery rake, which is 8 to 10 feet wide and is pulled by a team or a small tractor.

One make of tractor dump rake, which is hydraulically controlled, rakes a 24-foot width. It can be folded at the middle, the halves with their teeth facing each other, and it is mounted on rubber tires, so that it can be taken on a road.

A heavy-duty side-delivery rake, rubber-tired and designed for use with tractors, is useful for fast raking and for raking heavy crops. It is sometimes operated from the power take-off.

Many side rakes are fitted with three-bar reels, but the four-bar rake seems to be increasing in popularity. It rakes the hay more gradually and gently than the three-bar rake does, so that leaf shattering is less, especially if the hay is rather dry.

Tedding, an operation performed by a special hay tedder or by a side rake fitted for reversing the rotation of the reel, is sometimes (but less frequently than formerly) used to hasten field curing.

To eliminate the raking operation with some hay or grass crops, the mower cutter bar of both horse and tractor mowers may be fitted with a windrowing attachment. It consists of a series of curved fingers attached to the rear of the cutter bar for guiding the hay into a windrow as it is being cut. Sometimes a buncher attachment is used to gather very short hay that cannot be raked easily.

For loading windrowed material into a hayrack or truck, loaders can be had for cured and green hay and are available in the single-cylinder, double-cylinder, raker-bar, and combination types used mainly with cured hay.

The single-cylinder type has a pick-up cylinder mounted concentric with the axle. The cylinder picks up the hay and delivers it to a webbed or slatted carrier, which in turn carries it up the sloping deck and dumps it into the hay-rack or the truck that pulls the loader.

The double-cylinder loader is built almost the same as the single-cylinder loader except that a smaller or floating gleaner cylinder is attached to the rear.

The fork or raker-bar type makes use of reciprocating bars to which are attached flexible teeth. As each set of bars moves upward, the teeth rake the hay up the sloping deck and cause it to drop on the rack or truck ahead.

The combination type, much the same in construction as the plain raker-bar, has a cylinder, attached to the rear, which can be adjusted as to height by the castor wheels that support the rear end.

For loading green crops, such as clover, grasses, alfalfa, cowpeas, and soybeans, machines are used that are more ruggedly constructed and have the deck extended closer to the ground; otherwise they are of the same type as those I have described. They can be used also for loading cured or dry hay.

When storage space is small or the hay is to be shipped, it may be baled. Frequently a stationary baler is used. A portable type is mounted on rubber tires for moving from place to place. Essentially the baler consists of a chassis with a mounted baling chamber, in which the bale is formed; wooden blocks to separate the bales; a plunger for compressing the hay that is forced into the baling chamber feed opening by the feeder head; and a density regulator. The more common sizes of bales are 14 by 18, 16 by 18, and 17 by 22 inches in section; the length is about 36 to 42 inches; and the weight averages 75, 100, and 150 pounds, respectively.

To save work in baling, the windrow

pick-up baler was developed. In principle it is a combination of an ordinary pick-up device for taking the cured hay from the windrow and a conventional hay baler with a conveyor to conduct the hay to the baling chamber. On most pick-up balers—which form rectangular bales—is a slicer device, which consists of a knife on the plunger head and a stationary shear plate mounted at the edge of the feeder opening. As the plunger moves on its compression stroke, the hay projecting from the feed opening is sheared off so that each charge becomes a slice.

Available in this type of baler are the three-man wire baler, the two-man wire baler, one-man wire baler, and one-man twine baler.

On the three-man type, one man rides on one side of the machine and pushes the tie wire through to the man riding on the other side, who ties the wire; the third man drives the tractor.

On the two-man wire baler, one man does the tying and the other drives the tractor. On the one-man baler, either wire or twine, baling and tying are automatic, and the man drives the tractor. The heavy twine sometimes used in this type of baler has about three times the strength of ordinary binder twine. The bale is usually about 14 by 18 inches in section by about 36 inches long and weighs around 60 pounds. In bales tied with wire, the common sizes available are 14 by 18, 16 by 18, and 17 by 22 inches through and about 40 inches long; the weights are about the same as those given for stationary balers. Two ties are generally used, except in the larger sizes, such as 17 by 22, when three are commonly used.

One type makes a round bale. Its pick-up feeds the hay into a series of belts, so that the hay is rolled up like a carpet into a bundle 36 inches long and 14 to 22 inches thick. The machine can be regulated to bale tight or loose bales, so that their weight ranges from 40 to 100 pounds, depending on the density and diameter. When the desired thickness is attained, a tying mechanism causes a strand of binder twine to wrap around the bale near one end and then spiral around the bale to the other end, where it is cut. The bale is then discharged, and the process is repeated. This is a one-man baler.

As the hay is baled by the pick-up baler, the bales may be dumped in the field and picked up with a hook by hand or by a special bale pick-up, or pushed onto a trailing truck on an extension of the baling chamber.

This procedure is recommended when a pick-up baler is used:

1. Divide large fields into lands and cut in a clockwise direction—start at the edge of the field and finish in the center. Cut only as much as can be raked in ample time for a few hours of windrow-curing before nightfall. Do not mow while the grass is wet from a heavy dew or too soon after rain.

2. For windrowing after the swath has wilted to a loose fluffy state, if a left-hand side rake is used, enter the field and travel the same direction the mower traveled. The rake will lift the heads first and place most of the leaves in the center of the windrow with most of the stems exposed. This makes for uniform curing. After heavy rains, allow the hay to dry on top and then turn the windrow half over with the side-delivery rake. Under average conditions a 7-foot swath makes a good windrow. Avoid making windrows so large and dense as to hinder the free movement of the air.

3. After the hay in the first windrow is cured to the point when it could be safely stored in the barn if it were loose hay (that is, a moisture content of about 15 percent), it is ready for baling. Start baling at the outside of the field and travel toward the center in the same direction as the mower and side rake.

To facilitate curing of coarse-stemmed hay, a mower-crusher is available. It cuts the hay in the usual manner, as with a mower, but passes it through crushing rolls. This cracks the stems and speeds up curing in the swath. Thereafter the hay is windrowed in the ordinary way.

For quickly and easily moving large quantities of hay from the windrow to the barn, stacker or baler use may be made of the sweep rake. This consists essentially of a series of long wooden parallel fingers mounted 1 foot apart and varying in length and raking width according to make and capacity—usually from 8 to 12 feet. Commercially they are available for mounting on the front of tractors, directly or on support wheels, and on trucks. Several State agricultural experiment stations have published leaflets that describe the construction of home-made outfits.

Some farmers gather the hay from the swath, but most buck it from the windrow; they travel down the windrow until the rake is loaded and then tilt the fingers slightly upward to keep the hay from falling when it is enroute to the barn or stack.

If the cured hay is taken to the barn, it is placed in the mow usually by use of a sling or hay fork powered by a horse, gas engine, or electric motor.

If the hay is to be stacked, the farmer can use the buck rake itself (if it is designed for the purpose) or a special stacker. The several types of special stackers include the overshot, swinging, and cable stackers.

The overshot type is so called because the hay is carried up and over the stacker frame and delivered onto the stack in a fashion similar to pitching hay by hand. The swinging type can be swung around so that it drops the hay anywhere desired. The cable stacker has two sets of poles, each set bolted at the top and spread at the bottom, with a cable stretched across the top to act as a track for a hay carrier. The height of the stack is limited by the height of the poles; the spacing of the two sets of poles determines the length of the stack.

Mow curing, or mow finishing, consists in removing the surplus moisture by blowing atmospheric air, alone or with supplemental heat, through air ducts on which the whole, chopped, or baled hay is deposited. Hay ready for cutting has a moisture content of 60 to 75 percent, depending on the kind; in mow curing, the hay is left in the windrow for a few hours to wilt to a moisture content of about 50 percent before it is placed on the ducts.

Usually built in the haymow, the system is essentially a blower driven by an electric motor and a system of ducts. The blower forces cold air through the main duct and distributes it through lateral ducts that branch at right angles. From the laterals the air emerges through slots on the under side. The ducts usually are made of wood, although for the laterals other materials, such as sheet metal, have been used. The laterals are spaced about 5 feet on centers, and the system is so designed that about 15 cubic feet of air per square foot of mow space is delivered against a static pressure, generally about $\frac{3}{4}$-inch water, with long hay piled to a height of about 8 feet.

A modification of the duct-type drier is the slatted floor installation developed by engineers in the Department of Agriculture and the Virginia Agricultural Experiment Station. This type, simple in design, is now generally recommended in the eastern humid regions and is gaining in popularity elsewhere. Its main feature is a tapering central air duct that is open at the bottom on each side to allow the air to flow to a slatted floor and up through the hay. Its construction cost is low because the slatted floor can be built of rough lumber and laid by inexperienced carpenters. Experimental tests showed that duct pressure losses in driers of this design, properly operated, are considerably less than in the conventional duct-type system. Air distribution is better and the flow of air through the hay is increased.

Hay that is being finished in the mow should be dried to a moisture content below 20 percent in 8 days for best results; occasionally supplemental heat, from steam or hot-water radiators in the main duct, or hot air blown into it, is used to speed up the operation.

When large quantities of hay are to

be dried quickly and the costs of installation and operation justify its use,
artificial drying, or dehydration, can
be employed. In this so-called direct-
heat method, use is made of the gases
resulting from the burning of gas, fuel
oil, coal, and sometimes wood, diluted
with excess air in addition to what is
needed for combustion. These are applied directly to the green material,
which is thereby heated so that the
moisture is evaporated and carried off
in a vapor with the gases.

Two general types of forage dehy-
drators are available, the rotary-drum,
or high-temperature, drier, and the
conveyor, or low-temperature, drier.
Both supply the necessary heat from a
furnace designed to burn the particular
type of fuel available.

In the drum driers the temperature
of the furnace gases entering the machine range from 1,000° to 1,750° F.,
depending on the make of drier and
the requirements; the material, which
is cut into about 1-inch lengths, is
added at this point. The cut herbage is
advanced through the drying drum by
means of a suction fan. The flights on
the drum pick up the heavier particles
at the bottom and drop them near the
top, then move them along. The material remains in the drier from 1 to 3
minutes, depending somewhat on the
design of the drier and on the initial
moisture content of the forage. Then it
passes through a cyclone dust collector
into bags or into a grinder. The use of
high temperatures and a short period
of exposure in drum driers makes possible a rather small and compact unit.

Single drum driers are about 50 feet
in length and 7 to 9 feet in diameter.
Double or triple drum driers may be
shorter than that, because the use of
multiple drums increases the length of
the drying zone with reference to the
over-all length. The exhaust temperature is about 225°, the moisture content of the dry product around 10
percent.

Most driers are built as stationary
units, but portable units are available.
One manufacturer supplies a triple-
drum type with drying drums 7 feet
in diameter and 14 feet long.

The material remains in the con-
veyor-type drier for a considerable
time. The green forage, which may be
fed into the drier whole, crushed, or
chopped, is usually fed onto an endless
screen-wire apron and then conveyed
through the drying chamber. Driers of
this type may have a single endless
conveyor or several conveyors, one
above the other. The temperature of
the drying gases entering the machine
is usually 250° to 350°; the period of
exposure may vary from 15 minutes to
60 minutes, depending partly on the
initial moisture content of the forage
and partly on the final moisture content desired. The material coming from
the drier may be bagged if it is in short
lengths, or hammer milled for meal. It
sometimes is handled as ordinary hay,
if it is whole.

When the chopped material is to be
ground, it is generally dried down to a
moisture content of about 5 percent
and passed through a hammer mill.
The mill has a series of revolving hammers, rigid or swinging, mounted on a
shaft that is set centrally through the
middle of the grinding chamber. As the
material is fed through the hopper it is
struck by the hammers and broken up.
Close to the periphery of the revolving
hammers is the screen. The reduced
material falls through the screen into a
receiver; from there it is ordinarily
conveyed pneumatically into a cyclone
and then into bags. The fineness of
grinding depends on the size of screen,
which comes with openings from one-
sixteenth of an inch to around 1½
inches. There does not seem to be complete agreement as to the optimum
fineness of grind for feeding cattle,
poultry, and other stock, but it should
be pointed out that the finer the grind
the greater the power requirement.

THE AUTHOR«« *R. B. Gray is an
agricultural engineer in charge of the
Division of Farm Machinery of the
Bureau of Plant Industry, Soils, and
Agricultural Engineering.*

THE COSTS AND WAYS OF MAKING HAY

ALBERT P. BRODELL, MARTIN R. COOPER

AMERICAN farmers used about 970 million man-hours in 1945 to harvest the hay crop from more than 70 million acres. That was slightly less than 10 percent of all the labor spent directly on crop production and nearly 5 percent of all farm labor in agriculture. The acreage in hay is larger than the acreage usually used to produce any other single crop, except corn, and is about 20 percent of the harvested crop acreage of the United States. Corn and cotton were the only single crops that required more man-hours than hay. Furthermore, much of the haying is still hard hand work and most of it comes in June, July, and August, when other crop work is heavy and time, tide, and weather wait on no man. All those facts are reasons why farmers and economists are so keenly interested in machines and methods that will cut the costs, labor, and uncertainties involved in making good hay.

New methods of haymaking that reduce labor requirements and improve the quality of the hay have come into use in the past several decades. The most important changes have been the substitution of mechanical power for animal power and the increased use of power equipment.

Nation-wide studies of the 1939 and 1944 hay harvests gave us a general view of haymaking methods and the changes that occurred in the 5 years. Only 15 percent of the hay in 1938 was cut with tractor mowers; 42 percent of the crop was cut with tractor mowers in 1944. Since 1944 many farmers have bought tractor mowers because, for one reason, they had a large crop to harvest but little help.

The use of tractor power for operating rakes has increased also; 30 percent of the crop in 1944 was raked with tractor-drawn rakes. Raking is relatively light work, and the rate of performance often is about the same with tractor-drawn and animal-drawn

rakes. The use of side-delivery rakes has tended to increase.

Hauling hay to barns and stacks has been mechanized considerably since the 1930's, when rubber-tired tractors began to come into general use. Nearly one-half of all hay harvested in 1944 was hauled with mechanical power; in 1939 the figure was 15 percent. The increasing use of tractors and motor trucks for transporting hay at harvesttime is continuing.

More than three-fourths of the hay in 1944 was stored or sold at haying time as loose long hay. In New England, the Lake States, and the Northern Great Plains, more than 90 percent of the hay usually is so stored.

Baling has long been the practice when the hay was to be shipped to market, but because of savings in storage space and advantages in feeding, more and more farmers are baling hay from the windrow for use on their own farms. Less than 15 percent of the 1939 hay crop was baled, but about 27 percent of the 1944 crop was baled. In 1944, about a fifth of all hay was baled at haying time and 6 percent was baled from barns and stacks. Although windrow pick-up balers were used for only slightly more than half of the total baling, almost two-thirds of the baling at haying time was with these balers.

Only 2 percent of the 1944 crop was stored as chopped hay, and some hay was stored as loose long hay and then chopped. Chopping hay is of greatest importance in the Pacific Coast States and in Idaho, where from 7 to 12 percent of the 1944 crop was chopped at haying time.

About 62 percent of the total 1944 hay crop was stored in barns or sheds at harvest time. In the humid areas of the Pacific Coast States and in all States east of the Mississippi River, large quantities of hay are stored under cover. In the New England States, and in New York, Pennsylvania,

Rate of Cutting and Raking Hay and Cost of Use of Mowers and Rakes, by Type and Size, 1945

Crew	Work done per hour with machine	Average work done per year with machine	Cost per acre for use of machine [1]		
			Average use	One-half of average use	Double average use
	Acres	Acres	Cents	Cents	Cents
1 man, tractor, 7-foot mower............	2.1	100	25	40	17
1 man, 2 horses, 5-foot mower...........	.9	35	43	70	28
1 man, 2 horses, 10-foot dump rake......	2.0	50	16	28	9
1 man, 2 horses, side-delivery rake......	1.8	70	21	37	13
1 man, tractor, side-delivery rake [2]......	2.4	70	21	37	13

[1] Includes depreciation, repair costs (including labor, housing, taxes, and insurance), and an interest charge on the average investment in mower or rake.

[2] These data are for ordinary side-delivery rakes. Some of the newer types, operated with tractor power take-off, are operated at higher speeds and do more work per hour.

Michigan, and Wisconsin more than 90 percent was so stored in 1944.

About 32 percent of the hay crop of 1944 was stored in stacks and ricks at harvest time, a method that predominates in the drier areas of the Mountain and Plains States, and is fairly important in some localities of the Appalachian States. About 6 percent of the hay in 1944 was not stored on farms but was sold and delivered at haying time.

Although the use of grass silage is increasing, only about 0.5 percent of the production of the hay crop of 1944 was used for grass silage. Small quantities are produced in most States but grass silage is of greatest importance in the Northeastern States (where 75 to 80 percent of all farmers grow hay) and in the humid hay areas along the Pacific coast where it is often difficult to cure hay in the field.

Losses in quality and quantity of hay are pronounced in humid areas, and are usually heavier for early and late cuttings than for midseason cuttings, chiefly because more time is required for curing early and late crops.

Of all hay produced in 1944, more than 99 percent was cured naturally, or by sun-drying. Barn curing of hay is creating much interest in some areas, but only about 125,000 tons were so

cured in 1944. Use of barn driers was most important in the Northeast and Pacific Coast States. About three times as much hay was handled in 1944 by industrial dehydrating plants as was barn-cured. The industrial plants are widely scattered, but are located principally in important alfalfa areas of the Great Plains, the West, and the Corn Belt States.

Fairly standard equipment and power units are used in cutting and raking hay. According to a study made by the Bureau of Agricultural Economics in 1942, about 60 percent of the horse-drawn mowers had 5-foot cutter bars, and more than 65 percent of the tractor mowers had 7-foot cutter bars. The 7-foot tractor mower will cut an average of about 2.1 acres of hay in 1 hour, which is usually more than double the amount cut with a 5-foot horse-drawn mower.

The initial cost and yearly operating cost of tractor mowers is higher than for horse-drawn mowers, but in actual farm practice tractor mowers are used to cut more acres and the cost per acre of mower use is often less than with horse-drawn mowers. For example, a 7-foot tractor mower attachment cost about $160 in 1945 compared with around $120 for a 5-foot horse-drawn mower, but because of greater use per year the tractor-mower cost per acre was only about 60 percent as much as the acre cost of the horse-drawn mower. Furthermore, the 1945 acre cost of use for each mower that was used to cut 200 acres was only about two-thirds as much as the cost per acre of mowers that were used to cut 100 acres.

Side-delivery rakes drawn with tractors travel at a somewhat higher rate of speed and will rake about a third more hay in an hour than if drawn by horses. When dump rakes are tractor-drawn the labor required per acre is sometimes higher than if they are horse-drawn, as two men are needed to operate the tractor and rake unless the rake has been converted for one-man operation.

Cost of use for the dump rakes is less than for side-delivery rakes because of their lower initial cost and longer life, but the side-delivery rake is better adapted to tractor power and produces a more uniform windrow, and its use is increasing rapidly.

Selecting the proper method, machines, and equipment for putting up hay is not always easy. The kind and amount of hay, climate, topography, available farm labor force, whether the hay is to be fed on the farm where produced or sold, the amount of available storage space, feeding situations, and other factors influence farmers in their selection of haymaking methods.

About 80 percent of the hay in 1944 was stored as long loose hay, principally because the cost of machines and equipment for hauling long loose hay is relatively low and because long loose hay can be successfully stored with a higher moisture content than chopped and baled hay, so that less time is needed for field curing and there is less risk of weather damage during the field curing.

In the humid areas much long loose hay is hauled and stored in barns or sheds with simple, inexpensive equipment. On some farms that produce small amounts of hay, ordinary farm wagons and racks are used for hauling and the loading and unloading is done by hand pitching. With this method an average of about a quarter ton is hauled and stored per hour of labor. The cost of the hauling and storing equipment is small, as the wagons and racks are extensively used for farm work other than haymaking.

On many other farms with moderate amounts of hay, the hay is pitched onto the wagons by hand but unloaded with power forks or slings. The initial cost and the cost of use of power forks or slings are small. This equipment, which speeds up the haymaking, can be used to advantage on farms where the mows in the barns and sheds are fairly large and where the crop is too small to justify the purchase of a loader.

The most common method for handling long loose hay stored in barns, however, is to use a mechanical hay loader for field loading and power forks or slings for unloading at the barn. With this method of haymaking and a three-man crew, an average of about one-third of a ton of hay is hauled and stored per hour of labor. The hay loader is used with wagons drawn by horses or by a tractor, or with a motortruck. The loader method takes less labor than when the loading and unloading is done by hand, and with the forks and slings hay is stored in high mows that would be just about inaccessible by hand pitching. The cost of use of haying machines and equipment, including the loader, wagons, racks, track, cable, forks, and slings, with the loader method varies with the tonnage of hay handled; the cost in 1945 ranged from more than $1 a ton on farms handling 25 tons to about 40 cents when 200 tons were handled.

Some farmers use hoists powered with stationary motors instead of teams or tractor power for the forks and slings. Some barn mowers that help to distribute the hay are being installed. The new equipment and power hoists save some labor, but more importantly make it possible to use effectively fewer able-bodied workers for haymaking.

Use of Animal Power and Machine Power for Haying Operations, The United States, 1939 and 1944

Haying operation	1939		1944	
	Animal power	Mechanical power	Animal power	Mechanical power
	Percent	*Percent*	*Percent*	*Percent*
Mowing.............................	85	15	58	42
Raking.............................	....	....	70	30
Hauling at haying time.................	85	15	55	45
Hauled with wagons, sleds, etc	....	....	44.8	19.4
Transported with buck rakes and other rakes..............................	....	....	10.2	12.2
Hauled with motortruck..............	....	....	....	13.4

Buck rakes, powered with tractors or motor vehicles, under favorable conditions, provide a rapid and low-cost method of haymaking. With the buck-rake method, power slings are preferred over forks for lifting the hay into the barn. The load size of the buck rake is often around 700 or 800 pounds, and the rake can be used to advantage only for short hauls, on fairly level land, and where there are wide lanes from the field to the barn. Under these conditions a three-man crew can haul from windrows and store in barns about a half-ton per hour.

In many western areas hay is stored in stacks rather than in buildings, and specialized equipment is used for hauling and stacking grass hays and much of the leaf hays. In some places in the West and in humid areas about the same equipment is used for stacking leaf hays as is used for storing hay in barns. When wagons are used for hauling and the hay is loaded in the field and placed on stacks by hand pitching, an average of about one-fourth ton is hauled and stacked per hour. This method takes more labor than other methods of stacking, but the cost of use of machines and equipment for hauling and stacking is low.

Mechanical power has replaced much of the animal power that was formerly used in hauling hay with buck rakes and operating the mechanical stackers. This replacement has tended to reduce the size of the haying crew and to increase the amount of hay handled per hour of labor. The most rapid method of haymaking is the hydraulic buck-stacker method. This machine is tractor mounted and hauls and elevates the hay onto the stack. A small crew can be used effectively with this method, and the cost of use of the buck stacker is slightly less than the cost of use of machines and equipment for other mechanical methods of stacking hay.

Buck rakes are used more extensively for grass hays in the western dry areas than for leaf hays in the irrigated areas, because many farmers prefer to haul the leaf hays with wagons or sleds to limit leaf losses. The sleds are often equipped with slings and are loaded by hand pitching, and the hay is placed on stacks with derrick stackers.

About twice as much hay is now baled as was baled a decade ago. The increase in baling has come mostly from the increased use of windrow pick-up balers that reduce materially labor needs for baling. The storage space for baled hay often is only half of the space required for long loose hay, and many farmers prefer to feed baled hay because they can more easily regulate the amount fed and move it to feed lots.

Use of the pick-up baler continues to

increase rapidly although the period of field curing for baled hay is often somewhat longer than for long loose hay, and the likelihood of weather damage during field curing is greater. Cost of equipment for baling, which includes the cost of use of the baler, wire or twine, wagons, trailers, and equipment for storing hay, is much higher than the cost of equipment for harvesting long loose hay. For the more expensive balers, large tonnages must be handled to keep machinery costs at a reasonable level. It is not unusual for an automatic-tie, pick-up baler to handle more than 500 tons of hay and straw in a season.

Generally, baling crews must be composed of husky workers because handling baled hay, even with mechanical loading and unloading equipment, is heavy work. Types of balers include the stationary hand-tie, wire baler; windrow, pick-up, automatic-tie baler; and the windrow, pick-up, hand-tie, wire baler.

The machines of the third type probably did the bulk of the baling that was done in 1944. They are operated either with auxiliary motors or power take-off and are mostly tractor-drawn. A three-man crew is usually used for baling, although with some of the older types, a four-man baling crew is required.

With the hand-tie, pick-up baler, about a third of a ton of hay is baled, hauled, and stored in barns per hour of labor.

Windrow, pick-up balers of the hand-tie type cost an average of about $1,100 each in 1945; the annual cost of machine use when 200 tons were baled a season was estimated at $1.45 a ton in 1945; for 100 tons, the cost was $1.95 a ton; and for 400 tons, $1.15 a ton. These figures do not include the cost of baling labor or the cost of use of tractor or motor vehicles.

Most of the automatic-tie, windrow, pick-up balers now in use are twine balers. Either one man or two men are commonly used for operating this type. The twine bales are lighter and bale breakage is more common than with wire bales. The wire bales are preferred when the hay is to be hauled long distances, because the bales are denser and more tons can be hauled per load. More hay can be handled per hour of labor with the automatic-tie baler than with the hand-tie baler, but (chiefly because of the higher initial cost of the automatic-tie baler) the cost per ton of baler use is higher than for the hand-tie pick-up baler.

Stationary balers are sometimes used for field baling, the hay usually being transported from windrow or shock to the baler with buck rakes. It usually takes about twice as much labor to bale, haul, and store a ton of hay with the stationary field baler as it does with the automatic-tie, pick-up baler. The initial cost and annual cost of use of the stationary baler is low, however, and it is relatively well adapted for use on farms where the quantity of hay baled is too small to justify the purchase of the more expensive windrow, pick-up baler.

Only 2 percent of the 1944 hay tonnage was chopped before storing, and an additional small amount was stored as long, loose hay and then chopped before it was fed.

In the humid areas hay is sometimes loaded on the wagons with hay loaders and hauled to barns where it is chopped and stored with stationary choppers and blowers, which are also used for handling row silage crops and grass silage. This method takes about as much labor to process, haul, and store a ton of hay as is required when automatic-tie balers are used, but somewhat less labor than when the hay loader is used for loading and the hay is stored as long loose hay. The machinery cost of using the loader, wagons, and stationary cutter and blower averaged about 55 cents a ton of hay in 1945, when the hay equipment was used to harvest 50 tons of hay and the cutter and blower were used to harvest 50 tons of hay and 100 of silage.

The use of field choppers is increasing, especially in districts where the weather is particularly favorable for curing. The field chopper is tractor drawn and often operates with power take-off, although some of the larger choppers have mounted motors. When field choppers are used for chopping and stationary blowers are used for storing in barns, an average of about six-tenths of a ton of hay is handled per hour of labor.

When the field chopper was used to chop 100 tons of hay and the same amount of silage crops in 1945, the estimated cost of use of the harvesting machinery and equipment, exclusive of the tractor power, averaged about $1.30 a ton. On farms where the chopper was used exclusively on hay crops, the cost of use of machinery and equipment averaged $1.30 a ton when 200 tons were handled annually, $2.30 a ton for 100 tons, and 75 cents a ton for 400 tons.

In the West, when chopped hay is stacked, the wagons often are equipped with slings, and the hay is unloaded with derrick stackers. Stationary blowers and elevators also are used for stacking chopped hay.

Farmers who have small tonnages of hay also have ways to make use of expensive equipment. Some buy the equipment and then obtain economic amounts of use and get back some of the costs by doing custom work for others. Some rent out their machines. Sometimes several farmers buy the equipment for use on each of their farms. A more common method is to hire the machines or have the work done by custom operators, whose charges are usually somewhat higher than the costs that result when the machine is purchased and used extensively—although the custom charges often are less than the costs incurred when the machine is bought but used only a little.

THE AUTHORS《《 *Albert P. Brodell, senior agricultural economist in the Bureau of Agricultural Economics, has been engaged in studies of farm practices and costs for 27 years. One of his publications, F.M. 57, Harvesting the Hay Crop, treats of the economics of many aspects of haying.*

Martin R. Cooper, principal agricultural economist in the Bureau of Agricultural Economics, has been engaged in research in farm management since 1912. He is a native of Ohio and has conducted studies of farm organization and cost in all regions of the United States. He has published many treatises of the subject.

ENSILING HAY AND PASTURE CROPS

J. B. SHEPHERD, R. E. HODGSON, N. R. ELLIS, J. R. MC CALMONT

MAKING part of the hay and pasture crops into silage has several advantages.

The grasses and legumes usually grown for hay and pasture are mostly biennial or perennial and are produced more cheaply than annual or cultivated crops. Silage can be made from them with about the same equipment (except a silage cutter) and labor that is needed for haymaking.

Because the crops are taken off the field and put into the silo soon after they are cut, there is little risk of weather damage during harvesting. About 80 to 85 percent of their value (as shown by experiments at Beltsville) is preserved for feeding; only 70 to 75 percent of the value of field-cured hay is preserved, even if it is made during good curing weather. Properly made grass silage will provide much more protein and several times more carotene in the ration than field-cured hay, increase materially the carotene and vitamin A content of winter milk, and help prevent an oxidized flavor in winter milk.

Surplus pasture herbage and heavy or weedy crops that might make only low-grade hay can be made into a palatable, nutritious silage, thus preventing waste. Silage is the best form in which to preserve surplus forage crops from one year to the next as insurance against drought. Ensiling also destroys the germinating powers of weed seeds and thus helps eradicate weeds from the farm.

Storing forage as silage ends the hazard of fire from spontaneous ignition of inadequately cured hay. Less space is needed to store crop dry matter as silage than as long, baled, or coarsely chopped hay. Silage is an easy form in which to feed forage to livestock; grass silage is particularly useful for feeding cattle and sheep.

About half of 1 percent of the American hay crop was ensiled in 1944—roughly equal to 1,500,000 tons of silage but relatively little as compared with the more than 40,000,000 tons made yearly from corn and the sorghums. In the Northeastern States, 1.6 percent of the hay crop was put into silos—in Massachusetts, 3.3 percent, and in Rhode Island 4.6 percent. But as farmers turn more and more to grassland farming and as they learn more about making grass silage and the advantages of feeding it, we believe the amount of the silage made from hay and pasture crops will increase greatly.

Many crops can be made into silage: Timothy, bromegrass, orchardgrass, Sudangrass, Kentucky bluegrass, Johnsongrass, succulent range grasses, alfalfa, soybeans, lespedeza, red clover, Ladino clover, cowpeas, kudzu, alsike clover, crimson clover, and others, even though they differ widely in physical characteristics, in chemical composition, and in yield, as well as palatability.

Some of them can be ensiled in the same manner as corn or the sorghums. Others need a somewhat different kind of treatment.

Legumes or grass and legume mixtures usually make a more nutritious silage than do grasses alone. Adapted, high-yielding crops are the most satisfactory. Especially suitable for use as hay, pasture, or silage are combination crops such as alfalfa with timothy or bromegrass, and timothy, bromegrass, or orchardgrass with Ladino clover and red clover or alsike clover.

A rule of thumb is that crops that are palatable when grazed or fed green or as dry hay also make a palatable silage. Likewise, crops that are unpalatable when grazed or fed green or dry are usually unpalatable as silage. Furthermore, feeding trials conducted with some crops indicate that the dry matter contained in silage of good quality will have about the same feeding value as an equal quantity of dry matter in good-quality hay made from the same crop, and better than the dry matter contained in poor hay.

The transformation of green crops into silage is brought about by the changes that take place when the green forage is stored in a silo in the absence of air. Plant respiration, enzymes present in plant cells, and bacteria, yeasts, and molds present on the crop when it is ensiled all take part in this change.

After the crop is ensiled, plant respiration continues until the oxygen present in the air and trapped in the forage is used up and replaced by carbon dioxide and nitrogen. There follows a rise in the temperature of the forage, the extent of the rise depending upon the amount of oxygen present.

Enzymes are also active during this time. They break down sugars into alcohol, carbonic acid, water, and acetic, lactic, and butyric acids. The enzymes act on proteins to some extent, forming amino acids, peptides, and some ammonia.

As plant respiration and the activity of the plant enzymes slow down, the activity of the bacteria, yeasts, and molds increases. Molds cease growing as soon as the air is exhausted, yeasts soon disappear, and only the bacteria remain active thereafter. Bacteria produce additional acid from soluble car-

Suggested Quantities of Preservatives To Use in Making Silages

[Per ton of crop ensiled]

Silage	Molasses	Phosphoric acid (75 percent)	Corn and cob meal	Ground corn, barley, or wheat	Whey, dried [1]
	Pounds	*Pounds*	*Pounds*	*Pounds*	*Pounds*
Legumes, fresh green:					
Alfalfa, red clover..................	80	20	200	150	40
Soybeans, Ladino clover.............	100	30	250	200	60
Legumes, wilted: All crops [2]............	60	15	150	100	30
Legumes and grasses mixed, before grass is headed out:					
Fresh green......................	80	20	200	150	40
Wilted [2].........................	60	15	100	100	30
Legumes and grasses mixed, after grass is headed out:					
Fresh green [2].....................	60	15	100	100	30
Wilted...........................	None	None	None	None	None
Grasses and cereals before heading out:					
Fresh green......................	60	20	200	150	40
Wilted [2]..........................	40	10	100	100	30
Grasses and cereals after heading out:					
Fresh green [2].....................	40	10	100	75	20
Wilted...........................	None	None	None	None	None

[1] Concentrated whey may also be used, applying 2 to 3 times the weight indicated for dry whey. Liquid whey can be used only with wilted crops, but may be added at 10 times the rate indicated for dry whey, as a means of utilizing the product.

[2] Preservatives may be omitted when the silos are smooth and airtight, and when good silo filling methods are carefully followed.

Comparative Preservation of Dry Matter, Protein, and Carotene in Alfalfa Harvested and Stored as Field-Cured Hay and as Silage, 1945–46 [1]

Alfalfa	Dry matter	Protein		Carotene	
		Total yield	In dry matter	Total yield	In dry matter
	Percent	*Percent*	*Percent*	*Percent*	*mcg. per gm.*
Wilted alfalfa silage..................	83	85	20.6	34	92
Field-cured alfalfa hay................	75	69	18.2	3	9

[1] Silages and hays from same crop and fields harvested at the same time. Averages for 3 crops harvested at Beltsville in which the constituents retained in the silo and in the haymow are compared with those present in the green material as cut.

bohydrates and from alcohol, and are responsible for further break-down products from the other constituents of silage, notably protein. They are responsible for most of the losses of dry matter and feeding constituents that occur during fermentation and storage.

When the acidity of the silage increases beyond a certain point, bacterial action diminishes, and the silage-making process is completed.

The Massachusetts Agricultural Experiment Station found wide variations in the type of fermentation, the kinds of acids produced, and the quality of the silage. Many investigators have learned that the type of fermentation produced and the quality of the silage produced can be modified by suitable methods of silage making. They also learned that the inclusion of acids and sugars or other readily available carbohydrates at the time of siloing modifies the type of fermentation, increases the acidity, and tends to reduce the breakdown of protein compounds. Thus the farmer can control pretty well the fermentation process and produce good grass silage from many crops under many conditions.

Standards by which the quality of silage may be judged were set up by the American Dairy Science Association committee on silage methods in 1942. These standards are:

a. Very Good: Clean, acid odor and taste, no butyric acid, no mold, sliminess or proteolysis, acid pH of 3.5 to 4.2, ammonia nitrogen less than 10 percent of total nitrogen.

b. Good: Acid odor and taste, trace only of butyric acid, acid pH of 4.2 to 4.5, ammonia nitrogen 10 to 15 percent of total nitrogen.

c. Fair: Some butyric acid, slight proteolysis or some mold, acid pH 4.5 to 4.8, ammonia nitrogen 15 to 20 percent of total nitrogen.

d. Poor: High butyric acid, high proteolysis, sliminess or mold, acid pH above 4.8, ammonia nitrogen about 20 percent of total nitrogen.

Several factors influence the type of fermentation produced, the nature and extent of the losses occurring during fermentation and storage, and the quality of the silage produced. Among them are the maturity and chemical composition of the crop, the ratio of soluble carbohydrates to the mineral base content of the crop, its percentage of moisture when stored, the rapidity and completeness with which air is excluded from the silo, and atmospherical temperatures when the crop is ensiled.

In handling the crop for silage, the farmer should cut the forage when it has a high content of protein and carotene and when the yield of total digestible nutrients per acre is high. He should ensile it in a way that will produce a good, palatable silage with the least loss of feed nutrients and the least wear and tear on the silo.

In doing so, he will need to give proper consideration to the stage of maturity at which to cut; the moisture content at which to store; the need for and use of preservatives; the length of cut to use; the distribution and packing of the crop in the silo; and the sealing out of the air when the silo is full. He will have to adapt his methods to the type and condition of his silo. He also will want to use methods that permit the most efficient use of labor and the power and equipment he has.

To produce grass silage that meets those specifications requires first that it be cut at an immature stage while it is still reasonably high in protein and carotene and relatively low in crude fiber. This stage corresponds closely with that recommended for early-cut hay from the various crops.

Most grasses should be cut after the heads have emerged but before the plants have started to bloom. Alfalfa should be cut at an early bloom stage (one-tenth to one-fourth in bloom). Most clovers should be cut when they have reached half to full bloom, but before the blossoms have turned brown. Soybeans, lespedeza, and cowpeas should be cut soon after the first seed pods have filled. Cereal crops like oats, wheat, and barley may be cut any time from a prebloom to a milk or early dough stage, depending upon the relative importance of a high protein and carotene content compared with a high total silage yield. Where mixtures of grasses and legumes are ensiled, the crop should be cut at a stage best suited to the kind of crop that predominates in the mixture.

The moisture content of the crop at the time of ensiling is the most important factor in determining the character of the silage fermentation, the extent and character of the losses

Labor and Machinery Hours Required in Harvesting and Storing Alfalfa as Silage and as Hay, 1945–46 [1]

[Per ton of dry matter preserved]

Hours and operations	Wilted alfalfa silage	Field-cured hay
Man-hours (all operations)...............................	4. 87	4. 33
Tractor-hours (all operations).............................	1. 35	1. 57
Mower-hours (tractor-operated)...........................	. 47	. 53
Rake-hours (tractor-operated)............................	. 35	. 84
Loader-hours (truck-drawn)..............................	. 48	. 44
Truck-hours (loading, hauling, unloading).................	1. 66	1. 19
Silo-filler-hours (tractor-operated).......................	. 54	....
Hay-hoist-hours (tractor-operated).......................	....	. 30

[1] Average of 3 cuttings.

Dry Matter, Protein, and Carotene Losses in Grass Silage, With Palatability Data [1]

Experimental difference	Moisture	Dry matter eaten [2]	Losses in the silo exclusive of top spoilage		
			Dry matter	Protein	Carotene
	Percent	Pounds	Percent	Percent	Percent
Higher moisture.......................	70. 6	21. 4	10. 3	4. 8	22. 2
Lower moisture [3]......................	45. 0	24. 8	8. 3	2. 8	38. 3
Higher pH (4.76)......................	62. 6	22. 9	8. 7	7. 6	30. 5
Lower pH (4.36), by molasses [4]..........	61. 5	24. 2	8. 6	7. 8	23. 5
Higher pH (5.18)......................	66. 8	23. 6	7. 7	6. 6	26. 2
Lower pH (3.66), by 2–N acids [5]........	67. 9	16. 3	5. 0	2. 9	9. 3

[1] Averages obtained from a large number of trials.
[2] Dry matter consumed per cow per day.
[3] By wilting or added dry matter. Average of 25 comparisons.
[4] Various additions of molasses. Average of 19 comparisons.
[5] By additions of mineral acids.

through seepage and fermentation, and the quality of the silage produced.

An excessively high moisture content leads to large losses of liquid. Too little (under 60 percent) results in molding and spoiling of the silage. The silo should have adequate drainage so the silage will not become waterlogged and the silo damaged from too high pressures against the wall. Except during long dry spells, the moisture content of crops cut for silage at the stages of maturity indicated will usually range between 74 and 78 percent, but may sometimes equal or exceed 80 percent, being highest for the clover, soybeans, and grasses and cereals cut at a very immature stage. Lespedeza, an exception, usually does not contain more than 65 to 70 percent moisture when cut for hay or silage. During long dry spells, the moisture content of most crops may be down to 70 percent or below.

When crops are ensiled with a moisture content of more than 70 percent, fermentation takes place at a rapid rate, there is considerable seepage from the silo, and losses of most feed nutrients, except carotene, are large. If no treatment other than chopping is given, the type of fermentation will be desirable and the silage will be of good quality provided the crop ensiled consists principally or entirely of grasses or cereals that are cut after heading out and that contain a medium or low amount of protein. On the other hand, the type of fermentation will be undesirable and the silage will be of poor quality and have a strong, offensive odor if the ensiled crop consists principally or entirely of legumes or of grasses and cereals that are cut before heading out and that have a high protein content.

Long experience at the Agricultural Research Center at Beltsville, the Ohio Agricultural Experiment Station at Wooster, and elsewhere, however, has shown that a desirable type of fermentation and a mild, good-quality silage can be produced from these high-protein crops by simply wilting them slightly in the field to a moisture content below 70 percent.

When wilting is not possible because of unfavorable weather, the same results can be obtained by adding 5 to 15 percent of dry hay as the crop goes through the chopper. When the moisture content of the crop is reduced to 68 percent or below, the fermentation rate is reduced and seepage from the silo is eliminated. The best silage is made when the moisture of the material is not above 68 percent or under 60 percent. But occasional loads may contain as much as 70 percent or as little as 55 percent of moisture without materially affecting the quality.

Wilting high-moisture crops for silage, as we have indicated, not only produces a mild, palatable silage that will be consumed in normal roughage amounts; wilting also reduces the losses of nutrients (except carotene) that usually occur when the silo is filled with comparable unwilted materials.

For that reason, wilting all high-moisture crops for silage is advantageous regardless of whether preservatives are added. Even with the higher carotene losses, the carotene content of the silage will be considerably higher on a dry-matter basis than the carotene content of dry hay, and the liberal feeding of such silage will result in the production of winter milk with a higher vitamin A content than can be obtained from the feeding of dry hay. Furthermore, cows will eat more dry matter in wilted silage than they will in high-moisture silage. Wilting also reduces the weight of crop to be handled, causes less pressure against the silo walls and less softening of the mortar of masonry walls, and lowers the cost of ensiling.

But care should be taken not to wilt the crop too much, and the part that is wilted most should be placed in the lower part of the silo. The walls of silos used for wilted silage should be airtight and smooth. Wood-stave silos that cannot be made practically airtight by screwing up the nuts on the reinforcing bands should not be used for wilted silage because there is too little moisture in a wilted crop to swell the staves and cause them to tighten naturally.

A good deal of attention has been given to the possible benefits derived from the addition of other materials— commonly called preservatives—to grass silage. Investigators have tested many materials, including phosphoric acid, cultures of lactic acid bacteria, whey, molasses, ground corn, wheat and other cereals, salt, urea, dry ice (solid carbon dioxide), hydrochloric and sulfuric acid, and other acids.

Mineral acids increase the acidity of the crop immediately to a pH of 4.2 to 4.0 or below; prevent most of the plant respiration, enzyme action, and bacterial activity; and preserve the crop with the least change and with only small losses of nutrients.

Materials such as whey, molasses, and ground dry grains modify the natural fermentation process, produce a more desirable type of fermentation, and increase somewhat the acidity of the silage (pH range of 4.0 to 4.5). Dry grains also lower the average moisture content slightly and reduce the seepage from high-moisture crops.

Generally speaking, an acid medium (whether obtained by direct addition of an acid or by desirable acid fermentation) is the best preservative of carotene and other constituents.

Salt has little effect on the fermentation process and is of little practical value in silage making.

No desirable effects and no practical value have been found from the use of urea, dry ice, or cultures of lactic acid bacteria added with or without salt.

The preservatives most generally used in this country are phosphoric acid (68 percent or more of P_2O_5), cane or blackstrap molasses, and ground corn or wheat. The operator should be cautious in handling phosphoric acid because of its corrosive nature. It is necessary to feed ground limestone or some source of calcium or sodium carbonate to the animal at the rate of approximately 1 ounce for each 10 pounds of silage in order to neutralize the mineral acid and prevent any undesirable effects it might have.

Preservatives are most useful with high-moisture crops and crops high in protein. They have the least value with low- or medium-protein crops and crops low in moisture; often the preservatives do little more than to make the silage more palatable. If the crop is extremely high in moisture, the silage may sometimes be of poor quality even though preservatives are added. It is therefore generally recognized that a better silage is produced when the crop is wilted slightly as well. When the crop is wilted, less of the preservatives is needed because at that moisture level the fermentation process is slowed down, less undesirable fermentation is produced, and the losses (except of carotene) are usually small.

If the crop has been wilted to below 68 percent moisture, undesirable fermentations are seldom produced in high-protein silage, even though the acidity is relatively low, and the actual need for a preservative has usually been eliminated. Nevertheless, some farmers prefer to use preservatives with slightly wilted crops to insure the best preservation of nutrients and carotene under such conditions.

Another factor to be considered in using preservatives is their added cost, which is sometimes quite high, particularly the cost of ground grains. It is true that a considerable part of the nutritive value of the preservatives is usually retained in the silage, but if sufficient forage is available these additional nutrients are not required for their nutritive value. The use of preservatives therefore should be limited to the actual need for them.

Experience at Beltsville, at several experiment stations, and on thousands of farms demonstrates that good silage can be produced without preservatives from almost any type of crop if the proper methods are followed.

Grasses and cereals cut after heading out or a mixture of such crops with legumes can be made into a mild, good-quality feeding silage without preservatives when ensiled in the fresh green state. The fermentation rate will be slowed down, fermentation and storage losses will be reduced, and the palatability of the silage will be increased by wilting the crop slightly before ensiling.

Immature grasses and cereals cut before heading out, or crops consisting principally or entirely of legumes, can be made into good silage by wilting them down to a moisture content of 68 percent or slightly less.

We have pointed out that control of the fermentation process through the use of preservatives increases the acidity of the silage and makes for a better preservation of feed nutrients and carotene.

Wilted silages made without preservatives usually have an acidity within the pH range 4.0 to 5.0, depending on the crop. Wilted alfalfa silage often has a pH of 4.6 to 4.8. Even with a pH above 4.5, such silage nevertheless has good quality; the losses (except of carotene) are smaller, and it has greater palatability (as shown by the consumption of dry matter by dairy cows) than high-moisture silage made with preservatives.

Wilted silages made without preservatives also contain some protein break-down products, but these occur in only relatively small quantities if the silage is properly made. Part of these break-down products consist of amides and peptides, which are generally conceded to have a high nutritive value.

They also contain some ammonia nitrogen, which has generally been thought to have little value. It is now known that ruminants, for which silage is usually made, however, can and do utilize ammonia nitrogen for protein under favorable conditions when the ration fed is low in protein, through the activity of the bacteria in the rumen or paunch. The presence of a small amount of ammonia nitrogen in mild, palatable, wilted silage is therefore of little economic significance, as the production of cows fed wilted silage in feeding experiments at Beltsville demonstrates. We believe, then, that neither the pH of the silage nor the amount of ammonia nitrogen produced can be used as criteria of the quality of wilted grass silage in the same sense that they are used for high-moisture silage.

Sometimes farmers have failed to produce good silage by the wilting method. The cause can usually be traced to a failure to follow closely the methods required for handling and siloing the crop, to the use of a silo in need of repair, or to unfavorable weather during the silo-filling period. These failures are sometimes unavoidable and they demonstrate that making wilted silage without preservatives is not always practical.

As we stated previously, wilting slightly is desirable for all silage made from high-moisture crops. The discussion that follows on crop wilting, length of cut, and silo filling and sealing applies to silage made with and without preservatives. The problems of silo filling are somewhat different for trench, stack, and temporary silos than for the ordinary permanent upright tower silo or the permanent round pit-type silo.

In preparing the crop for silage, the usual tendency is to wilt it too much rather than too little, although with unfavorable weather it is sometimes impossible to wilt it as much as is desirable. With a little practice, the farmer can readily determine when the proper stage is reached.

The aim should be to wilt the crop slightly, to a moisture content between 65–70 percent but not below 60 percent. If the leaves become dry and curled, the wilting may have progressed too far unless the crop is heavy and the underside of the swath is in an unwilted state. The crop will have wilted sufficiently when the leaves and stems become limp. The stems can be readily twisted in two and the broken ends will have a dark, moist, but not excessively juicy, appearance. On rubbing the chopped crop between the hands, the material will feel cool and moist, but no free water will appear when a ball of the chopped crop is squeezed in the hands.

One or two hours on a good drying day may be sufficient to wilt the crop to the desired moisture level unless the crop is very heavy or very high in moisture. On a good drying day, therefore, the crop should not be cut too far ahead of loading and silo filling. During prolonged dry weather, crops cut at the usual stage will be ready to ensile within a few minutes after mowing. On very humid days, a half day to a day may be required to wilt the crop sufficiently. During rainy spells, the mowed crop may sometimes be in the field 2 or 3 days before it wilts enough to be siloed.

Too rapid wilting in good weather may make desirable the use of a wind-rowing attachment on the mower cutter bar or a side delivery rake to follow behind the mower. If the crop is not too heavy, combining two mowed swaths into one windrow will speed the loading and filling operations. If part of the crop gets too dry and is dusty when chopped and blown into the silo, fresh unwilted forage should be run through the cutter along with the drier material. Both partially dry and fresh green forage can be hauled on the same load if field conditions permit.

When rain interferes with silo filling operations, the rain-wet portion can be siloed without wilting by filling the silo at the slow rate of 3 to 4 feet a day so that some heat will be generated; or it can be siloed at a normal rate by running dry hay (10 to 20 percent), ground dry grain (5 to 12 percent), or molasses (3 to 5 percent), through the cutter with the wet crop.

Except for short and very immature crops put up under special conditions, it is necessary to chop the crop as it is siloed. The length of cut to use will depend upon the moisture content at which the crop is siloed. If the moisture content is 72 percent or more, the cutter should be set for a ½- to ⅝-inch theoretical cut. (The actual average length of cut will be much longer than this because many of the crop stems go through the cutter crosswise.) Crops with a high moisture content will pack well with this comparatively long cut and are less apt to clog up the blower pipe than when a shorter cut is used.

When the moisture content of the crop is 70 percent or less as ensiled, the cutter should be set for a shorter cut of not more than one-fourth to three-eighths inch. If the crop is wilted considerably, the cut used should not exceed one-fourth inch. Here, too, many of the stems go through crosswise with an actual longer average length, and this short cut must be used in order to get the crop to pack satisfactorily and exclude the air. The drier crop is not apt to clog the blower when a short cut is used. Failure to use a fine cut when the crop is wilted will prevent close packing, will cause considerable air to be trapped in the silage, and also will cause some mold.

When a field chopper is used, more crop stems go through the chopper lengthwise and a shorter average cut is obtained with the same theoretical cut than where a stationary chopper is used. For this reason, the theoretical length of cut used with a field chopper may be five-eighths or three-fourths inch with crops containing 72 percent or more of moisture; and three-eighths to one-half inch with crops containing 70 percent or less of moisture. If the field chopper used will not cut the forage short enough, this can be accomplished by rechopping through a stationary silage cutter.

During silo filling the cutter knives should be kept sharp. Knives should be changed just as soon as they fail to cut clean and begin to shred the material. The cutter bar against which the cutter knives operate should be changed or turned before its edge becomes rounded enough to cause shredding rather than cutting.

In making grass silage, satisfactory results will be obtained only if the silo has smooth, airtight walls and tight doors. The silo should be well reinforced so that it will withstand high silage pressures. It should be provided with an adequate drain so that any excess moisture in the silage can drain off easily and quickly.

When the silo is being filled, the crop material should not be allowed to pile up in the center of the silo. It should be kept well distributed over the entire area and well tramped near the wall. This is particularly important when the crop is wilted slightly. Good distribution and thorough packing are absolutely necessary in the top part of the silo.

Only heavy, unwilted crops should be used for the last few loads so that enough weight and pressure will be provided to force the air out and keep it out. No preservative will be needed in this wet top layer even if the crop is high in protein, because the material at the top warms up sufficiently to prevent undesirable fermentations and naturally makes a mild, palatable silage.

After the silo is filled, the top should be thoroughly tramped once a day for 2 or 3 days and kept packed tightly against the wall for 2 or 3 weeks until the silage has completely settled. Top losses can be reduced by seeding oats on top to help make a good air seal.

Top losses can be reduced also by covering the top of the ensiled material with a heavy, reinforced, waterproof paper, which is lapped 10 to 12 inches at the seams and against the wall and covered with enough wet crop or other material to keep it packed tight against the wall and against the silage below. If the silage is to be stored for some time, more material should be placed on top of the paper than if the silo is to be opened soon.

The rate at which the silo is filled affects the rapidity with which the air is eliminated from the silo and, consequently, the temperature which the ensiled mass attains. If the silo is tight and is properly filled and sealed, the temperature will seldom exceed 100° F., except at the top, and may sometimes not exceed 90°. If the ensiled material is high in moisture, or if the weather is cool, silo temperatures will be lower than when the crop is wilted or the weather is warm. When the silo is filled with a high-moisture crop, particularly in cool, moist weather, there may be an advantage in filling at a slow or moderate rate; that will allow the ensiled material to warm up slightly. That procedure also will help to prevent an undesirable type of fermentation.

When the silo is filled during a long dry spell or with a wilted crop, it should be filled rapidly in order to hold silo temperatures down to a desirable level. Spoilage is apt to occur on the surface of the ensiled material if more than 2 days elapse between filling periods. When such an interval occurs, the top of the material should be kept tramped thoroughly in the meantime, and any spoiled silage removed before filling is resumed. Where one crop only partially fills the silo

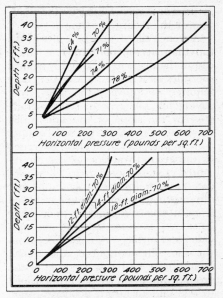

Grass silage pressures at silo wall: (Top) With different moisture contents in 12-foot diameter silos, and (lower) with a 70-percent moisture content in different sized silos.

and another crop is put in some time later, the silo should be tramped, sealed, and weighted down between fillings to keep silage temperatures and losses as low as possible.

So far we have discussed mostly the making of grass silage in permanent upright silos or in pit-type silos. Where permanent silos are not available or are too small to hold the entire crop, trench, modified trench-stack silos, or temporary fence silos and stack silos can be used with little or no cash outlay. Good-quality silage can be made in these different types from most grassland crops and cannery waste by the same general principles outlined in the foregoing, although certain minor modifications may be needed to meet specific conditions.

A trench silo, as its name implies, is simply a trench dug into the ground. The size of its cross section is limited by the smallest number of animals to be fed each day, so that 2 or more inches are removed from the entire cross section or open face every 2 days.

Its length is determined by the duration of the feeding season.

A trench silo should be wider at the top than at the bottom. This shape causes the silage to pack tightly against the sides as it settles, and is generally required to prevent the sides from caving in. The type of soil generally governs the slope of the side walls; the lighter, more friable soils require a greater slope. The depth is governed by the ground-water level and the required cross-sectional area. These silos can be made for the expense or labor of removing the soil. The soil removed from the trench is generally piled along its sides to increase its depth and provide good surface drainage away from the silo. The bottom of the trench should never be below the level of the ground water and should always slope to one end to afford good drainage. Trench silos are often made permanent by lining with concrete, cement plaster, brick, or stone.

Trench silos can be filled economically. A blower is not needed, although it speeds up the operation by using less labor to distribute the chopped material evenly. The silage should always be kept level and thoroughly tramped or packed during filling operations. Packing can be done by driving animals or some machine back and forth through the silo as the filling progresses. In completing the filling of these silos, the crop should be piled high enough so that it will be above ground level after settling, with an arch to the top. The surface should be covered immediately with a thin layer of freshly cut crop or weeds, which in turn should be covered with 6 to 12 inches or more of earth. Or, the surface can be sealed with heavy fiber-reinforced waterproof paper. If paper is used, the joints should be lapped about 12 inches and the paper weighted with enough earth to give a good seal.

If the silo is filled too rapidly and the forage is not packed sufficiently while filling, the forage may settle below ground level within a few days after filling has been completed. This may permit surface water to enter and produce a strong-smelling, unpalatable silage.

When the ground-water level is high, a modified shallow-trench type of stack silo can be used. The stack should be built up above the ground level with the sides of the chopped material straight and even with the edge of the trench. The stack can be built 4 to 6 feet above the ground level at the sides, and 8 feet at the center. When stacking is completed, the top should be well arched and covered with weedy material or reinforced paper and weighted down with 12 to 18 inches of earth to provide weight for packing and sealing. As the stack settles, earth should also be placed along the sides and ends to provide a seal.

When the silage is fed out, only one end is opened and the feeding is done from the vertical end surface. To prevent spoilage, only a short section of the trench or trench stack is uncovered at one time.

Good silage can also be made when uncut material is placed in trench or modified trench stack silos. When uncut material is placed in these silos, special care must be used to see that it is properly distributed and compacted. The portion of the pile above ground level should be well formed and the surface well sealed and weighted. Silage thus made is a little more difficult to feed out, but when it is sliced off the end with a hay knife, broadax, or machete, the work involved is not excessive.

Fence silos built with successive rings of 2- by 4-inch-mesh welded steel, triangular steel mesh, or wood slat fencing, and lined with a fiber-reinforced paper are valuable in putting up silage in emergencies, when permanent silos are not available, or when the cost is not justified.

Fence silos should not be built to a height of more than twice their diameter unless poles are set at from 4 to 6 points around their circumference. Poles, when they are used, should be tied together at the top; the fencing

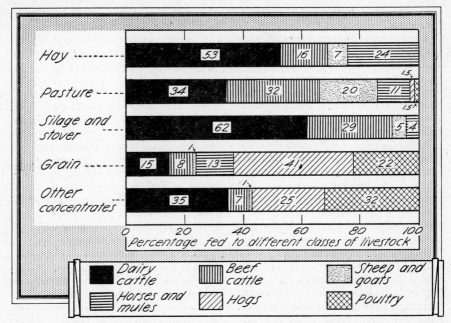

Percentages of each feed fed to different classes of livestock, the United States, 1941–42.

should never be fastened to them. When the silage is to be held from spring or early summer to winter feeding time, the silo should be lined with two thicknesses of paper.

These silos will make and preserve good silage, but care is needed during filling operations to keep the top of the silage level and well tramped. A space 12 to 15 inches wide should be leveled where the first ring of the fence is to rest. Special care is needed to keep this foundation level. When the first ring of fencing is half full, a second ring is placed inside the first, lapping 4 inches and temporarily lashed in place with twine. The lining for this ring is placed inside that for the first. When the second ring is half filled, a third ring is placed, and so on. When the third ring of fencing is half full, the twine binding the first and second rings together is cut to allow the second to telescope inside the first.

The chopped material should never be allowed to pile up in the center of the silo while filling but should be arched slightly at the top. An extra

ring of paper extending 18 inches above the fence is valuable in sealing the top surface. This ring is filled with silage and after the surface settles and has been tramped for 2 or 3 days after filling operations cease, it is folded in and a layer of paper is placed over the top and weighted down. Such a covering is desirable where the silo is not to be opened for several months.

Stack silos are often used for preserving cannery refuse, pea vines, beet tops, or pulp, and can be used for grass silage. The loss is much higher than in other types of silos, however, and the quality of the silage is lower. Bundles or bales of forage placed in a circle can be used to support and protect a stack of chopped material. In that case, the bundles or bales should be supported by bands of No. 9 wire spaced from 2 to 4 feet on centers as required. This system protects the silage better and offers the advantage of having chopped material to feed.

The cost of putting up grass silage will vary with the size of the operation, the efficiency with which machinery is used, and what equipment is at hand.

If a farmer ensiles several cuttings of forage crops, including pasture clippings, he will make much more silage with the same machines than a farmer who fills silos only once or twice a season. The machinery cost therefore will be lower. Labor can be saved by using a field chopper and a silage blower for filling operations.

A tractor mower with a windrow attachment offers a way to cut labor and equipment requirements. On light crops, a side-delivery rake can be used to throw two or more swaths or windrows together; loading operations are thus speeded up and labor and equipment requirements are reduced.

Studies on the cost of making grass silage at the New Jersey Dairy Research Farm show that the lowest cost per ton of silage is closely associated with high yield per acre and high tonnage per day. These costs are also lowest for the greatest mechanization. Since labor costs have gone up proportionately more than machinery since 1940, the efficient use of machines is a major factor in keeping down the costs of silage. Work at the Agricultural Research Center at Beltsville shows that more feed value per acre can be

obtained from forage crops with only slightly more labor and with about the same equipment requirements when the crop is preserved as silage as when it is preserved as hay.

THE AUTHORS «« *J. B. Shepherd is a dairy husbandman in charge of pasture and forage investigations, Division of Nutrition and Physiology of the Bureau of Dairy Industry. He is a graduate of the University of Nebraska and since 1917 has been engaged in research having to do with dairy production, pastures, forage, and grass silage and its utilization as feed.*

R. E. Hodgson is assistant chief of the Bureau of Dairy Industry.

N. R. Ellis is a chemist in charge of animal nutrition investigations in the Bureau of Animal Industry. His research has included the biochemistry of animal fats, swine nutrition, and vitamin requirements of animals.

J. R. McCalmont is an agricultural engineer in the Bureau of Plant Industry, Soils, and Agricultural Engineering. He was graduated from Iowa State College in 1927. Since 1930 he has studied farm structures, silage pressures, and silo construction. He is now in charge of livestock shelter investigations.

Grass and Rotations

GRASS AND THE YIELDS OF CASH CROPS

R. E. UHLAND

FARMERS generally recognize that continuous cropping to the same crop lowers the productive power of the soil. Data from tests at State and Federal agricultural experiment stations prove that when corn is grown after grass the yields may be several times greater than when corn is grown year after year.

In 1927 the Illinois Agricultural Experiment Station reported an experiment it had been carrying on for 39 years. For the last 9 years of the investigation the average yield of corn when the crop was grown continually on the same land was 24 bushels per acre. The average yield for the first 9 years was 41 bushels per acre—showing that the yield for the last 9-year period was 41.5 percent less than that for the first 9-year period. The average yield for the last 22 years was 25.1 bushels per acre, compared with a yield of 50 bushels for corn grown in a 3-year rotation following clover. When fertilizer and manure were applied, the yield of corn grown year after year on the same land averaged 40.5 bushels per acre. The same treatment applied to rotated land produced a yield of 66.6 bushels. The yield of corn on treated land following clover was 2.65 times as great as that for continuous corn grown on untreated land.

Research at the Indiana Agricultural Experiment Station, at La Fayette, offered proof that after 20 years of continuous cropping with corn, yields were reduced from 62 bushels per acre to 40 bushels. This decrease of 22 bushels occurred even though ample fertilization was practiced. When corn was grown in a rotation following clover and grass, the yield for the same period increased from 56 bushels to 65 bushels to the acre.

The accompanying figure on corn yields shows the importance of legumes and grasses in boosting yields in a number of sections of the country. For example, in a 14-year test at Wooster, Ohio, the yield of corn grown in a 3-year and a 5-year rotation with alfalfa was approximately three times as high as when corn was grown continually. That is, by following a good crop rotation, farmers in the Corn Belt can produce as much corn on a given acreage in 1 year as in 3 years of growing corn year after year.

The largest percentage increase in yield was obtained in a 3-year test at Auburn, Ala. Corn grown annually on untreated land yielded an average of 3.3 bushels an acre. This yield is in contrast with an average yield of 33.7 bushels when corn followed well-established kudzu. This land had been fertilized. When corn following kudzu received an application of sodium

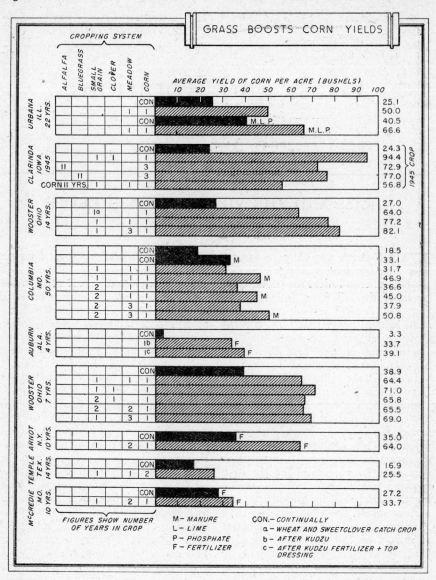

GRASS BOOSTS CORN YIELDS

CROPPING SYSTEM

AVERAGE YIELD OF CORN PER ACRE (BUSHELS)

FIGURES SHOW NUMBER
OF YEARS IN CROP

M — MANURE
L — LIME
P — PHOSPHATE
F — FERTILIZER

CON. — CONTINUALLY
a — WHEAT AND SWEETCLOVER CATCH CROP
b — AFTER KUDZU
c — AFTER KUDZU FERTILIZER + TOP
       DRESSING

nitrate in addition to regular fertilizer, the yield was 39.1 bushels.

The data from Clarinda, Iowa, show that this decline in corn yields was quickly checked by substituting a good crop rotation. The corn yield in 1945 for the fourteenth consecutive crop was 24.3 bushels an acre. On an adjacent area that had been cropped to corn for 11 years, then to oats in 1943,

and clover-and-timothy meadow in 1944, the 1945 corn yield was 56.8 bushels. That yield, however, was only 60 percent as great as the yield of 94.4 bushels on the field where a rotation had been followed for the 14 years.

It should be pointed out that the soil on this continuous corn plot at Clarinda had suffered a great deal because of erosion and deterioration. In-

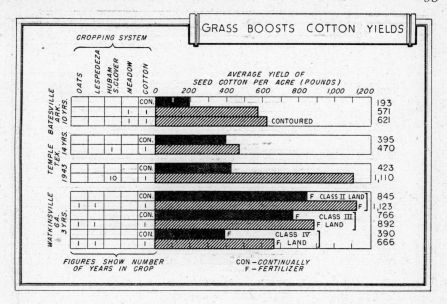

GRASS BOOSTS COTTON YIELDS

sects and diseases had become more injurious. The land, however, still possessed enormous soil resources, which made possible the 32.5-bushel increase in corn yield. This fact emphasizes the urgency of using rotations, including grasses and legumes, while there is still soil to conserve.

Corn after 11 years of alfalfa at Clarinda yielded 106 bushels per acre—compared with 86 bushels produced on plots where a 3-year rotation had been followed for 12 years, and 76 bushels an acre for corn following 11 years of bluegrass. The 1944 and 1945 yields for the rotated plots were 85.2 and 94.4 bushels, respectively. The yields of second- and third-year corn following 11 years of alfalfa were 83.5 and 72.9 bushels, respectively. Yields for second- and third-year corn following 11 years of bluegrass were 68.9 and 77.0 bushels, respectively. These data show that although corn yields following alfalfa were higher than yields following bluegrass, the decline in yield was more rapid when several crops of corn followed alfalfa.

The residual effect of grass in reducing erosion is also much greater than that of a legume like alfalfa

grown alone. For best results in controlling erosion as well as for boosting and maintaining yields, a grass-and-legume mixture should be used. At Clarinda the soil loss through erosion for first-year corn following both alfalfa and bluegrass was only 0.1 ton an acre. For second- and third-year corn following alfalfa, the total soil loss was 15.1 tons, compared with 5.6 tons from second- and third-year corn following bluegrass. The average annual soil loss from land cropped continually to corn for 11 years was 38.3 tons an acre. For this same period the average loss from land in corn following meadow in a 3-year rotation was 18.4 tons. The annual loss from rotation meadow was 0.3 ton an acre, from alfalfa 0.01 ton an acre, and from bluegrass 0.03 ton.

Cotton, like corn, gives much higher yields and permits less erosion when grown in rotation following a legume or a grass-legume mixture than when grown year after year on the same land. In a 10-year test at Batesville, Ark., reported in the accompanying figure, cotton in rotation yielded almost three times as much as when grown continually. By planting and

EFFECT OF CROP SEQUENCE ON YIELDS

AVERAGE YIELD PER ACRE (BUSHELS)

CROPPING SYSTEM	CORN	OATS	WHEAT
LA FAYETTE IND. 18 YRS. 18 YRS. 18 YRS.			
WHEAT AFTER CORN			23.0
WHEAT AFTER OATS			22.1
WHEAT AFTER CLOVER			31.2
OATS AFTER CORN		47.9	
OATS AFTER CLOVER		51.8	
CORN AFTER CORN	50.1		
CORN AFTER CLOVER	57.7		
ST. PAUL MINN. 29 YRS.			
CORN CONTINUALLY	36.7		
CORN CONTINUALLY		48.4	
CORN, OATS	40.2	62.8	
CORN, OATS, HAY	46.2	63.3	
CORN, OATS, WHEAT, HAY	48.6	65.7	24.4
CORN, OATS, WHEAT, HAY, PASTURE	49.7	64.6	23.6
URBANA ILL. 1888-1926			
CORN CONTINUALLY	31.1		
CORN, OATS	38.0	37.3	
CORN, OATS, CLOVER	49.3	45.9	

cultivating rotation cotton on the contour, the yield was increased 8.8 percent over rotation cotton not on the contour. Contouring saved both soil and water.

At Temple, Tex., the seed-cotton yield in 1943 for the tenth consecutive crop was 423 pounds to the acre. The same year cotton grown on land that had been alternately cropped with Hubam sweetclover yielded 1,110 pounds, an increase of 162 percent due to the use of sweetclover.

The results at Watkinsville, Ga., show that cotton grown in rotation following oats and Kobe lespedeza yielded much more than when grown continually. This was true for all Land Capability Classes. These increases were obtained on areas that were heavily fertilized. Fertilizers increase the yields but they do not take the place of good crop rotations.

As indicated in the chart on crop sequences, the arrangement of the crops in a cropping system is important. For example, corn in the 39-year test at Urbana, Ill., yielded 6.9 bushels more following oats than when grown continually on the same land. In the same experiment, corn in a 3-year rotation following clover yielded 18.2 bushels more than where corn followed corn year after year. None of these fields was fertilized. Both corn and oats gave higher yields when grown in a rotation including a grass and a legume than when grown continually at St. Paul, Minn. These findings are based upon 29 years of experimentation on land that received an average annual application of 2 tons of barnyard manure per acre.

Thus, farmers can grow as much, or more, corn, cotton, and small grains on smaller acreages when the cropping systems include grass and legumes.

THE AUTHOR≪≪ *R. E. Uhland is research specialist in agronomy and liaison officer between research and operations in the Soil Conservation Service. He was reared on a Missouri farm and educated at the University of Missouri, where he later carried on research for 7 years. For several years he was superintendent of the Soil Erosion Experiment Station at Bethany, Mo., and regional conservator in charge of Soil Conservation work in Missouri, Iowa, Illinois, Wisconsin, and Minnesota.*

ROTATIONS FOR PROBLEM FIELDS

R. Y. BAILEY, W. M. NIXON

THE IDEAL rotation is the one that achieves complete harmony between the farmer's demand for cultivated crops and the needs of the land for protection.

A good soil-conserving rotation includes enough grass and legumes to reduce losses of soil through erosion; reduce losses of plant nutrients through leaching; improve the structure of the soil so that it will absorb water readily; increase and maintain organic matter and nitrogen in the soil; and increase yields of the cultivated crops grown in the rotation.

Grass and legumes in rotation improve the structure of the soil by making it more granular and thus increasing its ability to absorb water. Residues from grass and legumes that are returned to the soil as green manure increase organic matter and nitrogen in the soil.

Samples taken at the Southern Piedmont Conservation Experiment Station at Watkinsville, Ga., from Cecil clay at the ends of the first and second cycles of a 3-year rotation of cotton, oats, and lespedeza showed on analysis that there was little increase in soil aggregation, nitrogen, or organic matter in the soil during the first cycle, but after the second cycle aggregation was increased, the nitrogen was almost doubled, and organic matter was more than doubled. These results illustrate the need for continuing rotations for more than one cycle.

Larger crop yields are often obtained from fewer acres as a result of rotations including grass and legumes.

Drayton Hopkins, who farms in the Fork Shoals Road community in the Greenville County Soil Conservation District of South Carolina, had 134 acres in cotton, 183 acres in corn, and 87 in small grain before he began using soil-conserving rotations. He was producing an average of 77 bales of cotton, 1,830 bushels of corn, and 1,670 bushels of oats and wheat. Under the rotation plan, he had 100 acres in cotton, 50 in corn, and 160 in small grain. The farm then produced 100 bales of cotton, 1,500 bushels of corn, and 10,300 bushels of oats, wheat, and barley. Annual lespedeza following small grain produced 70,000 pounds of seed. Fifty-five steep acres formerly in row crops were growing a perennial sericea lespedeza for seed and grazing, or kudzu for hay and grazing.

Soil-conserving rotations must be fitted to the land.

Kinds of ground cover, the extent of their use, and patterns of arrangement in rotations are determined by slope, soil type, drainage conditions, extent of erosion, and other characteristics of the land, which are the basis for land capability classification—a physical guide for assisting farmers in soil conservation districts to plan the use of their land and to determine its needed treatment. Of the eight classes of land, four can be cultivated safely; consequently, we are concerned here with grass and legumes in rotations on those four classes.

Such factors as rainfall and the system of farming affect the types of rotations recommended for the various classes of land in different regions and farming areas. Kinds of rotations recommended in the Southeast for the four classes of cropland are illustrative. The type of cropping system is determined by the crop needs of the farm.

Land in Class I—well-drained land of a desirable soil type, and flat enough so that erosion is not a problem—can be maintained in a productive condition under intensive use for cultivated crops, if such cover crops as vetch, crimson clover, bur-clover, or crotalaria are included in the cropping system. Cotton, if it is the main cash crop, can be grown on it each year, with a winter cover crop like vetch or crimson clover seeded between the cotton rows in the fall. On livestock farms, the cultivated land may be used for winter grazing and summer grain crops.

Short rotations may include mixtures of small grain or ryegrass and crimson clover or button clover for winter grazing and grain sorghum for grain production. Where ryegrass and hard-seeded crimson clover or button clover are grazed until late spring and followed by grain sorghum after seed is harvested, thick volunteer stands of ryegrass and clover come up between the sorghum rows in the fall. Such a rotation requires no land preparation for the winter grazing crop, because the summer cultivation of the grain sorghum leaves the soil in condition for the germination of grass and clover seed.

Several annual winter legumes make enough hard seed to fit into a cropping system that includes two or three successive years of corn and one year of grain sorghum following a legume seed crop. Such a cropping system permits a grain crop to be grown each year with a green legume to be turned under for corn and a heavy, dry legume residue for grain sorghum.

Land in Class II needs terraces, water disposal at terrace ends, contour tillage, and a rotation that keeps half the land covered while the other half is cultivated.

The effectiveness of a simple 2-year rotation in reducing erosion on Class II land was shown at Watkinsville. A rotation of peanuts the first year and a vetch-oats mixture for hay followed by a summer crop of crotalaria the second year was compared with continuous peanuts on runoff plots 105 feet long on a 3-percent slope in 1944, 1945, and 1946. The average annual soil loss from the 2-year rotation was 1.37 tons an acre. The value of the residue from the protective crops in the rotation is illustrated by the loss of only 1.52 tons an acre from peanuts in rotation, as compared with the loss of 6.97 tons where peanuts were grown continually. Peanuts in the rotation made an average yield of

1,634 pounds of nuts per acre, as compared with 1,079 pounds under continuous cropping.

Besides the protection that can be provided by terracing, proper water disposal at terrace ends, and contour tillage, Class III land, which is moderately good but subject to severe erosion, needs rotations that provide effective ground cover on at least two-thirds of the land while the remainder is under cultivation.

A rotation effective in controlling erosion at Watkinsville on Class II land did not control erosion on Class III land.

Soil losses under a simple 2-year cropping system of cotton and vetch the first year and corn and crotalaria the second year were measured on runoff plots on both Class II and Class III land. On a 105-foot plot of Class II land with a 3-percent slope, this cropping system lost only 3.45 tons of soil per acre annually during a 3-year period. During the same period, plots of Class III land 70 feet long on a 7-percent slope lost an average of 10.98 tons of soil an acre. Continuous cotton lost an average of 5.35 tons on Class II and 23.92 tons on Class III land.

Under a 3-year rotation of oats and lespedeza the first year, volunteer lespedeza hay the second year, and cotton the third year, on Class III land, average soil losses were only 3.79 tons an acre for the rotation. The average loss during a 4-year period under cotton in the rotation was 7.67 tons an acre, compared to 32.23 tons under continuous cotton.

Rotations that include a mixture of orchardgrass and red clover in a 3-year cycle with corn and small grain are effective on land in this class. Rotations that include more cover than either of the 3-year cropping systems described here are desirable. The high soil loss during the cultivated year should be as widely spaced as conditions permit.

Where livestock is a major source of income, a rotation that includes a cycle of alfalfa followed by a grass sod, or a mixture of perennial grasses and clovers, reduces soil losses and increases yields of other crops in the rotation.

The arrangement of the rotated crops in contour strips gives considerable additional benefit—particularly where the demand for cultivated crops is such that the rotation cycle is reduced to 3 years.

Even where strip cropping is used with terraces, there are advantages in this arrangement: It makes it more convenient to balance the acreage of various crops in the rotation where there are several fields of widely varying size. Under a strip arrangement, all the land in a field is not plowed up at the same time. When a terrace is overtopped or broken during a severe storm, contour strips reduce the total field damage by bringing the water under control when it reaches one of the vegetated strips. Contour-strip arrangement of the rotations helps to keep cultivation, including the operation of harrows and grain drills, nearer the contour. Anybody who has seen erosion in fields where grain drills have been operated up and down slopes knows the importance of the last point.

The rotation of crops in strips effectively controls wind erosion. The width of the trap or crop strip depends on a number of factors, such as the length of the jump of soil particles in saltation and the density and height of vegetation. The minimum width of the trap strip depends also on its capacity to hold the blown soil because the strip must be wide enough to store the soil moving into it and still have enough width to the leeward side to act as an effective trap. Taller-growing crops in rotation with strips of shorter-growing crops offer the best controls against blowing of surface soil.

In the Cross Timbers sections of Texas and Oklahoma, planting four to eight rows of peanuts in a strip-cropping pattern with crotalaria, grain sorghum, or other tall-growing crops has helped prevent wind erosion. Alternating the crops in the strips annually provides a sound conservation cropping system.

In the wheat-growing section of the High Plains, strips of summer-fallowed land are often alternated with strips of wheat. The wheat strips are approximately twice the width of the summer-fallow strips. If the wheat fails, grain sorghum is sometimes grown in alternating strips with summer fallow.

Land in Capability Class IV—fairly good land, but subject to severe erosion if tilled too often—requires long rotations that keep the ground blanketed with a sod of grass and legumes for several successive years, or rations that include deep-rooted perennial covers, like alfalfa with grass, or sericea lespedeza. Kudzu and sericea lespedeza have shown remarkable ability to reduce runoff and erosion where they are adapted. Kudzu has the further advantage of being able to reestablish itself from plants that survive the cultivation necessary in the production of one or two row crops. This ability of kudzu to maintain itself is indicated by results at Watkinsville, where successive crops of corn, cotton, and oats were grown on Class IV land without destroying the stand of kudzu. Oats were harvested in the spring of 1946 and the ground was again covered with kudzu before frost killed the foliage in the fall.

Erosion usually is not a serious problem on flat land where drainage is required. Grass and deep-rooted legumes (such as alfalfa, sweetclover, and sericea lespedeza) in rotation with cultivated crops help maintain a favorable soil structure so that the drainage ditches or tile lines are more effective. On heavy clay several years of clean tillage sometimes alter the structure of the soil to the extent that tile lines that formerly functioned efficiently fail to drain the land, and additional tile must be installed between the old lines.

Grass and legumes are not needed for erosion control on deep, highly permeable sands on gentle slopes, but they are essential for the maintenance of a desirable internal condition of these soils. Organic matter, the lifeblood of these soils, can be maintained only through residues of soil-saving crops.

Annual cover crops have an important place in rotations, particularly where row crops are so important in the farm economy that two successive cultivated crops are planted. A good example of a winter cover crop is blue lupine, which came into prominence in southern peanut-producing areas during the war—the demand for peanuts then was so great that farmers planted this soil-depleting crop on the land oftener than usual. Lupine did not completely protect the sandy peanut soils, but it did give late-winter and spring cover that materially reduced the damage to the land.

The maximum feasible use of all kinds of cover crops is extremely important in humid areas of the South, where climatic conditions cause the rapid oxidation of organic matter. This condition emphasizes the importance of including both winter and summer cover crops wherever there is bare land.

Grass and legumes can be managed after the plants are dead so as to reduce further the losses of soil and water. Dead residues, such as straw, stubble, and stalks, can be left on or near the surface while the land is cultivated by the use of special tillage practices. Residue so managed protects the surface from rain drops and from wind action and increases absorption of water by the soil.

Cooperative tillage studies were made on Cecil clay by the Soil Conservation Service and the South Carolina Agricultural Experiment Station at Clemson in 1943–46. A mulch disk method that kept a large proportion of a cover crop of rye and vetch on the surface reduced soil losses 46 percent and water loss about 50 percent, as compared with losses where the cover crop was turned under. Average yields per acre of corn were about the same, 49 bushels from the mulch tillage and 47 where the cover crop was turned under. Results to date indicate that mulch tillage causes greater

improvement in soil structure and a more rapid increase in soil organic matter and nitrogen in the first 5 inches of soil than conventional tillage methods.

Tillage methods that leave stubble and other residues on the surface protect the surface against wind erosion in the West where wheat is grown. Average yields of wheat in tillage field trials on farms in the Texas Panhandle during 1941–46 were 18.3 bushels an acre when the residue was kept on the surface and 17.3 bushels when the land was plowed and disked.

Hard-seeded annual legumes, such as Dixie crimson clover, bur-clover, button clover, Caley-peas, grandiflora vetch, smooth vetch, and crotalaria, can be managed in rotations as volunteering crops. Harvesting, processing, storing, and planting of seed are thus eliminated. Erosion losses are less than where the soil is disturbed in seeding other legumes.

Caley-peas grown in a 4-year rotation of oats, lespedeza hay, corn, and cotton at Watkinsville come up to thick stands each fall. Peas are plowed under for corn and cotton before blooms appear. The green peas are mowed for hay in April of the lespedeza-hay year of the rotation. Seed to keep the soil stocked is matured in the oats and on the stubble after peas are mowed for hay.

The ability of Caley-peas and other winter legumes to reseed proves objectionable where annual lespedeza is included in the rotation. Winter legumes crowd the lespedeza early in the spring and thin the stand. Mowing the winter legumes for hay early in the spring reduces the damage to the lespedeza, but is not fully effective. Close grazing of winter legumes during the spring reduces competition and increases survival of lespedeza plants.

Crotalaria and button clover produce plenty of hard seed, but require soil scarification for thick stands. Harrowing immediately after grain is harvested is necessary if a thick volunteer stand of crotalaria is wanted as a summer cover. Thicker stands of button clover are obtained through disking in late summer or early fall.

The application of lime and fertilizer is an important phase of rotation management. The total amount required may be larger under a good rotation than under a cropping system that includes only such cultivated crops as cotton and corn. Legumes supply nitrogen and reduce the amount of that element which must be applied for other crops, but they require more phosphate and potash fertilizers than some of the cultivated crops. The improved physical condition and the increased organic matter content of the soil where grass and legumes are grown result in more efficient use of fertilizer and lime than is possible on bare land where only cultivated crops are grown.

THE AUTHORS«« *R. Y. Bailey is head of the Regional Agronomy Division, Southeastern Region, Soil Conservation Service. He is stationed in Spartanburg, S. C.*

W. M. Nixon, head of the Regional Agronomy Division, Western Gulf Region, Soil Conservation Service, is stationed in Fort Worth, Tex.

T. C. Peele, of the Research Division of the Soil Conservation Service, Clemson College, S. C., furnished information on the influence of cropping practices on soil structure, nitrogen, and organic matter content. B. H. Hendrickson, project supervisor at the Southern Piedmont Conservation Experiment Station in Watkinsville, Ga., furnished information on results from runoff plots under various cropping systems.

FERTILIZERS FOR GRASS IN ROTATIONS

W. V. BARTHOLOMEW

GRASS CROPS in the rotation can be made to provide more pasture and hay and to impart a greater influence upon soil productivity if prudent use is made of fertilizers.

Let us examine some principles that determine the best use of fertilizer—the most efficient use, that is, in order to get the greatest benefit from grass crops. Four points are a part of such an examination: The peculiar nutrient needs of the crop or crops to be grown, the ability of the soil to supply the necessary nutrients to the plants, the tendency of the fertilizer to be lost by leaching, and the capacity of the soil to fix in unavailable form the elements applied in the fertilizer.

Soils vary greatly with regard to the kind and quantity of fertility elements they can supply to the growing crop. Alfalfa, a crop that can be grown in the several climatic regions of the United States if soil conditions are adequate, is an illustration. Alfalfa requires good drainage and moderate

to high levels of soil fertility. In the Southeast, lime, phosphate, potash, and some of the minor elements as well must be applied to the soil for alfalfa production. Good yields can be obtained on the better soils of the North Central region with little fertilization—usually only moderate to small applications of lime and phosphate. In some of the Western irrigated regions alfalfa has been grown extensively without fertilization. The soils of the West are normally calcareous and initially were generally high in fertility.

Soils differ locally as well as between regions. In some areas the local differences may be marked. The fact that one farmer gets excellent results by the use of high rates of fertilizer is not always an indication that his neighbor a few miles away can get similar results. Such local contrasts in soil fertility are common in the East.

For the better grass crops the nutrient requirements are high. This thesis runs counter to the belief that grasses,

Yield of Beets Per Acre Under Various Systems of Cropping at Huntley, Mont.

System of fertilization and cropping	6-year periods		
	3d	4th	5th
No fertilizer or manure:	Tons	Tons	Tons
Continuous beets............................	8. 22	7. 69	5. 06
2-year rotation—beets and potatoes.............	11. 49	8. 62	6. 71
6-year rotation—potatoes, oats, beets, alfalfa 3 years.	13. 49	9. 84	5. 09
Manure added:			
2-year rotation, potatoes and beets..............	17. 16	17. 74	14. 22
6-year rotation, potatoes, oats, beets, alfalfa 3 years.	17. 34	16. 70	13. 33
Manure and fertilizer added:			
Maximum production rotations (average).........	21. 58	22. 19	17. 98

because they are soil builders, find their best use in soil conditions of low fertility. Some grass crops will survive and grow on poor soils, but abundant experimental data, supported by extensive practical experience, have shown that grass crops, those that can grow on poor soils as well as those needing high minimum levels of fertility, respond markedly to the application of fertilizer.

An example of the capacity of non-leguminous grass crops to respond to nitrogen is provided by the Virginia Agricultural Experiment Station: Orchardgrass yields were increased from 1,099 pounds an acre where no nitrogen was added to 5,099 pounds when a hundredweight of nitrogen was applied. The protein yields in pounds per acre in the two treatments were 99 and 528 pounds per acre, respectively.

In South Dakota the average yield of several adapted grasses from experiments in four counties was 1,964 pounds an acre when no fertilizer was applied; 3,093 pounds when only nitrogen was used; and 3,240 pounds when nitrogen was added along with phosphorus.

Alfalfa yields in Michigan were increased from 3,032 pounds an acre when no fertilizer was used to 5,502 pounds where 500 pounds of 0–16–10 were applied. In an experiment in Sussex County, New Jersey, alfalfa yielded 3,118 pounds an acre without fertilization and 8,603 pounds when 370 pounds of bone meal and 200 pounds of potash were applied.

Some grass crops have a wide fertility tolerance. Such crops as peanuts, soybeans, lespedeza, and kudzu are effective foragers for plant nutrients and therefore can survive on poor soils and successfully compete with other associated crops under adverse fertility conditions. They grow best, however, under conditions of moderate to high fertility, and when they are grown on poor soils they have been found to respond markedly to additions of fertilizer. When such crops are grown on poor soils without fertilization, they contribute most by their limited fixation of nitrogen or by prevention of soil erosion—they neither conserve fertility nor hasten its liberation from the soil minerals. They merely postpone the time when it must be added to the soil as fertilizer if soil productivity is to be maintained.

Such crops as tobacco and cotton, when they follow soybeans and peanuts, commonly develop severe potash deficiency symptoms. This results from the high nutrient requirements of the peanuts and soybeans and their ability to take up large quantities of plant nutrients even at low levels of fertility.

The plant nutrients removed in a year's growth of grass harvested for hay are more than double the amounts contained in a crop of cotton or corn grain and more than three times the amount removed with a crop of small grain. A 3-ton crop of alfalfa contains about 140 pounds of nitrogen, 35 pounds of phosphoric acid, and 135 pounds of potash. A 3,000-pound crop of timothy contains about 40 pounds of nitrogen, 15 pounds of phosphoric acid, and 45 pounds of potash.

The grass and hay crops adapted to poor soils are also high in mineral elements. Each ton of peanut or soybean hay removes from the soil about 10 pounds of phosphoric acid and 25 pounds of potash. A 1,500-pound crop of peanuts and the accompanying 2,000 pounds of hay remove approximately 16 pounds of phosphoric acid and 56 pounds of potash.

Large amounts of plant nutrients also are immobilized in the extensive root systems of many grass crops. Approximately one-third of the plant nutrients taken up by alfalfa the first year is used to form roots. Similar proportions of plant nutrients are retained by the root systems of other grass crops.

Native prairie grasses have perhaps the most extensive root system. Yields of as high as 10,000 pounds an acre have been reported. The development and accumulation of roots in many of the cultivated grasses are not so great as are found in native prairies but yet are large in comparison to other crops. Root yields from bluegrass range from 2,300 to 5,000 pounds, and from bromegrass, 2,000 to 4,000 pounds an acre. For alfalfa, the yields range from 2,000 pounds an acre in young to 3,500 pounds in mature stands. From Sudangrass and sweetclover the root yields range from 800 to 1,400 pounds an acre. Small grains, sorghums, and corn produce only slightly less, the estimated root yield range being from 700 to 1,300 pounds an acre. Potatoes, peas, tomatoes, and similar crops have rather small root systems, the yields usually ranging between 200 and 500 pounds an acre.

Fertilizer recommendations based entirely upon crop consumption are not reliable. Crops seldom recover more than 75 percent of the nitrogen supplied in the fertilizer, and a 50-percent recovery is reasonable. Soil fixation may commonly prevent two-thirds or three-fourths of the phosphorus applied from contributing to plant growth. With potash the story is much the same. Leaching may account for some of the losses, but there is normally considerable fixation by the soil. At least part of the potash fixed by the soil may ultimately become available to crops, but the immediate crop cannot get it. One must, therefore, provide more nutrients than the amount that is equivalent to the demands of the crop increase that is expected.

Because of the tendency for fertilizer elements to be lost from the soil or to be fixed in unavailable form, placement and timing of fertilizer applications are important. Fixation of phosphorus and potassium is much less rapid when the fertilizer is placed in concentrated bands in the root zone. In such bands the fertilizer is conveniently located with respect to the plant roots, and because the fertilizer is in intimate contact with a smaller quantity of soil the nutrients remain available to the plant for much longer periods.

Because nitrogen is readily leached from the soil by heavy rains or excessive amounts of irrigation water, delayed seasonal applications have been found most efficient. If the nitrogen is applied too early, much of it may be lost before the period of crop utilization. Delayed applications may be so timed that the critical needs of the crop are satisfied with the least loss by leaching.

Maximum efficiency in fertilizer use is predicated upon the proper nutrient balance in the soil. Each element has a definite physiological role in the development of the crops. If the available supply of any element is deficient, low yields will result and a poor quality of plant will be produced.

For each crop there is a definite ratio of the amounts of each of these elements required to maintain optimum growing conditions. The ratio varies with the soil and climatic conditions under which the crop is grown. Failure to get response to high rates of fertilization, provided moisture and soil physical conditions are not limiting, may be because improper nutrient balances were produced by the fertilizer practices followed.

An example is given in data reported by the Iowa Agricultural Experiment Station. Nitrogen alone increased the yield of oats 16.1 bushels an acre. The addition of potassium and phosphorus, alone or together, brought about slight, insignificant increases in yields, except on calcareous soils. When nitrogen was added, with potassium and phosphorus, an average increase in yield of 23.6 bushels an acre was obtained.

Legume crops, through the medium of symbiotic bacteria, can utilize nitrogen from the air. The bacteria invade the plant roots; nodules are formed; the microbes live at the expense of the host plant; and in the process the legume obtains fixed nitrogen.

The nitrogen-fixing bacteria are sensitive to soil and crop conditions. Fertilization of the soil and the control of acidity with lime are of major importance not only as a means of inducing the greatest amount of nitrogen fixation but also for survival of the organisms in the soil between intermittant legume crops. There is increasing evidence that many of the minor elements play important roles in legume nodulation and nitrogen fixation.

Legumes respond to fertilization with potash, phosphorus, and minor elements and to additions of lime; many species also respond to nitrogen fertilization. Most of the leguminous crops need small amounts of available fixed nitrogen in the early stages of growth before the fixation of nitrogen in the nodules commences. Soybeans, for optimum growth on some Iowa soils, have been found to require moderate amounts of nitrogen fertilizer in the later stages of growth. Moreover, experiments indicate that some legumes fix larger quantities of atmospheric nitrogen when they have been fertilized with small amounts of fixed nitrogen.

The fertilizer needs of grass crops cannot be considered entirely apart from the need of the associated crops in the rotation. Often the total rotation requirement is of major importance, along with the most advantageous place in the rotation to apply each of the fertilizer elements.

For example, corn, clover, and alfalfa have higher potash requirements than wheat or oats. When a combination of these crops is grown in a rotation, the total potash requirement should be applied so as to favor the corn and legumes. On the other hand, wheat, clover, and alfalfa have higher phosphorus requirements than corn, oats, and soybeans. In the rotation, therefore, phosphorus should be applied to favor wheat and legumes.

The most general practice in the Corn Belt is to apply most of the lime and a large part of the phosphorus and potash at the time of establishment of the legume or grass crop.

In rotations containing potatoes, tobacco, vegetables, or other high-value crops, it is generally most efficient to apply a large part of the rotation fertilizer requirement to the high-value crop and only meager amounts to the associated grass crop.

When perennial grass crops are continued for a number of years, it is quite generally necessary to add annual applications of maintenance fertilizers. For alfalfa in New Jersey a yearly application of 500 to 1,000 pounds of 0–12–12 fertilizer is recommended; it should be supplemented with 80 pounds of borax per ton of fertilizer if boron is lacking.

THE AUTHOR≪≪ ← *W. V. Bartholomew, soil microbiologist at the Iowa Agricultural Experiment Station, was until August 1947 soil scientist in the Bureau of Plant Industry, Soils, and Agricultural Engineering where he was associated with the soil management investigations. He is a native of Utah and a graduate of Iowa State College.*

The Range, a Major Resource

HOW RANGE FORAGE GROWS

WILLIAM G. MCGINNIES, JOHN L. RETZER

TO UNDERSTAND and be able to practice good range management it is necessary to know the more important range plants and to know how they grow. How they grow is determined by the interactions of the climate, soils, plant competition, and grazing.

Range plants, like all other kinds of plants, are living factories that have importation, transportation, manufacturing, and storage facilities. They differ from man-made factories in that the manufactured products become a part of the plants themselves as new growth or seeds. Raw materials—water and nutrients—are taken in through the roots and transported through the stems to the leaves where, with the aid of sunlight and air, food is manufactured for life and growth. These food products are then moved to all parts of the plant. When the importation of raw materials through the roots runs low, the manufacturing process is slowed down or ceases altogether. Likewise, when leaves are reduced productive capacity is lowered.

The life of range plants, from seed germination to old age and death, may extend over a few weeks, as in annuals, or many years, as among perennials. Most range grasses and some weeds are perennials; a few grasses and many weeds are annuals. Perennial grasses and other plants that live over the unfavorable periods of the year have an advantage over annuals that die each year in that they can build up food reserves in their roots to be used for early growth the following year.

The annual growth cycle of mountain brome, a widely distributed and palatable perennial forage grass of western mountain ranges, has been carefully studied in Utah. Primary herbage growth begins before winter snow disappears and continues until the beginning of flower-stalk development. Active midsummer growth includes flower-stalk development, flowering, and seed production. During this period leaf growth is less active, but after seed ripening there is an important secondary herbage growth. The storage of food reserves and the beginning of bud development for the following year take place at this time. Dormancy begins with the drying up of seed stalks and leaves. There are three periods of root growth which alternate with herbage growth. The first occurs in early spring after melting of the snow, the second following flower-stalk production, and the third near the end of the season. The precise time when these various growth stages take place depends on favorable temperature and varies with elevation and from year to year.

Early spring is a critical period in the growth of established perennial grasses. As the food reserves stored in the roots and lower stems the previous fall are exhausted, further growth depends on plant food produced in the new leaves. Too early grazing of these leaves will weaken the plant; if such grazing occurs for several years, the plant will starve and die.

The most active period in the development of range grasses is from the time the flower stalk forms until the seeds are ripe. Immediately following and up to the time the seed stalks and leaves begin to dry up, the plant assimilates and stores most of its winter food reserves. This is the second critical period in the development of perennial range grasses. Growth then depends on current food production. Because food production depends on the amount of leafage, the greater the leafage the more food can be produced for use and storage.

If a range grass is grazed rather closely more than once during the season, the interval between such grazing must be sufficient for it to recover fully from each cropping.

In general, the life processes of range weeds and shrubs resemble those of grasses, but there are some noteworthy differences. The root systems of range weeds and shrubs usually penetrate more deeply and widely and often store more food than grasses. However, the perennial weeds and shrubs do not produce leaf and stem regrowth as readily as the grasses.

Vigorous range plants need nitrogen, phosphorus, and potassium. A dozen or more other plant nutrients are needed in small quantities. When ranges are in good condition, these essential elements are usually available in adequate quantities. Important amounts are returned to the soil by decaying herbage left after grazing.

Nitrogen is one of the most important and the most limited of plant nutrients. The air contains an abundance of free nitrogen but in this form it is not available to range grasses. By the action of nitrogen-fixing soil bacteria, which grow on the roots of legumes such as clovers and vetches, the free nitrogen is made available to all range plants. Legumes, however, are seldom abundant on dry, western ranges.

Individual plants with similar requirements and responses tend to group themselves into types. Although the members of these types are in competition with each other, they do contribute to the welfare of the group. Each plant species has its particular place on the range and holds that place as long as the combination of factors affecting it is favorable for its continued growth and development. A vigorous grass range owes its existence to the soil stability, fertility, and reasonably favorable soil moisture conditions maintained by the grass cover. If the stand of grasses has deteriorated, growing conditions are less favorable and the vegetative cover will show an invasion of weeds and shrubs.

Scientific range management, based on a knowledge of how range plants grow, aims to sustain optimum range forage and livestock production and to rebuild run-down ranges.

Available soil moisture is the most important factor in western range forage production. To be used by range plants, soil nutrients must be dissolved in water. Over most of the western range area the annual precipitation is under 15 inches, at best a low amount for plant growth. Unless the soil is mellow and porous not all of this is absorbed, but part is lost to plant growth by surface runoff. In humid regions grasses grow tall and closely spaced because they have adequate soil moisture for such growth. Such conditions also are favorable to the growth of turf-forming grasses. The low precipitation of western ranges, combined with high day temperatures, low relative humidity, high evaporation, high winds, and a high proportion of sunshine, causes plants to use the available water more quickly. These factors in turn favor the production of a thinner stand of vegetation than in humid areas and bunchgrasses rather than turf-forming grasses. Also, growth in height is usually not so great.

Perennial bunchgrasses have fibrous, spreading root systems, which on semi-arid ranges may be several times greater than above-ground stems and leaves. If bunchgrasses are as abundant as the normal soil moisture will permit, such as on ranges in good condition, these fibrous roots interlace between the tufts under what often appears to be small, bare soil spaces. This spreading root system helps to keep the top layer of soil mellow and porous and facilitates moisture penetration, which in turn makes more moisture available for growth. If the vegetative stand has become thin, exposing greater areas of the soil surface, or if the top few inches of soil have been eroded, leaving a compact subsoil, then part of the precipitation will run off no matter how

dry the soil may be underneath. The more moisture that is lost as surface runoff the less opportunity there is for adequate forage production.

THE AUTHORS ≪ *William G. Mc-Ginnies, the director of the Rocky Mountain Forest and Range Experiment Station, graduated from the University of Arizona, College of Agriculture, in 1922. He received his doctorate in ecology at the University of Chicago.*

John L. Retzer is a graduate of the University of Illinois and Iowa State College. He has worked in the Soil Erosion Service (now Soil Conservation Service), the former Bureau of Chemistry and Soils, as a soil surveyor in California, and, during the war, in the Emergency Rubber Project. He is a member of the staff of the Rocky Mountain Forest and Range Experiment Station.

THE MAJOR RANGE TYPES

E. J. WOOLFOLK, D. F. COSTELLO, B. W. ALLRED

MORE THAN half the area of continental United States produces native vegetation suitable for grazing by livestock. Three-fourths of this range area lies west of a line that roughly bisects the Great Plains from Canada to the Gulf of Mexico. About a fifth is grazeable forest and other lands in the South and Southeast, and the remainder lies chiefly in the Missouri Ozarks and the Ohio and Mississippi River basins.

These millions of acres can be classified into several broad range types which differ significantly in vegetative character and composition, climate, topography, and soil. Research and the experience of stockmen have defined kinds of operations and systems of management generally suitable for sustained production in each major type. Before we had that knowledge of true range values, widespread misuse brought serious deterioration, some of which has not been mended to this day.

Now that we have the knowledge, the future of the range livestock industry hinges on its application—on the restoration and sustained sound management of these major range areas.

The first is the tall-grass type. Under almost ideal conditions for the evolution of grassland, the tall-grass prairie developed throughout the Midwest and eastern Great Plains. The white man quickly converted the most fertile sites into farms, which today constitute a valuable agricultural section. About 20 million acres, mostly in private ownership, remain of the original tall-grass prairie, but they have been greatly modified by the introduction of exotic grasses and in places by deterioration.

The mixture of tall grasses and showy herbs, with an understory of short grasses and sedges, produces abundantly with average annual rainfall ranging from 20 inches in North

Dakota to 40 or more inches in parts of Oklahoma and Kansas. The grazing capacity is high; only ¾ to 1½ acres are needed to supply an animal-unit-month of forage. The prairie vegetation does not cure well when left standing, however, and is therefore of little value for late-fall and winter grazing.

The highly prized bluestem area in the Flint Hills and Osage sections of Kansas and Oklahoma are usually stocked lightly in summer to permit maximum gains on cattle marketed grass-fat in August. In the sand hills of Nebraska yearlong grazing of breeding cattle with considerable feeding of native hay in winter is the usual range practice.

As a result of severe drought and too heavy grazing, particularly during the middle 1930's, low-value weeds and shrubs in many places replaced the valuable bluestems, Indiangrass, switchgrass, and some other characteristic species. Although some recovery has since occurred with lighter stocking and favorable weather, present livestock inventories indicate that the remaining tall-grass ranges may again be too heavily stocked.

The tall-grass prairie has high recuperative power, and forage production may increase considerably through application of good range management and soil conservation practices. The native grasses have deep, fibrous roots and produce an abundance of natural mulch, which carries over winter; hence rainfall readily sinks in and excessive runoff is prevented.

Short Grass

The short-grass range, the largest and most important grassland type in the United States, extends from the Texas Panhandle northward beyond the Canadian border and from the foothills of the Rocky Mountains eastward midway into the Dakotas. An arm also extends westward from Texas across central New Mexico to northeastern Arizona. This area, now mostly in private ownership, has such valuable livestock forages as the grama grasses, buffalograss, bluestem or the western wheatgrass, and needle-and-thread.

Forage production coincides with the occurrence of spring and early summer precipitation, which totals about three-fourths of the 13-inch annual average in the Northern Plains and somewhat less of the higher annual average in the Southern Plains. Curing occurs toward the end of the hot, dry summer and the forage retains much of its nutritive quality throughout the winter. Grazing capacity is about 2½ to 4 acres per animal-unit-month in the Northern Great Plains and from 5 to 10 acres in the Southwest.

Range-cattle grazing in spring, summer, and fall is important throughout the type, and the nutritious native forage also provides adequate yearlong grazing in favorable winters.

Cow-and-calf operations predominate, but many grass-fat and feeder steers go directly to midwestern markets or into feed lots for finishing.

Sheep grazing is also important in the Northern Great Plains. Because most of the forage is provided by grasses which are normally dry during much of each year, only relatively few slaughter lambs are produced. Instead, the lambs are marketed largely as feeders. Yearling ewes produced on short-grass ranges are in good demand for breeding herds in other areas.

Yearlong maintenance of many antelope, deer, and game birds is another important function of the short-grass type.

Before and during the First World War, and in the early 1920's, widespread deterioration of short-grass ranges resulted from futile attempts to raise wheat on part of these semiarid lands, submarginal for crop production. This took millions of acres almost entirely out of range forage production for many years and reduced their grazing value to a fraction of what it once was.

Drought, a common phenomenon in the Great Plains, especially in the Southwest, reduces the stand and production of forage, causes heavy losses of livestock, and in the central and southern parts accelerates wind erosion. Severe drought and heavy grazing during the middle 1930's depleted the "upside down" ranges and severely reduced the unplowed cover. Additional acreages were devastated by the deposition of wind-blown soil. The forage species are phenomenally resistant to both drought and grazing, but, once depleted, require several years of good management and favorable weather for complete recovery. Nearly a decade of favorable weather and somewhat lighter stocking since the drought over most of the shortgrass country have enabled some sections, particularly the Northern Plains to recover to (or slightly above) predrought levels in vegetative cover and forage production.

Semidesert Grass

Good seasonal forage production, high nutritive values in cured forage, and mild winters place the semidesert grasslands of central and southwestern Texas, Arizona, and New Mexico among the best yearlong ranges in the country. The characteristic rich mixture of grasses, annual and perennial weeds, or forbs, and scattered shrubs and trees provide an average grazing capacity of 6 to 7 acres per animal-unit-month.

Variable topography and a wide range in elevation make for differences in climate and soil and in kind and amount of vegetation. Growing conditions are severe. Drought is frequent.

The grama grasses and curly-mesquite reach their maximum production at the higher elevations in the western part where annual rainfall averages 15 to 18 inches. These species cure well on the ground and are therefore suitable for summer, winter, or yearlong grazing.

At the lower elevations, where precipitation may be as low as 8 inches annually, black grama, the three-awns, and dropseeds usually predominate, with a heavy sprinkling of shrubs. In local low sites, which are alternately very wet and dry, tobosa grass and alkali sacaton often dominate the vegetation. Use in summer of tobosa grass, three-awns, and dropseeds renders more of the grama forage available for the remainder of the year. Extreme depletion of the tobosa areas through heavy grazing converts them into barren adobe flats.

Scattered throughout this rich grassland type are many shrubs, dwarf trees, yuccas, and cacti. Some of these, such as saltbush, mesquite, ratany, and scrub oak, are rather palatable and provide some forage, especially in winter and spring, and for goats yearlong.

Although especially adapted to grazing by breeding cattle, the semidesert grassland type in Arizona provides good winter sheep range. In the Edwards Plateau section of southwestern Texas both sheep and goats are grazed yearlong. There the production of feeder lambs is generally secondary to wool and mohair. Many lambs wintered in this area go grassfat to a spring market. Cattle, sheep, and goats are frequently grazed in common. Lighter stocking generally will aid sustained production.

Pacific Bunchgrass

Although greatly changed since settlement, the Pacific bunchgrass prairie is still a valuable grassland. Much of the area it once occupied from western Montana through the Pacific Northwest to southern California has been converted to wheat or other agricultural production. The remaining part forms a rather narrow belt along the foothills throughout the range.

Bluebunch wheatgrass, Idaho fescue, pine bluegrass, and California needlegrass, although well adapted to the long, dry summers and moist winters characteristic of the type, withstood grazing poorly and have largely been replaced by annuals. These annuals—alfileria, bur-clover, slender oatgrass, cheatgrass, and others—provide good forage when green. Growth starts in the fall and the plants, both annuals and perennials, remain green through the winter. Abundant growth starts rapidly in early spring. Because the annual type of forage dries up and declines in palatability and nutritive value after spring growth is completed, the type has rather low value for summer grazing.

Spring-fall grazing by cattle and sheep is most common in the North, but under favorable conditions and in the South or where perennials remain, yearlong use is feasible. On the average, 4 to 6 acres is now required to support an animal unit for 1 month. Improved management could doubtless double the productivity.

Sagebrush Grass

The sagebrush grass type occurs from northern New Mexico and Arizona northwestward into Montana and to the east slope of the Cascades in the Pacific Northwest.

It is typical of rather dry valleys and basins where most of the meager annual precipitation occurs during the winter and spring seasons. It is the third largest of all range types and twice as large as any other major shrub type. Its main value lies in the palatable herbaceous perennials that grow under and between the sagebrush plants. Bluebunch and bluestem wheatgrasses, and needle-and-thread, Indian ricegrass, Sandberg bluegrass, and palatable weeds provide most of an average grazing capacity of 9 to 15 acres per animal-unit-month, only one-third of what it should be.

Throughout its northern extension, this type forms an indispensable link, both spring and fall, between summer and winter ranges for cattle and sheep. To the south, at the higher elevations, winter grazing by sheep is somewhat more important.

The sagebrush itself provides little forage except in winter when heavy snows occasionally cover the grasses. For the sustained production of forage and livestock, sagebrush grass ranges should be stocked conservatively on the basis of the herbaceousperennial understory.

Salt Desert Shrub

The moderately productive salt desert shrub ranges of central Nevada, Utah, southwestern Wyoming, and western Colorado provide winter grazing for millions of sheep and cattle. Although forage production is less than one-third of potential and the grazing capacity averages only 18 to 20 acres per animal-unit-month, the type is of considerable value as winter range. The practice is to trail bands of sheep long distances back and forth from summer and fall ranges to the salt desert for wintering. Lack of dependable stock water often precludes grazing, except when there is snow.

The spiny hop-sage, black sagebrush, and winterfat, the most important browse species, are very palatable and provide considerable forage, especially when the grass understory is unavailable because of snow. Other browse species, such as small rabbitbrush, greasewood, and horsebrush, are of little forage value; they spread rapidly as heavy grazing of the more palatable species reduces the competition for soil moisture and nutrients.

In the understory, blue grama, sand dropseed, galleta, and Indian ricegrass are most important and provide considerable forage.

Southern Desert Shrub

The grazeable parts of the southern desert-shrub type are confined largely to the edges of the Mohave Desert and the valleys and adjacent mesas along the Colorado, Gila, lower Rio Grande, and Pecos Rivers. It has little grazing value because of the characteristically low rainfall and its undependable forage production.

Growing conditions are so severe that serious range depletion can result from only a year of too heavy grazing.

With pupils of Cheney elementary school in Washington, District Conservationist W. R. Spencer discusses a problem and a promise. The problem is: How can the farmer keep topsoil on the hills above them? How can he prevent gullies, like the one at their feet? How can we stop erosion by rain and wind?—which, as the air-plane view below reveals, scours unprotected land and exposes the lighter and harder subsoil. The problem affects us all. We have no more land to waste, but erosion yearly wastes productivity on hundreds of thousands of acres. Productive land is the basic resource from which this and all future generations must live.

And this is the promise: Grass and conservation farming will keep our country green and fruitful. An example is a drainageway in the Latah District of Idaho. To keep it from gullying, it was graded in the fall of 1944 and seeded to winter wheat. The next spring it was seeded to grass, alsike, alfalfa, and peas. In July 1947 (above) the second hay crop was in shock. Trees make a hilltop windbreak. On a West Virginia farm (below) rotations and strip cropping on exact contours protect the 37-percent slopes. Other soil-saving practices also stress grass and legumes—terracing, mulching, cover crops, pasture improvement, green manuring.

Kudzu, popular in the Southeast as a cover for eroded fields and for hay and pasture, is making a soil-building blanket on a road bank in Georgia (above). Kudzu is a long-lived, coarse vine and in some places equals alfalfa for hay. Less prepossessing is the picture of part of Santa Fe watershed in New Mexico, on which the city of Santa Fe depends for water. Before it was closed to all uses to protect it, it was dangerously overgrazed and nearly barren. Now it is recovering. Most range areas produce water, vital for western homes, irrigation, and industries; they must have a cover of plants to keep the silting of streams to the absolute minimum.

Several details of range management in the drier regions stand out in the picture (above) of the Espirito de Santo Ranch in New Mexico. Overgrazed areas are being restored by reseeding. Adequate stock-watering facilities are being installed. Grazing is limited to capacity. In Idaho (below) on land that has been farmed many years and plowed once—to establish a better stand of bluegrass—registered Herefords graze on an irrigated mountain meadow. Fields are rotated during the grazing period. Both scenes point up the principle of soil conservation: Use land to produce the most needed goods, but safeguard its productiveness.

The aim in making hay is to conserve the maximum of dry matter and nutrients at lowest cost. Good hay—the cheapest source of feed nutrients for livestock during nongrazing season—is weed-free forage dried without loss of leaves from handling, or deterioration in dry matter and nutrients, but with its natural color and sweetness. Several new machines lighten the hard job. One is a mobile drum drier in which the material, cut to 1-inch lengths, is quickly heated to 1,000° or more for a few seconds. The result (below) is feed of high carotene and riboflavin content. A cheaper and increasingly popular way is to dry hay over air ducts in the barn.

The field harvester shown above cuts the forage and blows it into a wagon, from which it is put into the silo. If the material wilts in the field so that it loses 10 to 20 percent of its moisture, no preservative is needed when it is ensiled. The scene below epitomizes the points made in these pictures. It is a view of the L. E. Martin farm in Harrison County, West Virginia, but there are many places like it in other parts of our country, where land is cropped on the contour, meadows grow good mixtures of grasses, pastures are fertilized, limed, and clipped, and there is no erosion—a green and fruitful place, and evidence of the promise we started with.

Once depleted, the palatable perennial grasses recover slowly. Forage production is largely on the basis of if-and-when it rains.

It is the practice to graze this range with cattle when the annual plants produce forage and stock water is available. This use, which saves forage on adjacent ranges and reduces supplemental feeding, gives some local value to the type. During unusually favorable winters, perhaps once in 5 years, the warmer sections, as in southern Arizona, provide valuable winter sheep grazing. Under those conditions, most of the forage is provided by annuals like alfileria, Indian wheat, bur-clover, and sixweeks fescue.

At higher elevations, black grama, tobosa, and dropseed sometimes persist in sufficient amounts to provide some grazing. Although many shrub species, such as the abundant creosotebush, characterize the type, most have little grazing value, but a few provide some forage in spring.

Pinyon-Juniper

The pinyon-juniper type forms an irregular woodland belt on rough topography and mesas having shallow, stony soils from southwest Texas to south-central Oregon. Over thousands of square miles at elevations just below the ponderosa pine zone, this open-woodland type often alternates with sagebrush, which occupies the better soils.

The type is of value for forage mainly in Arizona, New Mexico, Colorado, and Utah. In the North it is characterized by rather hot, dry summers, and an annual rainfall of less than 15 inches. In the Southwest, the rainfall is higher but comes mainly in the hot summer periods.

Spring-fall grazing is generally practiced in the North, but in the Southwest, where the forage cures on the ground and retains much of its nutritive value through the winter, yearlong grazing is prevalent. Deer find suitable winter forage in the pinyon-juniper

belt; where it is reasonably productive, it makes ideal lambing range.

The gramas, bluebunch and bluestem wheatgrasses, galleta, and such shrubs as mountain-mahogany and cliffrose give the type an average grazing capacity of 8 to 10 acres per animal-unit-month. Areas in good condition have capacities two or three times greater. Variations in the density of the trees affect grazing capacity. Some areas, particularly in the Southwest, which were once very productive of forage, now have little grazing value because of thickening of the juniper stands. Extensive areas in Texas have been cleared of juniper, often at considerable expense, in an effort to restore forage values.

Woodland-Chaparral

Woodland-chaparral varies from an open forest of orchardlike oak and other hardwood trees with an understory of herbaceous plants and shrubs to dense brush fields. It occurs throughout most of the foothills of the Central Valley of California. On its lower fringe, the type is quite open and now supports an herbaceous annual plant cover that provides forage for fall, winter, and spring grazing by cattle and sheep. At the higher elevations and in southern California, the many shrub species form almost impenetrable thickets, which are practically unfit for grazing but are extremely important for protection of the watershed values of the steep slopes on which they occur.

Introduced annuals such as alfileria, slender oatgrass, and bur-clover provide an average grazing capacity of 2 to 3 acres per animal-unit-month on the grazeable portions of the type. These plants are palatable and nutritious throughout the growing period, which begins slowly in the fall and ends in spring with the production of an abundance of forage. During the long summer the herbage remains dry and of low value, but it can be grazed satisfactorily if supplemented with cottonseed meal.

Most of the woodland-chaparral type is privately owned. Burning is widely used in an effort to reduce the shrubs, but on slopes serious damage is frequently done to watershed values. The brush sprouts aggressively so that any gain in production is temporary. The type has spread to higher elevations during the past half century as a result of logging and burning.

Open Forests of the West

The open-forest type of the mountainous West constitutes the second largest and most widely distributed range type in the country. In these forests of pine, Douglas-fir, aspen, or alpine spruce and fir with intermingled meadows and open grassy areas, grasses, other herbs, and browse species provide summer grazing for large numbers of cattle, sheep, and big game. Some spring-fall livestock grazing is practiced, and big game winter at the lower elevations, but because most of the type lies at high altitudes where snow comes early and stays late, summer use predominates.

Summering on these mountain ranges, over half of which are federally owned as national-forest lands, relieves ranches and adjacent winter ranges during this period. This facilitates diversification of livestock-farm operations and lends stability to outfits otherwise too small to operate successfully. Many grass-fat lambs, calves, and yearling steers go directly to the slaughter market from lush summer ranges. Other values of the open-forest type, such as lumbering and recreation, are important. Also, without the water stored as snow in the forests during winter, many agricultural and other communities could not exist.

Grazing capacity varies considerably throughout this type but generally averages 6 to 10 acres per animal-unit-month in summer. Meadows and alpine grasslands in good condition often have a potential grazing capacity 10 to 15 times greater than adjacent forested range.

Southern Forest Ranges

Eighty percent of the southern and southeastern Coastal Plain, the upland hardwoods, the Piedmont, and the loblolly-shortleaf pine-hardwoods of Arkansas, eastern Texas, and eastern Oklahoma is forest land upon which livestock graze at least part of the year. Much of it is privately owned and is generally grazed yearlong. High rainfall provides a long, favorable growing season. The vegetation is of four types.

The wiregrass type occurs in the longleaf-slash pine flatwoods of the Southeast and is characterized by pineland three-awn, carpetgrass, and bluestems. These grasses provide good grazing from March to June or July. One and a half to five acres of range per cow-month is needed during this 4- or 5-month period. About twice this acreage is needed monthly during late summer and fall. Carpetgrass, if available, adds grazing capacity and lengthens the desirable grazing period. In winter the forage is extremely low in nutrients, although Curtiss dropseed, if present, furnishes fair forage. If left on the range in winter, cattle require supplemental feeds even for maintenance, although the need for feeding is not generally recognized.

The broomsedge or bluestem type is characteristic of the longleaf pine and "upland" hardwood forests of southern Mississippi, Louisiana, Arkansas, east Texas and eastern Oklahoma, and the Piedmont. Bluestems, panicgrasses, paspalums, and weeds provide reasonably good forage in spring and early summer. Grazing capacity varies from about 1 acre per animal-unit-month on old fields and in open forests to 6 acres in dense shortleaf-loblolly-hardwood forests. In longleaf-slash pine forests grazing capacity averages from $1\frac{1}{2}$ to 4 acres per animal-unit-month. The grazing value of the type is very low in late fall and winter and many cattle are removed from the range to glean fields. Carpetgrass and Bermuda-grass, which occur on firebreaks, provide some fall grazing.

The switch cane or reed forage type is found mainly in the pond pine and river-bottom forests throughout the Coastal Plain and furnishes good summer or winter grazing. The reed, which is the main forage plant, must be protected from fire and too heavy grazing for best production. Grazing capacity varies, depending on the density of the reeds, from 3 to 12 acres per cow for 6 months from May to November with about twice the acreage for the remainder of the year.

The bottom-land hardwood type is typical of the Mississippi River delta and swampy areas throughout the Coastal Plain. Its shrubs and vines are valuable for winter grazing. The sprouts of many valuable hardwood timber trees are relished by livestock and grazing must be more carefully controlled than in the pine forest ranges, to avoid damage to forest reproduction. Grazing capacity is about 8 to 12 acres per cow in winter.

Coastal Prairie; Other Types

Extensive yearlong cattle grazing is provided by the coastal-prairie and marshland types which occur on low, poorly drained lands along the Gulf and Atlantic coasts and in the Everglades in Florida. Tall, coarse grasses, sedges, and rushes characterize these areas over which water stands to a depth of several inches during part of the year. In Florida the marshes are largely fresh water, and sawgrass is the dominant species. Even though inundated by salt water at high tide, the coastal marshlands are not extremely saline. Marshgrass is the most prominent species. The coastal prairies are usually not reached by high tide but otherwise are comparable to marshes.

Yearlong growth of the principal species, except during short periods when frost may occur, provides abundant forage. Although rank and coarse, the forage is nutritious for cattle. Brahman cattle, which are well adapted to southern coastal conditions, are becoming increasingly popular.

Grazeable native forage-producing lands outside the vast regions of the West, South, and Southeast consist largely of mountain glades or balds, scattered open forest areas, abandoned cultivated fields, and farm wood lots throughout the Missouri Ozarks, the Ohio and Mississippi River basins, and the Northeast forest region. Soils are generally thin, rocky, and erodible.

Many native broadleaved herbs, grasses, and browse species, including hardwood sprouts, and the introduced Kentucky and Canada bluegrasses produce the forage. The principal native grasses are big and little bluestem, Indiangrass, and switchgrass. The open forests and mountain glades are more productive of forage than the abandoned fields, because of less cultivation and a deeper, more fertile soil mantle. Grazing capacities are often relatively high during growing seasons.

Many farm wood lots, especially in the Corn Belt, are often excessively grazed, and damage to forest trees and sometimes to watersheds is serious.

The native vegetation on these lands not only maintains many livestock for a part of each year but measurably reduces runoff, which otherwise would deplete soil values and constitute flood hazards to lower areas.

THE AUTHORS ⋘ *E. J. Woolfolk is assistant to the chief of the Division of Range Research of the Forest Service. Previously he was in charge of range management and reseeding research at the United States Range Livestock Experiment Station, Miles City, Mont.*

D. F. Costello is a native of Nebraska and a graduate of the University of Chicago. He has been engaged in range research since 1934. Dr. Costello, senior forest ecologist in the Forest Service, is in charge of range-management research for the Rocky Mountain Forest and Range Experiment Station and is stationed at Fort Collins, Colo.

B. W. Allred is chief of the Regional Range Division, Soil Conservation Service, Fort Worth, Tex.

GRAZING ON RANGE LANDS

W. R. CHAPLINE

THE MAXIMUM production of our meat, wool, and other animal products calls for the use of the various types and parts of range best fitted for the different kinds and classes of livestock. The level and rolling grasslands, for example, can grow high-quality forage especially well adapted for production of high-grade calves and for growing out yearling steers. Such lands, too, are used in the production of feeder lambs. The higher mountain ranges with their cool summers and heavy growth of palatable grasses and range "weeds" are especially valuable for producing high-quality grass-fat lambs. Browse ranges of low value for cattle or sheep are often adapted to Angora goats. Ranges that produce an abundance of mast are sometimes used for grazing hogs. Many arid and semiarid mesa and valley lands, which often support a relatively scant cover of grasses, weeds, and browse, have proved to be well adapted to winter grazing by sheep. Also, if adequate water is available, they may be satisfactorily grazed yearlong or seasonally by cattle.

The belief, once widely held, that different kinds of livestock could not or would not graze in common has been disproved. Of course, on heavily utilized ranges or where more than one kind is allowed to concentrate on favored areas, there is definite conflict. When the forage best adapted to each kind is properly grazed, common use often furnishes maximum returns.

The best season to use most ranges is when the greatest grazing value can be obtained from the forage or the area can be used efficiently to save on cost of production. Thus, on high mountain ranges the green succulent growth is especially valuable in summer, but snow precludes winter grazing. In contrast, the semidesert valleys and mesas at the lower elevations, which have little snow, produce their forage in spring or summer, and often

would be suitable for yearlong grazing, but are especially valuable in winter when other ranges are snow-covered and when hay and other high-cost feeds would be required. Where the native grasses cure rather well and climatic conditions are not too severe, ranges can be grazed throughout the year. The highly productive grama ranges of the Great Plains and Southwest which produce their forage in a short spring or summer period have long been so used.

In every case it is advisable to adjust seasonal use so as to avoid damage to the resource. In many parts of the West the spring-fall ranges of the foothills are key units in the yearlong livestock operation since they furnish fresh green growth about the time lambs and calves are dropped. However, it is essential that grazing be delayed until the soil is sufficiently dry and firm to withstand trampling. Likewise, the plants should have made sufficient growth before grazing starts so as not to impair their vigor. On one central Oregon range, grazed too early for a number of years, the forage value was not only seriously depleted but the palatable forage plants developed much more slowly than those properly grazed in the spring. The vigorous spring range in good condition could be grazed 6 weeks earlier than the depleted range. This means much to stockmen who have difficulty holding their animals on hay and other feeds after some green grass starts. Moreover, it reduces cost of feeding and amount of feed required.

Research and experience have shown that removing steers, dry cows, and other marketable cattle from the range in late summer or early fall, about the time when they have attained maximum weight for the season, is the best practice. Often such animals are held for a month or even more beyond such time. When this is done, not only is part of the summer's gain lost, because the forage is not sufficiently nutritious to maintain weight, but the forage these animals eat is not available for the breeding herd or other cattle to be held over.

In simplest terms, grazing capacity means grazing the number of animals which the range unit will support for the period of grazing without impairing the vigor of the forage plants. It should assure abundant forage available for the livestock for the full grazing period. It not only permits vigorous production by the more palatable forage plants each year but also leaves sufficient stubble to give adequate protection for new growth.

Stocking at conservative grazing capacity provides maximum sustained profitable production of livestock over the years and adds stability to the industry. Numerous examples could be cited of the better results obtained from such stocking in contrast with either too heavy or too light stocking. For example, in a 12-year cooperative study, range pastures at the U. S. Range Livestock Experiment Station in eastern Montana, which were stocked approximately at grazing capacity, produced a calf crop 7 percent greater and calf weight per cow 43 pounds greater, on the average, than comparable range pastures stocked 25 percent heavier over the years. The cows on the overstocked ranges required practically double the expense for supplemental hay feeding as those on ranges properly stocked. Ranges stocked about 25 percent below grazing capacity produced a slightly greater calf weight per cow and required less supplemental feeding, but these advantages were not sufficient to offset the greater land costs.

Similarly, in cooperative studies at the Central Plains Experimental Range in Colorado, yearling Herefords gained an average of 252 pounds in 1946 on short-grass range stocked at 40 head per section for a 6-month season, approximately grazing capacity. But on comparable range, overstocked at 60

head per section, the average gain was only 174 pounds. The better developed animals on the properly grazed land sold for $1.25 more per hundredweight. Comparable profit in 1946 amounted to $1,807 per section for the range stocked at grazing capacity and $1,345 for the overgrazed, even though the latter produced slightly more beef. For the 7 years, 1940 to 1946, inclusive, the difference in favor of the moderate stocking was $43.13 per section annually. The heavy stocking has resulted in cumulative soil and forage deterioration during the 7 years of the study.

Two bands of ewes wintered in the salt desert shrub type of western Utah were placed on range grazed conservatively and heavily in alternate years. Each year the ewes grazing conservatively produced fully a pound more wool per head and were 12 to 20 pounds heavier at the close of winter than those grazed on adjacent heavily stocked range. Death loss from malnutrition was practically eliminated under proper grazing, whereas 3 to 5 percent losses were experienced year after year under heavy stocking. Lamb crops were 8 to 13 percent higher and financial returns were $1.00 to $1.50 per ewe higher on conservatively stocked range.

Even grazing a little heavier than proper reduces the forage crop and results in undesirable change in the plant cover and forage. As long as favorable rainfall occurs the loss in vigor and fewer and shorter stems and leaves of the palatable species and the breaking up of grass tufts resulting from such overgrazing may not be noticed. Heavy overgrazing very often causes rapid deterioration, especially when drought years occur, requiring many years for recovery. Such cumulative undermining of the range forage base has caused feed and financial difficulties for many stockmen during drought and depression periods.

The more palatable forage species are the key to proper grazing. When they have been grazed as fully as they can stand, the range as a whole must be considered properly grazed. There may be considerable herbage of relatively low value or unpalatable species left on the ground which might appear to be usable. An attempt to obtain greater utilization of this low value herbage, however, results in overgrazing the more palatable species.

Similarly, topography is an important factor in determining proper utilization of range units. Precipitation is less efficient in the production of forage and soil is more easily disturbed on slopes than on more level areas, particularly those which accumulate water from slopes above. Accordingly, it is not desirable to graze the vegetation on slopes as closely as on moderately level country. However, livestock naturally prefer to graze on the level or rolling country and on meadow areas that produce lush palatable forage. When such areas are properly utilized the range as a whole is fully grazed even though there may appear to be unused forage on the slopes.

Drought is the greatest hazard of the range livestock industry. Such drought years as 1934, which affected much of the western range country, or 1936 in the Plains bring home forcefully to stockmen the serious influence of inadequate precipitation in reduced forage production and in livestock losses incident thereto. Drought is unpredictable and occurs with irregular frequency. In the arid valleys of southern New Mexico, for example, three or four consecutive drought years may occur in each period of 8 or 10 years. Drought is almost as frequent in the semiarid range areas in other parts of the Southwest, in the Intermountain region, and in the Southern Great Plains. In less arid areas, however, such as the northern portion of the range territory and the high mountains, droughts do not occur so frequently. But even in these areas drought sometimes disrupts livestock production and causes financial losses. Accordingly, ranch and range management plans should recognize the drought factor and provide for emer-

gency adjustments to minimize effects of drought.

Range plants are adapted to contend rather well with low precipitation during drought. Adaptations include reduction in size or breaking up of grass tufts, production of fewer and shorter stems and leaves, the curling or folding of leaves to reduce transpiration, and even dropping of leaves by shrubs if moisture becomes too scant. It will be clearly evident why in drought years much less forage is produced. In severe droughts a considerable part of the stand may die out.

Although there is still much to learn about climatic relationships and the range resource, research results and practical experience clearly indicate certain broad principles, practices, and basic considerations that should govern ways to minimize the effects of drought in continued use of range lands for livestock production.

1. The outstanding requisite in guarding against the penalties of drought is conservative stocking year in and year out. Too often a few good years with increasing forage production encourage unwise increases in livestock numbers. The result, when drought brings short forage production, is overgrazing and heavy losses through death and sacrifice sales. Because there are more years below than above average in forage production, it is important to stock ranges on the conservative side as drought insurance. Under such use in good years some forage may be carried over ungrazed on the range but the resulting good cover of vegetation and improved vigor of the palatable plants help to sustain maximum production consistent with the current rainfall.

2. Another safeguard is to retain a reserve supply of forage by fencing off a portion of the range for use only during the critical period of each year. This assures ungrazed forage at that time and, if forage becomes short on the main body of the range before the reserve supply would normally be used, it helps to define advisable ad-

justments in the numbers of livestock.

3. A reserve of hay or other supplemental feed also provides good drought insurance. During drought the cost of harvested feeds and pasturage increases greatly and it is not sound business to wait until drought prevails before building up reserves.

4. When drought comes, the prompt marketing of steers, calves, and cull cows will minimize losses and save available forage for the closely culled breeding herd.

When abundant rainfall returns, new growth may be rather tall on the thinned forage stand; this growth in turn renews the weakened root system and general vigor of the plants. Sometimes this unusual height growth on the thin stand gives the impression of more abundant forage than actually prevails. This showed up clearly in the Northern Great Plains in 1935 when what appeared to some to be almost normal production turned out to be a short supply and left many livestock outfits, even after material reductions in numbers of animals in the summer of 1934, with a difficult forage and feed situation. Recovery from drought is often a slow process, especially so on ranges weakened by overgrazing. It took 8 years for conservatively grazed experimental pastures at the U. S. Range Livestock Experiment Station in eastern Montana to return to good condition after the 1934–36 drought. It is necessary, in other words, to avoid overstocking thinned stands, so as to give every advantage possible to rebuilding vigor and density of the palatable vegetation rather than to take the chance on even a slight degree of overgrazing following drought, which would further weaken the plant cover.

Alternate declines and recoveries of the stand of black grama on the Jornada Experimental Range in southern New Mexico have been followed through several extended drought and favorable periods which have occurred since 1915. Recovery has been reasonably rapid both under total protection from grazing and under conservative grazing, but seriously delayed under overstocking. Recovery was often more rapid on the conservatively grazed range than on the ungrazed, partly due to the fact that such grazing prevents the formation during good years of tufts larger than can be supported in drought years.

Reasonably uniform grazing of all parts on any range is necessary for most efficient use. If grazing over the whole range is not reasonably uniform the usable grazing capacity of areas where cattle naturally tend to concentrate seriously limits the number of cattle which can be grazed efficiently on the whole. Adequate distribution of grazing can be facilitated by proper salting, development of additional watering places, construction of drift fences, construction of trails to permit cattle to pass over rough spots and by attention from riders.

Salting, especially if correlated with feasible water developments and fencing, offers great possibilities for bringing about improvement in utilization on many cattle ranges. Water development and fencing often involve considerable expense as compared with salting, and accordingly it may not be possible to develop all the water or construct all the fences that might be desirable.

If possible, there should be a permanent watering place on level country at least every 4 to 5 miles, and in rugged country about every mile. Salt can then be placed at various distances from the water to attract cattle in such a way as to attain best seasonal use of the forage, to discourage excessive concentration around watering places, and to obtain desirable utilization of the forage away from water.

Open herding and bedding out of sheep has been widely used for years. In simple terms open herding means allowing the herd to graze quietly and openly over a part of the range during the day so as to avoid excessive concentration and to bring about reasonably even utilization of the forage on slopes, meadows and other areas. Dogs should be used only to guide the herd and prevent undue trailing. Bedding out allows the sheep to bed where darkness finds them instead of trailing back to a central camp or established bedground. They gather for the night on a convenient and suitable bedground wherever they happen to be. Such open herding and bedding out, in contrast to closer grazing and trailing back and forth for several nights to the same bedground, usually results in as much as 5 pounds a head additional weight in lambs and a greater quantity of wool. When the band is herded compactly and trailed back and forth, the lambs not only fail to make satisfactory growth but considerable forage is trampled and wasted, and the animals are inclined to eat many poisonous plants which they otherwise would not.

Supplemental Feeding

The use of supplements to offset nutritional deficiencies in the forage should be a common practice on southern forest ranges and on some western ranges during certain seasons. Supplementing low value range forage, especially in winter, with protein concentrates or grain, keeps young animals growing and breeding herds in good productive condition. On those lands where the forage loses much of its nutrient value late in the season but remains in sufficient quantity, supplements are especially important. In the annual type ranges of the foothills of California, for example, where there is lush production during the spring but the plants dry in summer, cooperative studies have shown that the dry herbage can be used to reasonably good advantage during the summer and fall provided it is supplemented with protein concentrates. Cows so supplemented produced greater numbers of calves; the calves developed better and brought greater value on the market.

In the southern Coastal Plain also, cattle that graze on forest range in late fall and winter when the forage is deficient in nutrients need a protein supplement as well as minerals. Cooperative experiments in southern Georgia show that range cattle fed cottonseed meal or cake as a protein concentrate go through the late fall and winter in better condition than animals maintained on harvested feeds. Cows on typical wiregrass range fed 2 pounds of cottonseed meal per day during late fall and early winter gained an average of 24 pounds per head during a 55-day period. In contrast, cows on similar range but not fed protein supplements lost 44 pounds on the average—a difference of 68 pounds.

Chemical analyses of range forage in nearly every State from Texas to North Carolina, and in many places in the West, show that the native forage is deficient in phosphorus and other minerals, particularly while dormant during winter months. The feeding of bone-meal or other mineral supplements is usually necessary.

Probably no greater satisfaction than ownership or use of highly productive range properly stocked with good quality animals ever comes to a livestock operator. Numerous examples could be cited of ranches which in the last 30 years have doubled forage production, increased calf and lamb crops 25 to 40 percent, increased calf weights 150 to 200 pounds and lamb weights 20 to 30 pounds at weaning time, produced several pounds more wool per ewe, cut death losses drastically, and obtained higher prices for marketable animals. All of these reflect better management in one form or another. And with better management over the years, greater stability will be generally attained.

THE AUTHOR ≪ *W. R. Chapline is chief of the Division of Range Research, Forest Service. He was born and reared in Nebraska and was graduated from the University of Nebraska. He has had wide experience in study of range and of cattle, sheep, and goat management throughout this country and has observed pasture and livestock production in several foreign countries.*

PLANNING RANGE CONSERVATION

W. T. WHITE, W. R. FRANDSEN, C. V. JENSEN

SUCCESSFUL ranchers have found by experience that the solution to grazing problems rests upon their adherence to four principles:

1. The prompt adjustment of livestock numbers to available forage supply.

2. The adjustment by seasons of the grazing use of each unit or pasture to meet the growth requirements of the main forage plants.

3. The proper location of fences, stock-water facilities, and salt to insure even grazing of each pasture or unit.

4. Keeping the kind of stock that will graze most economically the kind of forage found on the ranch.

The ranchers give several reasons why this is true:

1. The profits of planned conservation show up in increased and sustained forage yields, better calf and lamb crops, higher weights of market animals, and enhanced security against drought and other seasonal variations.

2. Grasses and other forage plants, effective protectors of the soil, are easily damaged by too close grazing, spotted grazing, and grazing too early in the spring. Even under normal or favorable conditions, grazing plans should be flexible enough to allow adjustments in time.

3. Grassland on the ranch must be used in relation to other lands that produce feed and forage crops for livestock. The rancher or farmer has to raise or purchase sufficient feed to meet his livestock requirements during those periods when forage is unavailable, improve the quality of farm-grown feeds, and produce feeds that will retain their palatability well into the winter and early spring. If he does not do so, he will have to hold his livestock on pasture or range too long in the fall or turn them out too soon in the spring. The result is bound to be injury to both forage and soils.

An inventory will help the farmer or rancher make practical plans. Several points are involved:

1. The first step is to record briefly on a map the location, area, and condition of the range and pasture lands; acres of cropland; kind and amount of forage and feed available by fields; and number and kind of livestock.

2. An analysis of the facts in the inventory will aid in deciding on the remedies needed to improve poor grazing land, designing of sound land-use practices for all the ranch, and determining an orderly sequence of applying the practices needed.

3. The next step is to provide in the plan for yearly or seasonal observations of the effect of the planned practices as a basis for determining the adjustments needed to meet current conditions of climatic economics.

4. Conservation planning for grasslands is facilitated by mapping the condition of each acre of grazing land on the ranch.

This classification of grasslands, with the associated facts, permits the rancher to understand the nature and cause of undergrazing and of the overgrazing of certain sites, and gives a basis for determining what needs to be done to restore poor grassland conditions and the degree and rate of improvement that can be expected.

One system classifies grasslands as "excellent" when they produce practically as much forage as they are capable of producing under the climatic conditions that normally prevail. Lands now producing less than their maximum under conservative use are placed in lower classes—"good" if they produce three-fourths or more of their potential; "fair" if production is one-half to three-fourths of full production; "poor" if it is one-fourth to one-half; and "very poor" if it is less than one-fourth of the production possible when the land has been restored. Grassland classed as "fair" means that the systematic application of sound grazing practices will about double its annual yield. Grassland classed as "poor" can be made to carry four times as many stock if it is put under the best management.

5. The inventory also provides information on the amount of forage available for use in terms of the number of livestock and the season when it may be grazed for greatest returns without injury to the best forage plants. Other factors affecting forage production and range and pasture use are also recorded: Periods of plant growth, which are closely related to the periods in which plants can be grazed without injury; possibilities for the subdivision of the grazing area into better management units; and possibilities for improved deferred-rotational grazing use. The adequacy and location of existing water supplies, the possibilities of additional water development, and sites in need of reseeding are especially important recorded facts.

The map can show the boundaries of each condition, class, or site and the location of lands suitable for cultivation and those that should be kept in grass or trees. The selection of croplands and crops is based on the character of the soil, slope, erosion conditions, fertility, and related factors. The cropping history of each field is useful as a guide in future planning.

It is important to know whether sufficient forage and feed supplies can safely be grown on the ranch for feeding the planned numbers of livestock. When such supplies are inadequate, the plan outlines the steps necessary to develop additional forage and feed resources, or to change the grazing use by adjustment in livestock numbers in order to balance the forage supply and livestock feed requirements.

The amount of green forage and other feeds needed annually and seasonally is influenced by the type of livestock operation and the number of animals that must be raised to fur-

nish a satisfactory income. The type of livestock, in turn, bears on the time the animals are kept before marketing. For example, the sale of cattle as yearlings rather than two-year-olds markedly reduces the annual feed needs.

6. To determine the adequacy of forage and feed supplies, a simple list is made of the number of each kind and class of livestock kept on the ranch and the feeds customarily grown or purchased. The grazing capacity of each pasture is estimated in terms of animal-units that can be supported safely each season.

Similarly, the current field-by-field production of cultivated forage crops and supplemental pastures and the season in which such crops and pasturage become available are analyzed.

Both the available and required feeds are calculated in terms of animal-unit-months (that is, the amount required to feed one cow or 5 ewes one month). Commonly recognized feed equivalents are used to convert tons of hay, bushels of grain, et cetera, to animal-unit-months of feeding value.

Though the number of livestock is governed chiefly by the total forage and feed resources available, the stocking of any individual pasture may depend entirely on the seasonal availability of the forage. Climate, elevation, condition of the range, kind of forage, and availability of water are some of the factors to be considered. Growth requirements of the plants themselves are important: Some forage plants require more sustained top growth for full production than do other plants; some will stand close grazing near the end of the growing season without injury. For example, other things being equal, stoloniferous grasses can be grazed more closely in the fall than the bunch grasses.

When the seasons of use of grazing units and the seasonal availability of feeds from croplands have been settled, a tentative distribution is made of the grazing and feeding yields for all lands of the ranch. A sketch map of the ranch shows the approximate location, size, and yield in animal-unit-months of the various fields and pastures. The estimated seasonal yields of the grazing lands and cropland are compared with the seasonal feed requirements of the livestock. Such a comparison provides information for determining initial adjustments of land use, livestock numbers, and grazing practices needed to obtain full use of grazing land and cropland without overuse, and to avoid the hazardous seasonal depletion of feed and forage supplies.

The conservation practices and remedial measures that will be used to restore and maintain the plant cover are decided upon and outlined in the plan, unit by unit. Particular attention is given to overgrazed and eroded areas and to areas where plant vigor is low. Reseeding of depleted grassland areas and abandoned croplands with adapted grasses may be an important consideration to overcome seasonal forage shortages. The planting of additional hay, silage, or grain crops, and supplemental pastures may be required for a balanced yearlong livestock operation.

The plan outlines a suitable system of grazing designed to improve the yield of depleted lands and to obtain sustained optimum production for each site now in good or excellent condition. It shows where fences will be built to make deferred rotational and seasonal grazing possible. Improperly placed fences hindering proper distribution of livestock on the grazing area are marked for removal. The plan specifies the water developments required to avoid destructive daily trailing and traveling of stock to and from water. It indicates the amount, location, and period of supply of salt necessary to encourage stock to graze under-utilized areas, and to avoid stock concentrations around salt and water, where they are located close together, so destructive to grazing lands. It outlines the action to be taken to control noxious and poisonous plants, install contour furrows and water-spreading systems, and protect the grasslands

from fires, injurious rodents, and insect enemies.

Because the growth of grass is seasonal and fluctuates from one season to the next, it is important that the conservation plan contain provision for timely evaluation of the measures specified in it and suggest possible adjustments. Seasonal or annual examinations of the current effect of grazing on the volume of available forage, on the adequacy of the reserves of ungrazed forage required for the remainder of the planned grazing period, and on the effect of the planned grazing on the productivity of the grasslands are needed.

Planning is progressive. Measures and practices may be established as the resources of the operator permit, but their establishment should always be in keeping with the comprehensive plan for the ranch as a whole, and should contribute to the conservation objective for the ranch as a unit. Generally, the more rapidly a comprehensive plan can be instituted, the quicker will the grassland respond to improved methods of management and supplemental treatment, and the earlier will economic benefits be forthcoming.

An example is given of the problems encountered, the practices designed, and some results on a typical 2,300-acre ranch, which comprises 1,800 acres of native grazing land, 250 acres of native meadow, 200 acres of cropland, and 50 acres of farmstead, corrals, and rocky outcrops. The operator has a grazing permit for 800 animal-unit-months (A. U. M.) off the ranch on public grazing land.

An inventory of the ranch listed nine problems:

1. The 1,800 acres of grazing land were in poor condition, with a heavy invasion of unpalatable weeds and brush, sheet erosion, and rilling prevalent. Ten acres were required for an animal-unit-month's grazing.

2. There were 250 acres of sub-irrigated meadow. About 100 acres were cut annually for hay; 150 acres were rough and cut by gullies; the an-

nual yield was 150 tons of medium or poor hay and 150 A. U. M. of grazing.

3. The 200 acres of cropland were poor. The yield was low because of erosion and 40 years of continuous cropping to barley and oats. The annual yield was 150 tons of hay and 150 A. U. M. of aftermath grazing.

4. The rancher customarily purchased 100 to 125 tons of hay and grain each year to supplement feed produced on the ranch.

5. Livestock traveled daily 1 to 2 miles to water on the 1,800 acres.

6. Salt stations near water supply caused concentrations of livestock that had depleted the palatable forage plants on about 150 acres; 150 acres more were almost depleted.

7. The calf crop was only 60 percent; 300 cows averaged 180 calves yearly.

8. Market cattle were sold as mixed-age classes, from short yearlings to long two-year-olds; average sale weight was 750 pounds. The mixed-age classes sold at a disadvantage.

9. A dozen or 15 bulls ran with the cows; calves were dropped at all seasons; the result was early-bred heifers, stunted winter calves, and winter calf losses.

Nine practices and remedial measures were designed:

1. The 1,800-acre range was fenced into four units. A 400-acre block of deeper soils was seeded to crested wheatgrass. A deferred - rotational-grazing system was designed so that one of the four units is deferred each year until after seed maturity of the principal forage plants.

2. The entire meadow was divided into three areas and surveyed for leveling and reseeding, about 50 acres to be treated each year. A system of water-spreading ditches was designed for each area—the water for irrigation to be diverted from a deeply cut gully.

3. Cropland was divided into units so that a rotation of 2 years of sweet-clover and 3 years of barley for grain may be grown on each unit. Sweet-clover is planted with the last grain.

4. The rancher will grow all his own feed.

5. Two stock ponds were located in newly established units on the 1,800-acre grazing area to assist in better grazing distribution.

6. Salt boxes were placed at distant points away from water in each unit.

7. The number of cows was reduced from 300 to 200 for better feeding and management.

8. Market cattle were sold as yearlings.

9. The number of bulls was reduced to 8 to be kept from cows in paddocks and pastures, except from July 1 to August 31, when they are to be turned with cows.

Some results and indicated further improvements were:

1. The 1,800 acres yield annually 200 A. U. M.; they will ultimately yield 400 A. U. M., as invigorated grasses crowd out unpalatable weeds and brush.

2. The meadow land yields 200 tons of hay and 200 A. U. M. grazing a year; it will ultimately produce 250 tons of hay and 300 A. U. M. of grazing.

3. Cropland produces 100 tons of barley grain and 125 A. U. M. of sweetclover and aftermath grazing annually; when full effects of the sweet-clover rotation are reflected on all cropland fields, an estimated 125 tons of barley and 300 A.U.M. of aftermath grazing will be realized.

4. No hay or grain is purchased.

5. No trailing to and from water.

6. The new salt stations have resulted in better grazing distribution.

7. The calf crop is satisfactory—200 cows average a 90 percent calf crop; the average sale weight is 700 pounds.

8. The market cattle are sold as even-aged class for better prices.

9. The better control of the bulls eliminates early breeding of heifers and gives an even-aged calf crop.

THE AUTHORS «« *W. T. White, a native of Kansas and a graduate of Kansas State College, is chief of the*

Regional Range Division, Soil Conservation Service, Portland, Oreg. He was engaged in range and livestock research, Alaska Agricultural Experiment Stations from 1917 to 1932. Since 1935 he has directed the technical phases of planning assistance rendered by the Soil Conservation Service to range-livestock ranchers in the western coastal States.

W. R. Frandsen, a native of Utah and a graduate of Utah State Agricultural College, operated a livestock ranch from 1930 to 1934. He has been a range-planning technician with the Soil Conservation Service since 1935; he is now a range conservationist in the regional office in Portland.

C. V. Jensen is a range conservationist in the Soil Conservation Service. He is stationed in Portland. Before joining S. C. S. in 1941, he was employed in range research in the Forest Service for 9 years. He was born in Montana and is a graduate of the University of Montana.

MANAGEMENT THAT RESTORES THE RANGE

R. S. CAMPBELL, LINCOLN ELLISON, F. G. RENNER

MOST run-down ranges can be improved. By improving the range, the stockman, the community, and the Nation gain. Restoration through wise use is witnessed by many specific examples in all parts of the range country. Many more ranges need such restoration. This article explains how to tell when grazed ranges need to recover, when they are on the mend, and how good livestock and range management can take advantage of natural processes to bring ranges back to greater productivity.

Restoration of range values can be accomplished most effectively and economically and in the shortest period of time by the wise use of all range techniques best suited to the type of operation involved, effectively coordinated with the natural growth habits and requirements of the principal forage plants.

The state of health or productivity of a range is known as range condition. Likewise, the steps or stages in the upbuilding of ranges are known in practical management as range condition classes, from very poor to excellent.

Range condition never stands still for long. It is either improving or declining. Range deterioration is but the effect of a downward trend of condition, the depletion of the plant cover and soil. Range restoration means stopping deterioration and bringing about an upward trend from an unsatisfactory to a satisfactory condition.

Five range condition classes are generally recognized, as mentioned previously.

A range in excellent condition has a fully productive stable soil and is producing all or nearly all the forage that it can. Good condition closely approaches excellent. Fair, poor, and very poor condition are all considered unsatisfactory because the soil is not fully productive and the range is growing only a part of the forage of which it is capable.

Even within each class, there may be a rather wide variation in density, composition, and vigor. Because each range has its own top or excellent condition, ranges must be classified in terms of their own best possible soil development and kind and amount of plant cover and forage production. For example, a mountain meadow naturally has a higher rainfall, deeper, richer soil, a thicker plant cover, and much greater forage growth than a semidesert grassland, even when both are in satisfactory condition. Hence, a mountain meadow cannot be judged by the standards one would use for a desert grassland.

Ranges in excellent condition do not need restoration because they are already producing all the forage possible under the existing climate. The plant cover protects the soil from abnormal erosion and maintains the fertility. The better forage plants, particularly the deeper-rooted, perennial grasses, predominate with palatable weeds and shrubs on some ranges. Better plants reproduce well in favorable years. Some litter covers the ground, and the topsoil is loose and friable, containing dark organic matter—more in areas of high rainfall than in the semidesert. The soil is porous and readily absorbs large amounts of moisture. The runoff water is clear. In other words, ranges in excellent condition serve every purpose as fully as possible.

Ranges in good condition are generally satisfactory although they produce less forage than those in excellent condition. The better perennial plants predominate, but there are some less palatable plants. The plant cover is thinner. There is less litter and the topsoil may show less organic matter. Erosion, if it occurs at all, is slight. Ranges in good condition offer an opportunity to increase production and value through conservative grazing and other management practices that encourage the more palatable plants. The job of restoration is not difficult or time consuming, as the better forage plants and soil are still there for quick improvement.

Ranges in fair condition are definitely unsatisfactory. Both soil and plant cover have been distinctly damaged, and restoration is no longer a quick or easy task. Valuable forage plants are considerably reduced in stand, their places occupied either by bare soil or by less palatable perennial grasses, weeds and shrubs. Annuals have usually increased. There is less total plant cover and litter and there is likely to be active erosion, particularly on the slopes. The dark topsoil layer is seriously disturbed, containing only moderate amounts of organic matter, and with only fair capacity to

hold available moisture. The exposed surface of clay and silt soils may be hard and crusted. Runoff water is heavy with silt. If neglected, fair ranges slip quickly to a poorer condition. If handled carefully, they can gradually be restored. Reseeding is often practicable.

Ranges in poor condition have lost so much of the forage stand and topsoil that they produce only a fraction of the forage grown on similar ranges in good or excellent condition. Few of the more valuable perennial forage plants remain, and low-value annuals or perennial weeds and shrubs such as snakeweed, juniper, and mesquite may predominate. Removal of topsoil by washing or blowing has exposed the subsoil or left a gravel "pavement." The soil has little organic matter and a low available moisture-holding capacity. There is active sheet and some gully erosion. Runoff is rapid and heavy with silt. The job of restoring poor ranges to full productivity is a major one. Years, even decades, may be required gradually to build back the organic matter in the topsoil that marks satisfactory condition. Where soil and moisture conditions permit, ranges in poor condition should be reseeded to adapted forage species, to hasten recovery.

Ranges in very poor condition have only a sparse stand of low-value plants, mostly annuals or unpalatable shrubs. Grazing capacity is very low, sometimes 5 percent or less of potential. The topsoil, with its organic matter, is largely gone, and the soil can hold little moisture for plant growth. The remaining soil is exposed to serious wind or water erosion. Gullies are extensive. Runoff from sudden summer storms forms flash floods, muddy with silt. Under such conditions natural restoration is a very long, arduous, and uncertain process. Where rainfall is sufficient, and where enough soil is left to support a forage stand, reseeding will usually aid recovery. Artificial aids such as furrows, terraces, and the like may be necessary on slopes to retain the soil in place long enough for better plants to take hold.

It is a matter of dollars and cents to the stockman to know the trend of his range condition—to be able to check when his management is improving its productivity. The indicators of an improving range vary in detail from one part of the country to another but in general may be summarized under three heads: (1) Improving soil character and stability; (2) increasing density and amount of vegetation; and (3) change in the kind of plant cover with better plants becoming predominant. All three must be considered together to judge range trend accurately.

Invasions of perennial plants into the bare soil openings are indicators of soil stabilization, as is the rounding of sharp erosional surfaces like the shoulders and bottoms of gullies as vegetation becomes established on them. A darkening and mellowing of the surface soil through addition of humus shows improvement. The old marks of erosion—gullies, wind-blown depressions, plant pedestals, erosion pavement—provide a record of deterioration that is written over, as it were, by a new record of plant invasion and building up of litter and dark soil. Building of soil means not only improving fertility but preservation of humus and tiny spaces between soil particles which store up needed moisture for vegetation. Plants growing on noneroded soil require less water than those on eroded soil. That means rainfall is used more efficiently on ranges in satisfactory condition—more forage is produced per inch of rainfall than on ranges in unsatisfactory condition and the soil is more adequately protected against erosion.

Change in density and amount of vegetation is a second important indicator of range trend. Vigorous forage plants, increasing in abundance by natural reseeding or otherwise on conservatively grazed range, are signs of stands being restored. Grazing must be so regulated that the better forage plants are allowed to spread.

Shifts in the kinds of plants present and the relative proportion of each kind are also important indicators of changes in range condition. From a very poor condition, the increase of any perennial plant cover is usually an improvement. A general thickening of palatable weeds and grasses is a mark of restoration from poor or fair. In most normal perennial forage stands there are young, "middle-aged," and old plants. The old ones die off naturally. A population of young palatable plants is a sign of an improvement in condition.

Conservative grazing keeps rundown ranges on the mend. It allows the more important forage plants to increase their density and vigor, avoids undue disturbance to soil, and retards runoff and erosion. Key forage plants are properly utilized on deteriorated ranges when enough of the leafage or stubble is left to maintain or increase their vigor and productivity and allow them to spread satisfactorily. Less valuable species will naturally be grazed less when the key species are properly utilized. For example, in the Southwest, when about 40 percent of the total herbage production of black grama has been grazed, the dropseed grasses usually are grazed only about 30 percent.

Sample utilization standards for ranges in good condition are shown in the table. Such general standards can be applied only with close study of the individual range, its soil, dominant forage plants, and their reaction to grazing use from year to year. Thus good condition and proper utilization of blue grama ranges are quite different in the Central Plains of Colorado than in the semidesert grasslands of Arizona and New Mexico. The stand is much more dense, and proper utilization may be closer under the favorable conditions of the Plains than under almost comparable rainfall, but shorter growing season, higher temperatures, and dry spring and fall periods of the Southwest.

One must know the condition of a

Indicators of Good Condition and Proper Utilization for Selected Range Types [1]

Type	Location	Soil	Plant cover	Proper utilization at end of grazing season
Short grass	Central Great Plains—Colorado and Wyoming.	Sod pieces not pedestaled. Slight to no erosion.	Almost unbroken sod of blue grama, buffalograsses; scattered tall grasses.	Blue grama—50 percent. Stubble height 1.5 inches.
Pinyon-juniper woodlands.	Southwest—Arizona, New Mexico.	Plant litter on surface. Little soil blowing or washing.	Blue grama predominant. Scattered other grasses, weeds, and shrubs.	Blue grama—40 percent. Stubble height 2.5 inches. One-fourth of stems ungrazed.
Sagebrush-grass spring-fall range.	Intermountain—south Idaho, north Utah, and Nevada.	Well protected by plant cover, accumulated plant debris. Sheet erosion limited, gullies lacking.	Slender bluestem, thick spike, and bluebunch wheatgrasses Idaho fescue dominant. Some arrowleaf balsamroot.	Grasses 50–60 percent. Stubble—3–4 inches. Equal use spring and fall. Reduce grazing as needed on steep slopes or erosive soils.
Subalpine grassland.	Pacific Northwest—eastern Oregon and Washington.	Half of surface covered by live vegetation. Soil stabilized by perennial grasses and weeds. Gullies lacking or stabilized.	Green fescue dominant, other grasses and weeds less than one-third of plant cover.	Green fescue—50 percent. Stubble—3 inches. Avoid undue soil disturbance by animals.
Mountain meadow.	Pacific Northwest—eastern Oregon and Washington.	Unbroken sod. Organic matter abundant. No erosion.	Tufted hairgrass dominant. Kentucky bluegrass, winter bentgrass, red fescue, sedges, and weeds scattered.	Tufted hairgrass—55 percent. Stubble—3 inches. Utilization even, giving mowed appearance.

[1] The information in this table is only approximate. For standards on range in poor condition, the references listed for further reading should be consulted for details. The proper utilization percentages are in terms of weight of the total herbage that may be removed by grazing.

range in planning grazing use that will allow forage production to improve. Let us illustrate with an example on mountain meadows of the Pacific Northwest. On ranges in good condition, tufted hairgrass is predominant, and dense vegetation covers about two-thirds of the ground surface. In poor condition, tufted hairgrass is limited to wet spots; vegetation is thin, patchy, and covers only about one-third of the ground surface; and weeds are abundant. When the condition is dropping from good to fair, the tufted hairgrass is replaced on drier spots by sod-forming grasses, such as Kentucky bluegrass. On the other hand, when a meadow in poor condition is improving, the perennial plant cover is vigorous and thickening, and weed patches are being taken over by sod-grasses. Later, as a fair condition improves toward a good condition, the more valuable tufted hairgrass will crowd out the sod grasses.

Grazing of palatable plants should be lighter on ranges in poor condition than on those in good condition. In the Southwest, for example, a properly grazed blue grama range in good condition will have about 40 percent of the weight of blue grama herbage removed at the end of the season. Average stubble height should be 2½ inches and one-fourth of the flower stalks left ungrazed. On deteriorated range, however, the blue grama is less abundant, has less vigor, and produces less forage, and the soil is eroding. Utilization of blue grama, therefore, must be lighter, not exceeding 30 percent, and leaving an average stubble of about 3 inches and two-fifths or more of the flower stalks ungrazed.

Conservative grazing is especially necessary in providing sufficient live-plant cover and litter to protect highly erosive soils from washing or blowing and to give the forage plants a chance to produce satisfactorily. Some soils on steep slopes practically melt away unless protected by plant cover. On heavily grazed range pastures within the ponderosa pine-bunchgrass type,

in fair condition on such soil in central Colorado, 51 percent of the herbage was utilized each year. After 5 years of such heavy use, plant cover was reduced about 12 percent, and herbage production was only 449 pounds per acre. On nearby moderately grazed pastures, where only 33 percent of the herbage was utilized each year, the grass density increased about one-third. Herbage production was more than 1,200 pounds per acre and of better quality. Thus, even though only a third of the herbage grown in 1946 was utilized on the moderately grazed range, the cattle had almost twice as much forage as with 51 percent utilization on the heavily grazed range.

The livestock production advantages of conservative grazing are well illustrated on two experimental ranches in the Southwest. After 27 years, these ranges, grazed conservatively yearlong, grow twice as much forage, have 50 percent greater net calf production, and have only one-fifth to one-third the death losses as compared to similar ranges that are heavily stocked.

Other Phases

In addition to conservative utilization, the other three basic principles of good range management—proper kind of animals, proper season of grazing, and even distribution of grazing use over the range—are important.

If overgrazing prevails, adjustments in livestock numbers or in season of grazing or both are essential. Sometimes changing the kind of livestock, combined with change in season and degree of use, is helpful. For example, a moderately steep range in central Arizona with erosive soil was used for many years by cattle yearlong. The valuable perennial grasses were grazed so constantly and closely that the trend continued downward until the range was in poor condition. Then a change was made from heavy yearlong cattle grazing to conservative winter sheep use. This allowed the vegetation to develop ungrazed during the full growing season. As a result, in fewer than 20 years, the range has improved greatly in both amount and quality of forage. Furthermore, since it is part of the watershed of an important irrigation project, the greater plant cover and improved stabilization of soil and runoff are protecting important values in the irrigated valley below.

Natural revegetation through deferred or deferred and rotation grazing has proved to be a very effective method for range recovery on many western ranges. It consists of deferring grazing on a part of a range each year until the more important palatable forage plants have matured a vigorous growth and gone to seed, or otherwise reproduced. The rotation feature comes through deferring grazing on different parts of the range in succeeding years. Under this practice, the mature seeds are shaken to the ground where they may be partly covered by trampling. During the following year light grazing or deferred use again may be desirable to promote establishment of seedlings. In a 10-year test in Colorado, for example, there was 47 percent more wheatgrass and 22 percent fewer weeds on a range where deferred and rotation grazing was followed, as compared to one grazed continuously. On the average, ranges grazed according to this method with conservative numbers of animals for 10 to 15 years have gained about 20 percent or more in forage value, an important step upward in condition. Through such management, which permits full use of the forage each year after maturity, individual range areas have improved in a period of 20 to 25 years from poor to good condition. Such improvement has usually meant doubling forage production.

Water-spreading devices and other structural aids speed up natural improvement where the plant cover has thinned by holding back the rainfall that is otherwise lost as surface runoff. Contour furrows have been found val-uable in the Great Plains, where blue grama, buffalograss, and other grasses make up most of the vegetation. Outside of the Great Plains, if there is a fair stand of grass, conservative grazing and other good management practices are likely to result in fully as much improvement as furrowing.

Water-spreading devices as a rule consist of a dam across a gully or arroyo, and a system of low dikes of earth, brush, or rock to spread the water on rather flat adjoining grasslands. Like contour furrows, water-spreading systems are chiefly effective by holding back the runoff water until the range grasses can use it. In the Southwest, as much as 1,500 pounds of forage per acre has been produced as a result of natural seeding and increased growth of forage on an area which was practically barren 2 years earlier. Small, inexpensive installations, which cause little damage in case of failure, have been found most satisfactory.

THE AUTHORS≪≪ *R. S. Campbell has been engaged in range research with the Forest Service since 1925. Dr. Campbell holds two degrees in ecology from the University of Chicago. He is now chief of the Division of Range Research, Southern Forest Experiment Station, at New Orleans.*

Lincoln Ellison, a native of Oregon and graduate of the University of California at Los Angeles, has a doctor's degree in ecology from the University of Minnesota. He has been in range research in Montana and Utah since 1933. He is in charge of grazing management studies, Intermountain Forest and Range Experiment Station at Ogden.

F. G. Renner was educated in forestry and animal husbandry at the University of Washington and Oregon State College. He was in administrative and research work with the Forest Service from 1916 to 1936, when he transferred to the Soil Conservation Service, where he is now chief of the Range Division. He works in Washington, D. C.

RESTORING THE RANGE BY RESEEDING

C. KENNETH PEARSE, A. PERRY PLUMMER, D. A. SAVAGE

FULL RESTORATION of much of the range land in need of improvement will require more than better grazing management. About 80 million acres of range land have been so badly depleted that they will have to be reseeded artificially if they are to recover in our generation. Satisfactory methods have not yet been developed for reseeding all situations, but progress is being made. Already more than 5 million acres have been planted.

Range reseeding is usually done on an extensive basis on lands unsuited for cultivation and at comparatively low cost. Plowing, except to reduce competition from undesirable plants, is usually not attempted; seedbeds are not generally prepared, except for reseeding abandoned cultivated fields in the Southern Great Plains.

On most reseeded ranges, correct grazing management alone is relied upon to maintain forage production, although in much of the South and on annual type ranges of California and in other areas where soils are poor, some fertilization may also be needed.

Reseeding, to be most effective, should be done where the chance of success is good and where increased forage will help most in making better use of the land and in increasing livestock production. For each area to be seeded, success depends on knowing what to seed, when to seed, and how to seed economically.

Practical answers to those questions are available on several important ranges, especially on depleted big sagebrush sites of the Intermountain Region, on abandoned cultivated lands in the plains and foothills, on mountain meadows below good condition in other parts of the West, and more limitedly on the other depleted ranges.

On some other range situations, promising leads have been developed by research, but are only now being tested on a practical scale. On others, research has made only a beginning. Here plantings of only small test areas, until proved procedures are found, will eliminate extensive and costly failures and save seed and effort for more productive planting elsewhere.

Even where specifications are available, sites for reseeding should be chosen with care. Ranges that have enough good forage remnants so that they can be restored rather promptly by better management alone seldom need seeding. Those whose production must always be low because of poor soil or unfavorable climate seldom produce enough forage to pay the cost. Where the valuable forage plants have been largely lost, but the good topsoil retained, the chance for success and the opportunity for improvement consistent with the cost is greatest.

A good appraisal of the site for reseeding may usually be made by observation of the terrain, the existing plant cover, and the soil. In semiarid parts of the West, experienced stockmen often can select the pockets, valleys, or parts of valleys that catch a little more rainfall, have subirrigation, or are subject to beneficial natural flooding. Where the range vegetation (even if composed of inferior forage plants) has a vigorous appearance and good color and makes good height growth and heavy seed crops, the site is apt to be above average.

Dark-colored, friable soil and a covering of humus and vegetable litter usually indicates a favorable site. Thus, where big sagebrush is dense, and the plants large and healthy, good stands of grass can be obtained once the sagebrush is removed. On the Fishlake National Forest in Utah, for example, 500 acres that was supporting a flourishing stand of vigorous big sagebrush and rabbitbrush furnished forage for only 8 or 9 cows for a 4-month season. Three years after it was reseeded to wheatgrasses and bromes at a cost of $3.22

an acre it provided forage for 100 cows for 4 months.

Reseeding will give greatest returns where it can best aid in meeting seasonal shortages in good forage. In most of the Intermountain West, for example, early spring forage is inadequate and sowing crested wheatgrass, an early spring- and fall-growing species, provides valuable grazing at that period.

Even in the Southern Great Plains, where the native grasses are noted for nutritive qualities, forage value drops markedly from early maturity and into winter dormancy. At Woodward, Okla., ranges seeded to western wheatgrass can provide nutritious forage throughout the fall, winter, and early spring. They have supported two to five times more cattle than nearby unseeded range, produced 50 to 80 percent more gain per head, saved 50 to 97 percent of the protein supplements required, and yielded three to eight times as much gain per acre.

In the South and Southeast, reseeding of fire lanes and other portions of piney woods ranges to adapted grasses that retain their protein and mineral content longer than the native species prolongs the period of good grazing, saves supplements, and permits better cattle gains.

Reseeding should be done only where good grazing management can be provided. Reseeded ranges need protection from grazing until the seedlings are established and moderate grazing in the proper season thereafter.

The success and productivity of artificially seeded ranges depends largely on planting species that are adapted to the local climate and that will persist under reasonable grazing use. Probably of first importance on most western ranges is the amount of precipitation and its seasonal distribution.

Less than 8 inches annually, even in the northern part of the western range country, is generally too little to justify the risk of large-scale reseeding. Even with as much as 12 inches annually, a considerable part of it must be available during the growing season, and very drought-resistant plants, like crested wheatgrass or some of the lovegrasses, must be used. Generally where precipitation is more than 15 inches and enough falls during the growing season, a number of forage plants, if soils and other conditions are satisfactory, are adapted.

Grasses withstand dry periods best when dormant. Hence it is necessary in each region to plant those that normally make their growth during the season when moisture is available. Where soil moisture is available in the cool spring and fall seasons, as in the valleys, foothills, and mesas of the Intermountain West, the wheatgrasses, bluegrasses, bromes, fescues, and other cool-season grasses can be used. Where summer rainfall is the rule, as in the Southwest, warm-season plants—native gramas, buffalograss, and the introduced lovegrasses—are best.

Low winter temperatures may limit the species that can be planted successfully. In the northern range country, only hardy native species (like slender and western wheatgrass, and mountain brome) or hardy introductions from comparable latitudes (like crested wheatgrass and Russian wild-rye from Siberia or smooth brome from Hungary) can survive.

In the Southern Great Plains and the Southwest, besides such natives as blue grama and side-oats grama, buffalograss, and sand lovegrass, three introduced lovegrasses from South Africa are promising. Of these, weeping lovegrass is the most cold-resistant, succeeding in northern Oklahoma and northern New Mexico. Boer lovegrass has less cold resistance, and Lehmann's least of the three. Since, however, both of these are more drought-resistant than weeping lovegrass, both cold resistance and drought resistance influence the selection for any specific area.

In the deep South moderate winter temperatures permit the use of such semitropical grasses as Bermuda, Bahia, and Dallisgrass, and among the legumes, the lespedezas, and crimson and white clovers. Each of these has its own cold tolerance which strictly limits its use. Cold-resistant strains of some are being developed by selection and breeding. Plants for reseeding in the piney woods also need the ability to grow in shade, under partial covering of fallen pine needles, and to withstand burning and competition from vigorous native grasses of lower value.

Mixtures of a few adapted species with similar palatabilities and seasons of growth usually take best advantage of differences in site conditions which may change frequently and sharply between parts of any large area. A single species may be largely eliminated by disease, pests, extreme drought, or winterkilling. In such instances, if several species are used together some will likely be much less affected than others and will fill in and maintain production of the stand. Mixtures also generally increase the nutritive value of the forage. Where the legumes are adapted, one or two should be included to add variety to the forage and add to soil nitrogen.

However, pure stands of species that differ in their season of usefulness and palatability, and so require different management, are often better than mixtures. Where both the cool-weather and the warm-weather grasses are adapted, separate seedings can be grazed when each is most nutritious. Each class can be managed according to its needs. Neither competes to the disadvantage of the other. Highly palatable species that cannot withstand heavy grazing, like sand lovegrass in the Southern Great Plains, can be maintained only if sown in pure stands or with other palatable species. Comparatively unpalatable but productive and nutritious grasses—such as many of the wheatgrasses—are best sown in pure stands or with species of similar palatability, and then grazed heavily enough to utilize them and maintain their succulence.

Source of seed is extremely important in successful establishment, productivity, and persistence of reseeded stands, especially for native species. Locally grown seed from plants that have proved their adaptability is preferred. Slender wheatgrass seed harvested in the Northern Great Plains, for example, is well suited for planting there, but in Utah produces small plants with little forage and no seed.

In the Plains it has been found that forage yield and length of growing period are greatly increased by using southern sources of seed. It is advisable there to use, at any given latitude, seed harvested south of that latitude. Seed may be used several hundred miles north of its source without much danger of winterkilling. Blue grama seed from northern Oklahoma, for example, has survived the winters in southern Alberta and produced several times the forage yield of Alberta blue grama.

In contrast with this, seed of most native grasses, when planted south of their source, produce plants decidedly lacking in vigor, production, and period of growth. Colorado and Kansas sources of blue grama and buffalograss, for example, produce in Oklahoma and Texas much less than half as much forage as plants from local seed.

Not only adapted species, but also adapted strains, must be chosen to give best results. Recent research has indicated immense possibilities for improving range grasses through genetics and selection. Some selections of smooth brome, for example, yielded under range conditions in central Utah five times as much forage as other tried strains. Differences in such important characteristics as leafiness, earliness or lateness of growth, seed production, ease of harvest, resistance to drought, cold, and disease have been found among selections of the grasses so far studied. Indications are that use of better strains can at least double forage production, make stand establishment more positive, and extend the usefulness of many species.

But proper choice of strains depends on careful consideration for each site. The most productive strain of mountain brome in the oak-brush zone of Utah, for instance, is entirely worthless in the next higher zone, where it winterkills.

How to Reseed

Growing conditions on most range land are difficult at best. Germinating seeds and young seedlings require a reliable and constant source of moisture. Range soils dry so rapidly on the surface that seed usually must be covered to provide adequate moisture as well as necessary anchorage for the growing seedling.

Correct depth of planting is also important. Until the young leaves have emerged from the soil and can build food, growth of the seedling depends on the food stored within the seed. Since this is limited, seeds planted too deeply cannot emerge and produce satisfactory stands. Generally seeds should be covered only enough to insure that they are kept moist until the roots can reach soil with a dependable supply of water. Satisfactory plantings of all species used in range reseeding have been obtained with covering of from ½ to 1 inch. Planting may be somewhat deeper for large seeds than for small, for light soils than for heavy, and for localities with light infrequent showers than where rainfall is more dependable.

Broadcasting seed with little or no provision for covering is of limited usefulness. It is most likely to succeed where rainfall is rather ample and dependable and where the small-seeded grasses like bulbous bluegrass, dropseeds, and lovegrasses can be used. Broadcasting on recently burned brush or timber ranges, if done before the ashes have settled or blown or washed away, can be effective. The seed will be covered by the loose ashes. Fallen leaves from aspen and possibly some other kinds of deciduous trees will give satisfactory covering of seed broadcast at about the time of leaf fall.

Airplanes provide an inexpensive means of broadcasting in some districts.

An accidental burn in young Douglas-fir-ponderosa pine on the Cabinet National Forest in Montana was seeded by airplane in the fall of 1944. Total cost was only $1.20 an acre. Two years later, the timothy, orchardgrass, Kentucky bluegrass, and bulbous bluegrass had fully protected the soil and were producing a ton of green herbage an acre. Obtaining uniform distribution of seed and flying accurately and safely are major problems over rough, mountainous range lands at elevations near the ceiling of the plane.

Airplane broadcasting of seed contained in soil pellets seems to offer advantages in facilitating uniform distribution of seed over large areas and increasing chances for success without covering. Further testing of this method is justified.

For planting at a uniform controlled depth, grain drills of either the single-disk, double-disk, or deep-furrow type are most useful. Flanges on the disks to control depth of planting, the addition of heavy press wheels to firm loose soil behind the disks, and strengthening and reenforcement to enable them to stand up in the rocky soils, thick brush, or rough terrain of range lands are desirable. Shallow plowing or heavy disking can be used to cover broadcasted seed, but since depth of covering with this method is somewhat haphazard, heavier rates of seeding than with drilling are necessary.

Perennial grass seedlings develop more slowly than most annuals and cannot compete for moisture, light, and space with annuals or established perennials whose period of growth coincides with their own. Reduction of this competing vegetation is difficult and costly, but essential to success. Complete removal, however, such as by burning or the preparation of a clean seedbed, may be undesirable because of drying and erosion of the soil and damage to the seedlings by wind, sand blasting, rodents, or frost heaving. Annual weeds which make most of their growth after seeded species are well started, such as Russian-thistles and tumblemustard in the Intermountain region and northern Plains, need not be removed. They are frequently beneficial in protecting seedlings.

One economical and effective method of reducing competition of many nonsprouting brush species, notably big sagebrush, is by prescribed or planned burning, when the conditions are suitable in the fall. Cheatgrass brome, an annual grass, can also be effectively reduced if it is burned just prior to the falling of the seeds. On many southern ranges in the longleaf pine type of the Coastal Plain, prescribed burning in winter is necessary to remove the "rough" and allow the seed to get to mineral soil. Burning is not recommended where desirable tree reproduction might be damaged or for brushy species which sprout vigorously, such as California chaparral. It is also a poor method on hot sandy ranges that are subjected to high winds and rapid surface evaporation.

Fire must be employed with care. It should be used only on range types where its value has been demonstrated, and in such a manner and where it will not jeopardize timber, watershed, or other values. Before burning, one must make sure that adequate fire lines have been made, and that ample help is on hand to take care of any emergencies. The topography should be sufficiently level that there will be no serious danger from erosion. Depleted ranges require seeding as soon as is feasible after burning to stabilize the soil and prevent reinfestation by undesirable plants.

Heavy one-way disk or wheatland plows are perhaps the most adaptable and effective machines for eliminating competition by many brush and weed species. The brush is left on the land, and the land is left rough so that it is not subject to severe erosion. As much as 80 to 95 percent of the competition can be eliminated by shallow wheatland plowing. Seeder attachments are available, so if work is done at the proper season, planting can be accomplished at the same time. The method is limited, however, to land with moderate slopes and little or no rock. A new-type plow with disks mounted on springs to reduce breakage even on rocky areas is especially promising.

Recently developed oversized and self-clearing harrows and rail drags with improved cutting edges are effective for eliminating undesirable plants where the one-way disk plow cannot be used because of rocky soil or broken topography.

The stubble-mulch method of land preparation has been effective in reseeding abandoned cultivated lands in the Southern Great Plains and subhumid areas east of the Plains. A close-drilled sorghum crop is grown on the land the first year. It is planted late enough in the season—in late June or July—so that the crop will not mature seed, volunteer the second year, and offer competition to perennial grass seedlings. Part of the standing sorghum crop is grazed off in the fall in order to pack the soil and realize some income. Sufficient stubble cover must be left by the livestock to control wind and water erosion, reduce surface evaporation, and prevent soil crusting. Grasses are drilled directly in the stubble the following spring. If the soil is still somewhat soft, a heavily weighted roller is run over the land. Rolling firms the soil around the seed, reducing moisture losses, and is often valuable wherever the soil is too loose.

When to Reseed

Reseeding should be done when seedlings will have the longest possible period of good growing conditions for establishment.

Planting should be timed so that seeds can germinate as soon as this favorable growing period begins. Seedling growth may be curtailed by low temperature, dry weather, or competition from weeds or other vegetation. In the intermountain valleys and foothills of much of the West, soil is usually moist during the winter and spring, but a summer dry period is the rule and seedlings must be big enough by early summer to withstand 100 days or more without effective rain. Fall planting, therefore, which gets the seed in the ground, ready to germinate with the first warm day of spring, is generally best for cold-resistant grasses. Where frost damage is severe, however, as on ranges with little vegetation or litter cover, and especially for susceptible legumes, early spring planting may be necessary.

Planting in the early summer is most successful in the Southwest, where the spring months usually are dry but good summer rains prevail. Where rainfall is rather well distributed during the growing season, as in the Great Plains, cool-weather grasses may best be sown in the fall, and warm-weather grasses at the beginning of the growing season in the spring. The exact date depends on the local precipitation pattern, the species used, the method of planting, and the time of weedy growth. Delayed seedings on abandoned plowed land in the Southern Great Plains meet with weed competition. Seedings, however, may be delayed in that area, where wind erosion is not important, until one or two crops of weed seedlings have been destroyed by surface tillage.

The growth requirements of the plant and the nature of the seed also affect the choice of planting season. Thus cool-season grasses, such as the wheatgrasses, can be seeded more readily in fall than warm-weather grasses such as the lovegrasses, which are killed by freezes, or legumes whose smooth taproots make them susceptible to frost heaving. Some seeds with hard coats, such as sand lovegrass, sand paspalum, and buffalograss, and others, such as fourwing saltbush and antelope bitterbrush, that need an after-ripening treatment, germinate better after freezing temperature. They should be sown in fall or very early spring.

During their first year, grasses used for range reseeding may make but little growth. Reseeded ranges do not develop so rapidly as cultivated pastures. Some range grass seedlings may show only a few small brown leaves in their first dry season and be almost invisible until they resume growth the next year. Because of this, plantings should not be plowed up or reseeded until they have had time—at least 2 or 3 years—to demonstrate success.

Reseeded ranges need protection from grazing until the seedlings are large enough to withstand pulling or trampling by livestock. This may require from 1 to 3 years, depending on the weather and other growing conditions. The plants are big enough to withstand grazing, however, when the first seed crop is produced, so that the best rule is to keep livestock off newly seeded ranges until seed heads show, whether that be at the end of the first growing season or after several years.

To assure maintenance of production from the reseeded stands, careful grazing management is needed. Principles of management described for native ranges provide valuable guides and should be used as a basis for grazing reseeded ranges. In addition, it is wise to keep a careful and frequent watch for any lowered vigor of the reseeded grasses—e. g., reduced height growth, small seed crops, poor color, and death of parts of clumps—and for invasion by low-value plants. If these signs are observed, livestock numbers will need to be reduced or the season of grazing shortened.

If wisely used, reseeded ranges will support more livestock for longer periods and in better condition than comparable unseeded ranges. Their production compares favorably with native ranges in good or excellent condition on similar sites and is far above that of ranges in poor, very poor, or even fair condition. The increased forage can be maintained indefinitely. Several experimental seedings on the Manti National Forest in central Utah have been grazed each year since they were planted in 1912. Many extensive plantings in other parts of the West have been grazed for 10 to 15 years and still produce from 2 or 3 times to as much as 20 times more forage than before seeding.

Total costs of reseeding, including seed, planting, supervision, and incidental items, range from $1.50 to $10 an acre, depending on the species and methods used. Most reseeding has been done for less than $5 an acre. The direct value of increased forage provided by reseeding varies from 15 to 50 cents an acre per year. In addition, many indirect values, such as soil and watershed protection, better balance of the year's forage supply, and more efficient livestock production, are realized. With such relationships between costs and benefits, very satisfactory financial returns on money invested are realized from seeding of carefully selected ranges to adapted species and providing proper grazing management.

THE AUTHORS≪≪   *C. Kenneth Pearse is assistant chief, Division of Range Research, United States Forest Service, Washington, D. C. He was formerly in charge of range-reseeding investigations at the Intermountain Forest and Range Experiment Station, Ogden, Utah. He received his training in plant ecology and plant physiology at the University of Chicago.*

A. Perry Plummer is range ecologist in charge of Utah reseeding studies for the Intermountain Forest and Range Experiment Station, Ogden, Utah. He is a graduate of the University of Utah.

D. A. Savage is an agronomist in the Bureau of Plant Industry, Soils, and Agricultural Engineering and is in charge of the Southern Great Plains Field Station, Woodward, Okla. He was trained at Montana State College.

GUARD FIRST THE BOTTOM LAND

R. V. BOYLE, J. S. MC CORKLE

OFTEN the heart of a ranch is its flood-watered bottom land. These acres of alluvial plains may comprise only one one-hundredth of the area of the ranch, but if they are in good condition they can produce 2 to 20 times more forage than do the adjacent uplands.

The flood plains often have significant value as a nursery for calving or lambing, a hospital for thin or ailing stock, a fattening pasture, a winter-feed pasture, or a hay meadow. On them the carry-over of soil moisture after flooding may insure green forage for months after the upland range has dried up.

Where only light runoff is available, grasses in the flood-irrigated valleys may be the same species found on the uplands although more luxuriant. The most significant increase in production, however, occurs when the volume of floodwater is great enough that the short grasses are replaced by taller, deeper-rooted species. Forage production then may be measured in tons as forage from the uplands is measured in hundredweights.

That is what happens when the range is in virgin state or in good condition. But often it is not: Depletion has been severe in many places. Upland vegetation has deteriorated. Much of the original grass cover has disappeared. The shrubs and grasses which follow are less able to resist erosion, and flash runoff increases.

And on the bottoms and flood plains misuse has been most concentrated: Cattle congregated on them; roads and trails appeared; the vegetation was thinned out; and channels were cut. When these areas were in virgin condition, heavy floods dug out pot holes, which usually filled with silt and debris and were revegetated without permanent damage. But as the vegetative cover was depleted, the holes grew in length and gullies were formed, made worse by the ruts and channels in the roads and trails. The bottoms were drained. Through the gullies, silt that had slowly accumulated in the valleys for centuries moved in damaging quantities to the stream channels and often spread over farm lands. Damage downstream from range deterioration is difficult to estimate, but is considerable. Silt fills river channels and reservoirs, and flash floods may damage irrigation systems and other property.

One can divide southwestern watersheds fairly readily into silt-producing areas and water-producing areas. Heavy water-yielding areas are generally at high elevations that have relatively good precipitation and vegetation. Their silt yield is relatively low because the vegetation on them resists erosion and rains are less intense.

Less favorable elevations are arid or semiarid, subject to long dry periods and torrential downpours. Soils are often erodible, and flash floods that carry excessive loads of silt are likely. Both flood and silt are greatly increased by range depletion. There are, of course, both uplands and valleys that have not suffered severe damage and others that have recovered.

Where damage has occurred, the remedy has two parts. The first is to correct the misuse responsible for depletion of the vegetation. The second is to restore flood-plain conditions by diverting the water from the gullies and to use whichever structures are necessary to insure a reasonable distribution or spreading that will control and prevent further gully formation.

It is usually impracticable to divert floodwaters to the uplands. The conditions required for successful diversion and spreading of water on range will usually be found on formerly flooded areas—be they a fraction of an acre or several thousand acres.

Several factors complicate the reclaiming of range bottoms. Water law is one. Irrigation of cropland has reached a high state of development, and the water from most western watersheds is appropriated for that purpose. Water laws in Western States are based on the principle of prior appro-

priation—whoever puts a water supply to beneficial use has a right to its continued use under State regulations.

Court decisions are somewhat vague on the point, but benefits to a rancher from natural spreading of floodwaters over grassland are seldom if ever contested. After floodwaters accumulate in a natural channel of sufficient size and permanence to be recognized by the courts as a watercourse, prior appropriations take precedence. Many large gullies now draining the range were caused by relatively recent activity of man rather than by natural geologic processes, and some authorities do not consider them "watercourses" in the legal sense. The rights of range operators to reclaim flood plains by diverting the water back to its original state of spreading over the area affected have not been generally defined.

Few specific data are available to determine the effect of this or other types of watershed treatment on total stream flow. Water that would drain off in a few hours through a gully may meander across a vegetated spreading area for days before finally draining off downstream, but there is little information to show the total yield of water in each case.

Diversions may vary from protective work to prevent further deterioration of natural spreaders to complete reclamation where gullies have been established for years. Many of the logical water diversions for range land occur on interior drainage basins where water appropriations do not introduce serious problems. In other instances the rights to the use of water for spreading may be recognized; it is possible also that the use of the water for farm irrigation is so remote that no question will arise.

Spreading floodwater on range is a type of irrigation. Such use of water may be less efficient than irrigation of cropland where flow is regulated and measured, but there are factors (such as saving water in transit) that are in favor of spreading. Flash floods may run off rapidly, where there are gullies and channels to carry them, but dry sand washes can absorb an enormous amount of water and may even entirely dissipate sizable floods before they join a permanent stream.

Other factors are of a physical nature.

Spreading may be impracticable because gully erosion has progressed too far. The arroyo may be too big or may carry too much water to handle on the area in question. Each site must be analyzed on its own merits, and its physical characteristics and limitations and engineering needs considered.

The type of diversion is determined chiefly by the size of expected floods and the size and character of the spreading area. Supplementary structures to effect a satisfactory spreading of water will vary with slope and topography. Small dikes, brush or rock percolators, wire diversions, or longer dikes with "weeps" to pass water in small quantities, are the types usually employed. Water should be in controllable quantities and flows frequent enough to saturate the soil one or more times a year.

An excessive amount of alkali in the soil is detrimental. Heavy textures and relatively impermeable soils may be suitable for water spreading if the gradient is flat enough that water will remain on them for some time—long enough to soak in thoroughly. Coarse, gravelly soil is usually not satisfactory.

Some diversions onto areas with not more than 2 feet of good soil are successful, but generally there should be 4 to 6 feet or more of good soil in water-spreading areas. This will provide soil enough for sufficient water storage in the principal feeding zone for grass roots.

The topography and slope must be such that water will spread naturally or with a limited amount of diking and supplemental structural work. The suitability of an area for spreading water will usually decline rapidly with increase in slope; 5 percent is about the maximum slope for practical application; 1 percent or less is better.

The type of vegetation already present is important. If there is a fair growth of perennial vegetation to retard and spread the water, greater amounts of water can be handled safely than if the cover has deteriorated. Seeding may be required on denuded areas or where desirable grasses have disappeared. For this purpose the native grasses found on the natural spreading areas are probably the best suited, but good seed of native species is not always available. Where reseeding is necessary, species should be selected for the site, considering alkalinity of the soil and the ability of the grass to endure flooding, silting, and drought between floodings.

Where a heavy silt load is expected, it may be practical to install stream-bottom fencing and gully plantings upstream from the diversion so that the heaviest silt will be deposited in the channel before it reaches the diversion. Sound range management (including proper use of the vegetation on the watershed) is, however, the most effective means of controlling silt.

Before a diversion is installed, one should plan the disposition of all the water to be diverted. If water flows out at the lower end of the area and drops into a raw gully, there may be danger of a head cut working back across the treated area. Occasionally small levees may be used to keep water out of gullies and supplemental outlet structures may be needed.

Getting the proper use of forage on spreading areas is often difficult. In dry periods, when the spreading areas contain the only green grass, animals tend to concentrate there and may seriously damage the cover. It is seldom possible to achieve proper use of the spreading area and adjacent range without fencing so as to control the use of each. Properly handled, the forage from the areas affected by water diversions will satisfactorily supplement the total range feed.

The importance of regular and systematic inspection and maintenance cannot be stressed too much. Water spreading by means of diversions is designed to be more or less self-operating as a rule, but no system can be expected to continue to operate without maintenance. The cost of maintenance will be much less if the system is observed closely and repairs and adjustments are made promptly. Rodents, for example, may burrow through dikes and cause destruction of the whole system unless repairs are made.

Unrepaired, a minor detail may become a major operation. Silting may necessitate adjustments such as shifts in location of spreader dikes. The main diversion is the key to the whole system and may be destroyed or made useless by lack of proper maintenance.

THE AUTHORS «« R. V. Boyle, regional chief of operations with the Soil Conservation Service in Albuquerque, N. Mex., is a native of Arizona. He began work in 1925 in the Department of Agriculture as a forest ranger and a specialist in range management. Mr. Boyle has been with the Soil Conservation Service since 1934.

J. S. McCorkle, regional chief of the Range Division, Soil Conservation Service, in Albuquerque, is a southwesterner. He was employed for several years in animal husbandry work following graduation from college. He has been engaged in range conservation work with the Soil Conservation Service since 1935.

SPACING WATER HOLES TO SAVE GRASS

B. W. ALLRED, HOWARD MATSON

THE RANCH that has poorly spaced and too few water holes for its cattle faces the danger of ruinous overgrazing around the water holes while little use is made of the forage that lies just beyond.

As the grass is tramped and grazed out, wind and water erosion takes a foothold and spreads rapidly. The eroding soil gradually loses its ability to absorb the water needed for good vegetation. The only remedy for this situation is to have plenty of well-distributed stock-watering places that will cause the livestock to spread out over the range and prevent the concentration of grazing in small areas.

To illustrate: East of Colorado Springs, ranges in poor condition near overused water holes absorbed only a third as much heavy rainfall as good grassland that was a long distance from water.

Another example: A rancher near Mangum, Okla., planned a soil conservation program on his 4,700 acres and developed a spring and 9 stock ponds to furnish fresh water at convenient locations for his cattle. Now

there is no sign of erosion or the destruction of forage grasses because of grazing concentrated around water holes. His lowland range is covered with western wheatgrass, Texas bluegrass, and Canada wild-rye, and the upland range has a vigorous stand of little bluestem, sand bluestem, and side-oats grama. Beneath the grass is a cushion of litter that breaks the fall of the rain and lets it sink quickly into the soil. The improved method of watering and other conservation practices have increased livestock production on the ranch 25 percent.

Springs, wells, and ponds are the most common types of stock-water developments. A dependable supply of good water at the lowest cost for installation and upkeep is usually the goal. Wet-weather springs, intermittent streams, and shallow ponds are used frequently as extra sources of water.

The correct installation of watering facilities is based on the number of animals to be grazed for a given number of days during a particular season, lay of the land, quality of water, con-

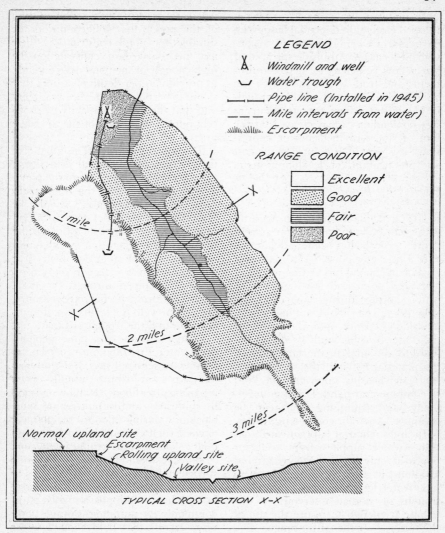

LEGEND

人   Windmill and well

∪   Water trough

⊢—⊢—   Pipe line (Installed in 1945)

— — —   Mile intervals from water)

⊸⊿⊔ⅇⅇ   Escarpment

RANGE CONDITION

▢   Excellent

▨   Good

▤   Fair

▥   Poor

1 mile

2 miles

3 miles

Normal upland site

Escarpment

Rolling upland site

Valley site

TYPICAL CROSS SECTION X-X

The improper placement of watering facilities led to the uneven use of forage on a 1,690-acre ranch near Marfa, Tex. The cattle grazed too much around the windmill and trough, and the forage there fell off 75 percent. The areas near the stream (indicated by the heavy shading) were next most heavily grazed. The animals were not forced to go for water to the upland area, where the forage was excellent.

dition of forage, spacing, ease of approach, and cost.

The rancher should plan for about 10 to 12 gallons of water daily per head for cattle, horses, and mules. Dairy cows and work horses need 25 to 30 percent more. Sheep and goats need 0.8 to 1 gallon.

The size and shape of pastures in-

fluence the location of water supplies. For example, livestock in the Southwest tend to graze into the wind; hence the windward side of a pasture is often tramped out. Some ranchmen change their fences to give the animals a wider pasture and place the water supply on the leeward side to bring about a more even use of the forage.

In many places springs can be developed easily into dependable sources, particularly when they are at a convenient location. A hillside spring that has a flow sufficient to meet requirements and from which the water can be delivered by gravity to a trough is ideal. But when springs occur as seeps extending over wide areas at the foot of slopes or in draws or depressions, it is wise to find out first the cost and practicability of developing them.

Wells and Ponds

If a dependable supply of ground water can be found at not too great a depth, a well has some advantages over a spring or pond. Usually there is greater likelihood of locating a well at a desired point and less danger of a water shortage during long droughts. Whether a well should be dug, driven, or drilled depends upon the nature of the water-bearing sand, its depth below ground surface, the character of the material between the surface and the water-bearing sand, and the kind of equipment at hand. Drilling, developing, and equipping wells can be complex—a job for competent drillers.

In areas where it is practical to develop water supplies from wells or ponds at only a few widely scattered locations, it is sometimes necessary to pipe water long distances to watering troughs or storage reservoirs to distribute it enough to insure the use of the forage over the entire range.

In the areas without year-round streams, springs, or good ground water close enough to the surface for economical well development, ponds are the main source of water for livestock. Even if such water is present, ponds sometimes can be developed more economically than other sources and can be used for other purposes, such as irrigation, orchard spraying, fish production, recreation, or extra water supplies.

For the greatest benefit and long life of ponds, it is essential that the drainage area be mainly grassland or woods to prevent rapid sedimentation of the pond; that soil conditions be suitable for pond construction; that any necessary dam construction be high enough, or the pond deep enough, to provide proper depth of water; that a suitable spillway site be available; and that the storage capacity be properly related to the size of the drainage area.

To reduce sedimentation, a band of dense vegetation is useful in desilting the water before it flows into the pond. The pond, including the dam, spillway, and desilting area, should be fenced against livestock to reduce pollution and the spread of disease, and to protect the vegetation on the banks of the pond. The stock get their clear, fresh water from a trough or tank to which it is piped through the dam. Wide platforms of concrete, masonry, or stone prevent the formation of mudholes around the trough or tank.

Economical use of a pond depends upon careful maintenance of installations. Grassed spillways and the various types of riprap usually need repairing after floods. Rank vegetation in spillways can be mowed to avert blocking during floods. Mechanical devices, such as troughs, pipelines, and float valves, require regular inspection.

All wells should be protected against surface pollution. Watering troughs or tanks are necessary at wells. In range areas where windmills are used most commonly for pumping, storage tanks or reservoirs that hold enough water to last for several days are needed for protection against a shortage in calm periods. Another protective measure is to equip the well with an auxiliary engine or motor.

Before extensive developments are begun, it is wise to learn the quality of the water available. In some localities neither surface water nor ground water is good for animals because of muddiness, salt solutions, or other impurities.

Properly spaced water supplies keep livestock from walking off their gains in weight. Spacings of a quarter mile are most convenient for animals but returns on the investment often will not justify such extensive water developments. At any rate, watering places should not be separated by more than 5 miles on level or gently rolling ranges and by not more than a mile where there are thickets, down timber, steep canyons, badlands, and mountains that impede travel. Sheep should travel no more than 3 or 4 miles for water in cool weather—half that distance in warm weather. Animals with young need water at closer intervals than do dry animals. Needless concentrations along one route can be avoided by providing several approaches to watering places.

Installation costs vary according to needs and conditions. Some authorities contend that $5 per animal unit is a reasonable expenditure, while others believe that the expense of water development is not justified at all on ranges where the potential grazing capacity is less than five or six animal units per section yearlong. On the other hand, the cost of quarter-mile spacing may be justified in high-rainfall belts and on highly improved tame pastures, and, of course, purebred

stock may justify greater outlays than grades.

THE AUTHORS ‹‹‹ *B. W. Allred was born in Utah and completed undergraduate work at Utah State Agricultural College and graduate work there and at the University of Nebraska. Before 1935 he was engaged in range livestock ranching and agricultural extension work. Since then he has been engaged in range management work. Mr. Allred is chief of the Range Division, Soil Conservation Service, Region 4, Fort Worth, Texas.*

Howard Matson received his bachelor of science degree in agricultural engineering at the University of Nebraska and his master of science degree at the University of California. From 1929 to 1933 he was employed as an extension specialist at Kansas State College of Agriculture and the University of Kentucky. Since that time he has been engaged in conservation engineering with the Civilian Conservation Corps, the Soil Erosion Service, and the Soil Conservation Service. Mr. Matson is chief of the Water Conservation Division, Soil Conservation Service, Fort Worth.

GRASS AND WATER AND TREES

CHAS. A. CONNAUGHTON

NEARLY EVERY acre of range has other uses and values besides forage production—to protect watersheds, produce timber, give wildlife a home, and provide places for recreation.

These are the "other" values of the range. Each is important; on some ranges, indeed, the demands of one or more may dominate or even exclude grazing. If grazing is properly managed, however, the various uses are usually compatible with the use of forage by livestock.

A description of how grazing can be coordinated with watershed and timber management is given here to pro-

vide a basis for a fuller understanding of the concept of management for multiple use.

In theory it is not particularly hard to coordinate grazing and watershed use on range land. In the main, it requires simply that methods and systems of grazing be practiced that will insure maximum production of forage so that grazing capacity is maintained and a cover of vegetation is provided to stabilize soil and help regulate runoff. Favorable watershed conditions are thereby insured.

There are exceptions to this general premise: On some steep slopes the loose soil is held in delicate balance by the plant cover, as on parts of the Boise River watershed in Idaho, the Salt River watershed in Arizona, and the South Platte River watershed in Colorado. On these slopes, it is unwise to attempt any grazing because the risk of erosion is too great. On most watersheds, however, properly managed grazing is entirely feasible.

In practice, the coordination of grazing with the watershed service of the land is not so simple. Grazing is often handled in such a way that the plant cover deteriorates and maximum forage production is not maintained; then the watershed values of the range are likely to decline because reductions in plant cover usually cause unfavorable changes in the soil, scarcely perceptible at first but ultimately strikingly evident in accelerated erosion and rapid runoff. These are marks of a damaged watershed.

Picture in your mind a range watershed with which you are familiar. Originally nature combined its soil, plant, and climatic factors in a way that imparted a given set of watershed characteristics, which were determined by the amount and kind of runoff, the movement of soil by wind or water, the quantity of silt in the runoff, and other elements. The natural factors may have created a stable balance. Well-vegetated slopes were yielding a steady flow of silt-free water, or, at the other extreme, the vegetation may normally have been scant, with considerable normal erosion and rapid runoff. The detailed characteristics are unimportant, however, because the general premises that follow are applicable regardless.

By and by, commercial grazing began on the watershed. If the numbers of domestic livestock were held at a point where the yield of forage was sustained at a maximum through the years, the natural characteristics may have changed little. There may be minor scars of use, such as trails and salt grounds, but, in brief, grazing and watershed use have been coordinated.

More than likely, however, the range with which you are familiar was subject to economic pressures and stocking was increased to the point where the forage was too closely cropped. When this happened, the plants began to lose vigor, and less and less organic material was produced to be returned to the soil. Fertility in turn declined.

The soil became less porous. This process probably started rather slowly without being noticeable in its early stages, but it is a vicious circle—the less vegetation produced the poorer the soil conditions, and the poorer the soil the less vegetation produced.

Without adequate plant material in and on the soil, the stage was set for erosion and rapid runoff. There again the effects pyramid, because a small loss of soil by erosion changes the surface by reducing porosity and creates small channels which concentrate runoff. This sets the stage for even greater soil losses and runoff.

Where such watershed deterioration proceeds unchecked and has reached an advanced state, we have the conditions which are all too common today—the silt-choked stream channels; flash stream flow with a heavy burden of soil; gullied valleys and meadows with lowered water tables; slopes barren of fertile topsoil; as well as irrigation and other improvements and even lives destroyed by flood and mud flows. Where these conditions prevail, coordination of grazing and watershed values has not been achieved, and to attain it after the damage is done may require drastic corrective measures.

What corrective actions will bring about belated coordination of grazing and watershed values on the range? Every watershed has its own peculiar set of conditions, but the first step is generally obvious. Grazing pressure must be removed or reduced so that the plant cover can restore itself to normal. This means reducing animal numbers or improving management practices and methods, or both. If the soil fertility has not been seriously depleted and perennial plants remain which can reproduce themselves, restoration may be accomplished fairly rapidly after grazing is gauged to permit abundant natural seeding or other revegetation.

If soil fertility or the plant cover has been badly depleted, natural recovery may be exceedingly slow even if all livestock is excluded. Where this is the case or where it is desired to hasten natural processes, attention should be given to supplemental measures. Artificial reseeding aids in reestablishing a normal plant cover. Engineering works (such as check dams and water-holding or water-spreading devices as were used with striking success on the mountain watersheds between Ogden and Salt Lake City, Utah) are means of arresting deterioration and hastening a return to a stabilized condition, especially when supplemented with reseeding. Whether these supplemental measures should be used will be determined by the potentialities of the land itself and the interests and needs of both the landowner and the public.

A further point: Watershed values of an entire range can be seriously damaged if misuse is permitted on localized key areas comprising no more than 5 to 10 percent of the total. Thousands of acres of slopes surrounding a few key meadows may have an excellent plant cover, but if the cover on the meadows only is depleted, erosion there may produce enough silt to make unusable the yield of water from the entire drainage. Or, runoff from these small, misused areas alone may be sufficiently accelerated and concentrated to overtax channel capacities and cause floods and aggravated channel erosion. This point has been demonstrated strikingly in the past when devastating flash floods and mud flows issued from certain canyons of the Wasatch Front in Utah as a result of grazing misuse on localized key areas that make up no more than 10 percent of the total watershed.

The coordination of grazing and watershed values on important range watersheds cannot, therefore, be a piecemeal arrangement. It must be accomplished on practically every acre if it is to be successful. One of the range manager's most important tasks is to hold the necessary scars of use, like trails and salt grounds, to an acceptable minimum, compatible with watershed values. If this cannot be done, watershed values can doubtless be protected only by the exclusion of grazing.

The Range and Timber

On millions of acres of land, particularly in the West and South, forage and forest are dual crops and their use must be efficiently coordinated— not generally a difficult task if conservative management practices are followed.

The best example that I know is the southern forests of longleaf pine, which characteristically grow in rather open stands with an understory of palatable forage. Grazing is common throughout most of this forest type. The forage can be grazed yearlong, although it has its highest nutritive values in spring and early summer.

Grazing cattle on average longleaf pine ranges offers few complexities if stocking is moderate—one head to 20 or 30 acres for a year. The damage done to small seedlings can ordinarily be avoided by light grazing for the first year or two after a large fall of pine seeds. Afterwards, stocking can be increased, not only to realize on the forage values but to reduce the accumulation of inflammable litter on the forest floor.

The real trouble with cattle grazing in longleaf pine stands is associated with the common practice of burning the woods to improve the forage. Under some conditions cattle make better gains in weight on burned range, but promiscuous wild fires set to improve grazing may damage the trees.

As a means of reconciling this conflict of uses, prescribed burning by owners of forest land is being viewed with increasing favor. Prescribed burning means simply that under competent supervision, controlled fires are set when weather conditions are right and allowed to burn over an area in such a way that little or no damage is done to the timber. If velocity and direction of the wind are right, humidity high, and the fuel fairly moist, the flames will not be hot enough or high enough to harm the trees much. Prescribed burning by competent men is not particularly difficult or hazardous. The forest can be burned over once every 3 or 4 years if there is need for it. If the area is segregated into blocks, part of it can be burned annually, thus making a freshly burned block available for the cattle each year.

Prescribed burning may benefit the forest by reducing brownspot needle disease on young longleaf pine. It also prepares the forest floor as a seedbed and reduces fuels for potential wild fires.

Grazing by sheep, goats, and hogs in these longleaf pine stands offer problems that are not so easily solved. Sheep and goats may graze the tender pine shoots even in places that have abundant forage. Furthermore, it is common practice where sheep graze to burn the range more frequently than where cattle graze. Grazing of the pine shoots stunts growth, and burning as often as twice a year is destructive. It is questionable, therefore, whether sheep or goat grazing and production of longleaf pine can be practiced on the same land without rather marked conflicts.

So far, no system has been devised to coordinate hog grazing and growing young longleaf pine successfully. In most localities one must supplant the other. Hogs cause high mortality in pine seedlings and saplings by digging up and eating the succulent bark of the tree roots. It has been estimated that one piney-woods hog can destroy a full acre of planted longleaf pine in a day. Natural seedlings are killed just as easily and quickly. But once the trees reach a height of 10 to 15 feet they are relatively proof against serious damage,

and hog grazing and timber production can proceed together.

Elsewhere in the East, in commercial forest types other than longleaf pine, open range grazing is considerably more limited. Where rainfall is abundant and soils are suitable, well-managed eastern timber usually grows so dense that forage beneath it is not plentiful. Consequently, fire is sometimes employed where grazing is desired, as in the Ozarks, to reduce the forest cover and permit greater forage production. This is poor land management, because it generally results in neither a good stand of forage nor a good stand of timber. Under such circumstances, proper coordination can be best realized by assigning grazing to improved pastures. Some grazing can always be obtained around the edges of openings in the forest, along roads, and on firebreaks, although it must be conservative to avoid damage to tree seedlings, soil, and watershed values. Timber production and watershed protection should dictate the basic policy of land management throughout most eastern commercial forests.

Grazing in the more or less noncommercial open-forest areas, such as the post oak belt in eastern Texas and Oklahoma, is similar to grazing in much of the woodland area of the Rocky Mountains. The use of open forest land such as this, unfitted to produce good timber, in both the East and West is governed quite largely by the grazing demands because livestock brings in more money than timber. Coordinated management here demands that range use determine the major land-management policies. In the extreme case, as with juniper in some areas in the Southwest, these policies might even call for reduction in the stand of trees if they encroach on and reduce forage.

On commercial timberlands in the West, where the land has a higher ultimate value for timber production than for forage, it is often necessary to handle grazing on a flexible basis. Stocking then should be maintained so that damage to tree reproduction does not occur. If the forest cover increases under management and thereby reduces available forage, livestock numbers should be adjusted downward to avoid damage by overstocking. By this system of coordination, grazing values can be realized to the fullest within the limitations of the prevailing objectives of developing the timber.

Grazing in the ponderosa pine type is probably the best illustration of this principle. This type, which is characterized by open stands of timber, is widely and successfully grazed by both sheep and cattle. Where rates of stocking are maintained so that the forage is not overgrazed, there is little damage to the timber. However, with good fire protection and timber management, the number of trees may increase and occupy space that formerly produced mainly forage. If that occurs, the reduced grazing capacity must be recognized and rates of stocking adjusted accordingly. Otherwise, overstocking

will result, with damage to both timber and forage.

Generally speaking, grazing on the commercial timber lands of the West offers relatively few complications as long as rates of stocking and livestock management are organized so that the forage resource is not damaged. If the forage is not damaged there will be little damage to the timber, and the two uses can proceed together without major conflict and to everyone's economic advantage.

THE AUTHOR ««‹ *Chas. A. Connaughton is director of the Southern Forest Experiment Station in New Orleans. Before his assignment to the South in 1944, he was engaged in forest research and administration, including studies of watershed management, in the Rocky Mountain and Intermountain Regions. He is a native of Idaho and a graduate of the University of Idaho and Yale University. He joined the Forest Service in 1928.*

WILDLIFE, A RESOURCE OF THE RANGE

R. J. COSTLEY, P. F. ALLAN, ODELL JULANDER, D. I. RASMUSSEN

MANY OF OUR major wildlife species inhabit the range lands. Elk, deer, and antelope normally depend upon the range grasses or the weeds and browse that are associated with them; equally characteristic of the range lands are the prairie chicken and sage grouse, and many rodents, rabbits, and predators.

The existence side by side of these wild creatures and domestic livestock sometimes brings a conflict for forage. Frequently the result has been controversy between persons interested in wildlife and the owners of the livestock, but from experience we know that the stockmen and the sportsmen can meet on a common ground and solve their problems if they have knowledge of the habits and ranges of the animals, the grazing capacity of

the land, and the factors of economics and sociology that each kind of range use involves.

Wild animals are a product of the land. The types that occupy any area are an expression of the nature and quantities of food available to them. Nearly as critical as food in determining the range of an animal is the kind and distribution of shelter and water.

The activities of man that bring about a change in the vegetation are soon reflected in a change in the kinds and numbers of animals. As with livestock, various degrees of use by wildlife have often changed the character of a plant cover. Sometimes deer that normally browse more than they graze overuse a cover so badly that the browse has been killed and excellent bunchgrass permitted to spread.

Journals of early travels tell glowingly of the teeming fish and game the pioneers encountered. Most characteristic of the prairie were buffalo, antelope, wolf and coyote, black-footed ferret, prairie chicken, badger, black-tailed jack rabbit, and black-tailed prairie dog.

Not so numerous, perhaps, but equally characteristic in the shrub areas were sage grouse, desert quail, road runners, jack rabbits, and kangaroo rats. These areas often were used by antelope yearlong and were the winter range or the seasonal spring and fall range of the mule deer, the southwestern white-tailed deer, and elk, which moved for the summer to the grasslands that were interspersed with woodland or forest. Besides the deer and the elk that summered there, some other animals that lived in the wooded areas were the bighorn sheep, woodland grouse, wild turkey, pocket gophers, ground squirrels, bobcats, lynx, and pumas.

Throughout the United States are places and topographic features named for the animals the first inhabitants encountered there—everyone has gathered wood on an Elk Mountain, drunk from a Deer Springs, fished in Salmon River, camped on Antelope Flat, enjoyed the scenery of Wolf Creek Canyon, irrigated his pasture with water from Buffalo River, or had something to do with Beaver Falls, Bear Mountain, or Goose Creek.

Those early settlers would have had an even more rigorous life had it not been for the venison, smoked fish, buckskin, and buffalo robes that the country supplied.

Much of the country was first explored by trappers in search of untrapped beaver streams, and the early transcontinental railroads depended upon their Buffalo Bills and other professional meat hunters.

Today the wildlife of America has values as important as during the pioneer era. On the national forests of Colorado and eastern Wyoming alone at least 10 million dollars were spent in 1947 just in the pursuit of fish and game, not counting the value of the meat and hides involved. It is often estimated that in some localities every deer is worth $150 or more on the hoof. In the next few years 26 million Americans expect to go hunting and fishing; each year they will spend more than 4 billion dollars.

Just as telling is the value that these creatures of the wild have to people who merely want to see and study them, the commercial value of the enormous annual fur take, the destruction of insects and the distribution of seeds by birds, and the stabilization of streams by beaver.

The different types of range with their characteristic animals were particularly significant to the early stockmen. The choice spots became cropland or hay and pasture lands. Most of the remainder was used as open grazing lands. In a few areas—only a few—the degree of use of the land has been consistent with its capacity; there the range is still in almost its original state and wild and domestic animals live in relative harmony.

Under heavy grazing or burning, the highest types of grasses disappear, and other plant species invade the range. When use of the vegetation is heavy and continues long enough, only annual grasses and weeds persist. Such a condition undoubtedly brought about the reduction of the number of greater prairie chicken. Damage to the desirable grasses and streamside vegetation adversely affect the sharptailed grouse, beaver, wild turkey, and white-tailed deer, but favor the increase of the ground squirrel, jack rabbits, and some other rodents.

Continued damage to this vegetation encourages shrubs; pricklypear, sagebrush, shadscale, yucca, and mesquite commonly come in. Such changes also result in increases in the number of prairie dogs, ground squirrels, and jack rabbits. Some ranges in relatively poor condition for livestock support many antelope and mule deer because they prefer this invading browse.

One of the notable game species of the southern coastal prairie, the Attwater prairie chicken, is close to extinction because of overgrazing, mowing for hay, and burning.

Although overuse of the range by livestock limits it as a desirable habitat for wildlife, there is abundant evidence that under proper range management satisfactory numbers of game animals can be maintained. Wildlife management and range management, however, must be completely coordinated before this objective can be realized.

Many good range-management practices are also an aid in the production of wildlife—the development of range water, deferred and rotation grazing, and range reseeding, the installation of flood-control devices, the control of fire, and other steps followed in watershed protection. Indeed, practically all measures taken to improve watersheds and ranges are steps toward bettering conditions for wildlife.

In general, the management of large acreages in such a way as to shift the trend of vegetation toward its original condition may have more profound effects than the treatment of small areas to solve specific local problems.

Not only does good range management tend to provide favorable conditions for many desirable wildlife species; it tends to lower the number of less desirable ones, such as rodents and rabbits, that are more abundant in low stages of plant succession.

The exact pattern and the intensity of the conflict between livestock and big game varies throughout the country. In many places the conflict has been overemphasized. Usually the different types of grazing animals do not prefer the same kind of plants for food. Deer, for example, take a little grass during the spring and some weeds when they are available, but they are normally browsers. Conversely, cattle and sheep select grasses and weeds. In addition, game animals, when they can, often inhabit different and more inaccessible parts of the range than do livestock.

On ranges in good condition both livestock and game animals can graze in fairly close harmony. If the range deteriorates, the competition for available forage becomes more severe and eventually the range, the game, and the livestock must suffer.

On some of the white-tail deer ranges of Texas that is the case. There is competition among sheep and goats and deer, although on some of the mule deer ranges of the more mountainous West it is not so pronounced.

An analysis of a sample area in Utah showed that when the range was properly managed and even when all the deer were removed, only 18.7 percent of the forage otherwise consumed by them was available for cattle. Serious conflicts do sometimes occur; however, certain plants, such as bitterbrush, are palatable to all grazing animals. When the bulk of a forage type is made up of such species there is likely to be competition, especially if either animal is present in numbers that more than fully utilize its other preferred forage plants.

Stockmen and wildlife managers have learned that they can never afford to let jointly preferred plant species become overutilized. To do so is to court disaster. Even on range areas where either livestock or game animals graze alone, their numbers must be limited and managed on the basis of the supply of palatable range forage.

A few words about rodents and rabbits are necessary. The effect on the range of the many different kinds of such creatures is quite variable; they often compete in some degree with livestock and big game for the forage produced.

Sometimes the competition is direct and serious, and cannot be ignored by stockmen or biologists. That prairie dogs, for instance, can denude the area around their towns is well known; under some conditions kangaroo rats, ground squirrels, and pocket gophers do damage.

But, as in the case of the deer we mentioned earlier, the damage may be less severe than it appears. Many species live in rocky ledges and other parts of the range not usually frequented by cattle or sheep, and many of the plants they select are not highly palatable to livestock. Besides the point of variable use, hasty observations all too often have obscured the true relation of cause and effect. Frequently many species of range rodents become more numerous as the ranges go downhill. In other words, they are found usually on an area because it is in poor shape—the area is not necessarily in poor shape because the rodents are there; in fact, naturalists often regard them as indicators of poor range conditions—actually "animal weeds."

Careful students of the problem know that if an operator is seeking to regulate most kinds of rodents on his range he can follow no more effective and inexpensive method than merely being sure that his range is stocked and managed in such a way that it will develop toward the highest type of vegetative cover that can exist on it.

Closely akin to the relationship of livestock to game and rodents and the dependence of all of them upon the range is the problem of predatory animals. Predators have a complex relationship to wildlife and domestic stock, and a controversial one. The main attack on the most important of all predators, the coyote (as is the case with most of the other predators), comes because he sometimes kills domestic stock; the coyote also feeds on antelope and other desirable species of game. Sometimes, because of special local conditions, there are possibly instances in which all predatory animals should be eliminated from particular areas to protect domestic stock and game.

But in more than 8,000 coyote stomachs collected from all over the Western States at all seasons of the year, the major food items were rabbits 32 percent, rodents 17 percent, carrion 26 percent, livestock 14 percent, and deer only 3.5 percent.

Further, careful observations during the past few years indicate that the initiation of predator campaigns merely because predators are present

may not only be unnecessary—it may be unwise. The hasty destruction of predators has resulted more than once in the increase of rodents or rabbits to the extent that the future of the range was threatened by extreme deterioration.

Essentially the same thing has happened in efforts to foster game herds through control of their predators. The history of the deer herd on the Kaibab National Forest is a classic example. An extensive campaign was inaugurated there to exterminate the puma, or cougar. The success of the "lion" hunters and the prohibition of hunting permitted the deer to increase so fast that before long they had actually eaten themselves out of house and home. The result: The range became so depleted that thousands of deer starved to death and the grazing capacity of much range was lowered considerably.

Because the predators feed upon the various kinds of big game, control measures may cause accelerated competition between these animals and range livestock. At the same time rodent control programs and big-game hunting may increase the loss of livestock to predators. The complexities of the whole situation are manifold and forcibly indicate the unsoundness of control measures without careful study and consideration.

What we have said may lead some to believe that an attempt to raise livestock and to maintain desirable wildlife species at the same time and on the same range is so fraught with difficulties that it is practically impossible. Such is not the case. When both the livestock and the wildlife are properly managed, common use of the range is not only possible—it is desirable.

In the past most of the conflicts have arisen because individuals and groups have failed to see the necessity for managing wildlife. They have not realized that game, as well as domestic animals, must not be permitted to reach a number greater than the number for which there is available food. Sometimes (but less frequently than before) they have been reluctant to admit that when such conditions exist it is desirable to remove the surplus, by hunting by sportsmen, for example.

Cooperative educational programs are rapidly convincing all groups that it is to the long-time advantage of all to coordinate their interests into an over-all management plan, and that the fundamental guide to be followed in such a plan is the maintenance of satisfactory range conditions. Even though this has sometimes resulted in a reduction of livestock in some areas and a reduction of game on the same or in other areas, the results have almost invariably been fruitful of more stable livestock operations and hunting conditions. We should like to emphasize that the success of these ventures has always been related directly to the degree of cooperation extended by the agencies and interested citizens.

An example of such a solution is the plan developed on and near the Dixie division of the Dixie National Forest in southwestern Utah. State and private land, a national forest, and a grazing district were involved. It had long been a good cattle and sheep range and the sportsmen were proud of the fine herd of deer.

The area was closed to hunting for a number of years and rather intensive predator control was carried out. As a result the deer made tremendous increases and before long the livestock operators were complaining of damage to their crops and of poor range conditions both in their fenced pastures and on the public grazing lands.

The interested agencies investigated the problem and agreed that the range, already fully stocked with livestock and subjected to the heavy forage demands of the increased deer herd, was threatened with rapid depletion and loss of value both as deer and livestock range. The area was opened to hunting of buck deer for several years, but the herd already was so large that buck hunting alone did not provide the necessary relief.

Then all the groups and individuals met. They studied the situation and determined the legitimate requirements of both groups. They determined the grazing capacity of all the range areas involved and the type of management necessary on each. This required that the use by livestock be drastically adjusted and that the number of deer be reduced. The decision was difficult but there was no alternative. The adjustments are being made in the use by sheep and cattle, and the deer herd has been reduced to only half its original size. The livestock operations are more stable, and there is still an adequate herd of deer which, despite its smaller size, provides a successful annual hunt, because both sexes are hunted. Most important, the range is recovering. This problem is being solved through an acceptance of the facts that management of all animals is imperative and that the range must not be misused.

THE AUTHORS «« *R. J. Costley is assistant chief of the Division of Wildlife Management in the Forest Service. He is a graduate of Utah State College and the University of Illinois and has been engaged in wildlife, range, and forest management with the Forest Service since 1935. As a naval officer, he organized the Department of Forestry in the Military Government of Korea.*

P. F. Allan has been chief of the Regional Biology Division of the Soil Conservation Service since 1938. His work has been primarily in the prairie and Great Plains sections of the country. He is a graduate of the University of New Hampshire and has done graduate work in mammalogy at the University of Michigan.

Odell Julander holds degrees from Utah State Agricultural College and Iowa State College. He was with the Forest Service from 1930 to 1936, engaged in studies of range and wildlife management. From 1936 to 1946 he taught and did research in range management and forestry in Iowa State

College and the University of Arkansas. Dr. Julander now is forest ecologist in charge of big-game range research at the Intermountain Forest and Range Experiment Station, Ogden, Utah.

D. I. Rasmussen began wildlife and range management research and ad- *ministration in the Intermountain Region in 1932. Since 1945 he has been in charge of wildlife management for the Intermountain Region of the Forest Service, with headquarters at Ogden, Utah. Dr. Rasmussen has degrees from Brigham Young University and the University of Illinois.*

RODENTS, RABBITS, AND GRASSLANDS

E. R. KALMBACH

A VARIETY of small mammals fall in the average man's ken of rodents. Among them are the rodents proper (*Rodentia*), mice, rats, squirrels, prairie dogs, gophers, and others. Hares and rabbits (*Lagomorpha*) are technically not rodents, but must be included in a consideration of the relation of small mammals to the range because sometimes they are of greater economic importance than the true rodents. Even the insectivorous moles are often associated with the rodents by those who have had to combat them.

Oddly enough there are many species of rodents whose feeding, life habits, or limited distribution make them individually of little significance as hazards in modern grassland agriculture. Some of them are even energetic destroyers of grasshoppers and other insects. With them we need not concern ourselves here; it is more expedient to indicate the few that do most damage.

On the long-grass and short-grass areas of the Plains and Intermountain regions of the West, extensive grazing under conditions of limited rainfall has aggravated the problem of balancing what Nature may produce as well as destroy with what man would like to utilize. In those areas we have spent our greatest efforts to control rodents and tip the balance in our favor.

Throughout those areas the primary problems arising from field rodents are those associated with prairie dogs (four species), ground squirrels (more than 20 species), pocket gophers (three

genera and numerous species), and kangaroo rats (fully two dozen species classified in two genera).

Not all the varied species of these groups are of paramount importance economically, yet problems connected with any one are essentially the same in their basic causes and in the economics of remedial measures.

Occasionally difficulties are had with other groups of rodents in the management of grasslands, although transgressions by these species are connected usually with other agricultural and horticultural pursuits. Among these rodents are the meadow and pine mice, rice and cotton rats in the South and Southeast, woodrats in the Southwest, and—when their numbers increase inordinately—even the commensal house mouse and the attractive little deer mouse become liabilities under certain field conditions. Less is known about the effect on grasslands of such species as harvest mice (*Reithrodontomys*), pocket mice (*Perognathus*), jumping mice (*Zapus*), grasshopper mice (*Onychomys*), and other more obscure forms.

Indirectly the valued beaver may play a part in grassland agriculture through impoundment and flooding of pasture land. The muskrat and its close relative, the round-tailed muskrat or water rat (*Neofiber*), may have the reverse effect through their undermining or perforating of irrigation structures adjacent to agricultural land.

The hares and rabbits may enter

into grassland economy whenever their cyclic increase has aggravated their pressure on the range. This is true of both the black-tailed and white-tailed species that affect the range and cultivated crops, especially when drought or early spring growth has concentrated them in the well-vegetated sections. This is also true of the antelope jack rabbit of the Southwest, but the related snowshoe and arctic hares, though capable of inflicting damage to hay crops at high altitudes or in northern latitudes, seldom become pronounced range-land pests. The diminutive but abundant cottontails, and brush and swamp rabbits, though capable of inflicting damage to young orchards, forest plantings, and truck crops, likewise are not looked upon as outstanding liabilities to range lands or hay crops, and their compensatory value as game animals must always be considered.

Whereas rodents and the associated rabbits have affected grasslands since time immemorial, their role in the ecology of modern agriculture and range use is far from being fully understood. These numerous vegetarian mammals always have been and will continue to be an influence on the range and farm. Their preferences for plant species may vary, however, and in that manner they may exert an influence on the succession of vegetative growth. The result may be for good or harm when judged in the light of man's prevailing range use.

Inseparately associated with the rodent-range complex is the degree of livestock use to which the grasslands have been subjected. This factor in itself may vary the rodent problem, according to circumstances, from one of little consequence to one of transcendent importance. To approach sound range administration and particularly range rehabilitation by giving consideration merely to one of these two elements (rodents or livestock) may be likened to a person, who, for some unaccountable reason, persists in merely dressing a wound without attempting to remove the disease. To carry the simile a bit further, it may be pointed out that, in the opinion of many who have studied such problems, the primary infection usually has its origin and persistence in excessive use by livestock. This has left a lasting wound, which rodent populations may be keeping in a state of constant irritation.

Some present-day conditions of depleted range are the result of many years of overuse. Whatever may have been their basic cause, it is evident that changes in the vegetative pattern did not take place suddenly. Even under abuse Nature often reacts slowly, and now that we are trying to rectify the trends that are against our best interests, we must not overlook the fact that readjustment also may be a slow process. This is particularly true at high altitudes and in arid regions where the struggle for readjustments is confined to short growing seasons or brief periods of rainfall.

Whereas rather rapid readjustments have been observed in experimental plots from which all controllable pressure elements have been excluded, it must be remembered that this drastic remedial treatment is not attainable on ranges that are being used. On most private and public lands there will be a certain degree of range use by livestock and it is under such conditions that we must appraise the role of field rodents and the economy of their control.

Prairie Dogs

The colonial prairie dog has been fought ever since the competition for forage between it and livestock became a matter of concern. More success has been attained in controlling it than any other group of field rodents. Being gregarious, its pressure on the range was emphasized wherever it had decided to occupy the land, and for that reason it was vulnerable to control since survivors would segregate at some point within their original colony. Here they would again become subject to attack.

The economic and ecological role of these mammals under modern agriculture and range use has been the subject of study through the use of experimental range plots and through an analysis of their food by stomach examination.

One of the earlier attempts to appraise the effect of rodent pressure on the range was the study carried out by Walter P. Taylor and J. V. G. Loftfield on the damage inflicted to range grasses by the Zuni prairie dog in Arizona. At the time of the work (1918), the authors stated, "Determinations under controlled conditions of the actual damage done by rodents, either in cultivated crops or on the open range, are, however, almost wholly lacking."

To determine quantitatively the damage done by these rodents to forage grasses, experimental areas were established at three points and their maintenance and appraisal became a cooperative project of the Biological Survey (predecessor of the Fish and Wildlife Service), the Carnegie Institution of Washington, and the Forest Service.

Results of 4 years of study in a wheatgrass forage type indicated that prairie dogs destroyed 69 percent of the wheatgrass and 99 percent of the dropseed (*Sporobolus*), or 80 percent of the total potential annual production of forage. In a blue grama type of range the loss caused by the rodents was computed to be 83 percent of the annual production. From the experimental testimony the conclusion was drawn that "in some overgrazed areas the total eradication of prairie dogs, as well as the reduction of the number of cattle per unit area, apparently will be necessary if the forage grasses are to continue in profitable quantity."

That "the prairie dog has not been shown to have a single beneficial food habit," though doubtless a true statement at the time it was made, is subject to qualification by later studies of the food habits of this quite generally despised field rodent. Some 20 years after the afore-mentioned field studies, Leon H. Kelso, having examined more than 500 stomachs of three species of prairie dogs collected under a great variety of conditions, disclosed that plants of forage or crop value are not the only ones eaten by these rodents. They did, however, comprise more than 78 percent of the food of the three species and wheatgrasses were highest in preference among the grasses. Of the range plants less attractive to livestock but eaten by the prairie dogs are sage, saltbushes, and Russian-thistle.

Taylor's and Loftfield's work on the Zuni prairie dog is worthy of repetition in the case of the black-tailed and white-tailed prairie dogs under range conditions differing from those in Arizona. Not only is there need for appraising more extensively the role of the other species of prairie dogs on which so much has been and still is being spent in control, but experimental procedures on range appraisal have improved since that earlier work. One would not expect that such later studies would materially change the estimate of the prairie dog's direct relationship to forage production but there is reason to believe that important facts in the concurrent use of the range by these rodents and livestock are yet to be disclosed.

Ground Squirrels

The control of ground squirrels has received attention throughout the West, but studies of their life habits and ecological relations have been carried out largely in the West Coast States, particularly in California and Washington. A treatise by Joseph Grinnell and Joseph Dixon on the California ground squirrels brought together for the first time much of the scattered information on life habits and economic status. Greatest emphasis was placed on the Beechey ground squirrel and its close relatives, the Oregon, Fisher, and

Douglas ground squirrels which collectively comprise most of the "'squirrel problem" of the State.

These were problems primarily of crop lands and, later, those associated with the curtailment and suppression of plague. Whereas the ground squirrel in relation to grassland agriculture in the sense of range protection entered the picture under many situations, much of the earlier work was conducted with the view of conserving highly valued crops. These early studies did not include detailed appraisals of the effect of squirrels on the range through the use of experimental plots. Estimates of over-all forage consumption were made by computations based on conservative estimates of the number of squirrels and the quantity of forage each would normally consume.

Whereas this approach is not considered as reliable as the methods used in more recent times, the conclusion reached was: "If the entire range of the California ground squirrel be taken into account and be supposed to consist purely of grazing lands (and so of minimum land value) grazed to their fullest capacity, the squirrels of this species take the place of 160,000 cattle or 1,600,000 sheep. Of course, it is not likely that the squirrels come into actual close competition with livestock in ordinary years; but in extra dry years, such as that of 1917–18, when all the living things which depend on vegetation for support are hard pressed to maintain existence, then the squirrels cannot help but crowd the cattle interests of the country, which are of such vital human importance."

In later years, appraisal of the effect of ground squirrels on the range was given much attention in California, particularly on the San Joaquin Experimental Range where, during the period 1935–46, a series of enclosures confining rather closely regulated numbers of ground squirrels, gophers, and kangaroo rats were studied and the results compared with those obtained on a comparable control area from which all of these small mammals were ex-cluded. Livestock was removed from the area.

According to preliminary findings, the heaviest toll on the forage was exerted in the spring when the digger squirrel population is at its highest. Broadleaf filaree, brome, and fescue grasses comprised the basis of their diet, but as the season advanced and vegetation dried, the squirrels turned increasingly to seeds, acorns, and tarweed. There also was great fluctuation in the abundance and character of their food because of variation in rainfall.

It is axiomatic that the effect of squirrels and other rodents on the range depends strongly on the density of population, which varies greatly from place to place and year to year. E. E. Horn and H. S. Fitch in 1934 computed the number of squirrels in one pasture on the San Joaquin range to be from 12 to 15 per acre. During subsequent years disease was prevalent among the rodents and a steady decline in numbers was noted until 1940, when it was estimated that not more than half the original number of squirrels was present.

In contrast with observations made elsewhere on the reaction of rabbits to intensity of grazing, the ground squirrels on the San Joaquin range appear not to be strongly affected by the extent of livestock use, and it was surmised that factors other than the degree of grazing pressure governed the density of squirrel population.

Although not directed toward an appraisal of the economics of the California ground squirrel, a recently published volume by Jean M. Linsdale outlines many fundamental reactions of this rodent that have a direct bearing on squirrel-grassland relationships. The studies cover the period 1937–44 and were carried out on the Hastings Natural History Reservation near the upper border of an area of grassland at the north end of the Santa Lucia Mountains in California.

A significant fact disclosed is similar to that observed in the case of rabbits; namely, that these rodents show a dislike for areas on which the vegetation is thrifty and tall enough to obscure their normal vision. A 100-foot square plot was created in 1937 as an observational area. At the time it was well populated with squirrels. With the removal of excessive grazing by livestock, vegetative recovery took place and the squirrels, still abundant enough in 1940 to permit adequate observations, decreased in number until in 1943 no squirrels could be found.

Dr. Linsdale commented, "This change has not been restricted to this one spot, but it has taken place generally over the protected parts of the Reservation. . . . It may be necessary to plow the land if we want to study this mammal in the future. . . . The ground squirrel thus exemplifies the notion that each species of animal has a type of habitat in which it survives permanently, but from which it spreads when population conditions are favorable to occupy other areas."

Generalizing on these findings, Linsdale stated: "The practice of agriculture in this region by white men involved changes which favored ground squirrels: the introduction and spread of new plants and an increase in the proportion of annuals resulted for the animals in a greater bulk of green forage in the spring and larger crops of seeds for storage. Repeated removal, by harvest, of the mat vegetation also improved the ground for squirrel settlement by permitting unobstructed daytime visibility and freedom to move over the ground."

It was clearly evident throughout these studies that in many instances the squirrels were so injurious to the cultivated crops that their summary removal was the only answer. It also was apparent that in other instances the presence of the squirrels was a symptom of excessive or unsuitable land use and with its correction squirrels may become less abundant. In fact, their presence was likened to that of weeds that do best on disturbed soil.

An example of the time needed to unravel the answer to some rodent-range relationships is that involved in studies now being conducted on Grand Mesa, Colorado. There, among stands of Englemann spruce at an altitude of about 10,500 feet, are grasslands that have been severely grazed for more than half a century and the original bunchgrass cover has given way largely to one of mixed weed type. The area also is heavily infested with pocket gophers on the control of which much effort has been spent with at best temporary relief following costly operations. Eventually the question arose: Is the control of pocket gophers on Grand Mesa economically sound from the standpoint of range rehabilitation and livestock production?

Pocket Gophers

Since no measurable appraisal had been made of the effect of gopher control on these particular high mountain pastures and no comparison of the benefits against the cost of gopher control had been drawn, a cooperative arrangement was effected in 1941 between the Rocky Mountain Forest and Range Experiment Station of the Forest Service and the Fish and Wildlife Service of the Department of the Interior to determine some of these facts.

Originally, 10 objectives were outlined, but several had to be dropped at the outbreak of the war and others could be carried through only on a restricted scale. One objective was to determine changes in volume, density, and composition of vegetative cover brought about through drastic control of pocket gophers.

The design of the vegetative studies involved four 1-acre plots replicated four times, once in each of four distinct vegetative type areas. Groups of the plots were well spaced over the 7,000-acre area on which gophers were to be generally controlled.

The treatments accorded the plots in each group may be defined by the following terminology: Gophers and cattle present; gophers present, cattle absent; gophers absent, cattle present; and gophers and cattle absent.

Of these, the plot with gophers absent and cattle present was the most significant from the viewpoint of translating experimental findings into range ecology and economics.

This plot most closely resembled the conditions that would prevail on used ranges where gopher control was practiced, a condition prevailing on many privately owned and public lands. Cattle were excluded by fencing; the gophers were removed by trapping and poisoning within the plots and for some distance around them. Unfortunately, the lack of adequate crews during the war to keep the gopher population of the surrounding areas within bounds permitted a certain invasion of the gopher-free plots. Although the removal of cattle from the stipulated plots was complete at all times, the absence of gophers was merely a relative matter which, however, improved as methods for their removal became more effective.

After 5 years of experimental treatment, when yearly clippings and measurements of the vegetation were made, followed in 1946 with a careful statistical appraisal of prevailing conditions, the following deductions were made:

"Analyses to date certainly do not point toward any marked vegetation changes following pocket gopher control. Neither do they reveal any great change due to protection from livestock grazing. However, the Grand Mesa area has been heavily grazed for 60 years, and is seriously depleted. Remnants of vegetation indicate the study area once supported dense stands of tall mountain bunchgrass; but now sneezeweed, lupine, needlegrass, etc., dominate the landscape. Gophers have riddled the area, leaving tons of bare soil exposed. Much top soil has been washed away. It is not surprising that more than 5 years of protection from both the cattle and the gophers may be needed before any prominent changes in vegetation occur."

The conclusions reemphasize that under some conditions of previous misuse vegetative regeneration, particularly at high altitudes, may be exceedingly slow, and the benefits from remedial measures may not become evident short of many years of application. If this proves to be the case when all possible curative measures have been used, it follows that the application of measures of relief singly or intermittently will fall still farther short of attaining the objective.

Because of their excessive and very evident movement of the soil, pocket gophers have been accused of playing an important part in soil erosion and hence range deterioration. When such erosive action has been the result of the undermining of dams or the banks of irrigation canals there is no doubt as to the sequence of cause and effect.

On open range lands, particularly at higher altitudes where gophers often are abundant, full appraisal of interlocking factors may lead to other conclusions. Lincoln Ellison studied the pocket gopher as an instigator of erosion on the Wasatch Plateau in Utah.

The gopher has been considered a factor in the general process of erosion. Its mounds of uncovered soil not only tended downwardly on the slope but they also exposed unprotected surfaces to the force of wind and water. Yet Dr. Ellison was convinced that action of gophers was not a primary cause of accelerated erosion; rather, it stemmed from excessive use by domestic herds, which created surface conditions highly conducive to erosion of all types.

Dr. Ellison found no evidence on the Wasatch Plateau "that tunnels of pocket gophers concentrate overland flow in a degree to create gullies, unless, possibly, abnormal surficial runoff is induced by other causes." Delayed infiltration, the cause of gully-cutting runoff, he learned, cannot be attributed to pocket gopher activities—on the contrary, loosening of and formation of minor irregularities on the soil surface by pocket gophers no doubt increase the rapidity of infiltration.

One of the earlier and more comprehensive appraisals of rabbits in relation to the range was made by Charles T. Vorhies and Walter P. Taylor in Arizona. They approached the problem through field observation, appraisal of fenced quadrats, and the analysis of stomach contents.

Rabbits

From their extensive field observations it became apparent that jack rabbits were not most abundant where the grass was best. The antelope jack rabbit (*Lepus alleni*) appeared in greatest numbers under conditions of moderate grass growth and was less abundant in the better, as well as in the extremely poor range types.

The California jack rabbit (*Lepus californicus*) was most common in the poorly grassed semidesert type. The men pointed out that the reasons for these findings were not entirely clear but they stated that jack rabbits may be "more partial to some of the weeds and herbs of the secondary successions that accompany overgrazing, than to an exclusive diet of climax grasses." They noted the possibility also that like so many rodents, the jack rabbits prefer open country with high visibility to areas where the grass prevents seeing far.

From their experimental plots Vorhies and Taylor deduced that rabbits and rodents were mainly responsible for holding the vegetation in a preclimax condition and the evident fondness of rabbits for grass, when available, greatly favors the encroachment on grass ranges of mesquite, cholla cactus, weeds, and other species. They also pointed out that jack rabbits exerted their most telling effect on the range during drought, a time when control operations were stressed.

More recently, R. L. Piemeisal made observations in Idaho on the effect of rabbits and rodents on abandoned lands that had been subjected to severe treatment through plowing, burning, or overgrazing.

A study conducted to disclose the history of plant succession on these abandoned fields in relation to the beet leafhopper revealed that even after all livestock had been removed there were variable and unexplained sequences in plant succession.

Experimental plots that had been free of fire, plowing, and all grazing by livestock, but accessible to rabbits, followed no uniform pattern of recovery even after 6 years of such protection. The establishment of downy chess, which was sought to combat the beet leafhopper, was irregular at best. However, within quadrats protected from rabbits and livestock, plant succession followed a regular course and finally terminated in stands of downy chess. Whereas some of the smaller rodents may have played a part in plant destruction, especially after a dense stand of chess was established, ample proof was disclosed of the persistent pressure applied to these severely abused lands by the jack rabbit population.

Significant in the history of the experimental plots was that, beginning in 1939 and continuing to the end of the experimental period (1944), a pronounced reduction occurred in the number of jack rabbits in the region.

This resulted in comparatively slight destruction of vegetation during the latter part of this period and a downy chess cover developed on the outside, although not to such a pronounced degree as inside the plots. What part these periodic reductions in rabbit populations have in the ultimate recovery of depleted ranges and what part they may have played in the pre-Columbian history of western grasslands is a matter for conjecture and a worthy subject of further study. The corollary of this, the need for control during peaks of rabbit population on range lands that have suffered depletion, requires little demonstration, provided, however, the economics of the particular situation indicate its soundness and if pressure from livestock also is kept within recognized range capacity.

Another area on which significant experimental work has been done to reveal the role of rabbits and certain rodents on southwestern ranges is the Jornada Experimental Range and the College Ranch in New Mexico.

On the College Ranch, exclusion plots were established first in 1936 on land from which livestock had been removed a year earlier. These plots were of three types, a small rodent-rabbit-livestock exclosure, a rabbit-livestock exclosure (open to small rodents), and a livestock exclosure (open to rabbits and small rodents). There also was a control area to which all of these mammals had access. After a few years significant vegetative changes had taken place in the plots protected from the feeding of rabbits while at the same time the areas that had been exposed to rabbits but protected from livestock showed little recovery from their previous depleted condition.

These facts led to the conclusion that severely depleted ranges may require relief from pressure from both livestock and small mammals before recovery may be effected.

Kangaroo Rats

Of the four groups of field rodents I have discussed, the kangaroo rats are the least important economically but even they are an element to be reckoned with in the Southwest, particularly during seasons of drought when pressure on the range becomes acute. Work by Charles T. Vorhies and Walter P. Taylor on the life history of the banner-tailed kangaroo rat (*Dipodomys s. spectabilis*) has brought together much of what is known of these odd rodents.

This rodent does not hibernate. It stores food against the time when the range becomes parched. These storage periods are during the growth period of spring and again in late summer and fall. Even so, during years of low vegetative growth these resourceful rodents may face starvation and, of course, it is in those same critical years

when their effect on the range is most pronounced.

The fact that much of the stored food of the kangaroo rats consists of seeds of plants makes their effect on the range more pronounced than that exerted by species that feed largely on the vegetative parts of the growing plants. Among the seeds eaten are those of some of the more important forage plants of the Southwest, particularly grama and needlegrasses. In quantity this stored food varies greatly, ranging to more than 12 pounds.

Vorhies and Taylor concluded that in ordinary seasons the banner-tailed kangaroo rat was not of great economic significance, but that during periods of extreme drought it may be of critical importance from the standpoint of the carrying capacity of the range.

Horn and Fitch in California found that, in contrast with the banner-tailed kangaroo rat, the Heermann kangaroo rat did not store food so extensively—no doubt the direct result of an ample supply of food yearlong. During the growing season much of the vegetative parts of range plants was eaten, but during the dry season the food consists almost entirely of seeds. Soft chess and filaree, common foxtail, and fescues are regular items of diet.

Great fluctuation in rat numbers was observed over a period of years. Counts of only 2 or 3 to the mile of roadway were observed in the spring of 1937; similar counts on the same area during the previous fall revealed as many as 75 to the mile. This wide fluctuation in numbers, as yet not fully explained, had much to do with the economic significance of these rodents on the California range.

That kangaroo rats may exert an effect on the range quite at variance with the expected has been pointed out recently by Albert C. Hawbecker in California. Confirming earlier observations by Joseph Grinnell, he recorded that in the San Joaquin Valley the giant kangaroo rat (*Dipodomys ingens*) occupied areas (to which the name of "precincts" was given) which were well covered with a healthy growth of filaree and red brome. Beyond the limits of the precincts these two plants were much less thrifty. Close study of the prevailing conditions led Dr. Hawbecker to conclude that the better growth was due to the agitation of the ground surface by the rats, resulting in better water penetration and possibly the formation of a more effective seedbed. This cultivating action of the kangaroo rats led to a fivefold increase of the two plants and they remained green longer.

In Conclusion

The problems arising in this country from the management of prairie dogs, ground squirrels, pocket gophers, and kangaroo rats, and the upsurging populations of other rodents and jack rabbits are endless in their ramifications. To appraise the economic implications has taxed the abilities of our best ecologists. Even when the analysis has been restricted to a single species, confined to a uniform environment, the results have often left the investigators confronted with many facts still unknown and indeterminable.

On costly and highly developed agricultural lands rodent control is seldom a matter for debate; the economics of the matter usually is plain. On open range lands, some of very low value, we are often confronted with decisions which are harder to make and for which adequate experimental data based on modern conditions of grassland use are lacking.

There is little question but that most of our present rodent-range problems have stemmed from some earlier abuse of the vegetative cover. It is also recognized that some of these depleted ranges on which the power of vegetative regeneration has been severely lowered may actually be kept in a state of perennial suppression by the resident populations of rodents or rabbits. Under such conditions rodent control presents an intricate problem in economics as well as in range management, and the correct answer will rest with the factors in each case.

One consideration, however, appears obvious: Rodent control alone, without provision at the same time for reducing livestock pressure and, where feasible for reseeding or otherwise aiding the depleted range, may be merely a temporary palliative.

THE AUTHOR≪ *E. R. Kalmbach, a senior biologist in the Fish and Wildlife Service, Department of the Interior, is in charge of the Wildlife Research Laboratory at Denver. Before joining the Biological Survey in 1910 he was engaged in museum work in Michigan.*

HOW TO CONTROL NOXIOUS PLANTS

JOSEPH F. PECHANEC, CHARLES E. FISHER, KENNETH W. PARKER

NOXIOUS range plants rob the livestock industry in many ways. In Texas alone, the annual loss from mesquite and juniper has been estimated to be 20 million dollars.

Some, like big sagebrush, mesquite, or oak, are shrubby or treelike, produce little forage, and obstruct grazing use. Other noxious plants, such as cheatgrass and snakeweed, produce poor forage and lower grazing capacity.

Poisonous plants such as larkspur, orange sneezeweed, and bitterweed sometimes cause such serious losses among cattle and sheep that some kinds of livestock must be taken off the range.

Still other noxious plants, like dry cheatgrass where it is predominant on a range, have been estimated to increase the fire hazard 500 times.

Against all noxious plants the charge

can be made that they occupy sites often to the almost complete exclusion of desirable species, use up limited moisture supplies, and produce little forage in return. Moreover, heavy stands often obstruct range reseeding or natural revegetation. Usually it is necessary to control or thin such growth before desirable forage species can be reestablished in abundance and, in many instances, accelerated erosion arrested.

The practicability and benefits of using proved methods of control have been demonstrated on a wide scale with sand sagebrush, mesquite, big sagebrush, and other noxious plants. Costs of mowing sand sagebrush in Oklahoma two successive years in June were mostly repaid in extra beef production and additional grazing capacity of the land during the first two winters.

Soil-binding qualities of the vegetation and water-holding capacity of the land also were improved, livestock movements over the entire area were facilitated, and screwworm infection was reduced. When the brush that protected them was removed, populations of kangaroo rats and other destructive rodents were reduced by coyotes and hawks.

The removal of mesquite has brought similar improvements. Trials in Arizona demonstrated that even though the potential production of range lands was low, the initial prewar cost of $1.89 an acre for killing mesquite with sodium arsenite could be repaid by increased cattle gains within 10 years. Control of the mesquite more than doubled usable forage production, improved the condition of the soil surface, reduced erosion, facilitated the handling of cattle, and probably reduced screwworm infection.

The control and removal of big sagebrush likewise has paid dividends. Burning to remove sagebrush (at a cost of 19 cents an acre) in southern Idaho, where reseeding to perennial grasses was unnecessary afterward, doubled the grazing capacity and greatly simplified the handling of range sheep and

cattle. Plowing to eradicate the sagebrush in southern Idaho and Utah (at a cost of $1.30 to $5 an acre), followed by reseeding, increased grazing capacity 9 to 12 times, increased soil protection, and made easier the movement of range sheep and cattle. On the basis of the increased grazing capacity alone, the initial cost of brush control and seeding was repaid in 7 to 10 years.

Some points to be considered in planning an effective program to control noxious plants are:

Undertake large-scale control only where practical, effective, and economical procedures can be used. Such methods are available for many sites and situations.

Control noxious plants when they first invade a range. It will cost much less then and may prevent further encroachment and deterioration of the range.

On heavily infested ranges, begin control work on parts where benefits can be most effectively utilized in the herd or range management plan. Start also on areas of greatest promise for forage production—those with fertile soils and with favorable precipitation or with possibilities for water spreading.

With widely distributed stands of poisonous plants first eliminate the toxic plants from areas near permanent water, along trails and stock driveways, or wherever livestock tend to congregate. This will eliminate likelihood of livestock losses.

Avoid areas where the elimination of dense stands of noxious plants seriously increases the risk of accelerated erosion. For example, it is well to leave sand sagebrush on sand dunes, big sagebrush in places where the soils are sandy or the slopes are steep, and juniper on rocky, shallow soils.

Choose a method suited to the site and type of stand. Hand methods of control are practical for sparse stands of juniper, but power machinery is the only practical attack on stands thicker than 150 trees to an acre.

Pick the most effective season. Mowing sand sagebrush in Oklahoma is most effective if done in June, for example. Burning sagebrush in southern Idaho is best done in the late summer and early fall. The use of 2,4–D is most effective during active plant growth.

In places where noxious plants make up most of the plant cover, reseed to desirable forage species after the noxious plants are killed. This will prevent serious loss of soil, insure a rapid increase in forage production, and retard the establishment of seedlings of noxious plants.

The choice of the method of attack is governed by its effectiveness, cost, adaptability to existing conditions, expected benefits, and possible hazards.

Hand pulling and grubbing the plants are efficient but costly methods for some species. Hand pulling waterhemlock along stream banks is a good way. For species such as larkspur, western sneezeweed, or the mesquite seedlings that have the taproot type of root system, grubbing thoroughly and for several years in succession gives good results. But on species like poison milkweed or St. Johnswort, which reproduce from underground rootstocks, grubbing and pulling are apt to give disappointing results. Because of its high cost, grubbing is practical only to clean out seedlings and sparse stands of noxious plants or to eradicate toxic plants from areas where cattle and sheep congregate.

Mechanical grubbing has been used effectively to remove dense stands of mesquite and big sagebrush, but it is relatively expensive because it takes a considerable outlay for equipment.

Mowing, an inexpensive method, is especially suited for controlling sand sagebrush. It is also good on such shrubs as burroweed and jimmyweed, which do not sprout readily from the stem base or roots. Often mowing may be used in rock-free areas to prevent seed formation by annual weeds or grasses like cocklebur and cheatgrass. But with most herbaceous perennials that die back to the ground each year (such as larkspur, St. Johnswort, or sneezeweed) or shrubby perennials that sprout readily from the roots (such as rubber rabbitbrush, chokecherry, or mesquite), mowing is rather ineffective unless it is carried on in conjunction with chemical control.

Railing is inexpensive and has been used widely to eradicate big sagebrush. It consists of uprooting, breaking off, or mashing down the old big sagebrush plants by dragging a heavy implement made from railroad rail over the area. Railing is adapted to nonsprouting shrubby species that are stiff and brittle. It has no value for herbaceous species or shrubby species that sprout from the roots or that have flexible tops.

Plowing with a one-way disk plow is moderately expensive but highly effective. It has been used widely to control big sagebrush and cheatgrass on relatively rock-free areas. It also has value with other annuals and nonsprouting perennials. Because plowing destroys most of the ground cover, it must be followed by reseeding. A heavy brush plow is useful for mesquite and similar shrubs.

Burning has been used with variable success. It is a successful and inexpensive way to control big sagebrush and cheatgrass. It is effective for nonsprouting noxious plants only. For wide-scale burning, a satisfactory combination of low moisture content and sufficient volume of inflammable material to carry a fire are essential. Burning with a flame torch has some value for the eradication of small colonies of undesirable plants. Burning must be done in compliance with State and Federal regulations. Considerable caution must be exercised to keep the fire under control and avoid damaging desirable plants, the soil, and property.

Chemical weed killers are generally expensive, but their cost is going down, and the new herbicides are finding wider usefulness, especially for destroying deep-rooted sprouting perennials and initial infestations of other noxious plants. They are especially useful where it is difficult or inadvisable to control by other methods.

Sodium arsenite and acid arsenic pentoxide, although hazardous to both grazing animals and workers, have been used successfully to control mesquite and pricklypear. Some stands of mesquite have also been killed effectively with kerosene and other oils.

Small areas of noxious plants can be controlled with more expensive materials like sodium chlorate, ammonium sulfamate, or borax.

Dichlorophenoxyacetic acid—2,4-D —is a selective herbicide that in low concentration kills some plants, roots and all, but unlike arsenic, chlorate, and oils, does not kill most range grasses. Properly used, it is not harmful to grazing animals. Its value for control of noxious plants on range lands has not been fully determined, but it has shown definite promise with several, including sand sagebrush.

Biotic control of native plants by insects and diseases is a natural phenomenon that often thins stands of certain noxious range plants. As such, it depends largely on the forces of nature and seldom results in lasting control. On the other hand, biotic control offers great possibilities with introduced noxious plants because the natural predators of these plants may be introduced unaccompanied by their own natural parasites and diseases. Remarkable success was attained by this method in Australia with cacti, and recent tests with St. Johnswort on the Pacific coast have been promising.

The benefits from noxious-plant control can be fully realized only through good grazing management. After the plants have been eradicated, the remaining forage plants or those reseeded must be permitted to increase in size and abundance, to develop a deeper and more extensive root system, and to mature and produce seed; they must be given a chance to compete successfully with any surviving noxious plants or new invaders.

Over big areas of range land, proper management is the only practical way to prevent the invasion of noxious plants or to thin out widespread infes-

tations. Where grazing use is heavy or untimely over a period of years, the perennial grass cover is weakened and a marked increase of snakeweed, pingue, and similar objectionable growth is inevitable. After that happens, moderate grazing may be the only practical way to thin them out.

On the other hand, after deep-rooted, undesirable plants (such as mesquite and big sagebrush) have become firmly established, moderation in grazing use alone is ineffective, and drastic measures must be used.

By following a few rules of good grazing management where the noxious plants are poisonous, the ranchman can reduce livestock losses and avoid having to use costly measures. Poisonous plants are usually eaten because of insufficient forage, depraved appetite of animals, or improper handling of livestock. Consequently, grazing should be delayed until there is ample forage on the range, stocking should be moderate, supplemental feeding should be used to correct mineral deficiencies, livestock should be handled properly on the trail and range, and classes of livestock should be shifted when necessary.

THE AUTHORS◄◄◄ *Joseph F. Pechanec was graduated from the University of Idaho. He has been engaged in research on grazing and range improvement since 1932, and now is forest ecologist in charge of range research at the Pacific Northwest Forest and Range Experiment Station.*

Kenneth W. Parker, a graduate of the University of California, is forest ecologist in charge of range research at the Southwestern Forest and Range Experiment Station in Tucson.

Charles E. Fisher is a graduate of Kansas State College and Agricultural and Mechanical College of Texas and has done research on range improvement since 1936. He is an agronomist employed jointly by the Texas Agricultural Experiment Station and Soil Conservation Service, Division of Research, at Spur, Tex.

Recommended Methods for Control of Some Noxious Plants on Range Lands

Species of noxious plant	Distribution, State or region	Recommended methods of control
Bitterweed (*Actinea odorata*)	Tex.	Proper range use, pulling, mowing, and sodium chlorate.
Burroweed (*Aplopappus tenuisectus*)	Ariz.	Burning, grubbing, mowing, 2,4–D.
Cheatgrass (*Bromus tectorum*)	Utah, Idaho, Nev., Oreg., Wash.	Burning or plowing and reseeding.
Cholla cactus (*Opuntia fulgida*)	Ariz.	Sodium arsenite.
Cocklebur (*Xanthium* spp.)	West.	Pulling, mowing, and burning, 2 years in succession.
Deathcamas (*Zigadenus* spp.)	West.	Grubbing.
Drymary (*Drymaria holosteoides*)	N. Mex., Tex.	Hoeing, burning with flame torch.
Gallberry (*Ilex glabra*)	Coastal Plain from La. to N. C.	Rotary brush chopper or plowing with disk plow.
Groundsel, threadleaf (*Senecio longilobus*)	Southwest.	Grubbing.
Huisache (*Acacia farnesiana*)	Tex.	Grubbing and oils.
Jimmyweed (*Aplopappus heterophyllus*)	N. Mex., Tex.	Grubbing, plowing, and reseeding.
Juniper (*Juniperus* spp.)	West.	Grubbing, sodium arsenite, burning.
Larkspur (*Delphinium* spp.)	West.	Grubbing.
Lecheguilla (*Agave lecheguilla*)	Tex.	Do.
Locoweed (*Astragalus* spp.)	West.	Do.
Lote (*Condalia obtusifolia*)	Tex., Ariz., N. Mex.	Grubbing, sodium arsenite.
Mesquite (*Prosopis* spp.)	Ariz., N. Mex., Tex., Utah, Colo.	Grubbing by hand and with heavy machinery, sodium arsenite, oils.
Milkweed, poison (*Asclepias galioides*)	South.	Sodium chlorate.
Oak, blackjack (*Quercus marilandica*)	Colo., N. Mex., Ariz.	Ammonium sulfamate, sodium arsenite, and oils.
Pingue (*Actinea richardsoni*)	West.	Proper range use, grubbing, mowing, and sodium chlorate.
Poisonhemlock (*Conium maculatum*)	Great Plains, Southwest.	Grubbing.
Pricklypear (*Opuntia* spp.)		Grubbing, acid arsenic pentoxide, grading, singe and grazing.
Sagebrush, big (*Artemisia tridentata*)	Utah, Nev., Oreg., Wash., Idaho.	Burning in fall, railing, shallow plowing and seeding.
Sagebrush, sand (*Artemisia filifolia*)	Great Plains.	Mowing in June 2 years in succession.
St. Johnswort (*Hypericum perforatum*)	Calif., Oreg., Wash., Idaho.	Plowing and reseeding, borax with sodium chlorate.
Sawpalmetto (*Serenoa repens*)	Coastal Plain from La. to Fla. and S. C.	Plowing or rotary brush chopper.
Snakeweed (*Gutierrezia sarothrae*)	Utah, N. Mex., Ariz.	Proper range use, grubbing, mowing, burning.
Sneezeweed, orange (*Helenium hoopesi*)	Colo., N. Mex., Utah.	Proper range use, grubbing.
Waterhemlock, western (*Cicuta occidentalis*)	West.	Grubbing or pulling by hand.
White brush (*Lippia ligustrina*)	Tex.	Grubbing.

Enemies of Grass

SOME DISEASES OF FORAGE GRASSES

J. LEWIS ALLISON

GRASSES, like all the other economic plants, are hosts to many diseases. To illustrate: In the United States, more than 45 diseases attack Kentucky bluegrass, 35 attack timothy, and 30 attack orchardgrass.

The bacteria, fungi, viruses, nematodes, and a few parasitic higher plants are among the pathogens that cause the diseases. The fungi are most to blame, but the others also are responsible for several economically important diseases. Nonparasitic disorders that frequently are mistaken for parasitic diseases are common to some grasses; actually they are caused by hereditary or physiological factors.

The diseases can be classified into three major groups according to the parts of the plant they attack: Root disorders, foliage disorders, and flower and seed disorders.

Root disorders are caused by the soil-inhabiting fungi and nematodes. Foliage disorders (blight, mildews, leaf spots, rusts, and smuts) are caused by bacteria, fungi, and viruses. Fungi and nematodes cause flower and seed disorders (ergot, head and kernel smuts, and seed galls).

Of these, root disorders are the least conspicuous, but they include several of the economically important pathogens and generally are responsible for the inability of grasses to establish initial seedings or the rapid depletion of already-established stands.

Foliage disorders, the most conspicuous group, include only a relatively small number of pathogens that are economically important. They destroy only the foliage, the part of the plant that is readily regenerated.

Flower and seed disorders have economic importance only when crops are grown for seed. Some of this group are highly destructive and seriously hamper seed production. One—ergot, a fungus disease—can poison livestock if infected grasses are heavily grazed.

The diseases generally are limited to certain regions. The pathogens are usually specific, attacking only a single grass species. Accordingly, the diseases of economic importance in a given region are those that attack the dominant grass or grasses in the region, although a few pathogens are destructive to several different grass species.

Environmental conditions, especially temperature and moisture, limit the range and destructiveness of the diseases. The two factors limit certain diseases to geographic regions; they may be the reason why a disease becomes economically destructive one season and diminishes to one of minor consequence the following season. Environmental factors are largely responsible for the common incidence of root disorders in the Great Plains region, the especial prevalence of leaf spots in the North Central and Southern States, and for the sporadic occurrence of rusts from year to year.

A few of the diseases occur in even more limited areas; for example, the blind seed disease, especially destructive to certain grasses when grown for seed, is localized in a small area in the Pacific Northwest. Most of them are not readily controlled by methods effective for other plant pathogens.

Sanitary measures, important in checking many diseases, are impractical in checking grass diseases under field conditions. For one thing, waste areas into which grasses spread by natural means are inaccessible for control practices. Crop rotation, important in combating many soil-borne diseases, is not readily applied to grasses. Many economic grasses are perennial and are used in permanent pastures where diseases can run an uninterrupted course. Chemical control of foliage diseases with sprays and dusts is impractical because of the possible poisoning hazard to livestock. Seed treatment for seed-borne diseases is not commonly practiced; many grass seeds are difficult to treat because they are so small or have awns and other parts that interfere with treatment. Sanitary handling and processing of grass seed can control diseases carried with the seed—ergot, blind seed, and nematode gall.

The development by means of selection or hybridization of strains and varieties of grasses resistant to the diseases that attack them is the only practical control for most grass diseases.

Such resistance has been demonstrated for many species. Breeding and improvement programs are under way in an effort to incorporate the factors for disease resistance into the germ plasm of improved varieties.

The knowledge that many pathogens causing grass diseases are themselves composed of physiologic races, each distinct from another, complicates improvement programs, but complete knowledge of any plant pathogen aids in assuring more complete success in breeding for disease resistance with any crop plant.

We cannot here consider all the diseases of grasses; rather, I have selected representative pathogens from each of the major groups—root disorders (damping-off, seedling blight, root rot, stem canker, sheath spot, brown patch); foliage disorders (bacterial blight, powdery mildew, brown spot, leaf blight, anthracnose, rusts, stripe smut); and flower and seed disorders (ergot, blind seed, heat smut, grass seed nematode).

Damping-off and Blight

Damping-off, *Pythium debaryanum,* is caused by a soil-inhabiting fungus that has a wide host range among economic and noneconomic plants. Disease symptoms are a seed rot and decay that occur during seed germination before the seedlings can emerge from the soil.

This fungus causes extensive seed rotting of many spring-seeded grasses in the Northern Great Plains. The disease is favored by wet, cool weather following seeding, which retards seed germination and allows the fungus a longer period to cause rotting. Many strains of the fungus are known to occur and these vary greatly in pathogenicity. Some strains isolated from infected grasses will attack many species of grasses but are mildly parasitic on nongrass crops, while in other cases the reverse is true.

No adequate control measures for this disease are known.

Seedling blight, *Pythium arrhenomanes,* is caused by a soil-inhabiting fungus and is destructive to many grasses. It has a wide host range among the grasses and cereals. It is not known to attack other crop plants. The fungus is widespread through the Northern Great Plains; in some years it causes almost complete destruction to spring seedings of crested wheatgrass, slender wheatgrass, and smooth brome.

Symptoms are a general blighting and dying of young plants a few weeks after they emerge from the soil. The fungus is favored by wet, cool weather.

Crop rotation, using crops other than grasses and cereals, is an effective control method. Fall planting of grasses is also effective because in fall environmental conditions are unfavorable for the development of the fungus, and after stands are established the fungus is no longer able to attack them.

Rhizoctonia solani

Rhizoctonia solani is a fungus present in most soils, especially acid ones. It has a wide host range among economic and noneconomic plants.

Disease symptoms on the plants it attacks vary greatly. On grasses alone its symptoms are recognized from the common names root rot, stem canker, sheath spot, and brown patch. The disease attacks most grasses after stands are well established; it is most severe in the spring during wet periods.

Brown patch symptoms occur on well-established turf such as golf courses, cemeteries, and lawns where Kentucky bluegrass is dominant.

Crop rotation is ineffective as a control method because the disease attacks so many different plants in one form or another and can thus persist in the soil indefinitely. With one exception, no other control methods are known. Brown patch can be controlled by treating diseased areas of turf with certain fungicides, among them tetramethyl thiuram disulphide (Thiosan), a mixture containing two parts of mercurous chloride with one part of mercuric chloride (Caloclor), and hydroxymercurichlorophenol plus hydroxymercuricresol (Special Semesan).

Parasitic races of the fungus are known to occur.

Bacterial Blight

Bacterial blight, *Pseudomonas coronafaciens* var. *atropurpurea*, is a destructive disease on smooth bromegrass throughout the North Central States. Initial symptoms appear as circular to oblong water-soaked areas of uniform size on the leaf blades, which turn purplish black and frequently coalesce to form typically blighted areas involving the entire blade and sheath. Blighted leaves wither and die.

The disease is favored by periods of warm, humid weather and is most severe about mid-June.

There are no known control measures for blight.

The second regrowth of smooth brome is rarely infected, because the disease does not develop during hot, dry, midsummer. Other bacterial diseases attack smooth brome but are not so destructive as blight.

Powdery Mildew; Brown Spot

Mildew, *Erysiphe graminis*, is a fungus disease that attacks many grasses. Among the economic grasses, Kentucky bluegrass is highly susceptible. Mildew produces conspicuous symptoms that appear to be more damaging than they really are. The white powdery growth visible on the surface of leaf blades is the vegetative and sporulating parts of the fungus. Dried blotched areas develop later at the points where the fungus has penetrated into the leaves. Severely infected plants become weakened and retarded in growth.

Mildew is widespread in its occurrence, but it is especially prevalent in the North Central States where bluegrass is a dominant grass.

The disease is seasonal in development, first appearing in the spring, diminishing during the summer, and reappearing again during the fall.

Resistance to mildew is known to occur in plant lines of bluegrass. Several physiologic races of the fungus have been determined.

Brown spot, *Pyrenophora* (*Helminthosporium*) *bromi*, is one of the many fungus leaf spots attacking grasses. It is selected as a representative example because both the asexual and sexual stages of the fungus are known. For most of the leaf-spotting fungi, only the asexual stage is known.

This fungus causes a serious leaf spot on a single grass, smooth brome. Initial symptoms appear as small black spots on the leaf blades in early spring. These are caused by the sexual or asco-spore stage of the fungus. As lesions enlarge, a yellow halo forms around each. Severely infected leaves wither and die. The asexual spores are borne on them and this spore stage causes secondary infection. As the season advances, small black bodies develop in the withered dead leaves. These bodies are perithecia, or enclosed cups, in which the ascospores develop. The fungus is carried through the winter months in this stage.

Brown spot develops most rapidly during periods of wet, cold weather and is most severe on the early-spring growth of smooth brome.

Resistance to brown spot is known to occur in selected lines of bromegrass.

Leaf Blight

Leaf blight, *Helminthosporium turcicum,* is a fungus disease that attacks Sudangrass throughout most of the range where that grass is grown. It is also a serious disease on sorghum and corn throughout the same geographic range.

As the common name implies, symptoms are a conspicuous blighted or scalded appearance of the foliage. Within a few days an entire field of Sudangrass may develop extreme blighting and appear characteristically burned or frosted. Blight makes its appearance about midsummer and continues until plant maturity. Disease development is favored by moist warm weather. Parasitic races of the fungus are known to occur.

Sudangrass is one of the few annual grasses important as a forage grass in the United States. Being an annual, destruction of its foliage by any cause reduces its forage value.

Resistance to leaf blight is known to occur in commercial varieties of Sudangrass. Plant breeders have made notable progress in selecting for leaf blight resistance. One variety, Tift Sudan, highly resistant to leaf blight, has been in production for several years. Others are being developed.

Anthracnose

Anthracnose, *Colletotrichum graminicolum,* is a fungus disease common on many grasses but a serious pathogen to very few. Sudangrass is susceptible and often is seriously damaged by it.

Initial symptoms appear on the basal leaves as small eye-spot lesions with visible black bodies in the center of each. These open structures are filled with large numbers of spores, which, being readily washed and splashed by dew and rain, account for much secondary infection. Individual lesions frequently coalesce and entire leaves wither and die. On Sudangrass, anthracnose appears about midsummer and develops rapidly from that time on until plant maturity.

Varietal resistance to anthracnose is known to occur among commercial varieties of Sudangrass. Plant breeders selected and incorporated anthracnose resistance with leaf-blight resistance in the variety Tift Sudan.

Rusts and Stripe Smut

Many rust fungi attack grasses, but the important grass rusts in the United States belong to the genus *Puccinia.* The four most important are stem rust, leaf rust, stripe rust, and crown rust. Leaf rust is the most common. None of the rusts is so destructive to the forage grasses as to the cereals.

Resistance to the rusts has been demonstrated for many grasses. The rusts are unique in their ability to hybridize in nature and each of the rust species is made up of many physiologic races. New races are being formed continually, and grasses resistant to known races may be completely susceptible to the new ones.

Stripe smut, *Ustilago striaeformis,* is a fungus disease that attacks many grasses and is sometimes rather destructive. Initial symptoms appear as chlorotic stripes on the leaf blades. When mature, stripes are filled with large numbers of smut spores. At this stage they rupture and so release their spores, and leaf blades become shredded and torn. Severely infected plants are stunted and dwarfed. Spores cause the initial infection of plants but after getting into its host the fungus is able to live within it from year to year. Accordingly, it is not seasonal in its development and can be found to a greater or less degree any time during the growing season. Physiologic races of stripe smut are known to occur.

Breeding for stripe smut resistance is the only way to control this disease.

Ergot

Two species of the ergot fungus, *Claviceps purpurea* and *C. paspali,* are of economic importance. The first is widespread and attacks a large number of grasses. The second attacks only members of the genus *Paspalum,* and so is limited to the South.

Ergot attacks only the flower and seed parts of its hosts and is of economic importance only when the grasses are grown for a seed crop or are allowed to flower and seed prior to grazing or cutting for hay.

The initial symptoms appear at flowering time when a sticky exudate called honeydew is noticeable. The exudate, which contains the conidial or asexual stage of the fungus, attracts flies and insects and much secondary infection of floral parts results from insect transmission. As the disease progresses, black, horny bodies called sclerotia develop in place of seeds. The sclerotia of *C. purpurea* are more conspicuous than those of *C. paspali.* When mature, these bodies fall to the ground or are harvested with the seed crop. In either case, they carry the fungus over winter. When planted with the seed or carried-over on the ground by natural means, they develop the perfect or sexual stage of the fungus each year. Ergot development is favored by periods of warm, moist weather.

Little varietal resistance is known among the varieties of the grasses which ergot attacks.

Thorough cleaning of seed to remove sclerotial bodies, crop rotation using crops other than grasses and cereals, and deep plowing of infected fields to bury the sclerotia are control measures.

Ergot is one of the few fungus diseases that can cause livestock poisoning. Substances in the sclerotia are highly toxic, and poisoning may result if severely infected grasses are grazed or fed for hay.

Blind Seed

Blind seed, *Phialea temulenta,* is caused by a fungus and was first recognized as being destructive to perennial ryegrass in New Zealand in 1938. Since then the disease has been reported in several other countries. In the United States it is confined to a rather limited area in Oregon, and it is thought that the fungus was introduced there in infected seed.

Blind seed disease has no recognizable symptoms and is manifested chiefly by low germination in the seed crop. The reason for the low germination is that the developing seeds infected by the fungus are in many cases nonviable. Infected or "blind" seeds are difficult to distinguish from normal seeds. When contaminated seed is planted in the fall, the fungus continues its development in the "blind" seeds to some extent and the following spring produces the spore stage of the fungus, which reinfects its host. These spores are normally produced at the same time that the grass flowers, and it is this stage of the host which is infected.

The development of the fungus and the severity of the disease are influenced by environmental conditions.

High soil moisture is essential for the production of the spore stage, and wet, cool weather after infection favors secondary infection and build-up of the disease.

Crop rotation, using crops other than grasses, and deep plowing to bury "blind seeds" are both effective control methods. Infected seed can be safely planted if such seed is at least 2 years old, because the fungus loses its viability in that time.

We used to think that the ryegrasses were the only grass hosts to blind seed in Oregon. More recently seed of Astoria bentgrass, Alta fescue, and creeping red fescue has been found infected with the disease.

Head Smut

Head smut, *Ustilago bullata,* is caused by a fungus that attacks several grasses, including both economic and noneconomic species of *Agropyron, Bromus, Elymus,* and *Hordeum.* It occurs wherever those grasses grow. As most of these grasses grow in the semiarid regions of the Western States, head smut is largely confined there.

In smutted heads, enlarged smut galls are formed instead of the seeds. Each smut gall is made up of a mass of dark-colored spores. Some of the spores released under field conditions are scattered to nearby heads, but most of them remain in the galls until the seed crop is threshed. Threshing breaks up the galls and spreads the spores to the healthy seeds.

When smutted seed is planted, the spores germinate along with the seed. The growing fungus invades the developing seedling and continues to grow inside the plant until after heading, when the smut galls which have formed in place of the seeds, become evident. Plants that are infected with head smut appear normal except for the smutted heads.

Head smut can be controlled by seed treatment, but it is an example of a grass disease where such control is not commonly practiced. Seeds of the grass species attacked by head smut are difficult to treat because of their light weight and the presence of awns and similar other seed parts.

Selection and breeding for head smut resistance is the only practical means of controlling this disease.

Physiologic races of the head smut fungus are known to occur.

Grass Seed Nematode

Grass seed nematode, *Anguina agrostis,* is an example of a grass disease caused by a nematode. Nematodes are known to occur in the soil in many regions, but specific nematodes become of economic importance only when the crop or crops completely susceptible to them are grown in such areas.

The grass seed nematode is important as a disease of Chewings fescue and bentgrasses in the Pacific Northwest, where these grasses are grown for seed.

The symptoms of nematode infection appear as swollen galls that replace normal seeds. These galls, when mature, may fall to the ground or be carried in threshed seed. Each gall may contain several nematodes. The disease is spread mainly through transport of the nematode galls in seed.

Sanitary measures, such as burning of infected grass fields to destroy galls which have fallen or shattered to the ground and thorough cleaning of galls from seed, are effective methods of control. Crop rotation, using crops other than susceptible grasses, is also effective in destroying nematodes in infested soil.

THE AUTHOR «« *J. Lewis Allison, a native of Montana and a graduate of Montana State College, has advanced degrees from Washington State College and the University of Minnesota and has been engaged in research on forage crop diseases since 1936. Dr. Allison is senior pathologist in the Bureau of Plant Industry, Soils, and Agricultural Engineering and is leader for forage crop disease investigations.*

SOME DISEASES OF FORAGE LEGUMES

HOWARD W. JOHNSON

ALL LEGUMES that we grow for forage purposes are attacked by diseases, some of them serious and widespread.

Because of the nature of forage legumes, direct control measures, such as spraying and dusting, have only limited application. Control must be sought in most cases through the development of disease-resistant varieties by selection or hybridization and the use of cultural practices designed to prevent infection from contaminated seed and soil—crop rotation, use of disease-free seed, time of planting, time of harvesting, and plowing under of crop residues.

Of the many diseases, a few can illustrate some of the types and demonstrate the progress that is being made in developing ways to fight them. The types of diseases considered here include bacterial wilts, anthracnoses, fungus and bacterial leaf spots, powdery mildews, rusts, mosaics and other virus diseases, and fungus stem and root rots.

Besides these are the diseaselike injury caused on numerous forage legumes by the potato leafhopper (*Empoasca fabae*); the root knot disease caused by a nematode (*Heterodera marioni*); and the diseases caused by mineral deficiencies in the soil. In the latter category, boron and potash deficiency are probably of most common occurrence on forage legumes.

A serious threat to alfalfa growing in the United States is the bacterial wilt disease that kills out stands of susceptible alfalfas in 2 to 4 years. When it was first discovered in 1925, bacterial wilt was most severe in the river valleys of Nebraska and Kansas, but it is now found in considerable abundance eastward to the Atlantic seaboard. It is prevalent and destructive also in the irrigated valleys of the Western States to the Pacific coast. The losses due to the disease include the crops that are destroyed, the costs of

seeding, and loss of production from the land until a new crop is established. If growers could maintain stands of alfalfa for even 2 years longer than at present by growing disease-resistant varieties, they would be able to save millions of dollars.

The first evidence of bacterial wilt in an alfalfa field is the presence of dwarfed plants with small, abnormal-shaped leaves of a yellow or pale-green color. Such top growth may wilt during summer droughts and the infected plants gradually weaken and die because water-conducting vessels in the alfalfa roots become plugged with bacterial growth. The wood of such roots is yellow; the color of a healthy root, uniform creamy white. In almost all sections, dwarfed alfalfa plants, with yellow or pale-green foliage and discolored wood in the roots, indicate the presence of bacterial wilt.

Efforts to control the disease by cultural practices have proved largely unsuccessful, and efforts have been directed toward testing alfalfa varieties for resistance and breeding new varieties that contain a large proportion of resistant plants and possess other desirable characters. Tests for varietal resistance have been made by inoculating large populations of seedlings and determining by examination those that remain free from disease at the end of a suitable period of growth in the field or greenhouse.

These comparatively rapid but controlled tests have not measured exactly the percentage of plants in a variety that will withstand wilt over a long period under all conditions, but they have made possible provisional estimates of relative resistance, and have been helpful in forecasting the outcome of long-time field trials.

F. R. Jones, of the Department, reported in 1940 that controlled tests show that Peruvian, Grimm, Hardigan, and the common varieties of alfalfa contain few resistant plants, usually fewer than 1 percent, and that Cossack alfalfa usually has fewer than 10 percent. In Ladak, on the other hand, about a third of the plants are highly resistant; in Hardistan, Orestan, and other more resistant strains from Turkestan importations, about one-half the plants are highly resistant. As a result of these tests and field trials of varieties, Cossack, Ladak, Hardistan, and Orestan have been recommended for use in wilt-infested areas until seed of new, disease-resistant varieties become available.

The introductions from Turkestan have provided the foundation material for a plant-breeding program for control of this destructive disease. Seed of these wilt-resistant plants, which were to prove so valuable to American farmers, had been collected in Turkestan and neighboring countries by plant explorers of the Department and had been grown in plant nurseries in various parts of the United States. The aim of the breeding program has been to combine the bacterial wilt resistance of the Turkestan alfalfa with the good qualities of commercial alfalfas, such as Grimm and Common.

Resistant plants for breeding purposes have been obtained by the same method of inoculation and subsequent examination that was used in the tests for varietal resistance. These selected plants have then been increased by vegetative cuttings and the resulting clonal lines have been inoculated artificially and tested for resistance in field nurseries.

By using that general method of getting wilt-resistant lines, workers in the Department and the Nebraska and Kansas Agricultural Experiment Stations have developed two new varieties of alfalfa, Ranger and Buffalo, which are highly resistant to bacterial wilt and possess good characteristics for growth and seed production. Seed of these varieties will soon be available to alfalfa growers in substantial quantities.

A bacterial wilt disease somewhat similar to the one that attacks alfalfa was reported on annual lespedeza by T. T. Ayers, C. L. Lefebvre, and H. W. Johnson, of the Department, in 1939. The disease is widely distributed in the lespedeza-growing areas of the United States.

The first visible symptom of infection is the appearance of dark, water-soaked spots on the leaflets. The infected leaflets soon become grayish brown, desiccated, and curled. Systemic infection follows rather rapidly in the case of susceptible strains of annual lespedeza, and within a few weeks entire plants wilt and die. Bacteria are abundant in the leaves and stems of infected plants, and it appears that the plugging of the water-conducting tubes is responsible for the general wilting and death.

Because the bacterium causing wilt of annual lespedeza may occur either in or on the seed, prevention of the disease requires primarily the use of disease-free seed. There seem to be no practical control measures that will check its spread once it appears in a field of annual lespedeza.

Greenhouse inoculations have shown that many strains of annual lespedeza are susceptible to bacterial wilt. In the field, the disease has appeared to be most severe on strains of Early Korean lespedeza in Illinois, Iowa, and Missouri. The disease has not yet been observed to affect perennial species of lespedeza in the field, although greenhouse inoculations have shown some species of perennial lespedeza to be susceptible.

Anthracnose of Clover

The two common anthracnose diseases of red clover are caused by the fungi *Colletotrichum trifolii* and *Kabatiella caulivora*. The symptoms they produce are similar, and most clover growers would be unable to distinguish them. In early summer, anthracnose occurs as small dark spots on the stems, petioles, and flower stalks. The girdling of these structures causes wilting and browning of the tissues above the girdles and results in breaking or bending over of the petioles and flower stalks to produce characteristic "shepherds' crooks."

Considerable defoliation may occur in the first cutting, but when anthracnose is severe during late summer the tops are sometimes killed completely and the crown and taproot of infected plants may be invaded and rotted. This type of general infection frequently destroys a stand of red clover after it has produced a satisfactory crop of hay and results in loss of the seed crop and a greatly reduced value for green-manure purposes.

Various methods of controlling red clover anthracnose have been suggested, such as crop rotation, seed disinfection, fall planting, and mixture with grasses. Such methods have decidedly limited application, however, and control by means of resistant varieties offers the most promise.

Varieties of red clover resistant to southern anthracnose (*Colletotrichum*) are known, and the development of strains of red clover resistant to northern anthracnose (*Kabatiella*) appears possible.

The Tennessee strain of red clover, which was developed at the Tennessee Agricultural Experiment Station during the first decade of the present century by selection of the surviving plants from badly diseased fields, is still highly resistant to southern anthracnose. Other strains of red clover, grown for many years in regions such as Kentucky and Virginia where they are subjected regularly to severe outbreaks of the disease, also possess considerable resistance to *Colletotrichum*. It appeared that mixing together the seed of several of these strains might yield an anthracnose-resistant red clover of wider adaptation than any one strain alone would possess.

Using this method of procedure, the variety Cumberland, which resists southern anthracnose and is adapted to the southern part of the red clover belt, has been developed and released

to farmers. Similarly, the variety Midland, which has some resistance to northern anthracnose and is adapted to the northern part of the red clover belt, was developed from old Corn Belt strains of red clover.

While the anthracnose caused by *Colletotrichum trifolii* is most severe on red clover, the disease is common also on alfalfa in the Eastern States. It is found also on sweetclover, crimson clover, sub clover, and bur-clover.

Leaf Spots

The common leaf spot caused by the fungus *Pseudopeziza medicaginis* is probably the most destructive of the foliage diseases of alfalfa. The disease is present in almost every alfalfa field; it does small damage to foliage under dry conditions and great damage under more humid conditions.

The disease has been regarded in the past as one of the unavoidable evils to which the alfalfa plant is subject, but recently resistant lines have been found in alfalfa breeding nurseries. It seems probable, therefore, that strains of alfalfa resistant to both bacterial wilt and leaf spot will eventually be made available for the humid areas of the United States. This fungus attacks other species of *Medicago* as well as alfalfa; a closely related but distinct fungus causes a similar leaf spot on clovers, as reported by F. R. Jones in 1919.

Leaf spotting and stem blackening of alfalfa are caused by the fungus *Ascochyta imperfecta*. The leaf spots are irregular and dark brown; when infection is severe the spots coalesce and the leaves turn yellow and fall. Infection by this fungus is favored by cool, wet weather and considerable defoliation may occur in the spring before the first cutting is made. Blackening of the stems occurs progressively from the base upward and in wet springs in some localities may result in the death of the less vigorous young shoots. Late in the season, in stands left for seed, the blackening may progress up to the racemes and even to the seed pods, according to a report by M. W. Cormack, of the Canadian Department of Agriculture in 1945. Dr. Cormack showed also that the pathogene is seed-borne; he suggests that seed infection occurs directly through the pods of severely diseased plants.

The causal fungus overwinters by means of pycnidia on dead alfalfa stems infected the previous autumn, and the spores produced in these structures are the source of new infections in the spring. M. L. Peterson and L. E. Melchers, of the Kansas Agricultural Experiment Station, reported in 1942 that they had produced a large supply of viable spores for artificial inoculations by growing the fungus on sterile, second-year sweetclover stems. They tested the susceptibility of alfalfa varieties and selections in the greenhouse and field and found that certain varieties and plants within a variety showed definite resistance, thus demonstrating that breeding for resistance offers a way to control this disease.

Cercospora leaf spot is widely distributed in the United States and occurs on alfalfa, bur-clovers, sweetclovers, and true clovers. On alfalfa, bur-clovers, and sweetclovers, the spots are circular; on the true clovers they are usually elongate, angular, and more or less delimited by the veins of the leaf. Although the color of the spots varies considerably, they are usually some shade of brown. Mature spots may appear ashy gray because of a covering layer of fungus spores and conidiophores. Infected leaves of sweetclover soon shrivel and drop, but this tendency is not so marked on the other legumes.

The disease occurs also on the stems and petioles as reddish-brown lesions. F. R. Jones reported in 1944 that on second-year sweetclover stems heavy infection with Cercospora can cause a stem blackening quite similar to that caused by Ascochyta meliloti. J. G. Horsfall in 1929 concluded from an examination of herbarium material that the fungus attacking all of these hosts

should be called Cercospora zebrina. More recently Dr. Jones has shown that the fungus on sweetclover has a distinct life history and proposes that the name Cercospora davisii be retained for it.

These fungi are known to be seed-borne, and seed treatment has been recommended as a method of excluding the disease from new fields. Dr. Jones has reported evidence of resistance to stem blackening by Cercospora in sweetclover, and it appears therefore that breeding for resistance offers a means of control.

A bacterial leaf spot is widely prevalent on several species of clover according to a report by L. R. Jones, Maude M. Williamson, F. A. Wolf, and Lucia McCulloch in 1923. The spots may appear at any time of the growing season on the leaf blades, stems, stipules, petioles, and flower pedicels. The lesions appear first as minute, translucent dots, but enlarge to become irregular, blackish-brown areas with a yellowish-green border. Older leaves become frayed because of the drying and falling out of the killed tissues. A milky-white bacterial exudate is formed on the lower leaf surface in rainy periods.

It seems probable that the clover seed becomes contaminated in the field or during harvesting and threshing operations, and that the disease is spread to new fields with the seed. If this disease should become destructive enough to warrant control measures, seed disinfection would warrant trial. No observations have been made to date on the resistance of clover to the disease.

Numerous other leaf spots occur on forage legumes in the United States, causing the same general type of symptoms and losses.

Powdery Mildews

Red clover powdery mildew, caused by the fungus Erysiphe polygoni, seriously alarmed growers of red clover in the United States when it appeared suddenly in 1922 as one of the widespread diseases of this crop. Much of the alarm at its appearance subsided when it was shown that animals were not injured by eating the hay made from mildewed red clover. The disease has been more or less prevalent each year since 1922, however, and causes an appreciable reduction in hay yields each season.

Powdery mildew covers the clover leaves with a dense white mat of mycelium and spores, making them look much as if they had been lightly dusted with flour. This covering reduces the ability of the leaves to manufacture food and increases the rate of water loss from them, thus resulting in the premature death of the infected leaves and a general stunting of the plants.

Soon after the widespread appearance of powdery mildew on red clover in this country, it was observed that our native strains of red clover were in general susceptible, while the European strains generally showed high resistance. Because the European strains are not winter-hardy and are highly susceptible to anthracnose and leafhopper injury, they are not suited for use in the United States. Attempts to control powdery mildew have turned, therefore, to a search for resistant individuals in our North American red clover strains. A small proportion of such individuals exists apparently in most strains of red clover.

It has been found that by crossing selected, mildew-resistant parents, one can obtain progenies that are highly resistant to powdery mildew. A number of them have been combined to produce a strain of red clover resistant to powdery mildew. Seed of this strain, developed by plant breeders in the Division of Forage Crops and Diseases of the Department and the Wisconsin Agricultural Experiment Station, is being increased as rapidly as possible, but none is available yet at commercial seed companies.

Powdery mildew of annual lespedeza caused by the fungus *Microsphaera diffusa* also covers the leaves with a white powdery growth and causes a certain degree of premature defoliation. Late in the season the white patches are liberally sprinkled with small black dots, the perithecia of the fungus. The perithecia constitute the overwintering stage of the mildew. Kobe and common lespedeza appear to be more susceptible to powdery mildew than the strains of Korean.

Rusts

Alfalfa rust, caused by the fungus *Uromyces striatus,* is widely distributed in the United States. It seems to do greatest damage to the crop that is being grown for seed but may be abundant in the later hay cuttings and cause loss of leaves and poorer quality.

The disease is characterized by dark-brown masses of fungus spores that rupture the epidermis of the leaves and stems and form typical, powdery, rust pustules. Marked differences in resistance to rust among species, varieties, and plant selections of alfalfa have been observed by J. M. Koepper, of the Kansas Agricultural Experiment Station, as reported in 1942, thus showing that the breeding of resistant varieties is a means of control.

All the common clovers are attacked by a rust (*Uromyces trifolii*), which is sometimes severe enough on white, alsike, and red clovers to be of economic importance. The summer stage of the disease is characterized by minute, cinnamon-brown powdery pustules on the leaf blades, petioles, and stems. The pustules occur on both the lower and upper leaf surfaces and, when abundant, cause the leaves to turn yellow and finally brown. The killed leaves fall to the ground, reducing the yield of hay. J. T. Sullivan and S. J. P. Chilton, of the Department, reported in 1941 that rusted leaves of white clover contain from one-fifth to one-third less carotene than do non-rusted leaves. It would appear, therefore, that the nutritive value of the crop is likewise reduced by clover rust. No experimental work on the control of clover rusts appears to have been reported, but it seems that breeding resistant varieties will be possible if it sometime becomes necessary.

Virus Diseases

Mosaic of alfalfa is a disease characterized by yellow and green mottling of the leaves. It becomes evident during the cool weather of spring and fall when the stunted, mottled plants may be observed scattered throughout alfalfa fields in all parts of the country. The disease does not appear to be of major importance, but its widespread occurrence and the stunted growth of mosaic plants indicates that some loss is caused each season.

Another virus disease of alfalfa, known as alfalfa dwarf, occurs only in southern California, where its symptoms and effect on alfalfa stands are quite similar to those of bacterial wilt. Dwarf can be distinguished from wilt, however, by the fact that the leaves of the dwarfed plants are normal in color, or of a slightly darker green than those of healthy plants, and, though small, they are practically normal in shape. J. L. Weimer, of the Department, presented evidence showing the virus nature of the disease in 1936.

A third virus disease of alfalfa, which is known as "witches'-broom," or "bunchy top," has been reported as prevalent and destructive in alfalfa fields in certain irrigated valleys in Washington State. Investigations there showed that the witches'-broom plants are more susceptible to winterkilling than are normal plants. The disease is considered to be an important factor in shortening the profitable life of alfalfa stands in the affected valleys, according to a report by J. D. Menzies, of the Washington Agricultural Experiment Station, in 1946. No control for these virus diseases is known, except the development of resistant strains of alfalfa.

Mosaic also occurs commonly on red, alsike, white, and crimson clover and sweetclovers. The disease is characterized by mottling, crinkling, and curling of the leaves. The size of the leaves is also reduced and the affected plants may be reduced almost one-half in size. Under field conditions it is difficult to determine the prevalence of the disease on account of the intermingling of healthy and diseased plants. In spaced plantings, such as occur in breeding nurseries, a high percentage of the plants are sometimes observed to have mosaic. It is probable, therefore, that this disease of clover is more important than has been supposed.

The pea aphid, *Illinoia pisi,* is the common insect vector for the clover mosaic.

Stem and Root Rots

Stem rot of forage legumes, caused by the fungus *Sclerotinia trifoliorum,* has been recognized in this country since 1890, and appears to be most prevalent in western Oregon and in the southern and eastern parts of the red-clover-growing area.

The fungus is most active in late winter and early spring, when it rots the stem bases and upper taproots of the attacked plants, resulting in their death. Serious outbreaks have been reported also on crimson clover, white clover, sweetclover, and alfalfa.

Control by growing selected, resistant strains seems possible. Serious outbreaks of stem rot in sweetclover fields in western Oregon led there to the development by selection of the Willamette sweetclover, which is highly resistant to stem rot under Oregon conditions. The Oregon Agricultural Experiment Station has likewise selected a strain of smooth crimson clover that is resistant to stem rot; growing that strain is said to have cut losses from stem rot by 50 percent. Observations in Kentucky indicate that adapted strains of red clover are more resistant to stem rot than are unadapted American and foreign red clovers.

Numerous other soil-inhabiting fungi also rot the roots of forage legumes.

Among these may be listed *Rhizoctonia* spp., *Fusarium* spp., *Cylindrocarpon* spp., *Plenodomas meliloti,* and *Phytophthora cactorum.*

In the semiarid regions where the cotton root rot fungus, *Phymatotrichum omnivorum,* occurs, alfalfa and sweetclover have been observed to be susceptible to attack by this omnivorous parasite. In the South, sclerotial blight and charcoal rot frequently attack the roots and stem bases of forage legumes and cause appreciable losses.

M. W. Cormack in 1942 reported the results of 7 years of field tests to determine the resistance of alfalfa and sweetclover varieties and strains to six root- and crown-rotting fungi in Alberta. He found that alfalfa was more resistant than sweetclover to all these fungi except one. Yellow-flowered alfalfa (*Medicago falcata*), Cossack, and Viking appeared most resistant.

Sweetclover varieties showed marked differences in their reaction to *Phytophthora cactorum* in these tests. F. R. Jones in 1939 obtained sweetclover plants resistant to Phytophthora root rot by selection from dug roots inoculated with the fungus. It appears therefore that selection and breeding offer a means of developing varieties of forage legumes resistant to the various root rots.

THE AUTHOR《《 *Howard W. Johnson is senior pathologist in the Division of Forage Crops and Diseases, Bureau of Plant Industry, Soils, and Agricultural Engineering. Dr. Johnson, a graduate of Ohio State University and the University of Minnesota, has been engaged in research on forage diseases since 1930. He is now stationed at the Delta Branch Experiment Station, Stoneville, Miss.*

SOME OF THE INSECTS

C. M. PACKARD

AN INCREDIBLE number and variety of insects live on grasses and legumes. Under favorable conditions many species compete successfully with domestic animals as consumers of these crops, as any farmer knows who has seen an outbreak of grasshoppers or armyworms ruin a good stand of grass or grain almost overnight or a whole cutting of alfalfa lost to the alfalfa aphid.

Often the number of insects runs into many millions to an acre and their large appetites more than make up for their small size. Hundreds of species are pests of grasses, legumes, and other forage plants. Herbert Osborn has written a book, *Meadow and Pasture Insects,* about them; only a few of the most important ones can be discussed in this article. Only brief mention can be made of the control methods used against them. Readers should consult their county agricultural agents or

State experiment stations when specific instructions are needed.

Grasshoppers are among the most widely prevalent pests of pasture and hay crops. Some species favor the uncultivated ranges; others like the cultivated grasses and legumes. In both environments their abundance and control may mean the success or failure of a year's farm operations.

Fortunately, effective means have been developed for controlling them. For many years the application of a poisoned bran or bran-sawdust bait broadcast thinly in the infested fields has been a standard, cheap, and, under most conditions, effective method of control. When bait is properly handled and applied there is no danger to livestock pastured in the treated areas. The substitution of sodium fluosilicate for the arsenical poisons formerly used in baits has practically eliminated the danger of stock poisoning.

Although much bait is still spread by hand, highly efficient power equipment for spreading it from the ground and from airplanes has been developed and is widely used. During the bad grasshopper year, 1938, United States farmers spread about 136,000 tons (dry weight) of grasshopper bait, supplied them by Government and State agencies, on 30,895,000 acres, and thereby saved crops valued at more than $175,000,000.

Baits are often rather ineffective in thick, succulent crops like alfalfa. Investigators have therefore been working hard to find a better method for use in the protection of such crops. Their experiments have shown that several of the new insecticides, particularly Chlordane, benzene hexachloride, and a chlorinated camphene, commonly called Toxaphene, directly applied in a spray or dust, with ground equipment or airplanes, are effective against grasshoppers. Proper use of these insecticides, it is found, is a practical supplement or substitute where poor control is obtained with bait. Until more is known about the residue hazards involved, however, these insecticides should be applied only to the early growth just after cutting if the crops are to be used for hay or feed, and to field margins, fence rows, roadsides, and idle lands in which the hoppers congregate and which are not to be pastured or cut for hay. Treated crops should not be fed to dairy animals or to meat animals that are being finished for slaughter.

The Mormon Cricket

The Mormons were the first ones to lose range forage and crops to the Mormon cricket, hence its common name. They encountered it soon after they first settled in Utah, about 1848. In the northern Rocky Mountain and Pacific Coast States the Mormon cricket often damages large areas of range forage severely. When very abundant, it depletes the forage supply in these areas and migrates to new pastures on foot in bands sometimes miles in extent. These bands will also attack cultivated grass, grain, forage, and garden crops athwart their path. They look like big, black, long-legged crickets, but they are really wingless grasshoppers. A closely related species, the coulee cricket, also occurs in some areas in the Northwest and has similar habits.

The early Mormon settlers knew no satisfactory way of fighting the Mormon cricket, but their crops are said to have been saved from destruction by an influx of sea gulls that appeared in answer to their prayers and ate up the crickets. A monument to the gulls has been placed near the Mormon Tabernacle in Salt Lake City.

Recently it was found that these crickets can be cheaply and quickly controlled by means of a poisoned bran or bran-sawdust bait. Although the crickets do not like a bait containing an arsenical, investigators finally discovered that they will readily eat one containing enough sodium fluosilicate to kill them. Baits containing this poison, broadcast by hand, power spreaders, and airplanes, have been widely and successfully used.

Cutworms and Armyworms

In an unpublished paper on the cutworms and armyworms of the central Great Plains, H. H. Walkden reports the observation of 54 species in cereal and forage crops, pasture grasses, and wastelands. Six of these species are known to be of major economic importance, the pale western cutworm, army cutworm, variegated cutworm, armyworm, fall armyworm, and corn earworm. Lawns as well as farm crops are sometimes attacked.

A few of the cutworms, like the pale western cutworm, work mostly under ground, whereas others bore within the stems of their host plants.

The only methods of control yet known for these species are cultural measures such as rotation of crops and properly timed summer fallowing.

Armyworms are really cutworms that occur in great numbers under favorable conditions and migrate in droves on foot in search of food as they deplete the supply in the infested fields. Most cutworms and armyworms feed on the above-ground parts of the plants and hide under the surface litter and soil during the day. Because of this habit they usually can be easily killed with poison bran or bran-sawdust bait broadcast in the infested fields late in the afternoon so that it is fresh and attractive to them as they emerge hungry in the evening. The bait may be applied by hand or with power or airplane equipment.

Another method of control sometimes used against armyworms is barrier furrows plowed along the side of the field being invaded. In plowing a barrier furrow, the dirt is thrown toward the crop to be protected. A log is then drawn back and forth in the furrow to work up a loose dust, which helps to keep them from climbing out, and kills them as they accumulate in the furrow. Sometimes instead of using a log, the furrow is left smooth and hard and post holes are dug in the bottom of it every 20 feet or so. The worms crawl along the furrow and tumble into the holes, where they may be killed by crushing or by the application of coal oil or crankcase oil.

Still another method is the application of an insecticidal dust or spray to the infested crop. Lead arsenate, calcium arsenate, and some of the new insecticides such as DDT have been found effective against certain species. Because of the residue hazards involved, however, their use on forage crops or pastures is inadvisable, except perhaps when several months of lush plant growth and heavy rains occur between treatment and harvest.

Range Caterpillar

A large spiny worm commonly called the range caterpillar has at times caused extensive losses of range forage in eastern New Mexico. Al-

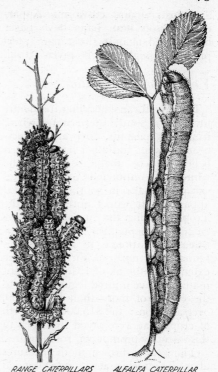

RANGE CATERPILLARS   ALFALFA CATERPILLAR

though it feeds on at least 40 different species of plants, including cultivated grain and forage crops, it is primarily a pest of the range grasses common to that region. It injures them in two ways: First, by eating them down to the roots over large areas; and second, by leaving on the plants the poisonous spines which it sheds as it crawls around or when it molts. Control measures such as burning over the range, the use of heavy corrugated iron rollers, and brush dragging have not been successful.

They can be killed with a lead arsenate spray if the value of the crop to be protected would warrant the cost. It is possible that cryolite or one of the new insecticides such as DDT might also be effective, though none of these have actually been tried against them. If one of them were to be applied, the same precautions concerning the attendant residue hazards should be observed as have already been mentioned in connection with the use of sprays and dusts against cutworms. Apparently poison bran baits have never been tested against the range caterpillar and might well be given a trial.

Velvetbean Caterpillar

The velvetbean caterpillar frequently invades the Southeastern States, where it attacks peanuts, soybeans, velvetbeans, kudzu, and other legumes. It is believed to be unable to survive the winter in continental United States except perhaps in southern Florida; apparently it works north from the Tropics during the summer until by August or September (after perhaps three generations) it is sometimes found as far north as Virginia. In the extensive outbreak of 1946 it was estimated to have injured legume crops to the extent of more than $5,000,000, over and above the $15,000,000 worth of crops that were saved from loss to this insect by prompt control measures.

The grayish-brown moth measures about 1½ inches across its expanded wings, both pairs of which bear a single dark diagonal line near their outer margin. The caterpillar is rather slender and about 1½ inches long when full grown, greenish or blackish, with several narrow light stripes along its back and sides. It is very active and will spring into the air, wriggling violently, when disturbed. When the worms are abundant, they rapidly cause "ragging" and defoliation of the infested plants. Susceptible crops should therefore be watched closely for them in the late summer, and control measures applied promptly.

A single treatment with cryolite dust at 12 to 15 pounds an acre has been widely and successfully used in the control of the velvetbean caterpillar. This treatment can be used safely on crops intended for hay or pasture. Quicker control can be obtained with 15 pounds per acre of a dust containing 2 to 3 percent of DDT, but crops treated with this insecticide should not be fed to dairy animals or to meat animals that are being finished for slaughter.

Alfalfa Caterpillar

Great numbers of a butterfly with bright yellow wings bordered with black and a spread of about 2 inches are a common sight in alfalfa fields of the Southwestern States. The so-called alfalfa caterpillar, from which it comes, is a green worm about 1½ inches long when full grown, with a fine white stripe on each side. There are several generations a year in the more southern part of its range. The worms eat alfalfa foliage and often ruin an entire cutting.

Although this insect is kept more or less under control by parasites and a wilt disease, artificial control measures are frequently necessary. Prompt, clean, low cutting of the crop and removal of the hay is often the best procedure. Cutting all fields in a neighborhood at about the same time, and keeping down the growth of weeds and volunteer alfalfa around the fields by mowing or pasturing aid in preventing serious infestations. Prompt dusting of infested fields with a heavy application of sulfur has also been found effective. Alfalfa growers in certain districts of central California have found it profitable to employ an experienced entomologist to watch their alfalfa fields during the growing season and advise them concerning the application of control measures.

Alfalfa Webworm

Alfalfa and clover sometimes become heavily infested by the alfalfa webworm. It was extremely abundant in 1947, when it was also reported attacking several other field crops. The small, greenish to nearly black worms web the terminal leaves together and feed on the enclosed foliage. When full grown, they are about an inch long and turn into small buff-colored moths. These hide among the plants during the day but will make short flights as when disturbed by one walking through an infested field and often swarm about lights on warm nights. There are several generations a year. In the fall the worms assume more of the habits of cutworms in newly sown alfalfa and hide in silk-lined burrows in or on the ground.

Prompt, clean cutting of the alfalfa and clean-up of weeds and volunteer growth around the fields are the most practical methods of controlling the summer generations. Fields of newly seeded alfalfa infested in the early fall may be protected by dusting or spraying with calcium arsenate, lead arsenate, or DDT, but crops so treated should not be used for pasture or hay the same season.

The alfalfa webworm is ordinarily held in check by its insect parasites.

Alfalfa Aphid

The alfalfa aphid, also called the pea aphid, thrives on alfalfa, the clovers, vetches, Austrian peas, and other legumes, and these perennial or winter crops serve as the major sources of the infestations that develop on canning and garden peas.

It is a pale-green, long-legged plant louse about one-eighth inch long when full grown. Although most individuals are wingless, many of them develop wings under crowded conditions and fly or are carried by winds for considerable distances.

Parasites and diseases usually hold down its numbers during warm weather, but it can multiply rapidly and often reaches extreme abundance on alfalfa, vetch, and Austrian peas during late winter or early spring. It bears living young, which begin at once to suck sap from the newly sprouted alfalfa shoots; the shoots rapidly become solidly encrusted with aphids in all stages and soon die. This aphid is present throughout the United States, and first cuttings of alfalfa are ruined by it somewhere in the country nearly every year.

The most practical methods of controlling the alfalfa aphid are heavy pasturing of the fields during the winter or early spring, or winter cultiva-

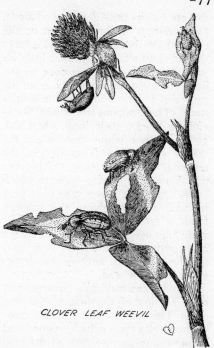

CLOVER LEAF WEEVIL

tion with a disk or spring-tooth harrow. These operations destroy most of the aphids that would otherwise survive the winter as eggs or adults on the fall growth and thus delay their increase until warm weather when their parasites and diseases can take over the job.

Recent experiments indicate that the use of one of the new insecticides, such as benzene hexachloride or hexaethyl tetraphosphate, on the small shoots early in the spring may be found effective and practical, but further trials of them are necessary before they can be recommended.

Alfalfa Weevil

The alfalfa weevil is an Old-World insect that appeared near Salt Lake City in 1904 and has since spread to 11 Western States. Little injury from it has occurred outside of Utah, Nevada, Idaho, Colorado, Oregon, and Wyoming. In some areas a little wasplike parasite brought in from Europe helps to keep it down. Alfalfa is the only crop that is damaged by it.

The adults are brown snout beetles about three-sixteenths of an inch long; they feed on alfalfa but cause little injury. The real damage is done by the little green worms that hatch from the eggs laid by the adults in the alfalfa stems. These worms are about three-eighths of an inch long when full grown, with a white stripe down the middle of the back. They feed on the terminal buds and leaves, eating out the tissue and leaving only the leaf-veins. Damaged leaves take on a gray or whitish cast, giving the infested fields a frostbitten appearance. The main damage is to the first or spring crop, although the second crop may also be injured in some seasons, especially if left for seed.

Damage can usually be prevented by early cutting of the first and second crops. This means cutting before many of the alfalfa flowers have opened and before many young shoots of the next crop have started out from the plant crowns. By clean cutting and prompt removal of the hay at this time, nearly all of the worms, eggs, and pupae are killed by starvation or heat in the bare fields. Early cutting of the first and second crops should be practiced if possible every year, even though these crops are not actually being injured. If this practice is not followed, enough weevils may be produced to cause damage the following year.

Where early cutting is not practicable, as in the case of fields left for seed, the weevil can be controlled by one application of 2 pounds of calcium arsenate per acre, diluted with a carrier dust or spray in order to obtain proper coverage. If the dosage is limited to 2 pounds an acre, evenly applied, the crop can be fed safely to livestock.

A single application of a dust containing 5 or 10 percent of DDT, at the rate of 1 to 2 pounds of the active ingredient per acre, has also given excellent control of the alfalfa weevil, but crops so treated should not be fed to dairy animals or meat animals that are being finished for slaughter.

Several relatives of the alfalfa weevil are more or less injurious to alfalfa and clover, including the clover leaf weevil, bud weevil, root curculio, and the root borer.

In general, no really satisfactory ways of controlling them have been developed. Most of them are mainly pests of clover and do not become extremely abundant if it is not allowed to stand more than 2 years.

Vetch Bruchid

The vetch bruchid, a little weevil that came in from Europe, makes a specialty of ruining the seed of hairy vetch although it also similarly attacks some other vetches. From 1941 to 1943 it greatly reduced the production of hairy vetch seed in this country—a serious matter, especially during wartime when no hairy vetch seed could be imported—as hairy vetch is an important cover crop in the South. Production of hairy vetch seed in the Eastern States ceased to be profitable 10 years or more ago on account of this weevil and recently most of the crop has been produced in the Pacific Northwest. The vetch bruchid found its way out there just before the war and was rapidly reducing production in that area also until entomologists found that it could be controlled by timely dusting of the crop with DDT.

The adults lay their eggs on the small newly formed seed pods; the little maggots hatching from the eggs immediately bore through the underside of the eggs into the pods and enter the seeds while they are still green. Infested seeds are hollowed out and ruined by the time they are mature and are eliminated in the cleaning process after the crop is threshed. A single application of about 25 pounds per acre of a dust containing 3 percent of DDT just as the pods begin to form kills off the adults as they congregate in the vetch for egg laying. Most of the seed infestation is thus prevented and a profitable crop can be produced. The straw and chaff from vetch that has been treated with DDT should not be fed to dairy animals or to meat animals that are being fattened for slaughter.

This weevil does not breed in mature, dry vetch seed although it can survive in them for months. It was undoubtedly brought to this country in vetch seed from Europe.

Chinch Bugs

The chinch bug must be included among the most important insect pests that are native to this country. Before the planting of large acreages of small grains and corn it probably lived on native perennial grasses. It finds modern farming conditions much to its liking, however, and in favorable seasons becomes extremely abundant in the Central and Eastern States. Chinch bugs feed only on plants of the grass family. They are most important as pests of corn and small grains but also attack forage and lawn grasses.

Chinch bugs are little black sucking insects with white wings folded on their backs to form a sort of X. They are about one-eighth of an inch long when full grown and have a typical "buggy" odor. When newly hatched they are smaller than a pinhead, red and wingless, but the red color is gradually lost and their wings develop as they mature. When abundant the adults hibernate in great numbers hidden away in bunchgrasses and various sheltered places. With the first warm weather they emerge from hibernation and fly to the small grains and grasses. By the time small grains are ripe the first new generation of the season is nearly mature and as these grains dry up, the bugs migrate in hordes on foot in search of green food. They swarm on corn, sorghum, Sudangrass, millet, or almost any green grassy plants they can find nearby and soon kill them. When full grown they migrate throughout the corn, sorghum, and grass fields.

Barriers are widely used to prevent chinch bug migrations on foot from small-grain fields to immature small grains and grasses, corn, and sorghums.

These are made in several ways, but the best of them include a narrow band of a repellant chemical, such as coal-tar creosote, or a poisonous dust, such as dinitro orthocresol, laid across the path of the migrating bugs.

The creosote is often poured in a narrow line along the smoothly packed brow of a plow furrow made by turning the soil toward the crop to be protected. Detailed instruction for building chinch bug barriers may be obtained from State agricultural experiment stations or the United States Department of Agriculture.

A different method must be used to control chinch bug infestations in lawns or on valuable grasses and grains being grown for seed.

Under those conditions it is necessary to make direct application of a spray or dust. Kerosene emulsion and nicotine sprays, dusts containing at least 1 percent of nicotine or rotenone or 10 percent of ground sabadilla seed, and a dust containing 10 percent of DDT have all been recommended. The nicotine or rotenone dust is applied at the rate of 25 pounds and the sabadilla dust at the rate of 2 to 3 pounds, per 1,000 square feet. The DDT dust is perhaps the best but it must be heavily applied (2 to 3 pounds per 1,000 square feet) and is very slow in action. Its full effects are not apparent in less than 4 days.

Animals should not be allowed to graze on grass that has been treated with DDT for at least 3 months after treatment, and clippings or hay from lawns or fields that have been treated with it since the last previous cutting should not be fed to livestock.

Leafhoppers

Unless leafhoppers are so numerous that they fly up in swarms when disturbed most people never see them. Some of the most injurious species, such as the potato leafhopper, are fragile, wedge-shaped, pale-green insects only about one-eighth of an inch long when full grown, but they make up in numbers for their small size. The potato leafhopper is a serious pest of alfalfa, peanuts, and potatoes. Severe injury by other species to clover and to range grasses being grown for seed in connection with a regrassing program in Southwestern States has also been reported.

The potato leafhopper as a pest of alfalfa and peanuts may be profitably controlled by the use of a dust containing 66 percent of a fine dusting sulfur, 10 percent of pyrethrum powder, and 24 percent of an inert powder, such as pyrophillite, to improve its dusting quality. A single properly timed application of 25 pounds per acre is sufficient on any one cutting of alfalfa.

On peanuts, three applications of 15 to 20 pounds each, 3 weeks apart, are usually necessary.

Promising results from experiments against various species of leafhoppers have recently been obtained with some of the new insecticides such as DDT but definite recommendations for their use on grasses and legumes cannot yet be made.

A delay of 10 days or so in cutting the first crop of alfalfa, if the crop is not too much impaired thereby, often serves to keep down leafhoppers because by that time large numbers of migrating adults will have deposited their eggs in that crop. These eggs will be taken away in the hay and the young leafhoppers that hatch from them will die of starvation. In general, the best procedure when a legume crop is being damaged by leafhoppers is prompt, clean cutting. This drives out some of them, starves others, and removes the leafhopper eggs that have been laid in the stems.

Lygus Bugs

The damage done to alfalfa and other legumes by several species of sucking bugs of the genus Lygus was not generally recognized until recent years, although their extreme abundance in such crops had long been noticed. They greatly reduce both the vegetative growth and the seed yield of alfalfa, and some evidence has been obtained that they do the same to clover. These insects are pale-greenish to brown, flat, oval-shaped, soft-bodied, about one-fourth of an inch long and winged when full grown. With their long slender beaks they suck the sap from their host plants. Many species occur in different parts of the country with corresponding variations in habitats and host plants.

The species prevalent in the irrigated alfalfa fields of the Southwest can be fairly well controlled by thoroughly cleaning up alfalfa and weed hosts in winter, cutting the first crop of alfalfa at the same time in all fields throughout a whole community, and starting the seed crop in all fields on or about the same date throughout the community. This system prevents the lygus from moving back and forth among fields in different stages of growth, and thus starves them out. It has been successfully demonstrated in certain districts of Yuma County, Ariz.

Conditions in other regions are less favorable for the community application of uniform cultural control measures and it is thus necessary to resort to other means. Fortunately, the advent of DDT has supplied this need, at least so far as seed alfalfa is concerned. Good control of lygus and large increases in seed yields can be obtained by a single properly timed application of DDT dust; this method has been widely used by alfalfa seed growers in the Western States since 1945. A good general recommendation is a 10-percent DDT dust at the rate of 20 pounds per acre, applied by either power duster or airplane, just before the first flower buds begin to open. The residual effect of such a treatment keeps down the bugs sufficiently to allow a good crop of seed to develop beyond the stage where they can hurt it.

When thus applied, there is no danger of killing the wild and domestic bees that are essential to the pollination and seed setting of alfalfa, since they are not attracted into the treated fields until the blossoms open and, for one reason or another, are not killed by the DDT residues. Incidentally, the much more abundant bloom following the control of lygus makes excellent bee pasture.

The one bad feature of this method of control is the uncertainty relative to the hazard of feeding the threshings of seed alfalfa, or the hay if a treated field should be cut for hay, to livestock. Although there is no danger of acute poisoning, enough DDT may remain in the threshings or hay so that it will be secreted in the fatty tissues and milk of animals to which they are fed. Therefore, alfalfa that has been treated with DDT should not be fed to dairy animals or to meat animals that are being finished for slaughter.

Some of the other new insecticides have also shown promise for the control of lygus in experimental trials but more information is needed before they can be recommended.

Other Sucking Insects

Spittle bugs are little sucking insects with the queer habit of living in small masses, of white froth or spittle which they excrete around themselves during their immature stages as a protection against their natural enemies. They were unusually abundant on grasses, clover, and weeds in the Eastern and Lake States during 1946 and 1947. These insects look like leafhoppers and cause a withering of the infested stems and blasting of the seed heads. Suggested methods of control are early mowing, burning the dead grass in the infested fields during the dormant season, and frequent rotation from grass and clover to some other crop. Recent experiments by T. R. Chamberlin and J. T. Medler in Wisconsin have indicated the possibility of controlling the spittle bugs in legumes with one of the new insecticides.

Several species of sucking insects more or less resembling lygus in habits, if not in appearance, attack grass and legume crops in various parts of the country. Among these are certain shield-shaped green or brown stink bugs, and the long, narrow green or brown plant-bugs that are somewhat larger than lygus. These insects often seriously reduce the yields of grasses and legumes grown for seed and undoubtedly reduce hay yields as well. Methods for their control have received comparatively little attention. In general, the cultural and insecticidal measures already suggested for the control of lygus and spittle bugs are recommended.

White Grubs

Pasture and lawn grasses in the Eastern and Central States are subject to severe and extensive injury by white grubs. These are the thick, white worms, about an inch long when full grown, with bodies curled in a half-circle and brown heads and legs, that are often numerous in the soil under and around the roots of grasses. They feed on the underground portions of the plants and when very abundant sever the roots of large patches of grass so that the sod can be easily rolled up like a carpet. Certain species are among the worst pests of permanent bluegrass pastures and lawns. Undisturbed sodlands are particularly favorable to them because most species require 2 or 3 years to mature. (The Japanese beetle completes its life-cycle in a year.) White grubs also attack cultivated crops that are planted on plowed-up sod.

When full grown the grubs turn into the well-known large, brown to black, May beetles or "June bugs." The adult beetles fly mainly to trees and feed on the foliage, returning to the soil during the day to hide and lay their eggs. Grasslands are their favorite places for egg laying. Long-time records have shown that in certain areas heavy flights of the injurious species occur in only 1 out of every 3 years. Where the years when these flights may be expected are known it is recommended that as much of the farm as possible be put into cultivated crops and legumes during those years. The beetles do not lay many eggs in such crops and grub infestations are thus avoided. A rotation of oats or barley, clover, and corn has proved satisfactory in some sections. This should be timed so that the maximum acreage will be in clover and a minimum in grass or small grain during the years of beetle flight.

Late summer or early fall plowing of infested lands, and heavy pasturing of such lands with hogs and poultry, help to reduce infestations where these practices can be followed. Hogs like white grubs and will root for them vigorously. Fields should not be hog-pastured oftener than once in 3 years, however, because these animals may become infested with the thorn-headed worm, a parasite of swine which passes part of its life in white grubs.

A system of renewing badly infested hillside pastures has been developed in Wisconsin, based on the knowledge that both the adult beetles and the grubs are partial to grasses but do not like legumes. The sod is thoroughly torn up with a disk, spring-tooth harrow, or field cultivator during late fall and early spring, treated with lime and fertilizer in accordance with need as shown by soil tests, and sown in the spring with a seed mixture consisting mainly of legumes. These soon provide good pasture and are gradually replaced by the original bluegrass. A more detailed description of this system can be had from the Wisconsin Agricultural Experiment Station at Madison.

No insecticidal treatment for white grubs has yet been found practical on pasture and croplands, but lead arsenate has been widely and successfully used on lawns and golf links for control of the grubs of the Japanese beetle. This treatment is also effective against other white grubs, and is applied to the turf at the rate of 10 pounds per 1,000 square feet. To obtain an even distribution, the lead arsenate should be mixed with sand or dry soil at the rate of 1 pound of lead arsenate to 1 peck of the carrier. In establishing new turf on ruined lawns the treatment should be applied at the time the seedbed is prepared.

DDT has recently been found effective against Japanese beetle grubs. It it applied to the infested turf at the rate of 6 pounds of a 10-percent powder per 1,000 square feet. Whether or not this treatment will control other species of grubs has not yet been determined.

After application of either DDT or lead arsenate the grass should be well watered to wash the poison into the soil.

When lead arsenate or DDT is properly handled, spread, and washed or cultivated down there is no danger of poisoning wildlife or domestic animals. It must be remembered, however, that these materials are poisonous and should be handled accordingly.

Certain species of the wingless May beetles are sometimes prevalent and injure field crops in the South Central States. A poisoned bran bait similar to that used for cutworms and grasshoppers has been used successfully against the adult beetles. The bait is broadcast thinly in the infested fields at the time the adults are abundant. These wingless beetles have also been trapped successfully where they are migrating from one field to another, by the use of steep-sided furrows containing post holes as already described for use against armyworms.

Sod Webworms

Grasslands, especially lawns and golf greens, are sometimes seriously injured by sod webworms, mainly in dry seasons. These are lively little grayish, blackish, or spotted worms one-half to three-fourths inch long that web particles of soil and litter together to make small tubes at or just under the surface of the soil at the bases of the plants. They hide in these tubes and come out at night to cut off leaves or stems which they often pull back into their tunnels to eat. When full grown they change into small whitish or buff-colored moths with long snouts and narrow wings. The moths fold their wings closely against their bodies and hide in the grass during the day. When very abundant, they fly up almost in swarms and quickly light again as one walks through the grass.

The damage done to lawns and golf greens by webworms is not usually noticed until the worms are nearly mature and it is almost too late to apply control measures. Hence, a close watch should be kept for them in dry seasons and treatment applied promptly. Various insecticides are effective against them, one of the most practical being a lead arsenate spray. The application of 2 pounds of lead arsenate in 10 gallons of water per 100 square yards, left on the grass for 48 hours without watering, is recommended. This treatment will also control cutworms. Another spray that has given good results against webworms is composed of one-half ounce of dichloroethyl ether per 1 gallon of water, applied at the rate of 1 gallon per square yard.

Leaf-Cutting Ants

Several species of ants that are common in the Southwestern and South Central States cut off the foliage or seeds of almost any plants available including grasses and legumes, and carry these materials into their nests in the ground. The Texas leaf-cutting ant is especially interesting because it does not eat the bits of leaves and stems which it harvests but uses them as the medium on which to grow "fungus gardens" in certain galleries of its nests. This ant feeds only on a certain white fungus which it grows in these galleries. Both the red harvester ant and the mound-building prairie ant make a specialty of harvesting seeds which they store in their nests and use for food. The last two species can sting and bite.

Single colonies of these ants may be many feet across. Some nests of the Texas leaf-cutting ant cover as much as 4,500 square feet and extend to a depth of 15 to 18 feet. Aerial photographs of Arizona alfalfa fields badly infested by the red harvester ant showed that the circular bare spots around their nests occupied one-tenth or more of the area. More than 33 colonies have been counted on a single acre. Successful control of the leaf-cutting ant is especially difficult because of the many scattered entrances to their extensive nests, and because each colony may have several queens laying eggs in different parts of the nest. By thorough treatment at the right time of the year, however, the colonies can be completely killed. The red harvester and mound-building prairie ant nests are easier to kill out because each one has only one opening and one queen.

One of the best methods of control is fumigation of the nests with carbon disulfide. The best time of year to apply it is early in the spring as soon as the ants have become active. The procedures followed in applying the fumigant depend on various factors, including the species involved. For this reason they cannot be described in this brief article. Anyone interested should write to his State agricultural experiment station or this Department for details.

Another method of control found successful against the red harvester ant and mound-building prairie ant is the use of a thin ring of london purple about 4 inches in inner diameter and 1½ inches wide on the ground around the opening of each nest. The results of this treatment do not become apparent for several days. Although a less certain method than fumigation with carbon disulfide, it is much cheaper and easier to apply. At least three treatments 10 to 12 days apart, and sometimes more, are usually necessary. Paris green may be used instead of london purple with fair success but has not proved so satisfactory. Dusts containing DDT or Chlordane are also reported to be effective when applied in the same way. Details on the best strength to use are not yet available.

Any of these insecticides must be handled with care. Carbon disulfide is highly inflammable, even explosive, and london purple, paris green, DDT, and Chlordane are all poisonous. Stocks of these, as well as the empty cartons which contained them, must not be left where children or livestock have access to them.

Many other insect pests of grasses and legumes could be mentioned. Wireworms, jointworms, sawflies, stem borers, mites, three-cornered alfalfa hopper, green clover worm, lespedeza webworms, and others injure one or another of these crops in one area or another every year. Then there are the special problems caused by alien insects that become established in this country, such as the alfalfa snout beetle in western New York, white-fringed beetle in the Southeastern States, and Rhodesgrass scale in Texas. But space will not permit a discussion of all these. In general, one or more of the control measures already described may be found useful against them, depending on the insect and its habits. Something can usually be done to reduce the losses caused by most of them if infestations are discovered in time and the grower is willing to make the effort.

THE AUTHOR «« *C. M. Packard is an entomologist in the Bureau of Entomology and Plant Quarantine. He has been in the Division of Cereal and Forage Insect Investigations since 1913. Until 1937, when he was put in charge of that Division with headquarters in Washington, he worked from various field stations on the biology and control of cereal and forage insects.*

[*Further information on the hazards in growing grass is given in the articles on rodents, by E. R. Kalmbach, page 248; noxious plants, by Joseph F. Pechanec and others, page 256; and in the discussions of lawns, by Fred V. Grau and others, page 302.*]

Points to be Stressed

WHAT MAKES A NUTRITIOUS FORAGE?

J. T. SULLIVAN, H. L. WILKINS

THE NUTRITIVE value of forages is determined by the presence of substances that are necessary for the health, growth, and productiveness of animals.

Nutritional experiments, or feeding trials, have indicated what are the desirable amounts of many of these substances. A chemical analysis will determine the amounts present in a particular forage and should indicate how forage meets animal requirements.

The high food value of certain feeds is to be expected because of the abundance of such materials as proteins, or vitamins, or minerals. While chemical analysis and feeding trials do not always agree in measuring nutritive values, the chemical method is much more rapid and inexpensive and much of our information about forages is based upon it. This discussion is limited to such information.

The chemical composition of forage crops depends on the conditions under which they grow. Natural factors that have a bearing on the chemical composition and correspondingly on the nutritive value are the kind of plant, whether true grass, legume, or other species; climatic conditions; soil fertility; the weather preceding and during the harvest; the age of the plant at harvesttime; and the season of year.

Young clover, for example, averages higher in moisture, protein, and calcium, and lower in fiber than grass and therefore is considered more nutritive for some purposes. But young grass grown in fertile soil can contain large amounts of protein. And because grass is higher in carbohydrates, it is better adapted for fattening animals and for preservation in silage.

Mature forages show similar differences. Alfalfa hay contains 12 to 16 percent of protein (on the dry basis) and 1.0 to 1.7 percent of calcium; timothy hay contains only 6 to 10 percent of protein and only 0.25 to 0.35 percent of calcium. Mixed herbage has a composition intermediate between grasses and legumes, depending on their relative amounts.

Protein tends to be less in midsummer than in the spring or fall. Temperature, light intensity, length of day, and moisture also control plant development and consequently chemical composition. No one factor works alone. The farmer therefore will do well to keep in mind these natural factors when he considers the influences (such as crop management and soil fertility) that are at least partly within his control.

In early spring grass is relatively high in moisture and protein and relatively low in fiber. As the season advances, visible changes take place, such as heading and flowering, and at the same time chemical changes occur, such as great carbohydrate storage and also lignification.

When, however, the tops of plants are cut off by the grazing animal or by the mowing machine, these natural developments are interrupted. The plants are stimulated to produce new foliage from shoots near the surface of the ground. At first this new foliage, like young grass, is high in protein and low in fiber, but in time it becomes more and more like older grass.

When the grazing is heavy or frequent, the plants continually produce new shoots and the foliage remains young and of high nutritive value. Grazing also influences the relative amounts of grasses and legumes where they occur together and may be managed so that legumes will thrive, but overgrazing may encourage the influx of weeds. These practices naturally affect the chemical composition of the mixture.

In a grazing experiment at Beltsville, it was shown that the herbage under continually heavy grazing was more nutritious than under light grazing. With a rate of one steer per acre the herbage contained, on a 2-year average, 14.6 percent protein, 0.75 percent calcium, and 0.32 percent phosphorus. With a steer to 2 acres, the herbage contained only 13.0 percent protein, 0.58 percent calcium, and 0.30 percent phosphorus.

These differences were due partly to the stage of maturity of the grass and partly to the higher clover content of the heavily grazed plots. When Napiergrass in Hawaii was cut every 6 weeks it contained as a year-round average 7.9 percent protein, 0.46 percent calcium, 0.72 percent phosphorus, and 29 percent fiber. When cut every 14 weeks, however, it contained only 3.8 percent protein, 0.26 percent calcium, 0.46 percent phosphorus, and as much as 39 percent of fiber. The more frequent cutting promoted the more continuous production of younger and more nutritious shoots.

Soil fertility not only regulates the amount of crop growth but also influences quality. Soils of high fertility produce forages of high nutritive value and inferior soils often produce forages of known deficiencies. Essential mineral elements are obtained only from the soil and valuable nonmineral substances of plants, such as proteins and vitamins, are produced in quantity only when minerals are adequate.

Most of our knowledge about the effect of soils on plant composition comes from observing changes following the application of fertilizers. These changes are not easy to explain entirely, but the application of fertilizers to the soil has certain general results. It has been stated, "Any increase in the percentage of protein, phosphorus, or calcium that forage crops may contain as a result of fertilizer applications may be considered to be an improvement in the quality of these crops as livestock feeds." Most fertilizer applications do increase one or more of these constituents.

Fertilization affects chemical composition of herbage in two ways.

In one way fertilization may favor the growth of some plants rather than others. For example, clover responds more readily than grass to some mineral fertilizers and as clover becomes more abundant the protein and calcium of the mixed herbage increase.

In another way fertilizers affect the quality of herbage by changing the chemical composition of the individual plant. Plants take up any element present in soluble form in the soil and may take up more when more is present. For example, the application of a fertilizer containing nitrogen will increase the absorption of nitrogen by the roots and this results in an increase of plant protein. Phosphate fertilizers will likewise promote a greater uptake of phosphorus; potash will promote the uptake of potassium; and so on. Lime, which is a salt of calcium, may increase the uptake of calcium.

The response to fertilizers depends on the fertility of the soil and on the

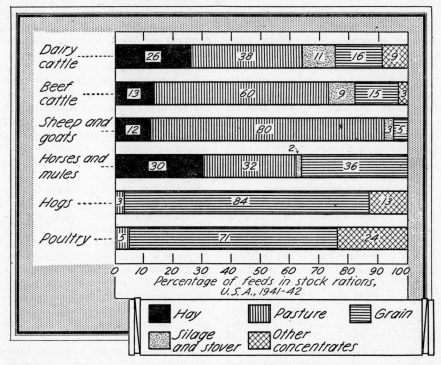

Percentage of various feeds in rations by classes of livestock, United States, 1941–42.

age and condition of the plant. If a soil is lacking in an element to such an extent that the growth of a plant is retarded, then the addition of that element should allow the plant to resume growth. For example, if a moderate amount of phosphate is applied to a phosphorus-deficient soil, some of the phosphorus will be taken up by the plants, which will thereupon make more rapid growth.

The percentage of phosphorus in the plant may not be any greater because the total dry matter will also increase. If larger doses of phosphate are applied, however, the percentage of phosphorus in the plant will rise, especially if some other factor becomes limiting and tends to retard plant growth.

The results obtained from fertilizers depend therefore in large part on the general fertility level of the soil.

Another point to be noted is that if growth is accelerated by any fertilizer the chemical composition of the plant changes because of the increase of new rapidly growing tissue. This may explain the increase of protein in grass after the addition of potash to a potash-low soil or the increase of carotene (provitamin A) after the application of ammonium sulfate.

The significance of age of the plant may be illustrated by saying that nitrogen applied to young pasture grass may increase yield or protein content or both. Applied to more mature grass, it will increase protein but is less likely to affect yield. When ammonium sulfate was applied to rather mature timothy in New Jersey 21 days before harvest, the protein of the hay was increased 50 percent over that in hay from an unfertilized area, but no yield benefit resulted.

Any effect of nitrogen fertilizer in increasing protein is usually apparent for a short time only. In Connecticut, when it was applied to bluegrass and bentgrass in the spring, only the first of successive monthly cuttings showed greater protein contents than those from unfertilized areas.

If high protein throughout the season is desired, the nitrogen must be applied frequently. In other cases, nitrogenous fertilizer has not affected protein percentage. In Ottawa, where fertilizers were applied to grasses in pure stands, a number of different fertilizer combinations had no effect on the protein content, but yields of dry matter were increased in most cases.

On peat soils of Florida, which contained ample amounts of nitrogen, nitrogen fertilization had no influence on yield or on the protein content of pasture grasses. Where other deficiencies occurred, fertilizer applications did affect composition. Potash fertilization doubled the yield and reduced the percentage of phosphorus in Dallisgrass. When both phosphates and potash were applied the percentage of phosphorus was raised.

Even though fertilizer experiments are carried out in a similar manner, the results do not always agree. In an experiment in Washington, nitrogenous fertilizers increased somewhat the protein of grasses growing on one type of soil but not that of the herbage on another type. It was not the soil type but its fertility that was important. Phosphate and potash fertilization increased the amounts of phosphorus and potassium, respectively, in the grass on both types of soils. When phosphate and potash were applied on mixed hays they indirectly increased the percentage of protein by increasing the proportions of clover.

Annual fertilization of a limed area of a Virginia pasture with superphosphate and either ammonium sulfate or nitrate of soda increased the average protein of a bluegrass and white clover mixture from 15.5 to 18.5 percent, digestible protein from 11.3 to 14.1 percent, and phosphorus from 0.25 to 0.43 percent. Fertilization had brought in more grass at the expense of weeds.

Phosphate and lime, with or without nitrates and potash, raised the protein, calcium, phosphorus, and potassium contents of West Virginia pastures. Under all the fertilizer treatments, Kentucky bluegrass and white clover came in to replace weeds and povertygrass. Nitrates increased protein in years when clover was light but did not affect it in the "clover" years. Carotene of mixed herbage in South Africa increased 28 percent as a result of monthly applications of sulfate of ammonia or nitrate of soda. Potash, also applied monthly, increased the carotene 6.2 percent.

The more commonly applied fertilizers, nitrates, ammonium sulfate, phosphates, and potash, and also lime, do promote an increase in one or more of the desirable major nutritive elements and thus may be said to increase forage quality. Soil applications also introduce minor elements such as manganese, copper, iron, and cobalt into the forage.

The effect of added fertilizers, however, has not always been detected by analysis of the forage. One experimenter fed fertilized grass to rabbits and observed better growth than with animals fed unfertilized grass. Chemical analysis had not revealed differences in the forage. Another investigator reported similar results in sheep grazing on fertilized lands.

We still cannot explain fully such observations, but there is no question that nutritive values are affected by cultural practices in ways we do not understand. Further research on soils, plants, and animals will uncover new and better methods of increasing the nutritive value of forages.

The question may be asked, What would be the nutritional significance of fertilizers applied in amounts beyond those economically profitable? We have no exact answer at present as to the effect of massive doses on nutritive values, but we may safely conjecture what may happen in some cases. More than 1 or 2 percent of nitrates in plants as a result of very heavy fertilization or of excessive amounts in soils is known to be poisonous to stock. Heavy nitrogenous fertilization of pastures may also increase other nitrogen compounds as well as proteins, and the former, in extreme amounts, may cause digestive disturbances.

Excessive quantities of certain other fertilizers may upset the mineral balance of animals. For example, too much potash may lower the calcium, magnesium, or sodium of the blood of animals to a dangerously low level. The cause of at least one disease, namely the so-called grass tetany, is suspected to be such an unbalance of minerals rather than a plain shortage in the diet. Excess lime also lowers the uptake by plants of certain soil elements necessary in nutrition, such as iron, copper, or manganese; some forages may become deficient in these minerals as a result. Further experimentation is needed before such questions can be answered.

THE AUTHORS≪≪ *J. T. Sullivan is a plant physiologist at the United States Regional Pasture Research Laboratory, State College, Pa.*

H. L. Wilkins is a chemist at the Agricultural Research Center at Beltsville. Both are members of the Division of Forage Crops and Diseases, Bureau of Plant Industry, Soils, and Agricultural Engineering.

MANURE AND GRASS-FARMING

FIRMAN E. BEAR, CARL B. BENDER

THE POSSIBLE savings in soil fertility in the best developed systems of livestock farming are such that they merit much more consideration than many farmers give them. If all the manure is carefully cared for and applied to the land, the losses of fertility constituents from the soil of a dairy farm are so small that they can be readily—and cheaply—made up.

Three important means of compensating for such losses exist: The growing of legumes, the purchase of extra feeds from which additional manure can be produced, and the supplemental use of fertilizers to balance the nutrient supplies in the soil.

Where large acreages of legumes are grown and feed purchases are high, the supplemental fertility needs can often be met by the use of liming materials and some form of phosphate. If the farmer is aiming for maximum efficiency in the use of his land, however, considerable amounts of complete fertilizer will be required to supplement the manure. This is especially true if the farm is located in an area where the climate naturally favors grasses.

When all factors, including protection against erosion losses and reduction in the rate of soil exhaustion, are taken into consideration, grassland agriculture is found to offer a unique opportunity for long-time, dependable profits. Some idea of the possible soil-fertility savings in such a system of farming is presented here.

An experiment at the New Jersey Dairy Research Farm at Sussex indicated a manure production of 21 tons a year for a 1,300-pound Holstein cow. Of this, 25 percent was urine and 75 percent feces. Each ton of the mixed excreta contained $9\frac{1}{2}$ pounds of nitrogen (N), 3 pounds of phosphoric acid (P_2O_5), and 8 of potash (K_2O).

It is apparent that the tonnage of manure from a dairy herd is large. But cow manure is a relatively dilute fertilizer that requires economy in handling. Unless its fertility is conserved and the handling costs are kept low, the profit potentialities from its use will be largely dissipated.

In this test 70 percent of the nitrogen in the feed, 63 percent of the phosphoric acid, and 86 percent of the potash were found in the manure. The unrecovered portion was contained in the milk and in the calf that was being formed. Such losses—or differences—can readily be compensated by the purchase of extra grain feeds. By that means, however, the fertility of a grassland farm can be built up only at the expense of a grain farm farther west.

But even for the farmer who feeds only what his own fields produce, the possible fertility economy in dairy farming is apparent. The 30-percent loss of nitrogen can be made up by growing legumes. The nitrogen of the harvested part of a clover crop is probably clear gain, the roots and stubble containing about as much of this element as the plant has taken from the soil. On this basis a 3-ton crop of clover or alfalfa hay, or its equivalent in pasture or silage, collects around 120 pounds of nitrogen from the air. Assuming a 70-percent recovery in the manure, this means a gain of 84 pounds of nitrogen per acre of clover grown and fed on the farm.

Manure is such a valuable and effective crop-producing agent that farmers can afford to put considerable effort and expense into protecting it against loss of its nutrient elements.

The first essential to this end is that all the urine be saved, either by the use of absorbent bedding or by draining it into a closed cistern.

A second need is to avoid loss of nitrogen as ammonia from stored manure. Such losses can be controlled by using superphosphate as an ammonia-absorbing agent and by keeping the mixed solid and liquid manures moist and well-compacted, as by the tramping of animals.

If possible, all manure, other than that in feeding sheds, should be hauled out daily and applied to the field. The most nearly ideal situation in getting the full value out of manure is found in grazed pastures, where the manure is dropped directly on the soil. The phenomenal growth of grass around spots where animals have urinated provides spectacular proof of the grass-growing powers of the liquid manure, much of which may be lost from stall-produced manure.

One of the important reasons why the grassland system of farming has come into such prominence as a conservation measure lies in the economy of fertility in grazed pastures. Under such conditions the loss of the fertilizing constituents, either by way of the drainage water or evaporation into the air, is reduced to the minimum. Since liberally manured grass provides a complete cover for the land, the principle of soil conservation is doubly met in such a system.

Both the solid and liquid droppings present problems in intensively managed pastures in that they make the surrounding grass unpalatable. The use of a harrow or some type of homemade drag is required to break the clumps of solid manure apart and scatter them about. Where labor is available, this work can often be readily done with a fork. The luxuriant growth of grass around the droppings necessitates the supplemental use of a mower. By this means the sward can be made much more uniform and attractive to the animals. Most of the dry grass clippings from around the droppings are consumed by the grazing livestock.

Standard practice in the use of superphosphate as an ammonia absorbent consists in scattering it over the floor and in the gutters behind the cows. If used only for reenforcing the phosphorus content of the manure, it can be applied over the spreader load before it is hauled to the field. The standard rate of application is about 50 pounds of the 20-percent grade of superphosphate per ton of manure. A 10-ton application of such phosphated cow manure, assuming that it contains the normal amount of bedding, will supply nearly as much N, P_2O_5, and K_2O as is found in 1,000 pounds of 10–15–10 fertilizer.

Horse and sheep manure are somewhat drier than cow manure and require less spreading. If such manures are stored, it may be necessary to add

Daily Record of Feed Consumed, Milk Produced, and Manure Excreted by 12 Dairy Cows, and Recovery of Fertility Constituents

Cow No.	Cow weight	Feed consumed			Milk produced	Manure produced	Recovery in manure			
		Silage	Hay	Grain			N	P_2O_5	K_2O	CaO
	Pounds	*Pounds*	*Pounds*	*Pounds*	*Pounds*	*Pounds*	*Percent*	*Percent*	*Percent*	*Percent*
1.............	1,407	51.5	6.5	14.0	42.6	116	76	46	84	64
2.............	1,322	47.2	5.4	16.0	60.1	97	70	67	83	64
3.............	1,259	56.3	6.0	10.0	33.0	115	72	69	97	73
4.............	1,291	54.0	7.0	14.0	44.6	106	72	64	90	69
5.............	1,270	58.0	6.0	16.0	49.5	114	66	58	82	66
6.............	1,223	56.0	7.0	14.0	40.1	141	68	58	95	65
7.............	1,415	52.0	7.0	14.0	36.9	118	72	70	80	64
8.............	1,334	48.6	5.7	16.0	54.0	105	66	54	74	53
9.............	1,293	60.0	6.0	10.0	31.1	114	73	73	91	68
10............	1,298	50.0	6.0	10.0	29.8	87	71	61	94	60
11............	1,261	51.7	7.0	14.0	42.3	116	69	65	78	65
12............	1,237	56.0	7.0	14.0	36.6	135	69	66	85	65
Average......	1,301	53.4	6.4	14.0	41.7	114	70	63	86	65

Proportions of Fertility Constituents in Urine and Feces of 12 Dairy Cows

Cow No.	Nitrogen (N)		Phosphoric acid (P_2O_5)		Potash (K_2O)		Lime (CaO)	
	Feces	Urine	Feces	Urine	Feces	Urine	Feces	Urine
	Percent	*Percent*	*Percent*	*Percent*	*Percent*	*Percent*	*Percent*	*Percent*
1................	52	48	99	1	21	79	99	1
2................	47	53	99	1	24	76	96	4
3................	52	48	99	1	20	80	97	3
4................	55	45	99	1	8	92	99	1
5................	53	47	98	2	9	91	99	1
6................	52	48	97	3	15	85	94	6
7................	49	51	99	1	34	66	99	1
8................	48	52	99	1	23	77	97	3
9................	44	56	98	2	11	89	97	3
10................	47	53	99	1	5	95	99	1
11................	51	49	98	2	10	90	99	1
12................	50	50	99	1	14	86	94	6
Average.......	50	50	99	1	16	84	97	3

Effectiveness of Superphosphate and Lime in Reducing Nitrogen Losses From Poultry Manure Under Natural and Artificial Drying [1]

NITROGEN LOSSES DURING NATURAL DRYING

Material used	Rate per ton	Test 1	Test 2	Test 3	Comments
	Pounds	*Percent*	*Percent*	*Percent*	
Superphosphate.....	200	2. 3	4. 6	6. 0	Conserved most nitrogen.
Quicklime..........	200	14. 9	13. 4	20. 2	{Reduced loss nitrogen. {Deodorized manure
Untreated..........	....	36. 9	16. 8	66. 2	High loss nitrogen.

NITROGEN LOSSES DURING ARTIFICIAL DRYING

			Test 4		
Superphosphate.....	200	....	48. 2	....	Reduced loss nitrogen.
Hydrated lime.......	275	....	35. 6	....	{Conserved most nitrogen. {Deodorized manure.
Untreated..........	....	....	75. 0	....	Very high loss nitrogen.

[1] In test 1, stored 20 days at 60° to 95° F.; in test 2, stored 20 days at 34° to 50°; in test 3, stored 60 days at 75°; in test 4, stored 40 days and then dried at 221°.

Water and Fertility Constituents in Undried and Oven-Dried Poultry Manure

Manure	Undried manure				Oven-dried manure		
	Water	N	P_2O_5	K_2O	N	P_2O_5	K_2O
	Percent	*Percent*	*Percent*	*Percent*	*Percent*	*Percent*	*Percent*
Laying hens:							
Fresh manure...........	77. 8	1. 05	0. 82	0. 51	4. 14	3. 70	2. 27
1 to 2 weeks old.........	66. 8	1. 41	1. 03	. 57	3. 02	3. 11	1. 73
Old litter manure........	47. 2	1. 83	1. 43	. 76	2. 50	2. 69	1. 43
Growing chicks:							
Fresh manure...........	74. 0	1. 64	. 94	. 64	5. 35	3. 57	2. 38
3 days old..............	66. 4	2. 87	1. 80	. 78	6. 50	5. 39	2. 33
Baby chicks:							
2 days old..............	63. 1	1. 72	1. 31	. 70	4. 45	3. 53	1. 89

Absorbing and Covering Capacities of Bedding Materials

Material	Absorptive capacity (in times its weight of water)	Covering capacity (in square feet to depth of 1 inch)
Shavings...	2 to 3	70
Peanut hulls..	3 to 3½	170
Sugar-cane residue..	3 to 4½	200
Straw..	2½ to 5	170
Peat moss..	10 to 11	200

water to prevent hot fermentation and consequent loss of ammonia. This water can be added as such or in the form of one of the wet manures, like those produced by cattle and hogs. Storage conditions are almost ideal in steer-feeding sheds where the steers are followed by hogs. Any horse or sheep manure that is available can be thrown into the feeding sheds where it is worked down by the hogs and compacted by the steers.

By reason of the harsh effects of cement floors on udders and feet, loose housing of dairy cows is now under study by State boards of health and may ultimately be widely adopted. The manure provides warmth in winter and increases the length of the effective life of the cow. The primary problem in such methods of handling the cows is that of providing plenty of bedding, so as to keep them clean. If such a system is put into effect, fertility losses from the manure will be greatly reduced.

A careful check was made of the manure production of 47 battery-fed White Leghorn hens over a 14-day period at the New Jersey Agricultural Experiment Station. During that period the hens consumed 136.1 pounds of feed and voided 259.6 pounds of manure. The production of manure amounted to nearly twice the weight of the feed consumed. The yearly production of 1,000 such hens would be about 72 tons.

Poultry manure presents a series of special problems, one of which is its marked tendency toward rapid decomposition and loss of ammonia. The ammonia losses occur both while the manure is fresh and while it is undergoing air drying.

One of the best means of preventing such losses is to apply hydrated lime to the fresh manure. Used at the rate of about 200 pounds per ton of wet manure, the lime stops the fermentation, serves as a disinfecting agent, and effectively deodorizes the manure. Hydrated lime is also being used to good effect in the loose litter on the floors of poultry houses. Here, again, it serves as a drying, disinfecting, and deodorizing agent.

Just as cattle, horse, and sheep manure is made into a better balanced fertilizer by the addition of superphosphate, so also is the effectiveness of hog and poultry manure increased by the supplemental use of potash.

Hog and poultry manures are largely the product of grain feeds and they lack potash, which the hays and bedding materials supply. The same applies to wet-sewage sludges, the potash in this case being lost in the runoff in the sewage-treatment process. When reenforced with 10 pounds of muriate of potash per ton, such sludges were found to be as effective fertilizers as fresh cow manure.

Plowing Manure Under

The manure of general livestock farms is most frequently applied on a sod in advance of plowing in preparation for the growing of corn. Applications of as much as 20 tons of superphosphate-reenforced cow manure per acre, or half that amount of potash-reenforced poultry manure, can be made to advantage in this manner.

The good effects of such manuring carry over several years, as evidenced by the better growth of the small-grain and legume-hay crops that normally follow the corn. In many cases, however, part of the manure can be used to better advantage on new clover seedings in small grains and on pastures. Similarly, reenforced manure is of great value as a late-fall or early-spring top dressing on hay lands, especially those that are largely covered with grasses.

Notwithstanding that most farmers have a deep appreciation of the value of alfalfa and the clovers as hay and pasture, at least 70 percent of the land that is devoted to such purposes in the northeastern dairy regions is covered with grasses. The reasons for this are found in the relatively cool, moist climate and in the natural acidity and low state of fertility of much of the soil. The grasses do not have as high fertility requirements as the clovers. Grasses are highly responsive to nitrogen and, for that reason, manure produces very marked effects on them.

But properly reenforced manure, applied at relatively low rates, also favors the clovers. Assuming that lime is applied to grass hay lands and pastures from time to time, the supplemental use of reenforced manure usually results in materially increasing their clover population. Thus, the manured grasslands produce better balanced hay and pastures than those that have not been so treated.

These same effects can be produced on both the grasses and clovers by the liberal use of well-balanced mineral fertilizers. Fertilizers have an advantage in that their composition can be altered to fit the variations in the need, and they are more easily applied. It usually develops that not enough manure is available to supply the entire soil needs of the dairy farm for optimum yields of the grain, silage, hay, and pasture crops. It is necessary, therefore, to develop a fertility program that involves the use of both manure and fertilizer.

Manured Grass

Horse, hog, sheep, and poultry manures can be liberally applied to pastures without reducing the palatability of the grasses and clovers to dairy cows. But cows tend to avoid grass that has been given an application of cattle manure. That being the case, it is necessary to consider carefully just how the manure on the dairy farm is to be used.

The order of preference is to apply it to the land in advance of plowing for corn, winter grains, or new seedings of grass-clover hay and pasture crops; as a top dressing for grass hays; as a light top dressing on new seedings of hay and pasture grasses; as a heavy top dressing on combination hay and pasture fields, the first cutting of which is

to be taken off for silage or hay; and as a light fall application on pastures.

Strawy manure is very troublesome in hayfields because the straw is often raked up with the first crop of the season. This difficulty can be overcome by putting the straw through a chopper before it is used for bedding. The chopped straw settles down to form a better mulch on the soil. It is also a better urine-absorbing agent and it is much more easily handled as bedding and as part of the manure that is hauled to the field.

Shavings, peanut hulls, peat moss, and sugarcane residues are the most important of the other bedding materials that are commonly used. These materials absorb from 2 to 10 times their weight of water, shavings being the least effective and peat moss the most effective absorbent.

Most of these bedding materials contain very little available nutrient material, except for the potash in straw and peanut hulls. Of the shavings, only those produced from the evergreens are ever troublesome in the soil. Thus, bad effects are sometimes noted from the use of pine shavings when applied at liberal rates to heavy soils, especially during wet seasons. As used in conjunction with manure, it is doubtful whether any such effects will be noted.

The widespread belief that shavings make the soil acid is without foundation. Pastures in acid-soil areas should be limed every 4 or 5 years, any acid effects from the manure being readily erased by this means.

Some dairy farmers are now growing bedding crops, of which reed canarygrass is one of the best examples. Others make use of hay that falls below classification grade. Fall harvesting of hay crops that were seeded in the small grains in the immediately preceding spring provides a considerable amount of straw that is discarded by the cattle, and this makes good bedding.

In many cases hauled-in bedding and hay bring large amounts of weed seed that are increasingly troublesome on dairy farms. The best means of getting rid of weed seeds is by putting the first hay and pasture crops of the season into the silo. The fermentation in the ensilage destroys the vitality of most of the seed, with the possible exception of a small percentage of those from bindweed.

Another way to eradicate weeds is to wait until time to reseed and then make use of one of the recently developed weed killers after the first crop of the season has been removed for hay. If this is followed by plowing and planting to corn and small grains, a large part of the weeds can be brought under control.

About 50 percent of the nitrogen, 1 percent of the phosphoric acid, and 84 percent of the potash excreted by dairy cows was found to be contained in the urine. Unless this urine is saved, fertility losses will be very great. Where bedding is scarce, some other method of saving the urine must be found. Some farmers have built storage cisterns and are making use of tank trucks, with spreading devices, by the use of which the urine is hauled to the field and spread. In any such storage of urine it is necessary to protect it from free access of air, because otherwise most of its nitrogen will be lost as ammonia. This means that the cistern must be kept tightly closed. Another way to protect the surface of the liquid is to keep it covered with a layer of mineral oil.

The fertilizing value of manure depends largely on the nitrogen and mineral-nutrient content of the feeds consumed by the animal that produced it. This ranges between wide limits, depending on the nature of the soil and the fertilizer treatments the feed crop has received. In an experiment with alfalfa that was grown on 20 different soils and through 8 successive harvests, the quantity of potassium in the harvested crop ranged from 0.51 to 2.89 percent of the dry weight. The greater the amount of available potassium in the soil the higher the potassium content of the crop. As potassium became deficient with the successive harvests, equivalent amounts of calcium (Ca) and magnesium (Mg) took its place. The sum of these three elements, calculated as their equivalents, remained practically constant. Liberal potassium treatment of crops results in the production of manure that has a high potassium-fertilizing value on the soil.

Minor Elements

Deficiencies of minor elements are becoming a major problem in many areas, especially on the rain-leached soils that occur in places in the Eastern and Southern States.

Such deficiencies were first noted on the sandy Coastal Plain soils, but, more recently, they have come into prominence in many of the areas farther inland.

Magnesium, which may be classed in this group, is known to be lacking in many soils, especially in those that have not been limed. But magnesium deficiency can readily be remedied by the use of manure from animals that have been fed either grains or legume hays, both of which are high in this element. Poultry manure has an especially high content of magnesium because the feed is made up largely of grain and concentrates, including bran, middlings, and cottonseed meal. About 90 percent of the magnesium in the feed of dairy cows is recovered in their manure, only about 10 percent of this being in the urine.

Evidence of the importance of poultry manure in relieving magnesium deficiencies was very apparent on sweetpotatoes in southern New Jersey in the summer of 1947. The leaves of the sweetpotato plants over large acreages were bright yellow, except for the dark-green veins, which are characteristic of magnesium deficiency. Where poultry manure had been applied no evidence of the yellow discoloration occurred.

Manure is of relatively little value in supplying boron, a second minor element that plays a highly important role in the production of the legume hay crops. Large acreages of land in the high-rainfall regions of the United States, especially that lying along the Coastal Plain, are deficient in this element. It is now standard practice to apply about 25 pounds of borax per acre broadcast at the time of seeding the legume hay and pasture crops. An additional 25 pounds of borax is applied in conjunction with the yearly manuring or fertilizing. Very marked increases in yield of legume hay and pasture crops and in seed production have resulted from such treatments.

THE AUTHORS≪≪ *Firman E. Bear is chairman of the soils department of the College of Agriculture and Experiment Station at Rutgers University. He is the author of a well-known textbook, Soils and Fertilizers, and is editor-in-chief of Soil Science, a technical journal in its field.*

Carl B. Bender is professor of dairy husbandry in the College of Agriculture and Experiment Station at Rutgers University. He is widely known for his contributions to the science and practice of grassland farming, with particular reference to the dairy cow.

Grass for Happier Living

SOD IS IDEAL FOR PLAYING FIELDS

FANNY-FERN DAVIS, GEORGE E. HARRINGTON

A SOD of perennial, relatively fine-leaved grasses is the ideal cover for school playground, recreational areas in parks, and athletic fields. Comfort, health, and beauty are the reasons.

The common alternatives to sod are bare soil, usually clay; cinders or gravel; and cement. The first is ubiquitous for no other reason than that the areas were planted originally to grass but the turf failed to tolerate the traffic of play. So, in rainy weather, the players slip in the mud and carry it into school and home; in dry weather, they fill their lungs and clothing with dust. This condition is particularly apt to exist on school playgrounds that were covered with subsoil when excavation for the building was made.

The roughness, the risk of skin injuries from falls, and the ugliness of the gravel or cinder surface speak against it, even as a rainy-day alternative for the turf field.

Often it is better for the health of the children and the health of the turf if a cement playground is available for use in wet weather. This keeps the children from getting wet feet as a result of playing in wet grass and prevents their tearing up soft wet turf and packing the clay soil on which the grass is growing, thereby permanently injuring the grass.

To establish and maintain a good, dense stand of grass on playing fields is difficult because the seasons in which the grasses should be growing into a tight sod are usually the ones when the areas are used most.

The abuse to which the turf on playing fields is subjected depends on the kinds of activities conducted on it and the time of year when play is heaviest.

Generally speaking, the larger the area the less the grass will be abused, particularly if the recreation director recognizes the importance of changing goal posts at intervals throughout the season or rotating the areas of hardest play in other ways to avoid bad scars.

The amount of hard use the turf will stand varies with the growing conditions (that is, soil and climate) and the species of grass used. The playgrounds connected with most schools must be built on the subsoil that was thrown out on the surrounding area at the time of excavation for the building. Subsoil usually consists of clay, the fine particles of which pack together tightly under heavy rains and traffic; thus the air spaces left in the soil, from which the roots must get air for respiration, are reduced. Packing also makes it extremely difficult for the grass roots to push their way into the soil to any considerable depth. If the roots do not penetrate, the plants will die when the surface soil in which the grass roots are growing becomes dry. Deep root growth is essential for any turf, particularly turf that is used hard.

Moreover, subsoil is usually low in plant-food elements, particularly in nitrogen and available phosphoric acid, both of which are essential to a satisfactory growth of grass. Regardless of its adaptation to prevailing climatic conditions, the grass cannot produce a satisfactory sod unless a sufficient supply of plant-food elements is available for growth.

Three problems must be solved if satisfactory turf is to be grown and maintained on playing fields:

First, the soil must be put into satisfactory condition before planting.

Second, a wise selection of the grass species to use must be made, consideration being given to climatic adaptation, planting season, planting method, and maintenance practices to be followed.

Third, the recreation director and grounds manager must cooperate to meet the requirements of the turf.

As for the soil, good drainage, both surface and subsurface, is one of the first essentials, both for players and grass. If satisfactory drainage is not obtained by natural means and grading, tile drainage should be installed before the final preparation of the seedbed. Usually a 4-inch agricultural tile, with a 6-inch tile for main lines, affords sufficient carry-off of the water. Athletic fields should be drained so that play can be resumed within 24 hours after a normal rainfall.

We mentioned compaction of heavy clay, which is sometimes so serious that no plants, not even the hardiest weeds, will grow. Air spaces are necessary between the soil particles, not only for the required circulation of air around the growing root tips, but also for an adequate movement of soil moisture both downward in drainage and upward through capillary action when the surface soil becomes dry. Therefore, when the soil is a heavy clay, coarser particles and organic matter should be disked into the top 4 or 6

inches. When grading operations are completed, 4 inches of topsoil should be added, if possible, to insure a satisfactory seedbed.

For a satisfactory soil, however, texture alone is not sufficient.

Adequate amounts of plant food must be present so that the grass seedlings or newly transplanted sod may be properly nourished. Nitrogen, phosphoric acid, and potash are the nutrients that the plants take from the soil in largest amounts.

Nitrogen, necessary for leaf production, is used by grasses in large amounts. If it is applied entirely in the form of inorganic fertilizers, leaching is inevitable; hence comparatively large quantities must be added to most soils.

Phosphoric acid, which encourages root growth and the production of flowers and seed, tends to be fixed where it is placed and does not leach down through the soil as does the available nitrogen. Therefore, in preparing a new area on poor soil for turf, it may be wise to place superphosphate 4 to 6 inches below the surface at the rate of 500 pounds to the acre before planting the grass in order to encourage root growth. This should be in addition to a balanced fertilizer which contains a relatively high percentage of nitrogen, such as 10–6–4, 8–6–2, or 8–6–4 grades, and which should be worked into the surface soil at the rate of 400 to 1,000 pounds to the acre along with the seed so that it is immediately available. The amount and grade of complete fertilizer required will depend on the fertility of the soil as indicated by soil tests, which can be made by State departments of agriculture or perhaps the county agent.

Most soils (except those in very sandy areas) have enough potash to satisfy the requirements of turf grasses, and little needs to be added in the form of fertilizer.

The possible necessity for lime also should be considered, particularly where the soil consists of heavy clay, but the applications to new seedbeds should be made only after soil tests have been made. Lime serves a dual purpose in the soil: It reduces acidity and it may improve texture by flocculating the finer soil particles, thus producing a more granular soil and improving the movement of soil moisture and air.

Choosing the Grass

Grasses for turf are not grown under conditions that normally occur in nature, but rather under unnatural conditions that cannot be tolerated by most of the many species of grass that are native to the United States. To produce sod, for instance, individual grass plants are not permitted to mature normally and produce flowers and seed. Instead, for a dense, uniform turf the individual grass plants, both roots and shoots, become so closely interwoven that individual plants cannot be discerned. Most bunchgrasses, those that do maintain their identity, are objectionable because they do not furnish a uniform or dense ground cover— and uniformity and density are two essentials of a good wear-resistant turf. This close interweaving of plants necessitates an abnormal competition for available food and water.

Moreover, throughout the season, large amounts of foliage are removed, although it is in the leaves that the carbohydrates, which must be returned to the roots for normal root growth, are produced. Yet roots should grow as deep as possible to tap the subsurface moisture when the few inches of surface soil become dry. In addition, flower and fruit production of grass is discouraged in favor of leaf production. It is therefore not surprising that not more than 30 or 40 of our native species will survive when grown as turf. The grasses that will survive under turf conditions are more or less limited in the climatic conditions they will tolerate. Consequently the correct selection of the species of grass may determine success or failure.

Some of the characteristics that should be sought in selecting a grass or grasses to be used on a playing field are:

It must develop a good root system in spite of almost constant defoliation throughout the growing season.

Its leaves should be erect, of a good color throughout the playing season, and reasonably fine in texture.

It should spread laterally and produce a dense, tough, wear-resistant ground cover either by the production of an interwoven mass of roots and rhizomes underneath the soil or an interwoven mass of stolons on the surface of the soil.

It should show a marked resistance to diseases and insect attacks.

All other conditions being equal, low-growing species and strains are more desirable than the tall strains because of reduced mowing costs.

The grasses that best meet these specifications differ in the various climatic regions. In cool, humid sections (the Northeastern, North Central, and Pacific Northwestern States), the most generally used mixtures contain high percentages of Kentucky bluegrass. In shady or cool, well-drained, or sandy areas, Chewings fescue or creeping red fescue does well. If a new area can be seeded in late summer or early fall, a seed mixture containing 85 to 90 percent of Kentucky bluegrass, 1 to 5 percent of colonial bent, and the remainder redtop, sown 100 to 120 pounds an acre, is usually satisfactory. On well-drained or sandy areas, the mixture can contain up to 50 percent of one of the fescues instead of an equal amount of Kentucky bluegrass.

When seeding must be done in spring, a higher percentage of nurse grasses, such as redtop, may be necessary. Lespedeza may be added to the grass-seed mixture; it will prevent erosion, reduce crabgrass invasion during the summer, and improve the soil. In late summer it can be removed by an application of 2,4–D; an additional seeding of the perennial grasses can be made immediately thereafter. In that way, the dying lespedeza and weed plants will prevent washing of the seed and may furnish some protection to the germinating seedlings.

For the southern half of the Eastern and Central States in the cool humid regions, the Zoysias offer a more wear-resistant turf. The two available species, *Zoysia matrella* (Manila grass) and *Zoysia japonica* (Korean lawn-grass) must be planted vegetatively because not enough seed is produced yet in this country for more than experimental purposes. The *Zoysia japonica* is more cold-resistant but considerably coarser than *Zoysia matrella,* which has a texture similar to blue-grass. Both produce dense, wear-resistant turf that requires a minimum of cutting because little upright growth is produced annually. The turf, once established, will thrive in soil of low fertility and it is relatively drought-resistant.

The Zoysias retain a good color in summer, when the bluegrass-fescue mixtures become semidormant. They are relatively slow to become established, however, and, being subtropical grasses, become dormant about the same time as Bermuda-grass and remain dormant till late April or early May, except in the Southern States.

On limited areas on which play is particularly heavy, the Zoysias could readily be established by sodding if space is available for a sod nursery. The purchase of sod to be used as such would be impractical at current high prices, but with a forward-looking program a sod nursery could be established for use the following year.

The United States Golf Association Green Section and several State experiment stations have directed attention to the values of Alta fescue for use on playing fields. It is naturally a tall-growing, tufted grass, about as coarse as *Zoysia japonica,* but it tends to form a "dense, well-knitted sod, free from clumps or bunches," according to the Green Section, and has real possibilities "where there is a premium on toughness, deep rooting, resistance to wear, and low cost maintenance." It has been grown from Canada to

Florida, is apparently immune to turf diseases, is naturally high in resistance to weed invasion, and tolerates wide extremes in temperature and soil moisture. At the Plant Industry Station at Beltsville, the best turf was produced when the grass was mowed at a 4-inch height. Seed is available commercially.

In the Southeastern States, in the warm humid region, Bermuda-grass still is probably the most widely used grass where wear-resistant turf is required. *Zoysia matrella* has possibilities as a more desirable and more wear-resistant turf producer, but even in the Southern States it takes more time than Bermuda-grass to make a dense sod.

Other possibilities for the South are centipedegrass for dry, sandy soils of low fertility; the Paraguay strain of Bahiagrass; and St. Augustinegrass, which thrives on a wide range of soil conditions if moisture is adequate.

In the more arid regions of the Western States, the buffalograss, which is a drought-resistant, low-growing, rapidly spreading grass, forms a tough sod and is therefore the most widely used grass for recreational areas unless irrigation is possible. Under irrigation, Kentucky bluegrass can be grown.

On the coast, in California, kikuyu, although coarse-leaved, has been used successfully because it is drought-resistant and crowds out Bermuda-grass.

Maintenance Problems

Once the turf is established, the constant vigilance of the grounds manager and the recreation director is needed to maintain it. Frequently the maintenance of good turf on playing fields is more difficult than its establishment.

Regular and frequent mowing is essential, even during seasons of nonuse. The top growth of grass is directly related to its root development. It is therefore advisable to set the mowers to cut at a height of 4 inches when the field is not in use and to bring the height down gradually to 2 inches as the playing season approaches. The grass should never be allowed to grow over 2 inches and preferably not more than 1 inch higher than the mower setting. Grasses do not make a dense sod if they are allowed to grow to a tall stage and then are cut short. Such a practice permits weed invasion and results in an open and loose covering that can be destroyed under heavy play.

A well-planned fertilizer program should be included in the maintenance plan. Depending on the grass used, the time of application is important. For the grasses adapted for southern regions a spring application is best. For the northern-adapted grasses, a fall application gives the best results.

Regardless of the most suitable time of application for the different grasses, an application of from 40 to 80 pounds of nitrogen to the acre in a well-balanced, complete fertilizer is a good practice. For example, a 10–6–4 fertilizer applied 400 to 800 pounds to the acre will supply the required nitrogen in addition to sufficient quantities of phosphorus and potash. Thirty percent of the total nitrogen content should be derived from an organic source. This will give a greater carryover effect to the fertilizer.

Applications of lime should be made only after soil samples have been taken and analyzed. The favorable pH range for most turf grasses is 5.5 to 7.5. Fertilizers are more effective at a pH range of 6.0 to 7.0. Dolomitic limestone is preferred to other types of limestone as it supplies not only available calcium but also magnesium, which is necessary for plant growth.

Sometimes grass growing on acid soil does not respond to an application of lime; in other cases, bluegrass growing in neutral soil has responded to lime. This is an indication that a turf test is the most satisfactory test for lime. Applications of lime to strips across the field at several rates, say, 1,000, 2,000, and 3,000 pounds to the acre, will show striking turf improvement within a few months if the lime is needed. If there is no improvement, the use of lime is not indicated.

After periods of heavy play, thought will have to be given to loosening the compacted soils if good plant growth is to be maintained. Several methods can be used to aerate and cultivate the soil beneath the grass without destroying the sod cover.

One way is to use a disk harrow, with the disks set straight. The sod is cut in opposite directions. But disking is not entirely satisfactory, as the slits made by the disks quickly close together and seal. A new aerifier, which shows promise for this type of operation, punches holes, 1 inch across and 5 inches deep, in the sod; the soil around each hole is loosened so there is better water penetration and a more economical use of phosphorus and potash fertilizers.

Athletic fields should be irrigated only during prolonged droughts or in dry sections of the country. Light waterings are more harmful than none at all because they stimulate shallow rooting and thus weaken the grass to such an extent that it will not survive the heat of summer. Irrigation, if any, should thoroughly wet the soil to a depth of 4 or 5 inches. The depth of the penetration of the water can be ascertained by removing a core of soil.

Weeds in turf can be controlled by products containing 2,4–D, which are effective against most turf weeds other than the weedy grasses and sedges. The arsenicals and dinitro compounds are perhaps the most effective against the weedy grasses and sedges, but must be used cautiously because they are apt to burn the turf grasses.

Good as they are, however, neither 2,4–D nor any of the other chemical weed killers can be considered panaceas for all ills: They are effective tools to be used with discretion in conjunction with good maintenance practices. Their wise use eradicates weeds from even the most severely infested turf, but only good maintenance will keep a turf dense and free of weeds.

Once a satisfactory turf of well-selected grass has been established, therefore, wise mowing programs, adequate applications of the fertilizers of proper grade for given soil conditions, the judicious use of lime and of weed killers, proper attention to soil conditions, and constant vigilance for diseases and grubs, chinch bugs, and other insects, all will contribute to keeping it dense, free of weeds, and wear-resistant.

THE AUTHORS≪≪ *Fanny-Fern Davis is turf consultant in the Horticulture and Maintenance Division of the National Capitol Parks, National Park Service, Department of the Interior. She received the degree of doctor of philosophy from the Graduate School of Botany of Washington University, located at the Missouri Botanical Garden in St. Louis. From 1938 to 1942 she was botanist, and from 1942 to 1945, acting director of the United States Golf Association Green Section.*

George E. Harrington is assistant director of the United States Golf Association Green Section. A graduate of the University of Maryland, he was a research assistant for the United States Golf Association Green Section for 2 years prior to the Second World War. During the war he served with the construction branch of the Army Air Forces as consultant on the establishment of turf at Army Air Forces stations.

POINTERS ON MAKING GOOD LAWNS

FRED V. GRAU, MARVIN H. FERGUSON

FOURTEEN steps are necessary in making a good lawn.

1. Before excavation is started for the house, the top 5 or 6 inches of soil should be pushed off to one side until the building and grading operations are completed. Afterward, the topsoil should be spread evenly over the surface of the lawn. Some topsoils may be little better than the subsoil, but in most cases it is worth saving.

2. Building debris—plaster, stones, trash—should be removed, not buried.

3. The subgrade should be sloped away from the house. Terraces should be avoided if possible; slopes should be gradual to the sidewalk. A gentle slope away from the house will carry off water and reduce the risk of a damp basement.

4. If, in grading and leveling, the surface is raised around shade trees, provision should be made to protect the trees. Shallow wells of brick or stonework should be built around the trunks of the trees to allow air to reach the roots. Deep layers of soil around the trunk of a tree may kill it.

5. In establishing the subgrade, special attention should be given to spots that are likely to be poorly drained. Sometimes tile may be necessary. The advice of competent authorities should be sought in putting in tile drains.

6. After the subgrade has been finished, about 75 pounds of lime (if soil tests show the need) and 25 pounds of superphosphate per 1,000 square feet should be harrowed or spaded into the subsoil to a depth of 3 or 4 inches. The lawn begins with the subsoil.

7. The topsoil should then be replaced and graded.

8. Lime, fertilizer, and other amendments, such as organic matter (peat, manure, compost, spent mushroom soil, and so on) should be incorporated into the topsoil before the finish grade is established. For many lawnmakers, cost and availability may determine the amounts. If one cannot get an analysis of degree of acidity from his county agent, State experiment station, or State department of agriculture, or if he does not test the soil himself with a soil test kit, a rough rule of thumb in the eastern half of the country is to apply 75 pounds of ground limestone on 1,000 square feet. Plenty

of balanced fertilizer is needed—say 25 to 50 pounds of a commercial fertilizer of 5–10–5 analysis.

9. The surface should be smoothed by raking and rolling.

10. Then seeding, sodding, or sprigging may be done, depending upon the type of grass to be used and the rapidity of cover desired. Because of its relatively high cost, sodding is recommended only when there is need for rapid completion of the job.

Hand sowing of seed is usually the most satisfactory method of securing a complete and uniform coverage on a small lawn. The seed may be diluted by mixing it with soil or fertilizer. It should be divided in two lots. One lot should be broadcast while walking lengthwise of the area and the other lot should be sown while walking at right angles to the direction of the first sowing. The seed should be covered lightly by raking.

11. Light rolling will press the seed gently into the soil where it will be encouraged to germinate in the shortest possible time.

12. Spreading a bale of straw or hay to 1,000 square feet on slopes will reduce erosion, conserve moisture, and facilitate establishment. It seldom is necessary to remove the mulch. Special types of netting also may be purchased to protect new seedings.

13. New seedings (or sod or sprigs) may be complete failures unless adequate moisture is available constantly during the period of establishment. Watering need only be light, but it must be frequent enough to avoid drying of the surface soil where the new tender rootlets are gaining a foothold.

14. Mowing should be started as soon as there is enough top growth to cut with the mower set at the proper height for the principal species of grass planted. Delayed mowing, so that the grass blades bend over and become matted, should be avoided.

There are 10 points to observe in keeping a lawn in good condition.

1. The lawn should be fertilized in the proper season—when the grass becomes thin or unthrifty. A commercial fertilizer of 5–10–5 (or similar) analysis is recommended. That means 5 percent nitrogen, 10 percent phosphoric acid, and 5 percent potash. A good standard is 20 pounds per 1,000 square feet. Because in some regions other types of fertilizers may be needed, it is wise to consult local and State authorities. In the cool humid regions, applications should be made in early fall and very early spring. In warm humid regions applications should be made in spring and early summer when the grass is growing actively. Fertilizer may be distributed by some of the fertilizer distributors on the market. Care must be used to prevent skipping and overlapping. Another good way is to broadcast the fertilizer by hand. If that method is used, the fertilizer should be divided into two lots. The first lot should be distributed while walking lengthwise of the area and the second lot should be broadcast while walking crosswise of the area, to insure a thorough and uniform coverage.

2. Soil tests are the basis upon which the need for lime should be determined. Generally speaking, soils in the eastern United States require lime.

Ground limestone is the cheapest form of lime. It is usually considered to be equal in value to other kinds.

Lime can be applied at any season— late fall or early spring are good times.

3. Frequent mowing with a sharp, properly adjusted mower will keep a lawn looking neat. Mowing also promotes tillering and spreading of the grass plants.

Height of mowing depends upon the dominant species of grass in the lawn. Stoloniferous (creeping or spreading) grasses—bent, Bermuda, Zoysia, centipede, St. Augustine—will withstand close mowing if they are kept fertilized. They may be kept mowed at ½ to 1 inch. The fescues, bluegrasses, and other grasses that do not produce stolons should be mowed at 1½ inches or higher.

4. Watering is the maintenance practice that is most often done incor-

rectly. The few rules are simple enough.

Do soak the ground thoroughly at infrequent intervals when the grass begins to suffer from drought. Water just often enough to keep the plants alive.

Do not sprinkle lightly every day "just to cool things off." Light sprinkling encourages shallow root systems and helps crabgrass more than it does the permanent grasses. It does more harm than good.

Many of the grasses of the cool humid region go through a dormant period in midsummer. If they are forced into active growth, the plants may actually be injured.

5. Rolling the lawn in the spring helps to firm the soil that has been loosened by the heaving action of frost. The ground should be moist, but not wet enough to "puddle" from the rolling operation. For the same reason, the roller must not be too heavy, or the soil will be compacted too tightly.

6. To keep weeds out, grow good grass—that is, proper management of the turf is the most important phase in the growing of a weed-free lawn. A good, healthy turf will not allow weeds to encroach. Any weed-control measure must be accompanied by appropriate fertilizer practices, and reseeding where necessary to fill in bare spaces.

Broadleaf weeds generally can be controlled by 2,4–D, which is sold under many trade names and in a number of forms. Manufacturer's directions should be observed strictly to avoid injury to shrubs or trees. Sprayers and other containers should be cleaned thoroughly after they have been used to apply 2,4–D; otherwise, plants sprayed subsequently with the equipment may be injured by the 2,4–D residue. In fact, it is wise to have two sets of spraying equipment; one for 2,4–D and one for other purposes.

Experiments to date have established that 2,4–D is not harmful to persons or animals, a point to be considered by those who have children and pets that play on the lawn.

Experimental work in controlling weeds has been done with a great many

other chemicals, arsenicals, chlorates, dinitro compounds, various petroleum fractions, and others. All have some value, but none of them (except lead arsenate) can be recommended without qualification. If they are to be used, workers at an experiment station or other authorities should be consulted. If used improperly the chemicals can be harmful to the grass and to the persons who handle them or come in contact with them.

Lead arsenate is a poisonous compound, but if one is careful he can use it with relative safety to himself, children, pets, and plants. It is effective against chickweed, Poa annua, and crabgrass in the more acid soils. In heavier soils high in lime and phosphorus its effects have been variable and repeated applications may be necessary. Lead arsenate should be applied at the rate of 20 pounds per 1,000 square feet. It may be applied at any time of year—fall is as good a time as any. Lead arsenate also is effective against most insects that live in the soil.

7. Insects most troublesome in lawns are beetle grubs, cutworms, armyworms, sod webworms, ants, chinch bugs, and mole crickets. Ticks and chiggers are not harmful to the lawn but they are a nuisance to the lawn owner and his children.

Most of the turf insects can be controlled by various DDT compounds. Ants, mole crickets, and chinch bugs are not readily controlled by DDT, but can be checked by the Chlordane products. These materials are sold under various trade names and in several forms. The manufacturers' directions should be followed. Advice about them can be had from county agents and State entomologists.

Most species of earthworms may be controlled by the use of lead arsenate at the rate of 20 pounds to 1,000 square feet. Lead arsenate is effective against grubs and other soil insects but it is not so economical as some of the newer insecticides. We mention earthworms because, although they are not insects and may not be pests, they might be numerous enough to make the lawn unsightly with their casts.

8. Disease control measures may be necessary on some specialized lawns. Bent lawns are susceptible to attacks of brownpatch and dollarspot.

Brownpatch may be checked by the use of Tersan. Dollarspot may be controlled by the use of mercury or cadmium compounds. These materials should be used according to the manufacturers' directions.

Most of the diseases attacking turf grasses are not easily controlled. Some new strains of grasses being developed at State and Federal experiment stations are resistant to disease. Your experiment station will be the source of information regarding the development of any new strains or species that may be adapted to your area.

9. Densely shaded areas under trees often present problems in the growing of a good turf. There are several reasons: Competition for nutrients and moisture by tree roots, the shading effect of the foliage, and the smothering of turf by fallen leaves.

There are ways to combat these difficulties. Deep placement of fertilizer around trees and heavy fertilizer applications on the turf may compensate for the scarcity of available plant food. The use of shade-tolerant species (the fescues and trivialis bluegrass in the cool humid regions, and the Zoysia grasses and St. Augustine in the warm humid regions) will overcome the shading effect. The prompt raking or sweeping of fallen leaves prevents any smothering effect which they might have. The grass should be forced into rapid growth during the period when the leaves are off the trees in order that strong turf will be established by the time trees begin growth in spring. If, despite good fertilization, grass will not grow in your shaded areas, ground covers like vinca, pachysandra, and thyme are sometimes used.

10. The growth of algae is a condition caused by standing water on the surface of the soil. Improving the drainage so that water may be removed from the soil and loosening the soil to provide conditions favorable for grass will eliminate the condition.

Slime molds are organisms that cause gray, unsightly patches in lawns during wet seasons. These primitive fungi are not harmful to the grass and may be brushed off the grass blades when it is dry. The fruiting bodies of the fungi may give off a "smoke" or "dust" of spores when disturbed.

Renovating the Lawn

To renovate a lawn:

Mow the old stand of grass closely.

Apply weed-control materials if necessary.

Rake severely or cultivate with a hand disk or spiker to loosen surface soil.

Apply fertilizer and lime as needed.

Seed, sod, or sprig.

Roll.

If the ground is bare, apply mulch on slopes.

Water.

Mow as soon as there is enough growth.

Renovation becomes necessary when the turf is wholly undesirable and when replanting to the same or to a different grass is contemplated.

It is essential first to determine the reason for the unsatisfactory turf and to plan a program that will correct the previous deficiencies. Unless all the factors for satisfactory plant growth are favorable, the turf will become unsatisfactory again in a year or so. The details of the renovation program will depend largely upon the conditions that must be corrected or modified. It is best to seek expert advice when planning renovation.

Destruction of all unwanted growth usually is the first step. To accomplish this it is best to mow closely and remove the clippings. The use of strong chemicals to kill weeds is justified in a renovation program.

Selectivity is secondary because the area is to be replanted and the loss of some desirable grass is not likely to be serious. Sodium arsenite is favored by many greenkeeping superintendents for the renovation of turf because planting can be accomplished very soon after its use. No general recommendations for any chemical can be made here—it is impossible on a subject like this to give suggestions that will hold good for the whole country. Always seek the advice of your county agent, extension specialist, experiment station, the greenkeeper near you, or the manufacturer or dealer of the product you plan to use.

Preparation of a seedbed is essential to a successful job of replanting the area. Lime (if needed) and fertilizer should be well incorporated by raking or spiking. Other operations follow in logical order and may be the same as for building the lawn.

Grasses for Lawns

In choosing a grass for his lawn, the owner usually has the choice of selecting a grass that will thrive under existing conditions or of selecting the grass that he wants and then modifying the conditions to meet the requirements of that grass.

Grasses suitable for lawns in the cool humid region are: Kentucky bluegrass, red fescue, Alta fescue, bentgrass, redtop, ryegrass, and *Zoysia japonica*.

Grasses suitable for lawns in the warm humid region are: Bermuda, centipede, carpetgrass, St. Augustinegrass, and the *Zoysia* species.

In the dry-land area, buffalograss and the grama grasses are suitable on nonirrigated areas. Crested wheatgrass (Fairway strain) is used in the Northern Great Plains. Where irrigation is practiced, Kentucky bluegrass and bentgrass do well in the cooler areas and Bermuda-grass in the warmer sections.

Generally recommended seeding rates are: Bermuda-grass, carpetgrass, and the bentgrasses, 4 ounces to 1,000 square feet; buffalograss, 12 ounces to 1,000 square feet; the grama grasses, 1 pound to 1,000 square feet; Kentucky bluegrass, red fescues, Alta fescue, redtop, the ryegrasses, and crested wheatgrass (Fairway strain), 2 pounds to 1,000 square feet.

Requirements

Grasses for which no seed is available and which must be planted vegetatively are centipedegrass, St. Augustinegrass, and the Zoysias. Selected strains of Bermuda-grass must also be planted vegetatively because no seed is available.

Grasses that require a well-drained soil are Kentucky bluegrass, red fescue, Bermuda, centipede, grama, buffalo, and crested wheat. Those more tolerant of poorly drained soils are bentgrass, the Zoysias, carpetgrass, and St. Augustinegrass.

Grasses that require a relatively high level of fertility are Kentucky bluegrass, Bermuda, and bent. Those tolerant of lower levels of fertility are red fescues, the Zoysias, carpetgrass centipedegrass, St. Augustinegrass, grama, buffalograss, and crested wheatgrass.

The grasses that do well in shade are red fescue, St. Augustine, and the Zoysias. Grasses that require more sunlight are bent and centipede. Those that have a high sunlight requirement are the Kentucky bluegrass, Bermuda-grass, carpetgrass, grama, the buffalo-grass, and crested wheatgrass.

Grasses that need a large amount of moisture are Kentucky bluegrass, bent, carpetgrass, and St. Augustinegrass. Drought-tolerant grasses are red fescue, the Zoysias, Bermuda, and centipede. Grasses that are extremely drought-hardy are the gramas, buffalo-grass, and crested wheatgrass.

Bentgrass should be mowed to one-half inch or less. The Zoysias, Bermuda, carpet, centipede, and St. Augustine should be cut at one-half inch or 1 inch. Kentucky bluegrass, red fescue, grama, buffalo, and crested wheatgrass should be cut 1½ inches or higher.

THE AUTHORS≪≪ *Fred V. Grau is director of the United States Golf Association Green Section and chairman of the Turf Committee of the American Society of Agronomy. He was reared on a farm in Douglas County, Nebr., and has degrees in agriculture from the University of Nebraska and the University of Maryland. Dr. Grau was extension agronomist at Pennsylvania State College from 1935 to 1945, with the exception of 1 year, when he was an agronomist*

in the War Department in Washington.

Marvin H. Ferguson was born in Texas and was graduated from Texas Agricultural and Mechanical College. He has been in turf work since 1940 except for a 2-year period of service with the Navy. He was formerly assistant agronomist with the Division of Forage Crops and Diseases, Bureau of Plant Industry, Soils, and Agricultural Engineering, and now is agronomist with the United States Golf Association Green Section.

GREENSWARDS IN THE COOLER REGIONS

H. B. MUSSER, J. A. DE FRANCE

THE GRASSES best adapted to make permanent turf for home lawns, parks, and cemeteries in the cool humid region (primarily the Northeastern and North Central States and also Washington, western Oregon, and northwestern California) fall into three general groups—bluegrasses, fescues, and bentgrasses. White clover is widely used in combination with these grasses for general lawn purposes. A fourth group of miscellaneous species has a limited value for general turf and may be used for temporary cover or under special conditions. The ryegrasses are the most important of this group.

Three species of the bluegrasses generally used for lawn turf in temperate, humid climates are Kentucky bluegrass, roughstalk bluegrass, and Canada bluegrass. Each has particular characteristics that adapt it for the production of good turf under special conditions.

Kentucky bluegrass is the most popular and widely used because it spreads rapidly and produces a dense sod of pleasing quality and appearance. It requires a fertile soil only slightly acid to neutral in reaction and grows best in cool moist weather, but it will not produce good turf in shade.

Rough-stalked bluegrass, with the same general soil and moisture requirements, is much less tolerant of drought and high temperatures, and its particular value for lawn use is in its high shade tolerance.

Canada bluegrass, however, has a wide tolerance for drought and low soil fertility. Although it spreads rapidly, Canada bluegrass forms an open, stemmy sod because of relatively sparse leaf development. Its use for lawns is limited therefore to mixtures for extensive areas where turf requirements do not justify the expense of soil modifications needed for the better turf-forming species.

The fescue species adapted to general lawn use have a wide tolerance of soil fertility and acidity conditions, will grow well in shade, and are persistent at high temperature and low moisture levels. They are not adapted to close clipping, poor drainage, and high temperatures accompanied by high humidity.

Creeping red fescue and Chewings fescue are the most important varieties. Both are in wide use, alone and in mixtures, for general turf purposes, particularly in the cooler sections of the region, where they grow best. The principal difference between the two species is that the creeping red has well developed, underground creeping stems that enable it to spread more

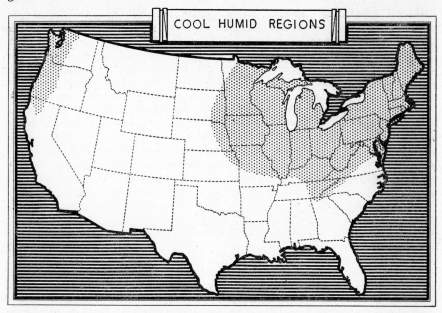

COOL HUMID REGIONS

The shaded areas are the ones where bluegrass, fescue, and bent species are best adapted for permanent turf; ryegrass leads those of limited value for general turf.

rapidly and heal more quickly than the Chewings variety.

A third member of this group is meadow fescue. Several selections of this species distributed under the names of "tall" and "Alta" fescue have a limited adaptation for parks, cemeteries, and home lawns. Its particular value as a lawn grass is in mixtures to establish quick cover in shade until slower growing permanent species develop.

The fine-leaved fescue, sheep fescue, hard fescue, and various-leaved fescue are typical bunchgrasses, but because of the inferior quality of their turf they are useful mainly for rough cover that will survive under the minimum of care.

Four species of bentgrasses—creeping bent, colonial bent, velvet bent, and redtop—have value for general turf use in the cool humid region. All have a wide range of tolerance to soil acidity and will persist under relatively poor drainage conditions. The velvet bent and redtop are highly drought-resistant, and velvet bent is somewhat

shade tolerant. Redtop is used primarily as a temporary grass in lawn mixtures for quick cover; it is short-lived under close clipping; the other species of the group are well adapted to clipping heights of three-sixteenths of an inch or less.

The bentgrasses, except redtop, produce the finest quality turf of all species adapted to the region, provided they receive adequate maintenance—frequent close clipping, periodic fertilization during the growing season, liberal moisture applications, yearly top dressing, and disease-control treatments. Because of the trouble and expense for proper maintenance of pure stands, bentgrasses are best suited for mixtures for general turf purposes on home lawns, parks, and cemeteries.

White clover is recommended for use with the permanent grasses for all types of lawn turf except where the sod is subject to hard wear. It spreads by creeping surface stems and does not compete too seriously with the grasses if liberal applications of nitrogenous fertilizers are used. Soil fertility, reaction, and moisture levels favorable for Kentucky bluegrass also are suitable for white clover.

Of the miscellaneous group, perennial ryegrass and Italian ryegrass are the two most useful for temporary lawn turf. Mixtures of the two species in various percentages are often sold under the name of domestic ryegrass. Both have the same general soil and climatic adaptations and growth habits, but Italian ryegrass is shorter lived and therefore more desirable in mixtures providing temporary cover until the permanent species become established. Because of their rapid growth rate, both species are well adapted for areas where a sod cover is required for only 1 or 2 years. They produce a brilliant-green turf of pleasing appearance at normal lawn clipping heights of 1 to 1½ inches.

Other species of the miscellaneous group, timothy, orchardgrass, tall oatgrass, and bromegrass may have a limited value under certain conditions. They are sometimes economical, considering costs and availability, for temporary cover or for use on outlying areas of parks, cemeteries, or estates where the chief requirement is cover for erosion and weed control, and where maintenance at normal lawn turf levels is not a factor.

Seed mixtures are designed for areas where growing conditions are so variable that a single species of grass will not meet all requirements. Thus, mixtures are used where locations are partially shaded, have poorly drained or droughty areas, or where variations in soil reaction, fertility, and physical condition cannot be economically adjusted to assure good turf establishment with a single species. Because of the slow rate of establishment of the bluegrasses and the fescues, individual species of these groups are usually seeded in mixtures with a temporary grass that can provide a quick cover for protection at the start against erosion and infestation of weeds.

The percentages of the various grasses in a mixture are adjusted in accordance with quality, purity, germination, relative growth rate, and number of seeds per pound for each species. Many formulae, varying widely in the kinds and quantities of permanent and temporary species, have been suggested as a basis for mixtures for general lawn turf.

It has been demonstrated repeatedly that the ultimate turf population resulting from a seed mixture depends to a greater extent upon the soil and climatic environment than upon the relative quantities of each species in the mixture. The best mixture is that which contains species best adapted to the particular location, in quantities sufficient to provide permanent turf at normal seeding rates. Because of the more rapid growth rates of the temporary grasses, it is generally accepted that they will seriously retard development of the permanent species when present in quantities exceeding one-fifth of the total.

Good seedbed preparation is basic to the successful establishment of lawn turf. Tillage operations should provide well-aerated soil to a minimum depth of 4 inches, but the seedbed must be firm because the small seeds of most grass species must be in close contact with the soil particles for good germination. Adequate provision also should be made, wherever practicable, to improve drainage on wet areas.

Soil modifications for establishment of lawn turf in the cool humid region include the use of peat and similar organic materials for improvement of physical condition, adjustment of soil reaction, and addition of fertilizing materials. The extent of such soil modifications will be governed by the area to be turfed and the requirements of the grass species used.

Under average conditions of soil fertility the grasses show a marked response to nitrogen fertilizers. Certain species, notably Kentucky bluegrass and white clover, also require liberal quantities of phosphorus and potash.

Time and rate of seeding are important factors in turf establishment. Under temperate climatic conditions seedings may be made either in early fall or in the spring. Generally the former is more desirable because the seedling grasses develop better during the cool, moist weather and are not subject to summer heat, drought, and weed competition before they are mature.

Rates of seeding must be adjusted to the species or mixture used. Individual grasses vary greatly in seed size, normal purity, and germination. The bentgrasses average about 6 million seeds per pound, with purity and germination normally above 90 percent; bluegrasses, from 2 to 2½ million seeds per pound, with an average purity and germination of 85 percent; fescues, from 600,000 to 700,000 seeds per pound, with an average purity above 90 percent and germination 85 percent; and the ryegrasses, about 225,000 seeds per pound, with approximately 95 percent purity and germination.

New seedings frequently require protection to prevent loss by drought and erosion, particularly when plantings are made in late spring or on terraces and slopes. Straw and many similar materials are adapted for use as mulches. Burlap and other types of coarse cloth are also satisfactory.

Maintenance

Maintenance of good turf in the cool humid region involves adjustment of the soil reaction by lime and fertilizer applications based on the growth requirements of the turf. A complete fertilizer is used where treatments are made in a single annual application, the ratio of nitrogen, phosphorus, and potash being adjusted to soil and turf conditions. When long periods of drought occur, irrigation is necessary, particularly for the bentgrasses that have relatively high moisture requirements. It is seldom necessary under normal seasonal conditions to water the bluegrasses and fescues unless it is essential that they be kept green and in an active growing condition.

Frequency of clipping and height of cut must be adjusted to the needs of the grasses. The bentgrasses thrive under frequent clipping at a height of one-half inch or less; turf that is composed principally of bluegrass and fescues is seriously injured when it is regularly clipped to heights of less than 1¼ to 1½ inches.

The use of selective herbicides for destruction of weeds has been highly successful as a part of turf renovation. The most important herbicides are 2,4-dichlorophenoxyacetic acid (2,4-D), dinitro compounds, and some of the arsenicals—arsenic acid and sodium arsenite.

Extensive experiments have shown that the various formulations of 2,4-D are specific for most of the broad-leaved weeds that commonly infest lawn turf (dandelion, buckhorn, broad-leaf plantain, and others). Crabgrass and other annual summer grasses are controlled by application of dinitro and arsenical herbicides at the seedling stage of the grass.

Besides weed eradication, a turf-renovation program includes correction of soil deficiencies by treatment with lime and fertilizer, improvement of drainage and physical conditions when necessary, and reseeding after appropriate soil preparation.

THE AUTHORS《《← *H. B. Musser is professor of agronomy in Pennsylvania State College. Born in Williamsport, Pa., he was educated at Bucknell University and the Pennsylvania State College. In the First World War he was a chief petty officer in the Naval Aviation Reserve. In the Second World War, as a lieutenant colonel in the Army Air Forces, he supervised the control of dust and erosion on Army airfields.*

J. A. DeFrance is associate research professor of agronomy and landscape gardening at the Rhode Island Agricultural Experiment Station. A native of Colorado, Dr. DeFrance holds degrees from the Colorado State College and Cornell University, and has taught in both institutions.

GREENSWARDS IN THE WARMER REGIONS

G. W. BURTON, D. G. STURKIE

THE TRADITIONAL barren yard, swept clean of all vegetation for generations, is rapidly disappearing in the South. Here, as elsewhere, people are recognizing that a beautiful lawn helps to make a house a home. It adds to the beauty of the landscaping, brings satisfying relaxation and comfort to the family, and increases the material value of the home. Without grass, parks lose their appeal, and cemeteries become drab, indeed.

Beautiful lawns can be grown in the warm, humid region of the United States. Success depends on the use and proper maintenance of grasses adapted to the environment. Often the environment must be altered by the application of fertilizer, by watering, or by the removal of dense shade. Changing the environment in this manner permits a wider choice of lawn plants. Heavy fertilization with nitrogenous materials will, for example, permit the growth of Bermuda-grass on poor soils where only carpetgrass and weeds would naturally grow. Generally, however, the best lawns are obtained when grasses are used that most nearly fit the natural environment.

The wise man will think of the grass as he chooses the site for a lawn, park, or cemetery.

Grass requires a fairly uniform supply of water throughout its growing season and can be grown with the least expense and effort on soils that tend to be moist.

If excavations are made for basements, the top soil should be stripped and set aside to be used later in covering the rough grade. If the subsoil is not needed to establish a desired grade, it should be removed from the lot.

All piles of building refuse, such as plaster and brick, should be removed. Good turf will not grow upon them even if they are covered with top soil.

Steep slopes should be avoided in the grading operation because it is hard to establish and maintain a good sod on them. The surface of the lawn should be smooth and sloped slightly away from the house to provide for surface drainage.

On the drier sites the lawn should be piped to facilitate watering if needed.

Extremely wet soils should be tile-drained if Bermuda-grass is to be grown. Carpetgrass will grow on them without drainage, but many species of shrubbery used in border and foundation plantings will not.

Trees compete with lawn grasses for light, moisture, and plant food, and it is often difficult and costly to grow grasses in association with them. Sometimes it is desirable to reduce the number of trees—best to do it before the grass is planted.

Lime, thoroughly incorporated in the heavier soils, generally improves their moisture-holding properties and favors the growth of the grass. A measurement of the acidity and lime requirements of the soil, which can usually be had from county agents and State experiment stations, will help in determining the need for lime.

Soils in the warm humid region are generally too low in plant food to grow good grass. Consequently a complete fertilizer, such as a 4–8–6, 5–10–5, or 4–12–4, should be worked into the top soil at a rate of 25 pounds per thousand square feet.

A good rule to follow in building the lawn is to prepare all the soil as if it were to be a flower bed. Pennies spent in such preparation will grow to dollars in savings in maintenance costs.

A lawn grass that will remain green the year around in the warm humid region is yet to be found. The nearest approach to this ideal is made by planting a summer grass that is adapted to the environment and seeding domestic ryegrass with it each fall to give a green cover after frost has turned the summer grass brown.

Principal Lawn Grasses for the Warm Humid Region

Species	Region where adapted	Shade tolerance	Soil-fertility requirement	Soil preference	Method of propagation	Period when green	Care required for satisfactory turf
Bermuda-grass	Throughout the region.	Poor	High	Well-drained medium heavy soils.	Seed (2 pounds per 1,000 square feet) or sprigs.	Spring, summer, and fall.	Medium to much.
Carpetgrass	South of Augusta and Birmingham.	Medium	Low	Wet sandy soils.	...do...	...do...	Little.
St. Augustinegrass	...do...	Very good	High	Sandy loam soils.	Sprigs.	...do...	Much.
Centipedegrass	South of Tennessee.	Medium	Low	Little preference shown.	...do...	...do...	Very little.
Manilagrass	Throughout the region.	Very good	High	Well-drained heavy soils.	...do...	...do...	Much.
Kentucky bluegrass	Tennessee north; in shade, south as far as Birmingham.	Good	...do...	Well-drained soils.	Seed (3 pounds per 1,000 square feet).	Varies with the region.	Medium to much.
Domestic ryegrass	Throughout region.	Very good	...do...	Well-drained heavy soils.	Seed (4 pounds per 1,000 square feet.)	Winter.	Much.

Much care and judgment should be exercised in the choice of the grass. An effort should first be made to choose a grass that will fit the environment. Bermuda-grass, for example, will never make a satisfactory lawn in the shade of trees. Carpetgrass will winterkill in Kentucky. Kentucky bluegrass will fail to grow in summer in the carpetgrass belt. Grasses having a low soil fertility requirement, such as centipede and carpetgrass, will make a good lawn on poor soils with less trouble and expense than Bermuda-grass, which has a high soil fertility requirement. The use of these poor-land grasses in park and cemetery plantings can result in a sizable reduction in the fertilizer bill.

The busy home owner who must neglect his lawn will do well to choose a grass like centipede that makes a satisfactory turf with a minimum of mowing and care. Centipedegrass should not be planted on farm lawns, however, because it may get into pastures and destroy their grazing value.

For seedings, weed-free seed of high germination should be purchased. Hulled Bermuda-grass seed, which germinates faster than unhulled seed, gives best results.

All grass seeds should be uniformly broadcast at the rates indicated in the table and should be raked lightly into the soil. The soil should then be kept moist by artificial watering when necessary until the seedling plants are well established. Frequent mowing will help to control the weeds and will aid the establishment of the seedlings.

It is often easier to establish Bermuda-grass and carpetgrass from sprigs or stolons than from seed. Centipedegrass, St. Augustinegrass, and the Zoysia grasses must be propagated in that way, because there are no commercial seed sources of them. In planting grass sprigs, the roots and a part of the sprig should be placed as deeply in the soil as possible; the tip inch or two of the sprig should be left protruding above the surface of the soil. Furrows may be opened, or a small garden shovel can be used to open a hole in which to place individual sprigs. After the sprigs are planted, the soil should be firmed around them and kept moist until they are well rooted. For rapid coverage, sprigs should be placed 6 to 12 inches apart in rows 12 inches apart. The Zoysia grasses spread so slowly that it is not advisable to set them farther apart. Carpet, Bermuda, St. Augustinegrass, and centipedegrass sprigs spread much faster, and may be set 2 to 3 feet apart in each direction for coverage in one or two growing seasons.

If they are adequately watered during dry periods, the summer grasses can be planted successfully throughout the spring and summer months, but generally spring plantings are most successful. The winter grasses, such as domestic ryegrass, should be seeded in early fall.

Maintenance

Perhaps the most important maintenance requirement and certainly the one most frequently neglected is adequate fertilization.

If the lawn received a good application of complete fertilizer when it was established and if the clippings are left on the lawn, nitrogen becomes the element most needed for satisfactory growth of the grass. Nitrogen improves the color, greatly stimulates the growth, and enables the grass to choke out competing weeds. Many nitrogen fertilizers are available, but nitrate of soda, cyanamid, and cottonseed meal are among the easiest to use. From 2 to 4 pounds per 1,000 square feet of nitrate of soda or granular cyanamid may be uniformly broadcast like seed over the lawn. These materials should be applied when the grass is dry and should be watered in to prevent burning of the foliage. Five to ten pounds of cottonseed meal per 1,000 square feet supplies the same amount of nitrogen and will not burn the grass. These materials should be applied only when needed to thicken the sod and improve

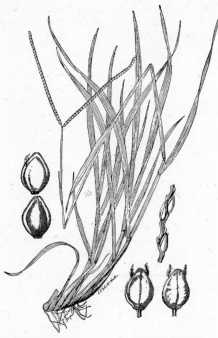

Bahiagrass (*Paspalum notatum*), useful for highways, airfields, and other places.

the color of the turf. Grasses like Bermuda-grass, having high soil fertility requirements, will require more frequent applications than species like carpet and centipedegrass. Putting too much nitrogen on carpet and centipedegrass may prove detrimental and cause them to give way to Bermuda-grass.

On the poorer soils, a spring application every third or fourth year of a complete fertilizer such as 4–8–6 at a rate of 10 to 15 pounds per 1,000 square feet is desirable. Adequate fertilization develops a dense, attractive sod in which weeds cannot become established.

Mowing encourages the grass to spread, makes the lawn attractive, and discourages weeds. The southern turf grasses should be mowed at a height of approximately an inch. Kentucky bluegrass and ryegrass will make better sod if cut at a height of 2 inches. The frequency of mowing depends upon the species, the season, and the mois-

ture and plant food available in the soil.

The clippings will fertilize the lawn and should be allowed to fall. To do this the turf must be mowed frequently enough that the clippings will not pile up and tend to smother the grass.

The lawn should be watered when evidence of wilting is apparent. Then it should be watered thoroughly to a considerable depth to favor root development.

If the grass begins to show unexplainable signs of dying, it is well to consult the county agent who can supply or obtain the assistance needed.

Most unsightly lawns that need renovation still have a fair stand of grass. Usually such lawns are starved for plant food. Fertilization with 25 pounds per thousand square feet of a complete fertilizer, such as a 4–8–6, followed by adequate applications of nitrogenous fertilizers when needed will usually transform the area into a beautiful lawn. Mowing and watering as needed are also essential features of the renovation process. Sometimes large areas in the lawn have no living plants of the desired grass. Such spots should be seeded or sprigged to the desired grass before the fertilization program is begun.

THE AUTHORS≪ *G. W. Burton holds degrees from the University of Nebraska and Rutgers University and has been engaged in research on grass since 1932. Dr. Burton is a geneticist in the Bureau of Plant Industry, Soils, and Agricultural Engineering and is stationed at Tifton, Ga.*

D. G. Sturkie, an Alabamian, has degrees from Alabama Polytechnic Institute, Iowa State College, and Michigan State College. Before he took his present position as agronomist at the Alabama Agricultural Experiment Station in Auburn, and assistant professor of agronomy and soils in Alabama Polytechnic Institute, he taught in the Agricultural and Mechanical College of Texas and in Clemson College, S. C.

SAFETY AND BEAUTY FOR HIGHWAYS

FRANK H. BRANT, MARVIN H. FERGUSON

AS MUCH as 80 percent of the right-of-way along a modern highway may be earth. If it is left bare, it is unsightly and subject to erosion. It can almost literally melt away, so that a goodly portion of the highway investment is destroyed and the roadside is made unsafe.

By improving appearance, bringing about economy of maintenance, and contributing to safety, grass is a prime item in the development of the modern complete highway.

In the pioneer work of making highways attractive, emphasis was placed on the planting of roadside trees regardless of the condition of the ground surface. During the past quarter century emphasis has changed from trees to ground cover, mostly grass.

Grass improves the appearance of the highway. It furnishes the ideal setting for trees and shrubs along highways, just as a lawn is needed as a foundation for plantings at home.

Grass also is important in that it contributes substantially to highway economy by controlling soil erosion. Soil that washes from cut slopes or sloughs off because of frost action fills ditches and culverts; erosion on fill slopes eats into the roadbed, sometimes to the extent of damaging the highway surfacing. On steep grades, erosion changes roadside ditches into gullies. These results cause expensive maintenance operations, which can be eliminated or greatly reduced by establishing a grass cover on the roadsides.

A grass-covered roadside protects agricultural land adjoining the highway. Constant, light sheet erosion and repeated sloughing of soil from slopes sends tons of soil from unprotected highways to adjacent lands to damage crops and deposit sterile soil on fertile fields. A highway is more than a path for vehicles—it is a part of the community, and roadside grass is a community asset in soil conservation.

Also, the control of erosion makes highways safer. Modern highways are constructed for safety with wide, smooth shoulders, rounded ditches, and slopes as flat as the topography will permit. If the earth surfaces keep their original shape, the highway will continue to be safe, with places of refuge for a vehicle to use without serious mishap when forced from the pavement in an emergency. To fasten down the soil, to keep shoulders and slopes from getting rough, and to prevent the formation of death-trap gullies in highway ditches is a job that grass can do.

Of course, grass is not a cure-all for every highway ill. On some shoulders, particularly in congested areas, traffic is too heavy to permit the maintenance of grass cover. On some steep grades, roadside ditches or other drainage channels may carry volumes of water so great and at such high velocities that even the best grass cover cannot prevent erosion.

It is generally possible to establish some type of grass cover on fill slopes as steep as are ordinarily used in highway construction, but cut slopes are frequently too steep to allow establishment of grass cover. In some cases an initial stand of grass can be obtained, but permanent maintenance of the grass on such steep slopes may be impossible. There has been a vast improvement in slope grading standards throughout the Nation in recent years, and the value of flatter slopes in more easily obtaining a completely effective ground cover is so apparent that further flattening of slopes in the initial highway grading would be justified.

Finally, grass is not some magic material that can be established by just scattering on a few seeds and then forgetting it forever. Grass needs attention. It needs mowing—to varying degrees on different roadside areas. In many roadside soils grass needs regular fertilization to keep it effective as a ground cover. Small failures need immediate repairs so that no serious or widespread erosion will develop.

A roadside has its use and nonuse areas. The use areas include the highway shoulders, next to the pavement, which are subjected to occasional traffic by vehicles forced from the pavement in an emergency or parked for repairs or rest. Drainage channels are also use areas because they carry away collected runoff water in excess of that which actually falls on the surface of an area.

The ideal grass cover for use areas is a low, dense, closely knit turf that will exist on stabilized soil on shoulders, survive any reasonable wear, and withstand the force of drainage runoff.

A similar cover of turf-forming grasses is also desirable at other locations such as median strips (the areas between the pavements of a divided highway), and on cut and fill slopes adjacent to lawns of homes, parks, golf courses, schools, and similar locations of intensive development.

Among the many species of grasses tested, Kentucky bluegrass, Bermudagrass, smooth brome, red fescue, and carpetgrass have been used most extensively. Prominent among the species currently being tried are Alta fescue, Bahiagrass, and the Zoysias.

Nonuse areas of the roadside are cut and fill slopes or other areas of the right-of-way where the primary purpose of grass cover is to prevent erosion and add to highway beauty. On such areas kinds of grass cover vary more widely; the less dense, more tufty, higher growing species of grasses and legumes are adaptable on them. Widely used are annual lespedezas, sericea lespedeza, redtop, hairy vetch, crown vetch, timothy, yellow sweet-clover, alfalfa, alsike clover, orchardgrass, and the wheatgrasses.

On some nonuse areas mowing is desirable, although perhaps not so frequently as on shoulders and drainage channels. On other nonuse areas, such as extensive cut slopes and fill slopes,

grass cover may be left unmowed and the natural sequence of growth, deposits of leaf litter, matting of stalks and decay, will provide protection against erosion and also a means of perpetuating the grass growth.

Since the term "grass" is used in a broad sense to include legumes and other herbs, one has sufficient license to include in grass cover for nonuse roadside areas some non-noxious weeds and wild flowers. In some agricultural areas there might even be objection to non-noxious weeds, but there are many miles of highway, particularly in wooded areas, where non-noxious weeds and wild flowers in the grass cover of the roadside are permissible and even desirable to strengthen natural appearances of the roadside.

Methods of establishing roadside grass cover are almost as numerous as the species used. Seeding is the most general method, but grass is also established by sodding, sprigging, topsoil planting (broadcasting topsoil containing grass roots) and mulch seeding (using a mulch that contains seed).

Techniques also vary widely. Seeding, for example, might be done entirely by hand methods, although the use of standard farm seeding equipment and specialized equipment for highway and airport work is becoming more common. Used with good results are a sprig planting machine; a combination harrow, seed and fertilizer distributor, and roller; and a device by which a mixture of soil, seed, fertilizer, and water is pumped onto steep slopes, where seeding has been limited to hand labor methods. The rotary type of soil pulverizer and soil mixer is being adapted to roadside work for preparing seedbeds, incorporating fertilizers, covering grass root sprigs, and incorporating mulch material.

In the maintenance of roadside grass cover, mowing methods vary from hand mowing of steep rough areas, through the use of conventional farm mowers to specialized tractor-type sickle bar mowers and large reel-type mowers constructed specifically for the high mowing (3 inches or more) necessary under highway conditions.

So far we have indicated many variations in kinds of grasses, techniques, and equipment used in establishing and maintaining roadside grass cover. These variations and changes occur because the specialized scientific and engineering approach to the use of grass on highways is a relatively new field; the kinds of plants, the methods, and the techniques must be adapted to the regional variations, and because a number of specific conditions are peculiar to highways.

One of these conditions is the soil.

The trend toward deeper cuts and higher fills for modern highways leaves larger areas of sterile raw soils to be covered with grass.

This soil is not just subsoil, but the rawest of raw soils from deep in the soil profile. Many home owners have first-hand knowledge of the struggle to get a lawn on raw soil spread out from basement excavation. To visualize the soil from a 30-foot deep basement on an area 40 to 60 times the size of an average city lawn is to realize one of the roadside grass problems on a mile of highway in many sections of the country.

Drought is another condition met with in highway planting—not only the spectacularly severe natural droughts but also the practically continuous droughty condition that occurs on many portions of the roadside and is caused artificially by the steepness of slopes and by the effort made to get the water to run off and thus protect the pavement and roadbed.

There is no chance for tillage of the soil on highways, so mulches are used to catch and hold moisture. Types of mulches vary widely; they include hay, straw, roadside mowings, sawdust, leafmold, and even a patented asphalt mulch material.

A third condition encountered on roadside planting is the need for establishing grass cover at practically any time of the year. New highway construction is susceptible to erosion, and the sooner it is protected with roadside planting the better.

The need to stretch the normal seeding seasons is met to a considerable degree by the use of mulches. Material for mulching these areas may be straw or clippings from mowing operations along the highway. The material should be weed-free if possible.

Mulch overcomes several difficulties usually encountered in a new seeding. It provides protection against heavy rains which would cut rivulets and gullies in the seeded area. It prevents the soil from drying rapidly and baking on the surface, and it reduces the fluctuation of soil temperatures. Thus it protects the young seedlings and enables them to become well established even under adverse conditions.

Mulch alone helps to prevent erosion, and mulching immediately after construction is finding favor since it provides at least partial erosion control until the next seeding season. Some States make widespread use of temporary cover crops to fill in between the seeding seasons for permanent grass cover; other States seed nothing but cover crops and depend upon a volunteer cover of the native grasses.

It is better to take some chances on stretching the seeding seasons or better to seed twice than to lose the soil—or even the entire pavement and roadbed—by waiting for just the right time to seed or sod or sprig.

A fourth condition is not exclusively a highway problem, because it is similar to a problem encountered on turf-covered airfields. Along highways the shoulder area requires sufficient stability to carry occasional traffic. Grass cover on a highway may be beautiful and it may control erosion perfectly; nevertheless, it should not hide a shoulder soil that is soft or slick to the extent that vehicles forced to the shoulder will be endangered or inconvenienced. This is one of the most important points to be considered in the establishment of a turfed shoulder because it affects the vital factor of highway safety as well as beauty.

The ideal soil for a highway shoulder is difficult to define in the light of existing knowledge. It must contain enough coarse particles to allow adequate drainage and to provide firmness sufficient to support standing vehicles without reaching a degree of compaction which would prohibit the growth of turf. On the other hand, there must be some organic matter, and enough clay to form a basis for nutrient exchange. Natural, unmodified soils that meet these requirements are not often found on highways. Perhaps further experimentation will enable us to define such a soil in terms of percentages of sand, loam, and clay.

The four conditions described give rise to the two major problems affecting the use of grass on roadsides—the selection of species of grasses and legumes for the specific highway conditions; and the specialized management and care of roadside grass cover.

At one time or another possibly every species that has been generally used in lawns or for hay and pastures has also been tried on roadsides. In the latter case there is a conflicting purpose between the two uses of the same plants. The highway need is not for heavy feed production or a particular nutritional superiority. The need is for low, spreading growth (to reduce mowing), resistance to weed invasion, deep roots for steep slopes, and wear resistance for shoulders. There is a decided need for drought tolerance and ability to grow at low fertility levels that is even greater than for hay or pasture species.

The species previously listed are some of those apparently best adapted to highway use. Each of them has one or more of the desirable characteristics but is deficient in other respects. There is still the need and the possibilities for developing plants closer to the ideal roadside grass or legume. The possibilities may be in new species; in new strains of established species; or in the examination, selection, and development of species in that commonly referred to but rather vague group of "native" grasses. It is quite possible that, in the quest for improved varieties of grasses and legumes, some of the useful plants discarded for agricultural use could be most valuable for roadside work.

The second problem is to find out the unknown factors in grass management under highway conditions. Some species of grasses and legumes now questioned for roadside use might become much more effective under different methods and techniques of management. New species might require management entirely different from that now being used.

These problems are a challenge to the many engineering and scientific fields connected with highways and plant life. It is a challenge that must be met because grass is and will continue to be important to highways. The use of grass along the roadsides can make the highway dollar go farther, be an asset to the community, and play an important part in providing a beautiful highway that is enjoyable and safe as well as useful.

THE AUTHORS«« *Frank H. Brant is a graduate in landscape design of the University of Wisconsin. He has been engaged in roadside development work since 1931 as landscape architect for the State Highway Commission of Wisconsin, and since 1935 as landscape engineer for the North Carolina State Highway and Public Works Commission at Raleigh.*

Marvin H. Ferguson is agronomist with the United States Golf Association Green Section.

A number of men experienced in roadside development with State highway departments gave assistance in checking this manuscript: D. D. Dupre, Jr., Albin Gries, W. L. Hottenstein, H. J. Neale, H. J. Schnitzius, N. M. Wells, and J. L. Wright; also H. L. Hyland, of Civil Aeronautics Administration, J. B. Dalhouse, of Public Roads Administration, and R. L. Lovvorn, professor of agronomy in North Carolina State College.

AIRFIELDS AND FLIGHT STRIPS

RALPH H. MORRISH, ALTON E. RABBITT, EDWARD B. CALE

THE ESTABLISHMENT of adapted grasses and grass mixtures is the most effective and economical means of checking dust and erosion on airfields and flight strips where soil and climate are favorable.

Paved runways, taxiways, and parking aprons of commercial, Navy, and Air Force airfields seldom constitute more than 15 percent of the total surface. Consequently, at least 85 percent of such installations and the entire landing areas of the smaller fields, which are used primarily for light aircraft and private planes, are other than hard surfaced.

To serve the purpose for which they are intended, these unpaved surfaces require inexpensive treatments that will eliminate dust and erosion problems and at the same time provide a satisfactory wearing surface on the shoulders of paved runways and on the entire area of smaller fields. Wear-resistant perennial species of grasses have proved to be most satisfactory for this purpose.

As a result of the excavation, filling, and grading required in the construction of an airfield or flight strip, most of the existing ground cover is destroyed, and a considerable portion of the topsoil is often removed or buried in a fill. The resultant graded surfaces on which a vegetative cover is necessary are usually made up of infertile subsoil materials, on which it is hard to establish and maintain desirable grasses. In contrast to agricultural practice, relatively high rates of seeding are necessary. Heavy applications of commercial fertilizers are essential, especially on infertile soils.

When several sites for a turfed airfield or flight strip are being evaluated, consideration should be given to the one having soil and drainage conditions most suitable for establishing and maintaining adapted grasses.

A well-drained and friable loam or sandy clay loam soil containing at least 2 percent of organic matter is most desirable. A tile drainage system may be necessary for turf production and to facilitate all-weather flying operations. Adequate surface and subsurface drainage must be provided. Construction that ignores these items may cause the failure of an otherwise well-built airfield or flight strip.

Drainage, especially surface drainage, must be considered in areas of relatively low rainfall no less than in humid sections. A soil covered by a dense sod may have as much as four times the water-holding capacity of similar soil that is devoid of vegetative cover. The infiltration rate changes with the type of soil structure, the ground cover, the moisture content of the soil, and the amount of organic matter present. The runoff of surface water from a turfed area is slow as compared to the rapidity of runoff from a bare soil or a paved area. To insure the rapid disposal of surface water from a sodded area, minimum slopes of 2 percent should be provided in construction.

Local soil and climatic conditions will govern the composition of the seed mixture to be planted and the rates and dates of seeding. The most desirable grasses are those that are adapted to local conditions; that can form a dense sod; resist wear, heavy use and abuse, and drought; recover quickly after periods of hard use; bear heavy loads; require relatively low fertility; and be maintained easily and inexpensively.

Few, if any, grasses now available possess all these characteristics, but experiments and field experience have shown that many of the known species of grasses occurring in the United States are satisfactory for use on airfields and flight strips. The sod-forming grasses are most desirable in the areas in which they can be grown.

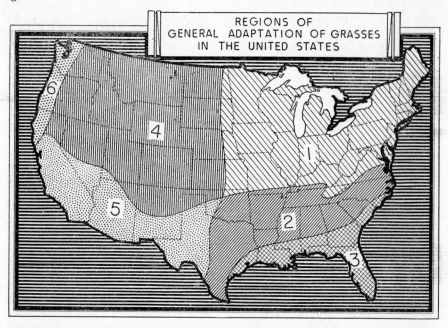

REGIONS OF
GENERAL ADAPTATION OF GRASSES
IN THE UNITED STATES

Grasses generally adapted to the regions are: *Region 1*—Colonial bentgrass, Canada bluegrass, Kentucky bluegrass, smooth bromegrass, Chewings fescue, creeping red fescue, quackgrass, and redtop. *Region 2*—Bermuda-grass and redtop. *Region 3*—Bermuda-grass, carpetgrass, and centipedegrass. *Region 4*—Buffalograss, smooth bromegrass (Eastern), blue grama grass, crested wheatgrass, and western wheatgrass. *Region 5*—Bermuda-grass (under irrigation), Indian ricegrass, sand dropseed, and weeping lovegrass. *Region 6*—Colonial bentgrass, Kentucky bluegrass, Chewings fescue, creeping red fescue, redtop, and perennial ryegrass.

Other species that have proved satisfactory for airfield use are the Zoysias, Lehmann lovegrass, Bahiagrass, kikuyugrass, and tall and Arizona fescues.

They and other species are being tested further to see if they can be used more widely on airfields. Several of the recommended grasses are not turf grasses in the true sense and do not form sods, but in the low-rainfall areas in which they are adapted they give satisfactory control of dust and erosion.

In Regions 4 and 5, as indicated on the map, the establishment of turf grasses, such as Bermuda, bluegrasses, and the fescues, is impractical without supplemental irrigation. The wheatgrasses, lovegrasses, sand dropseed, and similar species, however, have proved to be the best of those now available for use in low-rainfall areas.

In the cool humid region of the Eastern States, designated as Region 1, and in Region 6 of the northern Pacific coast area, the bluegrasses, fescues, redtop (and possibly colonial bentgrass in the northern parts of the regions) are preferred for airfields and flight strips. Mixtures of these grasses should be compounded according to the climatic and soil adaptations of the component grasses. Kentucky bluegrass will predominate on the heavier, more fertile soils and the fescues on the less fertile, sandy soils.

Bermuda-grass, the most important grass for vegetating airfields and flight strips in the Southeastern States and as far west as central Texas, may be established by seeding or sprigging. Most success with seeding has been attained by timely planting in the spring. When immediate germination is required, scarified seed should be used. If seasonal or other factors make it hard to decide which is the better method, a combination of sprigging and seeding is desirable.

In the Bermuda-grass area, where soil characteristics make it necessary to obtain the earliest possible protection against erosion, temporary grasses such as redtop, Sudangrass, cereal grains, and millets are preferable to annual lespedezas. Temporary grasses should be selected on the basis of effectiveness in control of erosion, ease of eradication, and degree of competition with perennial grasses. The tall-growing temporary grasses should be planted in drills spaced not less than 14 inches apart.

The establishment of buffalograss on flight strips and airfields in places where it is adapted has been facilitated by the use of processed seed. The low germination of untreated seed makes its establishment by seeding methods impractical, and planting by vegetative means is generally considered to be too expensive. By the timely spring planting of processed seed, buffalograss will provide a satisfactory cover on an airfield in one good growing season.

Crested wheatgrass is one of the best grasses now available for airfields and flight strips in the Northern Great Plains. Western wheatgrass is considered to be well adapted to the heavier soils where drainage is deficient.

When subject to extremely heavy traffic, the hay grasses, such as timothy, orchardgrass, and smooth bromegrass, are not considered as wear resistant as the sod-forming species, including Bermuda-grass, buffalograss, Kentucky and Canada bluegrass, Chewings fescue, creeping red fescue, and sheep fescue.

From the standpoint of wear resistance, the inclusion of such legumes as alfalfa, red clover, and sweetclover in seeding mixtures for airfields and flight strips does not seem advisable. Annual lespedezas serve well in providing temporary cover during the summer, but generally they do not stand up well under intensive use.

The use of domestic ryegrass in seed mixtures has been a common practice as a means of insuring a quick cover. The competitive nature of this species for available plant food and moisture is such that its presence is usually harmful and interferes with the rapid establishment of the desirable perennial species in the mixture. Where adapted, redtop is recommended in preference to domestic ryegrass for inclusion in seed mixtures where a temporary or semipermanent species is required to provide quick cover. Domestic ryegrass, if it is used, should not be more than 10 percent by weight of the seed mixture. Cereal grains, such as rye, oats, or wheat, as well as Sudangrass, may be used to provide temporary cover and dust control when the grading work is completed during the months when seeding with desirable perennials is not advisable.

Timeliness is one of the most important factors to be considered in all seeding operations. Seedings made out of season are extremely hazardous and usually result in partial or complete failures. In instances when the unseasonal planting of grasses is necessary because of the completion of construction, the use of mulching materials like straw will increase the chances of establishing a satisfactory stand. Successful seedings of perennial grasses may be made in the humid areas in summer when mulch is applied or when supplemental irrigation is provided.

The use of anchored mulch at the rate of approximately 2 tons an acre is recommended with all seedings of dry-land grasses on sites where stubble is not present. In the Northeastern and North Central States, dormant seedings made late in the fall are preferable to late spring seedings.

Sound practices should be observed in regard to the optimum depth of planting. Improperly prepared seedbeds that are not well firmed, plus the deep planting of grass seed, will necessitate many expensive reseeding jobs. The use of a seed drill or a seeding attachment on a cultipacker will insure an optimum depth of planting.

If the seed is to be broadcast, provision must be made for covering it; a spike-toothed harrow, cultipacker, or similar equipment can be used. Excessively high rates of seeding will not compensate for faulty planting methods. In seeding, an advantage in uniformity is gained by planting one-half of the seed each way across the airfield or flight strip. The rates and dates of seeding in the humid sections will be governed by local soil and climatic conditions. The rates of seeding in these areas will vary from 40 to 80 pounds an acre, depending on the species included in the mixture. However, Bermuda-grass should be planted at the rate of 10 to 15 pounds an acre. Dry-land seedings are usually made at rates of from 6 to 15 pounds an acre. Irrigation in the establishment of Bermuda and other grasses may be justified in areas of limited rainfall. Irrigated grasses are much less expensive to establish and maintain than mechanically stabilized surfaces.

Irrigation will insure a good grass cover in many areas where it would otherwise fail because of low rainfall or prolonged hot, dry seasons.

The expense of top-soiling airfields and flight strips is seldom justified in the establishment of desirable species of perennial grasses. Frequently the existing surface soil on an airfield site is of no higher fertility than the subsoil material. If it has suitable physical structure, the graded subsoil material, although it may be infertile, can be made to produce a wear-resistant cover by the timely planting of adapted species and the heavy application of commercial fertilizers of the correct analyses.

Top soil also is often high in weed-seed content. The cost of commercial fertilizer represents only a small fraction of the expense involved in the stock piling, hauling, and distribution of top soil. The top-soiling or mucking of runway shoulders at airfield sites where the soil is extremely sandy may be necessary to provide for the economical establishment of grass cover.

If the soil on the site of an all-over turfed airfield or flight strip will not permit the economical establishment and maintenance of perennial grasses without top-soiling, the field should be relocated on an area where soil conditions are more desirable.

Fertilization and Liming

The use of commercial fertilizers in high quantities is essential in both the establishment and maintenance of airfields and flight strips in the humid areas of the United States. Grasses grow vigorously, dominate undesirable weeds, and form dense sods if they are well fertilized and if soil moisture is not a limiting factor. Applications of as much as 800 to 1,000 pounds of a 10–6–4 fertilizer or a fertilizer of similar analysis at planting time is advisable.

Applications of nitrogenous fertilizers give economical results in the establishment of grasses in areas where its use has not been practiced in agricultural production. Applications of as much as 40 pounds of available nitrogen per acre at seeding time under some dry-land conditions will insure the early establishment of the desirable grasses.

Liming may be necessary on some soils to promote the healthy growth of adapted grasses. If soil tests indicate a need for lime, the required quantity should be applied before seeding.

Maintenance

The proper maintenance of an airfield or flight strip must include timely periodic mowing. The type of management followed on a hay field is not satisfactory in maintaining the intensively used areas on an airfield.

The grass cover on an airport should not be cut to a height of less than 3 inches. It should not be allowed to attain a height which will prohibit the use of a reel-type gang mower in its maintenance. If most grasses are allowed to grow to mature heights, they do not develop vegetatively and closely knit sods are not produced.

Extremely close mowing inhibits the desirable development of root systems, encourages damage from drought, decreases resistance to wear, and opens the soil surface to damage from propeller blast and erosion.

The frequency of mowing is governed by soil and climatic conditions, as well as the growth habits of the grass or grasses on the field. All grasses should be mowed often enough to permit the clippings to remain on the ground without danger of smothering the grass. If the clippings are allowed to remain on the field, their value as mulch and fertilizer is not lost. Gang mowers have been developed specifically for use in the maintenance of turfed airfields. These mowers can be operated at relatively high rates of speed and will cover six to eight times as many acres in a day as will the conventional sickle-bar mowers.

Annual applications of nitrogen are essential in the maintenance of grass cover on airfields and flight strips throughout the humid section. A minimum of 40 pounds an acre each year of available nitrogen will be required on most soils to maintain the grasses in a healthy condition. If the soil requirements for lime, phosphorus, and potash are fulfilled at seeding time, these elements will not usually be required again for 3 to 5 years.

The control of traffic, removal of debris, timely repair of eroded areas, the renovation of heavily worn or depleted critical areas, the control of weeds, the control of insects and diseases, and required irrigation are maintenance operations which must be attended to promptly on a seasonal basis if the grasses are to be kept in a serviceable condition for their intended use.

Any airfield or flight strip that warrants the expenditure of funds for the establishment of adapted perennial grasses also warrants the expenditure of additional funds to provide practical management and maintenance. A well-established sod represents a sizable investment and unless this investment is protected by timely maintenance operations, the turf soon deteriorates; dust and erosion problems become evident; flight hazards in the form of ruts and gullies develop; weeds become dominant, and expensive renovation and reseeding projects become necessary.

The best way to insure the proper and timely performance of the necessary grass-maintenance work is by the employment of a qualified and experienced grounds-maintenance supervisor. Such an individual will save his salary many times over if labor, materials, and equipment are made available to him as needed for the performance of the necessary maintenance work.

THE AUTHORS≪≪ *Ralph H. Morrish, as a colonel in the Army of the United States, was in charge of the maintenance of grounds at military installations during the war. He is now Chief, Grounds Section, Office of the Director of Air Installations, Headquarters, United States Air Force. He has the bachelor's and master's degrees from Michigan State College, where he has also taught and done research and extension work.*

Alton E. Rabbitt, as agronomist, Bureau of Aeronautics, Navy Department, Washington, is in charge of grassing of Naval Air Stations for dust and erosion control. He has also served as agronomist with the United States Golf Association Greens Section, and the National Capital Parks, Department of the Interior. Mr. Rabbitt received a bachelor's degree in agronomy at the University of Maryland.

Edward B. Cale is an agronomist in the Corps of Engineers, Office of the Chief of Engineers. A Virginian, he worked on golf-course construction and maintenance in New Jersey and Pennsylvania after he received a bachelor's degree in agronomy at Virginia Polytechnic Institute.

GOLF IS PLAYED ON GRASS

FRED V. GRAU, O. J. NOER

IN UNITED STATES there are six thousand-odd golf courses that occupy roughly 750,000 acres of land. The investment in land, buildings, machinery, clubs, balls, clothing, and the other necessities, and the labor required to maintain the courses make golf a multibillion dollar sport. This year more than 2,500,000 golfers played an estimated 70,000,000 rounds. To avoid belaboring the obvious, let it suffice to say that all these items depend on grass.

The regulation golf course has 18 holes, by tradition, but often courses in smaller communities have 9 holes; a few have multiples of 9, such as 27, 36, or 45 holes. The turfed areas of the course comprise the tees, fairways, greens, and roughs.

Of the hundreds of grasses that have been identified in the United States, only a few of the permanent turf-forming grasses are suitable for use on golf courses. They include the bluegrasses, fescues, and bents in the North and on the Pacific coast; Bermuda, carpetgrass, centipede, and Zoysia in the South; and buffalo, blue grama, and the Fairway strain of crested wheatgrass in the Great Plains region. Temporary grasses such as redtop and domestic and perennial rye are used to some extent. They are employed in the North to furnish a grass cover until the slower growing permanent grasses become established. In the South they are used to provide green turf on greens and fairways in winter when the true southern grasses are dormant.

Courses in the North, in the Great Plains, and in the Pacific Northwest use bentgrass on greens. In the early days the fescues and South German mixed bent were used. More recently seaside and colonial types of bent have been employed for this purpose. Another development has been the use of creeping bent selections which have been propagated and planted vegetatively. The bluegrasses, fescues, and colonial type of bent are used for tees and fairways; the first two are usually chosen for roughs. Recent studies indicate that hardier, coarser grasses more tolerant of drought and low soil fertility may find wide usage.

The first stroke on each hole is played from the tee, a flat area with a slight slope from front to back and from one to several thousand square feet in area. Most courses have a long tee for each hole, or several smaller ones, so the length or yardage of the hole can be varied. The back tee is usually known as the championship tee. The sharp spikes fitted into the bottom of the shoes worn by golfers to prevent slipping on dry turf have a severe abrasive action on the grass.

Further and greater damage is caused by the club head as it makes contact with the teed-up ball. The small clumps of sod, called divots, removed by the club head leave scars in the turf. Tees on short holes are injured the most because clubs with iron heads are used.

The best and most satisfactory turf is self-healing and produced from stoloniferous grass (creeping surface stems or runners) or from rhizomes (underground creeping stems).

The golfer demands a firm stance; a relatively "dry" surface is desirable. Drought-tolerance is therefore a good feature of tee grasses. Minimum quantities of water should suffice to maintain a turf.

Ability to withstand close clipping is more important than drought resistance. The teed ball must stand above and clear of uncut grass. The most common height of cut is one-half to three-fourths inch.

Disease resistance is extremely important in tee grasses because turf from them is easier and cheaper to maintain, invasion by clover and weeds is less likely, and the tee is more uniform in appearance.

A pleasing color throughout the playing season is highly desirable because it adds to the enjoyment of the game, even though it may not affect playability of the turf.

The grasses most widely used on tees are listed on page 328, along with several that have promise of being satisfactory. The list is divided according to regions. There is some overlapping in the border zones between North and South. For example, in places like St. Louis and Washington, D. C., Zoysia, which is usually looked upon as a southern grass, may become a good grass for tees. Bermuda-grass is another possibility; new cold-resistant strains, some of which are in use on tees and fairways as far north as Washington, have been developed.

Bermuda-grass is used in the South on tees for the summer play. Overseeding in the fall with domestic ryegrass, bent, or redtop is a practical way to provide green grass during the winter. Zoysia is an excellent new grass and may supplement Bermuda for summertime use.

We need new and better tee grasses, however. The grasses now available cannot survive, as well as we should like, the terrific punishment from heavy play on the small tees of the daily fee courses. The public courses particularly need a better grass.

In building new tees, or rebuilding old ones, it is good practice to follow these principles:

Make the tee large enough so there is time for the turf to recover before play is resumed from the same spot. Tees on iron-shot holes (the short par-3 holes) should be one-fourth to one-third larger than the others to permit more frequent change of tee markers.

Elevate the front end of the tee to make a slight slope (6 inches in 100 feet) from front to back.

Elevate the tee above surrounding terrain, but have gently sloping sides to permit mowing with mechanized units, preferably with tractor and fairway units.

If necessary, use humus and coarse sand to modify the texture of the surface soil and to produce a sandy loam soil that will support plant growth with a minimum of irrigation.

Fairways

Fairways comprise 20 to 30 acres on a 9-hole course and 40 to 60 acres on an 18-hole course. They average 50 to 60 yards in width and 100 to 600 yards in length. The quality of turf should be superior to that on the finest lawn.

The golfer prefers to play on a fairway where the turf can be mowed closely at $\frac{1}{2}$ to 1 inch—rarely higher. He desires a dense, tough grass to support the ball and firmness under foot to aid in making the shot. Maximum resistance to diseases, insects, drought, heat, cold, and invasion of weeds and clover is desirable for proper maintenance and play.

Modern golf demands weed-free fairways. A weed in golf turf is any plant that interferes with the accuracy of play and the enjoyment of the game—a definition that makes clover a weed on a golf course. Herbicides like arsenic acid, sodium arsenite, and 2,4-D can keep weeds out.

Most of the grasses used on fairways are the same as those used for lawns and pastures. The appearance of the turf is secondary to playability, yet golfers prefer well-kept fairways of a pleasing color.

Leading amateurs and professionals say they prefer well-kept Bermuda-grass; they like the good lies they get on the dense mat of evenly fertilized, closely cut Bermuda-grass. Bermuda is the principal fairway grass of the South, although there are a few courses with carpetgrass and centipedegrass fairways. Red fescue is rated high in the North; the next choice is a well-kept fairway bent. Kentucky bluegrass cannot tolerate the close clipping demanded by the golfers.

Old-timers talk about the fescue fairways of former times on northern courses; they bemoan the fact that modern courses do not have as good turf. Creeping red fescue is a wiry grass that gives a perfect lie when the turf is dense. Low fertility levels and infrequent cutting in the horse-mowing days enabled fescue to resist invasion by more aggressive grasses, such as Kentucky bluegrass and the bentgrasses. Only a few courses with fescue fairways remain; they are in less densely populated areas where maintenance standards are less exacting.

Kentucky bluegrass is commonly used for fairways in the North. Some clubs have good turf of it. Unless Kentucky bluegrass is cut reasonably high (1 to 1½ inch), it does not persist and becomes infested with clover, crabgrass, *Poa annua*, and other weeds. At 1½ inches a rather open, unsatisfactory fairway turf is produced.

The inherent weaknesses in a grass become apparent under intensive management of frequent and close mowing, heavy fertilization, and the overwatering practiced on some courses. These are the main reasons why fescue has disappeared from many fairways and why Kentucky bluegrass is faltering on others. Bluegrass suffers badly from leaf spot in cool, wet weather. As the bluegrass weakens, clover, knotweed, *Poa annua*, crabgrass, and chickweed become troublesome pests.

Bentgrasses have performed better than fescue or Kentucky bluegrass on the watered and intensively managed courses. They make a tighter and denser turf which resists invasion by clover and weeds. Bentgrass can be cut short. The erect-growing types, such as colonial bent, are best, but some of the creeping types have possibilities. Better selections of bentgrass would be desirable for watered courses; superior strains of fescue and possibly of bentgrass and Kentucky bluegrass are needed for unwatered fairways. New and better grasses for fairways are being requested everywhere. Their development is one of the pressing problems requiring solution.

Putting greens occupy only a small part of the total area on the golf course but they are the most important from the standpoint of the play. At least half the strokes in a round of golf are played on the greens. The average size of a putting green is about 5,000 square feet. The total area in the greens on an 18-hole course is about 2 acres.

Putting Greens

Many golf courses began with sand greens, and still have them in dry localities where water is not available to irrigate properly. A few of the first grass greens were seeded to bluegrass, red fescue, and redtop. Only traces of these grasses remain on a few isolated courses. Today, the world over, grassed putting greens are either bentgrass or Bermuda-grass.

Bentgrass greens are in use in nearly every section of the United States. Some bentgrass greens are scattered through Florida, Texas, New Mexico, Arizona, and southern California. The replacement value of the turf is about $1,000 a green, or $10,000 an acre. Some bentgrass sod sells for a dollar or two a square yard, which is at the rate of about $5,000 to $10,000 an acre.

The surface of the putting green must be as smooth and true as a billiard table, firm enough to avoid footprints, which deflect the ball, and sufficiently resilient to hold a pitched ball, even though the soil is on the dry side. Maximum density of the turf is demanded without any graininess. A grainy turf causes the ball to roll faster with the grain than against it. Putting-green surfaces are rarely flat. Gentle contours and slopes add to the interest by demanding greater skill and judgment on the part of the player.

Putting greens represent one of the most highly specialized uses of grass known. Without an excellent turf on the greens and a keen putting surface, golf would not be the popular sport that it is today. Maintenance of the turf is both an art and a science and it requires years of study and experience on the part of the greenkeeping superintendent.

When bentgrass began to be used for putting greens it was discovered that a mixture known as South German bent produced highly satisfactory putting surfaces. Many of these old greens still exist after 40 years or more of continuous play. When world conflict in 1914 made it impossible to get this seed, search was started for other types of bentgrasses. There followed years of collecting material, testing the value of various sources of seeds, and propagation of vegetative bentgrass (creeping bent) by the United States Golf Association Green Section. The present-day bent putting greens are South German mixed bent on the old greens, but on the more recently planted ones they are Seaside creeping bent from seed (with mixtures of colonial bent) or vegetative plantings of selected creeping bents.

A number of superior strains of creeping bents are being produced commercially and sold for vegetative planting. Many golf courses grow their own planting stock in nurseries. A mere handful of stolons of parent stock quickly produces a large quantity of stolons. The outstanding named strains are Washington, Arlington, Cohansey, Toronto, Congressional, Collins, Old Orchard, and Norbeck. All have been selected from established putting greens—none is the product of breeding and selection.

Bermuda-grass greens can be developed by seeding or by planting with stolons, an operation that sometimes is called sprigging.

Golf courses in the South use Bermuda-grass for summer play, and overseed with northern grasses for play in winter, when Bermuda-grass is dormant.

The secret of keeping a good Bermuda-grass green is to feed generously with nitrogenous fertilizers and to topdress whenever necessary to keep the surface stems buried.

Recent work indicates that fine-leaved strains of Bermuda-grass can be selected and developed. Under proper care they will produce a putting surface as true and as fine as bentgrass turf.

Imported seed of Italian ryegrass was first used for winter greens. Domestic seed produced in the Pacific Northwest has been equally good and less expensive. Those preferring ryegrass use it exclusively. A few clubs use only redtop and others prefer to mix a little redtop and bluegrass with the ryegrass. In recent years bentgrasses have been tried from seed. They have been satisfactory when seeded properly at the right time and given the right kind of aftercare.

Customary practice is to renovate the Bermuda turf before seeding in the fall, by slicing or raking, followed by close cutting, top dressing, and seeding.

In building a putting green, consideration must be given to a number of important details. Drainage to remove excess water quickly both from the surface and through the soil is a main consideration. By providing perfect drainage, the soil is better aerated and a deeper growth of roots is encouraged. Good soil texture, combined with drainage and aeration, also is vital. Drainage and aeration insure firmness and resilience, and prevent the soil from becoming puddled and compacted even under constant traffic by man and machinery. A sandy loam soil that contains 20 to 30 percent by volume of durable organic matter is considered ideal. Clay soils must be modified to produce a sandy loam. Coarse sands are less likely to become too compact for good plant growth than fine sands. Reed and sedge peats and peat moss are commonly used to furnish the organic matter fraction.

First the subgrade is prepared and given adequate drainage by the use of tile or porous gravel material. Then about 10 inches of the especially prepared topsoil is placed on the surface. This is graded for proper contours to avoid ponding areas and to allow the surface water to drain off in two or more directions. Lime (if needed) and fertilizers are then incorporated in the soil and the green is ready to be seeded

Grasses Most Widely Used on Tees; Also Those That Show Promise of Being Satisfactory

[All have pleasing color and stand close clipping]

Grass	Rapidity of healing	Drought tolerance	Disease resistance	Density
Northern region:				
Bentgrasses:				
Colonial type..................	Fair......	Good......	Good......	Excellent.
Creeping type.................	Very good.	Fair........	...do......	Do.
Bluegrass	Fair......	Good......	Fair.......	Fair.
Fescue.........................	Slow......	Excellent...	Good......	Good.
Poa annua [1].....................	Good.....	Very poor..	Fair to good.	Do.
Southern region (summer):				
Bermuda-grass.................	Excellent..	Good......	Good......	Do.
Centipedegrass.................	Good.....	Very good..	....do......	Do.
Zoysia.........................	Slow......	Excellent...	....do......	Excellent.
Southern region (winter):				
Ryegrass (winter)...............	....	....	....	
Redtop (winter)................	....	....	....	
Western Plains:				
Buffalograss	Very good.	Excellent...	Good......	Good.
Crested wheatgrass (Fairway strain).	....	....do......	....do......	Do.

[1] Usually considered a weed but tolerates shade and makes excellent turf where weather is cool and moist.

or, if necessary, planted with stolons.

If the green is to be seeded, the seedbed must be firm but mellow to avoid covering the tiny bentgrass seeds too deeply. Coverage of one-fourth inch is sufficient. Frequent light watering with a gentle spray is essential to obtain rapid and maximum germination and establishment. Usually 3 pounds of seed to 1,000 square feet is adequate—often less is used. Because the green will be mowed at one-fourth inch or less, it is highly important to start mowing as soon as the grass is one-half inch high.

Vegetative planting requires a different technique. The growing grass is lifted from a nursery, pulled apart or shredded, and the living plants scattered on the prepared surface. Usually 1 square foot of nursery stock will plant 8 to 10 square feet of putting green surface. This is equivalent to about 4 to 6 bushels of stolons for each 1,000 square feet. The stolons are scattered uniformly, pressed down with a roller, and top-dressed with about one-fourth inch of screened, prepared soil similar to that on the green. With frequent light watering, the grass will be ready for the first mowing in 10 days to 2 weeks. With excellent care, the green may be ready for use in 4 to 6 weeks. Frequent light top dressings are necessary to fill the low spots and to produce a true, smooth surface.

After the grass on the putting green has been established, a regular program of fertilizing must be considered. Normally it is general practice to apply in several applications a total of 6 to 8 pounds of actual nitrogen to every 1,000 square feet during the growing season. This amount equals approximately 60 to 80 pounds of a fertilizer containing 10 percent of nitrogen or 95 to 125 pounds of a fertilizer with 6 percent nitrogen. Calculations easily can be made on the amount to apply for the fertilizer which may be available. Every effort should be made to apply at least 30 percent of this nitrogen in the organic form to give a greater carry-over effect. Proportionate amounts of phosphorus and potash fertilizers should be included also to give a complete balanced feeding.

Accepted practice is to use lime judiciously on bent and Bermuda-grass greens and on turf in general, especially when soils become more acid than pH 6. The use of a dolomitic limestone of high magnesium content is desirable in regions where the acid soils are low in available magnesium.

Regular and frequent mowing of putting greens is essential to keep a true putting surface. The frequency of mowing is determined by the rate of growth; during the growing season, three to four mowings a week is not considered excessive. Many greens are cut daily. A mowing height of three-sixteenths inch during the growing season is necessary for the prevention of a mat, which will develop if the grass is mowed at a higher cut. Every effort should be made by close mowing, brushing, and raking to keep this mat from developing, as its occurrence will increase the disease incidence and make the watering problem more difficult during the hot, dry days of summer. It is generally a good practice to rake bentgrass greens heavily in the early spring and fall, at the beginning of the growing seasons, to remove any excess growth. At these two seasons, the grass will quickly recover from the rough raking treatment.

The principal diseases of closely mowed turf, particularly the putting greens, are brownpatch, dollarspot, snowmold, copperspot, pinkpatch, and pythium. Most of these diseases are controlled by the skilled use of chemicals, including calomel, bichloride of mercury, various organic mercury compounds, and nonmercury preparations. New materials which contain cadmium as the active ingredient appear very promising.

Insects have plagued the greens-keepers since the game began. Among the most destructive insects are chinch bugs, grubs of the Japanese beetle and the May beetle, cutworms, sod webworms, and armyworms. Pests that annoy but are not destructive are ants and earthworms. Arsenate of lead has been a standard insecticide for many insects. Recently DDT has found its place on golf courses, and other newer chemicals offer great promise. One of these is Chlordane.

The question of top dressing is a moot one, but generally is practiced on most golf courses today. Care should be exercised in applying a top dressing of any material that may cause layering in the soil. Peat or any other organic matter, heavy loam, clay, or sand when used alone will cause layering and ultimately stop root penetration. Layers in the soil create a shallow-rooted turf that will wilt and die during hot weather.

A good top-dressing mixture should contain approximately equal parts by volume of soil, organic matter (reed or sedge peat), and a coarse concrete sand. If the soil that is being used in the mixture is a sandy loam, then it would be best to use two parts of soil, one part of organic matter, and one part of a coarse concrete sand by volume. The normal rate of applying top dressing is 1 yard to a green of 5,000 square feet. The rate should be reduced one-half or two-thirds in midsummer if it is necessary to use the dressing then. Top-dressing material should be free of weed seeds; it can be made so by mixing fertilizers with the top dressing and storing for several weeks, or until heating ceases.

No specific recommendations can be made for watering putting greens. The use of water must be based upon the need for it, common sense, and judgment. Prevailing conditions, such as normal rainfall and drainage on the green, both surface and subsurface, will determine the amount and frequency of watering. The proper use of water is the key to good turf.

Many of the difficulties on putting greens can be traced to poor soil conditions which were either built into the green or have developed by compaction by foot and maintenance-machinery traffic.

Several methods can be employed to correct poor soil conditions. The tubular-tine fork can be used to good advantage, but it is a device that takes time and labor. Several mechanical devices can accomplish the operation with less manual labor. Although quite expensive, these pieces of machinery will more than pay their original cost in the saving of labor.

The roughs are penalty areas for the player who is off line. It is the region 75 to 100 yards in front of the tee, along each side of the fairway, and surrounding the green. The grass is cut at 4 to 5 inches—to penalize the golfer who has to play from it.

THE AUTHORS≪← *Fred V. Grau is director of the United States Golf Association Green Section and chairman of the Turf Committee of the American Society of Agronomy.*

O. J. Noer has worked as agronomist with the Milwaukee Sewerage Commission since 1924. After graduation from the University of Wisconsin, he conducted soil surveys in Wisconsin, worked as soil chemist for the Great Northern Railway, was State soil chemist in Wisconsin, and taught chemistry in the University of Wisconsin.

The Search for Better Grass

THE BREEDER'S WAYS AND MEANS

D. C. SMITH

THE MEMBERS of the grass family, like other plants, are classified into tribes, genera, and species, which represent successively smaller differences among types and, thus, closer relationships. Among the species are subspecies and varieties or strains. The latter are the smallest units in which the forage producer is interested.

The genus (the plural of which is genera) and species are the classification units of principal interest to the grass breeder; a knowledge of their botanical diversity and relationships and their natural occurrence over the world is important in planning a breeding program.

A genus may include several species of agricultural value, or it may have none. Its members may be widely distributed over the earth, or occur quite locally. In grasses the genus *Panicum,* for example, includes *Panicum virgatum,* the switchgrass of the Great Plains; there are, however, about 500 other species of *Panicum* throughout the world. Timothy belongs in the genus *Phleum,* which contains about ten species, only one of which, *Phleum pratense,* known as common timothy, is of great importance. This group is found naturally in northern Europe.

Among the numerous species of grasses few may be expected to be of value in cultivation. Many are important only as components of native range or pasture areas. Among some 1,500 accessions grown at the Northern Great Plains Field Station, Mandan, N. Dak., over a 10-year period, about 40 percent failed to survive climatic conditions there, and most of the others may fail eventually to meet all requirements.

After extensive trials of many native and introduced species and strains by the Minnesota Agricultural Experiment Station, it was reported, "No recently introduced species or varieties that were studied appeared as desirable as the cultivated grasses grown previously."

But one is prompted to ask whether the available species have been well sifted and whether the best ones are being utilized for all purposes and locations. It seems likely that further investigation will bring valuable new types into prominence.

In his presidential address to the Fourth International Grassland Congress in 1937, R. G. Stapledon, director of the Welsh Plant Breeding Station, said: "There is hardly a region in the whole world that has yet got the best combinations of the best agricultural genes (hereditary determiners) in its grassland plants while I make bold to hazard the opinion that there are many regions in the world that have not even yet gotten the right species to work."

Such being the case, much improvement might be expected from exploration for the introduction of new species and types and their testing under conditions similar to those where they are originally found. For some years now, workers in the Department of Agriculture have sought desirable species and varieties in foreign lands. Investigations by other workers in the United States since 1930 established that a number of native grasses may be successfully introduced into farming; among them are reed canarygrass, Canada ryegrass, green needlegrass, mountain bromegrass, big bluestem, big bluegrass, and slender wheatgrass.

Grass culture in the United States is especially notable because of the large number of species that may be of value in one region or another. Besides, there is a wide range of native species characteristic of the various geographical areas, but some (such as timothy, bromegrass, and the bentgrasses) may do well over wide areas.

Improvement of grass in any given area is therefore greatly restricted as to species according to the existing conditions. Similarly, introduction of kinds from other countries must be made upon the basis of special interest to certain areas and a particular introduction may or may not prove to be of wide interest. Grasses used for fine turf also require special consideration.

It is not always agreed as to which species are valuable enough to justify intensive improvement efforts.

Kentucky bluegrass, an important pasture grass in Sweden and one that is used there as an indicator of good growing conditions, has been thought to be a sort of weed in England and an indicator of poor pasture. Some fescue species generally acknowledged to be valuable in the United States and northern Europe have been in disfavor in parts of Australia. Such apparent disagreement is most effectively resolved by comparative trials of species and strains in areas and under conditions where they are to be used.

All factors associated with plant growth (including soil type and fertility, climate, latitude, management, and variety) are known to be active in determining adaptation. But it is not enough to test one strain or a few strains of a species. As with other plants, varieties differ widely, and if they show some desirable characteristics, further search needs to be made to isolate those that more nearly may meet the requirements. Extensive testing of strains is thus a forerunner and also a contemporary procedure of more complex breeding techniques.

The time required for adequate testing of a species and its subsequent incorporation into use is often unaccountably long. Crested wheatgrass, for instance, was first introduced into the United States from Russia in 1898 and was grown at several Northern Great Plains experiment stations in 1899. A second introduction was made in 1906 and the grass was again seeded at several stations. The first favorable record of performance was made in 1909 and others followed, but the crop received little attention until the mid-1920's. Even so, the cultivation of crested wheatgrass in the United States preceded similar use in some parts of the Old World where it is native.

The history of grass improvement is relatively short in the United States and other countries.

The efforts of Scandinavians to improve grasses are well known. The Swedish Seed Association, established in 1886, is an outstanding plant-breeding institution. Grass breeding began in Sweden in 1890 and in 1907 a regular division of the Swedish Seed Association was developed for improvement of forage plants.

The Welsh Plant Breeding Station at Aberystwyth, Wales, was founded in 1919, although grass improvement work was under way considerably earlier. Work in other European countries generally started between 1910 and 1920.

In the United States some of the earliest work in grass improvement was accomplished by workers with timothy in the early 1890's. Selections were made of a number of plant types of timothy and varieties were developed, although they were not distributed because they were found to be susceptible to stem rust.

Studies with timothy at the New York (Cornell) Agricultural Experiment Station began before 1902 and an extensive program was carried on for several years. In the early trials 223 lots were grown; 163 of them were from the United States, and 60 were from foreign countries. These included approximately 17,000 spaced plants—an extensive test, even in 1948!

The Colorado Agricultural Experiment Station reported results of studies of variation in smooth bromegrass in 1913. Differences in plant types were noted and parent and progeny relationships were investigated.

Since 1920 a number of experiment stations have undertaken improvement work with various grasses. Scientists in what is now the Bureau of Plant Industry, Soils, and Agricultural Engineering have coordinated studies of varietal behavior in a large number of grass species. The breeding work with grasses in the Bureau's Division of Forage Crops and Diseases was begun on an intensive basis in 1936. In that year also the Northeastern Pasture Research Laboratory at State College, Pa., began its work. In 1941 the Division of Forage Crops and Diseases initiated a uniform nursery testing system, which later included 66 nurseries in 41 States, the aim being to compare grass strains and varieties in nursery or small-plot trials under widely diverse conditions. Beginning in 1939, the United States Golf Association Green Section established a number of experimental greens for testing strains of bentgrasses. By 1944, some 40 strains had been tried at 19 stations.

Most grass species are pollinated with wind-borne pollen. Consequently they are usually cross-fertilized. Many annual species, however, are self-pollinated. The plants that are normally self-pollinated generally produce progenies of relative uniformity, with marked resemblance between parent and progeny. Cross-pollinated plants most frequently produce highly variable progenies.

The general situation with respect to self-pollinating crops is considerably different. In such species, strains may be separated immediately and then usually are expected to breed true. A number of types of such grasses may be present in any particular site, and wide differences among selected strains may be found.

Most grass species, particularly the perennials, are readily propagated vegetatively (clonally), from surface runners (stolons), underground stems (rhizomes), or from portions of aerial shoots or crowns; an advantage is that an individual plant may be increased into a number of clones or plants, as is commonly done with many horticultural varieties of flowers and fruits. An increase of that kind is of particular value for special purposes, as with varieties of creeping bentgrasses used for golf greens or elsewhere when vegetative propagation can be economical. Some of the best bentgrass strains are vegetatively propagated commercially. Stolon nurseries for vegetative increase of desirable varieties may be maintained by golf courses or others.

Much must be learned about the specific characteristics of any particular species before any well-planned breeding system can be developed.

Some grasses are annuals; some are perennials; others (like certain bromegrasses) are both.

The growth habit may be spreading or bunchlike. In the former, stolons or rhizomes (vegetative stems capable of rooting at the joints) tend to spread the plant outward; Bermuda-grass and bromegrasses are examples. Bunchgrasses have tufted centers and little inclination to spread.

Seed production in most grasses is sexual and depends upon pollination and fertilization of the female by the male elements, but in some species seed may be produced without fertilization. In such instances the plant may breed true; then the offspring may resemble the female plant or be identical with it. This condition has been studied especially in Kentucky bluegrass, but it is known to occur also in other species. In bulbous bluegrass, small seedlike bulbs that are proliferated in the seed heads serve to propagate the species.

The principal objective in grass breeding is to produce types with more desirable vegetative characteristics, including high yields of good forage.

A satisfactory method of propagation is necessary, either by seed or clonally, but the production of seed is relatively less critical than in crops grown primarily for the seed. Seasonal distribution or season of production of forage may be as vital as total yield. Eventually, most grasses may be utilized with legumes, because that combination is mutually advantageous. As early as 1910, it was shown that timothy grown with alfalfa contained a higher percentage of protein than when grown alone. Some species, such as orchardgrass, tend to smother less vigorously growing legumes, such as white clover. Strains may need to grow well with other species of grasses as well as with legumes.

Wide adaptability is desirable. Some strains appear to be better able to maintain productivity on poor soils than do others. Work has shown that some varieties of timothy and orchardgrass differ in their abilities to use nitrogen fertilizers when cut for hay, while comparable differences do not occur in seed production.

Uniformity, highly desirable in many crops, may be less important in the forage species. Maintenance of a highly variable variety becomes a problem, however, for it may be more subject to change because of the operation of soil, climate, and management on the plant population. It has been suggested that strains might best be maintained in a highly uniform or pure condition. Subsequently, they could be utilized in whatever blends with similar or different strains or species that might be desirable.

Quality of forage is important. Forage must be acceptable to livestock over a wide range of growth stages and conditions, contain high proportions of nutrients and vitamins, and have the ability to develop and retain those characters under adverse conditions of growth and handling. Significant differences in protein content have been noted among Kentucky bluegrass and bromegrass strains; the late-flowering Kentucky bluegrasses have been found to be higher in protein; darker green orchardgrass plants have been found to be higher in potential vitamin content. The darker green color may be associated with higher protein content. Significant differences have been noted in beta carotene (a vitamin source), magnesium, and potassium content among families of smooth bromegrass.

It may be necessary to consider other characteristics also in grass-breeding work. As early as 1901, for instance, it was pointed out that failure to get a stand of plants was the greatest difficulty experienced in trying to grow bromegrass on dry land. Investigations have shown that hull-less timothy, particularly if aged, is inferior for seeding. It has also been found that the tendency to hull in timothy is genetically controlled in part and thus may be reduced by selection. Marked variations in strains of side-oats grama and little bluestem have been noted with respect to the seed-dormancy period. A low germination rate may be an important problem with some species, for example, reed canarygrass.

Ability to grow at high temperatures is often another point. Smooth bromegrass plants may vary significantly in this respect. Variation in lines of bromegrass as to drought resistance also have been observed. Differences in ability of bluegrass and other species to withstand atmospheric drought have been noted in greenhouse studies.

Investigations in Australia have indicated a direct relationship between the amount of water loss that grass leaves can stand without wilting in artificial tests and in their actual resistance to drought.

Some species and strains of grasses are slow in becoming established because of poor seedling vigor and subsequent slow early growth. Notable differences have been observed in the ability of strains to develop roots. This may be related to conservation value.

Hardiness is an important problem with certain grasses. Significant differences among strains of bentgrasses with respect to winter injury have been found. Strains of some warm-temperature species show inherited differences in ability to survive low winter temperatures. Southern strains may be more susceptible to cold in both the seedling and later stages. Orchardgrass and meadow fescue have been insufficiently hardy in breeding trials in the Northern States. As early as 1910 it was noted that the orchardgrass could withstand winter cold but that it was injured by late-spring frosts. In the South, Rhodesgrass has suffered from winter injury.

Long- and short-day types—that is, types responding differently to the lengths of days of the growing season—have been noted in meadow fescue; this point is related to adaptation northward and southward, because longer summer days occur in northern areas. Various strains of timothy and sideoats grama respond markedly to different photoperiods or hours of daylight. Wide variations occur in most of the native species. Northern types moved southward react unfavorably, but a certain amount of movement northward may stimulate the development of larger, later, and leafier growth, although flowering and seed production may become more uncertain. The formation of stolons in some bentgrasses has been found to be associated with longer days.

Ability to produce sod is often a major object. Creeping strains usually develop superior turf and serve as better protection to tramping, weed encroachment, and soil losses. In smooth bromegrass, variations in type sufficient to change greatly the top and root proportions are known. Suitable turf strains are required for greens, fairways, roughs, parks, lawns, playfields, airports, roadsides, soil stabilization, and similar purposes. In such varieties, yield and nutritive quality are minimized; vigor in turf formation, color, texture, growth habit, density, firmness, uniformity, durability, and strength of turf are more important.

Occasionally a species may be so aggressive that crop rotation may be difficult—a principal fault of quackgrass and often of bromegrass under especially favorable conditions for spreading. Work in the Soviet Union has indicated that certain ecotypes of quackgrass may be valuable and that some nonweedy types outyield smooth bromegrass. Some workers believe that a vigorously creeping grass strain may be too highly competitive for its legume partner, as, for example, bromegrass growing with alfalfa.

The utilization of some species, such as tall oatgrass, reed canarygrass, meadow foxtail, Canada wild-rye, and other grasses, is greatly discouraged by their poor seed habits in one or more respects. In tall oatgrass shattering may occur. In bluestem, for example, seeds may be light, fluffy, and densely pubescent. Variations exist in ability of strains to produce seed well under different conditions. Other factors being satisfactory, a high yield of good quality seed is desirable.

Good health in grasses is another desirable virtue. In a survey of diseases and host plants in northern parts of the Great Plains and in the Western States, 221 kinds of parasitic fungi were recorded for approximately 500 kinds of grasses. As early as 1906, stem rust was reported to have destroyed some selected strains of timothy at Arlington, Va.; other strains showed relative resistance. Losses in bluegrass due to stripe smut have been estimated at 3 to 50 percent annually in one Northeastern State. Work at the Georgia Coastal Plain Experiment Station has shown that significant differences may be obtained in Dallisgrass in resistance to anthracnose and ergot. Work of the Pasture Laboratory in Pennsylvania has indicated that snow mold of orchardgrass, stripe smut of Kentucky bluegrass, leaf spot of orchardgrass, and crown rust of meadow fescue may do serious damage and that differences in plant reaction to the disease organisms may be found.

Comparatively little information is available about the insect resistance of grass strains, but variation in reactions of strains has been noted. Harshness of tissues has been found to be related to resistance to chinch bugs in certain species native to the Great Plains. In the blue gramas, important differences in the reaction of strains to grasshopper injury may occur. Variations in the resistance of Bermuda-grass strains to root-knot nematode have been noted.

Grass varieties may differ in response to fertilizers.

Bentgrass strains vary in their tolerance to applications of 2,4–D, the new chemical for control of broadleaved, weedy plants.

Even the most important species in farm use may have serious faults. Timothy is relatively hardy, widely adapted to soil and climate and to culture with clover, persistent, reliable in seed production, and easy to establish but unfortunately it tends to become woody when more mature, and is often severely affected by disease. It recovers poorly after cutting also and is quite susceptible to drought. Some of these faults may be improved by breeding.

One of the most practicable methods of obtaining new strains of grasses is through plant introduction from other countries, especially those where extensive tests are being conducted. But since growing conditions are seldom, if ever, comparable, it happens only infrequently that an imported variety is immediately adaptable to use here, and further breeding work may be neces-

sary. Some workers have suggested that the international interchange of varieties as such, and the installation of such varieties into agricultural production are definitely undesirable. Interchange of breeding material among workers is generally practiced.

Undoubtedly much may be accomplished in the future by further introduction of older, established species as well as by procurement of seed of those which have not yet been adequately tested. For example, a new strain of Dallisgrass from Uruguay was found recently to produce about twice as much fertile seed as strains already available in the United States.

Because of the wide ranges of variation in factors affecting plant behavior from continent to continent and from one locality to another, some breeders have come to rely primarily on improvement by utilization of old, local types. These presumably are well adjusted and best capable of economical production by virtue of their continued existence following competitive growth for long periods under the particular environment. Insofar as the conditions represent those typical of the proposed area of use, there is much to be said for this viewpoint; European workers have found it to be sound. If one is to rely entirely on this approach, however, selection would have to be operative on material comparable to that made available by breeding studies.

Strains within species that have become adapted to a particular set of local conditions are called ecotypes. Ecotypes are products of natural selection operating upon populations of more or less diverse plants, many of which were probably not well adapted to the conditions originally. A population of highly variable plants established in such a local area might therefore be expected to suffer differential elimination in a manner that would tend to increase the proportion of adapted types. The principle of selecting in such natural areas is based upon this assumption.

Lincoln and Achenbach varieties of

bromegrass have developed in this fashion primarily, although the latter strain was given some early selection by the Achenbach brothers in the 1890's. In timothy the effect of natural competition among plants in modifying varietal composition has been shown. It has long been known that growth types in orchardgrass vary notably with the habitat; other work with orchardgrass has indicated that ecological groups adapted to flood land, dry land, and mountainous areas may be segregated. Variations in plant type and reaction to disease have been noted in collections of switchgrass from various parts of the Great Plains.

Northern types appeared to be earlier, less vigorous, finer, and more disease-susceptible when grown in the South than those obtained from southern areas. Variations in blue grama, side-oats grama, and big bluestem also have been observed. These differences may be large or small, depending upon the species and the factors which are of importance in the delineation of strains.

Ecotype selection may not always prove to be advantageous. Much depends upon the variability and other characteristics of the material in question and on the conditions. Work in Australia has indicated that ecotypes have not developed in one species studied. In this instance, however, the strain traced back to one well-selected lot. It is generally known that plants of both varieties and species are relatively variable and that opportunity exists for continued plant selection, even among ecotypes and strains.

With some grasses, the type of seed production practiced commercially may have much to do with the eventual nature of a particular variety. Commercial seed production from one generation to another may tend to favor the types that produce seed most abundantly, and—while the species characteristics remain relatively constant—types that are inclined to produce less seed and more vegetative growth may be proportionately re-

duced and gradually eliminated. Thus, if improved forage varieties are developed, care should be taken that subsequent propagation by seed does not cause them to drift away from their original improved characteristics.

Since cross-pollination occurs in many perennial grasses, it is difficult to develop highly uniform strains without repeated selection. It is of interest to note, however, that a number of strains of meadow fescue, timothy, and red fescue have been obtained from selection and subsequent propagation of superior individual plants. Some of these strains have possessed a considerable degree of uniformity. At present, however, grass varietal improvement usually is based upon the combination of a number of desirable plants, this varying from a few to many. Natural selection is quite comparable in results to artificial mass selection where a large number of acceptable types are propagated as improved bulk strains.

Most varieties of grass now being grown are a result of natural or artificial mass selection. Workers in Russia have reported that they do not recognize closely bred varieties of smooth bromegrass but that they have grouped the strains being grown into meadow (northern) and the Steppe (southern) types. The principal agricultural strains are in the northern group, the southern ones being inferior in general desirability but better in drought resistance. Since the beginning of grass breeding, however, many workers have recognized the importance of selecting superior types of plants and determining by progeny tests which of these might be of most promise. This is the general basis for strain improvement at present.

It is expected that progenies derived from seed of plants after free flowering will, in part, have the characteristics of the parent plant. That is a maternal type of relationship, similar to the one which exists in the open-pollinated varieties of corn.

Modern methods of corn breeding have incorporated the practice of self-pollination, so that breeders can now determine more accurately the potential hereditary capabilities of the selected parents. The practice is comparable to mating related animals, but a higher intensity of inbreeding is possible with plants than with livestock. The inbreeding procedure has been incorporated in the breeding methods with open-pollinated grasses. Selection of superior plants from cross-pollination has not been discontinued, however, such individuals being subject to the usual testing procedures.

As early as 1912, studies with timothy indicated that progenies grown from open-pollinated seed were highly variable, and that there was little indication of a transmission of the characters for which the plants were selected. More recent work with timothy has indicated that selection among open-pollinated plants for earliness, culm length, and greenness of leaves was highly effective. Results reported by other workers have been somewhat different from this finding; in general, however, there may not be a very close relationship between parent characteristics and those of the progenies derived following open-pollination.

Because inbreeding tends to increase the relationship between parent and progeny behavior, selection among inbred plants is relatively more effective than selection among openpollinated individuals. As in corn, the inbreeding process also tends to result in a reduction in vigor and fertility and progenies in earlier generations are often quite variable. Odd and weak plant types may appear. During the inbreeding period, it is desirable that selection be made for plants which possess most nearly the desired agronomic characteristics. Breeding trials may then be used to determine relative abilities of the selected plants to transmit good qualities to the offspring.

Inbreeding, or self-pollination, of grasses normally cross-pollinated presents difficulties. Very few seeds may be produced by self-pollination. In others, seed is more readily obtained.

In all important forage species, however, the more comprehensive experiments have indicated that sufficient selfed seed may be obtained to propagate the families and to practice selection within them. The technique of controlling pollination in grasses is similar to that used in corn in that the flowering heads are covered with cloth or paper bags of various types which exclude foreign pollen.

Since grass pollen is very small, it may penetrate all but the finest mesh muslins. Most workers now use semiporous types of paper, like parchment, which serves to prevent pollen entrance into the bags but which allows for some interchange of air and does not raise the temperature unduly within the bag. Many studies have been made to determine the best means of accomplishing the selfing process. Under some conditions plants may fail to set seed under bags even though the plants are not entirely self-sterile.

Grass flowers are usually small, delicate, and difficult to manipulate individually. Several investigators have shown that it is possible to accomplish emasculation of the flowers by special methods. These include specific treatments with heat or cold, or with hot water. If flowers are immersed in water at a temperature of from 45° to 49° C., for from 1 to 5 minutes, the male elements of the flowers may be killed, while those of the female are uninjured. Subsequently, pollen of the desired types may be applied to the emasculated flowers, and this results in fertilization and seed formation. However, no methods of artificial emasculation and pollination control have resulted in seed yields comparable to those made with seed setting under natural conditions.

Intercrossing may be accomplished by bagging the plants together (mutual pollination) or by a method sometimes known as "shelter pollination," in which the selected clones or plants may be isolated in the desired combinations in fields of grain or other crops and allowed to interpollinate.

It has also been reported that grass culms bearing flowers detached from the parent plant before pollination may produce seed successfully if they are kept in water. This allows additional pollination control, which may be highly advantageous under some conditions. The use of potted plants in the greenhouse also permits considerable flexibility in intercrossing because such plants may be placed together in any manner, and mutual and other types of pollination control may be utilized.

Occasionally, in highly self-sterile species, individuals with a high degree of self-fertility may be isolated. Other things being equal, these would be advantageous since inbreeding could be conducted more readily with them. If, however, relative diversity and vigor are desired in the eventual plant group which is to become a new strain, it is generally believed that a relatively high degree of self-sterility and, therefore, cross-pollination should be present. This is thought to favor increased vigor. Often plants may be found that are male-sterile; in that case cross-pollination is mandatory, and there is a tendency toward increased diversity in the progenies.

As previously indicated, most breeders consider it desirable to take a number of selected plants as the basis for an improved strain. In corn, crosses between two selfed lines may produce relatively vigorous hybrids. Subsequently, double crosses are made from combinations of two single crosses. Such hybrid combinations of selected inbred lines have not yet been utilized in grass variety development. Breeders are concerned at present with the isolation of better plants and with possible methods of combining these plants into strains that will have superior value when compared with older types.

In selecting plants, the principal problem is one of determining the relative merits of a selected individual as a parent in transmitting desirable characteristics to its progeny. Various systems of testing this ability have been developed. Plants may be crossed in pairs and the progenies studied subsequently. Groups of selected plants may be allowed to intercross freely under field conditions and progenies of each plant compared with the progenies of other plants. This type of evaluation has been referred to as polycross testing.

A new variety that is produced by the free interpollination of a number of selected plants might be referred to as a synthetic variety. In general there might be little difference between a synthetic variety and one produced from mass selection except that in the former instance the number of parents would be greatly restricted and would have survived specific tests for their combining ability or value in hybrid combinations. Thus far, few grass strains have been produced as a result of inbreeding and subsequent recombination of selected plants.

Possibilities of hybridization between species and genera of grasses are of interest. Many such crosses have been made but such hybridization does not necessarily lead to improvement. In the United States one of the earliest crosses made was between Texas bluegrass and Kentucky bluegrass. Many grass species are thought to intercross naturally under field conditions, and many interesting hybrids have been observed.

In one instance a natural cross between two species of *Spartina* resulted in the production of a new species which was well adapted and which became widely distributed on the south coast of England and elsewhere.

Hybrids between genera may also occur naturally or be made by artificial control. Many such hybrids are highly sterile and propagation by seed may be difficult or impossible. In some instances, however, vegetative propagation of exceptional hybrids may be justified. New techniques have been developed that may be used to induce fertility in sterile hybrids. Studies concerning the nature of pollination and seed formation in interspecific and other crosses have served to define more clearly the problems involved in hybridization. Special methods of embryonic plants are now available.

The carriers of heredity, the chromosomes, have been the subject of much attention during the period of growing interest in grass improvement. Technical studies of these microscopic bodies are providing basic information concerning plant relationships within and between species and are a fundamental phase of grass breeding.

Because most forage grasses cannot be evaluated in the year of seeding, the complete growth cycle required for comparisons is considerably longer than that for many other plants. Compared with wheat, for example, at least 3 years would be needed to obtain information concerning bromegrass or timothy comparable to that obtained from wheat in one year of culture. Investigations have shown that there may be comparatively little relationship between the behavior of plants spaced in nurseries and similar plants grown together in a mass seeding typical of field conditions. In other instances, good agreement has been noted. This has caused breeders some concern as it is impossible to work with individual plants—the important breeding unit— on a mass-seeded basis. Fortunately, clonal row or mass row tests of selected plants may be made and a part of the difficulty avoided. A reasonably accurate evaluation of yield and other plant characters often may be obtained by estimation.

Many techniques to test individual plants or strains to various environmental and other influences in early growth stages have been developed. Artificial tests which indicate relative degrees of winter hardiness, drought and heat resistance, and reaction to cutting and fertilizer treatments are known. In small-plot trials, with plots 7 feet square or larger, it is possible to simulate grazing conditions to a satisfactory degree by clipping or other treatments, when livestock cannot be utilized.

The problems related to strain evaluation in grasses are much more acute than with most crops. One of the most perplexing problems with respect to grass improvement is to devise methods of testing new strains that may be developed. The principal reason for this difficulty is that the manner of utilization of grass may take a wide variety of forms and may vary over a great range of conditions. Class of livestock, type of management, harvesting practices, and duration of the forage crop all play important parts.

In experimental testing it is not always possible to study these variables in all of their various combinations. As a rule only a few alternative systems of production may be utilized in testing, and strains that fail to meet the requirements under these conditions are considered to be unadapted. In some instances, also, types that have been proved to be valuable elsewhere by other workers may fail to appear promising under different conditions.

Recent progress in the development of improved strains of grasses in the United States has made possible the distribution of new varieties of a number of species. These and other potentially valuable strains are being tested extensively in regions of adaptation.

Such cultural investigations usually tend to restrict new types in areas of best performance and permit more specific varietal recommendations by agronomists, turf specialists, and others concerned. While such restriction may result in better local production, a much larger number and greater diversity of strains may be required for a given region. For economical seed production by growers and more efficient distribution by the seed trade, the number of varieties grown in any given area should be a minimum to give maximum production of high-quality forage. Wide adaptation of any particular strain would be, therefore, highly advantageous.

Since seed of different grass varieties within a species is usually indistinguishable, some method is required for maintaining strain identity through the stages of production, processing, and marketing. The system of seed certification developed for other crops, comparable with respect to maintenance of varietal identity, is being adopted for grasses.

Through the efforts of the International Crop Improvement Association of the United States and Canada and its member associations, minimum standards for the production of seed and clonal stock of varieties of a number of species of grasses have been established. State crop-improvement organizations are usually responsible for administration and execution of the certification procedure. This provides a basis for the eventual user of a grass variety to be reasonably certain that he is utilizing the best strain available. If improved varieties of grasses are to attain effective utilization, the successful maintenance of such varieties is imperative and the interest of the breeder must continue to this end.

THE AUTHOR≪ *D. C. Smith is a native of Utah and a graduate of Utah State College. His graduate work was done at Oregon State College and the University of Minnesota. Dr. Smith has been doing grass-breeding research since 1936, having been formerly a member of the Bureau of Plant Industry, Soils, and Agricultural Engineering. He is at present professor of agronomy at the University of Wisconsin. For this article he drew freely on all published literature pertinent to the subject; he expresses appreciation to colleagues who offered suggestions.*

THE NEED FOR SEED IS URGENT

E. A. HOLLOWELL, H. M. TYSDAL

THE YIELDS of seed of some of the more important forage crops have declined seriously in the past two decades. The need for more and superior seed is urgent, but producing seed is usually an incidental farm enterprise because farmers put the forage crops to other, more certain uses.

Farmers often find seed production risky. Many factors may adversely affect seed yields of legumes and grasses: Unadapted varieties, poor cultural and management practices, harmful insects, lack of beneficial insects, diseases, unfavorable weather, soils deficient in major or minor nutritive elements, and losses in harvesting.

The farmer can direct the action of most of these factors, other than weather, toward an improvement in seed yields by following planned programs to make conditions as favorable as he possibly can.

Less than 1 percent of the legume and grass seed produced in the United States is of improved varieties. Selecting seed of the best variety for planting is the first step in successful production. The market demand for such seed is heavy; besides, the seed grower can benefit by having the most productive crops when he uses them for forage purposes.

In many of the major grass and legume crops, distinct and important differences exist in the adaptation of specific varieties for given regions or conditions: The valuable characteristics, such as the high yields and permanence of stands of Lincoln bromegrass, the earliness of Marietta timothy, the aggressiveness of Alta fescue for turf purposes, the resistance of Tift Sudangrass to leaf diseases, the high yields of Coastal Bermuda-grass, the resistance to bacterial wilt of Buffalo and Ranger alfalfas, the resistance of Cumberland and Kenland red clovers to southern anthracnose, the high yields and quality of Ladino clover, and the later maturity and high yields of Climax Korean lespedeza give greater returns of forage and persistency of stands than common kinds do.

In some regions where seed production is a main farm enterprise, the seed grower may find it more profitable to produce the variety having the greatest market demand, even though its yields of seed and forage may be less than those of the variety best adapted to his farm. Sometimes this is true of the western grower who wants to produce seed for the eastern market. But the fact remains that until seed of improved varieties is multiplied and made available to farmers, agriculture does not profit from the research in breeding and crop improvement that State and Federal agencies conduct.

Planting seed for seed production in a loose, cloddy seedbed that is low in the needed plant nutrients and foul with weeds or weed seeds foredooms failure.

Broadcast plantings of biennials and perennials seldom produce seed the first year.

Under favorable conditions, however, row seedings of many legumes frequently produce good seed crops the year of seeding. When the supplies of moisture are limited, row plantings yield more seed than broadcast sowings.

For most grasses and legumes, a steady, vigorous growth is conducive to high seed yields, but a rank vegetative growth, especially one that lodges, usually results in low yields. With most grasses and many legumes clipping or grazing, which checks the growth from which seed is to be harvested, reduces the seed yields. With alfalfa, red clover, and Ladino clover, however, the second crop is generally saved for seed. Removal of the first crop for hay or pasture reduces the number of harmful insects and brings the plants into bloom when warm, bright weather is expected; maximum flower development and activity of pollinating insects are thus encouraged.

Burning the dead growth early in the spring before new growth starts has given increased seed yields of Bahiagrass and centipedegrass in the South and on red and Chewings fescues in the North. Lower seed yields of orchardgrass and tall oatgrasses occur following burning.

The productivity of the soil is important. Studies in some places have shown that the addition of nitrogen even to relatively fertile soils has increased the seed production of grasses like brome, orchardgrass, tall fescue, Kentucky bluegrass, Dallisgrass, and some others. Where the soil is less fertile, it is well to add a complete fertilizer that includes phosphate and potash. To produce legume seed, adequate supplies of calcium, phosphate, and potash are essential. In some localities, the use of small amounts of the minor elements has proved beneficial.

Even when flowers develop in abundance, failures in seed setting occur frequently. Sometimes unusually hot, dry weather will blast the developing seed; a period of wet, rainy weather also is detrimental.

Many legumes and grasses require cross-pollination before fertilization will occur. Cross-pollination in grasses is brought about largely by wind; insects that visit flowers for nectar or pollen are the principal pollinators of many legumes. Self-pollinated legumes and grasses are less affected by weather conditions and the absence or scarcity of beneficial insects. Self-pollination of some species will occur before the flowers are fully open. After the flowers are open, pollination generally must occur within 3 to 5 days; otherwise the ovules will disintegrate and no seed will be formed.

In the following classification of species of grasses and legumes with respect to their mode of fertilization (a list prepared with the help of G. W. Burton, J. R. Harlan, H. M. Laude, Roland McKee, L. C. Newell, and G. A. Rogler), we give the best information we have on the behavior of the crops under field conditions. But in many instances the information is based on meager experimental data and is not necessarily final. Some of the species, particularly the grasses, contain many forms with varying numbers of chromosomes, so there is a tendency to produce wide variations within a species.

LEGUMES

Mostly Self-Fertilized

Crotalaria spp.	Crotalaria
Lathyrus spp.	
Lespedeza cuneata	Sericea lespedeza
Lespedeza stipulacea	Korean lespedeza
Lespedeza striata	Common lespedeza
Medicago spp. (annuals)	Bur-clover
Medicago lupulina	Black medic
Melilotus dentata	Banat sweetclover
Melilotus indica	Sourclover
Pisum arvense	Field pea
Soja max	Soybean
Trifolium dubium	Small hop clover
Trifolium fragiferum	Strawberry clover
Trifolium glomeratum	Cluster clover
Trifolium procumbens	Large hop clover
Trifolium resupinatum	Persian clover
Trifolium striatum	Striata clover
Trifolium subterraneum	Sub clover
Vicia spp.	Vetches

Mostly Cross-Fertilized

Lespedeza bicolor	Bush lespedeza
Lotus corniculatus	Birdsfoot trefoil
Lotus uliginosus	Big trefoil
Medicago falcata	Yellow alfalfa
Medicago sativa	Common alfalfa
Melilotus officinalis.	Yellow sweetclover
Trifolium hybridum	Alsike clover
Trifolium pratense	Red clover
Trifolium repens	White clover

Self- or Cross-Fertilized

Melilotus alba	White sweetclover
Melilotus suaveolens	Daghestan sweetclover
Trifolium incarnatum	Crimson clover

GRASSES

Mostly Cross-Fertilized

Agropyron cristatum	Crested wheatgrass
Agropyron desertorum	Desert wheatgrass
Agropyron intermedium	Intermediate wheatgrass
Agropyron michnoi	
Agropyron sibiricum	Siberian wheatgrass
Agropyron smithii	Western wheatgrass
Agropyron trichophorum	Stiffhair wheatgrass
Andropogon furcatus	Big bluestem
Andropogon hallii	Sand bluestem
Andropogon scoparius	Little bluestem
Bouteloua curtipendula	Side-oats grama
Bouteloua gracilis	Blue grama
Bromus inermis	Smooth bromegrass
Buchloë dactyloides	Buffalograss
Cynodon dactylon	Bermuda-grass
Dactylis glomerata	Orchardgrass
Digitaria pentzii	Pentz fingergrass
Digitaria stolonifera	Woollyfinger
Elymus junceus	Russian wild-rye
Festuca elatior var. *arundinacea*	Tall fescue
Festuca rubra	Creeping red fescue
Panicum virgatum	Switchgrass
Paspalum notatum hort. var. *Pensacola*	Bahiagrass
Pennisetum glaucum	Pearlmillet
Poa arachnifera	Texas bluegrass
Sorghum vulgare var. *sudanense*	Sudangrass

Mostly Self-Fertilized

Agropyron trachycaulum	Slender wheatgrass
Bromus spp. (annuals)	Bromes
*Bromus carinatus**	California bromegrass
*Bromus catharticus**	Rescuegrass
Elymus canadensis	Canada wild-rye
Elymus virginicus	Virginia wild-rye
Eragrostis curvula	Weeping lovegrass
Eragrostis trichodes	Sand lovegrass
*Stipa cernua**	Nodding needlegrass
*Stipa lepida**	Foothill needlegrass
*Stipa pulchra**	Purple needlegrass
*Stipa viridula**	Feather bunchgrass

(*Highly cleistogamous, especially first year.)

Possibly Apomictic

Bouteloua curtipendula	Side-oats grama var. Tucson
Panicum virgatum	Switchgrass (bottom-land type)
Paspalum dilatatum	Dallisgrass
Paspalum notatum	Bahiagrass (common broadleaf)
Poa pratensis	Kentucky bluegrass

Primarily Dioecious

Buchloë dactyloides	Buffalograss
Poa arachnifera	Texas bluegrass

Pollinating insects are essential for successful seed production of the species of legumes that we listed as mostly cross-fertilized. The insects may also enhance seed yields of some species listed as largely self-fertilized. A scarcity of pollinating insects is one of the chief factors that limit seed production of cross-pollinated legumes.

An example of the magnitude of the problems of cross-pollination in legumes is red clover. An acre of red clover in full bloom has approximately 300 million flowers, and 300 million visits by bees are necessary for perfect crossing and maximum seed setting. That tremendous job must be done in approximately 3 weeks. Alfalfa, white clover, and the sweetclovers are just as floriferous as red clover and require cross-pollination. And, aside from the number of pollinators needed, specific plant-insect relationships occur in alfalfa and red clover.

In alfalfa, fertilization and seed setting depend on tripping the flowers and on the transfer of pollen from one flower to another by insects, chiefly wild bees and honeybees. The alfalfa flower produces nectar and pollen that attract the honeybee. But when more attractive sources are available, the bee usually visits them instead of the alfalfa. When the bee collects nectar from alfalfa flowers, it avoids tripping them, possibly because it hates the slap in the face it gets when it trips the flowers. So, bees are effective alfalfa flower trippers and pollen-carrying agents when other sources of pollen are scarce.

The flower of the red clover has a long tube, at the bottom of which the secreted nectar accumulates. Under most conditions red clover does not produce an abundance of nectar, and the honeybee, when it thrusts its head into the top of the flower, cannot reach the nectar. But it does trip the flower; foreign pollen is transferred; cross-pollination occurs; and seed sets. The pollen of red clover is attractive to the honeybee, and the flower is tripped as the bee gathers pollen. The presence of other plants, such as sweetclover, alsike clover, or white clover, which provide good sources of both nectar and pollen, however, diverts the honeybee from red clover. Under such conditions it is a poor pollinator.

Wild bees for the most part are effective pollinators of alfalfa, red clover, and other legumes. Genera of wild bees that are good pollinators are *Megachile, Nomia, Bombus, Melis-* *sodes, Calliopsis, Halictus, Agapostemon, Anthidium, Augochlora, Anthophora, Andrena,* and *Tetralonia.*

In localities where wild bees are found, the seed grower will do well to protect their nesting places.

The only method now available to increase the number of pollinators is to place hives of honeybees near the seed field, as many as two or three strong colonies to an acre at blossoming time. When possible, cutting competing pollen-and-nectar-producing plants aids in forcing the bees to alfalfa and red clover. In some instances the time of cutting the first crop can be varied so as to bring the seed crop into flower when the competing plants are not in bloom.

Insects; Diseases

Many destructive insects attack forage crops. They may injure the roots, stems, or leaves, thus weakening the plant and indirectly reducing the yield of seed. Others directly attack the developing seed.

Chinch bugs, white grubs, stem maggots, grasshoppers, and others frequently cause low seed yields of many grasses.

Plant bugs, potato leafhoppers, root borers, root curculios, alfalfa weevils, sweetclover weevils, the grasshoppers, thrips, and others reduce yields of legume seeds. Some insects that directly attack legume seed are the vetch bruchid, clover seed chalcid, clover midge, and clover seed weevil. Indeed, the vetch bruchid is jeopardizing the production of the seed of hairy vetch in the United States.

DDT provides a means of controlling many harmful insects. One application of a dust containing 10 percent of DDT at 20 pounds an acre just before the flowers begin to open has given highly satisfactory control of lygus bugs and alfalfa weevil in seed alfalfa. Similarly, 25 pounds of a dust containing 3 percent of DDT, applied to hairy vetch when the first pods begin to form, has given good control of the vetch bruchid. So far, observations indicate that these treatments, properly applied, are not harmful to pollinating insects, but the straw and chaff from treated crops should not be used for feeding purposes, at least until more is known about the poison hazards involved.

The seed grower also has to be on guard against numerous diseases that may attack different parts of the plants, weaken them, and prevent seed setting.

Grass diseases, like the root rots, leaf spots, anthracnose, and stem canker, weaken or kill the plants outright. Others, such as ergot on Dallisgrass, destroy the developing seed. Blind spot on ryegrass reduces the germination. Bacterial wilt of alfalfa, anthracnose of red clover, stem canker on vetch, bacterial wilt of lespedeza, root rot, stem canker on sweetclover, and others are serious diseases of legumes that lower yields.

Some diseases are seed-borne. Others are widely present in the soil. The best way to control them is to use disease-resistant varieties. Infected seed should not be sold or used.

In the Eastern States many legumes and grasses will not produce consistently an abundance of seed under conditions under which they are grown profitably for forage. On many Corn Belt farms the forage requirements are high and the use of a forage crop for seed production conflicts with corn and soybean production. Many farmers are not interested in producing seed even if they could do so. But the local production of seed of improved varieties should be encouraged. Seed of varieties adapted to the locality, grown in other regions, should supplement the locally produced seed.

Several districts in the Western States now specialize in the production of grass and legume seed. Conditions mostly are favorable there, but the producers will do well to bear in mind that unless they grow varieties adapted to the regions where the seed is to be used the customers in the East will suffer losses and naturally will buy next year's seed elsewhere.

Weather is all-important. In a few days it can destroy a potentially profitable seed crop. It determines the regions where seed production can be expected to be successful. It influences plant development and insect life and activity.

Damp, rainy weather stimulates the growth and retards the blooming of several legumes and also retards the wind movement of pollen. On the other hand, bright, sunny weather favors blooming and increases the activities and numbers of pollinating insects as well as harvesting operations. The important thing is to bring the crop into seed production when the probability of bright warm weather is greatest.

Harvesting

The important factors in harvesting seed are time and method.

Many forage crops shatter badly if they are allowed to remain in the field until all seed is mature. It is therefore necessary to harvest most of them when most of the seed is matured, even though some of the seed is still green. Degree of shattering, length of blooming and seed-setting period, and the amount and conditions of growth differ widely among legumes and grasses. Weather, at the time of harvesting, affects the efficiency of harvesting and threshing methods.

The loss of seed in harvesting and threshing can be great: In an experiment where harvested red clover was cured under shelter, only 63 percent of the seed was removed in the first threshing when the combine was used as a stationary machine. The first rethreshing of the straw yielded 29 percent, and the second rethreshing 8 percent of the total seed yield.

Under the most favorable climatic conditions for curing the crop before threshing, experienced seed producers have found it profitable to rethresh the straw when using the combine as a stationary machine. Suction harvesters are also used with good results in harvesting such crops as bur-clover in the South, buffalograss in the Great Plains, and Ladino and sub clover seed in the Western States. Sometimes suction harvesters are used as gleaners to save shattered seed. Combine threshing now is probably used more than any other method for most crops, although with it seed losses often are high.

No one method can be used for all forage crops, but the best procedure for most is to cut and windrow the seed crop, cure it in the windrow, and thresh by using the combine with pick-up attachments or as a stationary machine. A stationary grain thresher equipped with hulling attachments does the best job in threshing legume seed that have tough pods.

To avoid losses from shattering, regardless of the method, the seed should be handled no more than absolutely necessary. When shattering is severe, cutting at night or early morning when the plants are damp with dew will reduce the losses.

The proper processing of grass and legume seed requires considerable expensive machinery. An inexpensive fanning mill may put the seed in condition for planting if the grower's field is free of weeds; if it is not, special equipment is needed to remove weed seeds and to obtain the desired purity. Sometimes, particularly among the grasses, special processes have been developed to remove glumes and chaffy material so as to facilitate cleaning and seeding. One of these methods is to put the seed through a hammer mill run at a low speed. Special equipment for cleaning and processing is too costly for the small grower, but this service is available by the seed trade. Another common practice is for the grower to sell his seed to the seedsman on the basis of pounds of recleaned seed.

Seedstocks of low moisture content may be protected from damage by insects while in storage if thoroughly treated with a very fine magnesium oxide powder at the rate of 1 ounce to the bushel. A dust containing 3 percent of DDT, used one-half ounce to the bushel, will protect the stored seed from insects, but seed so treated should not be fed to livestock.

Growers and dealers who offer forage seed for sale should inform themselves regarding the State and Federal seed laws. Almost always the seed must be properly labeled in order to comply with the law—a protection to both buyer and seller. Interstate shipments are subject to the Federal Seed Act.

To permit the user to take advantage of improved varieties, the seed he buys must be fully and clearly identified. Because most of the improved varieties cannot be distinguished from common kinds by the looks of the seed, a procedure is necessary that will identify the variety for both the producer and the consumer. State certified-seed programs perform this function. Seed of improved varieties is produced under regulations to protect it from contamination with common kinds in the field and at all stages of harvesting, processing, and distribution. The fields are inspected to determine the trueness of variety and freedom from noxious weeds. Certified seed from such fields is sealed in bags and identified by tags of the certifying agency, which is, in most cases, the State Crop Improvement Association. The variety name on the tags gives the purchaser the assurance of the trueness to variety.

THE AUTHORS «‹‹‹   *E. A. Hollowell and H. M. Tysdal are agronomists in the Bureau of Plant Industry, Soils, and Agricultural Engineering.*

Dr. Hollowell is in charge of the Bureau's clover investigations. Since 1924 he has carried on research pertaining to the cultural phases of clover production and the development of improved varieties. New superior varieties have been developed and their farm use expanded as a result of his work.

Dr. Tysdal, as a fellow of the American Scandinavian Foundation, studied plant breeding and plant physiology in Sweden and on the Continent in 1927–28. He has written numerous papers on the improvement of alfalfa.

WANTED: A PARAGON FOR THE RANGE

WESLEY KELLER

CRESTED WHEATGRASS is a good grass—more valuable perhaps than all other range-forage species that we now know about. It is largely responsible for the success of reseeding work on spring-fall ranges of the Intermountain region, where several millions of acres of denuded lands have been restored.

It is also a good example of the work and aims of investigators whose function is to discover superior strains for use in artificial reseeding and to supply whatever characteristics the reseeders desire in a species.

For, to be most effective, artificial reseeding must do much more than merely clothe the land with grasses. The grasses must be well adapted to the sites where they are seeded. They must be highly productive, nutritious, and palatable to livestock, long-lived or able to reseed themselves, tolerant of grazing, aggressive enough when moderately grazed to resist invasion by less desirable species, and effective in controlling erosion—not by any means a simple problem!

To get such a paragon, research workers have studied the sites that need revegetation. They have explored the relative merits for reseeding of a large number of native and introduced species. They have investigated most extensively the spring-fall ranges of the Intermountain region, the part of the range where acute yearly feed shortages occur. Their work began in 1902.

The first step in plant improvement is the careful evaluation of available material, including the introductions from foreign countries.

Among those introductions, several valuable range-forage species have been discovered. One of them is crested wheatgrass, which was brought to the United States in 1906. Many others have been imported since, but the merits of crested wheatgrass have remained outstanding. On the Northern Great Plains it proved to be longer-lived, more productive, and more drought-resistant than slender wheatgrass; it was found to be superior to smooth bromegrass, which, although long-lived, is less drought-resistant and becomes sod-bound.

Crested wheatgrass has been seeded extensively on the Northern Great Plains; its range of adaptation has been extended to all but the southern parts of the Intermountain region. It is well adapted to sagebrush lands and marginal or submarginal dry-farm lands that formerly were covered with grass or sage and are principally spring-fall range. Accurate figures are unavailable, but it is probable that more acres of range land have been successfully regrassed with crested wheatgrass than with all other species combined.

It has faults, however. Except under ideal conditions, seedling development may be slow. It is sensitive in the seedling stage to competition from cheatgrass. Growth ceases during the warm part of the year even though moisture is abundant—probably the main reason that it has not spread farther southward. Its palatability becomes less satisfactory as it matures.

To overcome these undesirable traits, plant breeders have imported seeds of crested wheatgrass, made simple mass selections from them, and have grown them in comparative tests in several parts of the range area. They have found some that are clearly superior to others, but so far have tested no selections very extensively because of limited quantities of seed or lack of time. Their work, however, progresses.

Recent introductions that give promise in range tests of challenging crested wheatgrass under some conditions are tall wheatgrass, stiffhair wheatgrass, and intermediate wheatgrass. As reseeding work is extended into the summer and winter ranges and the all-season ranges of the South, other species will grow in importance.

Crested wheatgrass, smooth brome-grass, and many of the other promising range-forage species are naturally cross-pollinated. Such cross-pollination (meaning that in the process of reproduction the pollen of each plant is shed freely and serves to fertilize the flowers of other plants of the species rather than its own) gives progenies in which the individual plants differ considerably. No two are exactly alike. Thus, when the available material has been compared, and the most promising strains identified, the breeder can take advantage of this variation within the strains.

The simplest form of plant breeding applied to variable strains is called mass selection. It consists of choosing from a large number of plants those that possess desired characteristics. The selected plants are then allowed to cross-pollinate among themselves as a means of concentrating these characteristics.

Unfortunately, plants arising by cross-pollination and reproducing by the same process frequently are not efficient in transmitting to their progenies the characteristics that they themselves possess. Thus mass selection may be a rather slow and relatively inefficient method of concentrating desirable characteristics in a strain and, in fact, may not achieve a very high degree of concentration even when applied to several successive generations. Nevertheless, because mass selection is easy and sometimes yields outstanding results, it usually is made use of in early phases of a breeding program with cross-pollinated species.

Some form of mass selection is the process used so extensively by nature, and, under natural conditions, has been effective in producing the many strains that characterize every widely distributed species. Most of the forage grasses as they exist today are the products of mass selection in nature.

Lincoln bromegrass, a notable example of cooperation between man and nature to produce a superior variety, is a mass selection made in southern Nebraska from plants that survived the drought of 1934. A number of other southern strains with somewhat similar history are being certified by various States in the Middle West.

Grass breeders are becoming increasingly interested in the controlled hybridization of selected plants. It is a refinement of mass selection. Each selected plant is crossed with every other selected plant. By this means a considerable number of distinct progenies are obtained rather than a single progeny of restricted but indefinite parentage.

The behavior of the separate progenies indicates which combinations are superior. The parent plants may then be vegetatively increased to provide larger quantities of seed. The method offers great possibilities, but preliminary experience indicates that it should be undertaken on a rather large scale in order to increase the chances of obtaining superior combinations. No strains of range-forage grasses produced by this method have as yet reached the stage where seed is available for widespread testing.

In the earlier years of breeding forage plants, along with mass selection, considerable interest and effort were expended on cross-pollinated species in the production of selfed lines. This no doubt stemmed from the remarkable accomplishments of the corn breeders in producing hybrid corn by the recombination of inbreds. It is too early to say that the use of selfed lines for producing hybrids will not be an effective method of breeding grass, but interest in the method has lessened, and more direct methods are being pursued.

Corn breeders use inbred lines as a means of preserving breeding stock of known characteristics. The perennial characteristic greatly simplifies the preservation of any available grass genotype. Thus grass breeders have come to a realization that selfing may be a method highly effective on some crops and probably useful on others, but not necessarily a fundamental procedure suitable to all. Some of the foundation work that has led the interest of grass breeders away from selfing has been done with alfalfa.

A number of important species of range forage grasses are naturally self-pollinated. Like wheat and barley, they produce uniform-appearing progenies.

Slender wheatgrass, a notable example, has a wide range of adaptation, and natural selection has produced many clearly differentiated strains. Some of them differ greatly in such characteristics as yield, palatability, seed productivity, date of maturity, and earliness. Species of this type require relatively simple breeding methods because progenies generally duplicate the characteristics of the parent.

A small amount of natural crossing is believed to enhance the breeding possibilities with slender wheatgrass. Even though slender wheatgrass requires only simple breeding methods, it is not receiving a great deal of attention from plant breeders. The reason is that the species, although widespread, is not dominant on any extensive area. This suggests that wherever it is reseeded it is soon invaded by other species. On the drier sites where reseeding is successful, crested wheatgrass is superior; on more favored sites, it will not compete with smooth brome and several other species.

An interesting recent development in the improvement of range forage is the establishment of a project for work with bluegrasses, partly because of their widespread occurrence, particularly in the Northwest, but even more because they are characterized by a method of reproduction known as apomixis, which offers the breeder many advantages.

Apomixis is reproduction without the union of gametes, so that apomictic progenies are genetically identical to the parent plants. The condition in species of bluegrass that makes apomixis of greatest interest to plant breeders is that it is accompanied by a variable degree of gametic reproduction. Gametic reproduction thus can be employed to produce a wide range of genetic variation and the desired types can be perpetuated indefinitely by apomictic reproduction. Other important range-forage plants reproduce by apomixis. One of them is Tucson, an apomictic strain of side-oats grama, which appears to be well adapted to the Southern Great Plains, where its breeding behavior is being studied.

The orthodox conception of what constitutes a species has recently been attacked by cyto-geneticists and cyto-taxonomists. The development is not particularly surprising; those who have classified grasses on the basis of their appearance and floral morphology have long recognized the limitations of the method. Some of the difficulties encountered by the old taxonomy are apparent from such names as *Elymus pseudoagropyron* and in the frequent renaming of some species as taxonomists have uncovered additional information concerning them.

On the whole, the established classification of forage grasses has been good, but on the basis of breeding behavior it is certain that many revisions eventually will be made. The following are a few of the many intergeneric hybrids that are known and that, in the aggregate, offer proof of this statement: *Agropyron saundersii* is the natural hybrid between slender wheatgrass and big squirreltail (*Sitanion jubatum*); Macoun wild-rye (*Elymus macounii*) is the natural hybrid between slender wheatgrass and foxtail barley (*Hordeum jubatum*); *Oryzopsis bloomeri* is the natural hybrid between Indian ricegrass (*O. hymenoides*) and western needlegrass (*Stipa occidentalis*).

These natural hybrids are easily recognized because they are sterile. The wealth of information that is accumulating in this field throws much light on the origin of many species of grasses and on their relationship to other species, and will eventually contribute directly toward the production of superior grasses.

The significant contributions of recent years that have enlarged our understanding of double fertilization have at the same time greatly expanded the horizons of wide crosses. It seems reasonable to believe that wide crosses, coupled with embryo culture where needed, will play an increasingly important role in the breeding of range forage plants.

There is one striking example of immediate benefit to the range from interspecific hybridization occurring in nature. In the arid interior of California, where summer droughts are long and accompanied by high temperatures, several species of *Stipa* occur naturally. Recent investigation has shown that some of these, when growing in association, produce natural hybrids quite freely. The hybrids are completely sterile, but they are more vigorous than the parents and remain green 4 weeks to 6 weeks longer in the summer. The establishment of the parent species in association with one another in areas where they are adapted appears to be all that is needed to insure the subsequent establishment of the superior hybrids.

So much information on all related subjects was available when range plant improvement began that some persons were led to predict that in a relatively few years many superior forage strains would be available. Substantial progress has been made, but some problems remain.

Several reasons come to mind. The range is collectively a highly variable area—really an aggregation of a large number of irregular sites, each differing from those adjacent to it in greater or lesser degree; it is not possible therefore to concentrate on a single set of conditions.

Another reason is that relatively few (if, indeed, any range lands) are adequately represented by the favorable environments found on experimental farms. One cannot stress too much the importance of conducting all vital phases of a range-forage breeding program on range lands. To use land that is adapted to the production of culti-

vated crops is merely to introduce an unnecessary variable (and one of unknown magnitude) into an already complicated problem. Certain phases of the work, such as seed increase, or the growing of plants to be used in controlled hybridization, may well be done on productive cropland, but the selection of those plants should be made on lands that represent as truly as possible the area which the species is expected to restore to grass. Only on similar sites can one hope to obtain an accurate appraisal of the products of a breeding program.

A third point is that any attempt to evaluate the products of a grass-breeding program without placing them on the range itself (in conjunction with direct measurements of yield and with grazing animals to harvest them) is incomplete and subject to errors of unknown magnitude.

Also: The large number of grass species that are native to the range and many introduced species that require testing have imposed on the reseeder and breeder a complicated job of evaluation before the foundation material for a breeding program can be intelligently selected.

And, finally, on nearly all range sites plant growth encounters serious limiting factors, such as long, dry summers, shallow, eroded soils, or competition from aggressive species of low forage value. For these reasons, reseedings frequently require several years to become established and additional time to demonstrate their adaptability to seasonal variations and management.

It is an established fact that in farm pastures a grass-legume association is more productive than grass alone. Agencies concerned with reseeding have given considerable attention to the appraisal of legumes for range lands and have found none that appears promising over extensive areas. As a result, reseeding practices usually include only grasses. Although the problem may be somewhat more complicated than the improvement of species already adapted to the range, the development of legumes suitable for use with grasses in range reseeding appears to be a plant-breeding problem that warrants considerable attention.

The browse plants present another important problem. Millions of acres of winter range lands in the Great Basin, represented by the lowest rainfall areas, probably never were dominated by grasses. On a significant part of these ranges, the most desirable browse plants, such as winterfat, are being—or already have been—replaced by species that are far less valuable as forage plants. Chamiza, a browse plant of considerable importance in the Southwest, produces a quality of forage comparable to alfalfa. It is clearly superior to most grasses in nutritive value. Because of a deep root system and drought-resistance, the seasonal production of chamiza is much more consistent than that of grasses under the same conditions. Winterfat, chamiza, and other desirable browse plants possess great possibilities.

Water is the limiting factor least susceptible to change by man over a large part of the range, and is a very critical factor over much of the range. Comprehensive studies of the water requirement of range-forage species should contribute greatly to forage-plant breeding. The water requirement is the pounds of water required by the plant to produce 1 pound of dry matter. Certainly the ideal range-forage plant would have, among other qualities, a low water requirement.

That is another of the problems that still stand between man and the improvement of his ranges.

THE AUTHOR≪ *Wesley Keller, a native of Utah and a graduate of Utah State Agricultural College and the University of Wisconsin, has been engaged in research on grass improvement since 1936. Dr. Keller, geneticist in the Bureau of Plant Industry, Soils, and Agricultural Engineering, is stationed at Logan, Utah.*

IMMIGRANTS TO OUR GRASSLANDS

C. O. ERLANSON

OF ALL the causes that disrupt the delicate balance between the native vegetation and its environment, man himself has been the most devastating and continuously destructive—and always with increasing effectiveness as he has evolved through the ages from a hunter to a herder and finally to a tiller of the soil.

He has destroyed the forest for fuel and lumber, by fire intentionally and by accident, replacing the cover with the sun-loving, mostly annual plants that have evolved with him from time immemorial. His herds have spread across the plains and savannas, often in such number as to overgraze the best grassland and destroy the most beneficial forage. And it is only recently that man in the more populous regions of the world has taken stock of his land

and its diminishing returns. He is beginning to realize that soil must be conserved, forests replanted, and valuable forage protected or augmented by the introduction of plant materials from elsewhere.

As man has evolved, his favorite plants have evolved with him; he carried them from place to place as he migrated just as he took with him his domesticated animals and the forage plants to which they are accustomed. Because the United States was settled largely by Europeans, it is not surprising that our agricultural methods, crops, and domestic animals are primarily European and differ only in the degree that the impact with a new environment changes them.

Happily, much that our colonists brought with them did well enough in the New World to allow the early establishment of self-sufficient agricultural settlements. From those early days the problems of plant industry in the United States have had to do mostly with the adaptation and improvement of our European heritage as the crops have spread to the limits of their adaptability throughout the country.

Not one of our major agricultural crops is native to the United States, not even those which the aborigines were cultivating when the first colonists settled here. Maize, tobacco, pumpkins, squash, and beans had been introduced by the migrating Indians from more tropical America. Through the years, from the time of the first settlements to the present, many crops and potentially valuable material—some new, others only variations—have been introduced from all parts of the world. A few of these have become eminently successful additions to our agriculture; others have played important roles in our breeding and improvement programs; and many have fallen by the wayside as unfitted to our needs of the moment.

Thus it would appear that the introduction of plants has been a fundamental factor in our agricultural development and will continue to be so to meet new situations and problems as they arise.

In general, the history of the forage plants we cultivate for grazing animals is the same as that of our other crops, except that all indications point to a shorter period of domestication. Probably no need was felt until rather recently to preserve specific kinds of forage, because the native range was ample and man needed only to shift to greener pastures. We can still find what appear to be the wild progenitors of many of our forage crops although some have been cultivated for centuries, and nature has a bountiful supply of close relatives with which to improve what we have.

Our present cultivated forage plants are by no means a haphazard conglomeration inherited from our ancestors; rather, they have outstanding characteristics that caused men to choose them from among the thousands upon which their stock grazed.

Many factors contributed to such choice, but the major attributes probably were food value, abundance, ability to reproduce freely, aggressiveness, and resistance to constant grazing. The two plant groups that furnish practically all of these are the true grasses and the legumes.

We have done well with the plants brought with us from the Old World. For a large part of the northeastern United States, with a climate much like that of Europe, our present forage needs are reasonably well satisfied. Here plant introduction is concerned mainly with bringing into the country new strains and varieties for the plant breeder to improve what we have, either in higher yield or resistance to pests and diseases. But in our Southeast and in large sections of the West, climatic conditions are so different that the common European crops do not thrive. To meet the needs of those areas, we must introduce cultivated or wild material from other parts of the world where conditions are nearly similar, or search among the native plants for promising types.

By 1900 it was recognized generally that formal procedures were needed to handle the introduction of new plant material. Seeds and plants brought from abroad by travelers, missionaries, explorers, and immigrants often were valuable but seldom received an adequate trial under proper conditions. No centralized record was available as to the results of trials. Foreign diseases came in and threatened our crops. Also, the development of the science of plant breeding caused a great impetus to the demand for specific programs of introduction for use in our plant improvement.

Within the Federal Department of Agriculture a unit was organized to centralize plant introduction activities for the Nation as a whole, a step which has since been taken by many other countries with progressive agricultural programs. Such centralization in no way precludes the free exchange of materials among Nations, individuals, institutions, or States, but is designed to implement and safeguard such exchange with expert services and knowledge gained by cumulative experience. It handles the needs of vast regions as well as local problems.

Foreign plant material is obtained in various ways. A continuous and active exchange with foreign research workers and institutions brings in the greater amount. Direct purchases from seedsmen and nurseries account for additional strains and varieties of cultivated materials. But potentially the most important and the hardest to obtain are the wild plants of foreign regions which are related to our important crops and may have characteristics needed to extend their adaptability and vigor, or which in themselves may become new crops to complement what we have. The procurement of such material usually requires specially planned exploration.

Each introduction by Federal workers is given a serial number. With the number is recorded all information that came with the plant as to source, collector, and possible value. The introduction passes through sanitary inspection, is fumigated or otherwise treated when necessary, or is grown under quarantine. Botanists verify its identity as closely as the material will allow; then the introduction may be ordered out for propagation and trial.

The material obtained deliberately for use in active breeding and improvement programs is immediately turned over to research workers. With the constant inflow of introductions, however, come valuable seeds and plants which are of no immediate interest in any program but which should be propagated and investigated to ascertain their future usefulness for the United States. For this purpose, the Federal Government maintains four Plant Introduction Gardens in Maryland, Georgia, Florida, and Cali-

fornia. They are supplemented by various State and Federal experiment stations that maintain special collections. The maintenance of these reservoirs of germ-plasm material is limited by funds available, but they have proved so valuable that recently some citizens have suggested that more such stations be established in all the important agricultural regions of the country.

One of the basic problems of plant introduction is the procurement of plants which may be used to diversify the agriculture of the several regions of the United States. A dependence on the one or two crops found to be most successful in a region often leads to trouble in a period of abnormal drought, pestilence, or overproduction. In diversification there is stability.

The determination of which world regions are most likely to supply new material requires an intimate knowledge of the climates and soils of the world in relation to those of the United States. Materials needed for specific areas in the United States should be obtained from as nearly similar climates as possible in order that the plants may grow as naturally as possible. Most plants have considerable tolerance to varying growing conditions, which is fortunate since no two areas are exactly similar. Often, if the areas are too divergent, the hot summers or cold winters, the humidity or drought stunt the growth of the plant immigrant. Sometimes the plant grows well enough, but fails to mature its seed. Some plants require lime in the soil, while others do well in acid soils; some plants tolerate alkali, but most do not. We must have at least a modicum of this kind of knowledge if an introduction is to receive a fair trial.

Of more importance to plant introduction in recent years is the study of the geographical distribution of the plant groups to which our crops belong. A detailed study of a group, whether its species are mostly cultivated or wild, indicates that, although the group may be widely spread across the world, there are centers within its area of distribution with high concentrations of variability. It is within these centers of variation that the plant explorer is most highly rewarded in his search for individuals with new habits of growth, productiveness, resistance to pests and diseases, and the many other characteristics of use to the plant breeder in his efforts to prevent degeneration and increase productivity of our crops.

The interval between the introduction of plant material and the day when results may be measured in dollar value to the country often is long. Through the tedious process of testing and evaluation, an introduction passes through many hands, and acquires new numbers and names until its identity as an introduced plant becomes obscure. Many times it is only one of several parents used in the development of a new variety. Too often by the time the new crop or variety has reached this final stage and may be

recommended to growers, the breeder alone is aware of the part that the imported germ plasm has played in its development. But just as a crop needs sun and water, so also it must have new blood from wherever it can be found to keep it healthy and productive.

A review of the introductions during the past few years shows that more than a third of the imported plant material was destined for trial as forage. Much of what has been received is from the wild, and little is yet known concerning cycles of growth and adaptability. The domestication of wild plants is not accomplished overnight, in a year, and often not in 20 years.

THE AUTHOR≪≪ *C. O. Erlanson, principal ecologist in the Division of Plant Exploration and Introduction, Bureau of Plant Industry, Soils, and Agricultural Engineering, has done research on the origin and utilization of economic plant materials since 1930.*

DOMESTICATED GRASSES IN CONSERVATION

A. L. HAFENRICHTER, A. D. STOESZ

ORDINARY GRASSES grow poorly on the eroded slopes of farmed-out land, in the Dust Bowl, and on denuded ranges. For them, new and better grasses and legumes are needed.

The task is big and complex because the country is big and complex. One has to find, assemble, test, and improve new materials and then grow large amounts of seed. Sometimes one has to devise special machines to harvest and plant the new grasses.

The search for new grasses naturally began on the prairies where the plants have survived centuries of drought, cold, fire, flood, insects, diseases, and heavy grazing; the American prairies are large, and combinations of soil, rain, wind, temperature, elevation, and seasons have produced many species of grass and a variety of strains of each one. Among the native species there is

a wealth of good material. But up to 1930, only slender wheatgrass had been domesticated from North American grasslands.

At first a large quantity of seed, harvested directly from the prairies, was used to seed back the arid lands that were devastated by the dust storms of the early 1930's after they had been used to grow wheat in the First World War. Many of the seeds were hard to harvest, troublesome to plant, and gave spotted stands—difficulties that had to be solved before the grasses could be domesticated.

The light, fluffy seeds of the bluestems, the bearded wild-ryes, and the needlegrasses and the ground-hugging burs of buffalograss were harvested by combines and threshers on which several adjustments had been made, but to harvest buffalograss seed a bigger change had to be made in the combine. It had a special reel and sickle bar and a device to speed up the reel.

Even after they were threshed, many native grass seeds could not be planted with farm drills. A notable contribution to domestication was made when processing was worked out simultaneously by G. L. Weber and by J. L. Schwendiman, R. F. Sackman, and A. L. Hafenrichter. Bearded and fluffy seeds were treated in a hammer mill and then recleaned.

Special drills and drill attachments were perfected to facilitate seeding into the stubble mulches, reseeding ranges and abandoned lands, and planting new grass-legume mixtures. A rotary hoe and a double drill box were combined so that mixtures of a large-seeded grass, a small-seeded grass, and a legume could be planted in stubble mulches. Drill-box attachments were made to handle tiny seeds, like those of lovegrass. Depth bands were fastened to double-disk drills so that grass seeds were planted uniformly at a shallow depth.

Even with the improvements for threshing, processing, and planting seed, many of the early stands of native grasses were poor and spotted. These plants were still wild, and each lot of seed contained good and poor strains.

Plant explorers, aware of the need for good strains and grasses with special qualities, set out to find the most vigorous strains, those that grew under difficult conditions, and those with better seeds, better roots, and other features that had conservation value.

The explorers collected more than 200 species and thousands of strains of native grasses and legumes from remnant stands on the prairies, railroad rights-of-way, and wastelands. The seeds were grown in soil conservation nurseries that were usually located on typical eroded farm land, but wide variations in their value were noticed at once, and it was certain that it would be better to grow seed under cultivation than to collect it from the wild.

Superior strains were found among the large numbers assembled in the nurseries when they were evaluated. From the original row nurseries, the best materials were taken to a number of smaller nurseries in typical farming areas to determine local adaptation. The strains found to be best in those tests were then planted in solid stands to determine their cultural requirements, conservation uses, and seed production needs. Finally, 13 of the outstanding native grasses were planted in farm fields in soil conservation districts, where they were compared with common materials. The plan has brought the grasses into use in a short time, and—more important—only superior strains of each good grass were put into common use on farms and ranches.

While the tests were being made, research workers in State experiment stations and in the Department of Agriculture were improving the grasses through breeding, analyzing their feeding value, studying their effect on soil improvement, and measuring their value for erosion control.

A need remains to get ample supplies of seed. Many farmers in soil conservation districts have their own seed plots. The best materials from the planned tests are supplied to the districts from increase blocks in the soil conservation nurseries. One nursery produced more than 11,000 pounds of selected fescue seed in 1946 and distributed them among districts in eight States. More than 200 production fields have been established from which other farmers can obtain seed.

In the States where the named strains are released through the Crop Improvement Associations, foundation seed stocks are maintained by the nurseries. When this seed is distributed to members of the Crop Improvement Association, the crop is eligible for certification, thus insuring the retention of the superior characters for which the strain was selected.

Another source of seed was the grasslands of other countries. From them special groups of investigators brought back hundreds of species and strains; other seed was furnished by scientists and experiment stations in those lands. Many were from eroded hillsides, wind-blown deserts, alkali flats, mountain plateaus, and the ruins of abandoned historical cities. They were also put in the conservation nurseries and evaluated. A typical result is the domestication of three lovegrasses from Africa. To date, 14 newly introduced grasses and legumes have been adapted to conservation uses on farms.

Also studied for possible use in specific conservation undertakings were improved strains of commercial grasses and legumes. A notable result has been the combining of grass with legumes in soil conservation rotations. Sweetclover and grass and alfalfa and grass mixtures were developed for many crop areas. The addition of the grass to the legumes increased the effective ground cover and improved the soil structure. Five grasses and two legumes are in this group.

Several native, adventive, and introduced grasses have proved worthy for conservation jobs but are not ready to be released. Unnamed material is in use from nursery production. Among these are big, little, and sand bluestem, side-oats grama, Boer and sand lovegrass, Indian ricegrass, sheep fescue, blue wild-rye, a southern mountain brome, and streambank wheatgrass. Several other grasses are in this category of testing and use; still others are in the beginning stages of domestication. Western wheatgrass, blue grama, and buffalograss are native grasses that are widely used, but seed is still collected from native stands because seed production from these stands is usually adequate and superior strains are not yet developed. These grasses are used for reseeding wind-eroded land. The uses for burnet, soft chess, and subterranean clover in conservation seedings are already known, but there are wide differences among strains from which material must be chosen to expand their usefulness.

There are problems of soil and water conservation for which there are still no satisfactory grasses; no legumes are available that can be grown successfully on semiarid lands of the West. Grasses are needed that will provide good pasture or range during parts of the season when those now in use are dormant. Some new materials that provide good ground cover cannot be established from seed, and others have weak seedlings or characteristics that make them hard to handle and manage. Both new materials and improvement of plants now in use are needed.

Seed supplies of new materials are still far from adequate, although many farmers are growing seed. For example, only enough seed was available to plant 20 percent of the waterways that needed grassing in one State—Kansas—in 1947. The soil conservation nurseries are maintaining production fields, and they and the State experiment stations are growing foundation seed so that new materials are available to growers—but the work of conservation requires more seed growers, more processing plants, and a greater flow of seed through commercial channels.

THE AUTHORS≪⋘ *A. L. Hafenrichter is stationed in Portland, Oreg., as chief of the Regional Nursery Division of the Soil Conservation Service. Dr. Hafenrichter, who is a graduate of Northwestern College and the University of Illinois, was a member of the research staff of the Carnegie Institution of Washington and the Washington Agricultural Experiment Station.*

A. D. Stoesz is a senior agronomist in the Soil Conservation Service. He has been chief of the Regional Nursery Division at Lincoln, Nebr., since 1935. Dr. Stoesz is a graduate of Bluffton College and the University of Minnesota.

[Three tables prepared by Dr. Hafenrichter and Dr. Stoesz appear in the section, Grass in Charts and Tables. Other articles on conservation include those in the section, Soil: Grass: Conservation.]

IMPROVED VARIETIES OF ALFALFA

H. M. TYSDAL

THE VALUE of the alfalfa crop to the Nation is being increased each year by the development of improved, disease-resistant varieties that are now getting into production. Alfalfa is one of the most important hay crops produced in the United States, but as with most crops, difficulties attend its cultivation. It is the problem of the alfalfa breeder to produce varieties which will be resistant to these hazards.

One of the greatest dangers to the alfalfa crop is plant diseases. Bacterial wilt (*Corynebacterium insidiosum*), one of the worst, has been reported in almost every State in which alfalfa is grown. Others include leaf and stem diseases, which, in general, are more severe in the humid sections of the country. The more common of these diseases are black stem (*Ascochyta imperfecta*), leaf blotch (*Pseudopeziza jonesii*), downy mildew (*Peronospora aestivallis*), leaf-spots (*Pseudopeziza medicaginis, Staganospora* sp., *Leptosphaeria pratensis*, and *Stemphylium* sp.), and rust (*Uromyces medicaginis*). The loss of leaves caused by these diseases greatly decreases the nutritional value of alfalfa hay and forage since the leaves carry two-thirds of the protein of the plant and almost three-quarters of the carotene (provitamin A).

Rots that attack the crown and roots of the alfalfa plant cause much damage in some sections. The cotton root rot (*Phymatotrichum omnivorum*) is confined largely to the Southwestern States. Other crown and root rots (*Rhizoctonia solani, Colletotrichum trifoli Sclerotinia* spp., and *Fusarium* sp.) probably cause more killing over large areas of the country than is generally realized because some of them weaken the plants enough that they become susceptible to winterkilling—to which the losses are charged instead of to the crown or root-rotting organism. Another group of alfalfa diseases is

the viruses. Little is known about them as yet and the extent of their damage has not been estimated. Three distinct diseases, however, have been reported: Dwarf virus, serious in parts of southern California; witches'-broom, found in Washington (although the latest reports on it indicate that it is not now causing serious damage); and the mosaic virus, which is found in various parts of the country but which as yet has not proved a limiting factor in alfalfa production.

Damage to the alfalfa crop as a result of harmful insect activity is of extreme economic concern. Leafhopper yellowing, caused by *Empoasca fabae*, probably damages the alfalfa crop in the eastern half of the United States more than any other one factor. In general, it is not serious in the Western States, although occasional infestations are found. Leafhopper attacks reduce the growth of the plants, cause them to yellow, and destroy the provitamin A content. Heavy infestations may result in killing the stand.

The alfalfa weevil (*Hypera postica*), and grasshoppers (*Melanoplus* sp., and *Orphulella* sp.) are pests found in sporadic outbreaks, chiefly in the Western States. Other insects such as lygus (*Lygus* spp.), alfalfa plant bug (*Adelphocorus* sp.), and chalcis fly (*Bruchaphagus funebris*) may cause seed failures.

The alfalfa crop is also susceptible to several climatic hazards. The most common ones are winterkilling, droughts, and heaving. Hot, humid weather, on the other hand, is conducive to development of diseases which may destroy the crop. Heaving of the soil causes severe damage to the alfalfa crop in the Eastern States.

The most effective means of combatting practically all of these problems is the development of resistant varieties through plant breeding. Often this is the only control. For example, rotations and soil amendments were tried for bacterial wilt control without success, but varieties resistant to the disease have been developed. Ranger and Buffalo alfalfas, developed by the United States Department of Agriculture in cooperation with the Nebraska and Kansas Agricultural Experiment Stations, respectively, are highly resistant to bacterial wilt and are recommended for areas where the disease is serious. Another example is Nemastan; it has proved resistant to the stem nematode (*Ditylenchus dipsaci*), a disease for which no other practical control could be found.

Atlantic, another new variety that yields well, is better adapted to the Eastern States than most commercial varieties. It was produced by the New Jersey Agricultural Experiment Station. Still another new strain was selected out of Kansas Common at the substation in Williamsburg, Va.

Through plant breeding methods, rhizomatous types of alfalfa, the crowns of which send out spreading rhizomes, are also being developed. Preliminary evidence indicates that they may be useful for both hay and pasture mixtures and that in pastures they will withstand more severe grazing than ordinary alfalfa.

A rhizomatous alfalfa has not yet been released for commercial production and no seed is available, but several different strains are being tested. Production is expected to start on the best of these types soon.

The utilization of hybrid vigor in the production of "hybrid alfalfa" also has definite commercial possibilities.

My article, *Breeding Better Alfalfa,* in the Yearbook of Agriculture 1943–1947, and Farmers' Bulletin 1731, *Alfalfa Varieties in the United States,* give further information on breeding for new and improved alfalfa varieties and descriptions of older ones.

Alfalfa was first successfully introduced into the United States about 1850 in the Western States, and it remained a "western" crop for many years. As recently as 1920–24, more than 80 percent of the alfalfa acreage in the United States was west of the 95th meridian (about the western boundary of Iowa). The acreage in the Eastern States has increased, however, and during the past decade 52 percent of the total acreage was east of this line. The expanded acreage in the East is due primarily to better information on methods of production, including information on lime, potash, phosphate, and boron requirements, and to recognition of alfalfa as a superior forage crop, rather than to development of varieties adapted to eastern conditions. As a matter of fact, there are no alfalfa varieties that are very well adapted to eastern conditions, chiefly because there have been relatively few intensive breeding programs in the East.

Alfalfa seed production in the United States has been largely confined to the Western States primarily because conditions essential to successful production are found more consistently in that region. Between 1935 and 1947 an average of 81 percent of the seed was produced in the Western States. A considerable seed production may be expected in the Eastern States in certain years, but consistent production is difficult—another reason why it is hard to develop an adequate breeding program.

Years of experimental testing show that there are varieties, such as Turkestan, that are adapted in the West but are poorly adapted in the East. On the contrary, varieties better adapted to eastern conditions, such as Hardigan and Atlantic, have done well under western conditions in approximately the same latitude.

In many areas of the West, the seed crop is secondary to hay production. Any of this region, however, may produce seed that will find its way into the eastern markets. The varieties grown in the West, therefore, should be those adapted to the East as well as the West.

It is not expected that a given variety will be adapted equally well to all sections of the country, but results indicate that varieties may be adapted to broad latitudinal belts. Thus, if in the breeding program consideration is given to adaptation in both the East and West, the problem of source of adapted seed will be largely eliminated.

These factors lead to the conclusion that it would be advantageous to have selection for disease resistance and adaptation made in the East on all strains to be increased commercially for use anywhere except in the deep Southwest. A specialized type of alfalfa for which there is no counterpart in the East is used in the Southwest for late-fall and early-spring growth.

With these problems in mind, State and Federal workers organized the Alfalfa Improvement Conference, which is composed of workers interested in the breeding and improvement of the alfalfa crop in the United States and Canada. Since 1945, the Conference has set up three groups—the Eastern, Central, and Western—to serve the regional interests to better advantage, but they continue to work as a unit on interregional problems.

Recent developments in alfalfa breeding methods have lent themselves to an integrated program, whereby selections can be made in one region while seed can be produced in another region from the same plant. Vegetative propagation of the plants make possible this attack on the problem.

Single plant selections are made under both eastern and western conditions, vegetatively propagated or "cloned," and the clones tested under various conditions. In addition, seed is produced in the West for testing of progeny performance in eastern and western United States and Canada. By vegetative propagation of the original selections, sufficient seed can be produced for a thorough testing program. The clones that prove best adapted by their own performance and by the performance of their polycross progenies over the widest areas are used for the production of either hybrids or synthetic varieties.

Summaries of performance and yield of new strains and polycrosses, as furnished by State and Federal workers, are given in the annual report of the permanent secretary of the Alfalfa Improvement Conference, who is the alfalfa project leader in the Division of Forage Crops and Diseases, United States Department of Agriculture. Seed of polycrosses and new strains are distributed through the Alfalfa Improvement Conference, and superior clones are given an Alfalfa Conference number and distributed to interested workers here and in Canada.

Once a new improved variety of alfalfa has been developed, there is still the problem of increasing the seed in quantity so that it can be made available to growers. The increase of foundation seed has been a bottleneck in the breeding program for alfalfa as well as for practically all forage crops. In some cases it has taken 30 years to get a definitely superior variety into wide use. There should be a well-developed cooperative program between State and Federal departments and the commercial seed industry. Once the foundation seed is increased, the seed should be produced and certified under regulations of the State Crop Improvement Associations to insure purchasers of the identity and purity of the superior germ plasm.

It is believed that improvements accomplished to date in the breeding of alfalfa are only the beginning. Resistance to various diseases and to insect depredations, as well as the promise of higher yielding, higher quality alfalfa through the utilization of hybrid vigor and the production of rhizomatous alfalfas, all through an integrated East-West program, presents a favorable picture for continued improvements to the ultimate benefit of all growers.

THE AUTHOR≪ *H. M. Tysdal, an agronomist in the Bureau of Plant Industry, Soils, and Agricultural Engineering, is a graduate of the University of Saskatchewan, Kansas State College, and the University of Minnesota.*

CLOVERS THAT MAKE A CROP

E. A. HOLLOWELL

MANY FARMERS plant clovers but do not reap a crop. The reasons for the failures might be several: The use of unadapted seed; a soil deficient in plant nutrients, particularly calcium, phosphorus, or potash; planting the seed in loose, cloddy seedbeds; failure to inoculate the seed with the proper strain of nodule-producing bacteria; and mismanagement of stands in grazing, clipping, or cutting. Even if all but one of the faults are corrected, complete or partial failures and low yields may still occur.

The most important single thing to do to get a good stand is to buy good seed—not unidentified seed purchased on the basis of looks alone—and give it a good chance to grow. There are several superior varieties, and it pays (in better stands, more feed, and more organic matter for plowing under) to buy them.

Nine different species of true clovers have regional or national importance in this country. Many other native or introduced species are of local value and add to the forage resources and furnish nitrogen to the associated grass. For five of the true clovers there are several varieties or farm strains: Red clover, white clover, crimson clover, sub clover, and strawberry clover. The varieties and strains have been developed by State and Federal improvement programs by natural selection for specific conditions, or are introductions from abroad.

Botanically the true clovers are perennials or annuals, but unfavorable factors of environment (diseases and insect pests, and climate) may make the perennials behave as biennials or annuals. Length of day is an important factor in varietal adaptation within many clover species.

The three most important sweetclovers are white sweetclover, yellow sweetclover, and sourclover. The first two have biennial and annual forms; sourclover is a winter annual adapted to the Gulf coast region, southern California, Arizona, and New Mexico. As with the true clovers, varieties and farm strains of each species have been developed in similar ways. All true clover species of agricultural importance and all the sweetclovers were introduced into this country by man for a definite purpose or by chance.

The principal red clover belt extends from the Atlantic Ocean to about the 97th meridian and is bounded by Canada on the north and approximately the Tennessee-Georgia line on the south. Recent studies indicate that red clover may have greater usage farther south. Red clover may also be successfully grown throughout the West under irrigation. It has long been a valuable crop in the Pacific Northwest. Through the extensive testing of strains and varieties, the eastern belt may be divided into three general regions of adaptation: The northern, approximately from the Wisconsin-Illinois boundary to Canada; the central, from the southern boundary of the northern region to the fortieth degree of latitude; and the southern, southward from the fortieth degree of latitude.

To be adapted to northern areas, varieties must be winter-hardy and tolerant to long periods of dormancy, resistant to northern anthracnose, and capable of making large yields in the long days of the growing season.

The clover root borer is widely distributed; it reduces the yield of the second crop, destroys the roots, weakens the plants, and makes them susceptible to diseases and winter-killing.

Other diseases, such as powdery mildew, crown rot, and leaf spots, contribute to reduction in stands and lower quality of the feed. Dollard, a Canadian variety developed at Macdonald College, has some resistance to northern anthracnose and appears to be one of the best in many locations of the region. Midland has also given good yields in the eastern and southern parts of the region. Numerous strains grown on farms in the region for many generations constitute a good source of seed, even though they do not have much resistance to diseases.

In the central region, factors of adaptation resemble somewhat those of the northern region. There is more alternate freezing and thawing, and the day lengths during the summer are shorter. The cool, rainy weather of 1944–46 favored severe epidemics of northern anthracnose. The yields of the Dollard variety, which has some resistance, have been high where previously it has not yielded so well. Midland and many farm strains that have been identified and tested, continue to give good yields.

In the southern region, the new variety Kenland, which has high resistance to southern anthracnose, has been strikingly superior to all others and in many places good stands remain through the second harvest or the third year from seeding. Cumberland, Ky. 215, and Tennessee Anthracnose-Resistant, have continued to be superior to others. In many localities the crown rot disease has become increasingly severe, and studies are in progress to develop more resistance in present varieties.

In the western region, where the practice of producing red clover seed is increasing, it is important that the varieties used be those adapted to conditions in the East. Such seed should be produced and marketed as certified seed in order that farmers in the Middle West and East may be assured of the trueness of variety. Certified seed is produced under regulations of the State Crop Improvement Associations. The regulations provide for protection of the superior characteristics of the variety during the growing, harvesting, processing, and distribution of the seed.

By using the superior varieties adapted to the region, greater yields of hay, pasture, and green manure are obtained, and the quality of the forage is improved. Comparisons of hay quality of varieties having some resistance and those susceptible to northern anthracnose show that the resistant varieties ranked one United States grade ahead of nonresistant varieties and also had a much higher carotene content.

White clover is grown in all regions of the United States wherever there is a good supply of soil moisture either from rainfall or irrigation. Under many conditions in the South, the plants usually behave as winter annuals, although some plants may live through the year.

The three general types of white clover are identified principally by growth characteristics, although, in any type, wide variation among plants may be present.

These types are large, intermediate, and small, of which there are one or more varieties and strains. They originated either through introduction or natural selection under varying climatic, soil, and management practices. Little is known about their resistance or susceptibility to most diseases and insect pests or other specific factors of adaptation. Variety and strain trials, however, have indicated their relative value to the conditions where tested.

The use of Ladino white clover, a variety of the large type, has spread more widely during the past few years than any other kind of legume. Its rapid spread from the Western States, first in New England, then through the Lake and Corn Belt States, the Piedmont sections of Southern States, and throughout the irrigated regions of the West has been the result of excellent performance.

But it should be pointed out that summer moisture conditions in most of those regions were exceptionally favorable to Ladino in 1944 to 1947. While it will tolerate short periods of drought, it is not drought-resistant. When planted in the deep South, true Ladino blooms sparingly; whenever it dies in the summer it fails to reseed as other adapted strains do. Ladino is used for pasture and hay in combination with one or more legumes and grasses. Seeds of all white clover look alike, and both genetic and mechanical mixtures may occur through growing, harvesting, and marketing. To insure trueness of variety, only certified Ladino seed is recommended.

Louisiana white clover, a regional strain, has developed under natural conditions in Louisiana over a large number of years. It is of the intermediate type and is adapted throughout the Southern States and as far north as the latitude of central Ohio. It also has given excellent yields in many places farther north, particularly where winter conditions are less severe or where it is protected by a snow covering in winter.

New Zealand white clover, which has been imported into the United States in large quantities, is mostly of the intermediate type. It is not tolerant of extremely cold weather and is less vigorous than Louisiana white clover.

New York Wild white and Kent Wild white are strains of the low-growing type. They are natural selections that have developed under close grazing conditions for long periods of years. They are less productive than strains of the other types but are persistent in certain regions.

The common white clover may be of the intermediate or low-growing types or mixtures of types. This clover often is called White Dutch clover, a name that is without meaning and should be discontinued.

Common white clover of the Northern States is not recommended in the Southern States because it produces low yields there and fails to reseed for volunteering. In the Northern States more than 95 percent is used in lawn grass mixtures. Wherever white clover has been grown, Common white clover need not be seeded in pasture mixtures because good stands will generally develop from volunteer seed after needed fertilizers have been applied and the crop is properly managed.

Two superior varieties of crimson clover are Dixie and Auburn. Both have hard seeds that facilitate the establishment of volunteer stands from shattered seed during the late spring and early summer. In preliminary tests, Auburn has been slightly less winter-hardy in the northern part of the crimson clover region. The hard-seeded characteristic of the Dixie and Auburn varieties minimizes the chances of stand failure, which frequently occurs in the fall during the period of germination. As the seed of Dixie and Auburn cannot be distinguished from common crimson, the use of certified seed only of these varieties is recommended. Neither variety resists crown rot or sooty blotch, which occur frequently in the Southern States.

There are many varieties of sub clover, the most recent winter annual species that is being extensively used in the Pacific Northwest. They are all of Australian origin and differ principally in adaptation and maturity. The early introductions were of the early maturing Dwalganup variety. Early in the 1930's many varieties were introduced, among them Mt. Barker and Tallarook, which are, respectively, midseason and late in maturity. In the Pacific Northwest, tests indicated that they were superior and would successfully produce good volunteer stands the following fall. They appear promising in several localities in the South. Almost all sub clover seed looks alike and the use of certified seed is recommended to insure trueness of variety.

There are several farm strains of strawberry clover and several varieties of Australian origin. The Australian varieties, for the most part, lack winter hardiness, and stands have winter-killed when planted in the Intermountain States. The farm strains locally grown on the same farm for many years are the best sources of seed.

Sweetclover is widely adapted throughout the United States where the effective summer rainfall totals 15 inches or more and there is an available supply of calcium, phosphate, and potash. Many factors affect the adaptation of varieties—diseases, insects, and climate. The sweetclover weevil is a relatively new pest and by far the most serious; the adults, when they are present in large numbers, frequently destroy seedling stands.

Of the many farm strains of yellow and white sweetclover, a few have proved to be superior. Madrid, an improved variety of biennial yellow sweetclover, has early seedling vigor, resists fall frosts, is slightly later in maturity, and produces greater yields than the common biennial yellow. It is particularly adapted to the Great Plains and the Corn Belt. Erector, an improved Canadian variety, when grown under Corn Belt and Great Plains conditions, is similar to common yellow. Willamette, a variety of biennial white sweetclover, resists crown rot, matures in midseason, and is particularly adapted to the Pacific Northwest, where the crown rot disease is a limiting factor in sweetclover production. Spanish, a variety of biennial white sweetclover, is midseason in maturity, has early seedling vigor, and is a high yielder.

Evergreen, a variety of biennial white sweetclover that matures late, produces a rank growth. These characteristics make it valuable for grazing and green manure. Seed yields are frequently low because of shattering, since it blooms over a long period of time when weather conditions are unfavorable. It is adapted to the Corn Belt and the eastern edge of the Great Plains.

Sangamon, a variety of biennial white sweetclover that is late in maturity, although slightly earlier than Evergreen, is adapted to the same conditions. Hubam, an annual variety of white sweetclover, blooms in the fall of the year when seeded. Under some conditions it produces a rank growth. It is being used extensively on the black soils of Texas for seed production, forage, and green manure. It is sometimes fall seeded, but may winterkill in severe winters.

Emerald is an annual variety of white sweetclover that is less vigorous than Hubam, but less coarse, having many stems of smaller size. It is adapted to southern Texas.

THE AUTHOR≪ *E. A. Hollowell, an agronomist in the Bureau of Plant Industry, Soils, and Agricultural Engineering, is in charge of the Bureau's clover investigations.*

THE OTHER PASTURE LEGUMES

ROLAND Mc KEE

FEW THINGS are more interesting than the quest for new legumes and their improvement. Locating basic material for an improvement program involves a wide search, and when promising plants are found, a program of breeding, selection, and increase of seed becomes possible.

Environmental complexes encountered are numerous: Each varying situation imposes special conditions and each location imposes limitations that determine the progress to be made. Many worthy achievements have been accomplished and recent efforts promise further accomplishments, but an extensive program of breeding and improvement of miscellaneous legumes has not been possible because of the large number of crops involved. As much time and work are required for breeding and handling a minor crop as for one that is more extensively grown.

Sometimes a plant, as originally introduced, is adequate, but later improvement adds to its efficiency. This is true of Korean lespedeza, an annual species which was widely adapted and serviceable as introduced and which today covers millions of acres. Breeding and selection developed varieties that now have extended its range both north and south and increased its yield, but further work remains to be done before utmost development is attained.

Climax Korean lespedeza, a late maturing strain, is the result of selection work with the crop. It extends the range of Korean lespedeza southward and lengthens the grazing season. Early maturing strains of Korean lespedeza also have been developed which extend its range to the north. The one now available commercially is known as Early Korean. The seed habits of Korean lespedeza are comparatively good; harvesting is not hard.

In pastures, as well as on cultivated land, the annual lespedezas are commonly maintained by volunteering. A large quantity of seed is usually necessary to effect volunteer stands because the proportion of hard seed is small. Hard seed is that which is impervious to water for an indefinite time and, consequently, will not take up moisture and germinate. Seed that take up moisture and germinate in the fall are killed later by cold weather or rot during the winter. Some progress has been made in the development of strains with more hard seed to insure volunteering.

Kobe lespedeza, a large-growing superior strain of common lespedeza (another annual species), was originally selected for its size. It has proved a heavy yielding strain of superior value for both hay and pasturage. It matures late and thus affords grazing at a time when green feed usually is scarce. The seed habits of Kobe, however, are inferior to Korean and for that reason the use of Korean has been more extensive in areas where both are well adapted.

From a large number of perennial species of lespedeza that have been tested, a few show some promise of serving as pasture crops. *Lespedeza cuneata,* commonly known as sericea lespedeza, is the one most extensively used. *L. hedysaroides,* known also as rush lespedeza, is similar to sericea lespedeza and perhaps equally serviceable. Several of the more shrubby species, such as *L. bicolor* and *L. thunbergii,* are eaten readily by livestock, but the coarse, woody nature of the plants makes them difficult to handle. Seed habits of perennial lespedezas are poor and harvesting is somewhat difficult, but with proper care and management a fair percentage of the seed crop can be saved. Selection and breeding for better seed habits is essential with Kobe and the perennial species of lespedeza before much increase in the percentage of seed saved in harvesting can be effected.

Second only to lespedeza in extent of use for pasturage are the bur-clovers, the annual species of *Medicago* (the genus to which alfalfa belongs). In California, bur-clover is the principal legume of the lower ranges, covering thousands of acres. It is also abundant in parts of Oregon and Arizona, and is extensively used in the southeastern United States from Texas to the Atlantic Ocean. The species most common in the West is *Medicago hispida,* which is known as California bur-clover. It is a variable species made up of many subspecies and varieties. Because of its aggressive nature in the West and its wide distribution, the development and use of improved strains have been impractical.

In the Southeast, the species most extensively used is *M. arabica,* which is known by the common name spotted bur-clover. This species in the Southeast is not so aggressive nor so widely spread as California bur-clover is in the West, and, for this reason, it has been possible to develop and maintain improved varietal strains. Manganese and Giant spotted bur-clover have become popular and are being used in many new pasture plantings.

Seed habits of bur-clovers make it difficult to harvest seed. This results in a limited market and high prices. Development of special harvesters with large suction fans that pick up the burs containing the seed has facilitated harvesting and has helped increase seed supplies.

Black medic is serviceable in pastures in both the South and West, and often is included in pasture mixtures.

Roughpea has been used satisfactorily in the pasture program of the Black Belt of Alabama and Mississippi. Strains have become naturalized and adapted locally and volunteer from year to year. Since roughpea has a high percentage of hard seed that carry over in the soil for a number of years, it is not difficult to maintain stands without reseeding. In fact, once a stand has been accomplished in pasture lands, it can be maintained indefinitely with proper management. Roughpea seeds abundantly, but the seed ripen unevenly and shatter badly when fully mature. Harvesting can be accomplished, however, with ordinary farm machinery and sufficient seed usually are available to meet demand.

Of the perennial legumes grown under cultivation, kudzu, which is adapted to the South, and birdsfoot trefoil, which is adapted to the North, are the most important.

Kudzu is propagated vegetatively and most of the plantings in the United States are made in that way. Because of limited facilities to carry on the breeding work, little has been done to improve the crop. Seedling kudzu plants are varied and selection should produce superior strains for forage and ground cover. The fact that the crop is propagated vegetatively will insure the maintenance of superior strains once they are established. Kudzu plants available from commercial sources are variable, but the crop has high feeding value and can be used advantageously for pasturage.

Birdsfoot trefoil is comparatively new in the United States. Although it was used in experimental plantings in the early 1900's, only recently has it attracted much attention. Naturalized plantings in New York, California, and Oregon demonstrated its value for pasturage and served as centers for increase of seed for additional plantings. Birdsfoot trefoil is variable and the regional strains that have developed show marked differences with reference to habit of growth and adaptation. Improvement of the species depends on the selection of strains adapted to the different sections, and the production of these strains under sectional or regional isolation in order to maintain them as selected.

Since birdsfoot trefoil matures seed unevenly and the seed pods split open readily upon maturing, the harvesting and increase of seed is difficult and the cost high. Harvesting can be done with ordinary farm equipment, although seed loss will be great and the expense high. A knowledge of the crop and experience in harvesting seed are essential if maximum yields are to be had.

Vetches are not used as extensively for pasturage as some of the other legumes, although three species, purple vetch, common vetch, and hairy vetch, are in common use.

There are no named varieties of purple vetch, and the species has been but slightly variable.

Common vetch is variable both with reference to the appearance of the plant and to winter hardiness. This latter factor has determined the varieties that can be used in the United States. Selection work for more winter-hardy strains resulted in the development of the Willamette variety, which is now most commonly grown. Willamette, like the species in general, requires a mild, cool climate for good seed production. Seed growing is confined almost exclusively to western Oregon, where adequate seed supplies undoubtedly will be maintained. It has good seed habits and gives good yields.

Hairy vetch is the most widely used of the vetches because it has greater winter hardiness and is better adapted to soils of lower fertility. A strain of hairy vetch has been developed recently which has little or no pubescence or hairs on the plant. It makes better winter growth in mild climates than the more hairy forms. This new strain—smooth vetch—has caused a wider use of the species for pasture. This improved variety was established in the seed-producing areas of the Pacific Northwest and most of the seed handled today under the name "hairy vetch" is of this improved form. The seed habits of smooth, or hairy vetch, are poor, the cost of production high.

Recently in Oregon damage by the vetch seed weevil (*Bruchid* sp.) has limited seed yields, thereby adding to the cost. This damage has been reduced to some extent by DDT, but seed production, nevertheless, is difficult and expensive. Increase of seed in sections where the weevil has not yet caused damage—Arkansas and central Texas—may be possible, but the seed supply may still be short.

Other legumes used for pasturage that should be mentioned are velvetbeans, crotalaria, and hairy indigo. These are all introduced crops that afford some grazing.

The velvetbean varieties most popular are early-maturing forms selected some years ago to extend the use of the crop to the north. Originally velvetbeans matured only in Florida, but the selected early strains extended its use to other parts of the lower South.

Crotalaria has received only minor consideration for pasturage but in recent years the increased plantings of nonpoisonous species for cover crops has resulted in their increased use for forage. *Crotalaria spectabilis* is poisonous and cannot be used for pasturage. Nonpoisonous species in use are *C. intermedia*, *C. mucronata*, and *C. lanceolata*. These volunteer almost indefinitely on cultivated land. Volunteering is less certain in pasture lands that are never cultivated, but occasional reseeding will insure stands. Selection of one large vigorous strain of *C. mucronata* is the extent of improvement within these species, and further improvement, no doubt, can be attained.

The species differ in manner of growth and adaptation and for best results it is necessary to determine the one best adapted to local conditions. These species of crotalaria set seed abundantly and have fair seed habits. Harvesting of seed can be accomplished by ordinary machinery but care

is necessary in handling the seed, both during and subsequent to harvest. Most of the seed harvested to date has been for use by the grower and only limited amounts have reached commercial channels.

Hairy indigo, which is a recent introduction, has been little used but has proved a good pasture plant for Florida. Late maturing of the crop makes seed production difficult but an early maturing selection now being increased promises a solution to this problem.

Many important though not too abundant legumes are found on the range lands of the West. One that occurs spontaneously in the Southwest is the so-called mesquite, *Prosopis chilensis*, a browse plant that furnishes considerable feed but in places crowds out more desirable vegetation. Its planting is never recommended. In some years mesquite matures seed in abundance and this affords good feed. The seed, however, is never harvested. In the far western range a few species, such as *Lathyrus leucanthus*, *Lotus wrightii*, *Hedyearum boreale*, and others, furnish much feed and are valuable in the pasture complex. They are entirely dependent on natural reseeding for their maintenance. Native legumes are not abundant in the Great Plains area or farther east, but a few species usually are present and serve to supplement native grasses.

THE AUTHOR⫷ *Roland McKee, a senior agronomist, has been with the Department of Agriculture since 1905. As director of investigations on miscellaneous legumes, he has seen the now well-known cover crops like Austrian Winter peas, Willamette vetch, purple vetch, Hungarian vetch, monantha vetch, blue lupine, Crotalaria spectabilis, C. intermedia, C. striata, and alyceclover come into use. He has also instigated the development of nonpoisonous strains of lupines in both the blue- and yellow-flowered species, and of high-yielding late strains of annual lespedezas, particularly the variety Climax.*

DEVELOPING GRASSES FOR SPECIAL USES

H. B. MUSSER, G. W. BURTON, H. A. SCHOTH

WORK TO develop superior strains of grasses for specialized uses—for lawns, playgrounds, landing fields, roadsides, and so on—has concentrated mainly upon seven characteristics.

The first is resistance to disease, an essential characteristic of any grass that is to be used for specialized turf. Although certain diseases like brown patch and dollar spot of the bentgrasses can be controlled by the use of fungicides, the development of resistant strains is the ultimate solution from the standpoint of economy in maintenance and permanent improvement.

The second is recovery from injury. Many types of specialized turf are subject to severe damage through use, particularly turf on airports and sports areas. Because the recovery rate is conditioned by growth habits that vary widely among individual plants within a species according to prevailing conditions, a breeding program designed to isolate the strains that can rapidly repair injuries presents a good opportunity for production of improved types.

Next is tolerance of cold, heat, and sudden changes in temperature. The ability of a grass to start early, retain its color late in the fall, and stand midsummer heat well is an important consideration. The wide range of variability in such response among individual plants of many species makes possible the development of improved types for particular regions or locations.

Appearance and wearing qualities of turf, the fourth item, are directly related to foliage texture and density.

Turf-forming quality is the fifth desideratum. Individual plants within a species may vary widely in ability to produce a close-knit turf under a given set of conditions. Types that fail to develop a dense sod often cannot resist weed encroachment or repair injury scars quickly. In either case, such types are undesirable, and improvement programs are designed to eliminate them.

The sixth item, the ability of grass to grow under conditions of low soil moisture and nutrient levels is primarily of regional concern. Breeding for such a character as saline tolerance is a good example of the opportunities for improvement in this category.

The seventh characteristic is adaptation to specialized uses and types of maintenance. A breeding program to develop strains adapted to use on putting greens of golf courses, for instance, emphasizes persistence and maintenance of a fine-textured uniform turf under a schedule that may require clipping every day to a height as low as three-sixteenths of an inch. In contrast, the particular demands for airport turf may require that a strain be capable of producing a tough, heavy cover under a maintenance program that includes clipping only two or three times during the growing season to a height of 3 inches or more.

The species of grasses best adapted for specialized uses are mixed populations composed of many strains varying in form, structure, and physiological responses. A breeding program, therefore, is concerned first with a study of the extent of natural variability within a species, and, as far as possible, attempts to determine the underlying genetic explanations for the observed differences.

When there is wide variability within a species and vegetative propagation is practicable, or when uniformity can be maintained through successive generations because of the asexual habit of seed production, simple mass selection followed by tests of turf quality is used successfully to isolate the best existing strains.

Considerable progress has been made by this method in developing better strains of creeping bent, velvet bent, Kentucky bluegrass, Bermuda-grass, *Zoysia,* Bahiagrass, and buffalograss. Sometimes it is necessary to use hy-

The Behavior of a Number of the Bermuda-Grass Selections Included in the Greens Test Established at the Georgia Coastal Plain Experiment Station, Tifton, Ga., in April 1947 [1]

Source	Relative values [2]							
	2–4–D injury 5–20–47	Coverage rating 5–20–47	Sod density 6–30–47	Sod density after mowing at 2½ inches 7–29–47	Fineness rating 8–13–47	Disease resistance 11–13–47	Frost injury 12–18–47	Quality for greens 10–27–47
Check (commercial seed)	3	3	1	1	3	5	2	......
Charlotte, N. C. (4) [3]	4	3	3	1	2	1	2	1
Atlanta, Ga. (18)	2	2	1	1	1	3	2	2
Hilton Village, Va	3	3	2	2	3	5	2	4
Pinehurst, N. C. (18)	4	3	2	1	1	3	1	1
Sea Island, Ga. (7)	5	2	2	1	3	2	2	3
College Station, Tex	3	4	5	4	3	4	2	3
Key West, Fla	4	4	4	4	3	6	2	3
Arcadia, Fla	4	4	2	1	3	5	2	2
Ona, Fla	3	4	2	1	2	5	2	2
Indian Creek, Fla. (1)	2	1	1	1	3	5	2	3
Do. (4)	5	4	4	4	2	5	2	4
Do. (7)	2	4	5	3	3	4	1	3
Do. (8)	3	3	1	1	3	4	1	3
Do. (9)	2	2	1	1	3	4	2	3
Miami Shores, Fla. (1)	3	4	4	4	2	5	1	3
Do. (2)	4	3	1	1	3	3	1	3
Belle Glade, Fla	2	3	1	1	3	2	1	3
Davie, Fla	2	2	3	3	5	4	1	5
Gainesville, Fla	1	4	4	2	3	3	1	4
Tifton, Ga	2	4	5	5	4	4	2	4
Pinehurst, N. C.	3	3	1	1	2	4	2	2
Harrisburg, Pa	3	4	3	3	3	7	2	5
Savannah, Ga	5	4	3	3	1	5	2	3
Sea Island, Ga. (6)	3	3	2	1	3	3	3	3
Do. (8)	4	3	2	1	2	5	3	1
Tifton, Ga., No. 12	4	4	3	2	1	2	1	1
Do	1	1	1	2	3	2	3	1
Do	3	3	1	1	2	1	2	1
Do	1	3	2	1	3	2	2	2
Do	2	3	1	2	2	4	2	1
Do	3	2	1	1	2	4	2	1
Do	3	2	1	1	2	1	2	1
Do	2	3	1	1	2	1	3	1
Do	2	2	1	3	3	3	2	3
Lansing, Mich	2	4	4	5	5	7	2	5
U. S. G. A. (U–3)	2	4	3	1	2	6	2	3
Do. (U–5)	3	4	4	4	2	1	2	1
Puerto Rico	2	5	3	2	6	2	6	4
Nashville, Tenn	2	6	4	2	2	5	1	2

[1] This is a partial table illustrating how different strains of grasses are evaluated.
[2] Relative values from 1 to 10, where 1 is the best expression of the character.
[3] Number of the green where selected.

bridization methods to incorporate additional desirable characters within a given strain. When successive generations of a strain are propagated from sexually produced seed, breeding programs include a study of the breeding behavior of individual plants with the object of controlling hybridization in such a way that the end product will retain the desired superior characters. Breeding work along this line is under way with selected material in the creeping bent, fescue, crested wheatgrass, and Bahiagrass species. A beginning has been made by breeders of grasses for specialized uses in the use of the polycross nursery for concentration of desirable characters of selected strains. It is possible that this method may be found to be well adapted to maintenance of superior stocks.

In the United States the intensive breeding of grass for special purposes has been limited in time and number of species. Earlier breeding work was confined largely to mass selection and testing of natural variants within the species; the improved strains now available are almost entirely the result of that method. Systematic programs to develop superior strains through controlled hybridization were inaugurated in 1942.

Definite progress has been made already with strains of bentgrasses adapted to use on golf greens. The staff of the United States Golf Association Green Section has collected and tested numerous strains selected directly from greens in all sections of the United States where the grasses are adapted. The Washington and Metropolitan strains of creeping bent were the first developments from this work. As a result of further collecting and testing in Green Section plots and by individual golf clubs and State agricultural experiment stations, six other strains have been named and distributed: Arlington, Congressional, Cohansey, Collins, Toronto, and Norbeck. Breeding and testing of selected strains are also under way at experiment stations in Indiana, Iowa, New Jersey, Michigan,

Oregon, Pennsylvania, Rhode Island.

Many strains of the velvet bent species have been selected and tested by the same methods. Three strains have been developed and are available in limited quantities: The Piper strain, selected at the Rhode Island Agricultural Experiment Station; the Raritan strain, selected by the New Jersey Agricultural Experiment Station; and the Kernwood strain, found at the Kernwood Country Club in Massachusetts.

Improvement work with Kentucky bluegrass is under way at a number of institutions, including the experiment stations of Indiana, Iowa, Kentucky, Missouri, Pennsylvania, and Wisconsin. Many strains have been isolated; some of them have been distributed locally for practical trials, but so far none has been tested long enough or widely enough to justify general distribution.

The development of types of Bermuda-grass for special purposes has been concentrated largely at the Georgia Coastal Plain Experiment Station at Tifton, where the work has been carried on cooperatively by the Department of Agriculture, the United States Golf Association Green Section, and the State of Georgia. In studying the variability of the species, striking differences have been found in type of growth, sod density, response to different methods of maintenance, cold tolerance, and other important characters. Several promising strains have been developed and are being multiplied for distribution.

Centipedegrass is being studied at the Florida Agricultural Experiment Station and the Georgia Coastal Plain Experiment Station to see whether types for lawn turf can be developed.

Breeding types of Bahiagrass for special purposes also is in progress at the Georgia Coastal Plain Experiment Station. Most of the work has been concentrated on developing types for use as heavy-duty turf on airfields and similar areas.

Many State agricultural experiment stations in the Great Plains are working to improve buffalograss, mostly with an eye to general agricultural use, but also in an effort to establish the value of new strains for specialized turf. No releases of superior types for such use have yet been made.

Crested wheatgrass is adapted for turf use over large areas of the Great Plains where rainfall is limited. A selection program to develop superior strains for specialized purposes is under way at the Oklahoma and Nebraska Agricultural Experiment Stations. The Fairway strain, developed in Canada, is considered more satisfactory for turf use than the regular crested wheatgrass. No general release of improved types has been made.

Breeding activities with the fescues have been limited largely to selection of types occurring naturally within various species. Work is in progress at the Kentucky and Oregon Agricultural Experiment Stations with meadow fescue, and two developments are in commercial production, Ky. 31, and Alta strains.

Breeding and testing creeping red and Chewings types of fescue are under way at the Indiana, Iowa, Maryland, New Jersey, Oregon, Pennsylvania, and Rhode Island Agricultural Experiment Stations and the United States Golf Association Green Section. Seed of several selected strains is produced commercially; of these, Illahee red fescue, developed in Oregon, is used most extensively. Another is F. C. 13706, tentatively named Rainier. It also was developed in Oregon.

Breeding work with *Zoysia* is limited to studies of variability and selection of naturally occurring types. This work has been carried on by the United States Golf Association Green Section.

THE AUTHORS«« *H. B. Musser is professor of agronomy in the Pennsylvania State College. Born in Williamsport, Pa., he was educated at Bucknell University and the Pennsylvania State College. In the First World War he was a chief petty officer in the Naval Aviation Reserve. In the Second World War, as a lieutenant colonel in the Army Air Forces, he supervised the control of dust and erosion on Army airfields.*

G. W. Burton holds degrees from the University of Nebraska and Rutgers University and has been engaged in research on grass since 1932. Dr. Burton, a geneticist in the Bureau of Plant Industry, Soils, and Agricultural Engineering, is stationed at Tifton, Ga.

H. A. Schoth, a native of Wyoming, is a graduate of the Oregon State College where he is now professor of agronomy. Since 1916 he has been engaged in forage crop and disease studies with the Bureau of Plant Industry, Soils, and Agricultural Engineering.

Some Aspects of Economics

THE LONG-TIME OUTLOOK

REED A. PHILLIPS

LIVESTOCK, poultry, and also the products from them form a large proportion, in value and output, of the total products of grassland agriculture.

The meat animals, milk cows, horses, mules, and chickens on farms at the beginning of 1947 were worth nearly 12 billion dollars, the highest value on record. The 13.2 billion dollars that farmers took in from the sale of livestock and livestock products in 1946 was 55 percent of their total cash receipts from marketing that year and was equal to about 7 percent of the gross national product—total output of goods and services—of 194 billion dollars in that year.

The outlook for those products of grassland agriculture is one key to the outlook for agriculture as a whole. The analysis that follows deals with what has happened and what might happen to the main factors that affect the demand for the products of the grasslands and income from them.

Changes in industrial activity, employment, and incomes of consumers usually are followed quite closely by changes in the demand for meat, eggs, milk, and the rest. Because livestock production tends to be relatively stable, changes in industrial activity and consumers' incomes are primary reasons for frequent and wide fluctuations in prices of livestock and livestock products. Those prices probably will continue to fluctuate more often and more widely than prices of industrial products. The fluctuations, however, may be modified somewhat through such programs as price supports and technological advances in production and marketing.

The level of consumers' incomes is highly important to the livestock producers. The total income of consumers has risen markedly since the early years of the century. The average income per person in 1946 was almost four times that of 1909 and twice as high as in 1930. (When adjustments are made for price changes, however, the increase in real income from 1909 to 1946 was about 65 percent.) The general level of consumer incomes probably will continue above prewar figures for many years.

The distribution of income also is important. A study in 1935–36 of consumer purchases and another of family spending and saving in 1941 indicated that families with incomes of $3,000 a year ate almost twice as much meat and poultry and dairy products as did families with incomes below $1,000. Families in the higher income group ate half again as many eggs as did the lower income group.

The recent trend in distribution of

income also explains much of the increase in the demand for livestock products. In 1935–36, about 53 percent of the consumer units (families and single individuals) in the United States had money incomes below $1,000. By 1941 this percentage had dropped to about 34, and in 1945 to only 20.

Our total consumption of livestock products has gone up a great deal since 1900. The rise reflects the expansion in production, population, and real income per person.

The population of the country was 57 percent larger in 1946 than in 1909; the consumption of livestock products in 1946 was almost 90 percent larger than in 1909. Further increases in the over-all production and consumption of livestock products are in prospect, but over the long run the increases probably will be at a slower rate than in the past. The recent sharp gain in population is generally considered a wartime phenomenon—the population probably will grow less rapidly in the future.

But while per capita income levels over the long run may not stay so high as during the Second World War and immediately afterward, they seem likely to continue above prewar levels. In light of the population gains already made and expected in the future, this income outlook points to further expansion in our total consumption of livestock products. Of course, this expansion probably will not be shared equally by all kinds and groups of livestock products. The consumption of dairy products and poultry products, for example, probably will rise more than the consumption of meat.

The gain in per capita consumption of livestock products from 1909 to 1946 about equaled the 20-percent rise in consumption of all foods. Livestock products made up about two-fifths of the total poundage of foods consumed, but their importance is even greater in terms of nutrients. In recent years they have furnished one-third of the calories in the average American's diet, two-thirds of the proteins, four-fifths of the calcium, one-fifth of the iron, two-fifths of the thiamine and niacin, and two-thirds of the riboflavin.

Among the livestock items, dairy products have increased the most in per capita consumption. Poultry and eggs are next. It is likely that these tendencies will continue.

The tremendous demand for meat during and immediately after the war raises questions about the prewar trend.

Meat consumption per capita tended to go down slightly from about 1909 to 1940. Consumption in the late 1930's was particularly small, an aftermath of the drought years. Civilian per capita consumption of meats increased about one-fifth during the war, despite heavy noncivilian use. Consumption per capita reached a record high in 1946.

The consumption of chicken and turkey averaged about 20 pounds a person before the First World War, and there was little change up to the beginning of the Second World War. During the recent war, when meat supplies were short and incomes were at new peaks, the average person ate about 23 pounds of chicken meat a year and about 3.7 pounds of turkey. Per capita consumption of eggs, which had fallen off about 10 percent during the 1930's, recovered during the war, and was 390 eggs a person in 1946, partly because the demand for meat was greater than the supplies.

The use of fluid milk and cream set new records each year during the war, and reached 430 pounds a person in 1945—primarily as the result of high purchasing power and the favorable prices to producers in relation to manufactured dairy products. The use of butter per capita eased downward during 1924–41. Heavy military purchases during the war reduced civilian supplies, but the smaller output of butter was even more important in cutting the consumption to 11 pounds in 1945 and 10 pounds in 1946; the 1935–39 average was 16.7 pounds. The consumption of cheese per capita was somewhat higher during the Second

World War than in 1935–39, when the average was 5.5 pounds; further increases are likely in the next few years.

The downward trend in the use of condensed milk was reversed during the war. There has been an upward trend in the use of evaporated milk and of dried whole milk and dried skim milk, which are particularly adapted for use in ice cream, bread, and prepared mixes. The use of all four is expected to increase, but the demand for ice cream is closely related to incomes of consumers. In the 1920's, the average person consumed about 8 to 9 pounds of ice cream, about 9.5 pounds in 1935–39, and about 14 pounds in the Second World War.

Lard has shown no decided long-time trend. Consumption per person was high in 1943 and 1944 as a result of unusually large supplies, but was down in 1945 and 1946, when much lard was exported. Lard competes rather directly with vegetable-oil shortening, but it might keep its place because hydrogenation improves it and its keeping qualities.

Livestock and livestock products in recent years have contributed a slightly larger share to the total farm income from all farm marketings than earlier in the century. In 1910, the sale of livestock and livestock products accounted for 49 percent of the total cash receipts from farm marketings. The proportion remained close to 50 percent of the total until about 1925; in 1931 the figure was 60 percent.

But over the past 35 years, cash receipts from livestock and their products have fluctuated widely, partly because of changes in the volume of marketings but mostly because of changes in consumers' purchasing power and differences in export demand. Changing tastes and changes in dietary habits also had something to do with it. Besides, variations in supply arise from cycles of livestock production, range and pasture conditions, feed supplies, incentives to feed to lighter or heavier weights, and outlook for prices.

Because livestock producers' incomes depend heavily on the level of general business activity, some uncertainty naturally exists regarding the future. But with prospects for a general upward trend in production of most livestock products and in population, farmers' cash receipts from livestock and livestock products would be proportionately greater than before the war under any given set of general business conditions. In 1910, farmers took in about 2.8 billion dollars from their marketings of livestock and livestock products; in 1919, their receipts from those sources amounted to nearly 7 billion dollars, but in the recession in 1921 dropped back to 4 billion. By 1929, the figure had climbed to more than 6 billion dollars, only to drop sharply again in the depression of the 1930's—to 2.7 billion dollars in 1932. In 1943–45, with high wartime prices and a large volume of offerings, farmers were paid more than 11 billion dollars a year from sales of livestock and livestock products. In 1946 the total was more than 13 billion dollars.

When such cash receipts are listed by major commodity groups and expressed as percentages of total receipts from all farm marketings, it is found that most of the gain in receipts from livestock since 1910 has been in dairy products and in poultry and eggs. Most of the gains in those products occurred during the few years after the First World War; more recently, income from dairy products has accounted for about 15 percent of the total cash receipts from all farm marketings. Receipts from the sale of poultry and eggs since 1920 have varied from 9 percent to more than 12 percent of the total, with a slight upward trend in the proportion. The share that income from meat animals contributes to total cash receipts from all marketings declined after 1918 from about 30 percent, and continued at a relatively lower level of from 22 to 27 percent until 1938.

Since then, the income from meat animals averaged slightly above 29 percent of the total cash receipts from the farm marketings.

Income from the livestock enterprise probably will continue to furnish half or more of farmers' total cash receipts from sales of all farm products. An indefinite upward trend in this proportion seems probable. Future shifts in types of farming in different parts of the country, price trends and price relationships, rates of production, and crop yields per acre will be among the chief influencing factors. A further tendency toward more diversified farming in the South, for example, would probably do much to raise income from livestock in that part of the country. Future trends will depend largely upon the effects of shifts in production in the different regions, as well as upon changes in prices.

The tremendous possibilities of improving the American diet by the greater use of livestock products are recognized. The need to include livestock in the business of farming in order to maintain soil fertility, improve the use of labor, and cut financial risks are well known. Unless new uses can be found for most crops for which we have exportable surpluses, it seems probable that future long-time shifts in land use will result in the diversion of larger proportions for the production of those crops that are necessary for producing livestock and livestock products, and smaller proportions for the production of crops for direct sale.

To meet the wartime needs for food, farmers boosted the numbers and production of livestock in the early 1940's. At the beginning of 1944, the number of livestock on farms, in terms of roughage-consuming animal units, was the largest on record and production, in terms of units equivalent to the production of one milch cow, also was the greatest on record. The next 3 years, the numbers and production declined, largely as a result of producers' difficulties in getting feedstuffs, although unusually favorable weather meant ample pasture and forage feed. In the

years immediately ahead it is unlikely that numbers of livestock and livestock production will duplicate the high levels of 1943 and 1944 unless stimulated by emergency. Over the longer period, however, those levels might be reached and possibly exceeded.

Some factors that point to future increases in production are: The development of better strains of livestock; better methods of disease control; improved management and feeding practices; a higher feed production potential, because of higher yielding varieties of feed grains and oilseed crops; improved pastures and ranges; and shifts from cash crops to livestock farming.

Some other factors, however, may operate on the down side. One of them is the weather—in most of the United States the weather was unusually good for 11 years, following the drought of 1936.

Total numbers of cattle have risen the past 80 years although not directly in step with the growth of population and often with considerable fluctuations. Since 1890, there has been a definite cyclical trend of 5 to 10 years of decreasing numbers of cattle, followed by 5 to 10 years of increasing numbers. The low point in the most recent cycle was at the beginning of 1938; the apex was at the beginning af 1945, followed by a drop in 1946 and 1947. Cattle numbers probably will continue to decline for the next few years and then resume an upward trend that, over the long run, probably will be more gradual than before the war, primarily because of limitations of grazing resources.

Most of the fluctuation in the number of cattle on farms and ranches has been among beef cattle. The number of dairy cows increased from 1900 to 1945, with little evidence of a cyclical movement and somewhat (but not completely) in keeping with the growth in population. Production per cow, however, has increased so much that the production of milk per capita has actually increased in the period. The trend in the number of beef cattle has been irregularly upward over the long period. The upward trend in the number of dairy cows probably will continue.

The geographical distribution of cattle numbers is likely to change noticeably over the next several years. The number of beef cattle in the South has already grown substantially, and further large increases in that and some other areas are likely.

Farm production of cattle and calves (live weight) set a new record in 1945, one not likely to be equaled for some years. The 1945 record in milk production also still stands, although production per cow in 1946 reached a new peak. The long-time trend in milk production probably will be influenced directly by changes in population, modified by the ability of people to purchase it, and further improvements in production per cow. It is possible that future demand and supply relationships will result in price levels for milk that will maintain the long-time relationship between milk production and population.

A decline in numbers of sheep during the war, the sharpest 5-year drop in history, was due primarily to the higher returns that could be obtained from competitive livestock and crop enterprises and a shortage of skilled labor. At the beginning of 1947 there were fewer stock sheep on farms and ranches than for any year on record— nearly one-third fewer than at the 1942 peak. Sheep numbers probably will increase during the next several years. However, they probably will not equal 1942 until conditions in the sheep industry become unusually favorable. Higher operating costs and competition from other fibers and foreign wools make the outlook for sheep producers less favorable than that for some alternative enterprises.

Tractors and trucks will continue to displace horses and mules, especially on the larger farms. At the same time, there are still certain kinds of farm work and certain types of farms for which horses or mules are better suited, both as to cost and to general adaptability. Future demands for horses or mules will come mostly from farmers of those regions where the land and type of farming preclude a great development of tractor farming.

Grass as a feed is not so important to hogs or poultry as to cattle, sheep, or workstock. But hogs and poultry are very important in the over-all outlook for products of grassland agriculture. Pork alone usually accounts for about half of the total meat produced in the United States.

Hog production tends to fluctuate in cycles of 3 to 5 years. Small or large production is usually reflected in correspondingly high or low prices. These prices, in turn, usually are followed by an increase or decrease in production, especially when there is a marked change in the relationship of hog prices to corn prices. Hog production went up markedly from 1910 to 1920 and then tended to be maintained at the higher level until the droughts of the mid-1930's. Production increased sharply after 1937, reached predrought levels in 1939, and was the largest on record in 1943. Production of hogs continued large after 1943, although moderately below the record peak.

There may be some tendency in the future toward greater production of hogs relative to production of cattle and sheep. Hogs consume nearly half of all corn grown in the United States and an even greater proportion of that grown in the Corn Belt. Improved technology and lower costs in the production of feed grains, particularly corn, will be conducive to increased hog production in this country.

THE AUTHOR«« *Reed A. Phillips was senior agricultural economic statistician, Bureau of Agricultural Economics, from 1944 to 1948. He was in charge of the livestock price analysis section, Division of Statistical and Historical Research in 1946 and 1947; his work then included economic research on livestock and meat, feed, fats, and oils, and poultry. He is now with a firm of commodity counsellors in St. Louis.*

MARKETING AND TRANSPORTATION

KNUTE BJORKA, W. F. FINNER

BECAUSE forage feeds are bulky and costly to transport, they are generally consumed near the place where they are grown. This is a general principle in production and marketing. For example: The production of feeder and slaughter livestock is heavy in the Western Range and the North Central States; dairying for the production of manufactured dairy products is important in the northern part of the Midwest; and the production of milk and cream for fluid use is more widely distributed, because it is concentrated near consuming centers.

Changes involving that general principle are now under way. Farmers and others who handle meat will do well to know these changes and to be aware of the relation of marketing and transportation to the economic utilization of grassland.

The extent to which the cost of transportation influences the location of production or of processing industries varies with the commodity.

The cost of shipping a bulky product of low specific value represents a relatively large proportion of its value and therefore may determine where it will be produced or processed.

On the other hand, the cost of shipping a concentrated commodity of high specific value is a rather small proportion of its value and may therefore not influence very much the place of production and processing.

Transportation costs are significant because of their differences for a particular product between areas, and, more importantly, because of their effect on the net income from different farm enterprises within an area. But a transportation disadvantage for a product may be overcome entirely by other advantages such as more favorable climate or lower costs of production, labor, or other items of marketing and processing.

The relative cost of transporting meat and live animals (plus other marketing and processing expenses) largely determines where slaughtering is done. Comparative transportation costs for livestock and meat are reflected by their rail freight rates. A rate on meat that is low in relation to the rate on livestock favors slaughtering near the place of production and the shipment of meat to deficient areas. But a rate on meat high in relation to the rate on livestock tends to favor shipment of livestock for slaughter at or near the place of consumption.

Freight rates increase with distance, but fixed relationships to distance are not maintained. For the longer distances, the rates are less per 100 miles than for shorter distances, and a through rate is less than the combination of two or more local rates. The through rate for livestock between Des Moines and New York City is 93 cents per 100 pounds, for example, but the combination of local rates of 41 cents from Des Moines to Chicago and 64 cents from Chicago to New York adds up to 105 cents for 100 pounds.

Freight rates per 100 pounds for livestock, the fresh meat, and packing house products between representative points where these commodities normally move are bases for comparison.

The relative advantage of shipping livestock or meat cannot be determined by comparing these rates directly, however, because the weight of the meat produced is considerably less than the weight of the live animal from which it is derived. Dressing yields vary among species and also among animals of the same species. The average dressing yields of the livestock slaughtered in packing plants in the United States in 1946 were 53 percent for cattle, 56 percent for calves, 76 percent for hogs, and 46 percent for sheep and lambs.

Other factors than rates also must be taken into account when comparing the relative advantage of shipping live-stock and meat, such as the relative shrinkage and other transit losses for the two commodities, and the relative consumers' demand for meat received from outside compared with locally dressed meat.

Rates from the northwestern part of the Corn Belt to Chicago favor the shipment of meat instead of livestock. In fact, the rate per 100 pounds of livestock is generally as high as (or higher than) the rate per 100 pounds of fresh meat or of packing-house products. From St. Paul to Chicago the rate on livestock is 129 percent of the fresh-meat rate and 132 percent of the rate on packing-house products. From Sioux City to Chicago the rates on fresh meat and packing-house products are the same, and the livestock rate is 102 percent of the rates on these products. From Omaha to Chicago the rates per 100 pounds are the same for livestock, fresh meat, and packing-house products.

Compared with the rates on live-stock, rates for fresh meat and pack-ing-house products are relatively lower to New York from the western part of the Corn Belt than from the eastern Corn Belt or from the South. Fresh-meat rates to New York are 136 per-cent of the livestock rate from Austin, Minn., 156 percent from Chicago, and 171 percent from Nashville, Tenn.

The relatively high rates on meat to the west coast from the Corn Belt and from the Mountain States tend to favor the shipment of livestock. How-ever, meat rates are not so unfavorable now as they were before November 1945, when the Interstate Commerce Commission adjusted the rates on meat shipped to the west coast from the ter-ritory east of Denver and Cheyenne. The fresh-meat rate to Los Angeles from Kansas City now is 153 percent of the livestock rate, compared with 239 percent before the rates were changed. From Ogden, Utah, to Los Angeles the fresh meat rate now is 183 percent of the rate on livestock, but the ratio was 174 percent before the adjustments in rates had been made.

Several important trends pertaining to dairying, slaughtering, transporta-tion, and marketing of slaughter live-stock have been under way since the First World War.

Important among these are the growing consumption of fluid milk, the shift in slaughter from eastern consum-ing centers to the heavy livestock pro-ducing areas in the Corn Belt and, in the Corn Belt, from plants located at the larger public stockyards to interior plants located in towns and smaller cities; a greater use of motortrucks for transporting livestock; and more direct marketing. The sale of frozen packaged meat and the sale of slaughter livestock by the carcass grade and weight are developments that might increase in importance.

Let us consider them in that order.

The consumption of fluid milk has gone up considerably in the past de-cade. This upward trend, which is likely to continue, has been due to larger per capita consumption as well as to the increase in population.

Because milk is bulky and perishable and there are restrictions on shipments, we can expect the increase in its pro-duction for fluid use to occur mainly near places where it will be consumed. But to a limited extent newer tech-niques of processing and refrigeration in transit may lower the shipping costs from outlying areas, and the territory supplying a given market might there-fore be widened.

We expect the principal expansion in the production of manufactured dairy products to be in the upper Mid-dle West, an area where such produc-tion is now concentrated and where the comparative advantage of dairying seems likely to be emphasized further by greater acreages and yields of grass. Increases in the Appalachian and southern regions will be consumed pri-marily in local markets.

Since shortly after 1918, the im-portance of shipments of livestock from the Corn Belt to slaughtering plants in the East has lessened, and slaughter in

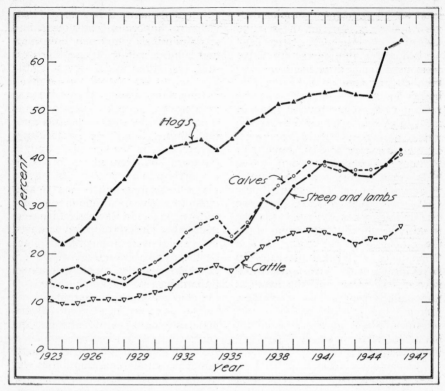

The percentages of slaughter livestock that were bought by packers direct, 1923–46.

plants in the Corn Belt and shipment of meat to the East has increased. The shipment of pork from the western Corn Belt to the west coast may increase as a result of more favorable rates on meat.

The shipment of meat instead of livestock from the Corn Belt saves transportation expenses and helps keep down shrinkage in weight during transit. Slaughter near the place of production is expected to increase, but will be limited somewhat because such western dressed meats cannot meet all the demand of some consumers for kosher meat and for some other locally dressed meats. Increasing amounts of kosher meat for supplying consumers in the East, however, have been produced in Corn Belt plants in recent years—the greater speed of trains has reduced the time in transit so that it is possible to make deliveries to distant centers fast

enough to meet market requirements.

Shifts in slaughter have also taken place within regions, particularly in the Corn Belt—primarily away from plants located at the larger public stockyards to those at interior points. Plants in towns and smaller cities in the producing area generally have easy access to livestock because most of it moves from farms in the area by motortruck. Lower site values for plants in the smaller communities also have encouraged the change.

In the Southern States, slaughter has grown in importance since 1935, the direct result of greater livestock production there. Because the South does not produce all the meat it needs, most of the greater supply resulting from local slaughter will be consumed locally.

Slaughter has increased on the Pacific coast (particularly in California) since 1942 because the expanding population there has boosted the demand for meat.

California has shipped in beef cattle from the Range States and hogs from the western part of the Corn Belt, largely as livestock, because livestock rates have been lower than those for meat. The new reduced rates to the west coast on meat originating between Denver–Cheyenne and the Mississippi River will encourage the shipment of pork instead of hogs from that territory to California.

No great shift to the shipment of beef instead of cattle to the west coast is expected, because those shipments generally originate west of Denver and Cheyenne in a territory that was not affected materially by the freight-rate adjustment of 1945. In the past some high-quality heavy corn-fed beef has been shipped from the western part of the Corn Belt to supply a special demand on the west coast. Such shipments might increase.

Direct Marketing

Slaughter near the source has been encouraged by the extensive use of motortrucks for transporting livestock—trucks need not follow prescribed routes or schedules, and they move livestock directly from farms to final destination.

Direct marketing of slaughter livestock has increased greatly. Hogs have been bought direct by packers (at places other than public markets) in larger proportions than other kinds of livestock since 1923, the period for which data on direct purchases are available. The increase in direct marketing of cattle and calves commenced about 1928 and that of sheep and lambs about 1931. Direct purchases by slaughterers comprised 64 percent of the total for hogs, 42 percent for calves, 41 percent for sheep and lambs, and 25 percent for cattle in 1946.

The greater use of trucks has been associated with the growth of direct marketing and the increase in slaughter at interior plants. Other factors have contributed, because feeder cattle and sheep in recent years have been marketed direct in fully as large proportions as slaughter livestock. Among the factors are lower costs in handling and more direct movement from farms to slaughtering plants or from ranges to feed lots. We see no indication now that the trend will be reversed.

Precutting of Meat

The precutting of meat at packing plants or in central warehouses for sale fresh or frozen is receiving considerable attention by processors and retailers. Precutting meat at a central plant helps the butcher-salesman to use his time more efficiently in his shop and thus tends to lower the cost of preparation and distribution of meat.

If the sale of frozen meat to consumers becomes more common, the cutting, boning, packaging, and freezing would logically be done at the packing plant where the slaughtering and processing can be carried on most economically. This probably will encourage slaughter in plants located near the source of livestock production.

The extra expense of selling meat in frozen-packaged form might be compensated for by the lower cost of retailing. The retailing margin for meat is high because it involves considerable service in cutting and preparing cuts. The margin might very well be reduced if the meat is prepared in central plants where precutting would also permit better utilization of byproducts; also, because some cuts would be boned and trimmed before they are packaged, the cost of transportation should be less.

State and Federal research agencies now are considering the possibility of selling slaughter livestock by carcass grade and weight—the packer would pay for the animals on the basis of the grade and weight of the carcass instead of on live weight; the quality of the meat could be determined in the carcass before final payment, instead of estimating it by the characteristics of the live animal. The weight of the carcass could be obtained directly by weighing, instead of by estimating the dressing percentage of the animal and then applying this estimate to the live weight.

Many practical problems need to be considered before this method of trading can be adopted: Identifying an animal and maintaining its identity until it is slaughtered and the carcass is graded; arriving at the price for the carcass instead of for the live animal; making settlement; and ascertaining the adaptability of the existing grade standards for carcasses of the different species, making the required modifications, and (for hogs) developing the necessary carcass grades.

More slaughtering will be done in the heavy livestock-feeding areas in the Corn Belt, especially the northwestern part, and in the South, as more feed and livestock are produced there. The expansion in both regions is expected primarily in interior slaughtering plants rather than in those at the larger markets.

These developments will be further encouraged by increased use of motortrucks for transporting livestock and the growth of direct marketing. Development of the frozen-meat industry might further encourage slaughter near the place of production.

Present slaughtering facilities generally are adequate but the shift in the location of slaughter that has already taken place and the expected further shift will result in considerable surplus facilities in the East and probably also on the west coast. On the other hand, some expansion of existing facilities probably will be required at the interior points in the Corn Belt. In the South the anticipated expansion in slaughter apparently will require an increase in slaughtering facilities.

Transportation

More slaughtering near farms naturally will affect transportation. The short distances will mean more trucking of livestock; rail transportation of livestock from the Corn Belt to the East will be less important, but rail transportation of meat between those regions probably will increase. It is likely that the rail shipment of livestock from the western part of the Corn Belt to the west coast will lessen, but the shipment of meat will increase.

Increased slaughter in the South will mean that less meat will be shipped there from the Corn Belt; in certain seasons surplus meat may be shipped to markets in the East. The net effect will be to cut the need for livestock cars and raise the demand for refrigerator cars. Refrigerated motortrucks also are expected to become more important.

Development of the frozen-meat industry will necessitate developing refrigeration equipment for both rail and motortruck transportation.

The expected changes would lower the costs of transporting livestock but increase the costs of transporting meat unless rates are modified. However, it appears that the combined transportation bill for livestock and meat will be less for a given volume of livestock than at present.

THE AUTHORS<<< *Knute Bjorka is a graduate of the University of Minnesota and has taken graduate work there, at Iowa State College, and at the University of Chicago. Since 1922, at Iowa State College, the Brookings Institution, and the Bureau of Agricultural Economics, he has engaged in research in livestock marketing, prices, margins and costs, and transportation. He is now an agricultural economist in the Bureau of Agricultural Economics.*

W. F. Finner did his undergraduate work at the University of Florida and the University of Wisconsin, and graduate work at the latter institution. Since 1937 he has been engaged in the study of interregional competition in agriculture and is now an agricultural economist with the Bureau of Agricultural Economics.

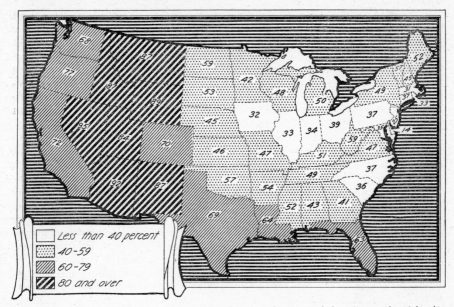

Percentages of all feeds from tame and wild hay and pasture fed to livestock, 1941–42.

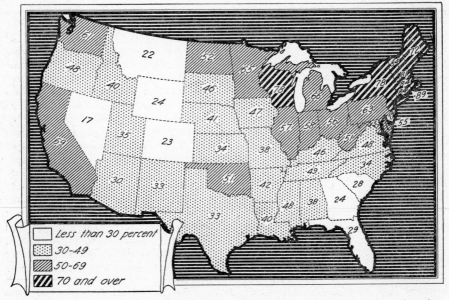

Hay: Percentage of total consumed in each State by dairy cattle, in 1941 and 1942.

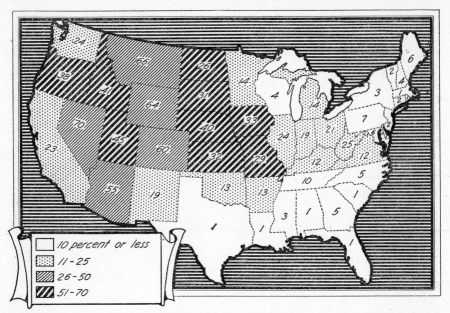

Hay: Percentage of total consumed in each State by beef cattle and sheep, 1941–42.

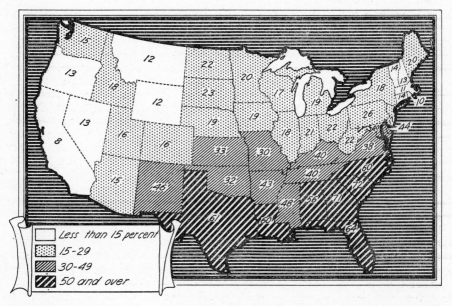

Hay: Percentage of total feed units consumed by horses and mules, by States, 1941–42.

ADJUSTMENTS THAT SEEM NECESSARY

C. W. CRICKMAN

WE HAVE three important criteria by which to measure balance in agriculture:

The kinds and amounts of foods and fibers that people want and need for adequate diets and comforts;

The tools and efforts needed to bring our soil budget into balance and, once balanced, to maintain the physical resource upon which agriculture is based; and

The ways in which farmers can best organize and operate their farms to utilize their individual resources efficiently and thus achieve sustained optimum farm incomes and improved levels of living.

Here, keeping in mind the potential demand for food and fiber and proved practices for efficient farming, let us examine the third point, some of our recent explorations into what would constitute a balanced and profitable pattern for agricultural production.

Even in peacetime too few farmers used systems of soil management that adequately sustained a high level of productivity of their lands. Then the war took a still heavier toll of their soil. To meet wartime needs, farmers in the Corn Belt alone increased their acreage of intertilled crops such as corn and soybeans by 11 million acres, mostly at the expense of grassland. Wheat growers increased their acreage of wheat, mainly in the Great Plains, from 62 million to nearly 72 million, mostly at the expense of grass and fallow. And stockmen in parts of the range country overburdened the range with too many grazing livestock.

Thus we have even farther to go now than before the war toward establishing a balanced agriculture. At least half of the acreage that our farmers are now using for intertilled and close-growing crops needs protection from damage by erosion. And even though during the war farmers increased their use of lime and fertilizers and such practices as contour farming, strip cropping, and growing cover crops, balancing the soil budget would mean even greater increases in the use of these materials and practices.

Almost as soon as the heavy demands of the war could be foreseen the need for a long-range production pattern that would serve as a bench mark for adjusting to a balanced agriculture was generally recognized. Even before hostilities had ended in Europe, State agricultural colleges and the Department of Agriculture began exploration of the opportunities for postwar agriculture. The opportunities for growing more grass and legumes for protecting and rebuilding depleted soils and for providing cheap and nutritious feed for livestock stand out among the many prospective adjustments appraised. Each suggested improvement in systems of farming, including the production and utilization of feed crops, was appraised on the basis of what would be both technically and economically feasible.

Preliminary results of these studies definitely suggest that within a reasonably prosperous national economy farmers can produce abundantly, profitably, and with progressive improvement of agricultural resources.

More specifically these studies indicate, first, that farmers in the United States may plan to maintain the total acreage of land used for crops and summer fallow at approximately the present level. Total cropland did not increase very much during the war. But to maintain and improve their soils for an efficient level of productivity, they should return to an even greater acreage of grass and legumes than before the war. The percentage increase needed in rotation hay and pasture combined would be about 20 percent more than the 1943 acreage.

Because of the increasing practice of using grass on cropland for both hay and pasture in the same year, it is difficult to separate the two uses. But the percentage increase in rotation pasture would probably be somewhat greater than that in tame hay. The percentage increase in permanent pasture would be small, about 2 percent, but the increase in acreage would be almost half as much as the increase in acreage of hay and rotation pasture.

Less attention has been given to improved practices in hay production than to any other feed crop except pasture. With favorable market outlets and favorable prices for livestock products, it would be profitable to go much further in the substitution of higher yielding and higher quality legumes for lower yielding and less nutritious grass hays. It would also be profitable to use more lime and fertilizer on more acres. And improved methods of harvesting and curing would enhance the nutritive content of the hay.

Available estimates indicate that under favorable conditions these improved practices would raise the United States yield of tame hay to about 1.8 tons (compared with an average of about 1.4 in 1937–41), an increase of about 25 percent. The combined increases in acreage and in yield per acre would increase total production of hay to about 40 percent more than was produced in 1943 and about 50 percent more than the average production from 1937 through 1941.

Considerable expansion in the acreage of grass and legume hay is desirable in all parts of the United States, except possibly in the Northeast. Compared with production in 1943, the largest increases (30–40 percent) would be in the Northern Great Plains, the Lake States, and in the Southern States that are largely outside the peanut-hay area. In the peanut-hay area there would be considerable substitution of other hays for peanut hay. The increases in the Corn Belt and other major agricultural regions would range between 15 and 20 percent.

Increases in yield per acre and improvement in the quality of the hay crop are feasible and would be profitable in all major groups of States. The opportunities appear to be greatest in the Mississippi Delta States—about 65 percent above the 1937–41 average. Regional increases in yield per acre ranging from 30 to 40 percent are estimated for the Lake States, the five Corn Belt States, the Appalachian States, and the Southeastern States.

Reference already has been made to the wartime shift of land from pasture to other more intensive uses, especially in the Corn Belt, the Lake States, and the Northern Great Plains. From the standpoint of a long-time program that will maintain or improve the soil and produce feed economically, pasture should occupy a more important place in those regions than it did during the war. Increases of about 25 percent in both the Corn Belt and the Northern Great Plains, and of about 15 percent in the Lake States seem desirable.

In the Appalachian and Southern States larger than usual acreages of better quality pastures are needed as a basis for a conversion to more diversified farming, including more livestock production. Increases in acreage of approximately 25 percent in these groups of States would be mostly in permanent pasture, although the percentage increase in rotation and permanent pasture would be about the same.

An increase of about 35 percent in rotation pasture in the Pacific States and 15 percent in the Mountain States would largely represent desirable increases in irrigated pasture.

The opportunities for improvement of the carrying capacity per acre by the use of better pasture-management practices are greater for open permanent pastures than for rotation pastures, measured in terms of animal-unit-months of grazing.

In the States east of the Great Plains, the estimated optimum carrying capacity for an average acre of open permanent pasture is about 30 percent above what it was in 1943, whereas for rotation pasture it is only about 15 percent more. Over-all gains in the carrying capacity of rotation pastures seem possible only in the central Corn Belt, the Lake States, and the Mississippi Delta States. In other groups of Eastern States, any improvement in carrying capacity of rotation pasture would likely be more than offset by the addition of more acres of lower potential carrying capacity. By the use of profitable improved practices, farmers in both the Corn Belt and the Lake States can probably increase the carrying capacity of the average acre of rotation pasture to 25 percent more than its carrying capacity with the pasture-management practices in use in 1943 and in normal growing weather.

In the same two groups of States—central Corn Belt and Lake States—comparable increases in the carrying capacity of an average acre of open permanent pasture are about 35 and 65 percent, respectively. A comparable figure for the Appalachian States is about 25 percent; for the Mississippi Delta States and the Northeastern States, about 15 percent.

Comparable estimates of the carrying capacity per acre of ranges and pastures in the Great Plains States and States farther west cannot be made from the available data.

Companion estimates for the four principal feed grains (corn, oats, barley, and sorghums), the other half of the "feed base" for livestock production, total in round numbers 150 million harvested acres and 127 million tons of feed. The combined acreage would be 3 percent more than the prewar (1937–41) average, but 4.4 percent less than the wartime acreage in 1943. Corn acreage would be about 4 percent less than the prewar average; the acreage of small grains would be about 10 percent more and that of sorghums harvested for grain almost 50 percent more. The production of feed grains would be 27.5 percent more than the average production from 1937 through 1941, and 14.5 more than was produced in 1943. The explanation of considerably larger production on approximately the same total acreage is the possibility of obtaining higher yields per acre under favorable conditions.

Besides better rotations, to which a reduction in corn acreage would contribute, it would pay more corn growers to use more fertilizer, green manures, barnyard manures, and crop residues; proper water disposal and moisture-conserving practices; and special practices to control insects and diseases. Hybrid seed is now used for almost 100 percent of the corn produced in the central part of the Corn Belt, but the development and use of varieties of hybrids better suited to other areas will considerably improve yields in those areas. Furthermore, adequate supplies of improved machinery will facilitate better cultural practices and make it possible to concentrate more of the work on corn in the periods when it is most effective.

The larger acreages of sod crops that are essential to balanced cropping systems would require a larger acreage of small grains in some of the Corn Belt States, to serve as a companion crop for new seedings of the hay and pasture crops. In the Southern and in the Appalachian States a considerable increase in production of feed grains is desirable and oats have been producing slightly more feed per acre than corn in these States since rust-resistant and higher-yielding varieties have been available. The opportunities for further improvement in yield appear to be more promising for oats than for corn.

The system of sustained feed-crop production here outlined would produce 34 percent more tons of tame and wild hay, 16 percent more animal-unit-months of pasturage, and 14.5 percent more tons of feed grains, than was produced in 1943. These larger supplies of forage and grains would provide feed for the production of about 8 percent more livestock and poultry products for food than was produced in 1943, and about 36 percent more than was produced in 1937–41. This estimate makes allowance for nonfeed uses of

The Old and the New in Dairy Farm Management on Trumbull County, Ohio, Experiment Farm

Item	Average of 3 years	
	The old, 1927–29	The new, 1940–42
Milking cows in herd............................number..	13.9	19
Annual production per cow:		
Milk..pound..	10,694	11,570
Butterfat...do....	368	382
Annual production per farm:		
Milk...do....	148,650	219,815
Butterfat...do....	5,118	7,262
Concentrates fed annually per cow:		
Corn and oats.....................................do....	1,791	1,604
Oil meals...do....	976	312
Bran...do....	807	199
Gluten feed.......................................do....	139	....
Total...do....	3,713	2,115
Total concentrates fed to herd annually...................ton..	25.8	20.6
Pounds of milk per pound concentrates fed..............pound..	2.9	5.3
Pounds of concentrates per hundredweight of milk.........do....	34.5	19.0
Approximate daily winter ration:		
Corn silage.......................................do....	45	20
Hay...do....	12	[1] 30
Hay purchased.......................................ton..	3	None
Hay sold..do....	None	16

[1] More than 30 pounds placed in mangers. Uneaten part used for bedding or for other livestock.

the feed grains, use of forage crops for green manure, and some margin of safety in the feed-livestock balance.

The larger production of higher quality hay and pasturage would provide efficient rations of these feeds, which involves greater substitution of forage for concentrates, for about the same total number of animal units of cattle and sheep as were on farms at the wartime high points of the cattle and sheep cycles; but with some shift from sheep to cattle in the interest of the most profitable utilization of the range and farm pastures. This would mean nearly 30 percent more cattle and calves than were on farms during the 1937–41 period, and about 5 percent downward change in the number of sheep and lambs.

The carrying capacity of hay and grazing land in terms of number of cattle and sheep has been increased progressively, especially in the humid regions, since 1918 by the decline in the number of horses and mules. Since 1918 the decline in the number of horses and mules has released enough hay and pasture to feed the equivalent of about 19 million additional cattle and calves at current rates of feeding. As the introduction of mechanical power gradually makes further progress, especially in the South, the numbers of cattle can be increased, because of the feed that will be released and because systems of farming are likely to be developed that include more hay, pasture, and grain.

Liberal feeding is one of the fundamentals of successful dairying. Improvement of the quantity and quality of hay and pasture would favor an expansion in the number of cows milked somewhere near proportional to the expansion in the total number of cattle. An increase, compared with the number in 1937–41, of about 25 percent in the number of cows milked would appear to be a profitable adjustment to the previously mentioned changes in feed supplies.

In prewar years 55 percent of the Nation's milk cows were in the Lake States, the Corn Belt, and the Northeastern States. About the same proportion of the suggested number would be in those three groups of States. But as the opportunities for increasing the feed base appear to be greater in the Lake States than in the Northeastern States, dairying would be expected to expand more in the Lake States. The expansion in milk cows in the Corn Belt would be about proportional to the total expansion in the United States.

Production of hogs and the supplies of corn are closely related. If farmers produce about 3¼ billion bushels of corn on about 89 million acres by using improved practices to increase yield per acre, and if the hog-corn price ratio is reasonably favorable, they would find it profitable to raise an annual pig crop of about 100 million head. This would be 18 percent less than the record pig crop in 1943, but 30 percent more than the average pig crop during the 5 years 1937–41.

An estimate of the total available supply of feed does not provide nearly so adequate a basis for estimating the numbers of poultry as for cattle and hogs. But on this basis, and keeping in mind a balanced agriculture, about 425 million hens and pullets on farms would seem to be comparable with the foregoing estimates. This would be about 13 percent more than the average number on farms from 1937 through 1941. Chickens, exclusive of commercial broilers, are ordinarily raised primarily for replacement of laying flocks, and thus would be in about the same relationship to prewar figures as the laying flocks.

Furthermore, under favorable con-

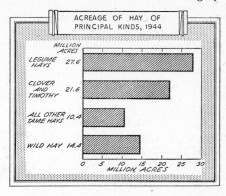

ditions, livestock and poultry producers would find it more profitable to give more attention to improved production practices. Estimates that have been made indicate that for beef cattle this would result in 6 percent more production per animal, with 5 percent fewer pounds of concentrates per 100 pounds of gain in live weight, compared with the 1943 figures. An estimated increase in the percentage calf crop from an average of 82.4 during 1937–41 to 84.6 with improved practices would be reflected in increased production per animal. Comparable estimates for sheep and lambs are 10 percent more production per animal with about the same number of pounds of concentrates per 100 pounds of live-weight production, and an increase in the percentage lamb crop from 84.1 to 87. The estimated average production of milk per cow and of eggs per hen is 13 and 24 percent, respectively, more than during the prewar (1937–41) period.

Combining these estimates of the numbers of livestock and chickens and of the rates of production per animal or per bird that would constitute an adjustment to a balanced agriculture, we get the following percentage increases in production over that in the prewar (1937–41) period: For milk, about 36 percent; net live-weight production of cattle and calves, about 40 percent; net live-weight production of sheep and lambs, about 10 percent; net live-weight production of hogs, about 40 percent; and for eggs, about 30 percent.

These estimates are to be considered as part of the potential production of a balanced agriculture in a national economy geared to full production. They are in a setting of full employment and a high level of national income, and they include the effects of the adoption of known improvements in farm practices that would be profitable under those conditions.

In this setting farmers of the Nation gradually can supply adequate diets for all of our people with a pattern of production that stresses soil-conserving practices and the livestock enterprises associated with grassland farming, and do it profitably and with pro-gressive improvement of their land. To move rapidly in this direction, however, more intensive educational and operations programs would be needed to encourage and accelerate the adoption of the improved practices that would be necessary for realizing the full potentialities of the grassland crops in the United States.

THE AUTHOR《《 *C. W. Crickman is principal agricultural economist, Division of Farm Management and Costs, Bureau of Agricultural Economics. He supervises farm management research in the Corn Belt and northern dairy region.*

Grass in the Ten Regions

The Northeastern States

GRASSLAND IS WELL SUITED

VANCE G. SPRAGUE, MERTON S. PARSONS

GRASSLAND agriculture is well suited to the Northeastern States. The nearness of markets for fluid milk and other dairy and poultry products has stimulated the production of these items. The rough and rolling topography of much of the land is not well adapted to growing grain and other feeds, and there is an increasing dependence on forage as a source of feed. The soils of the region need grass to improve them, and the climate favors its growth.

The climate is humid and temperate. The average annual precipitation is about 40 inches almost everywhere, although mountains may increase the rainfall in some localities and reduce that reaching the more level lands beyond. Much more important for the production of good forage is the fact that the greatest part of the yearly average comes in June, July, and August, when the requirements of the plants for water are greatest. Slightly less rainfall occurs in the spring and fall and the least during the winter. Unfortunately the summer precipitation of 12 to 14 inches often falls in heavy showers, so that much is lost through runoff, especially from intertilled crops.

Moreover, while the average precipitation indicates favorable conditions for growth during the summer, the variations throughout any one year often result in periods of drought. When these occur in midsummer, coinciding with periods of higher temperatures and greater evaporation rates, the production of forage may be seriously reduced.

Moderate temperatures prevail throughout the region, and seldom limit the growth of the common grasses and legumes. The variation in the average maximum temperatures (about 90° F. in northern Maine to 100° in Delaware and Maryland) is rather small; that in average minimum temperatures is rather large (minus 30° in northern Maine to plus 5° in Maryland and Delaware). Average July temperatures range from 75° in the southern part to 65° in the northern. Temperature alone does not prevent the use of a particular species in the region, although some plants (such as Kentucky bluegrass and timothy) grow much better in the central and northern parts, while other plants (such as orchardgrass) do better in the central and southern parts.

The length of the growing season varies considerably because of latitude, elevation, and proximity to large bodies of water. On upland farms in northern New England the frost-free period ranges from 100 to 125 days; in southern New England it is about 150 days;

near the seacoast it is 160 to 180 days. In central New York, Pennsylvania, and West Virginia the growing season ranges from 140 to 160 days. Along the coast of Delaware and Maryland a period of more than 200 successive frost-free days is not uncommon.

In general, the sunshine is adequate for excellent growth of grasses. During the summer 55 to 65 percent of the total possible sunshine is available. The average number of hours of sunshine daily during June, July, and August is between 8 and 9. The relative noonday humidity for July ranges from 50 to 60 percent, except along the seacoast, where it is 70 to 75 percent.

The topography is characterized generally by long ridges of low mountains and hills that extend in a northeasterly direction. Between the ridges are valleys of varying width; they comprise most of the good farm land, but the land is generally rolling and subject to erosion where cultivated crops are raised.

Most of the soils in the Northeast were developed under a natural forest cover in a humid temperate climate. They have been classified as Podzol, Brown Podzolic, and Gray-Brown Podzolic soils. The northern part, including most of New York and sections of northern Pennsylvania and New Jersey, was glaciated. In the southwestern part the soils were generally derived from sandstones and acid shales, with smaller amounts of limestone and calcareous shales as parent materials. In the south-central area the soils were derived from igneous rock, limestone, and shale. Along the coast, south of the glaciated region, the soils were derived largely from sand and silt.

After the forests were removed, the land was relatively high in fertility and abundant crop yields were obtained. Through years of cultivation, however, much of the original organic matter was destroyed, and large amounts of plant nutrients were removed. Serious erosion and leaching followed; the productive capacity of the soil was still further reduced, so that now many of the once-fertile hillsides and even some of the more level areas have been abandoned and have reverted to less desirable grasses, weeds, and brush.

During the past two decades there has been a growing realization of what has occurred. More lime and fertilizer are used on cultivated land to maintain the supply of plant foods. The soil organic matter is being increased through the use of more fertilizer for grasses and legumes and the adoption of rotations in which the sod crop supplies nutritious hay, silage, or pasture for three or more years. Similarly, abandoned fields are being reclaimed. Thus, through grassland farming, plant nutrients are replaced, losses from erosion and leaching are minimized, organic matter of the soil is maintained, and productivity of farm land is increased.

Still, productivity and farming opportunities vary greatly, even within small areas. Over the years, the interplay of several forces and of changing methods of farming—industrialization, a heavy concentration of urban and nonfarm populations with relatively high incomes, good nearby markets that favor the production of bulky and perishable items such as milk for fluid use, the development of part-time farming, and the influence of competition from other parts of the United States—have caused many adjustments.

Today northeastern agriculture includes about 640,000 farms, with more than 2.5 million persons on them. It includes approximately 60 million acres of land, 22 million acres of cropland, 4 million dairy cows, 70 million chickens, and smaller numbers of other livestock. The total value of sales in

1944 was about 1.7 billion dollars, 37 percent of it derived from dairying, 21 percent from poultry, 32 percent from all cultivated crops, and 10 percent from other sources.

Such statistics are impressive, but farming here can be understood better by looking beyond the total to the farm units and the separate farm situations that make up the whole. From one standpoint most northeastern farms are family farms, carried on primarily by the operator and his family. From another standpoint dairy farms are more numerous than any other type in the Northeast, and some of these, particularly in northern New England and northern New York, are specialized dairy farms. Others (such as those commonly found in western New York and southeastern Pennsylvania) are more diversified. Dairying is an important enterprise in every Northeastern State, and in some sections (such as most of Vermont, northern and central New York, and northern Pennsylvania) it dominates farming.

Grassland is behind this dairy enterprise and basic to it. In terms of acres, grass is the leading farm crop of the Northeast. During the past decade an average of about 10 million acres, roughly one-half the total area of cropland, has been used for hay. Further, the Northeast has some 15 million acres of pasture, most of it grassland. Woodland occupies about 22 million acres of farm land. Corn, the crop second to hay in acreage, has averaged around 3 million acres in recent years.

Aside from dairying, northeastern farmers are occupied largely with poultry, cash crops, and nonfarm work. Poultry is scattered throughout the region, with about half of the chickens in flocks of fewer than 400 birds. Even in New England, where poultry farming is more specialized than in other sections of the Northeast, roughly 40 percent of the birds are in flocks of fewer than 400, and about 10 percent are in flocks of fewer than 50. Many of the small flocks are on part-time farms or units that are classified as

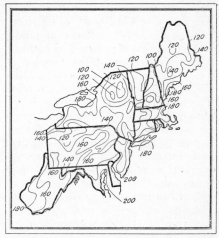

Average length, in days, of the frost-free growing periods in the Northeastern States.

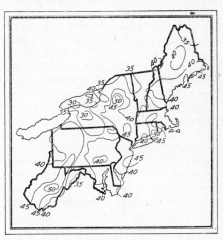

The average annual precipitation, in inches.

farms but are really little more than rural homes with gardens.

Cash crops, on the other hand, tend to be concentrated in certain areas where soils and topography are favorable. Much of the cash-crop production is highly specialized—potatoes in northern Maine, for example, or fruit along the Lake Ontario border of New York, truck crops in parts of New Jersey, Maryland, and Delaware, apples in the West Virginia panhandle, and tobacco in southern Maryland. Equally important in some areas, however, is the cash-crop production on dairy and general farms, such as found in western New York and the Piedmont areas of Pennsylvania and Maryland.

A considerable amount of nonfarm work is characteristic of farming in the Northeast, particularly in New England near manufacturing centers. The industrial development of the region makes it possible for many people to live in the country and yet depend primarily on nonfarm work for their cash income. Often they do enough farming so that their units classify as farms and thus become a part of the over-all farm statistics. For the region as a whole, 20 percent of the work done by farmers in 1939 was of the nonfarm type. For some sections the percentage was higher, amounting to more than 30 percent in the less productive farming areas.

Northeastern agriculture was not always like the picture we have sketched. In 1900 the number of farms in the region and the number of acres in farms were considerably larger than at present. Types of farming have also been changing. In general, the shifts have been away from beef cattle, sheep, and grain production toward dairying, poultry, fruits, and vegetables. As elsewhere, farming here has become more commercialized, more specialized, and more highly mechanized. In addition, the average farm is becoming larger, and production is concentrating on the better land. These changes have been in response to technological developments in farming and competition from other regions. There is nothing in sight to indicate that changes of this type are at an end.

Grass is a major item in northeastern farming, as the tremendous acreage of grass reported by the census would indicate. Acreage alone, however, does not tell the whole story.

Grass is not an end in itself, but rather a basis for livestock production; the progressive dairy farmer of the region is coming to realize that his success or failure depends to a considerable extent on how well he manages his grassland. Hay and pasture provide most of the roughage for his dairy animals and, if his is an average set-up, this forage represents perhaps 50 percent of the total feed nutrients used by the herd. If he handles his grassland so that he gets good yields of high-quality hay and grazing, the resulting income will be better than if he has a limited supply of inferior forage.

The production of nutritious forage as feed for livestock is increasing as its place in the farm program is becoming more fully recognized. A decade ago pastures and hay lands were generally considered separate entities. With a more liberal application of fertilizers, however, the quantity and the nutritive value of forage have been increased; the growing of larger grasses and legumes under improved management treatments for use as hay, silage, or pasture has made the distinctions between pastures and hay lands less evident.

At one extreme, land which is too rough, hilly, wet, or otherwise not adapted for the use of farm machinery is used for permanent pasture and from this all herbage is harvested by grazing animals.

At the other extreme, good cropland is used primarily for cultivated crops and is less often grazed. An increasing amount of land of intermediate fertility and topography is being seeded to grasses and legumes for use as intensively managed semipermanent or rotation pastures. Silage or hay may be harvested from these fields in June; later in the summer, when the production of permanent pastures is limited, the fields may be grazed.

Obviously, no single program of forage management will fit all, or even most, of the northeastern farms. Opportunities will vary according to physical conditions, such as soil and climate. They will also vary according to type of farm, markets available, the personality of the operator, and other factors that affect the problems on the individual farm. A dairy cash-crop farm in southeastern Pennsylvania is in quite a different situation and has different opportunities from a specialized dairy farm in northern Vermont. Likewise, a farm with a large acreage of permanent pasture presents a problem different from that of a farm primarily dependent on cropland pasture. Under some circumstances it may be good business to make heavy purchases of concentrates; in others, it may pay to make the most use of forage. Forage management, to be effective, must be related to management of the farm business as a whole and be part of it.

PERMANENT PASTURES

VANCE G. SPRAGUE

THE GREATEST acreage of grazing lands in the Northeast is in permanent pasture.

When the land was first cleared, even the soil on fairly steep slopes produced good crop yields, but after those lands had been tilled for some years, their fertility was reduced by losses from cultivation, erosion, leaching, and crop removal. Furthermore, the lands often were not adapted to modern equipment. It was no longer economical to crop them, and such fields were permitted to go to grass.

Thus pastures have been relegated to the more extensive and less productive areas of the farm where plowing is difficult and erosion hazards are greatly increased by tillage. The belief is general, therefore, that land which cannot be plowed easily or land from which the fertility has been removed by a continuous cropping system will make good pasture more or less by itself. It is true that cleared land which is grazed will revert to grass, but farmers have not fully realized how low is the quality and how limited is the amount of the herbage produced by such fields.

Environment determines the kinds of plants that grow on any land. The factors of environment are many, but several that affect pasture plants are moisture, temperature, soil fertility, and grazing management. All, reacting together, determine the species that will persist on any area. In an all-season grazing-management system, soil fertility becomes a leading factor in determining the predominant plants.

In this region, on land of low fertility, povertygrass prevails. It occurs on the poor hillside pastures from West Virginia to Vermont; it indicates a need for phosphate, usually lime, and sometimes potash. In the southern part of the region, broomsedge also indicates a condition of low fertility. On pastures of slightly higher fertility sweet vernalgrass and bentgrass occur in the cooler and more moist areas; Canada bluegrass is found in the drier and warmer parts. As the fertility level is raised still further, either from naturally more fertile soils or by the application of lime, phosphate, and manure, Kentucky bluegrass and white clover predominate.

This cycle of the occurrence of various grass plants in a pasture can proceed in either direction. Good pastures of Kentucky bluegrass and white clover may revert to povertygrass if plant nutrients are continually removed and none returned; a povertygrass pasture may be changed into a productive Kentucky bluegrass-white clover pasture if the necessary plant nutrients are added. Thus, change always is a factor for good or ill.

All stages in the improvement or degradation of these various types of permanent pastures may be observed in almost any part of the region. Pastures on droughty soils or steep slopes may not be economical to improve. Such areas probably should be reforested. There are also many acres of potentially productive pasture land on which Kentucky bluegrass and white clover could profitably be grown if the necessary lime and fertilizer were applied. Such land could then produce abundant and nutritious forage.

A survey of 232 farms in West Virginia has shown that 6 acres of povertygrass and weeds was required for one animal unit, but that only three-fourths of an acre of good Kentucky bluegrass and white clover was required to provide the same amount of grazing. Intermediate mixtures of povertygrass and Kentucky bluegrass and white clover provided intermediate amounts of forage. From this relationship a farmer is able to estimate the grazing capacity of his pastures and plan his farm program better.

Permanent pastures play an important role in a system of livestock farming. Since a considerable part of many farms is not easily tilled, this land is better suited to the production of forage. On steep, stony soils where difficulties would be encountered in working the land and seeding it to pasture plants, a permanent sod is most desirable. While the plants constituting permanent pasture sods may not yield so well as the grasses and legumes used under a system of intensive grazing management, they are not so exacting in their requirements. Thus, on land that is too remote to be cared for adequately or too rough for the use of farm machinery, a permanent sod may provide a valuable source of feed. Permanent grasses like Kentucky bluegrass and bentgrass are sod-forming, so that cattle may be turned out earlier in the spring with less injury to the turf. Pastures of such bunch-type grasses as timothy, orchardgrass, and meadow fescue are badly cut up if they are grazed when the soil is soft and wet in the spring.

Permanent sods are naturally most vigorous in the spring. A farmer can take advantage of this characteristic to supply nutritious pasture herbage while the hay land or the more intensively managed pasture land is producing a first crop for hay or grass silage. While permanent pastures do not produce so much feed during the summer months as some of the larger growing meadow and hay plants, sufficient herbage is usually available during this period to maintain young stock and dry cows. Thus the farmer during the summer months can turn his milking herd into his better pastures and meadow lands, which usually are located nearer the farm buildings.

Very few permanent pastures in the Northeast have actually been established by seeding. Perhaps most have come from land which had been in cultivation but which, after a number of years of cropping, was badly depleted in fertility. Such fields were usually seeded to a hay mixture, often to timothy and red clover, and the hay removed for several years or until productivity declined. Because timothy does not stand heavy grazing, Kentucky bluegrass, bentgrass, and white clover became established naturally as the timothy went out if the fertility was not too low; otherwise, Canada bluegrass, sweet vernalgrass, povertygrass, broomsedge, and weeds became the dominant species.

More recently, old fields as well as other rough land that had been cleared and grazed but not cultivated have been greatly improved through fertilization. To accomplish this improvement most effectively, at least 1 ton per acre of ground lime had to be applied where the soils were acid. Afterward, manure and superphosphate were applied liberally at approximate rates of 6 to 8 tons of manure an acre, fortified with 50 pounds of superphosphate per load. In subsequent years an application of phosphate (and on many soils, potash) was necessary to maintain fertility and thereby increase the stand and yield of desirable pasture plants.

Through the use of such fertility practices and good grazing management, Kentucky bluegrass and white clover will volunteer almost universally throughout the region. On soils where moisture is not seriously lacking, such pastures will carry approximately a cow on an acre.

Grazing Management

Besides adequate fertility, permanent pastures need care in grazing management if the greatest returns of palatable and nutritious herbage are to be had.

Grass by itself cannot produce the best yields unless it has a ready source of nitrogen for growth. Under most conditions this can be most economically provided by a legume growing in association with the grass. White clover is well adapted for the purpose. Unfortunately the very nitrogen that the legume supplies stimulates the grass to the extent that the grass may seriously crowd and thus weaken the clover. Unless the grass is removed either by grazing or clipping at or before its heading stage in early summer, the growth of the legume is inhibited and production again is lessened by a lack of nitrogen.

On some of the smaller pastures near the farm buildings it often has been found practical to apply 40 to 60 pounds of nitrogen in a commercial nitrogen fertilizer early in the spring. This practice stimulates the grass and provides grazing a week to 10 days earlier than would untreated pasture.

While the value of an intensive rotational system of grazing management on permanent pasture is questioned by some pasture specialists, it is rather generally agreed that all the permanent pasture should not be in one unit. Turning cattle into a large pasture (especially in the spring when bluegrass makes its most rapid growth and the fullest possible utilization should be made of it) often causes waste by trampling and spotty grazing.

It is better to divide a large pasture into two or three parts and graze each separately: There is less waste of the feed produced and the grass has a chance to recover before it is again grazed off. Mowing the pasture in early summer to cut off the ungrazed grass and seed heads and mowing again in July or early August to cut any weeds is desirable if the lay of the land permits the use of a mower.

A limitation of the permanent pasture is its low productivity in midsummer, when higher temperatures and low soil moisture are most likely. Low productivity is due largely to the growth requirement of the plant species that comprise the sward. While adequate fertility and soils more retentive of moisture aid in delaying the drop in production, low midsummer yields cannot be prevented, especially in the central and southern part of the region. In Maryland and some parts of West Virginia and Pennsylvania, midsummer production of permanent pastures is increased by the use of lespedeza, a warm-weather legume. In some of the northern parts, birdsfoot trefoil, another legume, has shown promise under certain conditions, but so far the problem of how to establish it on permanent pastures has not been solved.

SEMIPERMANENT PASTURES

VANCE G. SPRAGUE

SOME NORTHEASTERN farmers still think that pasture is one of nature's gifts but many others consider the production of high-quality forage the equal of cultivated crops.

In the Northeast, where a large part of the concentrate feed is shipped in from the Midwest, the possibilities of replacing part of this high-cost feed with locally produced nutritious forage cannot be ignored. Well-managed permanent pastures produce abundant herbage during the spring flush of growth, but are much less productive during the hotter, drier midsummer. Unless other forage is available, expensive concentrates must be fed if milk production is to be maintained;

the need is great for a source of succulent and nutritious summer forage.

To meet this need, some of the larger growing and deeper rooted hay-type plants—Ladino clover, alfalfa, orchardgrass, and bromegrass, which are better able to grow under summer conditions—are used.

They often serve doubly. The first crop may be harvested for hay or grass silage, and the aftermath grazed. That is a normal procedure where enough permanent pasture is at hand for spring and early summer grazing. This type of pasture, however, has flexibility and can supplement the forage program when the need is greatest. Such semipermanent pasture, called a short ley in England, is an intensive enterprise that requires adequate fertility and careful management if its full value is to be realized.

Because these pastures require careful grazing management and a liberal investment in fertilizer, they are usually located on potentially productive soils where good returns can be expected. Greater production may be had by using cropland, but rolling land that will allow the operation of hay-making machinery may be used. This will permit the more level land to be included in the regular crop rotation. Thin, droughty, poorly drained soils are not best adapted, although some progress is being made toward the discovery and development of plants and methods for their management so the use of borderline soils for forage production can be extended.

The large quantities of feed produced from intensively managed pastures indicate that the plants used are crops and not simply grass. Chemical analyses of the herbage produced by such pastures have indicated that, roughly, the equivalent of 500 pounds of ammonium sulfate, 150 pounds of superphosphate, and 150 pounds of muriate of potash is removed from each acre in a single season.

This liberal removal of fertility indicates the necessity for providing an adequate supply for growth. However, it is not necessary to supply nitrogen fertilizer when an adequate stand of legumes is present because the nitrogen, which is used to provide protein in the forage, is taken from the air by the nitrogen-fixing bacteria on the roots of the legumes.

Most soils in the region contain only a limited amount of phosphorus that is available to the plant. Besides, the soil itself exhibits a marked affinity for part of the phosphorus supplied in the fertilizer. Sufficient amounts of superphosphate, therefore, must be applied to fulfill the requirements of the plant besides the amount fixed by the soil. Soils in the region vary in the amount of fertilizer required to obtain good growth.

A general recommendation for potentially productive land in a low state of fertility would be an application of the equivalent of 600 to 800 pounds per acre of 20-percent superphosphate at the time of establishment. On more fertile fields 400 pounds per acre may be sufficient. In both cases about 200 to 300 pounds a year thereafter as a top dressing would be advisable.

Soils differ more in their potash requirements than in their need for phosphate. Potash, if it is needed, usually is applied at rates of 100 to 200 pounds per acre of muriate at the time of establishment and about 100 to 150 pounds per acre each year thereafter. When large amounts of potash are readily available, legumes and grasses often absorb more than they actually require for growth, and it may be advisable therefore to make two applications, half in the early spring and the other half after the first hay or silage crop is removed. If manure is applied liberally one year the potash fertilizer may be omitted that year.

Lime is needed on most northeastern soils. Before the seedbed is prepared, enough lime should be applied to reduce the soil acidity to near neutral (pH 6.5 to 6.8). Often that will take two tons or more an acre of finely ground limestone, or its equivalent in hydrated lime, burned lime, or marl.

The liberal amounts usually applied will last 5 years or more.

In some localities a lack of magnesium limits growth. It may be supplied by using dolomitic limestone.

Boron deficiencies, particularly on alfalfa, observed in a number of places, may be corrected by applying borax at the rate of 20 pounds per acre. Some mixed fertilizer of an 0–19–19 analysis is now available; it carries 1 percent of boron and obviates the separate addition of the required amount of boron.

Manure probably is of greatest value on croplands, but if a farmer has more than enough for that use, he can use it effectively on pastures. Manure supplies potash, nitrogen, organic matter, and minor nutrients, whose exact functions we do not understand fully. The addition of 50 pounds of superphosphate to a load of manure gives an almost complete nutrient balance and reduces the labor required to apply it.

Manure can be applied most effectively in the fall, winter, or early spring, and usually should be used only on fields from which the first crop is to be removed as hay or silage. If the first crop is pastured off after manure is applied, grazing is apt to be spotty, and the herbage will not be eaten so close to the ground as is advisable for the best growth of the plants.

Pasture Renovation

Pasture renovation means the improvement of any type of pasture. More specifically—and more recently—renovation is taken to mean a general improvement and a particular kind of improvement, that of breaking up the old sod and establishing on it some of the larger species of grasses and legumes. Further, the term is usually thought of in connection with the improvement of nonplowable land. It is particularly adapted to fields where plowing would be difficult because of a rough topography or stony soils and to those where plowing would be hazardous because of erosion.

Under such conditions the use of im-

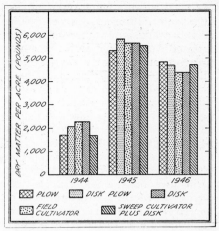

Yields of forage from a renovated pasture on which the seedbed was prepared with various implements and seeded to larger growing legumes and grass. Satisfactory results are had with any of these tools.

plements like the heavy cutaway disk (bush-and-bog harrow), the field cultivator, or the spring-tooth harrow is better than plowing. A seedbed prepared by surface tillage, where a layer of roots and stubble from the old sod remains on or near the surface, is not so susceptible to erosion. The layer of plant residues also makes it easier to establish seedlings and increases the amount of water absorbed during beating rains.

The actual preparation of the land for seeding is not difficult when one clearly understands the aims. As on plowable land that might be used for any crop, one must provide adequate lime and fertilizer to meet the needs of the plants used. The amounts required in pasture renovation are similar to those indicated for semipermanent pastures. Because the sites chosen for renovation are often on soils that had a low natural fertility or had been depleted of fertility by intensive cropping, it is wise to use liberal amounts of fertilizer at the time of establishment.

Just as important is the need to subdue existing vegetation. When an old sod is broken up and lime and fertilizer applied, the grasses or weeds that have been growing there will be stimulated. These old plants compete for light and moisture with the young grass and legume seedlings, and reduce their growth. This emphasizes a primary objective with the use of surface tillage implements—that of killing a large part of the old sod.

Some plants are more difficult to kill and have a greater competitive effect on the seeded species than others. Kentucky bluegrass, Canada bluegrass, and redtop sods, for example, can persist after surface tillage unless soil contact with their roots is broken, and the plants are thus made to dry out. Sods of povertygrass and broomsedge are more easily killed and, furthermore, they do not compete so severely with the new seeding. The composition of the original sod is therefore an important factor to be considered in preparing the seedbed.

The normal periods of higher temperature and lower soil moisture in midsummer may be used to advantage in renovation procedures. When the old sod is worked during this period, the unwanted plants are more apt to be killed than if the sod were worked in the spring or fall. Even during the midsummer it will be necessary to rework the field to loosen the sods that have rooted down after a shower.

As a general procedure for bluegrass and bentgrass sods, it is advisable to apply the necessary lime and begin working up the sod as soon as the spring or early summer flush of grass has been grazed off, about the latter part of June, and after a rain has softened the sod. A heavily weighted cutaway disk or bush-and-bog harrow is good for the purpose.

The field will probably require disking at least twice at right angles so that the roots of the sod will be broken from the soil below even though it may not all be turned over. Subsequent disking with a lighter disk or a strong springtooth harrow will be needed if the plants root down again. This procedure will kill most of the sod by mid-August. The fertilizer can then be applied and disked or harrowed in.

A spring-tooth harrow used for this operation will help level the seedbed although it may still appear rough.

A fairly rough seedbed is actually desirable because it halts erosion and improves the infiltration of moisture. In southern localities, where fall seedings of legumes have been successful, the field may be rolled and the seeding made in the usual way. In the central and northern parts, spring barley or spring oats may be seeded in August to provide late-fall grazing. Because these plants will be killed during the winter, they will not compete with the seeding made on frozen ground the following spring. Besides providing fall pasture, the ungrazed stubble and roots will reduce erosion during the fall and winter.

Over most of the region, a successful stand of legumes is more certain with a spring seeding. Better stands and larger midsummer yields are had with seedings made very early in the spring. Land prepared by surface tillage in midsummer is well adapted for seeding in late February or March as soon as the snow melts. Seed may be broadcast with a cyclone or wheelbarrow seeder on frozen ground. Alternate freezing and thawing of the soil surface covers the seed, and as soon as the temperature is warm enough to permit germination, the seedlings begin growth. Also, seeding in early spring does not conflict so much with other farm operations.

In most renovation seedings the use of a companion crop of grain does not seem warranted. If seeded in March, the forage grasses and legumes make enough summer growth to reduce the growth of annual weeds, and a small hay crop can be removed in July or the new seeding may be lightly grazed. There seems to be no advantage in seeding pasture species with a companion crop if the goal is to obtain forage.

Midsummer is the best time to prepare the seedbed in most of the region, but not everywhere. In West Virginia and other localities where open winters make soil erosion a serious hazard and where the original sod includes such bunch-type grasses as poverty-grass and broomsedge, the seedbed may be fitted in early spring. On this type of sod a spring-tooth harrow works well. Both of these species are relatively easily weakened by tillage: Neither causes such severe competitive effects on a new seeding as bluegrasses and bentgrasses. Lime and fertilizer may be applied, the land worked, and the desired species seeded, all within a short time. Again the earliest possible seeding date is preferable, and no companion crop is used.

Seeding Mixtures

Several factors determine which species is best for use in semipermanent pastures. Foremost are soil and climate and the intended use.

Legumes generally have more critical requirements than grasses, and because they usually provide nitrogen for the growth of the grasses, the selection of the proper legume to insure long life and good growth on a particular field and for a particular purpose should receive careful attention.

For example, alfalfa is one of the best plants for hay on fertile, well-drained, neutral soils. It is not adapted to wet or acid soils, nor will it persist even on favorable soils if it is heavily grazed. Ladino clover will grow well on moist soils and will persist under intensive grazing management, but it is easily crowded out by grass growing with it if the first crop is not removed at or before the time the grass flowers.

Whether a seedbed is prepared by surface cultivation or by plowing and disking is not a primary factor in the selection of an adapted mixture.

While many seeding mixtures may be adapted to the soil, climate, and farm conditions in the Northeast, only one legume combination, varied to meet local conditions, has been widely adopted. Its basis is Ladino clover, the giant form of white clover that has done much to improve the production

of nutritious herbage from intensively managed pastures in the Northeast. On a well-prepared seedbed 1 pound of seed to the acre is enough, and in Connecticut, ½ pound an acre is often recommended. To increase the production during the first and second years after seeding, 4 or 5 pounds of red clover are seeded with the Ladino clover. The two legumes form the basic legume combination.

On wet land and on slightly acid soils, 2 or 3 pounds of alsike clover may be added, or it may replace part of the red clover. On drier fields, 4 to 6 pounds of alfalfa per acre may be added to the mixture or replace part of the red clover.

Several grasses can be used with the basic legume mixture.

In the northern part, timothy is well adapted primarily for hay or silage, but its recovery in midsummer is limited. For spring seeding, 6 to 8 pounds per acre is used; for fall seeding, 5 pounds per acre is adequate.

In the central and southern parts, orchardgrass is rather widely grown, 4 or 5 pounds per acre being used with Ladino and red clovers. The first crop makes excellent silage or may be cut for hay, but the main value of orchardgrass is its ability to grow during midsummer when many other grasses become partly dormant.

Smooth bromegrass, which has been used widely in the Midwest, is being used more commonly on the better soils in the Northeast. Eight pounds of bromegrass and 1 pound of Ladino clover seed on an acre may be used for pasture, but if the combination is to be used as silage or hay, 8 pounds of alfalfa is a better adapted legume. Bromegrass is palatable, nutritious, high yielding, and productive of somewhat more aftermath than timothy, but for midsummer grazing it does not equal orchardgrass mixtures. Bromegrass makes a heavy first growth in the spring and unless it is grazed or the silage or hay crop taken before full bloom, the Ladino clover associated with it may be crowded out.

Several other grasses may be grown with Ladino under certain conditions, which I outline here.

Reed canarygrass, which in the past has been used primarily on wet land, is also adapted to upland. About 8 pounds to an acre is the usual seeding rate. Because of its rapid and rank growth throughout the year, it needs careful management to keep it from crowding out the Ladino and becoming too mature for the best feed.

Meadow fescue and tall fescue have been used with Ladino clover on poorly drained soils, and are seeded at about 6 pounds to an acre.

Tall oatgrass in association with birdsfoot trefoil is sometimes used on thin hillside soils; it is heat- and drought-tolerant and starts growth early in the spring, but it does not withstand continuous grazing. A satisfactory seeding rate for this species is 8 pounds to the acre.

In certain areas of New York State, birdsfoot trefoil is a valuable perennial legume for hay and pasture. It grows best on good fertile soil, but will survive under rather dry conditions and on poor soils. It will withstand less careful grazing management than alfalfa and Ladino clover when it is once established. In the seedling stage, birdsfoot trefoil is sensitive to competition from associated species. Sometimes a grass is seeded with it; sometimes it is seeded alone. If no volunteer grass is present at the end of the seeding year it may be seeded the following spring on frozen ground. The usual seeding rate of birdsfoot trefoil is 4 pounds an acre. Good inoculation is essential because most soils lack the strain of nitrogen-fixing bacteria that this legume is known to need.

Grazing Management

Semipermanent pastures are important in the forage-production program. They can supply feed in July and August, when palatable, nutritious herbage of permanent pastures is usually limited. The intensive pastures produce valuable feed during the spring, when it may not be needed for pasture, but because of the versatility of the plants used this crop may be harvested early for hay or silage and be preserved for future use. The later growth of the plants will then coincide with the period when permanent pasture production is limited.

The maintenance of the desired association of grasses and legumes in such pastures requires careful attention to management practices. Not only must adequate fertility be supplied to replace the large amount removed in the herbage or the animal products, but the time of harvesting the first crop and the length of time the pasture is allowed to recover before the cows are turned out to graze must be considered in determining management practices. The use of rapid-growing and high-yielding species of grasses and legumes increases the competition between them. Because both grasses and legumes are essential if a pasture is to produce maximum quantities of good herbage, grazing practices should be used that will permit each to maintain itself. Those practices are not especially difficult to follow.

An intermittent type of grazing is generally adapted to pastures or meadows composed of the larger-growing grasses and legumes. Under this system enough cattle are turned into a small area to remove the herbage in a few days. Then the plants have a recovery period of 3 to 5 weeks before being grazed again. This removes herbage before the grass becomes tall enough to crowd the legume seriously, and the legume has enough time before the next grazing to replace part of the stored plant food used to produce new stems and leaves.

The details of such a management system depend partly on the species of grasses and legumes used.

If alfalfa is the main legume in a mixture, especial care must be taken to provide a sufficiently long recovery to allow replacement of most of the stored plant food which was removed from the root in producing new stems and leaves. This period usually coincides with bud formation and early blooming. For Ladino clover the recovery period is shorter, but crowding by grass in the combination may be a serious factor. Therefore, it is important that the first cutting or grazing be done before the grass is in full bloom. During midsummer only limited blossoming of grasses occurs, but the crowding effects of the leaves of a vigorous grass must be prevented by grazing or clipping.

In actual farm use, grazing paddocks range in size from 2 to 5 acres. Often they are not supplied with water because the cows are turned in to graze in the morning and remain there only long enough to obtain their fill. They are then given shade and water in a nearby field. After milking in the afternoon the cows are again permitted to graze for about 2 hours and are removed before they lie down. This type of management provides clean, palatable forage and helps prevent trampling and waste of the ungrazed herbage. If the cattle are not given shade and water outside the grazing paddock it may be wise to spread the droppings with a chain harrow or other flexible drag.

Often milking cows are turned into the pasture first, when the herbage is 8 to 12 inches high, depending mostly on the kind of plants in the mixture. After the cows have eaten the more succulent feed and before their milk flow has dropped, they are moved to a new field. If pasture is needed for dry cows and young stock they may be turned in for a few days to graze the pasture more closely. On badly spotted fields, mowing a day or two before the cattle are taken out encourages them to pick up the ungrazed herbage.

The carrying capacity of such pastures is about two animal units an acre. In terms of 4-percent milk with high-producing cows, the equivalent of 9,000 pounds an acre may be had from the herbage produced in a 5-month growing season: Forage from such pastures is in effect a cash crop, and it deserves the careful fertilization and management that are usually given to cash crops.

ANNUAL OR TEMPORARY PASTURES

VANCE G. SPRAGUE

ANNUAL or temporary pastures, like semipermanent pastures, provide feed when the forage on permanent pastures is limited. One of these periods is late in the fall or early in the spring, when wheat, barley, rye, or other winter grains may provide good grazing.

If a grain crop is to be harvested the farmer must be careful to prevent trampling of wet soil and overgrazing lest the yield be reduced. Winter cover crops, like ryegrass, give excellent pasturage during both fall and early spring. In many northeastern areas, particularly the central and northern parts, a companion crop of oats is used for new hay seedings. If grain, and straw for bedding, are not required in the farm program, the oats may be grazed off when they begin to head, thereby providing summer feed. This practice results in more vigorous stands of the seeded forage and may yield more than when the oats are allowed to mature grain.

As a temporary pasture to provide midsummer feed in the central and southern parts of the region, Sudangrass is outstanding. This warm-weather grass may be seeded successfully in late May, in June, or up to the end of the first week in July. It often follows corn on manured and fertilized land that will go into wheat in the fall. Shallow seeding of 20 to 30 pounds of seed to the acre may be done with a grain drill on a well-prepared seedbed. Grazing usually begins 5 to 6 weeks after seeding and continues until frost.

Where Sudangrass is used, one has to be careful to avoid prussic acid poisoning. Such a mishap has been reported very infrequently in the Northeast, but plants of Sudangrass should not be grazed if they are stunted by drought or frost or when the plants are small. Experimental evidence indicates that there is more poison in the small leaves and young tillers.

Sometimes soybeans are seeded with Sudangrass to make excellent summer pasture or silage.

Japanese millet seeded in late May or June may also be used to provide midsummer forage.

FOR BEEF CATTLE AND OTHER STOCK

VANCE G. SPRAGUE

WHILE PASTURES for dairy animals are of prime importance in the Northeast, good pasture for other farm animals is needed. Because the forage requirements of beef cattle are not so exacting as those of dairy cows, the permanent bluegrass pastures farther away from the farm buildings are often used.

Beef cattle may gain well on herbage somewhat more mature than is desired for high-producing dairy cows, but high-quality herbage is most desirable. To maintain any particular association of grasses and legumes in a pasture, the grazing management of a beef herd is similar to that of a dairy herd.

For sheep (which lead farm animals in ability to use forage as a source of feed for growth) permanent bluegrass pastures are used extensively. Winter wheat or rye may provide late-fall and early-spring grazing; in midsummer, hay aftermath or a temporary pasture of rape may be used.

Internal parasites are a problem when many sheep graze continuously on the same pasture, but infection may be reduced by moving the flock to different pastures and by allowing at least several months between successive grazings. Recent advances in the use of phenothiazine, given in capsules or as a drench, and phenothiazine-salt mixtures during the summer grazing period have cut losses due to parasites. Sheep will reproduce regularly and maintain themselves in good flesh on permanent pastures when the phenothiazine-salt mixtures only are used. Often sheep may feed on pastures after cattle or sometimes may be grazed with them on the more extensive grazing areas.

Mechanized farming has reduced the importance of pastures for work horses in the region, but light horses for pleasure are increasing in number. Where horses and mules are kept they usually receive most of their feed in the barn. However, turning them out to pasture at night, or during the day when they are not working, keeps the animals in good physical condition and reduces the amount of barn feed required in the evening ration. Good bluegrass pastures or other pastures not intensively managed are satisfactory.

Pastures are important in hog production, but because swine have a limited capacity for bulky feed, forage cannot supply the same proportion of the total feed requirement as it can for cattle and sheep. Often permanent pastures are used for hogs. Alfalfa and Ladino clover make good pastures, but if these pastures are used year after year internal parasites may become a serious problem. A farmer who has to graze his hogs on the same area every year should plow the field and sow it to rapid-growing annuals like rape, soybeans, rye, or Sudangrass. In grazing any pasture with hogs, an adequate supply of forage should be available to prevent close grazing and the exposure of bare ground, which encourages rooting.

Permanent ranges for chickens are being used more and more. Ladino clover and Kentucky bluegrass together are suitable for a range that is to be maintained for several years. On some farms where small grains are being grown, Ladino may be used without a grass. Because Ladino alone does not form a heavy turf, it should be well managed to maintain sanitary conditions and prevent diseases. Pure Ladino ranges are sometimes used for only a year; then on some farms they are plowed and seeded to a small grain or corn or another crop.

Although forage cannot entirely replace grain and other concentrates in poultry rations, chickens raised on range do get minerals, vitamins, and high-quality protein from young herbage. We are not sure yet whether chickens must have green feed if a complete ration is fed, but if an incomplete ration is used, the herbage from a good clover-grass range will provide nutritional elements to supplement those fed in the hoppers. Any malnutrition in the flock can be prevented almost completely in this way.

Range is a good thing in the management of the flock. It does not replace the need for sanitation, but it will reduce losses if disease occurs. Too, less labor is needed for a flock on range than for one of the same size raised in confinement.

For a turkey range, in general farming, the aftermath of a red clover-timothy field in the farm rotation is commonly used. If a permanent range is used, Kentucky bluegrass, bromegrass, or orchardgrass seeded in combination with Ladino clover is good. To control disease, birds on permanent range must be most carefully managed. Shelters and feeders must be moved almost daily to maintain clean conditions and keep a good sward. If the shelters are not moved frequently, overgrazing occurs, bare spots develop, and the danger of disease from soil contamination increases.

Permanent ranges must be carefully managed early in the season to prevent the vigorous spring growth of the grass from crowding out the Ladino clover. Because it is not advisable to put the birds on range too early, or when they are too young to consume any great quantity of green herbage, it is usually necessary to cut and remove the first crop. This young, nutritious herbage may be preserved as silage for winter feeding, as it is believed to be beneficial in the normal ration of the breeding flocks.

HAY LANDS IN THE NORTHEAST

VANCE G. SPRAGUE

GRASSES and legumes grown for hay are vital in the crop rotation. Directly, they are a source of feed that may be preserved for use when fresh herbage is not available; indirectly, they improve the soil for the cultivated crops that follow.

Preserved forage is a first requirement (and often a limiting factor) in dairy enterprises in the Northeastern States. For many years hay has been grown to provide winter feed; more recently grass has been made into silage for the same purpose. Preserved forage has value for feeding during the grazing season, also—even when cattle are on good pasture, hay may be used to advantage to supplement grazing. In midsummer, when pastures are short, grass silage and hay produced earlier in the season may be used to furnish the high-quality forage required in a balanced ration. Another benefit: Feeding home-produced forage means that less feed has to be bought. Also, legume sods fix large quantities of at-

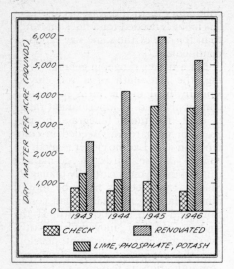

Herbage from an untreated (CK) permanent pasture in Pennsylvania compared with that from pasture top-dressed with lime, potash, and phosphate, and that obtained by disking, fertilizing, and seeding with larger growing grasses and legumes (renovated).

mospheric nitrogen; part of this is in the roots and will be added to the soil.

Organic matter in a soil is rapidly destroyed by cultivation, and a good soil becomes less productive as its organic matter decreases. The application of liberal amounts of manure to cultivated land helps maintain organic matter, but it is not sufficient to replace the amount lost. Grasses and legumes, through their extensive root systems, are excellent sources of organic matter to maintain a good physical condition of the soil. They facilitate the infiltration of moisture and adequate aeration and otherwise improve conditions for growth.

The use of longer-lived legumes and grasses under improved management practices increases the time which a meadow or hayfield is kept down. With them high production of nutritious herbage may be obtained from a minimum of labor for working the land, seeding, and cultivation. The species of grasses and legumes seeded on cultivated land for use in a long rotation are those primarily adapted for use as hay or silage during the first 2 years. The following years, the first crop is often removed for silage (which is equivalent in feeding value to corn silage) and the aftermath is grazed. If midsummer pasture is needed, during the first or second year, the aftermath also provides good grazing.

Thus, while hayfields are not established primarily for grazing, knowledge of the growth requirements of the plants used and selection of adapted species increase the use of the forage plants wherever the need is greatest.

Hay land in the regular rotation is usually the better land of the farm, with topography right for the use of machinery and fertility above that usually found in permanent pasture. On many farms, however, the amount of fertilizer returned to such land is not equivalent to that removed from it during the rotation. Greater production could often be obtained if adequate lime and mineral fertilizers were used.

Hay lands vary more than pastures in need for lime and fertilizer because of the differences in care given them in the past. Because most soils in the Northeast are low in phosphorus, 300 to 400 pounds an acre of 20-percent superphosphate could well be applied, generally after plowing.

On soils known to be low in potash, about 150 pounds an acre of muriate of potash should also be added. In certain areas, 20 pounds an acre of borax may be desirable if alfalfa is to be grown. For alfalfa, sufficient ground limestone or hydrated lime should be supplied to meet the lime requirement. Red clover and Ladino clover may be grown on slightly more acid soils. After establishment, an annual top dressing of manure reenforced with superphosphate helps to maintain high productivity.

To establish hay crops one must consider the separate plants of the desired stand. Some plants are seeded in the spring and some in the fall. Often red clover and timothy are grown with winter wheat as a companion crop.

Timothy is seeded in the fall with the wheat; the clover, early the following spring on frozen ground. If wheat is not included, the clover and timothy are both seeded in the spring with oats or barley as the companion crop. Alfalfa, likewise, is seeded in the spring, except in the southern part, where it may be seeded in August.

For spring seeding the land is plowed and harrowed and the fertilizer is disked in.

A firm seedbed is essential. It is firmed by rolling with a corrugated roller before seeding and again after seeding. The second rolling also covers the seed, and shallow covering of the small seed of these grasses and clovers is necessary.

Seeding early in the spring is important in order to permit development of root systems large enough to get moisture during the summer.

When the main idea is to establish the hay crop, the companion crop may be cut for hay at the time it comes into head, or it may be grazed. This early removal of the companion crop helps the seeded species to get more light and moisture and become better established.

When a small grain is used for a companion crop, it should be seeded at a reduced rate to prevent too severe competition with the clovers and grasses. If the grain is to be harvested, early maturing varieties should be used.

The companion crop does prevent the rapid growth of annual weeds, but it also reduces the growth of the seeded grasses and legumes. Where erosion is not serious, the land is relatively weed-free, and seeding can be done very early, the companion crop may be omitted. In these cases, the growth of the seeded clovers and grasses competes with the weeds and holds them in check, and at the same time will provide a small crop of hay or a period of grazing in July of the year of seeding.

Late-summer seeding of alfalfa is often successful in Maryland, West Virginia, southern Pennsylvania, and parts of New Jersey. The alfalfa may follow a small grain, canning peas, early potatoes, or soybeans cut early for hay. The seedbed is prepared by disking, harrowing, and cultipacking. The seed is sown without a companion crop, and the field is rolled again with a corrugated roller. In most of these areas, seedings should be made before the middle of August to permit good growth before winter.

Seeding Mixtures for Hay

Two basic seeding mixtures are used for hay in all parts of the Northeast: That for a long-time hayfield and that for a shorter rotation.

The legume component for a long-time hayfield is alfalfa. On well-drained neutral soils, alfalfa—seeded at rates of 8 to 10 pounds an acre for spring seeding and at higher rates for August seeding—can be expected to remain productive for 3 years or more if it is properly managed. Wilt-resistant varieties may make the field last longer. In the northern parts of the Northeast, 6 pounds an acre of timothy seed is often sown with the alfalfa. This mixture is productive and provides high-quality hay. Though predominantly a hay crop, a farmer can pasture it when necessary if he provides the adequate period for recovery.

Ladino seed is sometimes included in the mixture, at 1 pound an acre, to provide a legume if the alfalfa fails, and where neither of these does well, birdsfoot trefoil has been successful. Because of its slow seedling growth, fields of birdsfoot trefoil are not usually included in the rotation; once established, however, they are maintained as long as possible.

Orchardgrass seeded at 4 pounds to an acre with 8 to 10 pounds of alfalfa is used occasionally, but ordinarily the grass becomes too mature for the best hay by the time the alfalfa is ready to cut. However, if silage and aftermath grazing are required in the farm program, it may be desirable to seed one part of the alfalfa acreage to this mixture.

In the central and southern parts of the Northeast and somewhat in the northern, bromegrass seeded at 8 pounds an acre is proving well adapted as a grass for association with alfalfa used for hay.

The legume component for a shorter rotation includes red and alsike clovers. On soils that are slightly acid and only moderately drained, 4 to 6 pounds an acre of red clover and 2 to 3 pounds of alsike clover are mixed with 4 to 6 pounds an acre of timothy for the legume-grass association. This association grows well throughout the region, has good supplies of seed, and is easy to manage.

One pound an acre of Ladino clover is often added to provide a legume after the red and alsike clovers have disappeared, as this increases somewhat the longevity of the stand. In the southern part of the region, alsike clover is often omitted when Ladino clover is included.

Management of Hay Lands

Quality of herbage and maintenance of the legumes are the two main items in the management of hay lands.

Forage plants grow in a natural sequence—from the young succulent herbage relatively high in protein content and low in fiber, to a reverse condition at maturity of lower protein and higher fiber content. Consequently, if the plants are cut too young, the herbage is high in feeding value, but the yield is low and the plant is weakened; if the plants are cut too mature, the yield is high and the plants remain vigorous, but the quality of the forage is reduced. To insure good yields of nutritious herbage and maintain vigorous plants, harvesting is best done at a point about midway in the growth cycle of the plant.

If alfalfa is the primary legume, harvesting should not be started before the plant begins to flower, or at about the one-tenth-bloom stage. By that time reserve food has been stored in the roots to form new growth and maintain the vigor of the stand. If cutting is delayed until full bloom the loss of leaves will be greater. While the herbage cut before one-tenth bloom may be more nutritious, the plants will not have stored food in their roots, the vigor of the plants will be reduced, and if such cutting practice is continued the plants will not survive.

Similar conditions in quality of hay exist with red and alsike clovers. With them, however, the maintenance of a stand is not so essential as with alfalfa because, at best, they are naturally short-lived. The best time to cut red clover and alsike clover is when the plants are in about 50-percent bloom; then the quality of the hay is good, the yield is relatively high, and a good second crop can be expected.

Grasses have a growth cycle like that of alfalfa but are not weakened so much by early and frequent cutting. With grass, quality of herbage is the first consideration. To obtain more nutritious forage, grass hay should be cut after heading but just before blooming. This is a point that gains importance when Ladino clover is a component of the grass-legume association. Competition with the associated legume increases as the grass approaches maturity, so that Ladino is severely weakened and may be eliminated if the grass is allowed to mature.

High-quality hay is hay that has been cut at the proper time, has been properly cured, and (in the case of legumes) has maintained most of the leaves. Uncertain weather conditions are serious handicaps in making such hay.

Ensiling the first cutting of the earlier maturing grasses, such as orchardgrass, has been an important step in preserving and maintaining the original quality of the herbage. Other grass-legume combinations may also be ensiled if conditions are not suitable for curing hay. Freshly cut herbage is often ensiled with molasses or ground grain as preservatives. If the hay is allowed to wilt in the field until it contains only 60 to 65 percent moisture, it may be ensiled without a preservative.

The best hay usually comes from the second cutting; the stems are finer then, and the weather is usually more favorable for curing.

In the southern part of the region, three cuttings of alfalfa may be obtained, but the third cutting should not be taken later than the first week in September. After this time the plant is normally storing reserve food in its roots. Although the alfalfa may have grown enough to make a fair crop by the latter part of September, it is advisable to wait until the first or second week in October before removing it. Storage of food is sufficient by then and, although some recovery will be made after October, growth is so slow that only small amounts of stored food are removed from the roots.

Often a farmer will do well to pasture part of the hay land in midsummer, when permanent pastures become dormant. Proper grazing is highly important during such periods if the legumes are to survive.

Alfalfa particularly must be carefully managed. Cattle should not be turned into an alfalfa field before the alfalfa is well budded and beginning to flower, and the area grazed should be small enough to permit the removal of herbage within 10 days or 2 weeks. In no case should the cattle be allowed to graze continuously if it is desired to maintain the stand of alfalfa. Fall grazing should be avoided during September and early October. If feed is badly needed, light grazing may be done during the latter part of October. Grass-legume associations, where Ladino clover is the primary legume, may be grazed intermittently. Adequate recovery periods must be allowed, of course. Old grassy fields that are to be plowed may be heavily grazed in midsummer and fall.

———

Seeding mixtures for high-quality forage under careful management are given here. Before these mixtures are seeded, the land should be well limed and fertilized, and a good seedbed should be prepared. Seeding rates are given in pounds per acre.

1. For pastures or silage plus pasture on well-drained soils:

Seed		Pounds per acre
	Alfalfa_____	6
	Red clover_____	3
	Ladino clover____	1
plus	Orchardgrass [1] ___	4
or	Bromegrass [1]_____	8
or	Timothy [1] _____	5

2. For pastures on variable soils:

	Red clover_____	5
	Alsike clover_____	2
	Ladino clover____	1
plus	Orchardgrass ____	4
or	Bromegrass_____	8
or	Timothy _____	5

3. For pastures on wet soils: [2]

	Alsike clover_____	3
	Ladino clover____	1
plus	Reed canarygrass_	8
or	Meadow fescue___	6

4. Primarily for hay or silage in long rotations on well-drained soils:

	Alfalfa_____	10
plus	Bromegrass _____	8
or	Timothy _____	4
or	Orchardgrass ____	4

5. Primarily for hay in a long rotation on variable soils:

	Alfalfa_____	8
	Red clover_____	4
	Ladino clover____	1
plus	Bromegrass _____	8
or	Timothy _____	4

6. Primarily for hay in a short rotation on variable soils:

	Red clover_____	6
	Alsike clover_____	2
	Ladino clover____	1
plus	Timothy _____	6

[1] Timothy is primarily adapted to the northern part of the region, orchardgrass to the central and southern parts, and bromegrass to the entire region.

[2] On somewhat droughty soils for a pasture to revert to a permanent sod, birdsfoot trefoil 4 pounds per acre plus tall oatgrass 4 pounds per acre, and Kentucky bluegrass 4 pounds per acre is a suggested seeding mixture.

GRASS FOR CONSERVATION

E. B. COFFMAN

RUNOFF from land in crops means a loss of water, and water is needed for plant growth. Runoff also causes losses of soil and plant nutrients: Material washed off an experimental field in New Jersey contained 4.7 times more organic matter, 5.0 times more nitrogen, 3.1 times more phosphate, and 1.4 times more potash than the field soil from which it came.

From a field of tomatoes where no conservation measures were practiced, the loss of nutrients by erosion equalled 500 pounds an acre of 4-12-30 fertilizer. On an adjoining field of tomatoes where grasses and legumes were seeded as winter cover crops, the losses were about half as much. Besides, the cover crops increased the yield from 16.6 tons to 23.2 tons an acre.

Row crops cover only a small part of the total area of a field and much of the surface is exposed to the action of rain. To protect the ground, a grass or grasses and legumes are planted in late summer or early fall to protect the soil during the fall, winter, and spring. Some of the more commonly used species are rye, vetch, wheat, domestic ryegrass, and field brome. The last two are usually planted at the time of the last cultivation of the row crop. An application of fertilizer at the same time brings a heavier and more rapid growth of plant material. Wheat seeding should be delayed until after the fly-free date, but the rye can be seeded at any time up to the advent of cold weather.

Cover crops on cultivated fields give two benefits: Soil and water losses are reduced, and soil organic matter is increased. The loss of soil from a field where a rye cover crop had been used amounted to 6.8 tons of soil an acre, but the loss of an all-year fallow area was 16.3 tons. Ryegrass is better than rye in its ability to hold soil and water. Records were obtained from a field near Geneva, N. Y., on which ryegrass had been seeded at the last cultivation of corn with a moderate application of fertilizer. In May of the following year, the yield of the ryegrass amounted to 1.5 tons an acre of top growth plus 2 tons an acre of oven-dried roots, which protected the soil in winter, gave more protection after plowing than did rye, and added appreciably to the organic matter.

Pasture and meadow mixtures of grasses and legumes protect the soil the entire year; corn, potatoes, many of the vegetables and many other crops offer little protection during the critical months, even when cover crops are used. At the Arnot Experiment Station, near Ithaca, N. Y., the amounts of soil and water lost from fields on a 20-percent slope seeded to various crops were determined over a 9-year period. All crops were produced on the contour.

The field in fallow lost 1,000 times more soil and 20 times more water in the 9-year period than meadow protected by a vegetative cover all of each year.

Land in continuous corn also suffered severe soil and water losses. On such land continuously cropped with intertilled plants, soil organic matter is destroyed and little is replaced by the corn roots or stalks. Here a poor physical structure develops, the capacity to absorb water is reduced, and erosion increases.

Under a rotation of corn, oats, and clover, losses of water and soil were greatly reduced and the yields of corn were twice as large. The effectiveness of the rotation was due to the cover afforded by the oats and clover during the second year and by the clover during the third. The clover sod improved the physical condition of the soil for the corn, increased the water-infiltration capacity of the soil, and reduced erosion.

Almost no soil or water loss occurred

Effect of Crops on Losses of Water and Soil During the Growing Season
[Averages for the years 1935–43]

Crop and treatment	Loss	
	Water	Soil [1] per acre
	Inches	*Pounds*
Fallow..	3.81	19,583
Continuous corn, 200 pounds 5–10–5.........................	1.77	5,239
Corn, oats, clover—6 tons manure before clover............	.40	441
Idle, weeds, and clover....................................	.29	394
Meadow, fertilized...	.18	17

[1] Bath soil—20-percent slope.

on the fertilized meadow. Where grasses and legumes are grown, the soil has a more porous structure, soil organic matter is increased, and water can be absorbed more rapidly by the soil. Further, a greater percentage of the soil surface is covered by leaves and stems in the turf, and puddling action of raindrops is checked.

Much of the 22 million acres in pastures in the Northeastern States is steep and subject to erosion at some time of the year. To protect these areas, it is essential to maintain a good forage cover by means of adequate soil fertility and proper management. This protection brings about three distinct benefits: Loss of water and soil is reduced to a minimum, more forage is produced, and less land is required for pasture.

The amount of soil and water lost from a given field is in proportion to the intensity of the rainfall. When rains are intense the surface of the soil may be sealed by raindrop action. This reduces the infiltration of water into the soil, particularly on fields which have little or no ground cover.

In experiments on Bath soil conducted during 1935 at Arnot on fallowed ground, rains were of the highest intensity from June through September, in two cases exceeding 4 inches an hour. These intense rains caused a loss of more than 7 tons of soil to an acre.

Slow rains allow the soil to absorb a greater percentage of the water. On sodded areas, such as meadows and pastures, the vegetation breaks the fall of the raindrops—even of intense rain—and helps prevent sealing of the soil surface. It also slows the flow of the water, allowing more to be absorbed. On cultivated fields, the rapid runoff from high-intensity rains can be slowed down somewhat by contour planting, strip cropping, and such supplemental measures as terraces.

The amount of soil lost from grassland by erosion is small, except where active gullies are present. The water losses, however, are often great. The low midsummer production of Kentucky bluegrass pastures has often been ascribed to the injurious effects of hot, dry weather in July and August, but irrigated Kentucky bluegrass sods in Pennsylvania on a Hagerstown silt loam continued to produce during this period. It seems evident, therefore, that moisture rather than temperature is the primary factor in limiting growth. Further work was conducted to determine the moisture losses which may occur during thundershowers in midsummer on closely and heavily grazed, on lightly grazed, and on ungrazed pastures and meadowlands.

On heavily grazed pastures 45 to 70 percent of the rainfall was lost as runoff, on lightly grazed pastures less than 10 percent was lost, and on ungrazed pastures and meadows no water was lost by runoff. From this and further studies of water relations in the management of pastures, methods may be developed whereby more of the midsummer rainfall will be retained and made available for use by grass and legume swards.

FORAGE AS A PART OF FARMING

MERTON S. PARSONS, IRVING F. FELLOWS

OVER THE YEARS, farmers in the Northeast have raised more livestock than can be fed from home-grown feed.

Being close to markets, they generally have found it profitable to build their livestock production up to the forage capacity and labor supply of their farms and then to buy whatever grain was needed to balance their feed needs. In recent years this additional grain shipped in from other regions has totaled 11 to 12 million tons a year, most of it used by dairymen and poultrymen.

Nevertheless, since concentrate feeds are products of agriculture, the question frequently arises as to whether farmers should continue to purchase so much feed or whether they should produce more on their own farms.

Insofar as grass can be substituted for grain in feeding livestock, increased production of more nutritious forage is a method of reducing feed purchases. The farmer's problem is broader than that, however, and his opportunity in using his grassland to best advantage is a part of his larger problem—the best use of all his resources. If he is interested, as most people are, in a better level of living for himself and family, then one test of his success in farming is his income. Any change that will increase his income over a period of years and still maintain the soil is a good one, whether it is producing more and better forage, expanding cash crops and purchasing more grain, doing more nonfarm work, or some other adjustments.

The farmer's problem is complicated. He must decide on his best course of action. For example, how far should he go in improving permanent pastures? He must consider the costs: Cash costs for varying quantities of lime, fertilizer, seed, tractor fuel, and such; overhead costs of additional labor or new uses of regular labor; additional cash outlays. He attempts to measure the probable benefits: Increased pasturage, land released for other uses, or both.

Later he may find there is excess feed during the flush period of May and June, and he must decide between adding more cows, releasing land for other uses, or preserving the excess feed as hay or silage. In any case he can reach the best decision only after considering the use of all his resources, including land, labor, equipment, livestock, and managerial ability.

Furthermore, the pasture program may require several years to complete, and the major results may appear long after most of the costs have been incurred. There is always the danger, as in 1948, that items bought at high price levels may have to be repaid when prices are lower, but, of course, the reverse may happen.

Despite these difficulties, thousands of northeastern farmers have seen fit to undertake at least certain phases of long-range programs of forage management. On some farms originally quite typical of the area, such complete programs have been adopted and such good results have been obtained that they serve as examples for others. Possibly the problems and the opportunities can be brought out best by looking at what some farmers have done.

Farms A, B, and C are operated by

men who are recognized in their communities and, even more widely, as having done good jobs in the production and utilization of large amounts of high-quality forage. Farm D has made less progress with forage programs and is an example of the very common farm set-up in the Northeast, where forage management offers great promise for the future as a part of good farm management.

A New England Farm

Extending through a large part of northern New England and adjacent sections of New York is an area of rather specialized dairy farming. Conditions vary, but, in general, grass is the main crop. The growing season is short, tillable land tends to be limited, and large acreages of rough, hilly land are available for permanent pasture. Typically, most of the feed concentrates are purchased, but some hay is sold. Farmers here are at considerable distances from their fluid-milk markets, and dairying tends to be less intensive than in sections near markets.

In this area, in west-central New Hampshire, is farm A, a dairy farm. Originally the land and other resources were fairly typical of farms in the neighborhood. The roughage programs of the operator of farm A have attracted attention these many years. On 65 acres of tillable land, he now grows enough hay and silage for 35 to 40 milking cows, 20 head of young stock, and 2 horses, besides selling 25 to 30 tons of hay a year.

The story of such production began nearly 50 years ago when the present operator purchased the family farm. There were then only half the present number of livestock; yet it was necessary to buy hay. The operator knew that red and alsike clovers did not maintain themselves on hayfields for more than 2 years and believed that the best way to raise more high-quality roughage was to plow and reseed.

He adopted a 4-year rotation—corn, oats, clover hay, mixed hay—on most of the cropland. Some very stony fields were maintained in hay for longer periods by top dressing heavily with manure.

Working out this rotation brought about many other changes: The small hillside fields were enlarged by removing stone walls, labor-saving equipment was used wherever possible, and the first agricultural lime used in the locality was spread on this farm to improve stands of clover. Every attempt was made to conserve the fertility of the farm manure and use it wisely. These changes were all made by the operator and one hired man.

Progress in this roughage program continued with such success that in 1922 an extension circular of the University of New Hampshire was written, emphasizing roughage management on this farm and its contribution to the success of the business. At that time most of the hay was classified as clover, and two cuttings were made each year. About 50 head of livestock were kept, but there was usually 10 or more tons of hay available for sale each year.

One might expect little change from this point—but things have a habit of improving on this farm. Two main shifts have been made—the use of a longer lived legume and some improvement of permanent pasture.

Alfalfa was tried without good results about 1925. Gradually, however, alfalfa has been introduced on the farm by including small quantities in the seed mixture. (Ladino clover would serve a similar purpose and would probably grow in places not adapted to alfalfa.)

This is the management plan for one field under the present system. In the fall, a ton of lime per acre is spread. (Lime requirements are low because applications have been made for more than 40 years.) The land is then plowed. A heavy covering of manure containing superphosphate is made during the winter, corn is planted the next spring and 100 pounds of a high-potash, complete fertilizer per acre is applied. The following year oats are planted on the harrowed cornland and are seeded down with 4 pounds of alfalfa, 8 pounds of red clover, and 10 pounds of timothy. The oats are cut early and ensiled.

A year later two crops of clover hay are cut and the land is top-dressed with manure. After this, two cuttings of a mixed alfalfa hay are made annually for 4 to 6 years. Manure is usually spread on the fields each year. This system results in less frequent seedbed preparation than before and gives a high-quality, high-yielding hay.

Permanent pastures are so rough and stony that little improvement has been undertaken. An area of about 7 acres was plowed and seeded 10 years ago. This has been top-dressed annually—the last few years with poultry manure purchased from a nearby farm. Recently a 3-acre area was plowed and seeded to Ladino clover. The milking herd was pastured alternately on the permanent pasture and the Ladino pasture for 1-week periods during most of this season. As these practices allowed grass in the permanent pasture to become overmature, the operator believes that a better method might be to harvest the first crop of Ladino as hay and graze the permanent pasture more fully in the early summer. Second-cutting hay is fed to the milking cows beginning in September.

The increased returns obtained from the more intensive forage-production practices used on this farm are evident on comparing them with those of other farms in the vicinity. On farm A, 1⅛ acres of tillable land was required to provide forage for one animal unit; on 38 nearby farms 1⅞ acres of tillable land was required to produce the same amount of feed. Feed crops on farm A produced the equivalent in feeding value of 3.8 tons of hay per acre; 238 other farms in the same State indicated an average equivalent of 1.6 tons of hay per acre. Basically farm A was similar in land resources to many farms in northern New England. Excellent management plus a definite

plan and practices for forage improvement have made the difference.

Strong points in this program are:

1. Using legumes to increase yields and improve quality of hay.

2. Using crop rotation adapted to the characteristics of the legume used.

3. Reducing the frequency of land preparation by using a legume that maintains itself for longer periods than does red clover.

4. Enlarging fields and improving their arrangement to make field operations more efficient.

5. Working most intensively the land easiest to cultivate and using the rough and very stony areas for grass hay or pasture.

6. Preserving fertility value of farm manure by wise management.

7. Testing the adaptability of Ladino clover for permanent pasture.

Weak points are few. They are:

1. A pasture program has not been developed that will provide good grazing during midsummer and late summer. Hay land might be used for a hay-pasture combination instead of selling surplus hay or cutting the aftermath and barn feeding it as is done now.

2. A long period was required to build up soil fertility. At times, wider use of commercial fertilizers might have been practical as it would be under present price relationships.

In Southern New England

Most of southern New England and some sections of other Northeastern States can be called mixed-farming areas. Dairying is a major enterprise, but poultry and cash crops are also important, sometimes combined with dairying, sometimes on separate farms. The climate is less severe than that farther north, farmers are generally closer to their markets, and farming tends to be more intensive.

In this area, in the low rolling hills of eastern Massachusetts, is farm B.

The operator of farm B is a young man who has been making rapid changes in his roughage program—

changes that have permitted doubling the dairy herd in fewer than 10 years. Land and buildings are representative of many farm situations in southern New England. In fact, the fields are somewhat more stony and harder to work than others on similar soil types in the area. Although part of the pasture land and some cropland is rented, most has been handled as if it were owned by the operator.

The operator took over this farm in 1938 from his father, who had managed it profitably but conservatively. There were 22 cows, 1 bull, and 2 horses. About 1.2 tons of hay was available per cow after 5 tons of hay had been purchased. Beet pulp was also bought.

After talking with successful farmers, the operator decided to shift from clover–timothy to alfalfa. He considered clover a 1-year crop. The first step was to see the county agricultural agent, who believed the land suitable for alfalfa and made recommendations for seeding and management.

Soil tests were made, lime was applied in accordance with the tests, superphosphate and potash were applied, and a seeding was made. One of the best fields of alfalfa to be seen in the State resulted. Gradually the hayfields have been shifted over to this hay crop.

This is about the normal procedure: In the fall, lime is applied at rates determined by soil tests and is plowed under. During the winter, manure is spread; according to the operator, "There is only one speed on the spreader—wide open."

Sweet corn is planted to serve as a cash crop, and, once the ears are stripped, the stalks are fed green to the herd.

The next spring, after 300 pounds of superphosphate and a similar quantity of potash per acre have been spread, alfalfa is seeded in oats. The oats are pastured and by managing the grazing at least three and sometimes four periods of grazing are obtained. No harvests are made from

September 1 to October 20. Manure is used sparingly on alfalfa because the operator believes too much manure encourages the growth of grass.

About 15 tons of lime, 5 tons of superphosphate, and 1½ tons of potash are now required annually for seeding and top dressing. The amounts of fertilizer used have been increasing since 1938; practically none was used before that date.

It was the change to alfalfa hay that directed attention to this farm, but the pasture program that was followed proved to be equally interesting. Pasturage starts early in May when the herd is turned into a 10-acre orchard that has been top-dressed with a nitrate fertilizer. Feed for a week or 10 days is obtained at this time and at intervals throughout the pasture season when grazing will not damage the fruit or when cows will not be in danger from spray residues.

Next, 40 acres of permanent pasture are available and are used throughout the summer pasture period. About the middle of June, the herd is turned into the oats for about 2 hours each day. By dividing up the field, this crop is grazed several times over during the summer.

About July 1, the second growth of alfalfa is used for pasture in the same way, and a small acreage of millet is ready about the middle of July. These crops, along with the permanent pasture, carry the herd until the sweet corn is picked, about September 1. The stalks are then cut daily and fed in the permanent pasture. This is the only forage that is cut and carried to the herd in a system that provides an abundance of feed throughout the season.

It is hard to compare the present organization of this farm with that in 1938. For one thing, the herd has been expanded as fast as the amount of roughage or faster. Then, too, the present pasture system is far superior to the previous one. There are now 43 cows, 7 young stock, 1 bull, and 3 horses that require forage. Home-grown roughage is double the tonnage raised in 1938 but 30 to 40 tons of standing hay are now purchased from nearby inactive farms. Production per cow has increased from 6,000 to 8,500 pounds of milk with little change in the butterfat content. Feed concentrates fed per cow have risen from 2,290 to 3,100 pounds.

Strong points in the program on this farm have been these:

1. Using legumes to increase yields and improve quality of hay.

2. Requesting technical advice and assistance from local agricultural agencies concerning the suitability and management of a crop.

3. Wisely managing and using farm manure.

4. Applying commercial fertilizer materials at a time when price relations favored their use.

5. Incorporating early spring, midsummer, and fall pasturage as well as grazing management in the pasture program.

Weak points that might be mentioned are:

1. Small, scattered fields that reduce labor and equipment efficiency.

2. Unimproved permanent pasture which, if seeded to Ladino clover and a more productive grass, might provide more of the midsummer feed and thus make possible hay production from second-crop alfalfa.

One practice that might be questioned under ordinary conditions is the amount of grain fed in relation to the amount of milk produced. With the excellent forage available a grain-milk ratio of 1 to 3 or 1 to 3½ might be more profitable under normal price relations than the 1 to 2⅔ ratio now being used.

A Farm in Northern Delaware

Northern Delaware, and southeastern Pennsylvania and central Maryland make up an intensive general-farming area. Dairying is the leading enterprise; cash crops are a close second; poultry is also important. The growing season is long, markets are close, and the land is productive—but rolling enough to be subject to erosion. As compared with the more northern areas discussed earlier, a larger share of the feed concentrates are home-grown and the acreage of permanent pasture is generally smaller.

In this area is farm C, located in northern Delaware and having resources similar to many other farms in the section.

Farm C is operated by two brothers who have worked out a productive and flexible forage program. They have 84 acres of cropland that is medium heavy, well-drained, and easy to cultivate, although slopes are subject to some erosion. A shift to specialized wholesale milk production was made about 12 years ago. Previously 15 to 18 cows were kept and butter was sold; hogs used the skim milk and home-grown grains. About 75 tons of timothy, clover and timothy, and some alfalfa hay were grown; 50 tons of timothy and mixed hay were sold.

The shift to intensive dairying called for greater forage production. This was brought about by maintaining each acre at or near top production and by stressing pasture. These operators consider pasture one of the most valuable crops grown on the farm.

Part of the cropland is used in this general order—corn 1 or 2 years, wheat or barley seeded, hay 1 or 2 years, and pasture. There is no hard and fast rule, however, about the hay and pasture periods.

A recent seeding was made with Ladino clover, alsike clover, and alfalfa; hay is cut in the early part of the season and pasturage is obtained during the remainder of the period when the permanent pasture is less productive. When a recent summer was quite droughty, an 18-acre field used in this manner increased milk production 15 percent, according to the operators. In seeding this crop, 1½ tons of lime and 400 pounds of superphosphate were used per acre. An annual top dressing is made with 300 pounds per acre of 0–20–20 fertilizer or something similar.

Thirty-five acres of permanent pasture carry the herd during the spring and early summer months. Parts of the pasture have been plowed and seeded and it is all top-dressed with 1 ton of lime and 500 pounds of superphosphate per acre every 4 years. Manure containing superphosphate is also applied about once in 4 years. These treatments extend the period of abundant feed considerably beyond that of the usual native bluegrass-white clover pastures, but the hot summer weather retards the growth and the seeded pasture is needed. The farmer practices rotation grazing in order to realize maximum pasturage and to prevent killing out the Ladino clover.

The remainder of the cropland is in a hay rotation in which alfalfa is the chief hay crop. It is seeded in the small-grain crop following corn and is maintained with annual applications of liberal amounts of a phosphorus-potash fertilizer and by careful management. Mixed alfalfa-timothy fields are used both for hay and grazing. Some hay is made into silage. The Jersey herd now contains 28 cows, 20 young stock, and 2 bulls. Enough hay and silage is grown to feed about 2 tons of hay equivalent per cow during the barn feeding period.

Plus and Minus

Besides forage crops, 20 acres of grain corn and 20 acres of wheat are usually grown. For the most part, the grains are used for the dairy and a 200-bird poultry flock. Spring barley is sometimes grown to increase the amount of home-grown grains. A concentrate containing 1,400 pounds of corn and cob meal, 400 pounds of wheat, 400 pounds of oats, and 500 pounds of 28-percent protein supplement feed is mixed for the milking cows. The oats and supplement are the only feeds purchased. An average of 3,000 pounds of feed concentrates is fed per cow; average production for

the herd is 400 pounds of butterfat and 8,000 pounds of milk per cow.

Strong points in the forage production program on this farm include:

1. Using a variety of legumes to meet special needs and increase yield and quality of roughage. This point is put first, but three others are of equal importance.

2. Maintaining high soil fertility by good management of farm manure, using commercial fertilizer materials, growing green manure crops, and using cover crops and grass to reduce erosion.

3. Stressing a "full feed" pasture program throughout the entire pasture by using permanent pasture when it produces well and having hay-pasture combination fields to use during the midsummer.

4. Completely mechanizing hay harvesting and using methods to maintain high quality. (The opportunity to use grass for either silage or hay reduces losses that accompany hay making during unfavorable weather.)

Weak Points

It is difficult to find weak points in the forage program on this farm. One practice that might be questioned under ordinary conditions is the amount of grain fed in relation to the amount of milk produced. With the excellent forage available, a grain-milk ratio of 1 to 3, or 1 to 3½, might be more profitable under normal price relationships than the 1 to 2⅔ ratio now being used. This could also alter another practice that might be examined critically, that of using a large acreage for grain crops. Not only do these crops require considerable land preparation annually but the carrying capacity of the farm is limited to approximately the present number of cows. If a market for additional milk could be expected, the grain acreage could be reduced to that necessary in the rotation and at least 10 and possibly 15 cows could be added. This would be a marked shift in farm organization and would require additional investment in buildings, but it would tend to increase income and use existing management and labor more completely.

In Central Maryland

The discussion of farms A, B, and C has brought out many of the problems and many of the opportunities in forage management in the Northeast. The records available for these farms, however, do not permit a complete economic analysis to be made. Still needed to round out the picture is more information on the costs and returns to be expected from forage management and associated adjustments. Such information is available for farm D, a central Maryland dairy farm in the same farming area as farm C.

Farm D is fairly typical of the larger dairy farms in the general farming area that includes central Maryland, southeastern Pennsylvania, and northern Delaware. Many farms there may have more cash crops and less permanent pasture, but the opportunities in forage management would be similar. As on most dairy farms in the Northeast, some progress has been made in forage improvement, but the opportunities are still very great. This is in contrast to farms A, B, and C, where forage programs have already reached advanced stages.

As now operated, farm D has 109 acres of cropland and 70 acres of permanent pasture. About 20 acres of the cropland is used for pasture. Most of the land is rolling and must be farmed with conservation practices, such as contour cultivation, if soil fertility is to be maintained. Crops grown include corn, wheat, clover hay, and alfalfa hay. Livestock consists of 32 cows with enough young stock and other types to bring the total up to 49 animal units. Annual milk production per cow has been 6,800 pounds; grain is fed at the average rate of 1 pound for each 2.9 pounds of milk. The labor force is equivalent to two men who work full time and one who works a little more than 8 months of the year.

Farm D as now operated is a good-sized dairy farm with methods fairly typical of the area in which it is located. The cropping program could be improved first by adapting crops and methods to the capabilities of the land. Instead of following one rotation on nearly all of the cropland, several different rotations could be used. The flat, well-drained areas, about one-third of the cropland, could grow corn, wheat, and 2 years of clover-timothy hay. Another third could be in a longer rotation of corn, wheat or barley, and 4 years of alfalfa. The remaining cropland should be in a still longer rotation and might include Ladino clover with some of the adapted grasses. The first crop of this Ladino-grass mixture could be cut for hay or made into silage; the later growth could be used for midsummer grazing. About 10 acres of the permanent pasture could also be used for a hay-pasture combination, the rest improved by top dressing with lime and fertilizer. Another cropping adjustment that seems desirable is to increase forage production and reduce the amount of small grains and corn grown for grain.

Adjustments

These cropping adjustments, plus an increased use of lime, fertilizer, wider use of hybrid corn, and conservation practices where needed, should mean considerably higher crop and pasture yields. With larger acreages in forage crops, the roughage capacity of the farm would be much higher. This in turn opens the way for livestock adjustments. Sufficient forage should be available to carry about 55 animal units, and at higher rates of roughage feeding than at present. If more forage of a higher quality were available, particularly during midsummer and late summer, the rate of grain feeding could be lowered to about 1 pound of grain to 3.6 pounds of milk in contrast to the present ratio of 1 to 2.9 pounds.

At the same time production per cow should be higher because of better feeding. It could be increased easily 10 percent if, along with the feeding program, the operator adopted recommended practices for the control of mastitis and Bang's disease and carried out other recommendations on herd management.

At this point the question may arise as to the costs of such a program and whether or not the returns would justify it. It is true that costs would be increased. Annual expenses would be higher for concentrate feed, lime and fertilizer, seed, and several other items. Some remodeling of the barn would be necessary to house the larger herd and to make the routine chore work more efficient. This remodeling, plus improvement in methods of doing chores,

should permit the expanded herd to be handled with less labor than is now used.

Although costs would be higher, receipts would also be increased, primarily by larger sales of milk. At prices similar to those of 1943 it is estimated that total receipts would be increased by about $3,700. Expenses, including interest on a $2,000 higher debt, would be larger by approximately $1,500, leaving an increase in net cash income of $2,200.

On similar farms a variety of adjustments would be possible. A farmer interested in cash crops, for example, could take advantage of the increased crop yields to put more land into vegetables, potatoes, or some other crop while maintaining his present herd up to standard.

PRINCIPLES AND PROBLEMS

VANCE G. SPRAGUE, MERTON S. PARSONS

FOR MOST dairy farmers in the Northeast a few principles are basic in developing a well-rounded and productive forage program:

Relate land use to land characteristics.—Over a period of years farmers have tended to adjust land use to the topography and fertility of the land. More easily tilled and more fertile areas have been used for cultivated crops and hay; stony or rough areas have been used for permanent pasture or woodland. This adjustment could and should go much further. Land characteristics will determine the extent to which intensive methods will be practical. Larger quantities of labor, fertilizers, and seed can be used more profitably on some portions of crop and pasture land than on others. On easily tilled land shorter rotations may be followed; where fields are difficult to prepare, long rotations or semipermanent pastures may be most desirable.

Recognize growth requirements and limitations of various crops.—A suc-

cessful forage program must recognize the requirements and limitations of the crops used.

Alfalfa is adapted to well-drained neutral soils, on which it is very productive, but it will not persist on poorly drained or acid soils. On soils less well drained and slightly more acid, red, alsike, and Ladino clovers will grow. On thin, dry hillsides birdsfoot trefoil will persist under conditions where the other legumes will not.

Grasses have similar differences in adaptations. Orchardgrass grows best on well-drained soils, whereas meadow fescue and reed canarygrass will grow well under conditions of poorer drainage. The grasses and legumes that comprise most permanent pasture swards in the Northeast do not grow well during the hot summer months. With these species, the production pattern is a flush period in the spring, limited growth during midsummer, and moderate growth in the fall. Lime and fertilizers will change the extent of these periods somewhat, but unless different plants are used the same pattern persists. Species of forage plants which may be established on semipermanent pastures continue to grow during the less productive midsummer period and aid in leveling production.

Where alfalfa cannot be grown or where losses from winterkilling are frequent, a timothy-clover combination, if handled correctly, can provide high-quality hay. Since red clover usually will not maintain itself on fields for more than 2 years, frequent reseeding is necessary if a mixed legume hay is desired. The addition of Ladino clover to the red clover-timothy mixture will maintain a legume over a longer period. Where timothy or other grasses in association with these clovers are used for hay, early cutting and adequate fertilization will result in good yields of high-quality hay and increased longevity of Ladino clover.

Develop leguminous roughage.— Larger yields of higher quality hay and pasture are obtained through the use of legumes. Red clover and alfalfa have been used most widely, but Ladino clover with a grass has proved valuable both as a pasture crop and as silage and hay. Ladino is more persistent under grazing conditions than is alfalfa and it is longer lived than red clover. It makes an almost ideal pasture-hay crop—the first crop being cut for hay or silage and later crops being grazed.

Conserve fertilizer materials in farm manure.—Storing and handling farm manure so as to conserve its value as a source of fertilizer materials and organic matter is an important step in building up or maintaining soil fertility. Frequently half or more of the fertility value of manure is lost by poor management. An inexpensive manure pit together with a few simple management practices will hold this fertility on the farm to help produce better crops.

Use commercial fertilizer materials.—Lime and phosphorus are needed on almost all farms in the Northeast.

Good management often calls for potash and in some cases nitrogen applications as well. These materials should be used in accordance with the land and crop characteristics. Under present price relations, wide use of commercial fertilizer materials is generally profitable.

Understand the bookkeeping of soil fertility.—Basic to good management of cropland and pastures is consciousness of the flow of soil fertility—direct losses due to erosion and leaching, movement from the soil into the plants, and back to the soil from plant and animal residues and commercial fertilizers. In this way interest will be aroused in cropping and conservation practices that will build up and maintain soil fertility.

Problems

One of the greatest pasture problems in the Northeast remains that of increasing pasture production in July and August. The use of species of grasses and legumes better adapted for growth under midsummer conditions has aided appreciably. Still further advances may be expected from the breeding work now being done. Some legumes, like alfalfa, which may grow better during midsummer are also those which are most easily killed out under grazing conditions. Management practices that will provide more midsummer grazing have been developed; for example, the first crop is removed for hay or silage and then the aftermath is grazed.

The maintenance of the legume in a hay or pasture sward is another major problem. Since in most cases the legume is the primary source of nitrogen for the growth of the associated grass, production of the entire sward decreases if legumes are not present in adequate amounts. The reasons for the loss of legumes are undoubtedly many, a few of which are: Unadapted soils, inadequate fertilizers, overgrazing, undergrazing, winter injury, summer injury, diseases, and insects.

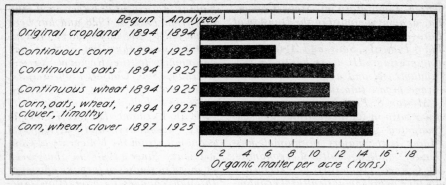

Effect of various cropping practices on organic matter content of unfertilized plots at Wooster, Ohio. Data provided by R. M. Salter, R. D. Lewis, and J. A. Slipher in 1941.

Any one of these causes is so general that it includes a number of separate problems. In some instances, the loss of Ladino clover has often been ascribed to winter injury, but whether the death of the clover was due to low temperatures, heaving, drying out by cold, dry winds, diseases that grow at low temperatures, or to a deficiency of some fertilizer element has not been determined. Information is now being obtained on these and many other problems affecting the survival of Ladino clover. These facts, when integrated and applied, will help maintain productive stands of Ladino clover for longer periods.

Diseases of forage legumes, with the exception of bacterial wilt of alfalfa, have received limited study. Diseases of red clover and more recently Ladino clover are being studied intensively to determine the effects of the various disease organisms and methods for their control. Similarly, diseases of some of the grasses like bromegrass, orchardgrass, timothy, and meadow fescue are being investigated.

Losses from insects on alfalfa and Ladino clover have been more evident throughout the region in recent years. Leafhopper injury to both of these legumes has seriously reduced the production of forage during midsummer, just when it is most urgently needed. Present control measures are far from satisfactory. Other insects which attack these and other legumes undoubtedly cause losses and reduce the longevity of the stand.

Recently several experiment stations have provided for more extensive studies of the insect problems. The breeding of disease- and insect-resistant plants seems to offer a promising procedure for reducing the losses. Management practices may also be valuable aids when life histories and growth habits of causative organisms are better known.

Careful studies of the fundamental principles of plant growth on various soils and under different climatic conditions will provide information that can be applied to the solution of forage problems. In addition, a thorough understanding of the economics of forage production and its utilization for different farm conditions in the region is essential. By an interpretation and integration of all these facts the northeastern farmer will be able to make the best use of his grasslands to meet the requirements of a stable and prosperous agriculture on his farm.

THE AUTHORS≪≪ *Vance G. Sprague is a native of Wisconsin. During graduate study at the University of Wisconsin, where he received a doctor's degree, he was engaged in research on forage species. He then spent a year at the University of Illinois working on pasture management problems. In 1937 Dr. Sprague joined the staff of the United States Regional Pasture Re-*

search Laboratory at State College, Pa., as an agronomist in the Division of Forage Crops and Diseases, Bureau of Plant Industry, Soils, and Agricultural Engineering. His work has to do with fundamental and applied problems of forage production in the Northeast.

Merton S. Parsons was reared on a dairy farm in southern Maine and was graduated from the University of Maine with majors in animal husbandry and agricultural economics. At Cornell University he received a doctor's degree in agricultural economics. From 1937 to 1939 Dr. Parsons was employed in the research division of the Farm Credit Administration in Washington; since then, as a member of the Division of Farm Management and Costs, in the Bureau of Agricultural Economics, he has worked on farm management problems of the Northeast.

E. B. Coffman is a graduate of Kansas State College of Agriculture. He was engaged in agronomic work at *Kansas Agricultural Experiment Station from 1922 to 1928 and has been employed by the Department of Agriculture since that time. He is an agronomist in the Regional Nursery Division, Soil Conservation Service, and is stationed in Big Flats, N. Y.*

Irving F. Fellows grew up on a dairy farm in Vermont. He has degrees in dairy husbandry and agricultural economics from the University of Connecticut. Since 1940 he has been engaged in studies of farming efficiency through changes in production practices and allocation of resources. He is an agricultural economist in the Division of Farm Management and Costs, Bureau of Agricultural Economics, and is stationed at Storrs, Conn.

J. B. R. Dickey, extension agronomist in Pennsylvania State College, and R. R. Robinson, agronomist at the United States Regional Pasture Research Laboratory, helped in the preparation of this manuscript.

Corn Belt and Lake States

THIS PROSPEROUS, BLESSED LAND

HENRY L. AHLGREN [1]

THE FIRST settlers in the eight Corn Belt and Lake States found dense forests in the northern and eastern parts of the region and tall-grass prairie in most of the rest.

Many of the pioneers lacked technical knowledge of farming; they followed trial and error and superstition; poor communication and transportation handicapped them—but climate favored them, the virgin soils were fertile, their first crops grew as high as an elephant's eye, and vision and will set the pattern of the diversified agriculture that now characterizes this prosperous and blessed section.

Difficulties arose, of course. Even before the settlers' sons took over, harvests had dropped quickly and alarmingly in places, particularly on the inherently less fertile soils of fields that had been forests. Selling all crops off the farm and returning little or none of them back to the land depleted fertility, and the introduction and extensive culture of certain crops for food or feed often were followed by losses caused by insects and plant diseases.

Help in solving the problems came from many sources. From individual and collective research and with knowledge gained by general experience

---

[1] All articles in this chapter were written by Henry L. Ahlgren.

there has come a better understanding of soil, plant, animal, and human interrelationships. Especially during the past 50 years agriculture has advanced from a venturesome enterprise guided by empiricism to a science based on tested knowledge. Many unsolved problems remain, but it is unquestionably true that science and technology already have done much to develop here a simplified and stabilized agriculture and reduce many of its risks.

Farming in the Corn Belt and Lake States now is devoted largely to supporting an extensive livestock enterprise.

Most of the crops are used to produce dairy and beef cattle, sheep, as well as swine and poultry, and to maintain horses and mules. The acreage of corn exceeds that of the small grains or tame hay in Illinois, Indiana, Iowa, and Ohio, but the acreage of tame hay exceeds that of corn or small grains in Michigan, Missouri, and Wisconsin.

Minnesota (except the southwestern part), Wisconsin, Michigan, and eastern Ohio are included in the hay and dairy region of the United States. Southwestern Minnesota, Iowa, Missouri, Illinois, Indiana, and western Ohio are an integral of the Corn Belt.

Forages for use as hay and pasturage and to a lesser extent for green manure, grass silage, and seed production are vital everywhere in the various farm

enterprises. The combined acreages of tame hay and pasturage exceed those of corn and small grains in Indiana, Michigan, Missouri, Ohio, and Wisconsin, and approximate those of corn and small grains in Illinois, Iowa, and Minnesota.

Rainfall generally is enough for growing grasses and legumes. The annual precipitation tends to increase from north to south and from west to east within the region. The average number of days without killing frosts is 80 to 180 days in northern districts and 140 to 210 days farther south.

Dairying is the leading farm enterprise in the northern States of the region. Meat production is of great commercial importance in the southern part. The deep, highly fertile prairie soils characteristic of much of this area are cropped more intensively than the forest soils of the dairy region. The use of soil-improving legumes has become increasingly important, but even when grain is largely fed to livestock, and cropping systems include forages for hay and pasture, corn frequently follows corn for 2 or 3 years in the rotations. With that system, soil losses by erosion and depletion of organic matter and fertility are often evident.

Destructive soil processes have been hastened during the period of agricultural development in both the dairy and the meat-producing areas by the effect of one or more of the following influences: Failure to restore fertility removed from the soil by cropping or by the sale of livestock and livestock products; the use of rotations and cropping systems that do not provide for the maintenance of organic matter;

failure to use such supporting practices as strip cropping, contouring, terracing, grass waterways, and other practices designed to reduce excessive soil losses by erosion; the waste of barnyard manure by improper handling; neglect and overgrazing of pastures; and improper use of wood lots, as evidenced by the fact that an estimated 20 million acres of woods is grazed.

Most farmers realize that the fertility used up by previous crops or lost by leaching and erosion must be restored. This is most important for the successful establishment and maintenance of productive forages of superior feeding value. Other factors of the environment, however, may drastically cut production and reduce quality—or even result in the total elimination of certain forages from seeding mixtures. Poor management of areas utilized for hay and pasturage, insufficient moisture on droughty soils or during the drier times in the growing period, severe winter conditions, shading of forage in wooded areas, insects, and diseases may adversely affect production and quality—and often do.

The production of most natural or unimproved pastures in all parts of the region is low. Likewise, cropland yields of forage harvested as hay or grass silage often are low and of poor quality.

The low production of natural or permanent pastures appears to be due largely to the following facts: Practices that increase production and quality are less easily applied to the pastures; they are often relegated to the poorest sites on the farm; barnyard manure and commercial fertilizer are diverted largely or entirely to cropland; and the pastures are used frequently as "exercise lots" where trampling by cattle and rooting by hogs damage the forage.

I give this telescoped account of the history and status of farming in the eight States to support the thesis that high production of feed, food, and fiber under conditions that provide an adequate and continuing margin of profit must come first in the development of a permanent agriculture.

A recognition of the basic importance of the soil and the urgent need for safeguarding and enhancing its productive capacity is fundamental in all the considerations relating to the future welfare of agriculture: The importance, that is, of superior grasses and legumes, supported by practices like terracing, strip cropping, contour plowing, and cultivation, liming, fertilization, and drainage, in safeguarding the soil and in fortifying its productive capacity has been clearly demonstrated as a result of many investigations.

Eight advances related to forages have been developed largely in the past two or three decades. The primary objective of the men and women who developed them was to investigate the possibilities of reducing hazards of production and processing, increasing yields, and improving the quality of the forages. The net effect has been to assure a greater measure of self-sufficiency in feed requirements within the region and conserve and improve the soil. The advances are:

The introduction and use of alfalfa, lespedeza, soybeans, sweetclover, La-dino clover, smooth bromegrass, and reed canarygrass.

The development of superior varieties or strains of alfalfa, medium red clover, lespedeza, soybeans, smooth bromegrass, timothy, and reed canarygrass.

New procedures for improving the production of permanent pastures.

The development of seeding techniques and management procedures for safeguarding the establishment of small-seeded grasses and legumes and assuring high production over a longer period.

The more extensive use of lime and commercial fertilizer to establish and maintain many important forages.

The use of grass silage as a means of preserving forages with a minimum of loss of nutritive value.

Continuing research on the development of labor-saving equipment for processing forages as hay or grass silage.

Studies on the use of barn drying as an effective means of reducing the time necessary for drying forages sufficiently for safe storage.

FIRST, THE CARE OF THE SOIL

THE SOIL comes first. It is the basis, the foundation of farming. Without it nothing; with poor soil, poor farming, poor living; with good soil, good farming and living. An understanding of good farming begins with an understanding of the soil.

In the Corn Belt and Lake States are a great many soil types, some widely different from each other and some different in only one or two respects. We can classify the prevailing soils in the region into six primary groups.

Podzols have a profile that consists of a very thin surface layer of partly decayed leaves and wood fragments above a gray leached layer that rests upon a dark-brown or coffee-brown horizon. Podzols are developed under a coniferous forest in cool, moist climates. They are usually acid and their inherent productivity for most crop plants is low. When limed adequately, fertilized, and carefully managed, those with a texture as heavy as sandy loam or heavier can be used satisfactorily in general farming. Extensive areas of soil types within this group are found in northern Minnesota, Wisconsin, and Michigan.

Gray-Brown Podzolic soils have a profile of a thin leaf litter covering an inch or two of grayish-brown, granular humus. This in turn is followed by a grayish-brown leached horizon extending to a depth of 8 to 10 inches and overlying a horizon varying from yellowish brown to light reddish brown. These soils develop in moist, cool, temperate climates under deciduous forests. They are generally acid, at least at the surface, but they are inherently more productive than the Podzols. They are found in all States in the region.

Red and Yellow Podzolic soils are strongly leached, acid, low in fertility, and generally deficient in organic matter. The surface soil is usually light-colored and sandy; the subsoil is heavier, and red, yellow, or mottled. These soils are relatively easy to till and, although low in inherent fertility, respond well to fertilization. They develop in humid, temperate climates under coniferous or deciduous forests. They occur extensively in Missouri and in a limited area in the southern part of Illinois.

Prairie soils grade from a very dark brown or dark grayish-black surface through brown to lighter-colored parent material at a depth of 2 to 5 feet. They have developed in a cool, moderately humid climate under the influence of grass vegetation. Their inherent fertility is high. Extensive areas of Prairie soils exist in Illinois, Iowa, Minnesota, and Missouri.

Planosols have a well-defined layer of an accumulation of clay or cemented material at varying depths below the soil surface. The group includes soils that range in value from some of the most desirable in the region to poorly drained types of low productivity. Planosol types are found in Iowa, Illinois, Indiana, Missouri, and Ohio.

Chernozems have a very dark brown to black surface layer. The underlying material varies according to the influence of the parent material, but a distinguishing characteristic is an accumulation of carbonates in the zone just above the parent material. Chernozems, which developed under the influence of the tall-grass prairie in temperate areas where annual precipitation ranges from 18 to 28 inches, have a high inherent fertility. Extensive areas of these soils exist only in western Minnesota.

The growth of plants is directly proportional to the available moisture and fertility present in the soil. Unfortunately, reserves of fertility present in virgin soils cannot be drawn upon permanently nor can yields be maintained indefinitely at high levels without the liberal and intelligent use of commercial fertilizer.

Soil depletion has been less severe in these States than in some other places, but it has been estimated that farm soils of the region have lost a third of their virgin fertility through cropping, leaching, and erosion.

Further, apparently only a small proportion of the farmers are maintaining the fertility of their soils by systematic applications of commercial fertilizer and by the use of effective cropping and soil-conserving practices. Similarly, the value of actively decaying organic matter in the soil is widely known, but few farmers employ cropping practices that provide for regular additions of large supplies of this vital material to the dwindling reserves of the soil. The rate of depletion of organic matter can be slowed down considerably by including forage grasses and legumes in the cropping system.

After investigations at the Ohio Agricultural Experiment Station, R. M. Salter, R. D. Lewis, and J. A. Slipher concluded that the changes and improvements of the past two or three decades should have increased production 40 to 60 percent—but did not: "The natural productive capacity of the land has been deteriorating at a rate almost fast enough to offset all of the improvements in soil and crop management."

Clearly, therefore, there is need to recognize the soil as a highly valuable natural resource that must be permanently preserved and safeguarded against the hazards of excessive leaching and erosion. Data from many sources show that forages are highly effective in soil and water conservation and soil improvement, and it appears that forages may be destined to serve a major role in the future in the development of a more efficient, simplified, permanent, and prosperous grassland type of agriculture.

No farmer can maintain a satisfactory standard of living on worn-out soils. With excessive cultivation of the soil, organic matter is depleted, structure is impaired, and the capacity of the soil to absorb water and resist erosion is decreased. In many areas drainage problems have been intensified, and increased tillage and fertilization are necessary to maintain yields. Thus there is a general need in the management of cropland for a shift from the system that involves excessive cultivation to one in which more extensive use is made of forage grasses and legumes for pasturage, hay, grass silage, seed production, and soil improvement. With this shift in the type of farming, livestock can be used more to convert the forages to marketable products like milk, beef, mutton, pork, and wool.

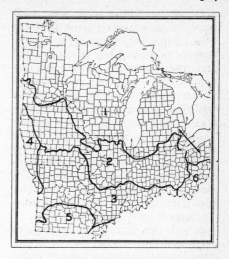

Details of procedure that can be applied effectively in increasing the content of organic matter of the soil and in reducing soil and water losses vary between the several soil and climatic areas comprising the region. Each of the six areas outlined on the accompanying map has differences in soil, topography, climate, and systems of farming great enough to necessitate individual consideration in designing practices and cropping systems for enhancing the soil resources.

Area 1. The soils of this area vary from sands and sandy loams to heavy clays. The farms may be broadly classified into two groups: Those having one-third or more of the land in permanent pasture or woodland, and those with relatively small acreages of permanent pasture or woodland.

On farms in the first group, planning for the best use of permanent pastures and woodlands should be given primary consideration. Data given on a later page show that open permanent pastures can be improved by renovation to a point where they produce good yields of high-quality forage. Wooded areas on better soils should be cleared and renovated under conditions where additional pasturage is required. The remainder should be fenced to exclude livestock and maintained as permanent wood lots. Because of the large acreage of permanent pastures available for grazing, farmers have not had to rely much on the use of rotation pasture on cropland. For that reason, strip cropping is used effectively as a supporting practice in reducing soil and water losses on cropped fields.

The acreage of permanent pasture and woodland is limited on farms in the second group, and under those conditions rotation pastures on cropland provide the major source of pasturage. Strip cropping appears to have limited application because more attention is necessary to regulate grazing than most farmers are willing to give when grasses and legumes of different ages in different strips are pastured at the same time. Where suitable slopes, soils, and outlets are available, terraces are used effectively as a supporting practice for reducing erosion and in developing rotation pastures. When terracing is not practical, the solution of the problem is found in longer rotations, which minimize the use of cultivated crops, together with contouring or across-the-slope tillage.

Grasses and legumes in long rotations are desirable on most farms of both groups for maintaining organic matter, improving soil structure, and preventing excessive runoff and erosion. Strip cropping or terracing (where feasible and practical) can be used to advantage as supporting practices for safeguarding the soil and for conserving and storing water in the soil. Grassed waterways are readily established and maintained with Kentucky bluegrass. The chief problem of silting in of grassed waterways is minimized by the use of adequate supporting conservation practices.

Area 2. The prairie soils of this area were highly productive in the beginning, but soil depletion has proceeded rapidly as a result of excessive and widespread use of cultivated crops. Continuing high yields of corn, soybeans, and small grains depend on more extensive use of forage grasses and legumes in rotations. Various investigations indicate that about one-third of the cropland must include grass and legume forages if maximum crop yields are to be maintained. Additional studies are needed to determine the extent to which such increases in forage production can be utilized effectively in supporting the extensive hog and beef cattle enterprises of this area.

Where cash-grain farming prevails, grasses and legumes grown in rotation and used for soil improvement are essential for continued high production. The most logical long-time objective from the standpoint of soil conservation in this area appears to be the use of enough legumes and grasses in rotations to improve tilth and maintain organic matter. On slopes of suitable topography, terracing is recommended as a supporting practice to reduce runoff and erosion. Contour strip cropping has limited application because of the attendant difficulty of controlling chinch bugs.

Many of the soils of this class are level, heavy, and imperfectly drained. Under these conditions, grasses and legumes are used to advantage because of their highly beneficial effect on soil structure and the resulting improvement in drainage.

Area 3. These soils are geologically older, leached, and of glacial origin. The subsoils are generally heavy and imperfectly drained. Many have been depleted as a result of excessive cropping with corn and small grains. They are generally strongly acid and require frequent and heavy applications of lime.

Lespedeza, well adapted to this area, provides much of the forage that is produced. With proper liming and fertilization, sweetclover, medium red clover, and timothy can be used effectively to provide hay and pasturage. On the better drained, rolling to gently rolling soils, mixtures of alfalfa and southern strains of smooth bromegrass produce good yields of high-quality forage. The soils of this area are naturally well adapted to forage production, and intensive effort is warranted in the development of forage mixtures and fertilization and management practices which will assure high yields of good quality.

Soils on slopes of more than one-half percent are subject to excessive erosion under intensive cultivation. Rotations that include productive forage grasses and legumes, along with such supporting practices as contouring and terracing, are necessary to reduce runoff and erosion. Because of the erosiveness of the soil, establishment of grassed waterways in gullied draws is more difficult here than in many other areas.

Area 4. Most of this area has deep, loessial soil, which has been cropped intensively with corn. Excessive erosion and many deep gullies point up the need for adopting practices that will safeguard the soil. Unfortunately, because of limited rainfall, deep-rooted, drought-resistant forages grown in long rotations tend to deplete the moisture content of the soil in 3 or 4 years to a point where the yields of the following corn crop are considerably reduced. Here the use of level terraces in combination with rotations that include 2 years of alfalfa-bromegrass is a practical way to conserve the soil.

It is hard to maintain grassed waterways because Kentucky bluegrass and timothy are often destroyed under conditions of excessive drought. Establishment of smooth bromegrass on grassed waterways seems a promising solution to the problem.

Area 5. These soils are similar in many respects to those in Area 3, but are shallower and more cherty. The acreage available for cropland is limited. Soil and cropping treatments suggested for Area 3 can be applied with equal effectiveness in Area 5.

Area 6. These soils are derived largely from sandstone and shale, and many are on slopes too steep to cultivate. They are generally shallow and acid and are subject to erosion when they are cultivated. Rotations that include productive forage grasses and legumes along with strip cropping as a supporting practice are necessary to reduce runoff and erosion. On many of the steeper slopes, corn or other cultivated crops should be used infrequently or not at all. The "trash-mulch" method has been used effectively by H. L. Borst and R. E. Yoder in Ohio for establishing productive forages such as alfalfa and smooth bromegrass in permanent pastures on steep, erosive slopes.

NATIVE FORAGES AND NEW FORAGES

THE IMPORTANT native forages that were common on the upland soils of the prairie areas at the time of settlement have been replaced largely by introduced forages. Lacking the aggressiveness, competitive ability, and good seed habits of most introduced forages, the native grasses failed to reestablish themselves after plowing or were eliminated by the usual grazing-management procedures.

Most of the native upland forage species still can be found in many places, but their habitats have been narrowly restricted. Generally they occur on infertile, abandoned sandy soils, undisturbed waste areas, and infertile slopes that are relatively inaccessible to livestock.

The native lowland species, however, have generally resisted the invasion of introduced species on wet, poorly drained, uncultivated soils.

The most important native upland species in the region at the time of settlement were big bluestem, little bluestem, broomsedge, Indiangrass, switchgrass, Canada wild-rye, junegrass, porcupinegrass, needle-and-thread, green needlegrass, side-oats grama, hairy grama, prairie sandgrass or sandreed grass, muhly grass, long-leaved rushgrass or rough rushgrass, prairie dropseed, and sand dropseed.

The most important native lowland forage grasses at that time were bluejoint, prairie cordgrass, American sloughgrass, the mannagrasses, reed canarygrass, and common reedgrass.

The most important introduced forage species in the region during the period of early agricultural development were medium red clover, alsike clover, white clover, timothy, Kentucky bluegrass, Canada bluegrass, and redtop.

From the various localities into which it was introduced by early settlers, Kentucky bluegrass, like white clover, has spread rapidly and spontaneously to all cleared, moderately fertile to fertile upland soils that are uncultivated or kept out of cultivation for a few years. These two species now represent the most important and extensively grown forages for pastures in almost all parts of the region.

With the gradual intensification of

Comparative Yield and Stand Survival of Alfalfa Varieties at Ames, Iowa, 1941–44 (Seeded in 1940)

Variety	Average annual yield per acre, for 4 years (12 percent moisture)	Stand survival Nov. 1, 1944	Variety	Average annual yield per acre, for 4 years (12 percent moisture)	Stand survival Nov. 1, 1944
	Tons	*Percent*		*Tons*	*Percent*
Buffalo...........	4.01	75	Grimm...........	3.34	11
Ranger...........	3.93	67	Baltic...........	3.33	2
Ladak...........	3.88	20	Kansas Common...	3.18	6
Cossack..........	3.45	16	Dakota Common...	3.14	3

Summary of Hay Yields of Domestic Alfalfa Strains at Ames, Iowa, During the Period 1927–40, Inclusive

Variety or strain	Average annual yield per acre (12 percent moisture)	Variety or strain	Average annual yield per acre (12 percent moisture)
	Tons		*Tons*
Ladak....................	3.23	Nebraska Common.........	3.05
Cossack..................	3.28	Oklahoma Common........	2.59
Ontario Variegated.........	3.06	Idaho Common............	3.04
Hardigan....	2.88	Hardistan................	2.63
Baltic.....	2.80	Colorado Common.........	2.79
Grimm...................	2.98	Utah Common.............	2.50
Montana Common........:.	2.87	New Mexico Common......	2.15
Kansas Common..........	2.89	California Common.........	1.51
Dakota Common..........	2.73	Arizona Common..........	1.11

Comparisons of Yields of Various Strains of Medium Red Clover at Columbus, Ohio, 1935–41

Strain	Yield in relation to adapted northern Ohio strain	Strain	Yield in relation to adapted northern Ohio strain
	Percent		*Percent*
Commercial northern Ohio..	100	Cumberland...............	106
Ohio Poland..............	87	Tennessee Anthracnose Resistant...................	99
Ohio Kirch.....:.........	104		
Ohio Van Fossen..........	107	Kentucky.................	108
Midland..................	104	France...................	62
Illinois...................	95	Poland...................	59
Kansas.....:.............	116	Roumania................	51
Iowa....................	122	Hungary.................	71

agriculture, some other valuable forages were successfully introduced.

Smooth bromegrass, alfalfa, soybeans, and the biennial sweetclovers are now grown extensively in many localities. The value of smooth bromegrass as a dependable source of nutritious, palatable forage was first recognized in the drier western part, but more recently it has proved valuable on fertile, well-drained soils in almost all parts of the region.

White clover and Ladino clover are of greatest value in the more humid eastern part. Timothy is replaced by orchardgrass to a certain extent in southern Ohio, Indiana, Illinois, and Missouri. Korean and common lespedezas, crimson clover, and cowpeas are grown only in the southern part, but meadow fescue is restricted primarily to the western part and to fertile, moist, heavy soils in Indiana, Illinois, and Missouri.

Reed canarygrass is grown generally on low, wet soils which may be subject to periodic overflowing, but its culture is most extensive in the north. Soybeans are grown successfully in almost all parts of the region, but the area of their most extensive culture corresponds with that of the Corn Belt. Sudangrass and sorghum are adapted to fertile soils in areas where 105-day or later maturing varieties of corn are grown.

None of the introduced forage grasses and legumes is adapted to all of the soil and climatic conditions in the region. The intended use of the seeding and the local adaptation of the species are the basis for devising seeding mixtures.

Here is a check list of the most important introduced grasses:

Kentucky bluegrass.

Canada bluegrass. This species occurs commonly only on relatively thin, infertile, acid upland soils.

Timothy. Marietta, Lorain, and Itasca are the newer superior strains. The first two were developed by the Ohio Agricultural Experiment Station and the Department of Agriculture; Itasca was developed by the Minnesota Agricultural Experiment Station.

Smooth bromegrass. Studies in 1945 by C. P. Wilsie, M. L. Peterson, and H. D. Hughes in Iowa showed that the "southern type" of bromegrass is superior to the "northern type" in yield and heat- and drought-resistance and for ease of getting stands in western and southern Iowa. The recognized strains of the southern type of bromegrass are Fischer, Lincoln, Achenbach, and Elsberry. Martin is a locally adapted, superior strain released by the Minnesota Agricultural Experiment Station.

Redtop. Redtop is limited naturally to relatively infertile, acid, poorly drained soils. The history and development of redtop and Canada bluegrass are like those of Kentucky bluegrass and white clover, but their spontaneous occurrence is more restricted and less widespread. Canada bluegrass occurs commonly only on relatively thin, upland soils.

Reed canarygrass. Introduced types are more aggressive and better seed producers than the native types. Only the introduced types are used in the establishment of new seedings. The Iowa Agricultural Experiment Station has developed a superior type of reed canarygrass known as Ioreed.

Orchardgrass.

Meadow fescue.

Sudangrass. Tift and sweet Sudangrass are new varieties that appear promising, particularly in southern parts of the region.

The primary introduced legumes are:

Alfalfa. Winter-hardy varieties such as Grimm, Cossack, Ladak, Hardigan, and Canadian Variegated are used in the northern part; regional strains of common alfalfa are grown farther south, where winters are milder. Ranger, Buffalo, Ladak, mixtures of Ladak and Cossack, or mixtures of Cossack and Ranger are recommended for soils infested with bacterial wilt disease (*Corynebacterium insidiosum*).

Medium red clover. Cumberland and Kenland are recommended in the

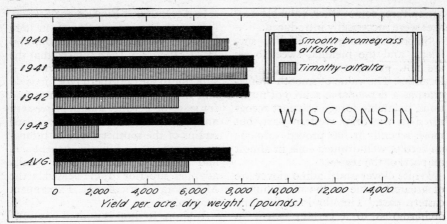

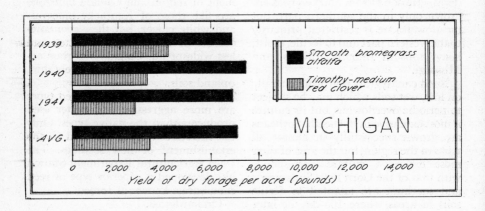

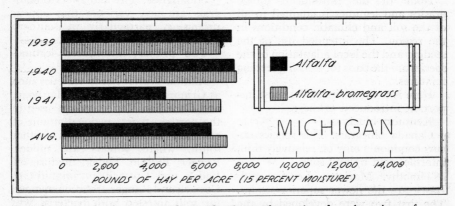

Introduction and subsequent widespread culture of superior, drought-resistant forages in the Lake States and Corn Belt have assured adequate forage production in dry years and during drier portions of the growing period as well as in wet years. The charts show the superior value of some of these forages as indicated by greater productivity.

southern part of the region. Midland is grown in south central localities. Kenland is adapted to the southern part, where southern anthracnose (*Colletotrichum trifolii*) is normally prevalent and frequently serious. Investigations in Ohio and elsewhere show that when the disease is prevalent Kenland will yield more than Cumberland and other adapted varieties. Seed from locally grown, hardy stocks have given best results in the Northern States.

Mammoth red clover.

Biennial sweetclovers. A new yellow-blossom variety known as Madrid appears to have considerable merit in a number of the southerly States in the region. It has vigorous seedling growth, leafiness, and resistance of the foliage to frost in the fall. Trials in some northern districts show that Madrid may be less winter-hardy than other sweetclovers commonly grown.

Common white and Ladino clovers.

Alsike clover.

Korean lespedeza. Three new strains earlier in maturity and superior in forage quality to commercial Korean lespedeza have been developed by the Iowa Agricultural Experiment Station. These strains are also more resistant to wilt disease (*Phytomonas lespedeza*) than strain 19604, which is the only other commercially available early type of lespedeza. The new strains are Iowa 6, Iowa 39, and Iowa 48. They are being increased for seed; Iowa 6 was distributed in 1947.

Common lespedeza.

Soybeans.

Other common but less important species of grass include: Rye (Balbo rye has shown recent promise of providing excellent pasturage in late fall and very early spring), oats, barley, wheat, corn, sorghum, millet, red fescue, orchardgrass, meadow foxtail, common ryegrass, and roughstalk meadow grass.

Other common species of legumes are cowpeas, vetch, field peas, annual white sweetclover, crimson clover, and birdsfoot trefoil.

Rape also belongs to the list of common but less important forage crops.

MIXTURES OF GRASSES AND LEGUMES

MIXTURES of grasses and legumes usually are more productive than seedings of grasses and of legumes grown alone.

Studies in Illinois in 1944 by R. F. Fuelleman, W. L. Burlison, and W. G. Kammlade, for example, showed that bromegrass and orchardgrass seeded alone produced approximately 40 percent less forage and 50 percent smaller gains in live weight than when grown in mixtures including alfalfa.

Likewise in Wisconsin, F. V. Burcalow and I noted that timothy, smooth bromegrass, and alfalfa seeded alone were much less productive than mixtures including one or more of these grasses and alfalfa.

Furthermore, weeds usually are better controlled when the seeding mixtures contain grasses and legumes. Such mixtures may lengthen the productive life of stands because grasses are hardier and last longer than the legumes commonly grown with them. Primarily for those reasons, mixtures containing grasses and legumes are commonly sown throughout the Corn Belt and Lake States.

The seeding mixtures vary according to the purpose for which they are intended and the soil and climatic conditions prevailing in the locality in which they are to be grown. Mixtures of grasses and legumes that are recommended in the various Corn Belt and Lake States generally include only two to four species, but under some conditions more complex mixtures containing five or more species are used.

Regardless of the mixture used, most sown species that comprise the initial seeding are eventually replaced by other species, even though they are not included in the original seeding mixture. Kentucky bluegrass eventually becomes the dominant species on fertile, upland soils in almost all sections of the region, but on comparatively infertile, upland soils the species that are sown are replaced by Canada bluegrass. Vegetation on impoverished soils, particularly in the eastern part, reverts eventually to broomsedge and povertygrass. Species sown on wet, poorly drained soils are gradually replaced by redtop. Well-established and managed stands of reed canarygrass on lowland areas, and smooth bromegrass on fertile, upland soils can resist the encroachment of most other species if they are not overgrazed.

GETTING GRASS AND LEGUMES TO GROW

ROTATIONS that include systematic use of small-seeded grasses and legumes are indispensable in maintaining a permanent and profitable system of livestock agriculture. Without them, high yields cannot be kept up even on the most productive soils of the Corn Belt and Lake States.

An illustration: On the Morrow plots at the Illinois Agricultural Experiment Station, corn yields averaged 48 bushels an acre from 1888 to 1944 when the corn was grown in a rotation with oats and clover but only 36 bushels in a rotation with oats alone. When corn was grown continuously the average yield was 29 bushels an acre.

The systematic use of forages in rotations depends a lot on their successful establishment after seeding. Failures apparently were rare just after the breaking of the virgin soil, but with continuing cultivation (and the subsequent depletion of lime, phosphate, potash, and organic matter from cropping, leaching, and erosion) soil conditions became less favorable.

A. J. Pieters says that there were reports of clover failures in Ohio as early as 1866; in 1908 the Ohio Agricultural Experiment Station found that failures of clover were becoming increasingly prevalent in eastern and southern Ohio. Later, particularly up to 1925 or so, more and more failures were reported in almost all parts of the region.

No matter what the cause, seeding failures are costly—in time used in preparing the seedbed, money spent for seed, labor of reseeding, and shortages of hay and pasture; also, the expense of establishing emergency hayfields and pastures, disrupted plans for rotations, increased erosion, and a reduction of organic matter and fertility.

Procedures that give reasonable assurance of success in the establishment of small-seeded grasses and legumes include: Liming and fertilizing with phosphate and potash; preparing a firm, moderately smooth seedbed; shallow coverage of seed; reducing competition from the companion crop and weeds; proper inoculation of legumes; use of adapted seed of good quality; seeding at the right time; mulching; maintaining adequate reserves of organic matter; control of grasshoppers in certain areas; and proper management of the seeding following establishment.

Forages capable of producing high yields of good quality cannot be established or maintained on impoverished soils. Increasing failures of red clover following long periods of cropping and the introduction of alfalfa with its highly exacting fertility requirements were factors of major importance in focusing attention on the need for improving the soil by the use of lime and commercial fertilizer. As a result, applications of lime, phosphate, and potash on the basis of soil and plant requirements have become relatively common for the establishment and maintenance of seedings for use as rotation pasture or for hay and grass silage.

Experiments have shown that nitrogen in an available form is likely to be a limiting factor in the production of forages on almost all soils except those that support a good growth of legumes; lime and phosphate are deficient in many soils, and potash is often the limiting factor in sandy soils, peats, mucks, and many heavy, poorly drained soils. When they are needed, lime, phosphate, and potash aid new seedings to withstand the hazards of drought, heat, and grasshoppers, and competition from the companion crop and weeds; they are also of utmost importance in maintaining production and quality at satisfactory levels following establishment.

Lime is usually applied every 6 to 10 years. It is often added to advantage 6 to 12 months before seeding. Recommendations for the several States are: Illinois, 2 to 4 tons of lime to the acre, depending on the soils; Indiana, 1 to 5 tons; Iowa, 2 to 4; Michigan, 1 to 3; Minnesota, 1 to 3; Missouri, 1½ to 3; Ohio, according to need; Wisconsin, 1 to 5 tons.

General recommendations for the use of phosphate and potash to establish new seedings (in pounds to the acre) are:

Illinois—100 to 500 pounds of 0-14-7, 0-12-12, 0-14-14, 0-20-20, or 0-20-0. From 500 to 2,000 pounds of raw rock phosphate may be substituted for the 0-20-0 fertilizer. (The figures, like 0-14-7, mean, in order, the percentage of total nitrogen; the percentage of available P_2O_5, which is phosphoric acid or less precisely phosphate; and the percentage of water-soluble K_2O—potash.)

Indiana—General: 200 to 400 pounds of 0-14-7, 0-10-20, 0-12-12, 2-12-6, 3-12-12, 2-18-9, or 3-9-18. Light sands: 300 pounds of 0-9-27, 0-10-20, 0-12-12, 3-12-12, or 3-9-18. Black sands: 300 pounds of 0-10-20 or 0-9-27.

Iowa—Typical well-drained soils except those high in lime and sandy soils: 200 to 300 pounds of 0-20-0 or 5-20-0. High-lime soils: 200 to 300 pounds of 0-20-20. Slowly drained and sandy soils: 200 to 300 pounds of 0-20-10 or 0-20-20; 250 to 350 pounds of 4-16-8.

Michigan—Acid muck: 200 to 350 pounds of 0-9-27, 3-9-18+2½ CuSo₄. Alkaline: 300 to 350 pounds of 0-9-27, 3-9-18+15 MnSo₄. Loams: 300 pounds of 0-20-0, 0-14-7, or 0-20-10. Sands: 300 pounds of 0-12-12 or 0-10-20.

Minnesota—General: 250 pounds of 0-20-0, 0-20-10, or 0-20-20; 300 pounds of 0-16-8; 350 pounds of 0-14-7 or 0-12-12. Peat: 350 pounds of 0-10-20.

Missouri—No manure: 200 to 500 pounds of 0-20-10 or 0-20-20; 300 to 500 pounds of 0-14-7 or 0-12-12; 150 pounds of 3-18-9; 200 pounds of 2-12-6, 3-12-12, 4-12-4, 4-12-8, 4-16-4, or 5-10-10; 250 pounds of 8-8-8. Manured: 200 to 300 pounds of 0-20-10, 0-20-20, 0-14-7, or 0-12-12.

Ohio—No manure; sands: 400 pounds of 3-12-12, 4-12-8. Loams: 350 pounds of 0-12-12, 2-12-6, or 3-12-12. Muck: 350 pounds of 0-10-20 or 3-9-18. Manured; sands: 350 pounds of 0-14-7, 2-12-6, or 4-12-8. Loams: 300 pounds of 0-12-12 or 0-14-7. Muck: 300 pounds of 0-12-12 or 0-10-20.

Wisconsin—Mucks and peats: 250 to 500 pounds of 0-20-20, 0-10-20, or 0-9-27. Silts and clay loams: 200 to 500 pounds of 0-20-0, 0-20-20, or 3-12-12. Sands and sandy loams: 200 to 500 pounds of 3-12-12, 3-9-18, or 0-9-27.

Lime and phosphate generally are more effective in stimulating growth of forages in most soils when they are thoroughly worked into the soil at the time the seedbed is prepared than when they are applied as a top dressing on the surface after the seedings are established. Responses following top dressing with lime, phosphate, and potash are likely to be small and of little practical importance unless other factors are introduced, like the presence of legumes or the addition of commercial nitrogen fertilizer.

Grasses in fields used for pasturage, hay, or silage can be kept productive after legumes have been eliminated by early spring applications of such quickly available commercial nitrogen fertilizers as ammonium nitrate, ammonium sulfate, and calcium cyanamid. In addition, in certain areas, commercial fertilizers as 8–8–8, 10–6–4, 5–10–5, and 6–10–6 are applied to advantage to increase production of forage. Treatment with all of these fertilizers should be limited to soils with a good supply of available moisture.

Broadcast applications of commercial nitrogen fertilizer are much less effective in increasing yields of forage on dry or droughty soils or on other soils during the drier times of the growing period. The usual rates of application are 125 to 175 pounds per acre for ammonium nitrate, 200 to 250 pounds for ammonium sulfate and calcium cyanamid, and 300 to 500 pounds for 8–8–8, 10–6–4, 5–10–5, and 6–10–6. Such treatments increase total production and improve quality; they also stimulate early growth so that grazing often can begin 10 to 14 days earlier.

Manuring

L. E. Thatcher, C. J. Willard, and R. D. Lewis in Ohio, and O. T. Coleman and A. W. Klemme in Missouri reported that manure added at rates varying from 4 to 10 tons to the acre and worked into the soil or applied as a top dressing after seeding may be a valuable adjunct in establishing new seedings, especially on infertile soils and soils low in organic matter. When it is applied as a top dressing to new seedings, the benefits are due largely to

the fact that the thin layer of manure not only adds nutrients but also serves as a mulch to conserve soil moisture, provides coverage for the seed, protects the young seedlings from drying and soil blowing, reduces fluctuations in soil temperature, minimizes soil losses from erosion, and protects the seedings from excessive heaving in winter.

In addition, studies by W. L. Burlison, H. P. Rusk, J. J. Pieper, and W. B. Nevens in Illinois; Drs. Coleman and Klemme in Missouri; D. R. Dodd and R. M. Salter in Ohio; R. F. Crim and P. M. Burson in Minnesota; K. E. Beeson and M. O. Pence in Indiana; and H. B. Cheney in Iowa showed that reasonably weed-free barnyard manure applied as a top dressing at the rate of 4 to 8 tons an acre (during the rotation to hay fields or rotation pastures, and every 3 to 5 years to permanent pastures) is highly effective in increasing yields of forage. Fresh, rather than composted manure, reenforced with 30 to 50 pounds of 20-percent superphosphate per ton of manure and applied before the soil freezes up in the fall, usually gives the best results.

Manuring pastures in the spring and summer months has been used as a means of regulating grazing in large permanent pastures. Observations show that when manure is applied to areas in overgrazed pastures livestock tend to avoid them until the forage has had ample opportunity to recover.

Most new seedings of grasses and legumes are made in a well-prepared seedbed in conjunction with a companion crop of small grain. Under some conditions it is highly desirable to graze, clip, or mow the companion crop to reduce excessive and harmful competition between the companion crop and the new seeding for light, moisture, and available soil fertility.

The Year of Seeding

As a rule the new seeding, when grown with a companion crop, does not produce a heavy growth of forage the year of seeding. Heavy grazing during midsummer or fall may result in considerable injury to the seeding. In general, best results are obtained if new seedings are not grazed heavily or mowed, except as necessary to control weeds after the small-grain crop has been removed. If sufficient growth is available, new seedings may be grazed moderately in July or August without subsequent injury to the stand. Grazing is usually withheld in September and October or until growth has been stopped or retarded by frost or cold weather.

Studies conducted by Thatcher, Willard, and Lewis in Ohio demonstrated that new seedings of alfalfa, alsike clover, and medium red clover may be clipped to destroy weeds and remove the grain stubble without injury to the seeding if the clipping is done before September 1.

Weeds and stubble are removed by such treatment, and cleaner forage of better quality results the following year. However, studies by Dr. Willard in Ohio in 1927 and D. W. Smith in Wisconsin in 1947 disclosed that sweetclover is injured by mowing or clipping during the year of seeding. Clipping is not recommended in August or September unless such treatment is necessary to destroy vigorous, competing weed growth. Willard's and Smith's studies show that cutting sweetclover for hay the first year is practical only when the value of the hay on the basis of individual need exceeds the value as green manure or pasturage the following year.

Medium red clover may blossom and produce seed the first year if seasonal conditions are entirely favorable. Some farmers believe that red clover that is permitted to produce seed will die, but this view is not supported by observations of Thatcher, Willard, and Lewis, who obtained heavy hay crops in fields in Ohio from which as much as 2 bushels of seed had been harvested the preceding fall. Cutting new seedings of red clover after September 1 may result in injury because of lack of a suitable winter cover.

Occasionally, however, tall, dense stands of medium red, mammoth, alsike, and Ladino clovers attract field mice and provide excellent cover for them. The mice live on the short young tillers or stolons during the winter and sometimes cause extensive damage. Then it may be desirable to cut or graze the seeding moderately to reduce the cover so that mice will not be attracted to clover fields in fall and winter. Likewise, on fertile soils well situated with respect to available moisture, the growth of Ladino clover may be so heavy that snow mats it down and plants may smother. The way to prevent it is to graze the fields moderately in the fall to remove some top growth.

In Permanent Pastures

Little commercial fertilizer is used on permanent pastures in many parts of the region, although its benefits have been widely demonstrated. Aside from increased production under conditions favoring the use of commercial nitrogen fertilizer, the greatest success in improvement of permanent pastures has been achieved where the practices have involved the establishment and maintenance of legumes and certain superior grasses.

Small-seeded grasses and legumes grow slowly at first and are poorly equipped to compete with weeds, other aggressive species, and with established plants. Cultural and grazing techniques designed to promote the establishment of sweetclover, medium red clover, white clover, lespedeza, alfalfa, smooth bromegrass, and timothy have been developed in various localities. Likewise, practical procedures for the reestablishment of sweetclovers, medium red clover, and lespedeza from natural reseeding and for the maintenance of white clover in grassy swards have been devised. These techniques are based on the recognized need for liming and fertilizing impoverished soils, and reducing harmful and excessive competition between the grassy component of

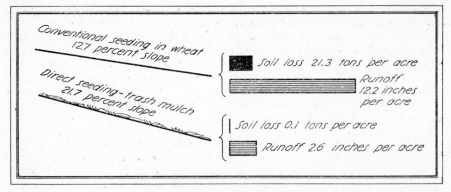

The effectiveness of stubble mulching in reducing soil and water losses under Ohio conditions as reported by H. L. Borst and R. E. Yoder. The conversion of existing vegetation
into a mulch by disking promotes infiltration, decreases and controls runoff, eliminates
soil erosion, and conserves the moisture by decreasing surface evaporation.

the sward and the seedling plants during their early stages of development.
I outline the techniques here.

*Alfalfa, medium red clover, sweet-
clovers, smooth bromegrass, and timothy.*—Various combinations of these
grasses and legumes are established in
permanent pastures by a procedure
known as renovation. The initial research leading to the practical procedure now in effect for establishing
grasses and legumes in permanent pastures was begun by L. F. Graber, of the
Wisconsin Agricultural Experiment
Station, in 1925 and reported in 1927.

Renovation is based on establishing
these forages in thin, unproductive
sods on hilly, erodible land without
plowing. A good seedbed is prepared
by tearing up the sod thoroughly with
a disk, spring tooth, or field cultivator.
Thorough cultivation is essential, because it is necessary to destroy most of
the grassy vegetation and incorporate
needed lime, phosphate, and potash
into the soil to assure the successful
establishment of the legumes. Except
for broken-up sods on top, a good seedbed should look as if it had been plowed
and harrowed. If the first and last of
the tillage operations are on the contour or across the slope, more moisture
will be conserved and the likelihood
of erosion will be lessened.

Studies in 1943 in Ohio by H. L.

Borst and R. E. Yoder have shown that
the conversion of the existing vegetation into a trashy surface mulch by disking promotes infiltration, diminishes
and controls runoff, eliminates erosion,
and conserves moisture by reducing
surface evaporation. Such protection
is not provided by the usual type of
moderately deep to deep plowing.

Studies by H. D. Hughes and M. L.
Peterson in Iowa in 1946 suggest that
very shallow plowing provides a good
seedbed at less cost than surface cultivation with a disk, spring tooth, or
field cultivator when the sod is tough
and heavy. The sod should be plowed
in late fall and left rough over winter.
Little or no loss of soil by erosion is
likely when this method of seedbed
preparation is used, if the sod is plowed
shallowly and on the contour. Lime
and commercial fertilizer in amounts
shown by soil tests to be necessary are
applied and worked into the soil.
Seedings of superior grass-legume mixtures are made with a small-grain
companion crop in early spring following the preparation of a good seedbed. On heavy sods seedbed preparation involving very shallow plowing
has provided better stands of seeded
grasses and legumes than methods
involving surface cultivation.

Scarification of the sod and the establishment of superior grasses and

legumes without plowing (or with very shallow plowing) has been used effectively in Wisconsin, Minnesota, Iowa, Illinois, and Ohio as a means of improving unproductive permanent pastures. Illustrative of results that may be obtained with pasture renovation are those reported by M. L. Wall, R. J. Muckenhirn, J. M. Sund, and H. L. Ahlgren in Wisconsin in 1946. We found that pasture renovated with sweetclover and medium red clover yielded an average of 3,210 pounds to the acre, against 1,453 pounds from ordinary pasture. Not only was the production doubled in these trials as a result of renovation, but, in addition, weeds and white grubs (*Phyllophaga* sp.) were markedly reduced, and more feed was available for grazing each year in July and August by the growth of the legumes.

How long the beneficial effects of renovation last depends largely on the success attained in maintaining the legumes. The common sweetclovers and medium red clover are biennials, and their continued survival is possible only as a result of natural reseeding.

This procedure has been outlined by workers at the Wisconsin Agricultural Experiment Station for reestablishing stands of sweetclover and medium red clover from natural reseedings in bluegrass sods:

(a) After ample seed production is assured during years in which sweetclovers and medium red clover produce seed, the pastures are grazed closely for the remainder of the growing period. The Kentucky bluegrass is weakened considerably by this treatment and the legume seeds are trampled into the soil by the cattle.

(b) During the following year the pastures are grazed closely very early in the spring when the sweetclover and medium red clover seedlings are still very small. This close grazing in early spring reduces further the competition of the Kentucky bluegrass.

(c) If the Kentucky bluegrass recovers from the first grazing to the extent that a 4- to 5-inch growth is produced by the middle of June, the pastures are grazed again to reduce shading of the legumes. The pastures are grazed in such a way that the growth of Kentucky bluegrass is reduced to the level of the legume seedlings, after which the cattle are removed.

(d) Moderate grazing may be practiced in July and August and occasionally in late fall after growth has been retarded by frost and cool weather. In general, however, best results are obtained if grazing is withheld in September and October.

Lespedeza. Korean lespedeza is grown more extensively in Missouri than any other legume. Studies by W. D. Etheridge, C. A. Helm, and E. M. Brown there in 1946 (and by Dr. Brown in 1941) indicate that when lespedeza is grown in permanent pastures it can be maintained indefinitely by natural reseeding, provided proper grazing management is practiced.

Permanent pastures in which lespedeza is grown are grazed moderately in April, May, and June. Moderately heavy grazing is suggested throughout this period to reduce the competition between the grass and the young lespedeza seedlings. The pastures are grazed lightly during July, August, and early September to utilize available forage and to keep down annual weed grasses. The cattle are kept out of the pastures from mid-September to December to give the grass an opportunity to replenish reserves which were depleted during the period of heavy spring grazing. The accumulated fall growth is grazed without injury to the plants after growth has been retarded or stopped by frost and cool weather.

White clover. E. Vandermeulen, G. McIntyre, and C. M. Harrison, of the Michigan Agricultural Experiment Station, discovered that proper management accompanied by appropriate top dressing with phosphatic fertilizer will result in the reestablishment of white clover in areas where this legume is adapted. Following the application of phosphate, white clover is established without seeding and maintained by continuous and close grazing. D. R. Dodd has shown that under less favorable conditions seasonal climatic conditions are of major importance in affecting the occurrence, fluctuation, and distribution of white clover in lawns and pastures in Ohio. In excessively dry seasons, white clover disappeared from lawns and pastures regardless of the fertility and managerial treatments.

HOW TO MANAGE GRASSLANDS

THE MOST important biennial and perennial forages grown for hay or grass silage in the Corn Belt and Lake States are alfalfa, medium red clover, alsike clover, smooth bromegrass, and timothy. Because alfalfa is inherently longer lived than the other important legumes but is more susceptible to winter injury than the perennial forage grasses, greater care is needed to assure its continued high production and survival.

Destruction of stands and reduction in yield and quality of alfalfa are due primarily to the single or combined effects of winterkilling, bacterial wilt disease, and injury by the potato leafhopper. Good management can safeguard alfalfa against these hazards.

Although better quality of hay and grass silage usually results from cutting alfalfa early, there is evidence that frequent or early cutting lowers vigor, reduces production and winterhardiness, increases summer mortality, provides more favorable conditions for weeds and undesirable grasses, and is less effective in controlling leafhoppers than cutting at more advanced stages of growth.

Studies in 1925 in Wisconsin by R. A. Moore and L. F. Graber showed that two cuttings annually in Wisconsin at the full-bloom stage yielded more than three cuttings at the tenth bloom. Dr. Graber and his coworkers pointed out in their summary: "The retardation of root and top growth of alfalfa plants and their ultimate death from cutting frequently and at immature stages is due, primarily, to the inability of the plants to elaborate food reserves . . . in sufficient quantities to provide for adequate translocation to and storage of such reserves in the roots for the future development of the roots, as well as that of the tops."

After further studies with alfalfa in Wisconsin in 1937, the men reported that optimum fertility greatly influenced productivity and survival.

The way stands of alfalfa are managed during the period of fall growth may have an important bearing on survival and the continued productivity. C. J. Willard, L. E. Thatcher, and J. S. Cutler found that, in Ohio, cutting in late September and early October was more injurious than cutting in early November, when root storage was complete and seasonal conditions prevented the initiation of new growth. V. W. Silkett, C. R. Megee, and H. C. Rather, of the Michigan Agricultural Experiment Station, found that alfalfa cut in September developed fewer crown buds per plant, had less dry matter in the roots, and produced fewer stems and a significantly lower yield the following spring than alfalfa that was cut in October or that was not cut. Studies in 1938 in Michigan by Rather and C. M. Harrison showed that least injury is likely to result when alfalfa is cut late enough in the fall that cold weather will prevent subsequent growth and the resultant depletion of reserves.

Critical periods during which fall cutting of alfalfa should be avoided range from about August 15 in the northern part of the region to November 1 in the more southerly areas. Moderate pasturing after growth has been retarded or stopped by cold weather is probably the best way of utilizing the fall growth. Such treatment has an added advantage over mowing in that it provides a taller stubble for more complete protection against winter injury. Other findings are that only two cuttings may be taken annually in the northernmost States and three cuttings in the more southerly States of the region if continued high productivity and maximum survival of stands are desired.

Pasture Management

Most of the forages utilized for pasturage deteriorate in feeding value and palatability as they approach maturity; thus, the highest feeding value and greatest utilization of forages used to provide pasturage for most of the important classes of livestock are usually obtained if they are grazed when they are relatively immature. Such grazing treatment is harder on the plants than harvesting at more advanced stages of growth. As a result, yields may be reduced considerably and survival, particularly of legumes, is jeopardized to a greater extent when forages are grazed than when they are harvested for hay or grass silage.

It is generally recognized that good pasture management includes the provision for sufficient pasturage so that there will be an excess during favorable seasons or portions of the growing period. It is only by such a procedure that the highly undesirable alternatives of costly barn feeding, increased use of purchased feeds, or overgrazing can be avoided. Excess forage of good quality produced during favorable parts of the growing period and not required for pasturage can be harvested and utilized to advantage later as hay or grass silage.

The period during which forage is available for grazing each year (or, with planning, can be made available) ranges from 5 months in the northern sections to approximately 9 or 10

months in Missouri. Few farmers anywhere make full use of improved pasture practices and cropping sequences to provide season-long pasturage of high quality. In many areas, unimproved permanent pastures represent the major source of pasturage during the growing period. Such pastures, which are composed largely of Kentucky bluegrass, Canada bluegrass, and redtop, often make 60 to 75 percent or more of their total seasonal growth by July 1. Where dependence is placed solely on them for pasturage, critical shortages are likely during warm, dry periods, and severe overgrazing often results.

The most important general considerations involving pasture management include:

The use of grazing procedures that permit maximum production and utilization of high-quality forage from any forage or forage combinations;

The development of rotation pastures on cropland and the use of other practices that assure continuous production of good quality throughout the growing period;

The availability of equipment and facilities for harvesting and preserving surplus pasturage as hay or grass silage with a minimum loss in nutrient value;

The use of safeguards to eliminate or minimize the danger of such hazards as bloat, prussic acid poisoning, or poisoning by certain weeds; and

The use of grazing procedures that assure the reestablishment of annual and biennial legumes in permanent pastures.

Effects of Close Grazing

When forages are utilized for pasturage the effect upon them of various degrees of defoliation is a matter of fundamental importance. In planning grazing procedures it is necessary to know the current effect of partial or complete defoliation upon the yield and quality of top growth and the extent of root and rhizome development.

It is well to appreciate that the residual effects of the treatment from the standpoint of production and survival are of great practical importance.

Early grazing of forages in the spring and close, continuous grazing throughout the growing period reduce vigor, root growth, and total yield of top growth. Intense grazing may result in the total elimination of certain forages from the stand during the course of a single growing period. Grassy swards occasionally are grazed closely to advantage during certain specified periods—to reduce the vigor of the grass component sufficiently so that short-lived legumes (such as lespedeza, medium red clover, and sweetclover) and long-lived legumes (such as white clover and Ladino clover) are more readily reestablished from natural reseeding. But if that is not the objective, close and continuous grazing is generally harmful.

After grazing, new growth starts primarily at the expense of previously stored food reserves. Unless there is enough time for the replenishment of the reserves between grazings, yields are likely to decrease progressively. For example, tests at the Wisconsin Agricultural Experiment Station demonstrated that timothy in association with alfalfa was less vigorous when cut three times annually than when harvested only twice at a later stage of maturity. Other studies there disclosed that the productivity of Kentucky bluegrass after 2 years of frequent cutting was reduced to less than one-fourth that of Kentucky bluegrass cut only once annually at maturity. Similar but less striking results were also reported for redtop.

Furthermore, in 1933, Dr. Graber found a much larger current production of Kentucky bluegrass from areas given close frequent defoliation than from those given tall defoliation at the same time and with the same frequency, but the following year—when production was measured by three uniform cuttings—the bluegrass clipped closely the previous year was less productive and weeds were five to seven times more abundant.

Studies in 1939 in Michigan by A. A. Johnson and S. T. Dexter revealed that quackgrass that was defoliated once a week for 24 weeks and that had a continuous supply of nitrogen had few functional shoots, although cultures receiving no nitrogen but also defoliated once a week for an equal period were still growing steadily. The quackgrass plants grown at a low level of nitrogen fertilization stored organic reserves in underground parts under more severe cutting treatments than plants grown at a high level of nitrogen fertilization.

In studies in Michigan with orchardgrass, timothy, smooth bromegrass, quackgrass, and Kentucky bluegrass, C. M. Harrison and G. W. Hodgson found the greatest total yields in almost every case from plants allowed to go unclipped. In general, the shorter a given grass was cut, the less top growth it produced. The yields of the underground parts decreased with increases in severity of cutting. Differences were noted between the species in extent of injury resulting from continuous close clipping. In this respect they rated the forages in the following order, beginning with the one injured least: Kentucky bluegrass, quackgrass, smooth bromegrass, with the orchardgrass and timothy about equal.

In studies in 1944 in Wisconsin, F. V. Burcalow and I learned that smooth bromegrass grazed whenever the forage was 2 to 3 inches tall produced only 54 percent as much pasturage as bromegrass harvested at a hay stage. On the other hand, bromegrass grazed when the forage was 6 to 10 inches tall produced 90 percent as much forage as bromegrass harvested at hay stage.

According to studies in Michigan in 1944, the palatability of forages may be of minor importance when they are grown in pure stands, but when forage species are grown in mixtures, relative palatability is of considerable practical importance; animals greatly preferred alfalfa to tall fescue and orchardgrass, and as a result overgrazed the alfalfa to a point where it disappeared from the mixtures in a few weeks.

Dr. H. C. Rather and A. B. Dorrance learned that root starvation by fall grazing in September and October and heaving of dead plants during the winter and spring were almost universal in fall-pastured alfalfa, although alfalfa not pastured in September and October showed no evidence of winter injury, and no heaving was apparent.

Early-spring grazing, close continuous grazing, and late-fall grazing are commonplace, particularly in localities where permanent pastures predominate. It is clear from the experimental data given that such grazing practices lead to serious curtailment of production of forage and the eventual elimination of all except the most persistent species from the sward.

In general, grazing should be delayed in the spring; if forages are closely grazed later, an ample period for recovery and replenishment of reserves should be permitted. But if grazing is delayed too long, particularly in the spring, the high palatability and nutritive value of most young forage is dissipated rapidly. Unfortunately, no exact rules of grazing management applicable to all forages under all conditions can be made, but it can be stated as a broad generalization that the ideal plan of grazing management involves maximum use of pastures at immature stages of growth while at the same time safeguards against hurting the forage itself are applied.

Woodland Pastures

An investigation in Indiana by D. DenUyl, O. D. Diller, and R. K. Day indicated that yields of forage from grazed woodlands are very low. Furthermore, their results showed that continued grazing such as is commonly practiced results in further lowering the carrying capacity of farm woods by the elimination of the better forage plants, and that grazing by livestock eventually destroys the woods.

They concluded, "Productive pastures and productive woods cannot be maintained on the same land at the same time, and continued protection by complete exclusion of livestock is essential for continued woods production."

F. G. Wilson and A. C. Arny have reported that in Wisconsin and Minnesota the forage value of an acre of open pasture equals that of 4 or 4½ acres of woodland pasture.

D. L. Weaver concluded that any soil type supporting a good growth of forest in Michigan could not be grazed economically.

F. A. Welton and V. H. Morris found that woods pastures in Ohio contained 32 percent more weeds and yielded 85 percent less dry matter per acre than open pastures.

Other investigations conducted in Wisconsin have shown that renovated and untreated open pastures produced annually an average of 3,210 and 1,453 pounds of dry matter to the acre, respectively, but comparable woodland pastures produced an average annual yield of only 276 pounds of dry forage.

It seems clear that continued grazing of wooded areas in this region is hardly worth while, especially because grazing will ultimately also destroy the woods. The results of various studies do not justify the conclusion, however, that wooded areas should be indiscriminately cleared to obtain higher yields of forage. The wise application of available information would lead to the selection, clearing, and improving of the best land for pasture and fencing out the remainder as permanent wood lots—which also contribute their share to the profit, permanence, and enjoyment of farming.

Rotational Grazing

Comparisons of rotational and continuous grazing in the region have shown no consistent advantage favoring rotational grazing.

J. E. Comfort and E. M. Brown, of the Missouri Agricultural Experi-

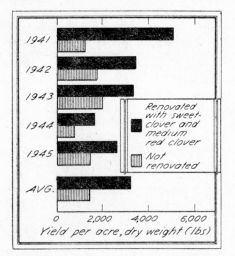

Illustrative of results that may be obtained from renovated and untreated pastures as reported by H. L. Ahlgren, et al., in 1946.

ment Station, found that the average yield of beef in pounds per acre from a continuously grazed pasture was 100 and that of a rotationally grazed pasture was 106.

Harrison, C. L. Cole, and Rather in Michigan, and four of us in Wisconsin reported nearly identical returns from rotationally and continuously grazed pastures.

M. L. Peterson, of the Iowa Agricultural Experiment Station, has presented results that show that yearling steers gained an average of 125 pounds an acre by continuous grazing of a moderate intensity and 144 pounds when pastures were grazed heavily in spring and early summer and in late summer and fall, with no grazing in midsummer.

Results elsewhere indicate that grazing rotationally may increase yields approximately 10 percent over those obtained by continuous grazing. We conclude that such increases are not large enough to justify the extra cost of fencing and of providing water for livestock so that pastured areas can be grazed rotationally. Nevertheless, whether pastured areas are grazed rotationally or continuously, sufficient leaf surface must be maintained so that food reserves utilized for growth can

be replenished. Otherwise yields are likely to drop and survival of the less hardy species may be jeopardized.

Burning to remove accumulations of previous growth of forage is common. Limited information indicates that the effect of burning may be comparable to that of frequent or close defoliation and might do lasting damage.

Findings in 1926 in Wisconsin by Dr. Graber were that Kentucky bluegrass pastures burned in March, when the soil was frozen completely, yielded 52 percent less the following summer than unburned areas. When pastures were burned in May the yield was 71 percent less than that of an unburned area. Weeds were more abundant in both burned areas and the weight of roots and rhizomes, dug to a depth of 7 inches, was 34 percent less.

Regardless of management, none of the forages available for grazing can provide continuous pasturage of high quality throughout the growing period. Too often unimproved permanent pastures are the primary source of forage for grazing; when this situation prevails, good pasturage is available usually for only a few weeks a year. Lengthening the pasture season by improving permanent pastures and using carefully selected crop rotations is an important measure of economy in all areas of the Corn Belt and Lake States where livestock predominate.

Forages and Treatments

Unless careful plans are made well in advance, critical shortages of pasturage are likely to prevail in early spring and midsummer in most areas. In sections where permanent pastures predominate, plans for providing continuous pasturage throughout the growing period should be centered around their improvement. In other areas, season-long grazing is possible by the use of carefully developed and well-executed cropping sequences, which provide sufficient fields so that rotational grazing can be practiced.

The following are examples of available forages and treatments that can be applied to develop sequences for providing continuous, season-long pasturage in various parts of the region:

For early-spring grazing:
a. Common and Balbo rye.
b. Winter wheat.
c. Winter barley.
d. Winter oats.
e. Crimson clover.
f. Common rye and hairy vetch.
g. Young, vigorous stands of alfalfa or alfalfa-grass mixtures in which the alfalfa has not been injured or weakened by bacterial wilt disease may be grazed evenly and heavily for about a week in early spring if the ground is firm. Excellent pasturage is provided by this treatment; it also delays the time of cutting and results in a finer and better quality of hay. Such early grazing, however, is suggested only if the stand of alfalfa is healthy and vigorous and when the following growth is to be harvested for hay or silage.
h. Early-spring applications of commercial nitrogen fertilizer to grassy sods well supplied with moisture will stimulate early growth of forage to provide grazing 10 days to 2 weeks before untreated grass is available for pasture.

For spring and early-summer grazing:
a. Permanent pastures (Kentucky bluegrass, Canada bluegrass, redtop, and white clover).
b. Renovated pastures.
c. Mixtures of grasses and legumes commonly sown in rotation.
d. Spring-sown small grains.
e. Sweetclover.
f. Ladino clover.
g. Reed canarygrass.
h. Mixtures of oats and field peas.

For summer or summer and early-fall grazing:
a. Renovated pastures.
b. Sudangrass.
c. Sorghum.
d. Soybeans.
e. Sweetclover.
f. Korean and common lespedeza.
g. Dwarf Essex rape.

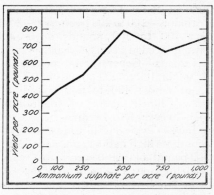

A 2-year old stand of smooth bromegrass, East Lansing, Mich., top-dressed with varying amounts of ammonium sulphate in April yielded seed as charted above.

h. Mixtures of alfalfa and smooth bromegrass.
i. Reed canarygrass.
j. Millet.
k. Mixtures of soybeans and Sudangrass or soybeans, Sudangrass, and corn.

For fall grazing:
a. Permanent pastures.
b. Hay fields or rotation pastures to be plowed.
c. Common rye or mixtures of common rye and hairy vetch.
d. Winter barley.
e. Korean and common lespedeza.
f. Dwarf Essex rape.
g. Reed canarygrass.
h. Cowpeas.
i. Crimson clover.
j. Moderate grazing of vigorous growths of new seedings and established stands after growth has been retarded or stopped by frost or cold weather.

For winter grazing:
a. Permanent pastures (in Missouri only).
b. Winter barley (in Missouri only).

Phosphate and Potash

Recommendations for using phosphate and potash to maintain the production of established grasslands used for hay, grass silage, rotations, and per-

manent pastures (per acre) are these:
Illinois—100 to 200 pounds of 0-20-0
and 100 to 300 pounds of 0-0-60
(where needed) every 3 years.

Indiana—General: 400 pounds of
0-20-0 or 400 to 600 pounds of 0-14-7.
Light sands: 400 to 600 pounds of
0-14-7. Black sands: 400 pounds of
0-10-20 every 3 to 4 years.

Iowa—Typical well-drained soils except those high in lime and sandy soils:
300 pounds of 0-20-0 every 2 to 3 years.
High lime soils: 300 pounds of 0-20-20
every 2 to 3 years. Slowly drained and
sandy soils: 300 pounds of 0-20-10 or
0-20-20 every 2 to 3 years.

Michigan—Acid muck: 100 to 150
pounds of 0-9-27 + 5 CuSo₄. Alkaline:
100 to 150 pounds of 0-9-27. Loams:
200 to 300 pounds of 0-20-0, 0-14-7, or
0-20-10. Sands: 200 to 300 pounds of
0-12-12, 0-20-20, or 0-10-20 annually
or every 2 years.

Minnesota—General: 300 pounds
0-20-0, 0-20-10, or 0-20-20; 350 pounds

of 0-14-7, 0-12-12; 150 pounds of 0-
47-0. Peat: 250 pounds of 0-10-20 or
200 pounds of 0-12-24 every 3 to 4
years.

Missouri—No manure: 300 pounds
of 0-20-10 or 400 pounds of 0-14-7.
Manured: 300 to 500 pounds of 0-
20-0 or 150 to 200 pounds of 0-45-0 biennially with alfalfa, every 3 to 5 years;
otherwise, 1,000 pounds of raw rock
phosphate every 4 to 8 years.

Ohio—No manure: Sands, 500
pounds of 0-14-7; loams, 400 pounds
of 0-14-7; muck, 400 pounds of 0-12-
12. Manured: Sands, 400 pounds of
0-20-0; loams, 300 pounds of 0-20-10;
muck, 400 pounds of 0-14-7 every 4
years.

Wisconsin—Mucks and peats: 200
to 500 pounds of 0-20-20, 0-10-20, or 0-
9-27. Silt and clay loams: 200 to 500
pounds of 0-20-10, 0-20-20, or 0-10-20.
Sands and sandy loams: 200 to 500
pounds of 0-20-20, 0-10-20, or 0-9-27
every 3 or 4 years.

SOME DANGERS TO GUARD AGAINST

SOME DANGER of bloat exists in
grazing forage mixtures in which legumes predominate. When grasses comprise one-third to one-half or more of
the forage mixture, the danger is lessened. Cattle should not be turned into
pastures when they are overly hungry
or if the forage is wet with dew or rain,
especially if the stand is made up
largely of legumes. Much less risk of
bloat exists if livestock grazing succulent growth of forage in which legumes
predominate have ready access to dry
hay, straw, or other grassy pasture and
have plenty of salt and water.

Sudangrass can be pastured with
comparative safety, but there is some
chance of prussic acid poisoning. Cattle
and sheep may be poisoned by it, but
horses and hogs are not poisoned. Several investigators have reported that
danger of prussic acid poisoning can be
reduced or eliminated by delaying

grazing until the plants are 2 to 3 feet
tall or taller, at which stage they are
relatively free of poison; limiting planting to fertile soils with good water-holding capacities; and feeding cattle
so they are not too hungry when they
are turned into a field of Sudangrass.

Undoubtedly poisoning of livestock
by weeds is less extensive in the Corn
Belt and Lake States than in some other
sections, but there are indications from
studies conducted by R. B. Harvey,
A. H. Larson, R. H. Landon, W. L.
Boyd, and L. C. Erickson in Minnesota,
and R. Graham and J. J. Pieper in Illinois that losses are often sufficiently
great to be of considerable economic
importance.

Most poisonous plants are restricted
to rough, swampy, stony, or relatively
inaccessible places and woodlands.

Mowing, pulling, hoeing, burning,
plowing, and cultivating where pos-

sible, drainage and reseeding, and applications of salt, gasoline, or certain weed killers like 2,4–D have been suggested as ways to kill poisonous plants.

Danger of losses of livestock can be reduced considerably by avoiding overgrazing in areas where poisonous plants occur. Usually poisonous plants are less palatable than the commonly grazed forages, and cattle will not eat them unless they are hungry and forage is scarce. When livestock are given free choice they usually graze the desirable forages in preference to weeds. The stage of growth of the weeds and the variations between species of livestock and individuals within a species in their susceptibility to poisoning are important factors in determining the extent and nature of illness and loss.

It can be stated as a broad generalization that in many cases of poisoning by weeds treatment is unsatisfactory and ineffective. If animals show recognizable symptoms of poisoning, a veterinarian should be called immediately. Purgatives are usually administered in an effort to empty the digestive tract. The identity of the plant that caused the poisoning should be determined as soon as possible, because treatment usually varies with the type of poison present.

The toxic agents in poisonous plants vary considerably; in some instances they have not been identified. Toxicity may be due to the presence in plants of widely different compounds like alkaloids, glucosides, resinoids, oxalic acid, and tremetol.

Plants that have been found in pastured areas in various parts of the region and that might sometimes be poisonous include bracken fern, male shield fern, horsetail, horsenettle, common or black nightshade, common or black locust, bitter buttercup, tall crowfoot or buttercup, pasqueflower, dutchmans-breeches or staggerweed, common sneezeweed, corncockle, wild lupine, dwarf larkspur, common poke, scoke, garget or pigeonberry, swamp milkweed, whorled milkweed, butterfly milkweed, cocklebur, hemp, jack-in-the-pulpit or Indian-turnip, marsh arrowgrass, Kentucky coffeetree, jimsonweed or purple thorn apple, Johnsongrass, white snakeroot, water hemlock, wild or black cherry, white oak, porcupinegrass, Indian-tobacco, and fetid or Ohio buckeye.

The Hazard of Drought

The major introduced forages used in the region during its early agricultural development could not produce satisfactory yields in dry years or the dry midsummers. So, as farming blossomed and the livestock population grew, the need for forage that could beat drought became more and more urgent.

To that end, many new forages were introduced for observation and testing. Some were found to be high in feeding value, agronomically desirable, and considerably more drought-resistant than the forages then in common use. Early trials were followed by intensive research on the cultural requirements of the most promising newcomers. The success of the efforts is indicated by the extensive use now of forages like alfalfa, smooth bromegrass, sweetclover, Korean lespedeza, soybeans, reed canarygrass, and Sudangrass. Examples of the superior value of some of these forages, as indicated by greater productivity in dry years, are the mixtures of smooth bromegrass and alfalfa over timothy and alfalfa, mixtures of smooth bromegrass and alfalfa over alfalfa alone, mixtures of smooth bromegrass and alfalfa over timothy and medium red clover, and alfalfa over medium red clover.

Winter Losses

Plants that complete their life cycle within the span of a single growing period are subject to fewer hazards than winter annuals or biennials, which must survive unfavorable factors of the summer environment plus winter hardships. In like manner, perennials, which must endure two or more winters and summers, are generally subject to more of the major hazards of environment than winter annuals or biennials, and the problems of their management in relation to survival are harder.

Aside from the management required during their period of establishment or the care necessary for re-establishment by natural reseeding in permanent pastures, where such is desired, the treatment given annual and biennial forages is of practical importance only as it relates to yield and quality. Unless provision is made for natural reseeding, annual and biennial forages fail to survive beyond the fixed period of their normal life cycles regardless of management, but with perennial forages yield and quality may be affected and, besides, they may be destroyed entirely by heat, cold, or other unfavorable conditions.

The important perennial forage grasses of the region are generally sufficiently winter hardy to survive prevailing winter conditions even though they are subject to abuses as overgrazing, inadequate soil fertility, and poor soil drainage. But perennial legumes, such as alfalfa and Ladino clover (and to a lesser extent their biennial counterparts), are considerably more susceptible than the forage grasses to injury or even destruction as a result of unfavorable winter conditions. It is not surprising, therefore, to find that the major effort of studies involving winter survival has been directed toward developing safeguards and procedures for protecting perennial and—to a lesser extent—biennial legumes against winter woes.

Three Conditions

Winter injury or winterkilling may result under the following conditions:

First, temperatures low enough to freeze the plants to death. Widely adapted forages are seldom injured or destroyed by low winter temperatures such as prevail in the region, but this factor is of major importance in limit-

ing forages like orchardgrass, crimson clover, and winter barley to the southern part, where winters are less severe.

Second, smothering under ice sheets formed in direct contact with the surface layer of soil. Studies in Wisconsin in 1940 and 1943 by V. G. and M. A. Sprague and L. F. Graber have shown that alfalfa plants maintained in ice for 7 to 12 days were weakened considerably; after 20 days of such treatment a high rate of mortality prevailed. They ascribe the injury and subsequent death of the plants to internal accumulations of the toxic products of aerobic and anaerobic respiration. Occasionally ice sheets formed in direct contact with the surface layer of soil occur in various areas; if they continue 3 weeks or more, intensive injury resulting in almost complete destruction of the legumes is likely.

Third, upheaval of plants due to alternate freezing and thawing. Injury of this type is less intensive than that caused by ice sheets, but it occurs more frequently and more extensively. It is probably the most important factor in the winter survival of legumes in all parts of the region where a cover of snow does not persist throughout the winter.

To Check Losses

Fortunately, losses from winter injury or winterkilling of biennial and perennial legumes can be effectively reduced by applying certain cultural and managerial controls; these in turn can be fortified by the use of adapted, hardy varieties.

The following controls, suggested for reducing winter losses of biennial and perennial legumes, have been developed specifically to provide protection against winter losses of alfalfa, but certain of them can be applied with equal effectiveness to other legumes, too.

First, fields selected for growing alfalfa should be well drained. Alfalfa established on level fields with good underdrainage or on sloping areas where there is little opportunity for water to accumulate is less likely to be injured by heaving or ice sheets.

Second, losses as a result of winter injury are likely to be less when alfalfa is grown on fertile soils than when grown on soils of moderately low fertility.

Third, old established stands of alfalfa are more susceptible to winter injury than young seedings. Thus, if alfalfa is grown as a source of forage, a good practice is to plan crop rotations so that alfalfa of several ages is available in different fields every year. There may be heavy losses due to winterkilling in older fields, but younger seedings are likely to survive.

Fourth, alfalfa should be managed so that there is ample opportunity for replenishment of food reserves following each harvest. Food reserves maintained at high levels are necessary for sustained production and continued survival. In addition, winter survival is enhanced by a fall growth that is sufficiently tall effectively to catch and hold snow, and with the snow, provide insulation and protection against low temperatures, ice sheets, or rapid changes in temperature.

Fifth, forage grasses like timothy and smooth bromegrass grown with alfalfa may reduce winter injury by providing insulation against low temperatures or sudden changes in temperature. Furthermore, if timothy or smooth bromegrass is included with alfalfa or other legumes, fair to good hay or pasturage will be obtained even if the legumes are totally destroyed.

Sixth, extensive trials for determining the relative winter hardiness and productive capacity of many varieties and strains of alfalfa and medium red clover have been conducted by almost all the experiment stations in the region. The results illustrate the importance and need for using adapted seed of hardy varieties.

Seventh, the gradual emergence of bacterial wilt disease as a factor of major importance in the survival of alfalfa undoubtedly represents the outstanding recent development in the culture of this valuable legume in many districts. The causal organisms enter alfalfa plants only if they are injured. Infected plants may not die immediately but are gradually weakened as the season progresses. They fail to harden in the fall and are likely to winterkill. Varieties such as Ranger, Buffalo, and Ladak, or mixtures of Ladak and Cossack or Cossack and Ranger are suggested for infected soils.

Insect Enemies of Forages

Insects sometimes cause heavy damage. All commonly grown forages are susceptible. Insects may injure or kill forage grasses and legumes in several ways, the most important of which are a result of sucking the sap, chewing and boring into the vegetative and floral parts, attacking and destroying the underground roots and stems, laying eggs on various parts of the plant, and transporting disease organisms to plants and implanting them there.

Practical controls have not been developed for some of the insects, but there are practical controls for almost all of the most destructive species. Among them are the use of selective insecticides, crop rotations, escape crops, tillage, variation in time of planting or harvesting, clean culture, and destruction of residues and weeds.

White grubs, cutworms, army worms, and grasshoppers are probably the most important among those injuring the grasses. The sweetclover weevil, clover root curculio, potato leafhopper, and the grasshopper are among the insects that cause the most injury to legumes.

Diseases of Forages

Many diseases have been reported as occurring on the grasses and legumes commonly grown for hay and pasturage in the region, but unfortunately our information about them is incomplete. Our general conclusion is that diseases affect the productivity and survival of biennial and perennial forage legumes more than they do perennial forage grasses. Likewise (except during seedling stages of growth) diseases of small grains, corn, sorghum, and Sudangrass appear to be of considerably greater economic importance than those affecting most perennial forage grasses.

Practical controls of diseases that attack hay and pasture forages are largely a matter of good crop management and of developing disease-resistant varieties. Fortunately, because plants vary widely in such important characteristics as disease resistance, leafiness, vigor, seed production, and date of maturity, we have opportunity of selecting plants for disease resistance and other desirable characters.

Ranger and Buffalo alfalfas, Kenland and Cumberland medium red clovers, Tift and sweet Sudangrass, and certain strains or varieties of bentgrasses are examples of disease-resistant grasses and legumes that have been developed by breeding or natural selection for use here and elsewhere.

Of the diseases known to occur commonly on important forage legumes in the Lake States and Corn Belt, the most important are spring black stem and summer black stem of sweetclover; northern anthracnose, southern anthracnose, and powdery mildew of medium red clover; and bacterial wilt of alfalfa. Likewise, bacterial blight, powdery mildew, helminthosporium foot rots and leaf blights, streak or brown leaf blight, stem rust, and leaf rust are most important among the diseases that affect forage grasses, but the extent of the injury they cause is still largely unknown.

THE PROCESSING AND USE OF FORAGE

HAY IS THE MOST important single constituent of the winter feed supply for livestock in most parts of the Corn Belt and Lake States.

Because of the uncertainties of the weather and the dependence on favorable weather for good hay, that fed to livestock varies more in quality than any other harvested feed.

Bleaching by the sun, leaching and spoilage by rain, excessive shattering during processing, and additional spoilage and loss of improperly cured hay in storage often reduce the feeding value as much as 20 to 40 percent.

Loss in feeding value begins from the day the crop is left standing in the field longer than it should.

In a survey conducted by G. Bohstedt, of the Wisconsin Agricultural Experiment Station, to determine losses incurred in average hay in the north central area, it was found that hay usually is harvested 10 days after it reaches its highest feeding value.

He learned further that $2\frac{1}{3}$ days commonly elapse between the time of cutting and the time the hay is stored in barns or stacks and that during this period it is exposed to 17 hours of sunshine, one light dew, and one heavy dew. One-half of the hay, he learned, was made without rain, and one-sixth with a heavy rain. One-half of the hay was windrowed within 7 hours of mowing, the other half 7 hours after mowing.

Hay of poor quality may cause mineral and vitamin deficiencies that may lead to rickets, scours, stiffness of gait, pneumonia, and night blindness in calves, lambs, and colts, and poor breeding performance and unthriftiness in older animals. Good, green, leafy hay, on the other hand, helps maintain the health of poultry and swine during the winter feeding period.

The feeding value of hay is largely conserved when most of the leaves remain intact on the plant and drying is fast enough to slow down fermentation, respiration, and enzyme activity.

Dr. Bohstedt reports that the greatest single benefit to the livestock industry might well be the development of procedures that assure the production, processing, and storage of leafy green hay, high in minerals, carotene, the B vitamins, and protein.

Standard or approved methods of haymaking usually involve windrowing the forage after 2 to 4 hours in the swath to reduce excessive shattering and bleaching. In the northern part of the region, where conditions for drying are less favorable, E. Vandermeulen, of the Michigan Agricultural Experiment Station, has suggested the use of pole stacks and tripods for curing hay.

Haymaking procedures commonly used take a great deal of heavy labor, and generally they depend on prevailing weather conditions. Speed of processing and economy of labor therefore are considerations of major importance; the problem of reducing labor costs and shortening the period required in processing is far from a solution, but there are encouraging indications of progress in this direction. The buck rake, field baler, bale loader, and field chopper are effective labor savers, and principles embodied in the hay crusher and in barn-drying hay may prove highly important in the production of good quality hay by reducing the length of time necessary for drying in the field.

Grass and Legume Silage

Ensiling hay crops as green forage eliminates field curing and reduces losses in nutritive value caused by leaching, bleaching, and shattering of leaves. Good grass silage can be produced even though weather conditions are generally unfavorable for haymaking. Ensiling forages has the additional advantage over processing them into hay in that only a third as much storage space is required, fire hazards are negligible, and the feed is cleaner and less dusty.

Forage legumes and most forage grasses are lower in content of sugar and higher in protein than corn; when ensiled, they provide an environment that is less favorable for lactic acid organisms.

Partial wilting to reduce the moisture content of the forage to 60 to 70 percent before ensiling and additions of molasses, phosphoric acid, ground corn, corn-and-cob meal, barley, or whey at the time of ensiling have all proved to be effective in preserving the silage and in improving its palatability and feeding value.

J. W. Wilbur, R. K. Waugh, S. M. Hauge, and J. H. Hilton, of the Indiana Agricultural Experiment Station, reported that silage made from a mixture of alfalfa and smooth bromegrass was similar to corn in feeding value for milk production. Usually silage made from legumes or grass-legume mixtures is higher in protein and carotene than corn silage, but corn silage is somewhat higher in total digestible nutrients than grass silage.

A. E. Perkins, of the Ohio Agricultural Experiment Station, has concluded that the dry-matter content of the forage at the time of ensiling is probably the most important single factor in determining quality of grass silage. He found that a dry-matter content of 30 to 40 percent results in good silage with or without preservatives.

Another aspect: Good soil-conserving practices often require less plowing and cultivation and greater acreages of grasses and legumes. With increased acreages of grasses and legumes, effective and economical procedures for utilizing and preserving the full nutritive value of the forage becomes increasingly important. Sufficient flexibility in use must prevail so that surplus forages not required for pasturage can be harvested economically at the proper stage of growth for high feeding value. Unless these objectives can be achieved, it is doubtful that practices involving more extensive use of grasses and legumes will find widespread acceptance in the region.

Despite its advantages, grass silage has not been widely accepted by the farmers here—maybe because of the greater labor and power requirements for handling the green forage; the general lack of suitable, low-priced equipment for harvesting and processing; the single or combined effects of the need for additional cash outlays for preservatives; the frequent necessity for reinforcing existing silos against additional pressures; the difficulty in controlling the moisture content of the material being ensiled; and the somewhat lower palatability, particularly for cattle accustomed to corn silage. The extent with which Midwest farmers accept grass silage appears to depend largely on the development of low-priced harvesters and other necessary equipment.

Pastures

Forages utilized for pasturage differ from all other commonly grown feed crops in that the period during which they are harvested is largely indeterminate. Unfortunately, however, many of the forages available for pasturage in the region deteriorate rapidly in palatability and feeding value as they approach maturity. Frequently in early spring the luxuriant growth of nutritious forage is in excess of that required by the livestock. The ungrazed forage continues to grow and at later stages it is utilized by livestock only because other more succulent and nutritious forage is not available. In areas where permanent pastures predominate, the generally low yields and poor quality of the more mature forages provide little incentive for harvesting them as hay or grass silage even where this is possible, and there is no ready solution to the problem of preserving the quality of the forage.

With rotation pastures, however, surplus growth of such forages as alfalfa, medium red, alsike and Ladino clovers, smooth bromegrass, and timothy can be harvested and preserved for later use as hay or silage. It is recognized that good pasturage is a more economical source of feed than hay or grass silage, but good-quality pasturage is not always available during all parts of the growing period. Good pasture management therefore involves plans that are sufficiently flexible so that surplus growth can be readily harvested and effectively preserved as hay or silage for later use or to supplement pastures during midsummer.

GRASS AND LEGUME SEED PRODUCTION

THE PRODUCTION of seed of forage grasses and legumes—a point of great importance to farmers—can be increased greatly by several cultural and management practices.

Incomplete data suggest that climate, variety of seed sown, soil type, moisture content of the soil, soil fertility, insects, diseases, density of stand, and method and time of harvesting may all affect seed yields of forage grasses and legumes.

J. F. Cox, C. R. Megee, M. G. Frakes, and I. T. Larson, of the Michigan Agricultural Experiment Station, found that the best yields of seed of red clover are obtained from the second crop rather than the first and that early cutting of the first crop for hay is almost invariably followed by an increased yield of seed.

C. J. Willard has shown that variegated alfalfas produce better yields of seed in Ohio than the common alfalfas and that the second crop is usually the more reliable for seed production. In the most northern part of the region seed is harvested from the first crop. If the first crop is harvested for hay under these conditions the second growth may not mature seed before frost and cold weather.

Most of the important forage legumes are cross-fertilized, and some (including medium red, alsike, and white clovers) are practically self-sterile. Wind-pollination is of little importance among the legumes. The flowers are usually pollinated by insects; unless enough insects are present, poor yields of seed are likely.

C. M. Harrison, R. H. Kelty, and C. Blumer concluded from a series of studies that honeybees, although essential for good seed setting of alsike and white clover in Michigan, had little effect on the setting of alfalfa seed. Their observations also show that alsike and white clover fields within a mile of an apiary produced two to three times more seed to the acre than fields located more than 2 miles away. E. E. Down reported that lack of tripping was a major factor in limiting production of alfalfa seed in Michigan in 1928 and 1929.

Proper crop management is a matter of considerable importance in seed production. For example, Megee, Frakes, and Larson found that early clipping of mammoth red clover reduced growth but did not affect seed production appreciably. Late clipping, however, was found to be hazardous. With alsike clover, seed yields were lowered decidedly by earlier clipping, regardless of seasonal conditions.

It may be that yields of seed of certain forages may be improved as a result of applications of commercial fertilizer.

Harrison, W. N. Crawford, and B. R. Churchill learned that yields of seed of smooth bromegrass were increased significantly in Michigan by annual applications of commercial nitrogen fertilizer. A 2-year-old stand yielded 356 pounds of seed to the acre without ammonium sulfate and 789 pounds of seed when 500 pounds of the fertilizer were applied. Their tests showed also that applications of commercial nitrogen fertilizer in September or in early spring were more effective in increasing yields of seed of smooth bromegrass than late-spring applications, and that better yields of seed are obtained from row plantings than from broadcast seedings.

Timothy seedings are usually made with medium red clover and growth during the first two crop-years is harvested as hay. The growth of timothy during the third crop-year is usually best for seed production.

Approximately 85 percent of the world production of redtop seed and 95 percent of the total redtop seed in the United States is produced in southern Illinois. Considerable quantities of seed of Kentucky bluegrass, reed canarygrass, white clover, and lespedeza are also produced in the Corn Belt and Lake States, but very few studies relating to seed production have been conducted with those species.

Much seed is lost in harvesting and threshing. Best yields of seed of medium red, mammoth red, alsike, white, and Ladino clovers are usually obtained by harvesting with a mower when most of the heads are plump and dry and before shattering occurs. Losses due to shattering can be reduced if the crops are cut and windrowed when the plants are somewhat tough. Clover hullers, grain separators, and combines are used effectively to thresh the seed.

Alfalfa is cut and windrowed with a mower or harvested with a grain binder and shocked when about two-thirds of the seed pods are brown or black. The straw should be handled no more than necessary because of the danger of shattering of the seed. Threshing is accomplished by means of a clover huller, grain separator, or directly from windrows in the field with a combine and pick-up attachment.

The seeds of sweetclover do not mature uniformly. They shatter very readily as they mature. Fields of sweetclover should be cut soon after the earliest maturing seeds have matured and when the plants are somewhat tough. They may be cut with a mower, windrowed, and threshed with a combine; or they may be harvested with a grain binder, shocked, and threshed with a grain separator.

Timothy is harvested when most of the seed is ripe but before much shattering has occurred. Timothy may be harvested with a grain binder, shocked and threshed with a grain separator, or combined directly from the field. The seed should be somewhat riper when it is combined than when a binder is used.

Farmers producing Kentucky bluegrass for seed usually sell their crop on a contract basis to a commercial concern. Rotary strippers are used to harvest the seed when the heads turn yellow and the stripped material is placed in long piles 1½ to 2 feet high. These piles or ricks are turned frequently to prevent heating. When dry, the rough, stripped material is sacked and shipped to commercial concerns having the necessary equipment for threshing and cleaning.

Seed of smooth bromegrass is ready to be combined when the lower branches of the head have become dry and have lost their green color. The crop should be combined as high as possible to minimize the effect of green leaves and stems. The harvested seed is spread out in a dry place and turned daily until it is thoroughly dry. Smooth bromegrass is also often harvested satisfactorily for seed with a grain binder, shocked, and threshed with a grain separator.

Fields of redtop are often harvested for 5 or 6 years before they are reestablished. Meadows to be harvested for seed are pastured for about 10 weeks the preceding fall and for 15 days in early spring. To reduce losses from shattering, redtop is usually harvested for seed about a week after blooming is completed. Redtop is cut with a mower, and dried in the swath, or harvested with a binder, shocked, and threshed with a grain separator.

Seed of reed canarygrass shatters soon after it matures. A header made by removing all unnecessary parts of an old grain binder with a large hopper constructed on the platform has been used successfully to harvest seed of reed canarygrass. The sickle is raised high so as to cut only the heads. The harvested heads are dried and threshed by hand flailing. Large acreages are harvested by combining.

It is clear from a review of the literature that critical and comprehensive studies are needed on the relation of factors of environment to seed production. The growing emphasis on the use of forage grasses and legumes in livestock production, their value and importance in soil improvement and conservation, the increased production of feed and cash crops which usually follow them in the rotation, and their potential value as a cash crop when grown for seed all serve to emphasize the need for additional research designed to assure and safeguard the production of ample seed of desirable forage species.

THE AUTHOR《《 *Henry L. Ahlgren, a native of Minnesota and a graduate of the College of Agriculture, University of Wisconsin, has been engaged in the cultural and managerial aspects of pasture research since 1935. Dr. Ahlgren is professor of agronomy in the University of Wisconsin; he devotes about half his time to teaching courses in agronomy and the remainder to research in pasture problems.*

For source material and suggestions in the preparation of this article, he thanks professors R. F. Fuelleman, Illinois Agricultural Experiment Station at Urbana; G. O. Mott, Indiana Agricultural Experiment Station, La Fayette; H. D. Hughes, Iowa Agricultural Experiment Station, Ames; C. M. Harrison, Michigan Agricultural Experiment Station, East Lansing; A. R. Schmid, Minnesota Agricultural Experiment Station, St. Paul; E. M. Brown, Missouri Agricultural Experiment Station, Columbia; C. J. Willard, Ohio Agricultural Experiment Station, Columbus; and H. Ream, Soil Conservation Service, Milwaukee.

Grasslands in the South

A WIDE AND VERSATILE EMPIRE

ROY L. LOVVORN

GREAT CHANGES are occurring in southern agriculture. To understand them and assess their chance of becoming permanent, one has to understand the finite facts of climate, soil, topography, and productivity of this wide and versatile empire.

First, the area. It extends from the Atlantic Ocean to approximately 96° west longitude, and from the Gulf of Mexico to approximately 37° north.

Mean January temperatures range from 32° F. in the coldest parts of Virginia and Kentucky to 70° in southern Florida. (Illinois, by way of comparison, has a mean January temperature range from 18° to 36°.) Summer temperatures are high, but the extremes are not so high as those often recorded in the Midwest. Mean July temperatures range from 68° in western North Carolina to 84° in southern Florida. Most of the area has a growing season of more than 200 days. The actual range is from 160 to 220 days in Virginia, 180 to 210 days in Kentucky, 180 to 240 days in Arkansas, and 240 to 365 days in Florida. The mild winters and long growing seasons are ideal for year-round grazing.

The relatively high rainfall, which averages more than 50 inches, is fairly evenly distributed throughout the year. Total rainfall ranges from approximately 40 inches in the northern and western parts to as high as 80 inches along the southern Appalachian ridge. Approximately one-half of the annual rainfall comes between April 1 and October 1, the period when most forage crops are making their maximum growth. Rainfall, although inadequate during certain short periods, is quite evenly distributed.

Most of the soils are in the Red and Yellow Podzolic groups. Other extensive soil groups are the Gray-Brown Podzolic soils, the Ground Water Podzols, the Lithosols, and the Bog soils. The relatively high rainfall and warm temperatures have induced strongly leached soils that are acid in reaction and low in organic matter and mineral plant nutrients.

The six physiographic regions are the Coastal Plain, the Piedmont Plateau, the Appalachian Province, the Limestone Valley and Uplands, the Mississippi Bluffs and Loam Uplands, and the Stream Bottom and Second Bottoms.

The low country bordering the Atlantic Ocean and extending from the vicinity of New York City south and along the Gulf of Mexico to the mouth of the Rio Grande is known as the Coastal Plain. Within the southern region the Coastal Plain consists of the eastern third of Virginia and North

Carolina, the eastern half of South Carolina, the southern three-fifths of Georgia, all of Florida, the southern and western two-thirds of Alabama, nearly all of the eastern half of Mississippi, a narrow strip in western Tennessee, the southern third of Arkansas, a fringe of southeastern Oklahoma, the western two-thirds of Louisiana, and the southeastern quarter of Texas. This area contains a plain-like country of sandy soils with an elevation beginning at sea level and rising to 600 feet.

The tidewater or flatwoods country is almost level; the Upper Coastal Plain is rolling and, in some instances, even hilly. The soils were formed from water-laid material that was brought down the rivers from higher and older land areas. Much of this material was carried to the ocean; the finer sediments were carried farther out to sea and the coarser material was laid down near the shore. The calcareous soils of the Black Belts of Alabama, Mississippi, and Texas were formed under water particularly favorable to marine life. The better drained soils have been largely in row crops; pastures and forage crops have never been important. Much of the tidewater country is poorly drained and vast acreages are still in woods. Considerable woods grazing is now done in the cut-over sections. Many of the soils that are inadequately drained for row crops are adapted to forage crops.

The area between the Appalachian Mountains and the Atlantic Coastal Plain is called the Piedmont Plateau. Within the Southern States, the Piedmont Plateau consists of a strip through middle Virginia and North Carolina,

western South Carolina, and northern Georgia to central Alabama. It is a rolling to hilly region, the elevation being from 100 to 500 feet along the Coastal Plain border to 700 to 1,500 feet at the foothills. Geologically, the Piedmont is very old. It was a land area when the present region to the east and west, except the Blue Ridge Mountains, was still covered by the ocean. The soils have been formed from complex rocks, including crystalline igneous rocks, highly metamorphosed sandstone and shale, and unmetamorphosed sandstone and shale. The soils were mostly clays and clay loams, although the surface of some is sandy. Erosion has been severe, but the soils can grow forage crops if adequately fertilized.

Like several other major soil provinces, the Appalachian Mountains extend beyond the South. Within the southern area, however, the western parts of Virginia, North and South Carolina, eastern Kentucky and Tennessee, northwestern Georgia, and northern Alabama comprise the Appalachian and Cumberland-Allegheny Plateau. The highest altitudes in the eastern United States are within this mountainous area. Most of the soils are loams, stony loams, sandy loams, silt loams, and clay loams that have developed mainly from granite, gneiss, schist, and quartzite. This is the area within the South where grassland farming has been practiced for many years. The soils, though steep, are well adapted to legumes like alfalfa and Ladino clover.

The Limestone Valley and Uplands Soil Province embraces the residual limestone soils lying north of the Atlantic and Gulf Coastal Plains and represents the limestone lands of the Appalachian region. The main valley is narrow and is known locally as the Cumberland Valley in Maryland, the Shenandoah Valley in Virginia, farther south as the Valley of East Tennessee, and as the Coosa Valley in Alabama. Two other areas, related in that they occupy rather low or basin country, are the Central Basin of Tennessee and the Kentucky Bluegrass region of north-central Kentucky.

These valleys are not lower than the surrounding country because of stream flow, but have resulted from the more rapid decay and removal of the original rocks by erosion and underground waters than has taken place in the rocks on each side of the valleys. The surface is undulating to gently rolling; the elevation is approximately 500 feet in northern Alabama to 2,700 feet in Virginia. Since the soils have been largely developed from limestone and from sandstone and shale associated with limestone, they are generally productive, especially the limestone soils; the famous grasslands of the region are located in these areas.

The Mississippi Bluffs and the Silt Loam Uplands are a long silty belt along the east side of the Mississippi River bottoms from western Kentucky to Louisiana. The topography varies from gently rolling and undulating to rough and hilly; erosion is serious in most of the area. The soils are underlain by yellowish-brown silty material that is believed to be wind-blown particles. The soils themselves have a brown silt loam surface layer that grades into a yellowish-brown silt loam subsoil. Farmers here have been shifting from cotton to a more diversified system and dairy farming now is important.

Bottom-land soils occur throughout the South along the intricate network of the streams. The width of the bottom lands varies generally with the size of the stream and the hardness of the rocks or deposits through which it flows. Many small runs have flood plains only a few yards across; the Mississippi River bottom is sometimes 75 miles wide. The soils, formed from material that has worked downward from the uplands, vary from fine clays to sands in texture, depending upon the distance from the banks. Many of the poorly drained bottoms of the Piedmont can be used for shallow-rooted forage crops; the better drained soils lend themselves to sod or row crops.

Although eastern Texas, eastern Oklahoma, and eastern Kansas are included in the South, as outlined on the map, they are not included in the statistical survey because we have no way to calculate data for part of a State.

The Farms

In 1945 there were 2,183,157 farms within the 11 Southern States, which had 186,450,505 acres in farm lands. One of the difficulties in developing a grassland agriculture has been the great population density on the small farms. The average North Carolina farm contains 65 acres. Elsewhere the average is a little higher, but as a rule the farms are too small for ideal livestock agriculture. (In Wisconsin, for comparison, the average-size farm is 133 acres.)

Historically, the South has been a row-crop region: Cotton and tobacco, peanuts, and sugarcane have been the cash crops, and great acreages have been in corn. Such a system demanded much hand labor, and small size was no great handicap.

A more efficient use of the present cropland plus some reduction in the amount of land now idle would aid in developing a livestock industry in the region. Larger corn yields through adapted hybrids, heavier fertilization, and better cultural practices will mean more grain from fewer acres, the direct production of more concentrates, and the indirect production of more forage through a shifting of tilled acres from corn to forage crops.

Against 57 million acres of cropland in 1945, more than 10 million were idle. Some of the unused land is submarginal and cannot be tilled economically, but some of it can be used for pasture and hay.

On these idle acres much of the expansion in grassland farming will come.

There were about 13 million cows and calves in the South in 1947; more than 1,700 million gallons of milk were produced; approximately 93 million chickens laid nearly 641 million dozen eggs. Other livestock included 1,172,-000 horses and colts, 2,133,000 mules, 11,514,000 hogs, and 1,868,000 sheep.

To provide grazing and hay for this livestock, the 11 Southern States had 13,962,663 acres of permanent pasture, 26,288,311 acres of other land used for pasture, and 9,037,944 acres in hay crops. That was not enough: The southern livestock farmer had to import hay.

The problem of creating larger farms involves complex adjustments that are closely tied to industrial developments within the South. More jobs in cities mean fewer laborers on the farm and eventually larger farms. During the war and immediately afterward, the tremendous demand for livestock products swelled livestock farming in the South, notably dairying.

Is this a permanent change? Time will tell, but right now we have enough information in our notebooks and heads and fields to develop a permanent grassland agriculture in the region. The key words are "permanent" and "grassland." The transition can be made without reducing the cash crops now grown. It will mean a healthier and more prosperous people. The key words there are "healthier" and "more prosperous."

STARTING AND MAINTAINING GOOD PASTURES

HUGH W. BENNETT, ROY L. LOVVORN

GOOD PASTURES can do great good in the South. Every farmer knows why. His aim is to provide a large yield of nutritious forage over a long grazing season. If he does so he has a cheaper source of minerals and vitamins and other nutrients for his stock, a tool against erosion, a way to revive abandoned land, a chance to raise more cows and pigs, an opportunity to stabilize his income by getting away from too much row-crop agriculture. He needs them all.

But to get a good pasture started he must remember two points: His pastures must include both grasses and legumes; he must fertilize his fields.

Evidence we have from all parts of the South indicates that, regardless of the starting point for establishing and improving a pasture, a legume must be maintained in the sod. Grasses need nitrogen more than any other item of fertilizer. Legumes add nitrogen to the soil, and any treatment that increases the growth of legumes will indirectly increase the growth of the grasses. The increased forage that results also has a higher nutritional value because of the addition of the legume.

In the South, soil fertility is by far the most important factor and major problem in the establishment and production of pastures; almost without exception, the fertility of land available for pastures is low. The best way, and almost the only way, to start a good pasture is to use appropriate amounts of lime and fertilizers and thereby provide soil conditions that favor the growth of desirable plants.

The response of pastures to any fertilizer element depends upon the degree to which the element limits growth, the level of fertility, and the type of plants that are present in the sod.

Many levels of fertility are so low that adding one element alone will produce no effect; in some places two elements or more are necessary for substantial increases in yield. Nearly every agricultural experiment station in the South has found by test that this is true, and farmers who need information for their own land should not hesitate to ask their State experiment stations or agricultural colleges for it.

Many people think that seeding and

cultural practices come first. Actually, however, experimental data from all parts of the region demonstrate that if the soil is not fertile enough no amount of seed will produce a satisfactory sod, and nothing is gained by reseeding poor pastures that have not been fertilized and limed.

Seedings made on soils that have been treated with lime and mineral fertilizer will contain relatively small amounts of grasses and clovers the first year. But weeds and bare ground are markedly reduced, and yields of herbage are increased 30 to 50 percent. Desirable plants are increased 20 to 150 percent, lespedeza and low hop clover are usually doubled, and the seeded grasses and clovers show some increase.

The addition of nitrogen to the lime-mineral fertilizer benefits the young grass but is often detrimental to the establishment of the legume, and does not appreciably increase the total yield if the legume stand is adequate.

Idle land can be greatly improved for grazing with a minimum of expense by seeding low hop clover and lespedeza and establishing adapted grasses as time and facilities allow. Summer legumes, such as soybeans or cowpeas, have been grown for turning under as a preliminary step in soil improvement before seeding a legume and grass mixture, but this is not necessary because the growth of the tolerant legumes furnishes enough nitrogen for the growth of adapted grasses.

Adequate fertilization is therefore the first step. As the phosphate level of the soil is increased, it is possible to seed clovers which are more productive and provide a longer growing season. The stimulation of clover with applications of phosphoric acid—phosphates—will tend to crowd out the lespedeza. Better seasonal distribution will be had by seeding only a part of the lespedeza-low hop clover pasture to clover under conditions of high fertility. On some alluvial soils it is better to use spring clover as a supplemental crop rather than include it in the pasture mixture.

Besides increasing yields, fertilization increases the proportion of desirable plants. The effects of continued fertilization become more noticeable as time goes on. Adapted grasses and legumes replace weeds, bare ground, and less desirable plants. So pronounced is the effect upon botanical composition that, unless seed is available at a relatively low price, we question whether seeding always justifies the cost in many areas.

The increase in the percentage of desirable plants, mainly legumes, is reflected in the higher feeding value of the herbage produced. Legumes usually surpass grasses in calcium, phosphorus, and crude protein. Fertilization expands the feeding value of total herbage produced by increasing the percentage of legumes present and also the nutritive content of the plants grown. Increases in the composition of the adapted plants range from 30 to 100 percent for phosphorus, 10 to 50 percent for calcium, and 5 to 40 percent for crude protein, as compared to no fertilization. Thus, almost twice as much herbage is required per pound of gain for an unfertilized as against a fertilized pasture.

The Need for Lime

Pasture soils vary considerably in their need for lime, depending upon their texture and acidity, the type of plants to be grown, and whether the lime is used for top dressing or for establishment. In general ½ to 1 ton is the proper amount to apply to light soils and 1 to 2 tons on the heavy soils.

Data from several Southern States show that the maximum response is obtained with the first 2,000 pounds applied. Other tests indicate that applications of not more than 1,000 pounds should be applied as a top dressing. Experiments indicate that lime should be applied every 8 to 10 years. Light rates should be applied oftener than heavy rates. Surface-applied applications may be repeated every 5 years. The clovers need more lime than lespedeza. Liming gives two benefits: It increases the yields of herbage and it helps fertilizers do their most good.

Phosphates are needed on pastures throughout the South. Pasture legumes vary considerably as to their response to phosphorus. The white clovers require more, and low hop clover less than any of the commonly used pasture legumes. Heavy initial applications are necessary for the establishment of clovers; smaller amounts are sufficient later to maintain the proper level of phosphorus. Heavy soils respond more readily but may require more phosphate than light soils. An application of 600 pounds of 20 percent material applied every 3 years, or 200 pounds applied annually, seems to be adequate for most sods. Ladino clover and other legumes may require more.

The response to potash is less general. Legumes—especially alfalfa and Ladino clover—are heavy feeders of potash, however, and, if productive stands are to be maintained, adequate quantities must be applied. The rate depends on the amount in the soil, as determined by a soil test and the particular legume. It is not advisable to delay applications of potash until deficiency symptoms occur.

Southern agronomists are not in agreement as to the use of commercial nitrogen on permanent pastures. Their different viewpoints come from an interpretation of the data, however, rather than from experimental results. The response that will be obtained is closely associated with the botanical composition. Sods in which grasses predominate respond to nitrogen. The yields from such sods are usually lower than from sods containing both legumes and grasses even when nitrogen is applied. Most of the response of a grass-legume sod to nitrogen fertilization is in the early spring, and whether such a practice would be profitable depends on the value of the early-spring grazing. For much of the region it is not a sound practice, but special cases,

notably on dairy farms, undoubtedly exist where it would be profitable.

We do not have all the facts we need on the response of legumes to minor elements, except boron. Light applications of boron, 5 to 10 pounds to the acre, appear desirable for legumes on some soils. In any case, adequate amounts of lime, phosphate, and potash should be supplied before treating with minor elements; a farmer will do well to consult his State experiment stations, agricultural college, or county agent before he uses any of the minor (or trace) elements.

Recommendations for Planting

Climate and elevation divide the South into three rather distinct regions: The sections of "cool" climate, or high elevation; "warm" climate, or upper Coastal Plains; and the extreme southern Coastal Plains and the Florida peninsula. Pasture plant mixtures will vary within and between sections so that no certain rule can be offered for a seeding mixture for a specific location. The mixture and rate of seeding will depend on climate, fertility, the cost of seed, the rate at which establishment is desired, and management.

Recommended mixtures for cool sections will contain orchardgrass, redtop, Kentucky bluegrass, Ladino and white clovers, and lespedeza or a mixture of the lespedezas. Kentucky bluegrass is eliminated and the orchard and redtop grasses are increased on the less fertile soils. More recently the tall fescues, Ky. 31 and Alta, have shown promise. Dallisgrass may be added when used in the Piedmont from Virginia southward.

Ladino clover has become an outstanding legume in the upper South. Thousands of acres have been seeded to it in Virginia, North Carolina, Tennessee, and Kentucky, and farmers have been pleased with its performance. It is being seeded at the rate of 2 to 3 pounds an acre with 10 to 12 pounds of orchardgrass. This legume is more productive than white clover in the upper South, and recovers more quickly after a dry spell.

Mixtures for the warm or upper Coastal Plain section will contain Dallisgrass and Bermuda-grass, Kobe or common lespedeza, and some spring clover. Additions of orchardgrass in the northern one-third of Alabama, Mississippi, and Arkansas will furnish grazing while the other grasses are becoming established. The spring clover will furnish more and longer grazing, but low hop clover will grow on a much lower level of fertility. As fertilization is increased or continued, the clovers will change from low hop to Persian to white. For high-phosphate soils, there should be grass-clover and grass-lespedeza combinations in separate pastures. Korean lespedeza, lappa clover, sweetclover, and black medic are adapted to the calcareous soils.

Mixtures for the lower Coastal Plain and for the Florida peninsula consist of Bahiagrass, Bermuda-grass, carpetgrass, Dallisgrass, Napiergrass, the clovers, and annual lespedezas. Paragrass, Bermuda-grass, Napiergrass, and St. Augustinegrass are suited to the muck soils of south Florida.

The exact seeding date for lespedeza will depend upon elevation and latitude, but is usually begun about February 1 in the southern part of the region. Korean lespedeza is better suited to the upper half of the region than to the southern portions.

Kentucky bluegrass, orchardgrass, redtop, and the white clovers are commonly seeded in the fall, although they may be seeded in the spring. White clover in the lower South should be seeded from August to October.

Dallisgrass, Bermuda-grass, Bahiagrass, and carpetgrass should be seeded in the early spring. Dallisgrass may be seeded in early fall in the lower South. Bermuda-grass and other grasses usually propagated by vegetative means should be sprigged or sodded in the spring because of more favorable moisture conditions.

For new seedings the seedbed should be well prepared but firm. This usually means that a thorough job of disking is enough. A rain between the time of disking and seeding should firm the seedbed satisfactorily. The seed should be covered to a depth of one-fourth to one-half inch.

There are several ways of reseeding an old sod. The extent to which the sod should be broken up depends upon the species that is to be used. Lespedeza may be added to an established grass sod with little preparation. Renovation of an established carpetgrass or Kentucky bluegrass sod should be accompanied by a thorough disking. Legumes may also be successfully added to established grasses following a slicing of the old sod with a weighted disk set at a slight angle.

The Management of Pastures

Pasture management throughout the South fits into the same procedure pattern as for establishment. Fertilization to maintain legumes is the cardinal principle of maintenance in all sections. Maintenance fertilization can best be accomplished by replacing the minerals that have been removed by plant growth. Proper management is essential to good pasture establishment, maintenance, and utilization. When the items of fertility and establishment have been attended to, maximum production of pastures depends on proper management.

A pasture that has been properly prepared, fertilized, and seeded at a rate sufficient to give a satisfactory stand of desirable plants usually has fewer weeds than a poor pasture. The desirable plants compete with the weeds for soil moisture and plant food. Grazing animals find the weeds unpalatable and allow them to grow and produce seed; the desirable plants are grazed in preference and their seed production is greatly reduced. Mowing, usually twice a season, is therefore necessary to prevent the production of weed seeds.

The rate or intensity of grazing is probably the most important management practice for pastures in the South. The principal factor in grazing management is the prevention of overgrazing, which reduces ground cover and permits erosion. Overgrazing also results in severe selective grazing with weeds replacing the desirable plants.

Erect or semi-erect plants are readily exterminated by continuous heavy grazing because all or most of the leaves are removed. When most of the leaves are continuously removed the food reserves in the plants are removed faster than they are replaced. A good practice is to manage grazing so the pasture is never grazed closer than 2 or 3 inches. Some foliage must be left on the plants at all times. Overgrazing favors one plant over another in the pasture combination, and the proper balance for maximum yields is disturbed. Summer grasses tend to be reduced, and the sod contains a greater percentage of spring clovers. The excessive growth of spring clovers further reduces the population of grass and lespedeza.

Undergrazing is perhaps just as undesirable because of the loss in quality of pasturage. New seedings may be exterminated by rapidly growing native vegetation if undergrazed. The calcium, phosphorus, and crude protein content of pasture grasses drops rapidly as the plants approach maturity, and the herbage is not readily eaten because of low quality. A grain ration of higher protein content is required by cattle for meat or milk production on undergrazed pastures.

Undergrazing also favors some plants over others in the mixture and the proper balance for a good pasture is not maintained. If spring grasses, like Kentucky bluegrass and orchardgrass, are allowed to make excessive growth in the spring they will crowd out lespedeza.

With the uneven distribution of rainfall, it is almost impossible for permanent pastures, no matter how fertile or well managed, to provide uninterrupted and sufficient nutritious forage for efficient livestock production throughout the season. Peaks of production furnish more feed than animals can consume, and periods of lessened production will result in overgrazing. It is not practical to remove animals from permanent pastures during periods of low production unless other provisions for their maintenance can be made. This means that supplementary pastures are necessary to a good farm program.

Every section of the South can make use of supplementary pastures. Many such pastures can be used for hay, seed, silage, or soil improvement when not needed for emergency grazing crops. Kudzu, soybeans, lespedeza, Sudan-grasses, millet, small grains, Italian ryegrass, and annual clovers are well adapted for the purpose. Relieving permanent pastures during periods of drought will enable them to produce efficiently later into the fall, as compared to pastures that have been either under- or over-grazed. The use of supplemental crops is often the key to good pasture management and economical livestock production.

Legumes are necessary to increase the yield, extend the grazing period, and improve the quality of permanent pastures in the South. Applications of lime, phosphate, and potash must be made if the legumes are to be maintained in the sod. Supplementary leguminous crops like kudzu, lespedeza, soybeans, and annual clovers should be fertilized in the same way. Sudangrass, millet, small grain, and Italian ryegrass are excellent supplementary grazing crops that require liberal applications of commercial nitrogen. Grazing can be had every month of the year through a combination of these crops.

[*Recommendations regarding initial and maintenance fertilization required for pasture and forage crops in each of the Southern States are given in tables found in the section, "Grass in Charts and Tables."*]

HAY AND SUPPLEMENTAL GRAZING

T. H. ROGERS, GEORGE E. RITCHEY

WE LIST HERE the more important crops used in the South for supplemental grazing and harvested forage.

Johnsongrass can be considered a pest or a desirable forage crop. It is used primarily for forage on the Black Belt soils of Alabama and Mississippi. It can be used for hay silage or temporary grazing. Frequently the first growth is cut for hay and the new growth is grazed either just before or just after the first frost in the fall. If a good stand of the grass is to be maintained, it must be permitted to approach maturity at least once during the growing season. This late growth is necessary to allow root stocks to form so they can make new plants the following season. Winter oats, or one of the winter legumes, may be seeded in Johnsongrass stubble during the fall. The oats can be cut for hay or grain in the spring; the Johnsongrass grows the rest of the season. The winter legume provides winter grazing or hay and also stimulates the growth of Johnsongrass.

Sudangrass is well suited to southern conditions. Its susceptibility to a leaf disease has limited its use, but plant breeders have succeeded in producing high-yielding, disease-resistant strains that should be popular for grazing and hay. It is an annual and can be used to supplement the permanent pasture in periods of low grazing, or as a hay for use in winter. A rotational plan of grazing will give a large tonnage of succulent green feed for a long season.

The saccharine, or sweet, sorghums (sorgo) are grown mostly for silage through the South. Sorghum silage is slightly lower in nutritive value than corn silage, but the greater yield of sorghum more than offsets the difference. The use of silage in the lower South has declined since the introduction of clovers and disease-resistant oats which may be used for winter grazing.

Grain sorghum is becoming quite important in certain sections of the South. Some of the combine varieties commonly grown in the West have been found to be well adapted to the more humid conditions of the South. In the lower South, grain sorghum can be planted after a winter crop, such as oats, has been harvested. This crop is grown for grain, fodder, and for harvesting with cattle and hogs. The entire plant is cut just before the seed is mature and shocked until cured. It may be fed either whole or chopped. It is as well adapted for silage as the sweet sorghums.

Sugarcane is grown mainly for sugar and sirup, but several hundred acres of cane in the southernmost South are harvested each year for forage. Two methods of preservation are used. The crop is cut and hauled to the silo and ensiled in the ordinary manner, or it is often cut and shocked with the butts in close contact with the ground, thus reestablishing the flow of moisture into the stem. The crop is left standing in the shock until needed and is then run through a feed cutter and fed.

Corn is often grown in combination with velvetbeans, cowpeas, soybeans, peanuts, or some other summer legume and grazed by hogs and cattle during late summer and autumn.

Pearlmillet, or cattail millet, is grown in the extreme South as a grazing crop—occasionally as a silage or soiling crop. It is particularly adapted to a warm humid climate; it makes its best growth when planted on a rich loam soil although it does well on medium sandy loams. With enough plant food and moisture, the crop makes a rapid, succulent growth.

Napiergrass is grown principally in Florida and the Gulf Coast districts. It is used mostly for grazing, but it can be used for silage and as a soiling crop. Napiergrass can be cut for silage when the stems are mature, in July and again in autumn. The plant is cut and hauled to the silo where it is cut with the silage cutter and ensiled. Often water must be added to offset the dryness of the stems and leaves. The plant is propagated vegetatively.

Orchardgrass, a short-lived perennial, is well adapted to permanent pastures, particularly in the upper South. It is primarily a pasture plant, but it can be used for hay.

Tall fescue survives longer than orchardgrass either in meadows or pastures. It is used in the same way as orchardgrass.

The small grains, when planted early in the fall and fertilized with a complete fertilizer high in nitrogen, will furnish abundant fall and winter grazing. They may also be grown in combination with winter legumes and harvested for hay. When grain or hay is desired, grazing is stopped in February. Relatively light grazing reduces the yield of grain or hay little or not at all; heavy grazing may reduce the yield considerably.

Alfalfa is not yet an important crop in the South, but its use is increasing. Recent research at several Southern experiment stations has shown that with liberal applications of lime, phosphate, potash, and boron, alfalfa may be grown successfully on most of the fertile, well-drained soils of the South. When it is well fertilized and managed, a good stand of alfalfa can be maintained for 5 years or longer. Alfalfa is used primarily for hay, but it is also an excellent temporary grazing crop. There is danger from bloat when it is grazed, but the hazard can be reduced by feeding straw or some similar material. Alfalfa should be permitted to make sufficient growth in the fall to restore the food reserves in the roots.

Sericea lespedeza is rapidly becoming an important summer grazing crop in the South. It is not entirely palatable, but cattle will eat it well enough if grazing is started when the plants are 3 or 4 inches high. Sericea should be grazed at the rate of one cow to the acre in order to keep the plants from becoming coarse and woody. Grazing starts in early spring and lasts until frost. Gains of more than 300 pounds of beef an acre have been obtained. Sericea is also used for hay, but for good hay it must be cut when it is 12 to 15 inches tall and handled as little as possible to prevent loss of leaves.

The annual lespedezas, important forage crops in the South, are used in permanent pastures, for hay, and for temporary grazing. They will grow on soils of low fertility, but will respond to good fertilizer treatment; commercial fertilizers enhance both yield and quality of forage. Seeding is done during late winter or early spring; a crop of hay or seed is produced the same year. Usually enough seed is shattered to produce a volunteer crop the following year. Korean lespedeza produces less satisfactory volunteer stands than common and Kobe in the southernmost areas.

Kudzu is more commonly grown on rough, badly eroded areas. When it is used for hay or temporary grazing, kudzu must be handled carefully if a good stand is to be maintained. For hay, it should be cut once in early summer and again just before or just after the first frost. It makes good hay, but its viny growth makes it harder to handle than alfalfa or sericea. Kudzu should be grazed periodically or only lightly. It should not be grazed so heavily that the ground is visible. Kudzu is propagated vegetatively.

Soybeans and cowpeas are often used for hay. Both usually produce better when planted in rows and cultivated once or twice. The plants are rather difficult to cure because of their woody stems. Hay from soybeans and cowpeas is usually more expensive to produce than from perennial crops, such as alfalfa or sericea. The use of soybeans and cowpeas for forage is decreasing as the acreage of perennial hay crops increases.

Red clover is grown as a forage crop primarily in the upper South. It makes excellent hay and is well adapted as a soil improver in short rotations. Best results are usually had when red clover is seeded on a well prepared seedbed in early fall. On most soils liberal applications of commercial fertilizers are necessary for best growth. Only adapted, disease-resistant strains should be grown. In the lower South red clover acts like a winter annual and is grown only to a limited extent.

Crimson clover, wherever it can be grown, is one of the favorite winter grazing crops. If it is planted on a well-fitted seedbed in late summer and early fall, it furnishes abundant grazing in winter and early spring. New strains of reseeding crimson clover with a high percentage of hard seed have recently been released to farmers. They eliminate the expense of seeding the crop annually and will probably result in a greatly increased acreage.

Vetches are grown as winter forage crops for grazing or hay and, in many regions, as a cover crop that can be plowed under to improve the soil. Vetches most commonly grown are the common and hairy species. Promising new strains are being tested. Vetches, usually used to supplement the permanent pastures, furnish a succulent, high-protein feed. The vetches are also grown in combination with the small grains and cut for hay.

Lathyrus hirsutus, known locally as rough peavine, wild winterpea, Singletary pea, and Caley-pea, is an important forage crop in the Black Belt section. It is grown there as a winter crop primarily in combination with Johnsongrass. A winter legume, it is used for late-winter and early-spring grazing or for hay. It should not be grazed after seed pods have set, as it may cause serious upsets in digestion of cattle and horses.

Bur-clover, an excellent winter grazing crop, grows well in combination with Johnsongrass or in rotation with grain sorghum or Sudangrass. The Manganese strain, a selection from southern bur-clover, is the most popular. Because of its susceptibility to cold, California bur-clover is adapted only to Gulf coast areas.

The use of sweet or nonalkaloid lupine as a forage for the lower South is still in the experimental stage. The use of the nonalkaloid strains for grazing offers the possibilities of a cheap, high-protein feed.

In several sections peanuts are often used for fattening hogs. Spanish peanuts can be hogged earlier in the season than the runner type, but they must be hogged soon after maturity to prevent them from germinating and rotting. Runner peanuts are more resistant to rot and can be grazed over a much longer period than Spanish. Hogging peanuts tends to increase soil fertility; digging has the opposite effect. Farmers usually figure that 3 pounds of peanuts hogged will produce a pound of pork.

Hairy indigo, a native of northern Africa recently introduced into Florida as a cover crop, is used to a limited extent as a summer grazing legume in permanent pastures. Its use as a pasture plant is increasing.

USE AND IMPORTANCE OF PASTURES

J. C. LOWERY, E. N. FERGUS

SOUTHERN farmers can use pastures much of the year because winters are mild and the growing season is long. New species of grasses and legumes and new methods of fertilizing pastures have extended even longer the grazing period.

Livestock raisers consequently depend less than before on harvested types of forage; they use cultivated forage crops in large measure as hay, silage, grazing, and soiling crops to supplement pastures; their use of supplemental grazing crops during times of low production of permanent pastures further reduces the need for feeding concentrates or harvested forage.

Now the Alabama Agricultural Experiment Station at its Tennessee Valley Substation has developed a system that furnishes grazing for dairy cows practically the year around. The system involves four separate plots.

Plot 1 consists of an acre of permanent pasture per cow.

Plot 2 consists of a half acre of alfalfa per cow.

Plots 3 and 4 rotate.

Plot 3 consists of an acre per cow of crimson clover-ryegrass mixture seeded in late July. The crimson clover-ryegrass mixture is grazed and then harvested for seed, and is followed by oats seeded in September.

Plot 4 consists of an acre of oats per cow. The oats are grazed and then combined for grain and followed by crimson clover-ryegrass seeded in July.

The system allows $3\frac{1}{2}$ acres per cow and, in addition to the grazing and hay, furnishes a crimson clover seed crop and two grain crops. Alfalfa is used for temporary grazing during summer drought periods and, in addition, is cut two or three times for hay. This hay is fed during the most severe weather when the cows cannot be turned into the fields.

Other experiment stations constantly are releasing new facts about production and management of grasses, especially in grazing programs. Particularly impressive are the results of research with grass-legume combinations for winter grazing and the use of phosphate, potash, and lime.

Thousands of demonstrations have been conducted in the application of this research. A State-wide program of demonstration has been in operation in Louisiana for a decade. Demonstrations in the Tennessee River watershed area show a marked decline in row-crop acreage and an increase in fertilized and managed grass-clover sod. Records show that cotton farmers usually have increased their cash income when they made grass a definite,

steady part of their cropping system.

Grass has enabled farmers in the Black Belt of Alabama and Mississippi to set up a new system of farming. Cotton was the main source of cash until 1914 when the boll weevil almost destroyed the cotton business. Johnsongrass and pastures were tried. At first the drop in yields of grass was such that production could not be continued on a paying basis; a decade ago workers at the experiment stations discovered the great value of phosphate and potash for the area.

As a result of demonstrations, farmers in the Black Belt now grow grasslegume combinations on most of their land. A new agricultural system has been set up. Winter and summer the land is protected against erosion. Farmers have seen the contrast in growth on untreated plots and those treated with phosphate, potash, and lime. They have seen animals select the treated areas in grazing. Another index of the interest in grasses is the experience of many county agents; they say they get more questions about pastures than about any other problem.

Experiences in Kentucky

The combined experiences of the farmers of the inner bluegrass region of Kentucky are significant for farmers in many other parts of the South. Here is a region in which Kentucky bluegrass and white clover have grown together naturally for 150 years. Farmers of the region, therefore, have always followed an essentially permanent-pasture type of agriculture. Corn and other grains yield profitably in the region, but not enough to meet the need for feed, and farmers have found it generally better to buy corn rather than to break their sods to produce the corn. They believed that the grass was as valuable as the corn that would replace it. Besides, the reestablishment of the sod was an expensive experience.

Tobacco was an important cash crop of the early settlers of the inner bluegrass region, and it has remained a good source of cash income. But the farmers have never allowed it to occupy more than a small part of their land. The small grains that have been grown have been largely for soil cover, winter pasture, and nurse crops, although they have generally been harvested for grain.

The wisdom of following a pasture type of agriculture rather than a grain and hay type is indicated by a comparative study of the agriculture of five counties of the inner bluegrass zone that are not affected by the horse industry, and of five counties in southwestern Kentucky.

In topographical features and size of the farms (approximately 113 and 118 acres, respectively), the two groups of counties are similar. The soil of the latter region is perhaps the most productive of the major soil areas outside the bluegrass region but it is substantially less productive than the soil of the inner bluegrass.

Crop-acreage data in the 1940 census reports indicate points of agricultural similarity and contrast between the two areas: Total cropland harvested was 28.4 percent and 29.8 percent, respectively; idle or fallow cropland, 0.9 percent and 7.8 percent; tobacco, 5.0 percent and 2.9 percent; hay, 8.5 percent and 8.3 percent; plowable pastures, 57.4 percent and 30.5 percent; woodland, 3.3 percent and 20.3 percent; and all other land, 8.9 percent and 10.8 percent.

Thus, the farmers in the two groups of counties are harvesting essentially equal acreages of crops, but those of the bluegrass region are utilizing most of the remainder of their land for pastures, whereas those in the southwestern Kentucky counties have about one-half of the remainder in idle and fallow land, in woodland, and nonplowable pastures. Approximately 64 percent of the farm land in the bluegrass counties is in productive pastures, whereas only about 43 percent of the farm land of the southwestern Kentucky counties is in similar pastures. The total acreages of hay and pasture in the two areas are, therefore, about 72.5 percent and 51.3 percent, respectively.

The farm income derived from the two types of agriculture provides some measure of their relative economic merits. In arriving at these figures, tobacco should not be considered because the bluegrass farmers have the advantage of a greater acreage of burley tobacco than those in the southwestern Kentucky counties.

After deducting this source of income, the farmers of the bluegrass counties had 88 percent larger gross income in 1939 from crops and livestock than the farmers of the western Kentucky counties. We recognize, of course, that this difference in income is due partly to a difference in soil productivity that favors the bluegrass farmers, but it must be remembered also that differences in productivity to some degree are the culmination of the grass type of agriculture in the former region and its absence in the latter. That the apparent income advantage of the bluegrass farmers is a real one is indicated by the efforts that the western Kentucky farmers are making to achieve a larger pasture acreage. During the decade from 1929 to 1939, their plowable pasture acreage increased 28 percent, as against an 11-percent increase in the bluegrass counties.

The grassland agriculture followed in central Kentucky rests upon many years of experience in the utilization of hay and bluegrass pasture in the production of sheep, beef cattle, and dairy cattle. The farmers are convinced by the net income achieved from these enterprises and the conservation of their soil that their type of farming is the best for them. Despite a topography that would permit a grain type of farming, almost three-fourths of their land is in pasture and meadow. It is the desire of these farmers to increase their pasture acreage rather than to decrease it. The principal obstacle to such an increase is the difficulty of providing stock water gencrally throughout the region. A few farmers, however, have found it profitable to make the necessary installations to provide the water where needed, and it seems safe to predict that these experiences will lead to a larger acreage of grass on the farms of the central bluegrass counties.

Limited supplies of stock water are also retarding the development and utilization of pastures in southwestern Kentucky counties, but experience of a few farmers in that region also indicates that they can afford to provide an adequate supply of good stock water in good permanent pastures. It has been the experience of numerous farmers that such pastures can be produced by proper soil treatment at reasonable cost.

GRAZING ON FORESTED LANDS

JOHN T. CASSADY, W. O. SHEPHERD

THE CHEAPEST feed for livestock in the South is obtained from native grasses on some 200 million acres of forest land. Since early Colonial times the clearings and cut-over forests have provided free grazing. On them an important livestock industry developed—at first, the unmanaged grazing by poor-grade stock and later, increasingly and gradually, the yearlong management of improved herds.

Progressive stockmen realize that although native forage is inexpensive it is valuable only when it is used wisely. Most native grass furnishes good forage for about 3 months in the spring and a few weeks in early fall. During the rest of the year ranges usually furnish roughage only. Cultivated pastures, harvested forages, concentrated feeds, and minerals are needed for balanced yearlong nutrition.

Conflicts have developed between forestry and grazing because forest lands produce most of the native forage. Close grazing and fires set to remove old grass are often detrimental to forest reproduction. Most farm wood lots are so badly trampled and grazed that they produce very little forage or timber. Forestry and grazing, however, can be worked together successfully.

Most Southern forest lands are 5 to 10 times more valuable for timber production than for native forage. Thus forestry must be given first considera-

tion on forest lands. Grazing may furnish the major income from clear-cut lands while the new crop of trees is growing to merchantable size. Grazing has a real value in lowering the forest-fire hazard by reducing the amount of rough. Forested areas are really better suited for grazing than open areas because the trees furnish shade and a greater variety of forage. The most ideal native grazing is found on lands where open areas, young trees, and mature timber are somewhat mixed. Such mixtures usually exist where good forestry is practiced.

To make good use of native forage it is well to know the different range plants and their grazing values. Natural vegetation occurs in distinct types composed of certain dominant or abundant plants from which the types are named. Grazing management is based largely on characteristics of the types.

The Southern range area can be divided by forest types and geographic regions. Most Southern forest range is in the longleaf-slash pine forests extending through the lower South near the coast from the Carolinas to Texas. This area of 55 million acres was heavily cut over and has been slow to reforest. Forage is abundant in it.

Next in importance for grazing are the shortleaf-loblolly-hardwood forests, which cover nearly 80 million acres. They usually are dense; forage is sparse. The bottom-land hardwood forests of the Mississippi and other large river valleys cover about 30 million acres. Not much grass grows under dense hardwood forests, but there are considerable amounts of browse forage.

The upland hardwood forests of the hills and mountains cover nearly 35 million acres. Grazing capacity of the uplands is low, and soils are easily eroded so that grazing should be carefully regulated.

Of the three major geographic land areas in the South—the Coastal Plain, Piedmont Plateau, and Mountain regions—the Coastal Plain is the largest and most important for grazing. It includes Florida, Mississippi, Louisiana, and parts of Texas, Arkansas, Alabama, Georgia, the Carolinas, and Virginia. The longleaf-slash pine, shortleaf-loblolly-hardwood, and bottom-land-hardwood forest types are mostly in the Coastal Plain. The region is essentially a low plain with flat to rolling land, low elevations, slow drainage, sandy loam soils, and relatively open forests with much forage.

The principal range types of the Coastal Plain are wiregrass, bluestem, switch cane, bottom-land, coastal prairie, and marshgrass. We describe these types in the approximate order of their importance.

Wiregrass, the leading grazing type in the Southeast, extends from South Carolina into Georgia, Florida, and Alabama, mainly in longleaf-slash pine forests. Frequent burning has created a type of wiry, fire-tolerant bunchgrass. Important grasses are pineland three-awn, Curtiss dropseed, several bluestems, panicums, cut-over muhly, and carpetgrass. Shrubs such as gallberry and palmetto, which are characteristic of the type, are useless for grazing. A few others and hardwood tree sprouts are browsed to some extent.

From mid-March to late June, wiregrass range furnishes good grazing, and cattle gain about a pound a day on it. Cattle barely maintain weight from July to October, however, and lose weight rapidly the rest of the year unless they get supplemental feed.

Grazing capacity varies from about 1.5 acres a cow-month on open wiregrass range to more than 5 acres in well-stocked timber stands. Grazing capacity, as used here, means the number of acres of range needed to furnish ample forage to a mature cow for a month without damage to the forage or timber stand.

Curtiss dropseed and pineland three-awn furnish the best forage in March, April, and May. From then until fall the bluestems, panicums, and carpetgrass are important. Curtiss dropseed furnishes a good share of winter grazing. The foliage of this species (and of many others) remains green in winter, but the nutritional value of the forage is particularly low at that season.

A dozen species of bluestem grasses—also called broomsedge, sedge, and sage—furnish half of the native forage on the pine and upland hardwood forest lands of Mississippi, Louisiana, eastern Texas, eastern Oklahoma, and Arkansas. This important bluestem type also occurs in other Southern States. The principal forage plants are pinehills bluestem, little bluestem, slender bluestem, yellow bluestem, panicums, paspalums, carpetgrass, blue dropseed, muhly, and three-awns. Grasses furnish 80 to 90 percent of the forage. Grasslike plants called beakrushes and green sedges furnish 5 percent of the forage. Other imported species include beggar lice, common lespedeza, and swamp sunflower.

Certain shrubs as well as hardwood sprouts are grazed in winter and on heavily forested ranges where grass is sparse. Grazing capacities of bluestem ranges vary from about an acre a cow-month on old fields and clear-cut areas to more than 6 acres a cow-month on the heavily forested areas typical of shortleaf-loblolly-hardwood forests.

Bluestem ranges furnish excellent forage from March 20 to May 1, and beef cattle gains of more than 2 pounds a day are not uncommon. Thereafter forage values decline. Poor forage is produced in July when it is hottest, fairly good forage for 4 to 6 weeks in late August and September, and very poor forage from October to March. Without supplemental feed, mature cattle on bluestem ranges lose up to 25 percent, or 200 pounds, during fall and winter. Similar losses occur on many other southern ranges.

Switch cane, a tall reed of the bamboo tribe, forms the best native grazing type in the South. Although cultivation, fire, and heavy grazing have reduced former stands, extensive areas of switch cane still remain on uncultivated bottom lands of the Mississippi Delta and in large swamps of eastern Virginia and the Carolinas. Other forage plants found with switch cane are bluestems, panicums, beakrushes, cinnamonfern, greenbrier, and various hardwoods.

Grazing capacities of the switch cane type vary from ½ acre a cow-month in the tall canebrakes on deep organic soils to about 2 acres a cow-month on less favorable sites. Switch cane furnishes the best grazing from May to November, but some farmers save this type for winter use. Heavy grazing in the spring or soon after a fire seriously damages this type.

A large variety of trees, shrubs, vines, grasses, and sedges grow in the bottom lands of the Mississippi and other rivers throughout the South. Prominent forage plants are carpetgrass, bluestems, beakrushes, sedges, switch cane, greenbrier, and many hardwood sprouts. Some of them provide nutritious winter forage. Spring and summer grazing is even better, but care must be taken to protect valuable hardwood-timber reproduction from excessive grazing damage.

The true grasslands of southeastern Texas, southern Louisiana, and southern Florida support large cattle operations. The marshgrass type hugs the coastline and the coastal prairie is situated on slightly higher ground bordering the flat pinelands.

Principal forage plants in the coastal prairie are bluestems, carpetgrass, Bermuda-grass, maidencane, and several paspalums. The grazing capacities are higher than on bluestem ranges and closer grazing is permissible because damage to tree reproduction is here of no concern.

The marshgrass type includes large areas of fresh-water marsh and a fringe of salt-water marsh along the southeastern and Gulf coasts. Predominant species are cattails, bulrushes, maidencane, sawgrass, cordgrasses, saltgrasses, and black rush. The fresh-water marshes provide the best forage, but some grazing is obtained in the salty marshes at low tide.

Southern range grazing is concentrated in the Coastal Plain. The Piedmont Plateau and Mountain regions have little open range and, as a whole, furnish limited range grazing. Forage values are low in comparison to timber and watersheds. Soils and hardwood tree reproduction are easily damaged by unrestricted grazing. Livestock production is largely a farm-pasture operation and native ranges are best used in spring to supplement farm pastures.

The Piedmont Plateau occupies a wide belt between the Appalachian Mountains and the Coastal Plain. It is characterized by rolling topography, sandy loam to clay soils, mixed pine-hardwood forests, farms, and old fields. A common practice is to abandon fields when soils are worn out or eroded. Weeds and grasses soon cover the fields and furnish fairly good spring forage until new crops of trees shade out the grass. The forage is composed of about the same plants found on bluestem ranges. Grazing capacities vary from 2 acres a cow-month on open areas to about 10 acres on forests that are well stocked.

In the southern Appalachian Mountains such excellent forage plants as Kentucky bluegrass, orchardgrass, and clovers grow naturally in the clearings. As long as the land is clear these plants furnish excellent forage, but when the forest stand recovers, forage is sparse and the grazing capacity is low. It is not practical to combine forestry and grazing on the same areas in the mountainous districts.

The southern range-livestock industry developed on a philosophy of minimum investment in capital and labor. Large areas of free range on cut-over lands and the mild climate favored haphazard management. Most range livestock are still left to forage for themselves. Under this system the return per animal is low, but the investment is lower still and some profit is made.

Problems and Benefits

The prevailing practices have several undesirable features. Yearlong grazing on strictly seasonal ranges results in severe weight losses in winter, high death losses, low calf crops, and poor calves. With mixed herds and yearlong breeding, one man who tries to salt or feed supplements on the range also feeds his neighbors' stock, and good bulls compete with scrub bulls. With free grazing on open ranges, the range is free only as long as the landowner permits; it may be fenced and leased to some other stockman, so that former users are left without sufficient range. Uncontrolled grazing, frequent burning, and hog rooting have kept trees from growing on valuable forest lands. Under a system of large and absentee ownership of unfenced forest lands, the average farmer is not interested in protecting forest reproduction from fires and grazing; even his farm wood lot is used more like a feed lot than a pasture.

Under prevailing practices, a few individuals have profited, but the community and forests have lost. More and more people have gone into the livestock business and the ranges are becoming crowded. Young trees are growing up and there is less forage. The answer lies in proper seasonal use of the range, more cultivated pastures and home-grown feeds, a higher grade of stock, and careful yearlong herd management.

A change toward better livestock management is evident throughout the South. Experience has shown the necessity for improved practices. The greatest need in range livestock production is for adequate nutrition when native forage is poor. This can be provided by the use of cultivated pastures, home-grown feeds, and supplements.

Ways to increase production and improve the quality of native range are being developed by experience and research. In central Louisiana, for example, 300 pounds of commercial fertilizer per acre on bluestem range doubled the yield and improved the quality of native grasses. The range was further improved by broadcasting lespedeza seed on fertilized areas. Best results were obtained by burning to remove rough and by fertilizing, seeding, and harrowing. Costs were high and pine reproduction was damaged.

A large number of forage plants are being tested on native ranges at the Georgia Coastal Plains Experiment Station. Lespedeza, carpetgrass, and Bahiagrasses have given best results so far. Carpetgrass is already widely distributed in cut-over lands. It is spread by cattle droppings and will grow on relatively poor soils. Common Bahiagrass will also grow on poor soils. It produces better forage than carpetgrass but is harder to get started and is less frost-resistant. The production of beef must be fairly high to offset the cost of improving native ranges. This leads to close grazing and damage to forest reproduction. In many cases it may prove more practical to establish permanent pastures on selected areas and manage forest lands for maximum tree production.

Because livestock belonging to many individuals frequently use the same range, cooperation is needed to improve the stock and their management. The formation of community associations of cattle growers provides an efficient way to handle cattle on forest ranges. Some of the operations that an association can effectively perform are to obtain grazing rights on forest lands; to purchase good bulls, feed, and minerals; to hire riders; and to effect the necessary improvements and operations in management. A good association will give stability to the local livestock enterprise.

The major problem on forest ranges in the South is to obtain integration of grazing and forestry on a basis that will result in utilizing the forage resource without damaging the forest. Forest range grazing, cultivated pastures, farming, and forestry, if properly coordinated, will provide a higher income for southern farmers.

THIS IS OUR UNFINISHED BUSINESS

W. W. WOODHOUSE, JR., R. E. BLASER

SOUTHERN CLIMATE permits the growth of a wide variety—an embarrassingly wide variety—of pasture and forage plants. So many new ones appear and so great has been the upsurge of interest in them that it has been hard to keep up with them and their specific requirements. Faced with so many possibilities, farmers and research workers have tended to dissipate their efforts on the many while learning too little about any one. Research workers particularly need to develop facilities and methods for evaluating properly the new plants and reevaluating some of the older ones.

We do know enough about the available plants, however, to build a fairly satisfactory pasture and forage program for most southern farms and to realize that other plants are urgently needed to fill gaps in the program for certain sections.

A major item of this nature is a warm-weather grass, high in nutritive value, that will grow well with legumes and at the same time allow legumes to grow—a plant, that is, to replace carpetgrass. It should be easy and rapid of establishment and disease-resistant. Unlike carpetgrass, it should be palatable and nutritious and should lend itself to a type of management that would encourage the growth and survival of legumes in the sod.

Dallisgrass, with all its limitations, seems now to be the most promising candidate for this spot. Dallisgrass will require considerable remodeling before it will fill the bill because it is a poor seed producer, it is slow and expensive to establish, and its nutritive value is less than desired.

Also, a good perennial hay legume is needed for the districts where alfalfa does not do well.

Alfalfa promises to go a long way toward solving the problem of hay production in much of the region, but, elsewhere, the perennials now in use are low-yielding, unpalatable, slow to establish, or difficult to manage and harvest. As a result, most of the hay produced there is from annual crops, which have the added risk and expense of establishment each year. The plant to fill this gap should be nutritious, persistent, high-yielding, and fairly easy to establish. Such a plant is not now in sight.

Disease resistance is a prime requirement in any plant to be grown in the South, where leaf and stem diseases are intensified by the warm, humid climate. Lack of resistance to any one of them can completely eliminate a plant from certain areas and lessen its value everywhere. For example, the annual lespedezas and white clover are almost useless on some of the sandy Coastal Plain soils because of their susceptibility to nematodes. Thus, while several fairly good grasses are adapted to these soils, the lack of legumes makes good pastures scarce. We have little hope for anything better than unproductive, pure-grass sods on these soils until the nematodes can be overcome. The incorporation of disease resistance into plants is a major objective in breeding new or improved forage plants for the South.

The old problem of grass-legume competition in sods is perhaps more acute here than elsewhere in the United States. With few exceptions, the low nitrogen level and high rate of nitrogen losses from southern soils make the need for the nitrogen supplied by legumes extremely vital to successful pasture production. Also, a high proportion of the grasses used are sod formers—carpetgrass, Bermuda-grass, Bahiagrass, and Kentucky bluegrass, for example; all form tight sods and tend to make life difficult for any legumes among them.

An example: A good growth of white clover or Ladino clover will supply adequate nitrogen for the growth of a sod and (for a while, at least) will convert the lowly carpetgrass into a productive and fairly nutritious plant. Such a combination, without the benefit of any applied nitrogen, actually has produced more than 600 pounds of beef an acre each year. Yet, when the summer rains come, the carpetgrass may get sufficiently out of hand to crowd out the clover. When this happens, both the early grazing and the nitrogen supplied by the legume are lost. As soon as the nitrogen supply declines, carpetgrass reverts to its usual role of a carpet on which the animals may walk in search of grazing.

Apparently this adverse situation may be prevented by holding back the carpetgrass by heavy grazing or mowing. Unfortunately, animals forced to graze so closely drop off in production. Frequent mowing is expensive. Another solution supposedly would be to substitute Dallisgrass for carpetgrass. Dallisgrass is more tolerant to clover growth, better able to utilize the high fertility level, and more palatable. But to survive in most areas, Dallisgrass must successfully compete with carpetgrass. Studies show that two factors largely determine the outcome of carpetgrass-Dallisgrass competition—fertility level and grazing intensity. Low fertility, particularly in nitrogen, and intensive grazing both tip the balance in favor of carpetgrass. Thus a

management system that would encourage Dallisgrass would tend to exclude the clover. Loss of clover would lower the nitrogen level. This, in turn, would favor the carpet and cause the sod to revert to a pure carpet stand. While not impossible, the process of permanently substituting Dallisgrass for carpetgrass is one calling for astute management.

The example cited is one of the most acute in the region, perhaps, but it illustrates the factors operating in most grass-legume combinations. Certainly it presents a type of problem whose solution, of vital interest to southern livestock growers, lies in improved plants and management.

Nutritious forage cannot be produced on soils low in the essential minerals. Examples of the importance of proper soil treatment are everywhere. Povertygrass-broomsedge pastures are frequently converted to bluegrass-white clover sods without the addition of seed. Carpetgrass sods are changed to productive white clover-Bermuda-grass pastures by soil treatment alone.

Fertility studies with grassland plants in the South have never been very extensive. The fact that many of these were largely empirical trials, accompanied by only scanty information on the properties of the soils involved, makes it difficult to interpret their results in terms of new plants and practices. The recent adoption of superior species and strains, coupled with changing cultural and management practices, has made much of the previous work obsolete. More productive plants will require higher fertility levels. Improved methods of application and incorporation may require major changes in fertilizer and liming practice. Enough is known of the fertility requirements of the common grasses and legumes to grow them satisfactorily on many soils. Much remains to be learned to enable the livestock grower to make most efficient use of these materials.

Since most southern soils are naturally low in calcium and magnesium and are rather acid, lime must be applied for the satisfactory growth of many plants. In fact, lime is the first essential for successful pasture and forage production on many soils. Most soils in the region, fortunately, have a comparatively low lime requirement, but at present neither the lime status desired nor amount necessary to attain and maintain it are very well known for most soils and plants. In order to make intelligent use of liming materials, we need to know what level of lime in the various soils is most desirable for the growth of the adapted plants and how much of what materials must be applied to reach this level. Further, we need information as to the rate of loss of lime from these soils through leaching and plant removal to enable us to maintain the proper lime level once it has been reached.

Information on time and place of application of liming materials is still sketchy for most soils and plants. Most of the natural grassland soils of the world contain free lime in the subsoil, yet most lime treatments in the South have taken into account only a few inches of surface soil. Indications are that depth and distribution of lime may be quite important for some plants on some soils. Nodulation of legume roots sometimes occurs only in the limed zone of the soil. Liming the deeper soil horizons may be of considerable value in such cases. Present practice in this field is certainly open to question and offers fruitful possibilities for investigation.

Phosphorus is frequently a limiting factor in the growth of forage plants and in the diet of the animals that consume them. Most of the field crops in the region benefit from annual applications of the element. Apparently some forage plants are able to utilize available forms of phosphorus slowly. It may be advantageous in some cases to build up to the level under sods and eliminate the necessity of frequent applications. The extent to which this may be practicable is still an open ques-

tion in many localities in the South.

Widespread phosphorus deficiency in the South is due to the low phosphorus content of most soils and also to the ability of the soils to fix considerable amounts of this element in unavailable or very slowly available form. Phosphorus fixation seems to depend largely on the amount of fixing agents present in the soil and the extent to which the phosphorus is exposed to them. For this reason the concentration of applied phosphorus in narrow zones within the soil should greatly reduce fixation. The efficiency of phosphorus applications for pasture and forage plants might be greatly improved in this way. The value of localized phosphorus applications for these plants on southern soils should be studied. Methods and machinery must still be developed.

Legumes, particularly the more productive plants like alfalfa and Ladino clover, feed heavily on potassium. Some southern soils have large stores of potash minerals, but others are low in total potash. In order to use fertilizer potash intelligently, we need to know the extent to which the native potash supply of the various soils may be drawn upon. The development of methods of increasing the availability of soil potash would lower the cost of producing forage.

Some plants tend to absorb potash far in excess of need when a plentiful supply is present. Apparently about 1.25 percent of potassium in the alfalfa plant is adequate for normal growth, yet alfalfa sometimes may contain 3.50 percent. This luxury consumption of potash may result in wasteful use if the material is applied at the wrong time. For example, in a single season an acre of Ladino clover may take up potassium equivalent to that contained in 200 to 300 pounds of muriate of potash. On soils low in potash it may be necessary to split this up into more than one application in order to maintain the supply throughout the season.

The use of minor elements has been explored only to a limited extent. Boron, zinc, copper, manganese, and sulfur deficiencies have been found in some plants. Cobalt deficiency in livestock has developed in certain areas. The highly leached condition of some soils, plus the trend toward more productive plants and the use of heavier lime and fertilizer applications, may be expected to increase the drain on the soil supplies of the various elements. Undoubtedly, it will become necessary to apply some of these more generally than has been done in the past. Plant requirements and tolerance to minor elements must be worked out.

We should have better ways to make hay. The frequent periods of high humidity and rain during haying season bring considerable losses in field-cured hay. Barn drying systems, already in use in the South, may be the solution. But tests have shown that much dry matter is sometimes lost during barn drying and storage. Present barn drying systems still require considerable labor or expensive equipment and, consequently, the effect of curing and storage methods on feeding value should be thoroughly studied.

The relatively small amounts of forage stored as silage in the South should be supplemented by grass silage made from surplus hay and pasture crops. There are flush periods of growth accompanied by inclement weather when much material could best be conserved by ensiling. Our present information on methods of preserving grass silage and its feed value is inadequate.

And so, along with the numerous serious and urgent conservation problems in the South there are corresponding opportunities for correction and improvement. No other section has a larger number of useful grasses and legumes with which to build a conservation program. Proper planning of cropland, grazing land, woodland, and wildlife land, the use of necessary lime and fertilizer, and the application of vegetation according to the needs of the land and the capabilities of the plants, will give the South a sounder agriculture in which crops, livestock, and woodland products contribute to a better balanced income.

THE AUTHORS ⋘ *Roy L. Lovvorn holds degrees from the Alabama Polytechnic Institute, the University of Missouri, and the University of Wisconsin. He is professor of agronomy in North Carolina State College of Agriculture and Engineering and agent in the Bureau of Plant Industry, Soils, and Agricultural Engineering. Dr. Lovvorn has been engaged in research on forage crops since 1935 and has written many articles on the subject.*

Hugh W. Bennett was born in Alabama. He is a graduate of the Alabama Polytechnic Institute and Iowa State College and has been engaged in forage crop research since 1934. Dr. Bennett is associate agronomist of the Mississippi Agricultural Experiment Station at State College.

T. H. Rogers attended Alabama Polytechnic Institute and the University of Minnesota. He has been engaged in forage crop teaching and research since 1938, and is associate agronomist of the Alabama Agricultural Experiment Station at Auburn. He was born in Alabama.

George E. Ritchey, a native of Nebraska and a graduate of Iowa State College and Cornell University, has worked with grasses and legumes since 1929. He is an agronomist in the Bureau of Plant Industry, Soils, and Agricultural Engineering and in the Florida Agricultural Experiment Station at Gainesville.

J. C. Lowery, a native of Alabama and a graduate of the Alabama Polytechnic Institute, has been engaged in agronomy extension for a number of years. Mr. Lowery is extension agronomist, Agricultural Extension Service, Auburn, Ala.

E. N. Fergus, a native of Ohio and a graduate of the Ohio State University and the University of Chicago, has been engaged in forage crop research for a number of years. Dr. Fergus is in charge of the forage crop investiga-

tions, Kentucky Agricultural Experiment Station, Lexington.

John T. Cassady is in charge of a branch of the Southern Forest Experiment Station in Alexandria, La. He was born in Alabama and is a graduate of the University of Arizona. Except for 5 years in the Army, he has done research on range management since 1933.

W. O. Shepherd is a forest ecologist in the Southeastern Forest Experiment Station. He has been engaged in grazing research since 1941, except for a period of military service. He holds degrees from Utah State Agricultural College and the University of Nebraska.

W. W. Woodhouse, Jr., is a graduate of North Carolina State College and Cornell University. He has been engaged in research with fertility problems in forage production for the past 13 years. Dr. Woodhouse is now associate professor of agronomy in North Carolina State College, Raleigh.

R. E. Blaser studied at the University of Nebraska, Rutgers University, and North Carolina State College, and has conducted forage research for the past 14 years. Dr. Blaser is professor of agronomy in Cornell University.

The Northern Great Plains

WHERE ELBOWROOM IS AMPLE

GEORGE A. ROGLER, LEON C. HURTT

THE NORTHERN Great Plains covers about 300,000 square miles, roughly a tenth of the total land area of the United States. Approximately the western three-fourths of North Dakota, South Dakota, and Nebraska, the eastern two-thirds of Montana, the eastern one-third of Wyoming, and the northeastern one-tenth of Colorado are included in the Northern Great Plains, which is part of an extensive midcontinental belt known as the Great Plains.

The natural boundary on the east is a zone of transition that may be defined in terms of climate, soil, or natural vegetation. The ninety-eighth meridian represents the average of these changing characteristics. Precipitation there averages about 20 inches a year; westward it is less. The western boundary is the foothills of the Rocky Mountains, which form a natural barrier to the Plains type of vegetation. The Canadian border is the northern boundary of the Great Plains in the United States; actually, the Great Plains include about 150,000 square miles in Canada. The southern boundary of the Northern Great Plains is the Nebraska-Kansas line projected westward to the Rocky Mountains, a line that represents the transition from the northern to the southern short-grass or mixed-prairie type of vegetation.

Generally the land is gently rolling, but some areas are rough and broken. Soil types and structure vary widely. The surface features of lake beds, river valleys, plateaus, and buttes are the result of glacial action or erosion. Part of the area is deeply covered with glacial drift. There are heavily eroded localities along the Missouri River and in the Badlands of North Dakota and South Dakota. Mountainlike formations are the Black Hills in South Dakota and the Bear Paw Mountains in Montana.

The climate is semiarid and has wide extremes. Rainfall is the greatest limitation on crop production. Moisture comes as slow rains, or cloudbursts sometimes accompanied by hail, or gentle snowfalls, or blizzards of severe intensity. The average precipitation is 27 inches in the southeastern part and less than 10 inches in some places in the northwestern. Much of the rain falls in the spring and early summer.

Temperatures vary widely from north to south and in a given locality from day to day. A range of more than 130° F. often occurs between maximum summer and minimum winter temperatures. A summer temperature of 117° and winter temperature of 57° below zero have been recorded at the same place. The average growing season is about 160 days in the southern

lished ranch headquarters along the streams before the close of the century, when buffalo still grazed plains forage. Then a tidal wave of land-hungry settlers arrived to plow under millions of acres of grassland. This high tide quickly subsided after the First World War; thousands of people deserted their drought-stricken homesteads that were not adapted to regional limitations. National alarm was aroused when yet another series of drought years—the most devastating on record—struck repeatedly in the 1930's. The rural population continues to decline.

part and 116 days in the northern part.

Medium and short grasses are the predominant vegetation. Tree growth is absent except along streams, coulees, and north slopes of rough terrain. The native grasses of the Northern Great Plains are hardy, drought-resistant species such as blue grama, buffalograss, western wheatgrass, and needlegrass. Several less important grasses and dry-land sedges are also present.

The Northern Great Plains is sparsely populated. There are no large cities. Three out of five people live on farms or in towns of less than 2,500 population. The average density of population is approximately six persons to the square mile.

About 25 percent of the land is under cultivation, but the cropland is not evenly distributed. In some counties more than 80 percent of the land is under cultivation; in others it is less than 1 percent. The proportion of cropland decreases generally from east to west, but not in regular belts. Between cultivated areas are large expanses of native grassland that have not been plowed and should not be plowed.

Production varies greatly from year to year and from locality to locality because of the limited and variable precipitation. Precipitation must occur in sufficient quantity and at the right season if pastures and forage and grain crops are to yield satisfactory returns. Any degree of departure from the average annual rainfall usually results in bumper crop or near failures.

For nearly a century after the Lewis and Clark explorations across the plains this grassland empire was largely unpeopled. A few pioneers had estab-

A realistic look ahead shows that opportunities for industrial developments are restricted by long distances to central markets, high transportation costs, and a sparse population. Experience has demonstrated that future developments must be built largely on this range forage and hardy crops adapted to a semiarid climate of a northern region. Long and severe winters, high winds, and early-spring and late-fall storms that frequently destroy promising crops and range livestock are a part of the environment. But drought that strikes at unpredictable intervals has been the nemesis of thousands of farm and ranch ventures. At Miles City and Havre, precipitation has dropped below 75 percent of the 13.2-inch normal on the average of once in 5 to 8 years, respectively, since records were started more than 66 years ago. Range forage has withstood these drought periods more successfully than most cultivated crops in the drier parts of the region.

M. A. Bell reports yields of spring wheat at the North Montana Branch Station, near Havre, averaging 9.1 bushels an acre on spring plowing and 15.3 bushels on fallow for the 30-year period after 1917. In 13 of these years yield was less than 5 bushels on spring plowing. Hot winds, hailstorms, grasshopper invasions, as well as dry weather, were partly responsible for these crop failures and low yields; it is unsafe to rely on crop farming.

To achieve safety, farming practices must be adapted to existing climatic hazards. A livestock economy based on the proper utilization of native range and seeded pastures supplemented by locally produced annual forage and feed crops can do much toward stabilization. In some places irrigation developments are under way; they will assure the production of forage and other feeds. These developments will bring a new era of stability in livestock production if the forage and other feeds thus produced are properly integrated with the use of large acreages of native range.

Yet despite its extremes, the climate is healthful for men and livestock. Certain diseases and pests of southern ranges do not molest northern ranchers. The people here come largely from pioneer stock and have been tested by adversity. Many remain because they treasure the wide horizons and ample elbowroom of the Northern Great Plains. Their experience and tenacity will be invaluable in developing a more stable program of range husbandry supplemented by crop agriculture in a region that normally produces at least 15 percent of the national total of cattle, sheep, and horses.

THE PLACE OF GRASSLAND FARMING

M. M. KELSO

THE NORTHERN Great Plains is a transitional region.

From east to west, about 500 miles, it passes from the intensity of cultivation and management of the Corn Belt to the semiaridity and extensive operations found in range country.

From north to south, about 600 miles, it passes from the short summers and long cold winters, with wheat and small grains, to the longer summers and shorter winters, with corn, sorghums, and winter wheat. An hour's drive (particularly just east of the mountains) can take one abruptly from areas in which tillage (if there is tillage at all) depends upon natural rainfall into areas wholly dependent upon irrigation for crops and forage.

The economy does not depend uniformly on grassland. Its basis varies from area to area as the degree of its dependence upon cash grain or livestock varies, and as the degree of its dependence upon beef cattle and sheep or upon hogs and poultry changes. These variations fall into a pattern that reflects roughly the increasing aridity and climatic variability from east to west, and the increasing length of the summers from north to south.

Agriculturally, there are four subregions—the spring-wheat area, the wheat-range area, the corn area, and the range area.

In the spring-wheat area, grassland is secondary to cropland, and grassland as pasture is secondary to grassland as hay. Livestock and livestock products in 1944 produced only about a third of the gross cash agricultural income of the area, and grassland furnished only about a half of the nutrients required by the livestock that produced that income. Grassland as pasture produced about a tenth of the feed nutrients for this livestock; grassland as hay produced about 40 percent, and concentrates about 50 percent. Apparently this comparatively heavy use of hay and concentrated feeds arises from the rather large proportions of hogs, chickens, and dairy cows and from the striking fact that the native tall-grass pastures in the relatively humid spring wheat area should be no more productive than native short-grass ranges in the half-arid range country to the west.

One need not assume that the pastures of the spring wheat area are not used to capacity and that the feed they produce is wasted. Their unproductive condition apparently results from a greater degree of depletion of the grass cover. On this point the report, *Post-war Program for Conservation and Improvement of Range and Native Pasture Lands in the Northern Great Plains,* said in 1944: "It is paradoxical that the grazing lands east of the 100th Meridian are in a relatively poorer condition than those in other parts of the region. Of the 15 million acres in poor condition, 9½ million acres are located in this area. The native grazing lands remaining in this area have lost so much of their original grasses from hard use that it generally requires complete new seedings before the potential production can be restored."

Free land and the Homestead Act influenced sharply the pattern of settlement. Peak periods of homesteading often coincided with relatively abundant rainfall and abnormal prices for wheat. Hidden then was the fact that under more normal rainfall and prices the homestead tracts were too small to produce adequate livelihood. Overcultivation, overdevelopment, and overstocking were the consequences.

The drought and depression of the 1930's brought widespread economic distress. The fundamental need was less dependence upon wheat and more on feed crops and pasture and livestock. But that was largely impossible without making farms larger—and that meant that some farmers had to sell their land to neighbors and move away. During the depression the lack of alternatives for these "surplus" farmers held many of them on their farms, and the adjustment was largely blocked. The new employment opportunities during the war helped the situation somewhat. According to estimates in the report, *Adjusting Agriculture in the Northern Great Plains for War and Postwar Needs,* in the long run it is desirable (in comparison with 1939 conditions) that the number of farms throughout the spring wheat area decline some 11 percent and that about 11 percent of the cropland be regrassed

as additional pasturage. Although the number of farms has dropped, it is doubtful if much regrassing occurred during the war years.

The Wheat-Range Area

The wheat-range area lies west and north of the spring wheat area in southwestern North Dakota and north-central Montana. Here, too, grassland is less important than cropland, but grassland as range is more important than grassland as hay. Diversity characterizes the area. Dry-land wheat farms, wheat farms with range livestock, and livestock ranches sometimes are right next to one another.

Livestock and livestock products produced here in 1944 brought in only about a third of the gross cash agricultural income. But grassland supplied about three-fourths of the nutrients required by the livestock that produced this income; grassland as pasture alone produced almost half of the feed, grassland as hay produced about a fourth, and concentrates about a fourth.

The relatively heavy dependence of livestock in this area upon grassland, particularly pasture, comes from two factors: Only 5 percent of the livestock is swine and poultry, which use little roughage; beef cattle and sheep, animals that use relatively little concentrate feed and utilize hay only during a part of the year, comprise 80 percent of the livestock. Dairy cattle, so important as consumers of grain and hay in the spring wheat area, constitute only about a fifth of all roughage-consuming livestock in the wheat-range area. Almost three-fourths of the land in this area is in pasture.

Here, too, overcultivation and overexpansion of cropland caused distress. Farms of the usual homestead size frequently could not survive drought and depression.

The war encouraged many families on undersized farms to leave the area; the excellent market for agricultural goods encouraged the farmers who remained to add those properties to their

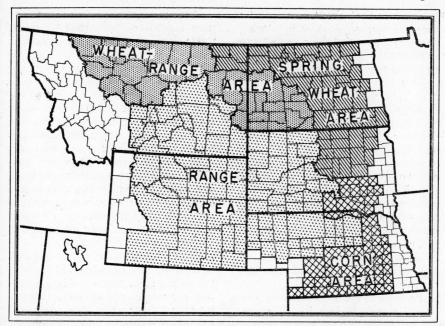

Generalized types of farming areas in the Northern Great Plains showing areas where grassland's place in farm economy differs. The map is adapted from "Generalized Types of Farming in the United States—Delineation on County Boundaries," U. S. Bureau of Agricultural Economics, 1946. Here, the Northern Great Plains is the sum of these farming areas and consequently may not correspond exactly with the other definitions given.

holdings. As a result the size of farms has gone up and the number of farms down since 1940. Now, with farms of more adequate size (although still further adjustment is needed) the prospect is favorable that high-risk cropland will be regrassed with the return of more normal weather and prices.

Here, more than anywhere else in the Northern Great Plains, grassland is the balance wheel. Climate, soils, and topography are variable, sometimes favorable for wheat, sometimes unfavorable. Wheat is at the margin—a risky venture in all but limited spots. Livestock production is not subject to irregular fluctuations to the same degree that crop production is in the wheat-range area. Between 1924 and 1945 crop production in all of the Great Plains varied less than 28 percent from average in two-thirds of the years, but livestock production in the same period varied less than 14 percent from its average, or only one-half

as much. Thus stability of the agricultural economy of the wheat-range area rests on an emphasized livestock enterprise, which, in turn, rests upon grasslands. Natural grasslands of the area provide the cheapest and most abundant forage. Native range grasses supply most of the nutrients needed by cattle, sheep, and horses.

The Corn Area

In the corn area, grassland is subordinate to cropland, and grassland as pasture is less important than grassland as hay. But, unlike the spring-wheat area, livestock and livestock products furnish two-thirds of the gross cash farm income of the corn area, where only about 40 percent of the feed nutrients for the livestock that produces this income is derived from grassland—25 percent from grassland as hay and 15 percent from grassland as pasture.

The fact that about 60 percent of the feed requirements of livestock in this area is supplied from concentrates indicates the importance of the corn crop as a base for the stock enterprise.

This relatively heavy dependence upon concentrates and upon grassland as hay rather than as pasture reflects the importance here of hogs and chickens (17 percent of all livestock) and of dairy and feeder cattle.

Possibly because of this importance of corn and grain-consuming animals and the concentrated settlement of the area, pastures have been so abused that—although they are in an area of greater humidity and originally in the tall-grass belt—they supply only about twice as much nutrients per acre as do the short-grass ranges of the drier range area.

To conserve soil resources and to enhance and stabilize incomes, grassland in the corn area should be made more productive and plentiful. In the long run, we think, the acreage of cropland should be reduced about 9 percent (from the 1939 figure) and put back into grass. Although it might be profitable to use the poorer croplands for pasture, it is probable that they will yield less income than when they are cropped. To maintain or to enhance incomes, larger farms, about 20 percent fewer than in 1939, will be necessary if this needed regrassing is to be carried out.

The Range Area

The range area is the part of the Northern Great Plains where climate, soil, or topography make crop production too risky.

Generally it lies south and west of the Missouri River and includes the sand hills of north-central Nebraska. The economy rests primarily on livestock ranching, although spots of dry farming and irrigation are scattered throughout the area. Beef cattle and sheep predominate and are run mostly under range conditions, rather than on farm pastures.

Crop production is less important than anywhere else in the Northern Great Plains. In 1944, crops occupied only 10 percent of the land, produced about 28 percent of the gross agricultural income, and supplied about 15 percent of the nutrients fed to livestock in the area.

Grassland as range occupied some 85 percent of the land in 1944 and supplied about one-half of the nutrients needed by the livestock, which furnished about three-fourths of the gross agricultural income. Grasslands as hay furnished about 30 percent of the feed required by the livestock.

These grasslands have suffered from overextension of cultivation and overgrazing, although, by and large, they have suffered less than grasslands of the wheat area. Homesteading spread into the range area as it did through the wheat area; many farm units were too small; livestock pressure on the range was severe; taxes were too high. Drought, depression, and the recent war caused a reduction in the number of operating units, the extent of cropland cultivated, and numbers of range-using livestock. But in this area limited rainfall and considerable wind make range recovery and regrassing of abandoned cropland extremely slow, unless actively assisted by man.

The vital importance here of grassland makes its protection and rehabilitation essential to stability and welfare. In the long run, we believe, approximately 20 percent of the land in crops in 1939 should be regrassed; in local areas, where wheat is grown, there should be a reduction in use of land for crops and, on the land retained in cropland, there should be a considerable shift to feed crops and away from wheat as a cash crop.

Although the size of units has increased during the war years, it is doubtful if the recommended reduction in cropland has taken place to any significant extent. In fact, there probably has been some recropping of formerly abandoned lands.

The need is still before us to widen

the extent of grassland and reduce cropland, increase the economic reliance upon range-using livestock, and put the relation between livestock and grassland in such shape that grasslands are protected against deterioration.

Importance of Grassland

To the individual farmer or ranchman the value of grass is reflected in how much another acre of it will affect his net income and whether the effect will be plus or minus. To him, whether he adds an acre of grassland to his farm or whether he shifts an acre of cropland to grass, the question is the same—how much does it add to or subtract from his net income? As an individual farmer, he will be concerned with which added acre adds the most income—if either adds to income at all.

To the individual, grassland may have economic importance in two directions. An additional acre added to his farm area may enable an increase in the size of his business from which added gross income can be received with less than proportional increase in costs, thus adding to his net income. Or it may enable him to carry the same size of business as before but with less pressure on resources, less resource deterioration, and lower costs but with equal gross income and hence a greater net income.

An acre of cropland converted to grassland will add to the farmer's net income when the relationship between costs and returns is such that the net is larger from the grassland than from the cropland. This condition may arise for one of two reasons—first, as a result of climatic uncertainty or quality of soil or topography, the spread between costs of tillage and gross returns on the acre may not be so large when it is in crop as when it is in grass; and, second, the acre when in grass may fit so well with other aspects of the farm business that it affects the gross farm income or costs or both so that its net income is enhanced.

How does the economic importance of grassland look to most individual operators in the major areas of the Northern Great Plains in the light of these considerations?

In the spring-wheat area and the corn area the farmer is faced with like problems when evaluating the importance to him of adding another acre of grassland to his farm or converting another acre of cropland to grassland.

In either area, when one operator wants to acquire additional grassland to add to his farm he usually will have to buy some other farmer's entire farm unit—not only the grassland he wants but cropland he may not want, and improvements (e. g., buildings) that are of little value to him. Under such circumstances the grassland must be worth considerably more to him than to the adjoining farm to warrant the investment, or the farm he is buying must be so poor that these unwanted values are small, or the public must step in to assume the loss occasioned by the value of the unwanted improvements. Only rarely and under unusual circumstances can the operator who wishes to do so expand his grassland in the wheat area and in the corn area by adding additional land to his farm.

What economic considerations face the individual farmer when he is considering converting some of his cropland to grassland in these areas?

The most common kinds of farms in these areas are only big enough to produce a minimum adequate livelihood under normal price and weather conditions and then usually only by pushing the resources to their productive limit. Except under conditions of unsuitable climate, poor soil or topography, and down to a point of proper relation between cropland and grassland on the farm, an acre of grassland will not produce as much net profit as will the same acre in cropland use. On farms that must be pushed to the limit to make a minimum living for the operator's family, a sacrifice of net income cannot be made by a shift of cropland to grassland use.

Even where the farm produces more than enough for a comfortable living, the shift cannot be made unless the farm is oversupplied with cropland relative to its labor and machinery, or unless it is undersupplied with grassland relative to the needs of the livestock necessary to utilize the feed crops produced, or unless the farmer includes "resource deterioration" as a cost in his accounting and can reduce this cost more than his income by shifting certain crop acres to grass. Farms on which these possibilities occur are few in the spring wheat and corn areas, however.

Rapidly expanding mechanization in both areas also retards the spread of grasslands even though farms are growing in size. Not only can the operator with modern equipment handle more crop acres, but he is compelled to do so in order to carry his investment in machinery. In the spring-wheat area, the wheat-range area, and the corn area, the increasing size of farms is only just barely keeping up with the expanding pressures of mechanization—if it is doing even that.

Thus, though grassland is important in these areas, its expansion, if left to the judgment of individual farmers, faces economic obstacles. Mechaniza-tion of hay and silage equipment may help to increase the use of grass.

In the range area economic pressure for more grassland is a more compelling force; the tendency among ranchmen is to acquire lands from those who have moved away and to stabilize and secure the business by getting firmer control over grasslands that formerly were used but not leased or owned. Mechanization and high wheat prices with favorable weather have retarded the expansion of grassland, but conditions are more favorable for regrassing to take place with the return of weather and wheat prices more normal than they have been since 1920 or so.

The grasslands are essential in the economy of the Northern Great Plains. Without them there would be no economy at all (as in the range area) or a crippled economy (as in the corn area). Yet it is true that the importance of the grasslands and the need for managing them well are not yet appreciated.

To too many persons the grasslands need no management, only harvesting. To too many, they still are only an adjunct to farming—not farming itself. To too many, the yield on grassland is as natural as the weather—not to be affected for good or ill by man.

THE TYPES OF PLAINS VEGETATION

LEON C. HURTT

THE FORAGE that grows on 176 million acres in the Northern Great Plains is the basic raw material for a great range livestock industry.

Hundreds of species, mostly grasses but including shrubs and weeds, make up the total forage crop. Even if they are not grazed, all are of value for holding the topsoil and as a source of humus to retain moisture and enrich the soil.

The plains vegetation is of five types, based on the native vegetation on 231 million acres before a fourth of the total was plowed.

The northern short-grass (mixed prairie) type covers about 228,000 square miles—most of eastern Montana and adjacent parts of the Dakotas and Wyoming, where average precipitation is from 11 to 17 inches a year. The dominant species are blue grama, bluestem wheatgrass or western wheatgrass, needle-and-thread and green needlegrass, buffalograss, Sandberg bluegrass, and threadleaf sedge. These seven provide about 75 percent of the total range forage, but shrubby plants (such as big, silver, and fringed sagebrush, greasewood, and saltbush) are widely distributed and provide some winter forage. This type occupies the rolling plains, but badlands, semibadlands, and roughs of broken topography sometimes considered a separate type, are also included. These occupy many thousands of square miles along the Missouri, White, and Little Missouri Rivers, where geologic formations of low resistance sometimes erode into fantastic forms.

More productive roughs with natural shelter and browse feed are especially valuable for winter grazing. Grazing capacity on any large acreage of this type seldom exceeds 2 acres per animal-unit-month (that is, 1 cow or 5 sheep), but the average is now 3 to 4 acres. Ten acres or more a month is required for some of the roughs that have thin stands.

The tall-grass prairie type grows in northeastern North Dakota and in a zone 50 to 100 miles wide westward from the 98th meridian through South Dakota and Nebraska, a total of about 50,000 square miles, where precipitation ranges from about 17 to nearly 30 inches, and much of the best land is cultivated. This is the most productive type because of a thicker stand of taller grasses. The main species are prairie beardgrass, bluejoint turkeyfoot, blue- and side-oats grama, bluestem wheatgrass, prairie dropseed, and bluegrass. The grazing capacity of the better parts was originally ½ to 1 acre per animal-unit-month, but up to 3 acres is now required for large areas. A large acreage is cut for wild hay of good quality.

The sand-hills type occupies about 21,500 square miles, mainly in west-central Nebraska; there are smaller areas in adjacent States. Precipitation there ranges from 15 to 22 inches, and is absorbed so rapidly by the sandy soil that there is little or no surface runoff. Stream flow is thus remarkably uniform, so that this is one of the best watered of all plains types. The principal species are prairie sandgrass, sand dropseed, sandhill muhly, and three of the *Andropogons*—prairie beardgrass, bluejoint turkeyfoot, and turkeyfoot— often called bluestems. Ranchers of the sand hills have weathered drought periods better than elsewhere, partly because of the relatively stable water supply. Overgrazing, because it is so promptly followed by serious wind erosion, has been less prevalent. Any undue disturbance of the loose surface by plowing or heavy grazing accentuates soil drifting.

The sagebrush-saltbush grassland type (two closely associated and somewhat similar browse types are here considered together) includes a total of about 43,000 square miles of the driest part of the region, where average yearly precipitation drops to 7 to 12 inches. Soils are often highly alkaline or saline, and elevations reach upward to 7,500 feet. The principal species are bluestem wheatgrass, needle-and-thread, bluebunch wheatgrass, Indian ricegrass, Sandberg bluegrass, and sand dropseed. Black and big sagebrush, two or more saltbushes, and greasewood are important shrubs. This type, mainly browse, grows in the Big Horn and Wind River basins, and parts of the so-called Red Desert, a high, windswept, dry area of scanty forage. It is grazed mainly by sheep in fall, winter, and spring, when snow supplements the water supply.

The open-forest type grows on mountain uplifts—Black Hills, Big Horn, Little Snowies, Laramie Mountains, and others—that break the monotony of the plains. Ponderosa pine, Douglas-fir, and spruce occur at the higher elevations. About 18,000 square miles is within this type, a large part of which produces usable forage. Still more important is the extra water for irrigating ranches from snow stored in the mountains. The grasses include bluebunch and bluestem wheatgrass, Idaho fescue, mountain bromegrass, pinegrass, and others. Some of the better forest-range areas can carry one animal-unit-month for 3 or 4 acres, but on the average more is required because of waste range on steep slopes and in dense timber. Succulent forage for a short summer grazing period and ample water make this type especially desirable for producing fat range lambs.

Though not abundant in the Northern Plains, some plants need special attention because they are poisonous. Among these are deathcamas, lupine, loco, waterhemlock, and several selenium-bearing plants. Cockleburs, leafy spurge, and other noxious plants tend to increase with poor management.

FOR A BETTER RANGE MANAGEMENT

LEON C. HURTT

EVEN ON the mixed farms that predominate in the eastern part of the Northern Great Plains many cattle are produced. Farther west, as precipitation declines to 15 inches or less, crop farming is secondary to range-livestock production. Large units are needed in these drier areas, where ranches of 100,000 acres and more are not uncommon. Up to 100 acres may be required on some ranges to carry one cow a year—in the East many complete farms have fewer than 100 acres.

Public land, usually the rougher areas too poor for private ownership, is concentrated in the western part. Counties, States, and various Federal agencies control these lands, which are widely used under lease by local ranchers.

County ownership changes from month to month, so recent totals for the region are not available. R. R. Renne and O. H. Brownlee, in publications of the Montana Agricultural Experiment Station, reported that more than 3.1 million acres were owned by 37 eastern Montana counties in 1936. For all Montana counties the total was approximately 4.5 million acres; 4.5 million acres more were tax delinquent 5 years or more, and thus were subject to county tax deed. All phases of the economy, including income for schools and local government, are disrupted by such high tax delinquency.

This tangled ownership pattern is complicated further by thousands of privately owned tracts that are leased to the highest bidder, often for only a year or two. These ranchers are under a severe disadvantage as compared with those who have leases or permits for 10-year periods. Overcompetition for leases has been especially prevalent in favorable periods among in-and-out speculators and established ranches. Excessive prices paid for poor range land is even a greater, more permanent burden than high prices for leases. Land bought at inflated prices has bankrupted hundreds of ranchers.

The experience of the past half century has somewhat clarified broad outlines of a program of better use of range and water resources, so essential for the welfare of this semiarid region.

Good range management aims to regulate grazing to safeguard resources and get sustained, maximum production of livestock and the best forage species.

The need for it is plain enough: Thousands of cattle and sheep were shipped out of the region as a result of the 1919 drought; there were heavy death losses besides. In 4 years, 1934–38, reductions amounted to 1,200,000 animal-units (43 percent) for Montana as a whole, and nearly 900,000 units (30 percent) for South Dakota. On some ranches more than 80 percent of the livestock were liquidated during the 1934 drought. Heavy shipments were again necessary in 1936.

State averages can give no adequate idea of the distress on thousands of drought-stricken ranches after all feed reserves were exhausted. Forced sales of half-starved livestock brought only a fraction of prices paid during long

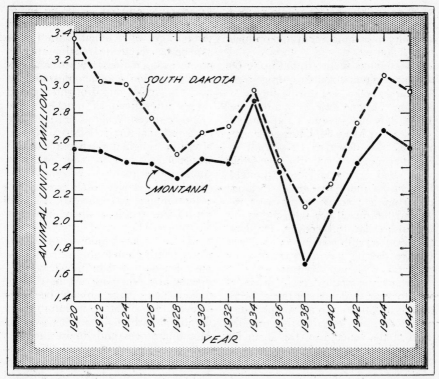

Trends in total animal-units (sheep divided by 5, plus cattle and horses) for Montana and South Dakota, 1920–46. Drought and heavy shipments from 1934–38 accounted for the greatest reduction in animal-units: Montana, 43 percent, and South Dakota, 30 percent.

restocking periods. For years after each emergency, income was painfully inadequate and mountainous debts piled up. Many operators who stocked too heavily lost savings of a lifetime, but a few who maintained more adequate grass and hay reserves saved more from the wreckage.

Many factors besides drought have contributed to widespread range depletion. Reduced forage density, vigor, and production are important indicators of depleted ranges. Careful research has established the principle that excessive trampling and grazing result in increased floods, siltation, and runoff, which reduces soil moisture available for forage growth.

Excessive trampling and damaged range occur on unnumbered sheep bedgrounds, lambing ranges, and key areas that have been used too heavily for long periods. An enormous population of rabbits and mice destroys and consumes untold quantities of forage. Thousands of acres are utterly devastated by prairie dogs that congregate in dog towns.

Striking examples of depleted ranges are found on fields that have not been cropped for many years but which now provide a fifth to a half as much forage as they could if restored to full production.

Dead and dying grass clumps and browse plants are common on some ranges that have been overstocked for years, whereas a healthy, vigorous stand grows on better-managed areas.

Erosion-damaged range occurs on innumerable gullied slopes. Weakened and dead plants perched on pedestals several inches above the present soil levels indicate widespread erosion.

Seedlings of the better plants needed to maintain the range have increasing difficulty in gaining a foothold on such eroded soil.

Investigators reported that up to 60 percent and more of plains forage over wide areas was killed during the great drought. On one series of quadrats at the U. S. Range Livestock Experiment Station near Miles City, forage density in 1937 was down to 10 percent of the predrought level. By 1944 this range had recovered to predrought production under moderate stocking. Unfortunately many ranges were restocked too quickly or with too many animals to allow full recovery. Drought depletion is still evident on a large acreage despite several years of generally favorable weather since 1937.

Considering all the causes—drought, overstocking, rodents, localized overgrazing around key areas, and poor distribution—it is estimated that on one-third of the range area (or about 60 million acres) production is now only 60 to 80 percent of what it could be under good management.

Some Objectives

Make no mistake about it: A more stable range program for the region requires constructive action on many fronts.

Land use practices must be designed to safeguard topsoil and avoid unnecessary erosion, siltation, and waste of water or soil moisture. Uncertain tenure and the crazy-quilt pattern of land-ownership should be corrected. So, too, the evils of overcapitalization due to excessive prices for lands that do not yield any net return. More adequate reserves of range forage, hay, or concentrates, and also financial reserves, need to be built up against the inevitable droughts, grasshopper invasions, or other emergencies. Social opportunities and living conditions for ranch families can be bettered.

Depleted ranges can be rehabilitated profitably. Range reseeding is a cheap, quick way to restore depleted ranges to full production and, in doing so, to check erosion and unnecessary loss of topsoil and water. That many ranges can be economically rehabilitated by no more than reduced stocking and better distribution was demonstrated on a large scale on drought-depleted ranges after livestock numbers were greatly reduced. Where a third or more of the original forage density remained after the drought and where restocking was delayed long enough to allow young forage plants to become firmly established, recovery often was apparently complete in 3 to 5 years. A longer period was required where depletion was more severe.

Reseeding artificially is necessary where nearly all desirable native forage has been destroyed by plowing, overgrazing, or otherwise. More than 3 million acres have already been reseeded in the six States within the past decade. Nearly half of this was on Montana ranges, and almost a million acres in Wyoming. Most of this acreage has been reseeded since cheap methods were developed to convince ranchers that benefits greatly exceeded costs. At the Range Livestock Experiment Station and at the Montana Branch Station at Moccasin, areas reseeded to crested wheatgrass produced two to three times more forage and cattle gains an acre than nearby native range. Reseeded fields frequently produce five times more than fields that have been allowed to revert to weeds of low value.

Little or no soil preparation is necessary where seed is drilled in relatively clean stubble the first or second season after a grain crop, before competing weeds take over to increase risks and costs. Seeding has been successfully done without seedbed preparation on a large acreage of Russian-thistle and certain other weeds. However, competition from a few aggressive species must be controlled for consistently successful reseeding.

Crested wheatgrass and smooth bromegrass make up more than 90 percent of the range acreage of the region successfully reseeded. The latter is used mainly in the eastern portions where annual precipitation is 15 inches or more, but splendid stands of crested wheatgrass now grow where precipitation drops to 10 inches. It starts growth 2 weeks or more earlier than grama and some other native grasses— a great advantage for lambing and calving. Crested wheatgrass also makes splendid hay when cut at the proper stage before maturity. Hay reserves can thus be built up at low cost without irrigation. Early growth, high value for grazing or hay, and low cost account for the high popularity of crested wheatgrass.

Crested wheatgrass drilled in the fall or early spring on a firm seedbed with good seed covered 1 inch or less has been successful. Three to five pounds of seed to the acre with drill rows about 14 inches apart have given excellent stands, but 5 to 8 pounds is often used since the supply increased and the price dropped to 20 cents or less a pound. A much greater seed supply will be required to accomplish the large reseeding program needed.

Several other introduced and native species and some mixtures have shown promise in extensive experimental plantings. Better varieties are also being sought by selection and plant breeding. Methods are also being tested to find which is better or cheaper for various sites, especially where certain aggressive weeds of low value— such as annual brome—provide severe early spring competition.

No comprehensive survey has been made to determine definitely the acreage that should be artificially reseeded, nor have suitable standards been developed for such a determination. Estimates vary from about 3.5 million acres (based on a questionnaire sent to the six States) to something more than 20 million acres (estimated in 1942 by the National Resources Planning Board and in 1944 by the Agricultural Advisory Council for the Northern Great Plains). A large acreage of this is unplowed land on which forage production is a third or less of the original range. The rest is land that has been cropped and abandoned or which will soon be idle. A report by the Bureau of Agricultural Economics, *Wheat Production in War and Peace*, suggests that the Nation's wheat acreage may well be cut as much as 10 to 16 million acres below recent high levels. Much of this is in the Northern Great Plains, where range forage is the most logical alternative use for this land.

Stocking should be for maximum stability. The rate of stocking can be controlled to avoid range depletion, and it should be.

Heavy stocking on short-grass experimental cattle range at the U. S. Range Livestock Experiment Station since 1932 resulted in range deterioration and wasted soil moisture: Principal forage grasses in 1946 averaged more than 25 percent taller on moderately stocked (30.5 acres per cow yearlong or 21 cows per section) than on adjacent heavily stocked pastures (23.1 acres per cow, 28 per section). Production of air-dry forage was 30 percent greater on lightly stocked (38.8 acres per cow yearlong) than on heavily stocked range. Quality of forage was also lower on heavily stocked areas.

Plant litter needed for soil maintenance and for conserving soil moisture was only one-third to one-half as abundant on heavily as on adjacent moderately and lightly stocked range. Heavily stocked areas were more compacted by trampling, which retarded water intake by the soil. Rate of intake was less than half on one heavily stocked soil type as on a lightly stocked type just across the fence. Height of growth, quality, and vigor of forage all dropped under heavy stocking before density was materially reduced.

Besides better soil and range conservation, conservative stocking also gave increased cattle production at lower cost for all feed used and with less risk from drought emergencies.

In November 1945, soon after calves were weaned, the cows from conservatively stocked pastures averaged 98.7 pounds more than those from the heavily stocked pastures, and sold for $12.69 more per head after 8 years on the same pastures. Total feed cost, charging range rental at 10 cents an acre plus supplemental hay feed at $8 a ton, was $1.48 a cow-year less for the conservatively stocked group than for the heavily stocked group. At the recent higher prices, the total advantage in feed cost plus greater production would be more than $12 per cow-year for conservatively over heavily stocked range. As heavy stocking continues year after year penalties grow heavier, whereas better managed range with limited livestock numbers give maximum sustained economical production.

At the same station, experimental sheep ranges deteriorated even more rapidly than cattle ranges under heavy stocking, closer repeated cropping, and trampling by sheep. These experiments demonstrated that ranges and watersheds are more stable with conservative grazing by either class of stock.

Even distribution is a good practice. Thousands of additional watering places are needed to avoid unnecessary penalties in reduced livestock gains, in wasted forage, and in range damage that occurs when livestock are not evenly distributed in relation to the forage supply. Even when the range as a whole is not overstocked, a third or more of it that is around watering places may be damaged; another third may be utilized properly; but on more remote areas forage is wasted when livestock are poorly distributed. Salt placed at strategic locations away from water helps to insure more uniform distribution. Only a few extra pounds of gain per animal will pay handsomely for the added cost of good salting and herding practices.

The class of livestock and season of use also have a bearing on proper use. Thousands of grass-fat beef shipped directly to slaughter pens have established the high quality of Plains forage. Thinner cattle go as feeders; some "two-way" cattle may go directly to butchers or feed yards in the Corn Belt for further fattening. Growthy lambs from Plains ranges are also in keen demand for replacements in breeding herds or for feeders. Midwestern finishers depend on western ranches for a large part of high-quality feeder steers, calves, and lambs that require finishing for the fat-market trade.

Certain varieties and combinations of forage permit grazing of both cattle and sheep if skillful management is practiced. Unless very carefully regulated, however, grazing two classes of stock may result in slow but serious range deterioration.

Segregating winter from summer range provides a change to fresh forage late in the fall and again in the spring. These are critical periods for breeding herds when ample forage of the best possible quality is needed. Fresh range available in December may save the costlier winter feed that otherwise would be required. Spring is also a critical time for young forage plants that are easily destroyed by trampling or heavy grazing. Moving from winter to summer range about midway in the active spring growing season helps to minimize damage when soil is loose and plants are easily destroyed.

Deferred and rotation grazing to aid natural reseeding can be arranged by dividing summer range into three or more parts and grazing each at successively later dates in rotation so that one is grazed after seed maturity each year.

Plants that are poisonous or noxious only at certain seasons sometimes dictate the best season of use on certain ranges.

Ample feed reserves are essential for emergencies. Old cured forage that accumulates under conservative stocking will sustain livestock for a considerable period, but hay, byproducts of cottonseed, soybean, or other reserves should be available.

Any temporary increase in stocking in favorable periods to use up accumulated reserves should be made with caution; production costs are increased by the use of supplemental feed for excess numbers. And when reserves are inadequate, the operator risks damaged range and forced sales of foundation stock with heavy losses. Rather than incur such risks, it is not too serious if some reserve feed deteriorates.

Bad marketing practices also burden the range. Late-fall marketing often presents a problem. After Plains forage matures, normally in August, the lignin content, of little or no feed value, increases while the protein content drops. On matured forage, weight gains tend to level off or may decline after late August. Too often cattle are not marketed till 60 days later, when heavy shipments may break the market. Even when late-marketed cattle do make a slight September gain, it may not compensate for the extra forage used and the risk in the interim.

Other practices should be tested and developed.

For instance, sagebrush and numerous other noxious or low-value species have increased over large areas to the point where reliable guides as to the cheapest and best control measures are urgently needed.

More specific information is needed on how to minimize losses where mineral and vitamin deficiencies cause sickness or reduce breeding efficiency among various classes of livestock.

Better control is needed of range fires that rob wildlife of food and shelter and destroy forage, humus, watershed values, and sometimes lives.

This semiarid region depends heavily on the development and wise use of limited water supplies. Even though the range country contributes only a minor part of the runoff, local floods are increasingly destructive. Because 3 acres is used for range for each acre used for other purposes, range-management practices exert great influence over total runoff. Increased runoff and siltation waste soil moisture, which means reduced forage growth. This vicious circle can hardly fail to fill storage dams and do other damage at an accelerated rate. So, better management is needed on 175 million acres of range for maximum yield of usable water, with a minimum of floods, siltation, and damage to new structures planned for the Missouri River Basin, as well as to those already existing. Values running into billions of dollars are involved.

CULTIVATED GRASSES FOR PASTURES

GEORGE A. ROGLER

SEEDED PASTURES have many values. They can supply cheap and good feed when they are grazed in combination with the native range. They cut the amount of harvested forage or other feed that livestock needs. They can provide a long season of abundant pasturage for spring grazing to supplement native range or pasture that is ready later in the summer. They have a unique place in rotations with other crops. They help to control erosion and make the soil more absorptive of rainfall. Established near farm buildings, seeded pastures enable the farmer to keep stock under close observation.

They can be restored if their stands of grasses or legumes are weakened or destroyed by overgrazing or otherwise.

The use of seeded pastures has been growing in the Northern Great Plains in recent years, but not enough.

Pastures established from seed differ in several respects from native range. Generally they are rather limited in area and may be located on land that could be used for other crops. Native range, on the other hand, occupies relatively large areas that would be unprofitable or impractical for crops. Seeded pastures, even though they consist of perennial grasses and legumes, may be considered as temporary; native range is considered permanent.

We cannot stress too strongly the importance of planting grasses or legumes that are hardy and drought-resistant enough to withstand the severe climate of the Northern Great Plains.

Species and Mixtures

Grasses that can be grown here are ordinarily classified as cool-season or warm-season grasses, depending upon their period of maximum vegetative growth.

Cool-season grasses make most of their growth early in the season and very little in the heat of the summer. They often make considerable growth until late in the season if autumn moisture conditions are favorable.

Warm-season grasses, which make most of their growth in summer, generally start growing after the last frost in the spring and stop growing by the time of the first hard frost in the fall.

Cool-season grasses are the more important by far for cultivation in the Northern Great Plains. Only in the southwestern part are grasses of the cool-season group less well adapted. Local strains of cool-season grasses generally can be moved greater distances north and south without affecting their adaptation than can the warm-season group. Bromegrass is the most important exception to this principle; northern strains of bromegrass are not well adapted in the southern parts. Improved strains of some of the grasses that are well adapted for use under cultivation in the Northern Great Plains are now available, among them are Nebraska 36 and 44 bromegrasses; Mandan wild-rye, an improved Canada wild-rye; and green stipagrass, an improved feather bunchgrass. Others are being developed at experiment stations.

Warm-season perennial grasses of value in the region are all native species. In general, strains of this group should not be moved either north or south more than 200 miles from their origin; otherwise they are not sufficiently well adapted to be of value under cultivation.

Alfalfa and sweetclover are the only legumes now grown to any extent in the Northern Great Plains. Because they help to keep up production and add to the quality of the forage, at least one of them should be included in small amounts with grass in most pasture plantings.

Alfalfa is the best legume for growing in mixtures with grass toward the eastern border of the region. Under good management it may be expected to remain in the mixture for several years. One of the most important points in good management is to avoid close fall grazing because it tends to eliminate alfalfa from the mixture. In the western part, alfalfa may kill out, especially on dry, eroded sites, unless moisture conditions are unusually favorable. Ladak is one of the best varieties to use in mixtures with grass for pasture. Other hardy varieties are available, however.

Sweetclover is the best legume for use in mixtures with grass in the western part and on many dry, eroded sites in the eastern part. Madrid and Spanish are two new varieties that are excellent for use in pastures.

The use of mixtures of grasses or of grasses and legumes is generally preferable to pure seedings for pastures. A combination of species will often provide better grazing over a longer period than pure seedings. Cattle prefer to graze a variety of species.

There are other advantages of mixed plantings. The hazards of seeding will not affect two or more species equally, so that a mixed seeding is more likely to give a stand than is a pure seeding. Several species growing together can better accommodate themselves to a wide range of varying conditions than a single species can.

In cases where fencing and water facilities are such that several adjacent pastures can be planted, it may be well to seed several kinds of grass in pure stands, so that the maximum use of each grass can be made during the proper season. If farmers want a seed crop, as well as pasturage, pure seedings are best.

Despite the recognized advantages of mixtures, the actual interrelationships of associated plants and their effect on livestock need further study.

Establishment

The careful planting of high-quality seed of adapted species at the correct date, a well-prepared seedbed, and proper attention after emergence will assure the successful establishment of grass in most cases. The only other difficulty is dry weather.

Four periods of seeding to be considered are late summer or early fall, late fall, early spring, and midspring.

Late-summer seedings are made about August 15 to September 15; the seed then has time to germinate and establish seedlings well before winter. Plantings of cool-season grasses made at that time are usually the most successful, provided sufficient moisture is available for rapid germination and growth, and grasshoppers do not cause damage.

Alfalfa and sweetclover can generally be seeded successfully in late summer from the southern border of North Dakota southward without danger of severe killing, except when the seedlings do not become well established before heavy frost. From that line northward, the hazards of winterkilling are generally too great for seeding these legumes at that time. If grass-legume mixtures are to be established, the grass can be seeded in late summer and the legume seeded the next spring. The chief advantages of late-summer seedings are that there is less competition from weeds, and the seedlings are well established by the time heat and drought become serious the following summer. Fall-established seedlings also have a better chance to escape June seedling blights.

Late-fall seedings are made so late that germination does not occur until the following spring. Plantings made in late fall have been successful, except in the southernmost parts. The greatest use of late-fall seedings has been on abandoned areas or stubbleland that were seeded without seedbed preparation. An advantage of late-fall seedings is that they do not depend on favorable moisture conditions at the time of planting; late-fall seedings also may be extended over a long period and are better for planting large acreages.

Early-spring plantings made as soon as the ground can be worked are used extensively and successfully throughout the region. Early spring is a good time to seed mixtures containing alfalfa or sweetclover.

The warm-season grasses are best planted in midspring, after the soil has become warm, the first crop of weeds has germinated, and the ground has been worked to destroy weeds.

Shallow seeding is important in the establishment of grasses and legumes. The proper depth is determined by species, size of seed, soil type, and moisture conditions. Ordinarily, planting depths should be no greater than $3/4$ inch—except on light, sandy soils, on which most species can be seeded successfully up to $1\frac{1}{2}$ inches deep. Warm-season grasses should never be seeded deeper than $\frac{1}{2}$ inch.

Poor preparation of seedbeds often causes failure. The soil must be firm in order to make shallow seedings and to enable the seed to be placed in close contact with the soil. A well-packed soil will also retain moisture longer and germination will be faster. Pastures are generally seeded on relatively small areas that can be worked rather intensively if necessary for the preparation of a good seedbed. The additional expense of good seedbed preparation will be repaid by the more rapid establishment of high-yielding pastures.

Well-prepared summer fallow is the best seedbed preparation for late-summer seedings. If erosion threatens, however, a light cover crop of oats may be seeded with the grass. The reserve

Grasses Adapted for Cultivation in the Northern Great Plains Region

COOL-SEASON GRASSES

Common name	Scientific name	Part of region to which best adapted	Pure seed to plant per acre
			Pounds
Crested wheatgrass..	Agropyron cristatum...	Entire region..............	10–12.
Intermediate wheat-grass.	Agropyron interme-dium.	Southern portion on favorable local areas.	10–12.
Western wheatgrass.	Agropyron smithii.....	Entire region especially on heavy soils.	12–14.
Slender wheatgrass..	Agropyron trachycaulum.	Entire region; in mixtures only.	
Bromegrass........	Bromus inermis........	Eastern border and favorable local areas.	10–12.
Canada wild-rye....	Elymus canadensis.....	Entire region; in mixtures only.	
Russian wild-rye....	Elymus junceus........	Entire region..............	10–12.
Feather bunchgrass .	Stipa viridula.........	Entire region; in mixtures only.	

WARM-SEASON GRASSES

Common name	Scientific name	Part of region to which best adapted	Pure seed to plant per acre
Big bluestem.......	Andropogon furcatus...	Eastern border and favorable local areas.	10–12.
Side-oats grama....	Bouteloua curtipendula.	Entire region; best in south central and southwest; in mixtures only.	
Blue grama........	Bouteloua gracilis......	Entire region, especially on eroded sites.	6–8.
Buffalograss	Buchloe dactyloides....	Southwest and on dry heavy soils.	8–10 (burs).
Switchgrass........	Panicum virgatum.....	Eastern border and favorable local areas.	6–8.

moisture stored in fallow results in faster growth and stronger plants than those grown on any other preparation. Successful seedings can be made in clean grain stubble if the soil needs a protective covering. Seedlings that emerge in stubble have protection against soil blowing. Besides, snow that is caught will form a cover that greatly lessens the danger of winterkilling. Grain stubble also furnishes a desirable seedbed for late-fall seedings.

Spring plantings can be made on protected fallow or corn ground. Plowed grain stubble is somewhat less satisfactory, but can be used if the soil is well firmed before seeding. Tillage treatments that tend to leave the soil so fine that it is susceptible to wind erosion should be avoided.

A drill is best for sowing because it distributes the seed uniformly and places it more nearly at the proper depth for good germination and establishment. Drill spacings of 6 to 12 inches are satisfactory for pasture. The wider spacings may be better in the drier areas toward the west.

On well-fitted seedbeds a press drill can be used to advantage, as it will place the seed in closer contact with the soil than other types of drills. Single-disk drills are used when the farmer wants to leave the soil surface as rough as possible. Deep-furrow drills have been used successfully for seeding abandoned lands without previous seed-bed preparation. On limited acreages and on unstable soils, hay that contains mature seed may be spread over the surface and disked or pressed into the soil to afford some covering.

Broadcasting the seed usually is not satisfactory, but in localities where the land is too rough for machinery, broadcasting is sometimes successful. Some method of covering the seed should be used if possible.

Unless they are needed to protect the soil, companion or nurse crops should not be used with grass or legume plantings in the Northern Great Plains. If nurse crops are used, they should be seeded at very low rates; otherwise competition for moisture and shading by the companion crop is likely to be too great for the survival of seedlings.

Newly established stands of grass ordinarily should not be grazed or cut for hay the first year. Occasionally, when seed is planted in the late summer on fertile soil that has a favorable moisture content, enough growth will be made the next year so that a light crop of hay or seed can be harvested or a small amount of pasturage may be available.

Weed growth is generally rather heavy the first year, especially where late-fall or spring plantings have been made. Weeds should be clipped only when they are so tall and vigorous that the grass or legume seedlings are seriously hampered in their growth. Clipping, if it is necessary, should be done only in cool weather, and the weeds should be cut high to avoid injuring the seedlings. A high stubble also will provide protection to the seedlings and catch snow.

In early spring it is wise to mow and remove any old heavy vegetative or weed growth that has been allowed to remain over winter. It is best not to burn old growth because of the serious damage that may be done to tender grass or legume seedlings. Stands are usually well enough established by the second year so that weeds cease to be a serious problem.

MANAGEMENT OF SEEDED PASTURES

GEORGE A. ROGLER

The maintenance of stands or of high production of grasses and legumes depends greatly upon proper management. Pastures that do not have legumes generally show a marked reduction in yield the third or fourth year after establishment. This reduction is frequently caused by a lack of available nitrogen and may be as high as 50 to 75 percent. Alfalfa or sweetclover planted in mixture with grasses is the cheapest way to provide the nitrogen to maintain yield, but it may be difficult to keep those legumes in the mixture in dry seasons. Alfalfa may kill out because of drought. Sweetclover seedlings generally do not become established by natural means in old stands of grass.

Yields can often be increased somewhat by tearing up thoroughly the sod of old pastures, but the beneficial effects of the practice are usually short-lived. Seeding alfalfa or sweetclover into disturbed sod offers some possibilities in favorable years.

Application of commercial nitrogenous fertilizers often boosts yields sharply, but in dry periods they should be applied sparingly to guard against severe burning. Manure also will often increase yields.

The best way to get continuous high production of grass is to have the pastures in a crop-rotation system. When production falls off, the pasture can be broken and cropped for several years and then returned to grass. Old, low-producing grass stands can be broken and fallowed for a year and then reseeded; this method, however, may not be practical on marginal land or erosive areas.

In the Northern Great Plains the most efficient and economical method of utilizing both seeded pastures and native range is to graze the seeded pastures in combination with (and as a supplement to) the native range. Experiments have shown that this combination system of grazing will provide a longer grazing season and give a higher production on fewer acres.

Pastures of cool-season grasses can be grazed 2 to 3 weeks earlier than native range, and on them livestock can be grazed at a rather high intensity for 60 to 75 days in the spring. During that time grazing on the native range can be deferred. By the time the livestock have fully utilized the grass in the pasture, or after it has become too mature for good grazing, the deferred native range is in excellent condition for livestock, and because it has been deferred for approximately 45 days, the intensity of grazing on it can be greater than if it had been grazed early in the season.

Cattle grazed on seeded pastures should be moved to native range while they are still making good gains. If pastures of cool-season grasses are grazed too late in the summer, the grass will mature and lose quality and livestock gains will often drop rapidly.

Native range grasses remain in good condition for grazing much later in the season and greater gains can be obtained on them during this period than on cool-season grass pastures. With favorable moisture in the fall, pastures may still make considerable growth. It is generally not advisable to graze this new growth heavily, because doing so will cut production the following spring.

When cattle or sheep are grazed on a combination of native range and cool-season grass pasture, it is advisable to fence the pasture separately so that the stock can be restricted to one or the other. Proper utilization will not be made unless the cultivated grass

and native range are separate. Livestock will graze the cultivated grass early in the spring, but will tend to leave it and graze the native grass as soon as it starts to grow. The cultivated grasses will then be underutilized and become coarse and stemmy. If this old growth is permitted to accumulate on the seeded pasture, grazing will become patchy in later years.

Because grasses differ as to maturity and the period when they can be grazed, a series of pastures of different grasses can be established and grazed in rotation. Good results have been obtained in experiments with sheep in Wyoming by grazing them first on crested wheatgrass very early, then on Russian wild-rye, which makes somewhat later growth, and then on warm-season grasses for the rest of the summer. Gains were much higher on these pastures than on native range alone.

Temporary Pastures

Temporary pastures are a possibility on farms that do not have sufficient native range or enough cultivated grass pasture for their livestock needs. The best crops for this purpose in the Northern Great Plains are winter rye, Sudangrass, and sweetclover. Individual farm needs will determine which of these crops can best be used for pasture purposes. Their use as supplements to native range and pastures will provide a full season of grazing.

Winter rye planted in late summer will usually provide considerable grazing later in the fall. It is very productive the following spring.

Sudangrass, if conditions are favorable, will give an abundance of pasture during the hot part of the summer. Care should be taken to use pure seed—it is generally wise to plant only certified seed in pastures.

Mixtures of cane with Sudangrass sometimes cause prussic acid poisoning. Precautions should be taken not to allow livestock to eat too much when they are first turned on the pasture even when grazing Sudangrass that is thought to be pure. Poisoning can usually be avoided by feeding hay to livestock before turning them on the pasture. Another precaution is to turn only a few head of stock on the pasture until it is determined that there is no danger from poisoning.

Sweetclover also makes an excellent temporary pasture. Sufficient growth is usually made during the first season to provide some pasture during late summer and fall. Second-year sweetclover will furnish an abundance of pasturage in midsummer. There is a danger of bloat, but it is not serious and can be avoided in most cases by feeding enough dry feed before turning the stock on sweetclover so that they will not immediately gorge themselves. Another way to avoid bloat is to have dry roughage available to stock while they are being pastured.

HAY, FODDER, AND SILAGE CROPS

L. C. NEWELL

ON THE BASIS of acreage, wild hay is the outstanding hay crop of the region. More than 9 million acres of it were harvested in 1946. Nebraska, South Dakota, and North Dakota lead the United States in the production of wild hay. It is the principal return from virgin, unbroken lands other than the grazing.

Wild hays, made up chiefly of the tall and mid-tall grasses of the prairie regions, are the prairie hays of commerce, although their most important use is within the region. On the market they are graded as Upland Prairie or Midland Prairie hays according to the kinds and qualities of the grasses they contain.

Prairie hays are composed of a large number of grasses and grasslike plants, with smaller admixtures of native and introduced species belonging to many different families. In any particular case, the large percentage of the grass in the hay will be of a few species.

The principal grasses found in Upland Prairie hays are the bluestems, needlegrasses, and wheatgrasses, with such grasses as junegrass, the grama grasses, the dropseeds, Indiangrass, and switchgrass contributing smaller amounts in different hays. The principal species of Midland Prairie hays are those adapted to growing in wet areas; among them are sloughgrass or cordgrass, bluejoint, and switchgrass.

Studies of the composition and nutritive value of native vegetation at Mandan, N. Dak., showed that western needlegrass comprises 50 to 75 percent of the total weight of the grasses. Fifty or more different kinds of plants were found. Since the droughts of 1934 and 1936, the needlegrass has largely been replaced by western wheatgrass.

Wheatgrass hay is produced on the fine-textured soils largely to the north and west of the Nebraska sand hills. It is especially important along river bottoms in northeastern Montana. This hay is frequently harvested from nearly pure stands of western wheatgrass. Feeding tests have shown it to be equal or superior to alfalfa hay for wintering cattle.

In the Nebraska sand hills, which are unique in ranching and haying operations, a good balance is achieved between range and hay land. Ranges of the sand hills or adjacent hard lands provide grazing. Meadows of the subirrigated valleys produce abundant hay crops in which the bluestems predominate. These hay lands are a postclimax development resulting from the westward extension of the tall grasses along the valleys. Studies of these hay meadows have shown that the relative amounts of the many kinds of grasses are closely associated with distances to the water table. The quality and yield of hay have been greatly improved by the introduction of clovers into some of these subirrigated meadows. Haymaking, the principal harvesting operation in the sand-hill ranching area, continues from June until September. Some of the early-cut hay of best quality is baled and shipped out of the region to terminal markets. A large tonnage of stacked hay is required for overwintering operations within the area.

Haymaking and hay-feeding methods have become largely mechanized with either improvised or modern machinery within the past 15 years.

An experiment to measure the effects of time of cutting on the yields and quality of typical bluestem hay was started recently in southern Nebraska on a section of unbroken prairie given to the University of Nebraska for experimental purposes. The effects of different clipping treatments on the meadow are to be measured over a period of years and the results interpreted each year in terms of the feeding value of the hay. The first experiments showed that early-cutting and aftermath harvests gave the best hay.

High quality is important in haymaking. Studies of the different kinds of prairie hays indicate that the protein content drops as the grasses mature. There also seems to be a close association between protein and carotene content of hays. Although the early-cut hays usually contain enough protein to exceed minimum feed requirements, the later cut hays frequently are deficient. Feeding of protein supplements has become common in wintering cattle on native hay or on the range, with the result that a maximum return is had from the hays fed.

Cultivated Perennials

Seed of adapted strains are needed when croplands are put back into perennial grasses. Most of the commonly cultivated forage grasses have never been successfully established under the variable and severe climate of the Northern Great Plains. The native grasses provide some of the best adapted plant materials for this purpose, but until 1934 seed of these grasses was not available. Since then much progress has been made in domesticating them, seed has been machine harvested in large quantities from native stands and nurseries, and methods of establishment have been developed. It is now possible to obtain seed and establish stands of such important grasses as western wheatgrass, feather bunchgrass, wild-rye, big bluestem, switchgrass, sand lovegrass, side-oats grama, blue grama, and buffalograss. A continuing problem, however, is to increase seed supplies of the adapted superior strains in order that they may become generally available for conservation plantings and for hay and pasture production.

In general, cool-season grasses—which grow early in the spring and mature seed in early summer—have been shown to have a much higher content of crude protein than those of the warm-season group, which reach their greatest growth in the hot months. As such, they are important species for consideration as hay. The cool-season group, including native western wheatgrass, wild-ryes, feather bunchgrass, and the introduced crested wheatgrass, intermediate wheatgrass, and bromegrass, offers the best possibilities for hay crops in the region. These tall grasses are suited to hay-harvesting methods, but require considerable amounts of moisture for maximum yields. However, they combine varying degrees of ability to withstand drought with the ability to produce good yields when moisture conditions are favorable. They are important for use in supplementing the warm-season group, which predominate in native hays and on the range.

On the other hand, adapted strains of the warm-season grasses such as big bluestem, switchgrass, sand lovegrass, and the grama grasses are important for reseeding on sandy soils and in the southwestern part where the cool-season species are less well adapted.

Crested wheatgrass is the most important introduced species in the region. Stands of this grass are useful supplements to the range for early spring pasture; they make it possible to defer grazing of the warm-season range grasses until a proper growth has been made. If it is not used early in the season as pasturage, crested wheatgrass will provide a hay or a seed crop. For the best hay it should be cut before a maximum of heading has taken place in order to insure a high protein content. When properly handled, the feeding value of crested wheatgrass is high, ranking with other cool-season grasses and alfalfa. Another introduced wheatgrass that shows promise through the southern half of the region is intermediate wheatgrass.

The demand for grasses to be used for soil conservation purposes has greatly increased the acreage of bromegrass along the eastern edge of the region. The Dakotas have long been recognized as one of the principal producing areas of bromegrass seed in the United States. Nebraska grew more than 50 percent of the bromegrass seed in the United States in 1944 and 1945. It is estimated that plantings in Nebraska have increased from a few thousand acres to more than a half million acres in 10 years. Originally planted for conservation purposes, bromegrass is now being used for pasture, hay and seed production, and as a crop in rotations.

Increased acreage in the southern part has been made possible by the discovery of adapted strains. Lincoln bromegrass, certified in Nebraska, and the Achenbach strain, produced in northern Kansas, are the leading strains adapted for establishment on critical planting sites and under the relatively longer hot summers of that part of the region. These varieties are thought to be derived from an early introduction of seed of Hungarian origin in contrast to northern-grown strains of Russian origin. Bromegrass is primarily considered best adapted along the eastern edge of the region,

but the use of adapted strains and the recent favorable seasons have extended its use farther westward. It is especially recommended on fertile soils and under irrigation in mixtures with alfalfa.

Legume Hays

Alfalfa, the most important legume hay in the Northern Great Plains, is especially valuable in the finishing ration with grains for cattle and sheep. It is also grown for shipment to dairy centers and for use as a component of commercial feeds.

The alfalfa plant has a deep root system and, once established, can draw heavily on subsoil moisture. It can therefore survive moderately dry weather for rather long periods under proper management. Alfalfa is grown to best advantage on fertile soils with naturally favorable moisture conditions or under irrigation, where it reaches its greatest production and is valued as an important crop in the rotation. With sufficient moisture, three good cuttings are usually obtained a year in the southern part and two cuttings in the northern part.

Varieties for this region must carry a high degree of winter-hardiness to withstand the typical cold weather that often occurs without a snow cover. Hardistan, Grimm, Cossack, Baltic, Ladak, Ranger, and the Northern Commons are the most important varieties with sufficient winter-hardiness to survive.

Bacterial wilt is prevalent in districts where soil moisture conditions favor maximum production. The disease is not serious on upland soils, but wilt-resistant varieties are desired for seed production because of favorable price considerations. Of the new wilt-resistant varieties, Ranger is the most likely to prove adapted. It yields about the same in seed and forage as Grimm in the absence of bacterial wilt.

Spring seedings of alfalfa are the more common, although good stands can be obtained by seeding in late summer if moisture conditions are favorable and grasshoppers are not too numerous. A firm, moist seedbed is essential. If the field has not grown alfalfa or sweetclover previously, inoculation of the seed with cultures of the proper strains of nitrogen-fixing bacteria may be beneficial for establishment and early growth in certain localities. Planting with a drill provides the best means of obtaining even distribution of seed and uniform depth of seeding. It will usually pay to compact the seedbed with a corrugated roller following broadcasting or drilling. Best stands are usually obtained without a nurse crop.

The climate of the region favors the production of high-quality alfalfa hay. When properly cured, hay cut at the one-tenth bloom stage provides a nutritious product, without danger to the stand. Harvesting procedures should be adopted that retain the maximum percentage of leaves with a rich-green color in order to obtain good quality of protein and high vitamin content. If properly cured and stored, the hay will provide these essentials to animal health during periods of the year when other green feeds are not available.

Sweetclover is widely adapted, but its importance as a hay crop is secondary to its value as pasture or as a soil-building crop in the rotation. Adapted new varieties include Evergreen, Spanish, and Madrid sweetclovers, which have been shown to be superior to the common white and common yellow varieties that are still being grown widely. If it is harvested at the proper stage and properly cured, sweetclover hay is comparable in composition and feeding value to alfalfa.

Grass-Legume Mixtures

Special care must be exercised in curing sweetclover because when it is spoiled it might kill livestock. The bitter quality of sweetclover is due to a substance known as coumarin. Changes in coumarin resulting from spoilage are considered to be the cause of the blood-thinning effects of feeding the spoiled sweetclover hay. Extensive research is being directed toward the development of new varieties of low coumarin content.

Growing grasses and legumes in mixtures is a desirable practice for improving and maintaining yields and providing high protein content. Such mixtures are more practical under conditions where moisture may be the limiting factor during parts of the season than are legume crops grown alone. Soil moisture is made available to different types of root systems and growth is distributed during different parts of the season. Nitrogen accumulated in the soil by growth of legume plants can be used effectively by perennial forage grasses during periods of favorable moisture supply. Grass roots assist in stabilizing soil against erosion.

Alfalfa and sweetclover are the best legumes now available for inclusion in mixtures. Their use with cool-season grasses is particularly desirable, since these grasses require a readily available supply of nitrogen during the cool months of the year when nitrogen release by the soil is slow. The development of drought-tolerant strains of alfalfa and sweetclover and of other legumes which may be adapted for growing with grasses is extremely desirable.

Where annual rainfall is low, growing grass in rows is feasible for obtaining maximum yields. At the Archer Field Station in Wyoming a practice of growing a mixture of crested wheatgrass and alfalfa in rows with cultivation has been a successful method of producing a mixed hay.

On poor soil, plantings of sweetclover in the rotation ahead of the seeding of grasses is proving practicable in building up a readily available supply of nitrogen for the benefit of the grass crop during its period of establishment. Volunteering of the sweetclover in the grass stand is also desirable if the plants are not so thick as to compete with the establishment of the grass.

Cereal hays, chiefly rye and wheat, are sometimes used in the western part of the region to provide a quick-growing hay crop. The hay is cut in an early stage to insure a high protein content. Such hays are especially valued as roughage for small dairy herds.

The millets are summer catch crops that are well adapted here. They produce hay crops in about 50 to 75 days from planting and usually give a good yield. Their short growing season makes them especially valuable to replace crops destroyed by hail in the early part of the growing season. The chief varieties are Common, German, Hungarian, Siberian, White Wonder, and Proso. Millet is usually cut for hay just after blooming. Hay cut later is inferior in quality but may be fed with little danger to cattle and sheep. Millet hays, especially if mature, are considered unsatisfactory for horses.

Sudan hay, another summer crop, is extensively used as supplemental feed. Valued as a summer pasture in the eastern counties, it is frequently harvested as hay if the summer forage supply is ample for grazing. It is usually close-drilled to provide a fine-stemmed hay, which should be cut well before maturity in order to insure maximum quality and ease of handling.

Fodder and Silage

A common practice is to grow a mixed cane as a bundle feed. Mixed sorghum, seeded with an ordinary grain drill, gives a summer crop that is relatively fine-stemmed and can be harvested with a grain binder or mowed and stacked for winter use.

Results at experiment stations indicate that better yields and quality can be had by growing selected varieties than by planting mixed seeds of unknown adaptation. Seed should be treated to insure good stands and to control grain smuts. The best fodder yields are usually obtained by seeding in rows with cultivation, harvesting with a corn binder, and placing in shocks for curing. For fodder the forage sorghums should be cut when the seed has reached the medium-dough stage.

The sorghum crop is second in acreage and production to alfalfa as a cultivated forage crop in the Northern Great Plains. It is grown chiefly in the southern half, where it may supplant corn in the rotation because of its greater tolerance to drought.

Varieties like Black Amber, Fremont, Rancher, and Dakota Amber are comparatively drought-resistant and well adapted. In the eastern and southeastern districts and under irrigation, Atlas, Box, Leoti, and Axtell are the most productive. These long-season varieties are also sometimes grown farther north in areas where they are not expected to produce seed.

Forage varieties of sorghum and corn are used sometimes as silage, the early-maturing varieties of corn being the most important in the northern counties. When used as silage, sorghums produce a good grade of roughage with a somewhat higher yield than corn. They should be cut at a more mature stage for silage than for fodder. Cutting too early promotes spoilage. Silage can be stored for a longer time than fodder without material loss of quality or palatability. It can be carried over as an emergency feed for years of drought.

Some waste of hays, fodders, and silage is inevitable if sufficient reserves are carried from year to year. These wastes may be held to a minimum if old supplies are used up periodically, along with other feeds of good quality. The value of such supplies cannot be overestimated from the standpoint of their insurance against feed shortages during recurrent droughts and periods when the normal disposal rate of livestock is interrupted by unfavorable markets.

THE AUTHORS ≪ *George A. Rogler grew up on a farm in the Flint Hills area of eastern Kansas. He attended Kansas State College and the University of Minnesota. Mr. Rogler has been engaged in research with grass since 1934; he is now an agronomist in the Bureau of Plant Industry, Soils, and Agricultural Engineering at the Northern Great Plains Field Station, Mandan, N. Dak., where he has been located since 1936.*

Leon C. Hurtt was reared on a western Nebraska farm and was graduated from the University of Nebraska. His early Forest Service assignments were on Utah and New Mexico range studies. Later he was forest supervisor in Idaho and Montana for 8 years. Since 1932 he has been in charge of range research for the Northern Rocky Mountain Forest and Range Experiment Station.

M. M. Kelso is ranch economist for the Montana Agricultural Experiment Station and professor of agricultural

economics at Montana State College at Bozeman. From 1934 to 1937 he was associated with the Land Utilization Division of the Resettlement Administration; from 1937 to 1942 he was head of the Division of Land Economics of the Bureau of Agricultural Economics. From 1942 to 1946, he operated a cattle ranch in Montana.

L. C. Newell, a native of Nebraska, has been engaged in research on grasses in the Central Great Plains since 1935. Dr. Newell is an agronomist in the Bureau of Plant Industry, Soils, and Agricultural Engineering. Now he is delegated to the Nebraska Agricultural Experiment Station in Lincoln where he has charge of the cooperative grass investigations, including the selection and breeding of superior strains of native and introduced forage grasses.

The Southern Great Plains

THE REGION AND ITS NEEDS

D. A. SAVAGE, D. F. COSTELLO

THE Southern Great Plains is a big expanse of range country, dry-land farms, and some irrigated areas. Unintentional but widespread misuse of its soils in the past and a cataclysmic drought depleted the ranges, destroyed land and property, upset community stability, and brought a need for subsidies, relief, and other outside aid. People then called a part of it the Dust Bowl.

It has now regained some of its prominence as a leading cattle-producing and livestock-farming area; to maintain and improve this position requires a grassland agriculture geared to climate and the nature of the soil.

This hopeful trend is still in its infancy. Much remains to be done. Millions of acres of the erosive, less fertile areas need to be returned to grass; farming needs to be restricted to the better lands. Extremely alarming is the tendency in some sections to repeat the serious mistake made in the First World War by plowing up the native pasture land and placing it under cultivation. The great drought of the 1930's emphasized the fallacy of straight wheat production in the region, pointed up the importance of a more diversified grassland agriculture, and focused public attention upon the critical need for expanding, improving, and conserving the acreage of good

range grasses. The lesson was a costly one. It must be remembered. Severe droughts are certain to recur. We must be ready for them.

The Southern Great Plains includes about 130 million acres south of the Nebraska-Kansas and Wyoming-Colorado borders. It extends from the eastern slope of the Rocky Mountains in Colorado and New Mexico to about the 98th meridian in Kansas and Oklahoma. The boundary swings southwest in Texas to the southern border of New Mexico and includes the Texas Panhandle and adjacent areas of western Texas and eastern New Mexico. The region represents about a third of the total area of the five States.

Wide variations occur in surface features, soils, and plant cover. The general aspect is a fairly level plain with shallow drainage channels often interspersed with rolling lands or steep broken areas. The principal rivers flow eastward. Only two of them, the South Platte and the Arkansas, furnish much water for irrigation. Most of the region slopes gently from elevations of 5,000 to 6,000 feet on the west to 2,000 feet or less on the east and south.

The climate is highly variable from month to month and year to year. Rainfall is comparatively light and infrequent; humidity is low; there are high winds and quick evaporation.

503

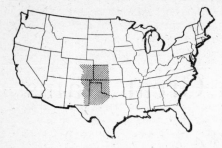

The yearly precipitation ranges from 10 to 17 inches in the west to 20 inches or more in the east; about two-thirds of it falls during the active growing season, April to September. Much of the rainfall occurs as torrents or light, ineffective showers; often hot weather and high winds further reduce its effectiveness. Drought periods, which occur nearly every year and occasionally last for several seasons or years, make dry-land farming hazardous.

The winters here are generally mild, open, and fairly dry, with an infrequent shower or severe snowstorm and sharp fluctuations in temperature. Wind velocities reach a peak late in winter or early in the spring and are usually higher throughout the year than elsewhere in the United States.

Plants to be fully adapted to the entire region must be able to withstand these conditions and temperature extremes from 118° to −30° F. The average yearly temperature ranges from about 50° in the north to 65° in the south, with a summer mean usually above 70°. The daily range is high. The frost-free season varies from 125 days on the higher slopes of Colorado to 200 days at the lower elevations in the southeastern part.

The soils range in texture from dune sand to heavy clay. Most of them are well supplied with minerals and other essential elements in available form. They were developed mainly from materials originally washed from the Rocky Mountains, and contain a variety of minerals that have not been leached below the depth of plant roots, except in some sandy soils.

Farmers recognize two broad classes of soils in the region: The hard lands, that can grow wheat and cotton, and the sandy lands, where sorghums or corn are best suited.

Two other broad distinctions are made in considering proper land use: The heavy, semiheavy, and sandy soils adapted to cultivation; and the loose sandy soils, heavy clays, and rough broken lands suitable for range. The heavier and more fertile soils consist of a fine-grained layer of topsoil composed of silt or clay loam and underlain with a clay or clay loam subsoil. These soils absorb water slowly but retain it well.

On January 1, 1947, the five States that include the Southern Great Plains had about 18 million cattle, 13 million sheep, and 1½ million horses and mules. The five States had 22 percent of the Nation's cattle, 35 percent of the sheep, and 16 percent of the horses and mules—or 25 percent of the total animal population and 17 percent of the valuation of these classes of grass-eating livestock. Sheep numbers in the five States were 75 percent of the cattle numbers in the area, but the valuation of sheep was a tenth of that of cattle.

Texas led the United States in number and valuation of cattle and sheep and in number of horses. Kansas ranked second in the region and fifth in the country in number of cattle; Colorado ranked correspondingly in number of sheep. New Mexico had fewer cattle than any State within the region but more than 11 other States. The importance of the region as a cattle-producing area is much greater than the figures indicate; they were recorded after millions of feeder cattle had left the region for finishing in the Corn Belt.

The cattle population in the region on January 1, 1947, was 4 percent below that for the same date in 1946 but 8 percent above the previous 10-year average. This large population is certain to result in damage to range resources in the event of another severe drought unless adequate supplies of extra forage and other supplements are provided.

The Southern Great Plains is outstanding in the production of feeder cattle, most of which are fed on native grass alone or with a limited supply of protein concentrates. The comparatively high feed value of the native grasses at all stages of growth accounts for the reputation of the region for yearlong grazing.

Many of the large ranches depend on range forage for most of their livestock feed. But most of the farmer-stockmen and increasing numbers of the ranchmen, particularly in the northwestern and southern parts, are making considerable progress in using a combination of range, pastures, and harvested crops for producing and fattening feeder-cattle and other classes of livestock.

This desirable practice could be expanded to advantage throughout the area and should include the increased use of reseeded pastures. For wintering and fattening their livestock, Colorado stockmen make excellent use of harvested crops, among them sugar-beet byproducts and alfalfa from irrigated farms, and sorghums, corn, and small grains from dry-land areas. Grain sorghums, supplemented with concentrates, are being extensively used for wintering and fattening cattle in the southern part of the Texas Panhandle. Wheat pasture also is important in the livestock economy of the region.

Grassland agriculture in the Southern Great Plains is represented by all gradations of land use, ranging from complete livestock grazing to strict crop production. Individual holdings vary in size from farms of a half section or less to large ranches of several thousand acres. The majority are small operating units of less than 2,000 acres, although the trend is toward a larger and more permanently self-sustaining unit in which livestock and crop production are conducted as well-balanced enterprises. Cash grain and feed crop production receive more emphasis than livestock on the smaller units.

The dry-land ranching units are used mainly to produce breeding herds and feeder cattle. Most of the livestock are finished in the Corn Belt, although some fattening is done in irrigated sections, on dry-land farms, and in the subhumid bluestem areas east of the Plains. Only a few livestock are moved in from other areas for summer grazing. Some sheep are shipped in from mountain areas for winter grazing.

Yearlong grazing of range land is a common practice in most of the region, especially with breeding herds. Cultivated forage crops are used to replace or supplement the winter range in the northern part of the region and on some smaller units elsewhere. Cropland aftermath, wheat pasture, and other supplements are common winter feeds. Most native ranges are used from April to October or November in Colorado and Kansas and on a yearlong basis farther south. Some ranges are retained for exclusive winter use, although most of them are grazed continuously. Most operators use protein concentrates to supplement their winter range. Only a few supplement their summer range with a light feeding of protein concentrates in late summer.

Approximately 20 percent of the heifers are saved for annual replacements in the breeding herd. Prices and feed supplies affect the number retained. The general practice is to have the heifers calve at 2 years of age, although the better stockmen prefer calving at 3. A crop of 2- and 3-year-old heifers and dry cows is usually culled from the herd to add to the livestock sales.

Purebred bulls are used generally. The individual merit of the bulls varies greatly from ranch to ranch. Some effort toward the improvement of herds through cooperative purchase of better bulls is evident.

Feeder yearlings and feeder calves represent the principal sales from farms and ranches. Some grass-fat yearlings and 2-year-olds are sold. More feeder calves are sold in years when prices are relatively high and winter feed supplies are short.

In the few places where sheep are

grazed on the range, the general practice is to use a herder and to provide night corrals and some shelter. Supplemental feeding in winter is the common practice. A few small operators cater to the spring lamb market, but the bulk of production goes to the fall slaughter and feeder lamb markets. Range sheep production is of minor importance in the region. This accounts for the fact that range lands of the Southern Great Plains have suffered somewhat less from overgrazing than many other ranges in the West.

The beef cattle industry in the Southern Great Plains can be placed and maintained on a much more stable basis through the adoption of improved practices for the care and management of both the range and the cattle. These possibilities are indicated by the results of range studies and grazing tests conducted in the region.

Stockmen are urged to make annual appraisals of the condition of their range lands and determine the trend for better or worse. Accurate inventories of this kind are dependent upon a thorough knowledge of, and ability to recognize, the desirable and undesirable plants. Every stockman needs a practical working knowledge of the production capacity of his grasslands. He needs to know what degree of forage utilization will result in optimum returns from his livestock and at the same time allow sustained maximum production of grass.

If this knowledge were generally available, the evil effects of "grass inflation" and "grass depression" could be diminished. In good years, a large volume of vegetation, much of which consists of low-value weeds, springs up and gives false hopes of prosperity. The tendency under such conditions is to graze more livestock than is proper or profitable. The result is overgrazing in dry years and enforced sale of a portion of the breeding herd laboriously built up over a period of time. This lowers the herd quality and frequently causes the operator to conclude that purchase of high-grade animals is hazardous and uneconomical. Stockmen need guides for judging condition of the range, yearly forage production, and current use of the grass.

An occasional overhaul job of the ranch is just as important as a motor tune-up on the family automobile. There are very few farms and ranches where the efficiency of operation cannot be improved. Higher income can usually be obtained after a little trouble-shooting, usually without an expansion of facilities. This can be accomplished by giving proper attention to forage, livestock, and equipment.

The forage should receive attention at all times. It is the crop which the livestock operator has for sale; the animals are merely a means of harvesting and processing it. In the long run, conservative use of the grass pays the best dividends in grass and livestock production. It provides assurance of a sustained forage supply and results in optimum weight gains. An understanding of range conditions is necessary before correct use can be attained. An examination of different ranges in any locality will show that the forage is better on some than others. An exchange of ideas among stockmen frequently reveals the cause.

DRY-LAND PASTURES ON THE PLAINS

D. A. SAVAGE, JAMES E. SMITH, D. F. COSTELLO

IN THE Southern Great Plains a steadily increasing acreage of pastures is being established by seeding native or introduced grasses on cultivated and abandoned farm land. Other grazing lands include small areas of irrigated pasture and extensive native range.

Millions of acres of the more erosive

and less productive lands in the region are unprofitable for cultivated crops but they can produce excellent pasture grasses if they are properly handled.

Investigations by research agencies and experience of farmers in the past decade show that it is simple enough to get good stands of palatable and nutritious grasses on land once tilled unwisely and unprofitably, and, in doing so, to reclaim vast areas of otherwise unproductive land, make the agriculture more permanent, and achieve proper land use.

Further and faster progress is expected when planting equipment and seed become more plentiful, more farmers and stockmen understand and appreciate the methods and values of this new undertaking, and the prices of wheat and other crops are at stable levels.

More rapid expansion of grasslands may be expected when farmers more fully realize the economic returns obtainable from pastures. Much of the region that has been cropped during the past 50 years was unprofitably used for the purpose.

Most of these fields produce more net returns in grass than in crops, and the reseeded pastures usually yield much higher net returns than adjacent native range land. Every reseeded pasture on the United States Southern Plains Experimental Range near Woodward, Okla., has supported many more cattle and produced much greater total live-weight gains than the native range. In these comparisons, both the native range and the reseeded fields on abandoned farm land were stocked to capacity on a moderate basis so as to obtain the maximum beef production without causing injury to the existing vegetation.

A reseeded field of native sand lovegrass carried 186 steers per section of land (640 acres) throughout the year, produced 403.9 pounds of liveweight gain per head, and yielded 117.2 pounds of gain per acre. This reseeded pasture was superior in every respect to native range. It carried 119 more

steers to the square mile, produced 41.8 more pounds of gain per head, and yielded 78.6 more pounds per acre, or nearly three times that of native range.

A reseeded mixture of cool-weather and warm-weather native grasses showed similar advantages over the native range. This mixture included about 6 pounds of blue grama an acre, 4 pounds of side-oats grama, 3 pounds of western wheatgrass, and ½ pound of Texas bluegrass. This pasture combination supported 152 steers per section and produced gains that averaged 385.6 pounds per head and 92.6 per acre. The yearlong grazing advantages over native range were 90 head per section, 23.5 pounds per head, and 54.0 pounds per acre.

The mixture, therefore, produced nearly two and one-half times as much gain per acre as the virgin range.

Weeping lovegrass produced 67.6 fewer pounds of gain per head than native range, but carried 233 percent more cattle and, therefore, returned two and one-half times as much gain per acre. This vigorous-growing importation from South Africa is much more fibrous and much less palatable than the other grasses. Therefore, the cattle consumed less of this grass and produced 109.4 pounds less gain per head than on sand lovegrass and 91.1 pounds less than on the reseeded mixture.

A reseeded field of buffalograss, not yet fully established, produced about the same gain per head as native range, but supported about twice as many cattle, and returned nearly twice as much gain per acre.

The results are conservative, since the reseeded pastures had been established on some of the most highly erosive and least productive land in the Southern Great Plains. They were compared with some of the best sandy range land in the area that had been moderately grazed since 1940 and supported a good growth of blue grama, sand dropseed, sand bluestem, sand lovegrass, and numerous other grasses, weeds, and brush.

In the spring of 1943, crested wheatgrass supported 125 head of cattle on 1,200 acres near Briggsdale, Colo., for 2 months. It is estimated that the abandoned fields on which this grass was grown would have supported only 20 cattle for the same period if the fields had been allowed to remain in their original weedy condition.

At Amarillo, Tex., a reseeded pasture of blue grama and western wheatgrass produced 69 pounds more gain per steer in 213 days than comparable steers made on native range that included principally blue grama and buffalograss. The native short grasses had barely started growth by April 1, when the western wheatgrass was growing actively.

Most native ranges have become infested more or less with the competitive growth of weeds and other objectionable plants. Many of the more palatable grasses have been seriously reduced in vigor and replaced with less palatable ones. The result is that reseeded pastures have many natural advantages at the outset. Pure or mixed stands of the very best grasses in the region may be established over an entire field and, if properly grazed, will remain deeply rooted and persist for many years.

Range surveys in 1936 disclosed that abandoned farm land which had become completely regrassed by natural revegetation before the drought of 1933–36 began withstood the drought much better than adjacent range land that had never been plowed—evidence of the superiority in persistence of grass on formerly cultivated lands. From 15 to 30 or more years were required, however, for abandoned farm land to revert naturally to a good stand of native grasses. That process may be accomplished in a few seasons or years by modern reseeding methods.

Nearly all reseeding efforts now being made throughout the region are directed to establishing permanent pastures on the less productive farm land. This will doubtless continue to be the main purpose of regrassing work for many years.

Some interest, however, is now being displayed in the possibility of including grasses in rotations with cultivated crops on the better farming lands. Research work at Hays, Kans., and Woodward shows that long-term grass-crop rotations may be important in the future agriculture of the region. Only about 3 years was required for a good stand of native grass to refill cultivated land with grass roots to a depth of about 4 feet and leave the soil in a condition comparable with that of virgin sod. In the absence of a legume, the grasses used in these studies had no material effect on soil fertility and caused no essential changes in the carbon or carbon-nitrogen ratio. The grasses, however, greatly improved the general physical condition of the soil and its ability to absorb water, retain moisture, and resist erosion.

It seems evident that even the more productive cultivated lands could be improved in tilth and farmed with less erosion if grasses were included in long-term rotations with other crops. Although the grasses soon restore the soil to virgin-sod conditions, it would seem advisable to leave the grass on the land for several years to justify the expense of establishment. Grasses grown on good farm land in rotation with crops can produce more forage than do pastures reseeded for permanent grazing on the less productive lands. Crops grown in rotation with the grass may not be greatly increased in actual yield, but the soil can be handled better and with fewer hazards.

Land Preparation

Many methods of land preparation have been successful in regrassing cultivated and abandoned farm land when local climatic conditions were favorable. Few methods have resulted in successful stands under the adverse conditions that usually prevail.

Choice of methods depends on wind velocities and rainfall expected in a locality and the kind of grasses used. The occurrence of high winds and torrential rains in spring and early summer and the tendency of most soils to blow and bake when bare of cover were major factors in the determination of a suitable method of grass establishment.

A stubble-mulch method of the land preparation that we have developed has been consistently successful in wind-erosion districts. It is also regarded as an excellent method to use in the eastern part where water erosion, soil crusting, and rapid surface evaporation are important problems.

The method consists of drilling adapted grasses early in spring in the protective stubble left by a previous crop of close-drilled kafir, sorgo, Sudangrass, or other sorghum. Seedbeds of this kind are usually more firm than those prepared in other ways. The noncompetitive mulch of stubble and hay residue helpfully controls wind and water erosion, reduces surface evaporation, and prevents crusting of the surface soil until the shallow-seeded grasses can become established.

The sorghum is sown the first year and pasture grasses the second year. The object is to drill the preparatory crop late enough in the season to prevent seed maturity, but early enough to insure adequate forage production. This is usually accomplished to best advantage by drilling the crop in late June or July, except in chinch bug areas where earlier plantings are necessary. Delayed seedings reduce or eliminate the number of mowings necessary to prevent seed maturity. Rates of seeding are the same as those ordinarily used in producing a sorghum hay crop.

Whenever the cover crop shows signs of maturing seed, it should be mowed at a stubble height of 8 to 10 inches to insure maximum protection to the seedbed the following spring. A light hay crop left on the land adds to the protective value of the mulch. The heavy hay crops may be removed without unduly lowering the quantity of stubble and aftermath required for soil protection.

A better seedbed can be prepared and the cost of preparation reduced by grazing part of the standing sorghum crop in the fall. This makes excellent feed for weaner calves. Their trampling is extremely helpful in packing the land, especially on light sandy soils that are hard to get in a desirably firm condition. The livestock, however, should be removed in time to leave enough stubble cover on the land to control wind and water erosion, prevent crusting, and reduce surface evaporation. The crop residue should be left evenly distributed and sufficient to cover at least 75 percent of the ground. More of the preparatory crop may be removed by mowing or grazing in the eastern part of the region, or on special sites where soil blowing is less serious or where the slope of the land is such that severe washing is not a problem.

Many abandoned fields have a poor cover of good grasses as much as 10 years after abandonment. They are usually covered with a dense growth of weeds and poor grasses. Farmers are reluctant to plow up and establish a suitable seedbed on these lands. To do so, however, will pay dividends in rapidity of establishment, completeness of coverage of good grasses, and higher grazing returns. Seedings made in weed residues usually result in consistently poor stands or in failures. Successful stands are sometimes obtained in exceptionally wet seasons or when grasses capable of withstanding weed competition are used.

Cool-weather grasses, such as western wheatgrass (or crested wheatgrass at the higher elevations), may be seeded in weed cover with fair success under favorable conditions. They start earlier and compete better with weeds than most warm-weather grasses. Of the latter group of grasses, sand lovegrass and sand dropseed are superior in resistance to weeds and can be sown sometimes with fair success in weed cover. All these grasses, however, respond with better stands and fewer failures when sown in well-prepared seedbeds.

Until the cost of grass seed is much lower than at present, it is not advisable to risk failure, delayed coverage, and undesirable final plants by seeding in weed cover.

Small-grain stubble is rarely satisfactory for grass seedings, except perhaps in the northwestern part. Volunteer cereal plants and weeds usually develop after harvest and before grass-planting time the following spring. Cool-weather grasses have the best chance for success on this method of land preparation, if sown in the fall or very early in the spring. Other grasses can be drilled satisfactorily in grain stubble if the land at planting time is unusually free of volunteer plants and weeds.

Clean-tilled cropland or fallow land may be used for grass seedings only in protected areas or localities where soil blowing is not severe. Fine, firm, mellow seedbeds are essential in grass establishment and are difficult to obtain without danger from wind and water erosion, surface evaporation, or baking of the soil. Bare land is rather widely used in northwestern and extreme eastern districts. Sorghum stubble, with its additional protective features, however, is gaining favor there and elsewhere. That cultivated crops can withstand wind erosion on a particular field does not prove that grasses will do likewise. Seedling grasses are less able to survive the hazards that occur on clean-tilled seedbeds.

Sorghum crops usually continue growth until late in the fall and make a poor seedbed for fall-sown grasses. The hay millets have been used successfully for the purpose. Their fall growth is slower, stops sooner, and is less competitive than the sorghums. Sown after a rain in midsummer, the millets usually produce sufficient growth for soil protection. The millets are like the sorghums in that they need mowing to prevent seed maturity and competition from volunteer plants. Leaving a high stubble is likewise essential in providing adequate protection to fall-sown grasses.

When to Plant

The time to plant grasses depends on the kinds used, the method of seedbed preparation, and general location in the region.

Spring seedings give optimum results for most grasses best adapted to the area. Exceptions are the cool-weather grasses that respond about equally well to seedings made in fall or very early in spring.

Grasses adapted to fall seeding may be sown following rains late in August or September. Spring seedings in crop residues should be made directly in the undisturbed stubble. The protective value of the stubble should not be destroyed in advance by tillage operations. Hence it is important to make these seedings before weeds start. Satisfactory seeding dates for the purpose range from about February 15 in southern localities to April 10 in the north; the fore part of the period is preferred for seeding cool-weather grasses and hard-seeded species, such as sand paspalum and sand lovegrass.

Where it is possible to use clean-tilled seedbeds, the drilling of warm-weather grasses is delayed until the latter part of April or early May, when wind velocities are usually lower and rainfall heavier than earlier in the season. But too much delay means rapid surface evaporation and severe crusting of the soil from heat and heavy rains. Light surface tillage would destroy one or two stands of weed seedlings and prepare a firm seedbed.

How to Plant

Drilling is superior to broadcasting. Drilling makes application easier, distributes the seed more uniformly, places it more nearly at proper depth, and requires lower seeding rates.

Unfortunately, common methods of harvesting and cleaning permit the seeding of only a few adapted species with ordinary farm drills. Common grain drills have been used successfully to plant especially clean seed of buffalograss, western wheatgrass, and crested wheatgrass. New and carefully constructed alfalfa drills or grass-seeder attachments can be used for weeping lovegrass, sand lovegrass, sand dropseed, switchgrass, and sand paspalum. These small-seeded grasses may be seeded more satisfactorily, however, by using drills made from garden-planting equipment.

Important native grasses usually incapable of being drilled properly with ordinary farm machinery include all the gramas, all the bluestems, Canada wild-rye, Indiangrass, and Texas bluegrass. Processing the light, chaffy seed of these grasses with hammer mills and fanning mills removes part or all of the hulls and facilitates seeding with ordinary drills. Most of these grasses have to be sown in the "rough," since the processing work is not done commercially on an extensive scale.

Special drills have been made and used successfully in seeding all these grasses regardless of the fluffy nature of the seeds. The first such drills were developed at Woodward through the cooperative efforts of the Bureau of Plant Industry, Soils, and Agricultural Engineering and the Soil Conservation Service.

The machines are assembled by mounting cotton-planter cans in the place of the grain box on regular drill frames. A stirring mechanism in the seed hoppers, when used in conjunction with an assortment of cotton plates, provides uniform flow of chaffy seeds. The machines, when further equipped with alfalfa-seeder or garden-seeder attachments, can be used to drill all seeds of grasses, legumes, and field crops. The separate nature of the hoppers aids the seeding of different grasses in mixtures, rows, or close drills. The machines cost more than regular drills, but are more useful. Many of them are now in use, but the number hardly begins to meet the needs of the farmers.

Ordinary grain drills can be used to seed many chaffy grasses when the machines are equipped with sugar-beet agitators or similar devices. H. C. Hyer, of the Oklahoma Extension Service, and Hi W. Staten, of the Oklahoma Agricultural Experiment Station, have devised simple and effective drills of this kind for seeding chaffy grasses.

Depth of planting is important. Shallow depths of $\frac{1}{4}$ inch usually give best results under ideal moisture conditions, but such conditions rarely prevail long enough to insure successful stands in dry-land areas. Shallow seedings often germinate and die before additional moisture is received. It is essential in dry localities to plant the seed at or near the maximum depth from which it can emerge. Planting at a regulated depth of 1 inch, followed by heavy press wheels to give a firmed coverage of $\frac{1}{2}$ to $\frac{3}{4}$ inch, has proved successful on many soil types with every grass adapted to the region. Grass drills give best results when equipped with double-disk coulter openers and depth-regulating bands set to prevent seeding deeper than 1 inch. These special items enable the operator to apply enough lever pressure to insure proper penetration of crop residue and firm soils without seeding too deep on light soils.

When drills are not available, the seed can be broadcast by hand and covered with a drag harrow or packer on clean-tilled land or with an ordinary disk or disk drill on stubble land. The seed should be covered at depths like those recommended for drilling. More even distribution of broadcast seed can be had if the seed is divided into two equal lots and each lot used to cover the entire field. A simple means of broadcasting is to scatter the seed from the rear end of a tractor, in front of the machinery used to cover it.

Firmness of seedbed also is highly important in establishing grass. Heavy press wheels should be standard equipment on every drill. Surface rollers may be used advantageously in packing the soil before and after seeding. In wind-erosion areas, the crop residue must be sufficient to prevent soil blowing after the packing treatment. Loose sandy soils may be made desirably firm before seeding by rolling them when the ground is wet if the stubble mulch is sufficient to prevent clogging of the roller.

Companion crops (or nurse crops) of small grains should not be sown with the grasses; they compete too much for moisture to justify the practice in dry-land areas.

One has to reduce competition in seedling stands of perennial grasses by mowing weeds whenever they get so high they shade the grasses or use up too much moisture. Two mowings are usually required the first growing season; one mowing will do the second year.

Seedling stands of native grasses often seem to be failures when actually they usually develop into satisfactory stands if left undisturbed. No seeding should be destroyed without first determining definitely whether a stand failure exists.

Most perennial grasses of the region can be grazed the second fall after seeding. In some instances the growth is sufficient to warrant grazing the first fall or second summer after seeding. Grazing may start when the height and vigor of growth are comparable with moderately grazed native range. Management practices for the maintenance of heavy production on reseeded pastures are similar to those recommended for native range.

What to Plant

The naturally high mineral content of Great Plains soils results in the production of native grasses superior in yearlong grazing value to those of most other parts of the world. The principal native grasses possess a superb combination of desirable characters. Most of them run high in calcium, phosphorus, protein, carotene, and other food essentials during the growing season. Many retain much of these values during the winter, according to intensive studies of Woodward grasses conducted by the Oklahoma Agricultural Experiment Station and the Bureau of Plant Industry, Soils, and Agricultural Engineering. (See U. S. D. A. Technical Bulletin 943.)

These grasses are also outstanding in high palatability at nearly all stages of growth. They are long-lived perennials that rarely require reseeding when well established and properly managed. Many can resist heat, cold, drought, close grazing, and trampling. They have the ability to recover remarkably fast from the effects of adverse climate and abuses. The soil-binding qualities of their rather dense turf and extensive root systems make them extremely effective for erosion control.

For these reasons, and because few introduced grasses are fully adapted to all parts of the Southern Great Plains, native grasses have received major attention for regrassing purposes. Most of the native grasses best adapted to the area are warm-weather species that start growth rather late in the spring, cease growth early in the fall, and remain dormant most of the winter. A few cool-weather species of native and imported grasses are adapted; they provide much green palatable and nutritious grazing early and late in the season in the northern part of the area and nearly all winter in the south.

Chief among the warm-weather natives are blue grama, buffalograss, side-oats grama, sand lovegrass, sand bluestem, switchgrass, Indiangrass, and little bluestem. The principal cool-weather natives include western wheatgrass, Texas bluegrass, and Canada wild-rye. The main introductions include Caucasian bluestem and Turkestan (or yellow) bluestem throughout the region, crested wheatgrass in the northern and higher locations, weeping lovegrass in the south, and Lehmann lovegrass and Boer lovegrass in the southwestern corner.

No perennial legumes have been discovered that are fully adapted for inclusion with grasses in dry-land pastures of the Southern Great Plains. Alfalfa is grown to some extent on bottom lands and other areas favored by extra moisture. Manchurian milkvetch shows some promise for use on similar sites. Sweetclover is grown widely in all parts of the region, but is rarely suitable for use in seed mixtures with grasses. It competes too severely with the seedling grasses and usually fails to maintain itself by natural reseeding in a grass mixture. A well-supported program of intensive research in the development and testing of legumes should be started. Legumes are badly needed to maintain soil fertility and add to the nutritive value of pasture mixtures.

The source of the seed of native grasses merits close attention. Although adaptation to local conditions may be best assured by using in a given area seed harvested in that area, the forage yield and length of growing season are greatly increased by using seed from southern sources. The seed may be used several hundred miles or more north of its source without much danger of winterkilling. Seeds of most native grasses, when grown very far south of their harvested source, produce forage decidedly lacking in vigor, production, and period of growth. Seed of blue grama and buffalograss from sources in Colorado and Kansas, for example, produce in Oklahoma and Texas much less than half the forage yield of the same species native to the latter States. Seed of native grasses from sources in Oklahoma, New Mexico, and Texas produce higher yields throughout the region than that from northern sources.

Blue grama grass occurs naturally throughout the region and is best adapted to heavy and semiheavy soils but is widely distributed on sandy land and does well when seeded there. This short bunchgrass is palatable and nutritious during the growing season and retains much of these values during the winter. It can be used to excellent advantage as the basic species in most upland mixtures. The seed is comparatively easy to harvest with small combines, usually runs fairly high in purity and germination, and emerges promptly after planting.

Blue grama is not quite so resistant to

close grazing as buffalograss is, but is slightly more palatable, more drought-resistant, and equally nutritious. It withstands closer grazing and heavier trampling than any other well adapted species except buffalograss. Pure seedings of blue grama at 6 to 10 pounds of combine-run material or 1 pound of dehulled seed to the acre give good stands. Mixtures of this grass with others usually give more satisfactory results.

Buffalograss thrives best on the heavier soils, but has been grown successfully on land containing some sand. It occurs in about equal mixture with blue grama in native ranges on heavy soils, except in the southern areas where buffalograss predominates in association with blue grama. These two species constitute the famous short grasses of the Plains and are well known for their nutritious qualities.

Buffalograss has nearly all the valuable characteristics of blue grama and has the added advantage of spreading rapidly by surface runners. The current high cost of buffalograss seed and its comparatively low germination, unless especially treated, limits its use in mixtures or pure seedings. Chilling treatments developed at Hays and dehulling methods devised at Woodward greatly improve the germination. Nearly every mixture seeded on heavy or semiheavy soils in the Southern Great Plains should contain at least 1 or 2 pounds of buffalograss seed burs or ½ pound of dehulled seed per acre.

The proportion of buffalograss may be increased to advantage when seed becomes cheaper and more generally available. It is rarely considered advisable, however, to establish a pasture exclusively with buffalograss. The inclusion of blue grama and other grasses with buffalograss in a mixture improves the immediate and ultimate value of the pasture. These grasses add desirable qualities not possessed by buffalograss alone and provide helpful indicators of overgrazing to assist in pasture management.

Side-oats grama usually shows a

natural preference for the rocky, "caliche," open soils, especially in the drier parts of the region where lack of available moisture retards its development on extremely heavy soils. This medium-tall, rather large bunchgrass, however, is not too particular in its soil requirements. It may be used as an important part of most mixtures on soils containing some sand or other pervious materials. It is usually more productive than either of the short grasses but requires more moisture for maximum growth.

Side-oats grama is eaten readily by cattle, especially during the growing season, when it is often preferred to the short grasses. It is slightly less palatable and somewhat less nutritious than the short grasses during the winter, but is superior in these respects to most other grasses in the dormant stages of growth. The seeds are borne on medium-tall, erect stems, are easy to harvest with ordinary machinery, and are increasing in availability each year. Pure seedings of this grass usually require about 15 pounds of bulk seed or 2 to 2½ pounds of dehulled seed per acre for satisfactory stands. The grass is an excellent one to use in mixtures with others.

Sand lovegrass has proved to be one of the most valuable native grasses under trial at Woodward, and on sandy soils elsewhere in the region. Its natural occurrence is limited to very sandy soils, but it grows well on semiheavy soils. This lush-growing, fine-stemmed, medium-tall bunchgrass, with its rich growth of soft basal leaves, is much more palatable than weeping lovegrass, which it resembles in general habit of growth and adaptability to reseeding purposes.

Sand lovegrass starts growth several weeks earlier in the spring and continues later in the fall than most other warm-weather species. It is superior in palatability to most other grasses during the growing season and is eaten readily by livestock during the winter. It is less drought-resistant and probably is shorter-lived than the short grasses, but it compares favorably with them in nutritive qualities.

Sand lovegrass produces an abundance of very fine seeds when conditions are reasonably favorable. Considerable quantities are now commercially available. The seeds ripen in the fall and are fairly easy to harvest with a binder or combine. Many of them are semihard and delayed in emergence. Their germination increases with age and is promoted somewhat by freezing temperatures. The grass reseeds itself better in natural stands than most other species, with the possible exception of sand paspalum and sand dropseed. It is one of the best warm-weather grasses to use in seeding weed-infested abandoned land or depleted range land of a sandy nature.

Sand lovegrass is highly satisfactory for use in mixtures with side-oats grama, blue grama, and other palatable grasses on sandy soils. It is so highly palatable, however, that it should represent a substantial part of the mixture. A light sprinkling of this grass in a mixture is likely to be sought out by cattle, heavily overgrazed, and eventually eliminated. A pure stand of the grass or a heavy proportion of it in a mixture can be stocked properly to obtain maximum gains without abusing the stand by excessive use. Sand lovegrass should never be used in a mixture with the much less palatable weeping lovegrass. Recommended rates of seeding are ¼ to ½ pound in mixtures and 1 to 2 pounds in pure stands.

Sand bluestem is well adapted to deep sandy soil throughout the region, where it often occurs as the most productive if not the principal component of the native vegetation. This tall, vigorous, broad-leaved grass spreads slowly by rootstalks to form large clumps or extensive colonies. It serves equally well as an excellent summer grass for grazing purposes on sandy uplands and for hay production on bottom lands. It rates high in palatability and nutritive qualities during the spring and early summer months, but becomes coarse and stemmy in the fall and is eaten much less readily than most other grasses during the winter. It is similar to big bluestem of the sub-humid area east of the region. It is actually a more drought-resistant, sand-expression of big bluestem.

Sand bluestem rarely sets a heavy crop of seed; the seed is usually very chaffy and low in purity but high in germination. The seed has not yet become extensively available in commercial quantities but can be harvested with fair success in native stands or increase plantings. The chaffy seed usually requires seeding rates of 15 to 30 pounds to the acre to give satisfactory stands from pure seedings. Dehulled seed gives equally good results when sown at 3 to 5 pounds an acre. This grass is an excellent one to include in mixtures with other grasses for pasture or hay production on sandy soils.

Switchgrass occurs somewhat sparingly but widely distributed in favored sites on sandy upland. It is usually the principal grass on sandy lowland. It has a natural preference for sandy soils but does well on semiheavy soils when seeded there. It grows in somewhat the same manner as sand bluestem and has nearly the same grazing value. This tall, vigorous, leafy grass makes excellent hay, especially when cut before the heads appear. It usually produces satisfactory yields of seed that are easy to harvest, clean, and drill with ordinary machinery. The seed runs high in purity and its germination is usually satisfactory after a period of after-harvest ripening. The seed is easy to harvest and increase, but little of it is yet available commercially.

Indiangrass resembles sand bluestem and switchgrass in soil requirements, grazing value, and general habit of growth. It exceeds them in seedling vigor, and is slightly superior in palatability. The seeds are somewhat less chaffy and easier to handle than those of sand bluestem.

Little bluestem is one of the most important prairie grasses in the sub-humid area east of the Southern Great Plains, where it and big bluestem are highly regarded for palatability and beef-producing qualities during the late spring and early summer months. Little bluestem is fairly common on sandy or rocky soil throughout the region, but it usually ranks fairly low in palatability unless the previous year's growth has been removed by grazing or other means. It is eaten readily, however, in reseeded stands when grazed reasonably close or when the old growth is mowed. This grass is more susceptible to drought injury and heavy consistent grazing than most other grasses, and is shorter lived. It is valuable, however, for reseeding purposes in the eastern and southeastern parts, where it may be used advantageously in mixtures with other tall grasses. Much the same difficulties are experienced in harvesting and handling this chaffy-seeded grass as were described for sand bluestem. Seeding rates of 15 to 20 pounds of chaffy seeds or 2 to 2½ pounds of dehulled seed an acre usually give satisfactory stands in pure seedings.

Sand paspalum, a short, semiprostrate, native bunch grass with broad, crinkly, soft, fuzzy leaves, is one of the most palatable grasses for summer grazing on sandy lands. The leaves, however, become dry, brown, and papery in the fall and have little grazing value in winter. The grass is a fairly rapid invader and stabilizer of sand dunes and blow-out areas, where it is ultimately replaced to a large extent by more permanent species; usually, however, enough of it remains to constitute a big part of the vegetation.

Seed production in the customarily thin native stands is usually too meager to justify harvesting, and consequently only a limited quantity of the seed has been available commercially. Row plantings, however, produce fairly good yields of seed. The hard-coated seeds require aging, freezing, or processing to germinate well. The extent to which the grass reseeds itself in native stands indicates, however, that it could be used very satisfactorily in reseeding.

A few pounds of sand paspalum

added to the grasses already discussed would improve the mixtures for sandy soils. Its comparatively short life makes pure-stand seedings undesirable.

Western wheatgrass is one of the most valuable cool-weather natives. It is best adapted to heavy soils where its natural occurrence and greatest development is usually restricted to areas benefited by runoff water from adjacent land. It occurs generally throughout the region but becomes successively less abundant from north to south and from high to low elevations. It is less drought-resistant and less palatable than many others in summer, but it is highly palatable and extremely nutritious when growing actively in other seasons. It is a cool-season grass in the northern part of the region and a true winter grass in the south. It continues active growth through fall, winter, and spring unless the weather is extremely dry or temperatures fall near or below zero for long periods. Reseeded stands of western wheatgrass have survived more than 10 years on upland at Woodward, and remained highly productive in the cooler months.

In grazing tests, reseeded pastures of western wheatgrass have supported more cattle and produced greater winter gains with much less cottonseed cake than were obtained from native range.

The rotation of cattle from western wheatgrass during the cooler months to native range during the warmer months has been clearly superior to continuous grazing of native range. This system of grazing resulted in a saving of protein supplements during winter, supported more cattle on a yearlong basis, and gave more gains.

During the winter of 1944–45, the gain advantage of western wheatgrass over native range was 69.3 pounds per head. The second winter the cattle on western wheatgrass were fed half as much cottonseed cake as those on native range and still showed a gain advantage of 62.2 pounds per head. Two lots of cattle were grazed on western wheatgrass the third winter. One lot received no protein supplements except 9 pounds during a blizzard and the other lot was fed half as much cottonseed cake as comparable cattle on native range. The first lot showed a winter gain advantage of 21.9 pounds per head over native range, with a saving of nearly all the protein supplement. The second lot produced a gain advantage of 39.1 pounds per head on half the protein fed to cattle on native range.

The 2-year average gain advantage over native range was 50.7 pounds per head for the lightly caked cattle on western wheatgrass during winter. When rotated to native range during summer, these heavy winter-gaining cattle made 25.2 pounds less summer gain than the cattle on continuous native range. The rotation system showed an average yearly gain advantage of 25.5 pounds per head, supported 8 percent more cattle, and yielded 9.3 percent more gain an acre.

It seems advisable to establish a separate pasture of this grass for exclusive use during the cooler months, to be used in rotation with warm-weather grasses during the summer. A mixture of the two types of grass involves difficulties in establishment and management. They respond best to different times of seeding and have the greatest grazing value at different times in the year. A separate pasture of western wheatgrass would provide excellent grazing while the warm-weather grasses were being protected from use during their spring and fall growth.

Commercial seed supplies of western wheatgrass are limited, although the grass usually matures good seed crops following wet winters. The seed can be harvested readily with wheat combines and, when it is thoroughly threshed and cleaned, can be seeded satisfactorily with an ordinary grain drill. The plant spreads rapidly by rootstocks. A rate of 10 to 12 pounds per acre is sufficient in pure seedings and 2 to 3 pounds in mixtures.

Texas bluegrass is more palatable than western wheatgrass but is similar in habit of growth, nutritive qualities, and general grazing value. Limited investigations at Woodward indicate that it is less able to withstand competition from other plants than western wheatgrass. It occurs on sandy and semiheavy soils from southern Texas to southern Kansas. No seed of this extremely valuable grass is now commercially available. The fluffy seed is hard to harvest and thresh. These disadvantages have been overcome at Woodward by processing the threshed material with a hammer mill.

Canada wild-rye, another cool-weather native, grows naturally on sandy soils in the region but shows a preference for roadside and lowlands favored by extra moisture. Good stands failed to survive heat and drought on semiheavy upland soils at Woodward for more than 3 years. The grass, however, is being used successfully on sandy soils in southwestern Kansas. The seed can be harvested and handled fairly well with ordinary farm machinery, but the bearded heads make these operations more difficult than with western wheatgrass. The fall, winter, and spring growth of this grass is highly palatable. The mature growth is coarse, stemmy, and rarely eaten by livestock.

Caucasian bluestem and Turkestan bluestem are the only exotic grasses that have fully withstood cold winters and hot, dry summers from northern Colorado to southern Texas.

Both are medium tall, fine stemmed, and leafy. They are equally nutritious, but the Caucasian variety is more palatable to beef cattle. They are finer stemmed than the native bluestems, usually produce more viable seed, and reseed themselves more readily. Seeds of these imported grasses are being increased in the region, but only Turkestan is available commercially. Recommended seeding rates per acre for pure stands are 5 to 8 pounds of combine-run material or ½ to ¾ pound of dehulled seed.

Crested wheatgrass, an introduction from Siberia, is a promising grass for reseeding in the higher elevations of eastern Colorado and northeastern New Mexico. Numerous tests conducted for many years show that it suffers from intense heat and drought and grows poorly below an altitude of 4,000 feet. During the recent favorable years, however, it has given good results in parts of the Texas Panhandle and southwestern Kansas.

On the basis of experience, seedings of crested wheatgrass in these areas should be limited to fairly small trials until these later plantings have been subjected to prolonged heat and drought and have demonstrated ability to survive the adverse conditions. This grass grows well on a wide range of soils but prefers the heavier types and is slightly tolerant of alkali. It equals most native grasses in forage production at the higher elevations of the region. It provides much palatable early-season and late-season grazing but lacks palatability in midsummer. It produces good hay when cut early. Recommended rates are 6 to 8 pounds an acre in close drills.

Weeping lovegrass is much less palatable and shorter lived than most native grasses, but is usually more productive for at least a few years. It is prompt in germination, easy to establish, strong in seedling vigor, makes rapid vigorous growth on a wide range of soil types, and resists heat and moderate cold. It has survived winters in the southern half of the region and has winterkilled only to a limited extent farther north. In many instances, vigorous initial stands of this grass have gradually died out in 5 years, even in southern Oklahoma where winter temperatures were not severe. Losses from drought, cold, or the natural short life of the plant have been replaced by natural reseeding in some cases.

Weeping lovegrass compares favorably with the natives in nutritive qualities, but its high fiber content at all stages of growth and its offensive odor at flowering time reduce the palatability and quantity eaten by livestock. Cattle usually graze every other grass in preference to it, if given free choice.

Beef steers grazed exclusively on weeping lovegrass at Woodward produced 91.1 pounds less yearly gain per head than similar cattle on a reseeded mixture of native grasses, 109.4 pounds less than on sand lovegrass, and 67.6 pounds less than on native range. Weeping lovegrass has proved to be the poorest grass included in the grazing tests. It supports more cattle than native range for at least a few years. Its palatability is improved by heavy grazing. Perhaps it should be grazed heavily and reseeded when the stand expires.

Applications of ammonium nitrate, at the rate of 30 pounds of nitrogen per acre, to a pasture of weeping lovegrass in 1947 caused a significant increase in cattle gains and produced profitable returns. The fertilizer, however, failed to improve the naturally poor grazing value of weeping lovegrass sufficiently to make it compare favorably with native grass. The gain per head on fertilized weeping lovegrass was less than half that recorded on fertilized or nonfertilized sand lovegrass during the same period.

Weeping lovegrass forms a distinct bunch of many long, slender, drooping leaves and tall, slender, erect stems, with a spreading panicle producing numerous very small seeds. The grass greens up earlier in the spring than most warm-weather natives and remains green later in the fall. Some green growth is often present at the base of the clumps in midwinter, especially in the south. Its palatability is less inferior to the natives in winter than in summer. Seed yields are high and easy to harvest with properly adjusted farm machinery. Considerable quantities are now available.

Weeping lovegrass is adapted to a wide range of soil types. Its production is greatest on fertile soils but it grows unusually well on worn-out land in the southeastern part of the region. Seeding rates of ¾ to 1 pound give good stands in pure seedings. Its competitive effect on native seedlings and the superior palatability of the natives indicate that this grass should not be grown in mixtures with native species.

Boer lovegrass and Lehmann lovegrass are adapted to the extreme southern part, where they produce more palatable growth than weeping lovegrass and show promise for reseeding.

Many other perennial grasses are used to a limited extent. Big bluestem is a valuable grass on favored sites along the eastern and southeastern borders. Smooth bromegrass is grown on a limited scale under favorable conditions at high altitudes. It is more palatable but less drought-resistant than crested wheatgrass. Rhodesgrass and Dallisgrass thrive on the Gulf coast, but usually winterkill even in the extreme southern part of the region proper. Bermuda-grass is used to a limited extent for pasture purposes on sandy upland and moist lowland in the southeastern sections.

Blue or giant panicgrass has shown promise in recent years for tall, vigorous, palatable production in the far southern areas. It becomes severely injured or killed by freezing temperatures in the central districts. Native sand dropseed occurs widely throughout the region. It rapidly invades abandoned fields and depleted ranges on sandy or semiheavy soils. It has considerable grazing value, but is less palatable and more difficult to establish artificially than most other native grasses.

Johnsongrass has been used successfully to stabilize sandy uplands and furnish considerable seasonal grazing. Cultivation about every other year improves its forage yield and ability to withstand drought. Although its best use should be made on areas where it now occurs, it seems unwise to expand the acreage. The grass has long been regarded as a noxious weed difficult to eradicate on bottom land. It may be grown on dry uplands with considerable expense for cultivation, but it offers a source of infestation to adjacent farm land. It occasionally causes severe death losses of livestock from prussic acid poisoning.

Other more desirable grasses can be established with equal ease and maintained much longer with less expense. If Johnsongrass is used, it should be limited to fields permanently removed from cultivation where there is no danger of contaminating adjacent lands or seed supplies of sorghums. It should be grazed with the full realization that stock losses are likely to occur periodically. Losses are reported every year along the river bottoms in northwestern Oklahoma.

Slender wheatgrass is a cool-weather native perennial sometimes used at high elevations in Colorado. It is comparatively short-lived, but is strong in seedling vigor and produces fairly large yields of palatable forage.

Mixtures of Grasses

Mixtures of two or more species of somewhat related palatability and growth habits are usually preferred to pure stands. Seeding a mixture of well-adapted species is usually considered to have four advantages over the others—greater success in obtaining a stand, a greater variety of forage, a longer grazing period, and more rapid and complete occupancy of the land.

Mixture seedings are not always desirable. Separate pasture seedings of the cool-weather and warm-weather grasses offer greater possibilities than mixtures of the two types. The separate seedings of these two classes of grass can be grazed in rotation with each other and when each is most nutritious. Each class can be properly managed and protected when it needs protection. Neither competes to the disadvantage of the other when planted separately.

Mixture seedings are not always possible. Most native grasses give good results when sown in pure stands, and this method is permissible for special conditions and when no other seed is available. Some highly palatable species cannot withstand exceedingly heavy grazing pressure. This difficulty is avoided when such grasses are sown in pure stands or as heavy components of a mixture. Comparatively unpalatable but vigorous-growing grasses give best results when sown in pure stands, grazed heavily to maintain some semblance of palatability, and reseeded when the stand finally succumbs to heavy use.

Grama-buffalograss mixtures have been widely and successfully used in the Southern Great Plains. A suitable mixture of unprocessed seed for heavy and semiheavy soils consists of about 6 pounds of blue grama, 3 pounds of side-oats grama, and 1 or 2 pounds of buffalograss per acre. This mixture may be improved for the extremely heavy soils by increasing the proportion of buffalograss and reducing that of side-oats grama. The combination may be modified for sandy soils by increasing the proportion of side-oats grama, reducing or eliminating the quantity of buffalograss, and adding substantial quantities of one or more of the sand-tolerant grasses. These include sand lovegrass, switchgrass, sand bluestem, and Indiangrass.

Many improved strains of grass are being developed by plant breeders. A few of these have been released and others are being increased for further testing and general distribution in the future. Preliminary work indicates that this line of investigation will result in the development of strains greatly superior to bulk species now used.

Achenbach, a southern strain of smooth bromegrass released by the Kansas Agricultural Experiment Station, appears to be greatly superior to ordinary bromegrass in the region. The station has also released the Blackwell strain of switchgrass, selected for rust resistance from Oklahoma bulk material. The El Reno side-oats grama is another selection from an Oklahoma source that has been certified for distribution by the Kansas station. An improved selection of buffalograss has been released as Hays buffalograss by the Hays branch of the Kansas station.

J. R. Harlan, of the Bureau of Plant Industry, Soils, and Agricultural Engineering, is devoting full time to the selection, breeding, and improvement of native grasses at Woodward. He has several promising strains in the process of being increased or tested. Chief among these to date is Tucson side-oats grama, a vigorous, tall-stemmed strain of buffalograss, and a sand-tolerant strain of western wheatgrass. Tucson side-oats grama shows special promise for seed production, early and late growth, and the ability to remain green and grow vigorously in the face of summer heat. The varietal purity of this strain can be maintained more easily than that of other strains because it does not cross with the others.

Temporary Pastures

Temporary pasture crops used extensively in the region include Sudangrass, sweetclover, and wheat. These crops, when grazed in rotation with each other and with permanent pastures or range, often provide green, succulent grazing through a greater part of the year. Wheat produces considerable grazing from early in the fall until about April 1 when moisture and temperature conditions are favorable. Second-year sweetclover usually supports heavy grazing from about April 1 to late June or early July. Sudangrass when grown on well-prepared land and favored by good rainfall distribution, can be grazed heavily from early summer to late fall. First-year sweetclover can be grazed lightly in the fall.

Seasonal grazing of this combination of crops is particularly helpful in providing succulent and nutritious feed for dairy cattle. Growing the wheat and Sudangrass on fallow land assures maximum production from these crops. Sudangrass and sweetclover may be grown advantageously in rotation with each other. Three fields are used for the purpose, one for Sudangrass and one each for first- and second-year sweetclover. Sudangrass stubble makes an excellent seedbed for sweetclover. This biennial crop gives best results

when seeded annually to provide first- and second-year growth every year. After grazing is completed on the second-year sweetclover, the land may be plowed and fallowed for the subsequent crop of Sudangrass.

The Madrid and Spanish varieties of sweetclover are superior to ordinary commercial lots. Redfield sweetclover remains green later in the season of its second-year growth than other varieties, but it is a poor seed producer. The Madrid variety is about equal to Spanish in forage production and remains green much later in the fall of its first year. Most of the early, yellow-flowered varieties of sweetclover are less productive than the white-blossom strains but are more palatable and reseed themselves better.

Wheat pastures occasionally cause severe death losses in cattle because of grass tetany, a malady locally known as wheat poisoning. The difficulty increases with an increase in the lushness of growth. The principal losses occur among pregnant cows and in cattle being transported from wheat pastures. A disarranged metabolism due to high protein and unbalanced minerals is considered responsible. A coordinated research program on the problem is now in progress in Texas. Wholly effective remedies have not been developed to date. The indications are that giving cattle access to dry roughage before and during the grazing period reduces the ailment.

Irrigated Pastures on the Plains

An irrigated pasture is profitable if it yields returns equal to those from an alfalfa hay crop on similar land, according to D. W. Robertson and his associates at the Colorado Agricultural Experiment Station. A heavy carrying capacity for 5 or 6 months of the year makes an improved pasture highly useful in maintaining a dairy or breeding herd. If these goals cannot be attained, the pasture should be replaced by higher-yielding forage crops.

The Southern Great Plains has little land suitable for irrigated pastures. Consequently, few investigations have been made to determine methods of establishment and care of such pastures. The development of irrigated cropland, particularly in Colorado, has been accompanied by an increase in dairying and livestock feeding to market a surplus of bulky crops. Continuous cropping of irrigated lands results in a rapid decrease of soil fertility. Since fertility can be replaced cheaply through the use of manure, livestock play an important part in maintaining a balanced agriculture in irrigated sections. Considerable acreage is used for the production of pasture, hay, fodder, and silage crops.

Methods of establishment and care of irrigated pastures are similar to those practiced for related purposes in other regions, according to Charles G. Marshall and J. S. McCorkle of New Mexico. These practices include proper attention to land leveling to conserve water and soil fertility, a firm seedbed, shallow seeding, frequent light irrigations during establishment, rotation of grazing, not grazing when the land is wet, scattering of droppings, fertilizing to maintain the production through the use of nitrogen for grasses and phosphates for legumes, and timely irrigations.

Grasses commonly used in irrigated pasture mixtures are smooth bromegrass, orchardgrass, timothy, Kentucky bluegrass, and meadow fescue. In the extreme southern part of the area, smooth bromegrass is replaced with perennial ryegrass. Several of these grasses are usually grown in mixtures with one or more of the following legumes: Ladino clover, White Dutch clover, alsike clover, red clover, or alfalfa. Reed canarygrass, Alta fescue, redtop, and strawberry clover are often used on very wet lands. Most of these plants are cool-weather types that produce green growth throughout the winter in the southern part of the region and from early spring to late fall when irrigated in the northern part, especially at the higher elevations.

The suggested pasture mixtures for irrigated land under different site conditions are:

Site condition and crop:	Pounds per acre
For heavy irrigation:	
Smooth bromegrass	8
Orchardgrass	8
Meadow fescue	6
Perennial ryegrass	4
Legumes	4
Total	30
For limited irrigation:	
Smooth bromegrass	8
Orchardgrass	8
Crested wheatgrass	6
Alfalfa or yellow sweetclover	12
Total	34
For wet alkaline land:	
Kentucky bluegrass	8
Slender wheatgrass	8
Redtop	4
Strawberry clover	2
Total	22

Smooth bromegrass often becomes sod-bound after a few years. This condition can be corrected by disking, using the grass in mixtures with alfalfa, or making applications of ammonium nitrate.

Orchardgrass is not adapted to sandy soils, is less drought-resistant than is smooth bromegrass, and should be grazed closer to prevent accumulation of old growth. Timothy is best adapted to the higher elevations where the summers are cool. It is not suited to sandy soils. Timothy is not resistant to trampling, but its cheap seed and ease of establishment make it useful in mixtures. The stands are not permanent; the grass is medium in palatability but furnishes considerable forage throughout the season. Kentucky bluegrass is highly palatable and grows on a wide range of soils, but does not withstand hot weather in the lower and southern parts of the region.

Early spring or fall are the best times to sow these cool-weather grasses and legumes for irrigated pastures. It is advisable, however, to delay seeding until a clean, fine, firm seedbed is prepared and a continuous supply of irrigation water is available. Good, weed-free seed, properly tested and tagged in accordance with seed laws, should be used. The seeding may be done by methods we have described for dry-land pastures, except that heavier rates of seeding are used.

Regardless of the method used, from four to six light irrigations should be applied to the pasture each season. The grass should never be allowed to suffer from drought. The flooding and border methods of irrigation are used in northern Colorado. The furrow, or corrugation method, which is common in the Arkansas Valley, permits the use of a head of water ordinarily too small to apply by other methods.

Conservative grazing is the first essential in management of irrigated pastures. Grazing should be rotated by fencing the pasture into separate fields. Three fields are better than two. One can be grazed while the others are being irrigated or allowed to grow. Livestock should be withheld during the first year after planting. Mowing may be necessary to kill weeds and to cut down unpalatable growth. In some instances a light crop of hay may be cut the second season, after which the animals can be allowed to graze. Growth should be allowed to reach a height of 5 or 6 inches before grazing

is permitted in the spring. The pasture should be harrowed once each season to spread the animal droppings. When the yield or carrying capacity begins to drop the stand should be plowed. Irrigated pastures should be included in rotation with other crops.

Pastures that are used for winter grazing should be left unused during the summer. A lush growth of grass protects the soil from freezing and permits later growth in the fall. Thawing is lessened during the winter and thus trampling damage is reduced. Pastures should not be used more than 2 years at a time for winter grazing. More extended use permits the sod to thicken and loss of grasses may result.

Manure should be applied in February or March. The application of manure should be followed by disking or treatment with an alfalfa renovator. This permits aeration of the soil and stimulates new growth. Ammonium sulfate or ammonium nitrate will produce earlier pasturage and frequently increases the yield. Phosphate will increase the yield of legumes on many soils and will produce forage with a higher phosphorus and lime content. Before the entire pasture is treated, small areas should be fertilized to see if the grasses respond.

RANGE MANAGEMENT

D. A. SAVAGE, D. F. COSTELLO

NATIVE RANGE is the major source of forage for livestock in the Southern Great Plains. It furnishes the entire forage supply of livestock for about half the year in most localities and nearly all of the yearly requirement in some areas.

The principal range forage types consist of the short-grass vegetation that occupies the heavier soils and the tall or midgrass association that occurs on sandy soils along nearly every stream in the region. Many modifications of these major types exist.

The general occurrence, relative importance, and soil adaptations of the leading native grasses we have already described. The famous short grasses, blue gramma and buffalograss, are largely responsible for the enviable reputation of the region as a yearlong grazing country. These grasses often occur in nearly equal proportions and together represent up to 90 percent of the vegetation on the hard lands.

Some valuable taller grasses, or midgrasses as they are commonly called, mingle with the sod-forming short grasses on conservatively grazed ranges. These taller grasses are more abundant in localities favored by heavier rainfall. The taller grasses increase in evidence in wet years and decrease during dry years. Their expansion into the drier areas increases on the lighter, more pervious soils.

The more valuable midgrasses on short-grass ranges include western wheatgrass in the northern part and on low sites farther south. Side-oats grama, hairy grama, and little bluestem occur on rough broken lands that have shallow soils underlain or intermixed with gravel. Little bluestem also occurs with big bluestem on the eastern border of the region. Needle-and-thread and junegrass often accompany the short grasses on the high plains of Colorado.

Other less valuable midgrasses invade the short-grass association on special sites or following abuse by overgrazing or drought. Red three-awn is a decidedly unpalatable grass that increases rapidly on the semiheavy to heavy soils when the better grasses are injured. Sand dropseed, a fibrous grass of only fair palatability, increased rapidly on the lighter types of short-grass land following drought injury to the better grasses. Tobosa, a grass of secondary grazing value, is often an important associate of the short grasses in southeastern New Mexico and the southern part of the Texas Panhandle. Galleta, a grass of slightly more palatability than tobosa, often occurs to the near exclusion of short grasses on the misnamed "tobosa" flats of northeastern New Mexico.

Black grama occurs sparingly in association with blue grama or in place of blue grama in the drier sections of the Southwest.

The comparatively dense short-grass turf usually supports fewer weeds and fewer shrubs than the sandy ranges. Some of the weeds associated with the short grasses are palatable to livestock, but most of the weeds lack palatability. The scarlet globemallow, particularly abundant in the northern areas, is high in protein content and is eaten readily by livestock. Dense stands of lambsquarters, prairie pepperweed, annual broomweed, western stickseed, Indianwheat or tallow weed, and other annuals occasionally appear on shortgrass ranges in wet years or when the ranges are overgrazed.

Very few shrubs of browse value occur with the short grasses over the region as a whole. Chamiza or fourwing saltbush and winterfat grow in the higher elevations of Colorado and New Mexico. These plants are especially valuable for winter browse in Colorado. Mesquite is rapidly invading many of the shortgrass ranges in the southern half of the region. The mesquite bean is highly nutritious and palatable to livestock, but the plant competes seriously with the better range forage species.

Pricklypear are abundant in some short-grass areas. Recent investigations indicate that the increase of these cacti is more closely related to a succession of drought years than to excessive grazing. Broom snakeweed is generally present throughout the Plains, particularly on shallow soils underlain with caliche gravel. The increase of this unpalatable and competitive plant is regarded as an indicator of overgrazing.

The sandier types of range land are characterized by a highly variable mixture of tall grasses and midgrasses. Most of these grasses are bunch types which usually present a thin open stand associated with many weeds and considerable brush. They are usually interspersed with a thin understory of blue grama on the sandy sites and a dense short-grass turf on small areas of heavier soil. The density of brush and weeds usually increases and that of grass declines with successive increase in slope and depth of sand.

Much of the sandier types of range land are seriously infested with sand sagebrush and considerable quantities of skunkbush and sand-hill plum. The Miles series of sandy soils along the breaks of the High Plains in Oklahoma, Texas, and New Mexico is heavily in-

fested with shinnery oak. Soapweed occurs thickly on many of the shallow
sands, particularly in the northern and
western parts of the region. Mesquite
brush offers serious competition to
grasses in Texas and New Mexico.

The more valuable tall grasses of the
sand hills include sand lovegrass, sand
bluestem, and switchgrass, with some
side-oats grama and Indiangrass. Little bluestem is a dominant species in
the shinnery areas, is occasionally important on other sandy areas, and frequently occurs abundantly on rocky
outcrops bordering the sands. Sand
dropseed is a prominent transition grass
on sandy land.

The less valuable sandy-land grasses
include blowoutgrass over the region as
a whole, sand reedgrass in the north,
and giant reedgrass in the south. Purple three-awn and purple sandgrass
occur as indicators of overgrazing on
many sandy ranges.

Switchgrass, with some admixture
of sand bluestem, Indiangrass, Canada
wild-rye, silver beardgrass, and western
wheatgrass, represents the principal
component of the more valuable hay
meadows on bottom lands in the region.
These grasses are often replaced or accompanied by the less valuable vine-
mesquite, inland or desert saltgrass,
and alkali sacaton on moist soils of
moderate alkalinity. These saltgrass
types are less palatable than the others,
but remain in active green condition
through long grazing seasons and therefore provide much nutritious forage.

Range Condition

Short-grass ranges may be divided
into five classes, based on the amount
of forage, the kinds of plants present,
and other factors such as the amount
of bare ground and the degree of erosion, according to studies in Colorado
reported by D. F. Costello and G. T.
Turner. These classes of range condition are: Excellent, good, fair, poor,
and severely depleted. The grazing capacity decreases in the order named
and improvement of the lower condi-

tion classes or maintenance of the forage on the better ones cannot be had
without wise stocking and use.

The excellent condition on short-
grass ranges is evidenced by an almost
complete cover of blue grama and buffalograss. At the end of the grazing
season the turf may appear to be
broken into bunches separated by
spaces of bare ground 1 to 2 inches
wide. Some of the more valuable taller
grasses are present, especially in wet
seasons. Pricklypear and other undesirable plants, such as broom snakeweed,
are seldom present. Annual weeds are
scarce or absent. Such areas are generally limited in extent and care must
be exercised that stocking based on
these sites does not result in overgrazing surrounding ranges in good or only
fair condition if livestock have access
to both. The allowable stocking rate
for ranges in excellent condition averages about 2½ acres per animal unit
month in Colorado and slightly fewer
acres farther south.

The excellent condition in general
is characterized by ranges where the
soil and plant cover have been little
changed by grazing. The grass cover
and litter on the ground is sufficiently
abundant to prevent undue loss of
moisture. Erosion is negligible and the
runoff following rains is relatively
clear and free of silt.

Good condition on short-grass ranges
is found when the sod pieces are separated by space not more than 3 to 6
inches wide. The plants are not elevated above the ground surface. Taller
grasses occur as individual plants or
clumps in wet and average growing
seasons. Perennial weeds are a normal
part of the stand, but are not conspicuous except in abnormally wet seasons.
Annual weeds may temporarily obscure
the short grasses in late spring and
early summer, following periods of
excessive precipitation. In dry years
practically all weeds are absent or inconspicuous. The vigor of the vegetation is somewhat reduced. Some washing of the topsoil may be apparent
during heavy rainstorms. The allow-

able stocking rate for ranges in good condition is 20 to 40 percent fewer cattle than on excellent range. The objective of management should be to maintain the range in good condition at least, and on the better sites to improve it to excellent condition.

Fair condition on short-grass ranges is characterized by grass clumps separated by spaces 6 to 12 inches wide. The plants are usually slightly pedestaled and wind and sheet erosion are evident in the bare spaces. Taller grasses are scarce or absent. In some localities poorer perennial grasses have replaced the more palatable short grasses. Vigor is usually low; few seed-stalks are produced and the better plants do not spread rapidly onto new ground. Runoff is generally heavy with silt. These ranges may be stocked with only about half the cattle allowable on ranges in good condition. The fair condition usually indicates a combination of drought and overgrazing. The immediate objective of management is to improve the range to good condition.

Poor-condition short-grass ranges have scattered grass tufts or bunches separated by bare spaces 1 to 4 feet or more in width. The sod pieces or tufts are frequently elevated above the ground surface and sheet erosion is very evident. The ground frequently cracks after rainstorms. Annual and perennial weeds may be scarce or abundant, depending on the amount of precipitation that has been received. The condition results from drought and overgrazing. At least 10 acres or more per animal unit month are recommended for this range condition in Colorado in order to permit recovery of the better grasses.

Severely depleted ranges are generally denuded to the extent that reseeding and mechanical treatment of the soil are necessary to stop blowing and prevent excessive removal of the topsoil by sheet and gully erosion. Grazing should not be permitted until the soil has been stabilized by a cover of grass or other vegetation.

The range should be examined periodically for signs of deterioration or improvement. Deterioration is generally indicated by decreases in plant cover, vigor, and numbers of the better plants. Other indications are increases in bare ground, soil washing, and number of gullies. Improvement is indicated by increase in plant cover, number of palatable plants, and protective litter on the ground, with a decrease in erosion as shown by healing of gully slopes and invasion of bare ground by perennial grasses.

Range recovery is usually a slow process. It may not be indicated at first by the remnants of short grass which characterizes the deteriorated range. Relief from grazing pressure or cessation of long continued drought is frequently followed by an immediate growth of weeds. Gradually the grasses crowd out the weeds and become dominant. The most positive indication of range recovery occurs first on key areas or sore spots, such as trails, driveways, bedgrounds, congregating areas, gully slopes, and heads of canyons. Evidence of reduced erosion or increase in forage cover on these areas usually indicates that the entire range is recovering.

Degree of Use

When the condition of a range has been judged and the estimated proper number of livestock placed on it, the degree of forage utilization should be watched closely. The plants should not be grazed too closely if they are to maintain their vigor and protect the soil. In eastern Colorado 1¼ to 1½ inches of leaf stubble should remain on the short grasses at the end of the grazing season. A stubble height of at least 2 inches should be left farther south. One or more checks should be made during the season to allow for needed adjustments in livestock numbers. The final check at the end of the grazing season is very important. This should be made in the fall for ranges grazed during the summer and in spring before growth starts for ranges grazed during the winter. Taller grasses should have a stubble at least 4 or 5 inches high. Check not only the grasses, but also the palatable shrubs. They should not be grazed in excess of 20 to 30 percent of current twig growth.

Artificial seedings, already discussed, offer the most effective means of regrassing abandoned plowed lands. However, natural regrassing on many of the long-abandoned fields may be encouraged by judicious grazing.

Grazing of these lands should be deferred until the heavy stand of Russian-thistle has disappeared naturally and a perennial-weed cover has been established. All stages of recovery that follow should be stocked very conservatively. The following rates are suggested for stocking abandoned fields in eastern Colorado: The annual weed stage, no grazing; perennial weed stage, 40 to 60 acres per cow month; mixed grass stage, 20 to 40 acres; red three-awn, 10 to 20 acres; and the early stage of short-grass range, 4 to 10 acres per cow month. Grazing of the perennial-weed stage should be deferred until late summer or early fall to allow grasses to complete their growth cycles. When short grasses appear in the advanced stages of recovery, desirable rates of grazing should be based on the production and use of these grasses. The plants to be perpetuated should be grazed lightly. Abandoned fields should be grazed in conjunction with native ranges. Do not plow up abandoned fields which are making a good recovery unless they are to be reseeded.

Conservative grazing is imperative at all times on seeded pastures and native ranges. The greatest total pounds of beef or the greatest number of animals do not always show the greatest profit. A relatively high income may be obtained even from light grazing, which permits the most rapid recovery of deteriorated ranges. The cumulative result of heavy grazing is a gradual decrease in the plant cover, the loss of desirable grazing plants, and erosion. The results of grazing studies made on short-grass pastures at the U. S. Central Plains Experimental Range near Nunn, Colo., strikingly illustrate the benefits of conservative use of forage. Yearling Herefords have been grazed May 10 to November 10 for 7 years, at three rates, heavy, moderate, and light (57, 38, and 22 head per section, respectively). The heavy rate has caused both soil and forage deterioration. The moderate rate has resulted in some improvement of the range, and the light rate has brought about marked improvement. The 7-year average gross returns per section for these three rates were: Heavy, $1,024.93; moderate, $1,068.06; and light, $744.05. This shows an annual advantage of more than $43.00 per section in favor of moderate use of the forage. In 1946 the income under moderate use was $352 more than under heavy use.

Similar but less positive results were obtained on sandy range land at the U. S. Southern Plains Experimental Range near Woodward, Okla. Three degrees of continuous yearlong grazing and two degrees of continuous summer grazing of native range were much more evident in their effect on the vegetation than on cattle gains during the 5½-year period, 1941–46. In yearlong grazing rates of 6.6, 9.8, and 12.9 acres per yearling steer, the heavier rate produced annual gains 25 pounds per head less and 22 pounds per acre more than the average of the two more conservative rates of stocking. The detrimental effect of overgrazing on the vegetation was increasingly evident throughout the period, but the experiment had to be continued into the sixth year before heavy grazing caused sufficient reduction in gain per head to result in less gain per acre than was obtained from the moderate rate. More total gain was produced with fewer cattle during the winter of 1946–47.

Other sets of pastures at Woodward were grazed only from April to October on both a continuous and rotational basis at the overgrazed rate of

4.1 acres per yearling and the moderate rate of 6 acres per head. In these comparisons, the heavier rate reduced the average gain per head to the extent of 35 pounds and seriously damaged the vegetation, but caused a 15-pound increase in gain per acre. Of primary importance, however, is the fact that the moderately grazed pastures have been maintained in good condition while the overgrazed vegetation is rapidly declining in vigor and becoming seriously infested with less palatable plants.

Indicators of abuse on the overgrazed pastures in these studies included the gradual elimination of the taller, broad-leaved grasses, the opening effect displayed by clumps of blue grama, the grazing of weeds not eaten in other pastures, and the breaking down of brush branches by cattle in their effort to seek out and eat the grasses that grow in the protection of brush. Other evidences of misuse included a rapid transition from a mixed-grass to a short-grass association, the increase of purple three-awn and many other unpalatable weeds, the tendency of cattle to spend more time seeking food and less in resting near the water supply as the season advanced, and the increased tendency of cattle to walk the fence lines and reach through the fences for grass in adjoining pastures.

Nearly all of the surface growth of palatable forage and many unpalatable plants are removed in the overgrazed pastures by the end of the season. In contrast with this, the moderately grazed areas possess a good reserve of forage with considerable head development of the principal grasses as the season closes.

These degree-of-grazing tests at Woodward indicate that a stockman should give more consideration to the condition of his pasture plants than to his cattle, in deciding whether or not he is obtaining proper range use. The studies also showed that the optimum carrying capacity of nonmowed, sandy range land in the vicinity was 10 acres per steer on a yearlong basis and 6 acres from April to October.

Light grazing showed outstanding advantages over heavy grazing in a 4-year test with yearling steers on buffalograss-blue grama-tobosa range at the Spur, Tex., substation. The average gains for a 158-day summer grazing season were 178 pounds per head and 36.7 pounds per acre under light grazing, as compared with 114 pounds per head and 36.6 pounds per acre under heavy grazing. The gain differences in favor of moderate stocking were much greater the last year than on the average, indicating the cumulative ill effects of heavy grazing and beneficial effects of light grazing.

Season of Use

Most grasses are considered especially susceptible to heavy use early in spring. Protection from grazing at that time is essential in renewing the vigor of depleted ranges. Some grasses are equally if not more vulnerable to heavy use in late summer. Extremely heavy grazing at Woodward, for example, was more damaging to the vegetation when the abusive use was conducted in August and September than at other times in the year. Grasses that were most seriously affected by heavy use in late summer were blue grama and related species that head out in late season. These plants apparently exhaust the food in their roots by the production of surface growth during the summer and are likely to be damaged if grazed before the root reserves are replenished. All grasses injured by grazing late in summer respond slowly to protection from grazing during the next spring.

Deferred Grazing

Excluding livestock from range pastures during the entire growing season has proved to be extremely beneficial to the vegetation. Most range plants, when allowed to develop the maximum of surface growth and mature seed, produce a deeper and more extensive root system, enlarge at the base, and become generally more productive. The more palatable grasses are encouraged and enabled to compete with and crowd out those less desirable. The summer-deferment practice not only builds up the vigor of the grasses but provides an excellent reserve of winter forage which reduces requirements for supplemental feeds. This desirable practice should be applied at intervals of several years to every range unit of a ranch, provided of course that the undeferred portions of the range are not overstocked by cattle removed from the deferred areas.

All of these advantages were particularly noticeable in comparisons of range deferred during the growing season with those grazed continuously throughout the year in the experiments at Woodward. The deferred range supported twice as many cattle as the continuous range during the winter, and the winter gains of steer calves were 10 pounds per head more on the deferred areas.

Rotational Grazing

In contrast with the advantages derived from season-long deferment, the deferred-and-rotation system of grazing gave poorer results than continuous summer grazing at Woodward. Continuous grazing of native range from April to October through the 5-year period, 1942–46, gave consistently higher gains of yearling steers and left the grass in better condition than deferred-and-rotation grazing. The comparisons were made in duplicate pastures at both heavy and moderate rates of stocking and included rotation pastures containing both two and three divisions. The rotation cattle were moved from one division of the pasture to another at monthly or bimonthly intervals during the growing season.

Continuous grazing was superior to deferred-and-rotation grazing in every comparison. The two-division system of deferment was superior to the more intensive three-division method, indicating that the less frequently cattle are rotated on native range during the summer, the better are the results. This may be explained partly by the inability of yearlings to make maximum use of the coarser and more mature forage on deferred portions of the range. Another explanation may be that the continuously grazed cattle have free access to all the forage when it is highest in food value, while the rotation cattle are restricted in acreage at any given time. Rotation grazing at Spur, Tex., proved damaging to the vegetation, since heavy use for short periods left the soil unprotected when torrential rains occurred.

Forage Value and Gains

Stockmen are urged to take advantage of seasonal trends in range forage quality and animal gains in grazing and marketing their cattle. Monthly weighings of cattle in the Department's cooperative grazing tests at Nunn, Colo., and at Woodward, Okla., show that the rate of gain is highest in spring and declines successively by months from spring to fall. Colorado yearling Herefords produced 6-year average monthly gains of 68.8 pounds per head in May, 66.0 in June, 58.2 in July, 53.7 in August, 30.3 in September, and 4.0 in October, or 281.0 pounds for the season as a whole. Yearling Hereford steers used in the Oklahoma tests gained at the 5-year average daily rate of 2.37 pounds per head in April–May, 2.11 in June, 1.62 in July, 1.32 in August, and 1.23 in September–October. These rates represented an average seasonal gain of 306.4 pounds per head.

At both of these locations, the cattle produced nearly 90 percent of their total seasonal gain by the end of August. A practical suggestion would be for stockmen to take advantage of this fact by selling their fattest steers early in the fall, when prices are usually higher than later on, and thereby leave more forage for the remaining cattle and build up the future vigor of the grass. Marketing the entire herd by the end of September or soon after the first killing frost would appear to be a profitable practice, especially in Colorado where actual losses in weight are common in October if the weather is cold and stormy.

The downward trend in rate of cattle gains during the growing season is the direct result of diminishing nutritive qualities in the range forage. This is fully substantiated by analytical work conducted with 29 Woodward range plants at monthly intervals over a 6-year period through the cooperation of V. G. Heller of the Oklahoma Agricultural Experiment Station. The range forage ran extremely high in protein, phosphorus, calcium, and carotene in April. It declined slightly in these respects in May and somewhat more in June but usually maintained a minimum level above that required for rapid growth and fattening of beef cattle during these months. Cattle gains on grass alone during this period were comparable with those obtainable on a full feed of grain.

The food values of the grasses showed further decreases as the plants approached maturity during the summer and became dormant in the fall. However, they rarely fell below a minimum of 5 percent in protein content during the last half of the season. This quantity of protein kept the cattle gaining well but was not sufficient for maximum development.

Protein Supplements

The quantity of protein supplements required by beef cattle on native range and the time to use concentrates are important considerations in range livestock production. The winter feeding of limited rations of protein-rich supplements is a common and usually profitable practice. A daily ration of 1 pound of cottonseed or soybean cake containing 41 to 43 percent protein is usually considered sufficient to satisfy the protein requirements for thrifty growth and proper maintenance of most classes of beef cattle on native ranges in the Plains. Greater quantities, however, often result in profitable gains. At Woodward, for example, steer calves fed a total of 270 pounds of 41 percent cottonseed cake (1.8 pounds a day) during the 147-day winter grazing season of 1946–47 gained 57.5 pounds per head, as compared with only 16.6 pounds for comparable steers similarly grazed and fed half as much cake.

The decreasing food content of range grasses and gains of cattle in late summer indicate the advisability of feeding protein supplements at that time, although that is not commonly done in the region. Further evidence in support of the practice was obtained in feeding trials conducted at Woodward in 1945 and 1946. Feeding a daily ration of 1 pound of cottonseed cake after July 1 increased the summer gains of yearling steers on native range by an average margin of 41.3 pounds per head, when compared with similar lots receiving no cake. Doubling the late-summer ration of cake increased the advantage over noncaking by an average difference of 56.0 pounds per head. The 1-pound rate of feeding was profitable both years; the 2-pound rate, 1 year.

Many cottonseed-processing companies plan to make most of their cottonseed cake in the future by the new solvent method of extraction. The relative feeding value of this product and the standard hydraulic-extracted material as supplements for beef cattle on native range was tested at Woodward during the winters of 1945–46 and 1946–47. Both products contained about 41 percent protein, but the extra oil removed by the solvent process for other uses left the solvent cake containing about 3.5 percent less fat. Despite this difference in energy value, the two supplements produced about the same rate of gain. There was a statistically insignificant gain difference of 11.2 pounds per head in favor of the hydraulic cake the first winter and a minor difference of 0.9 pound in favor of the solvent product the second winter. It may be concluded, therefore, that the two products have about the same feed value when processed to the same protein content.

Brush Control

Various types of brush control offer possibilities for improving many native ranges in the region. Mowing has given outstanding results in controlling sand sagebrush and increasing grass production in experiments conducted at Woodward, since 1935. Mowing the brush in June for two successive years and keeping livestock off the range from June to September of those years resulted in greatly improved pastures.

These treatments eradicated many of the sagebrush plants, greatly reduced the vigor of the remainder, and doubled the density and vigor of the grass. Other advantages included the reduction in grazing pressure on individual grasses by making all plants in a pasture accessible to livestock. The mowing also improved the naturally low palatability of the shrubs that survived.

The results on the range, as well as in the chemical laboratory, showed conclusively that June is the best time to control sand sagebrush by mowing in the central part of the region. Chemical analyses of the sagebrush roots, conducted through the cooperation of J. E. Webster of the Oklahoma Agricultural Experiment Station, showed that the roots contain the least quantity of carbohydrates and other stored food in June and, therefore, are controlled most effectively by removal of surface growth at that time. The plants exhaust most of their root reserves in completion of their forage growth by June and thereafter begin to replenish the reserves.

Most any heavy-duty power take-off mower, when properly equipped, can be used satisfactorily in mowing heavy brush. The operation merely requires a series of special attachments manufactured by most machine companies. Rubber-tired tractors have been used in heavy brush without evidence of damage to the rubber.

For the first mowing of heavy brush, use a 5-foot cutter bar equipped with (1) a complete set of snub-nosed pea guards having extra rear bracing and square bolt holes, (2) heavy underserrated sections (they are about $\frac{1}{16}$ of an inch thicker than ordinary sections), and (3) a double set of hold-down clips (one less than twice as many as are ordinarily supplied with a regular mower bar). Mow in low gear the first time to obtain maximum sickle speed, setting the mower to cut as close to the ground as possible. Insert an extra gear in the mower or power take-off, if necessary, to obtain high sickle speed. Keep sickles sharp and all mowing equipment in snug working order at all times.

For the second mowing of heavy brush or the first mowing of light brush, use a 6-foot cutter bar equipped with (1) a set of heavy pointed rock guards having extra rear bracing and square bolt holes, (2) heavy underserrated sections, and (3) a double set of hold-down clips. The snub-nosed guards will handle heavier brush than the rock guards but the latter will do a cleaner job and should be used if the brush is not too heavy. In mowing the second year, cut the brush in a direction opposite that of the first cutting, using the same speed as in mowing hay. The opposite direction of the second mowing removes prostrate branches that escaped the first operation. The plant parts, if left uncut, will replenish the food in the roots and retard control.

The detailed brush-control studies were tested on a larger scale by mowing two of the experimental pastures in June 1941 and June 1942. Grazing was deferred on these pastures during the summers of those 2 years to enable the grass to recover and compete to the further detriment of the weakened sagebrush plants. Increased gains of yearling steers during the first winter, and the extremely heavy carrying capacity which the deferred vegetation afforded a large herd of beef cows the second winter, defrayed much of the cost involved in conducting the two mowings.

These mowed pastures were also grazed in comparison with nonmowed pastures during the summer grazing seasons of 1943–46. Mowing was shown by this comparison to have increased the carrying capacity of the land by a margin of 60 percent, raised the gain per head to the extent of 16 percent, and nearly doubled the beef production per acre.

The 4-year average summer gain on the mowed pastures was 353.1 pounds per head, as compared with 304.6 pounds of comparable steers on nonmowed land. The average carrying capacity was increased from the equivalent of 95 head per section of nonmowed land to 152 head on the mowed areas. These increases in gain per head and carrying capacity resulted in raising the gain per acre from 46.6 pounds on the nonmowed pastures to 89.0 pounds on the brush-controlled pastures. The actual increases due to mowing amounted to an average of 57 head per section, 48.5 pounds per head, and 42.4 pounds per acre.

In another set of pastures grazed on a yearlong basis after the first 2 years of June mowing and summer deferment, mowing increased the yearlong carrying capacity 70 percent and yearlong gains 36.1 pounds per head and 35.7 pounds per acre.

All pastures used in these mowing comparisons were moderately grazed and possessed a reserve of unused forage at the end of each grazing season sufficient to maintain the vigor of growth. The extra moisture and plant food saved by the removal of brush promotes maximum growth of grass. Mowing also exposes and increases the more palatable grasses which enable the cattle to fill up with choice forage in less time and with less interference from brush.

This method of improving sage-brush-infested range land is a highly effective and profitable practice. However, it is tedious, slow, and expensive, and only a limited acreage can be mowed at the optimum time in June.

Other types of equipment used with varying degrees of success in brush-control work include brush beaters, rolling cutters, one-way disk plows, and railroad rails. The brush beaters, when properly constructed and kept in good working order, remove the brush equally as effectively as mowing. The rolling cutters disturb the soil considerably and leave a high uneven stubble, but are satisfactory in subduing brush too heavy to be handled with other equipment. This implement and the one-way disk destroy some of the grass but may be useful in reducing some brush and preparing a partial seedbed for artificial reseeding.

C. E. Fisher, of Spur, recommends the use of sodium arsenite, oils, grubbing, or power machinery for the control of mesquite brush.

Use of 2,4-D in Brush Control

Investigations for the control of sagebrush and other shrubs have been conducted extensively since 1937 at Woodward, Okla. The studies included comparisons of various mowing attachments; detailed date-of-mowing tests with sagebrush, skunkbush, and shinnery oak; comparisons of the mower with other implements; chemical analyses of the root reserves in sagebrush, skunkbush, shinnery oak, and prickly-pear at semimonthly intervals during the growing season and at monthly intervals during the winter; grazing tests on mowed and nonmowed pastures to determine the effect of the treatment on grazing capacity, cattle gains, and range forage production; and a 2-year test of chemicals for brush control. Here we are interested in the last—specifically, the use of 2,4-D.

Excellent results in the control of sand sagebrush, skunkbush, sand plum, and many range weeds were obtained in preliminary tests with various types of 2,4-D chemicals on small plots in 1946 and on extensive areas in 1947. None of the treatments gave satisfactory control of shinnery oak. Several commercial and home-made formulations of 2,4-D were tested on 1,000 acres of range land in the Texas Panhandle and on 500 acres of similar land near Woodward in 1947. These 2,4-D materials included several methyl, ethyl, isopropyl, and butyl esters, four sodium salt solutions, and two antifreeze solutions. An amine was included in the 1946 tests. These studies were conducted through the cooperation of chemical companies, an airplane-spraying company, and stockmen. The work was done by both air and ground-spray equipment. These and other range studies were under the supervision of E. H. McIlvain.

Mr. McIlvain and his coworkers, among them Jack R. Harlan and Albert L. Brown, found that time of treatment is extremely important. Treatment should be made when the plants are well leafed out and growing actively. Date-of-spraying tests indicated that the best time for controlling sagebrush extends from about April 15 to June 1 in the Woodward area. A somewhat earlier time may be advisable farther south and somewhat later farther north. It cannot be too strongly emphasized that spraying at the wrong time is a complete waste of money, labor, and materials.

All commercial formulations of 2,4-D (the esters, amine, and salts) gave satisfactory control of sagebrush, skunkbrush, sand plum, and many range weeds when properly applied at the rate of 1 pound of pure 2,4-D acid equivalent per acre, in volume sufficient to insure complete coverage. Three gallons of an ester solution and 5 gallons of a salt solution usually represent the minimum required for adequate coverage. Further work may indicate that these volumes can be reduced, but lower volumes cannot be recommended now. Applications of 2,4-D in quantities less than the equivalent of 1 pound of the pure acid per acre cannot be recommended for brush control on the basis of results to date.

Most commercial formulas are too costly at present for use in brush control on cheap range land. A home-made solution was much less expensive than the others. It was also one of the most effective, if not the most effective, treatments included in the 1947 tests.

Suggested Formula

It consisted of applying the following materials with an airplane at the per-acre rates indicated (5 gallons per acre):

A solution of:
> One pound of pure (98 percent) 2,4-D acid.
> Six-tenths pound of sodium carbonate.
> Four gallons of water.

In emulsion with:
> One gallon of Diesel oil.

This home-made formula is prepared by dissolving the acid and sodium carbonate in the water by vigorous agitation in a mixing tank. The sodium carbonate is used to get the acid in solution. The quantity required to accomplish this purpose varies with the alkalinity of the water. A true solution is formed in this manner. Further agitation is needed only to keep the Diesel oil in emulsion with the salt-water solution. This is accomplished by vigorous agitation in the mixing tank and by an agitator in the airplane tank. The Diesel oil reduces the volume of water required, keeps the spray from evaporating and landing as a dust, and aids in distributing the 2,4-D over the leaves.

Method of Spraying

Large-scale applications on range land can be done best by airplane. Biplanes of the Stearman type are recommended and should be suitably equipped with tank, pump, mechanical agitator, underwing boom, and nozzles. It is extremely important to have the plane fitted with a positive cut-off valve to avoid releasing any of the spray on areas not intended to be treated. The effectiveness of control depends to a considerable extent on the operator of the plane. The plane should fly as low as possible, crosswind, and at intervals of 30 to 50 feet depending upon a wind velocity. A plane should not be expected to operate economically at more than five miles from a landing strip. Adequate ground equipment and a convenient source of water are essential to fast, efficient use of the ship. Flagmen are required to mark the course of the plane across the range, changing their location for each flight. The cost of this labor is comparatively small, because a plane can cover up to 1,000 acres a day.

The use of ground spraying machines on sagebrush range presents certain difficulties. Most equipment is not made to stand the rough treatment to which it is subjected in bouncing across the average sage-land pasture. Much breakage can be expected unless special braces are welded to the boom and other similar precautions taken. The operator experiences further difficulty in trying to tell where he has been or where he is going. With a ground spraying machine, flagmen may be prohibitive in cost and of little help because of the short range of vision of an operator on the ground in rough, rolling range. The strips can be marked with flagged stakes moved by a man on horseback following the sprayer. Despite the difficulties in using ground sprayers, they have advantages for small areas, or for spraying near crops susceptible to injury from 2,4-D.

Many equipment companies make various types of sprayers for use in low-volume, high-concentration spraying of the kind found successful in the Woodward work. In some cases machines used for livestock sprays and other purposes have been converted for use in ground application of 2,4-D. A boom is available that is equipped at intervals of 18 to 20 inches with special flat atomizing nozzles and designed to spray as low as 5 gallons per acre when operated from a tractor or tank trailer at about 3½ miles an hour. A powerful truck of the four-wheel drive type may be substituted for the tractor. The conveying tank should be equipped with a suitable agitator and designed to provide a nozzle pressure of about 30 pounds. A mechanical agitator is essential in keeping the Diesel oil in emulsion with the salt solution.

Rain may nullify or reduce the effectiveness of the treatment if it falls within 8 to 12 hours after applying a salt solution or within an hour after using an ester solution. Close attention to weather reports is advisable.

The spray is capable of drifting 400 yards or more in high winds. Extreme care should be observed to avoid damage to susceptible crops, trees, gardens, and ornamental plantings. Cereal crops, sorghums, corn, and all other grasses, except in the seedling stage, are highly resistant to 2,4-D, but alfalfa, sweetclover, cotton, and many other broad-leaved plants are subject to lethal damage by the chemical. Osage-orange and hackberry are highly resistant to 2,4-D, but black locust, chinaberry, and cottonwood are easily damaged and sometimes killed by drifting spray.

The dusts of 2,4-D usually drift much farther than the sprays, and, therefore, often cause more damage to susceptible crops. Moreover, the dusts are considered less satisfactory than the sprays in dry regions.

Adequate precautions should be taken against fire around the mixing tank and airplane. Prolonged personal exposure to 2,4-D liquid or fumes should be avoided.

All traces of 2,4-D must be removed from spray equipment before spraying crops, orchards, and ornamental plantings for insect control or other purposes. This can be accomplished by thorough rinsing with water, soaking overnight with a solution containing 1 part of household ammonia and 100 parts of water, and rerinsing with water.

The spray treatments had no apparent ill effect on the grasses and none on the livestock. In every comparison the sprayed areas produced fully twice as much grass as the nonsprayed ones. The advantage in grass improvement through the control of weeds alone appeared to be sufficient the first year to defray the total cost of the home-made treatment.

The spraying company that cooperated in conducting the 1947 tests is contracting with stockmen to have the home-made solution of acid, sodium carbonate, water, and Diesel oil furnished, mixed, and applied at a total cost of $2 an acre, exclusive of flagmen. Several other fliers are making the same contract and many others have shown an interest in the program. A current shortage of the pure 2,4-D acid is delaying the plans of some of these fliers.

Shown below are some desirable and undesirable plants listed in approximate susceptibility to injury by 2,4-D when applied from April 15 to June 1 for sagebrush control.

Susceptible to 2,4-D

Alfalfa.	Pigweed.
Annual buckwheat.	Plums.
Black locust.	Puncturevine.
Black walnut.	Rabbitbush.
Cherry.	Ragweed.
Chinaberry.	Russian-thistle.
Cocklebur.	Sagebrush.
Cotton.	Sand plum.
Cottonwood.	Siberian pea.
Evening primrose.	Skunkbush.
Grapes.	Sumacs.
Lambsquarters.	Sunflower.
Marestail.	Sweetclover.
Mustard.	Tamarix.
Persimmon.	Willows (some).

Intermediately susceptible to 2,4-D

Chinese elm.	Perennial broom-
Gaillardia.	weed.
Honeylocust.	Prairie thistle.
	Loco.

Resistant to 2,4-D

Blackjack oak.	Osage-orange.
Cereal crops (all).	Pine.
Grasses.	Red cedar.
Hackberry.	Roses.
Mesquite.	Sand legume.
Pricklypear.	Shinnery oak.
Oaks.	Yucca.

Mineral Supplements

Phosphorus is about the only mineral that is occasionally deficient in the range forage of the region. Excepted localities include the shinnery oak area where both calcium and phosphorus often occur in quantities below the minimum requirements of beef cattle. The deficiencies in phosphorus are most evident during winter and periods of drought, but are rarely so great in the region generally as in many other parts of the country. The feeding of bonemeal or other phosphorus supplements is a common practice in the region and is recommended by most experiment stations as a safeguard to proper nutrition, especially in eastern Colorado, the lower Texas Panhandle, and eastern New Mexico.

Deficiencies in phosphorus appear to be less evident in the central part of the region than elsewhere. In range experiments conducted at Woodward since 1942, yearling steers fed a mineral mixture of steamed bonemeal and salt, or of steamed bonemeal, ground limestone, and salt, showed no advantage in gains over comparable steers fed salt alone. Analyses of the range forage used in these studies were conducted at monthly intervals over a 6-year period by V. G. Heller, of the Oklahoma experiment station. All of the forage had an excess of calcium every month in the year and ample supplies of phosphorus from April to October, inclusive. A minor phosphorus deficiency was revealed in many of the dormant range plants during the winter, although the shortage was much less than that recorded in southern Texas, southern New Mexico, and many other parts of the West.

A series of analyses of the blood from the salt-fed and mineral-mixture-fed cattle showed that the blood from all lots was high in calcium and phosphorus at all times in the year, indicating that the diet contained ample quantities of these elements. The phosphorus deficiency in some forage plants during the winter was apparently overcome by an excess of this element in other vegetation and by the feeding of cottonseed cake containing considerable phosphorus.

Further evidence that the range forage, when supplemented with cottonseed cake during the winter, contained sufficient phosphorus to meet cattle requirements was the reluctance of cattle to eat the minerals unless forced to do so by the absence of salt on the side. Even then the consumption of the mixture was much less than that of salt alone in adjacent pastures. When salt was fed exclusive of other minerals, the average quantity consumed was 18.1 pounds per head during the summer and 26.6 pounds in winter, or a total of 44.7 pounds for the year. The average consumption of the mineral mixture was 11.8 pounds in summer and 22.6 pounds in winter.

Cattle having access to separate bunks of the two minerals ate 2.6 times as much salt as they did bonemeal during the winter and 7.8 times as much in summer. These figures indicate that the cattle had no special craving for phosphorus. The results are in direct contrast with those recorded in such phosphorus-deficient areas as southern New Mexico where cattle eat more of a mineral mixture than they do of salt alone.

Most grasses in the region generally are high in calcium content. Because of this and the fact that an excess of calcium often accentuates phosphorus deficiencies, it is wise to dispense with the use of ground limestone or similar high-calcium supplements except perhaps in the shinnery oak belt. The feeding of steamed bonemeal as a mixture with salt corrects phosphorus deficiencies and also provides some calcium in localities where the element may be questionably low. The use of phosphorus supplements is often advisable when soybean cake is fed. This protein supplement contains less phosphorus than cottonseed cake.

Many stockmen are interested in the relative grazing value of short-grass hard land and tall-grass sandy land.

Grazing comparisons at Woodward indicated that gains per head were nearly identical on the two types of vegetation but carrying capacities and gains per acre were higher on pastures containing the most short grass. The outstanding results obtained from mowing sagebrush on tall-grass sandy land shows, however, that this type of pasture is superior to short-grass areas when the brush is kept under control. The sandy land supports a wider variety of vegetation and produces more green forage throughout the year than do the heavier soils.

Conservative or deferred grazing alone will result in reestablishing good stands of grass on most depleted range land in the region. However, the process of natural revegetation is slow and can be greatly hastened by reseeding the area with adapted grasses. Starting reseeded stands on thin pasture land is more difficult than in prepared seedbeds on formerly cultivated land. Competition from weeds and remnant grasses on native range makes it difficult to thicken up the stand by artificial seedings.

Grasses best suited for use in range reseedings are those most capable of withstanding competition from other plants. In the northern and higher elevations of the region, these include crested wheatgrass, western wheatgrass, and other cool-weather grasses that start early and often become established before weeds are numerous. Sand lovegrass has proved to be most successful in range reseedings at Woodward, in southwestern Kansas, and elsewhere on sandy ranges. Other grasses that have given fair success in range reseedings include blue grama, side-oats grama, and switchgrass.

Care of the Herd

Keeping the livestock at top performance is one of the best methods of assuring a sustained income. The management of many ranches and farms can be improved by giving attention to the care of livestock and the performance of the breeding herd, the quality of bulls, breeding season, death losses, and calf crops.

The control of external parasites is an important factor in promoting gains of range livestock. Numerous tests and practical demonstrations show that spraying cattle with DDT for horn fly control increases gains. Yearling steers sprayed at Woodward with a 0.25-percent solution of DDT at monthly intervals throughout the summer of 1946 gained 26.7 pounds per head more than comparable lots not sprayed. Another lot sprayed at semimonthly intervals gained only 1 pound more than the group sprayed once a month. Greater advantages may be expected from the sprayings when horn flies are more numerous than they were in this test. The work was conducted during the driest growing season in 60 years, when the horn fly population was unusually low.

Cattle lice may be effectively controlled and gains increased by dipping or thoroughly spraying the cattle with a solution containing 8 pounds of 50-percent DDT per 100 gallons of water. A single treatment of this kind usually destroys most of the lice. Cattle grubs may be destroyed and heel fly infestations helpfully reduced by spraying the backs of cattle 3 times in the late fall and early winter with a solution containing $7\frac{1}{2}$ pounds of rotenone per 100 gallons of water. Heel flies cannot be controlled effectively unless these treatments are applied by all stockmen in a locality.

Nonbreeders and poor-quality animals should be systematically removed. The calf crop and the basis of heifer replacement will largely determine the amount of culling needed. If the calf crop is 90 percent or better, approximately 8 dry cows per 100 may be expected at inventory in January or February. The lower the calf crop the larger will be the number of cull cows. A good replacement basis requires about 20 heifers each year for 100 cows. This includes expected death losses and marketing of overaged animals.

Good bulls add to the quality of the herd. It is generally considered good practice to dispose of bulls at the age of 5 or 6 years to insure having virile and active breeders. Many owners find it profitable to pool their purchases of range bulls. A saving in price is frequently possible and greater uniformity in marketable livestock is achieved when herds are run in community pastures.

A controlled breeding season allows the rancher to take advantage of grass and markets for his calves at the most favorable times. Greater uniformity in age and weight of marketable animals is also possible where the bulls are not turned with the cows until a given date.

Some death losses are caused by lightning, poison plants, parasites, and diseases. A record of the causes will often suggest the remedy or the precaution that should be taken to prevent recurrences. The lightning hazard can be reduced by grounding all fences every quarter of a mile. The rancher should familiarize himself with the poisonous plants which cause losses: Larkspur, milkweed (various species), loco, suckleya, and others. Some plants are selenium bearing; others cause bloat. Ergot-infested plants occasionally cause abortion and other losses in wet years. The remedial measures include eradication, avoidance during the dangerous period, fencing, and proper distribution of salt and water. A plentiful supply of forage, developed through conservative use of the range, is the best insurance against poisonous and noxious plants. Animal diseases are best handled by an experienced veterinarian.

A 90-percent crop of calves should be the goal of every cattle grower in the Southern Great Plains. A calf crop that is first-class will produce a given amount of beef with fewer animals in the herd, a lower investment, less work, and less feed. A 50-percent calf crop requires twice as much feed for every cow that weans a calf as a 100-percent calf crop.

The production of cultivated forage

crops is most important as a means of carrying the breeding herd through the winter. The most widely used of these harvested feeds are sorghums, corn fodder, corn or sorghum silage, and alfalfa hay.

Many varieties of sorghums are well adapted and provide the bulk of harvested forage used in the area. They are much more drought-resistant and better adapted than corn in most sections. They usually produce greater yields of grain and forage. Sorghum forage is often superior in feeding value to that of corn, and the grain has about 95 percent of the value of corn for livestock.

Procedures for growing sorghums and other forage crops are well known. Information regarding their local adaptation and use can be had from county agents and State and Federal experiment stations.

Procedures and results involved in feeding the crops are discussed in the article, *Grass for the Production of Beef,* by W. H. Black and D. A. Savage, page 103.

THE PRODUCTION OF SEED

D. A. SAVAGE, JAMES E. SMITH

IN THE FINAL analysis, all phases of grass establishment and utilization become valueless if seed supplies of desirable grasses are inadequate. Much is known about species adaptation and methods of establishment, but wholesale production of native grass seed is still in its infancy.

So far, most market supplies of native grass seed have been derived from natural range stands. Blue grama, buffalograss, and little bluestem can be found in natural stands pure enough to warrant temporary dependence on this source. Many other desirable native species, however, are usually found in undesirable mixtures, small areas, or inaccessible sites on which harvesting cannot be done with machines.

Set of seed is normally low and extremely uncertain under the conditions of severe competition generally present in native stands. The cost of harvest is much lower and the quality of seed much higher from cultivated stands than from native stands.

The steps to follow in growing grass seed on a commercial scale are relatively simple. The increasing demand for seed fully justifies the effort and makes it a highly remunerative undertaking. Of first importance is the use of seed from well-adapted southern sources or improved strains if they are available.

Land free from perennial pests, such as Johnsongrass, should be selected for cultivated seed production. The sorghum-stubble method of land preparation is suitable for establishing seed increase plantings of warm-weather grasses. An excess of surface litter is to be avoided, however, as it may interfere with cultivation of seedlings.

Row plantings of all except spreading grasses are recommended for seed increase. Clean-cultivated rows usually produce more and better quality seed than close drills. The width of rows may be varied to suit the available equipment. The average is generally about 40 inches. Rates of row planting for seed production are one-half to one-third the quantity recommended for close-drilled pasture seedings. Thick seeding rates are desirable to reduce weed competition in the rows.

Cultivation should begin as soon as the rows of young plants can be seen from the tractor seat. The first cultivation is slow and tedious, and front cultivator gangs should be equipped either with reversed disk hillers to throw dirt away from the rows or with fenders to protect the rows if shovels are used. Once the rows are clearly defined, cultivations are as rapid as for any other crop.

Yields of seed will be low the first year, though usually high enough more than to repay costs of cultivation. Good yields of seed should be realized the second year, and by the third year the field should be in full production. Maximum yields can be expected in most instances from the third to the tenth year, after which time production goes down rapidly.

An alternate course during the first season is simply to control weeds by mowing, and start intensive cultivation the second season. No seed yield can be expected the first year by this method, but the rows usually attain sufficient size to be seen readily and cultivated more rapidly the second year. When cultivation is postponed until the second season, the field is at least a year slower coming into full production.

Cultivation should be continued as intensively as necessary to keep the fields free of weeds. If good stands are obtained, the few weeds that appear in the rows are usually crowded out by the end of the second season.

All the native and introduced grasses important to the region, except buffalograss, can be readily and efficiently harvested with the ordinary farm machinery. Several basic changes in the combine are necessary in harvesting buffalograss.

Binders, headers, and swathers or windrowers can often be used to advantage in harvesting most grasses, because their use serves to lengthen the harvest season by allowing cutting to start before seed is ripe enough to combine. The extra labor involved in the use of these machines, however, makes them secondary to the combine in importance for general use.

Timeliness of harvest determines success in seed production. After seed has reached the hard-dough stage and is ready to combine, only 10 to 12 days are available for profitable harvest. The total acreage to be handled at a given time must be planned with the available harvesting equipment in mind. A 5-foot combine can be expected to cut only about 10 to 12 acres of grass seed in a day.

Combines having angle-bar or rasp-bar cylinders are more satisfactory for grass-seed harvest than those having toothed concaves and cylinders. It is possible to vary the number of teeth in the latter machines and reduce straw chopping, but better quality seed material can be obtained by using the angle- or rasp-bar type.

The cutting width of the combine is not important, but a high ratio between separating capacity and width of cut is essential. In harvesting seed of such grasses as the gramas, bluestems, Canada wild-rye, and western wheatgrass, the seed separates slowly and with difficulty from the straw, and care must be exercised to insure that the combine separator does not receive more material than can be handled without wasteful loss of seed in the tailings. This can be accomplished by adjusting the rate of forward travel to the capacity of the separator and type of seed being harvested.

Regardless of the size or make of combine used, the following initial adjustments are necessary: Render the air-blast fan inoperative either by removal of the fan blades or by disconnecting the fan drive. Set the clearance between cylinder and concaves at about $\frac{1}{2}$ inch for bluestems and Indiangrass; $\frac{3}{8}$ inch for gramas, western wheatgrass, and Canada wild-rye; $\frac{1}{4}$ inch for switchgrass; and $\frac{1}{8}$ to $\frac{3}{16}$ inch for lovegrasses. Set the cylinder speed at about 800 to 1,000 r. p. m. for bluestems and Indiangrass; 1,100 to 1,300 for gramas, western wheatgrass, and Canada wild-rye; and 1,400 to 1,600 for switchgrass and the lovegrasses. Remove the perforated sieve if one is present—its use will not eliminate recleaning, and it is almost certain to cause trouble by becoming clogged. Equip the reel bats with belting flaps or brushes to sweep the sickle guards clean at each revolution. Make certain that the flanging of the clean-grain auger extends full length into the bin elevator boot to avoid clogging of the bin elevator.

In harvesting most chaffy grass seed, the lower adjustable sieve should be removed and final separation of seed accomplished by means of the upper adjustable sieve. If an adjustable tailer is in place, the vanes should be closed; if a tailings rake is employed, it should be covered by tin or cardboard so that material riding over the upper adjustable sieve cannot fall into the cylinder return auger.

In harvesting such grasses as switchgrass or the lovegrasses, the tailer may be left open so that unthreshed material is returned to the cylinder. Seed of these grasses is easy to reclean in ordinary fanning mills. Finely chopped trash is not so objectionable as in seed of the bluestems or gramas which are difficult to reclean.

When starting to use a combine with bin and unloading auger, place a post or a piece of 4″ x 4″ lumber inside the bin with one end resting in the auger opening. Removal of the timber when the bin is full provides an opening through which the unloading process can be facilitated.

Since switchgrass, the lovegrasses, and other small seeds are easily recleaned in ordinary fanning mills, it is always best to use fast cylinder speed with a close cylinder-concave spacing to thresh all possible seed without regard to the quantity of trash included.

Seed of such grasses as the bluestems, gramas, Indiangrass, Canada wild-rye, and western wheatgrass are relatively difficult to reclean. Every effort should be made to avoid short pieces of stems and trash in combining them. This can be accomplished by cutting fairly long straw, and by using the slowest cylinder speed in conjunction with the widest cylinder-concave spacing at which most of the ripe seed is threshed in one trip through the machine.

Freshly harvested seed of all grasses must be spread and dried, to prevent spoilage from heating and molding, before final cleaning and sacking. The depth to which such seed material can be safely piled during the drying process depends on the stage of maturity at which it was cut, the amount of weeds and other succulent material present, and the degree of air circulation in the drying shed. A layer of seed material 8 to 12 inches thick usually requires turning at least once a day for 3 or 4 days.

A valuable adjunct to any cleaning operation is a simple screening device called a scalper, which is used to remove coarse trash from combine-run seed material. It consists essentially of an inclined screen held in a supporting framework, made to shuttle back and forth through the action of an eccentric drive connected to a small engine or motor. The screens are usually constructed from hardware cloth, but regular fanning-mill screen stock can be used. Two sizes of hardware cloth, 8-mesh and 4-mesh, are satisfactory for rough cleaning of most combine-run material. The scalper, when used in conjunction with fanning mills or other cleaning equipment, greatly speeds the entire operation and can be used alone to produce good-quality seed from combine-run bluestem, grama, and similar seed material.

Ordinary 2-screen fanning mills are used to clean such seed as switchgrass and the lovegrasses, as well as others that normally produce free grain when threshed. A wide range of screen sizes is essential to best cleaning operations. Openings in the top screen in each case should be just large enough to allow the largest seeds to fall through, and openings in the bottom screen small enough to hold small but sound seeds while allowing sand, small weed seeds, and other such impurities to fall through.

In cleaning lovegrass, a $\frac{1}{23}$-inch perforated zinc top screen and a 36 x 36-mesh bottom screen are desirable. For switchgrass a size 6, 7, or 8 top screen and a $\frac{1}{23}$-inch bottom screen are suitable. For western wheatgrass and side-oats grama, a slotted screen, size A, B, or C, is proper for the top, with a $\frac{1}{18}$ or $\frac{1}{20}$ perforated screen on the bottom. Canada wild-rye, the blue-stems, and most gramas cannot be cleaned readily in fanning mills without processing to remove the awns or hairs.

Many of the native and introduced grasses produce seed having hairs, awns, or other appendages which make them difficult to clean and plant in any but special drills. Ordinary farm hammer mills, operating at speeds of about 800 to 1,400 r. p. m., have been successfully used to "trim" such seeds so that they can be readily seeded with regular grain drills equipped with an agitator.

Steps to be followed in adjusting the hammer mill are outlined by M. M. Hoover, James E. Smith, Jr., A. E. Ferber, and D. R. Cornelius thus:

Place in the mill a screen having openings slightly larger than the seed to be processed. Start the mill at slow speed. Fill the cylinder with seed material and keep it full. After a short trial run, carefully examine the seed that has passed through the mill. If few or no cracked or hulled seeds are found, but many of the seeds retain the appendages you wished to remove, advance the cylinder speed by about 100 r. p. m. Be careful to prevent cracking or damaging the seed. Over-processing may reduce germination.

Repeat this process until the greatest amount of trimmed material is obtained with the least breakage of seed. Differences in seed size within a given lot makes it necessary, after running the lot through the hammer mill and cleaning it in a fanning mill, to rerun the portion still untrimmed through a finer hammer-mill screen. The hammer mill should be fed to its full capacity. Then the cylinder and hammers will roll the material around repeatedly and squeeze out through the screen whatever seeds have been trimmed enough to pass through readily. If the rate of flow drops and the cylinder speed remains the same, the cushioning effect of seed on the hammers is greatly reduced and the hammers begin to perform their usual grinding function.

THE AUTHORS≪≪   *D. A. Savage has been engaged in research on grass and related forage crops since 1924, the year of his graduation from Montana State College. He is senior agronomist in the Bureau of Plant Industry, Soils, and Agricultural Engineering and is stationed at the United States Southern Great Plains Field Station at Woodward, Okla. The station was established in 1913 for dry farming investigations. In 1936 it became the headquarters for grass breeding, regrassing, and range-improvement investigations conducted by the Bureau of Plant Industry, Soils, and Agricultural Engineering in the Southern Great Plains. The station includes 1,080 acres near the headquarters at Woodward and 4,315 acres on its United States Southern Plains Experimental Range near Fort Supply, Okla., where more than 500 head of beef cattle are grazed annually to determine how best to manage the native range and reseeded pastures of the region. Mr. Savage is assisted in the grass work at Woodward by J. R. Harlan, associate agronomist in charge of grass breeding, and E. H. McIlvain, assistant range ecologist in charge of range and pasture-improvement studies.*

D. F. Costello has done range research since 1934. He is senior forest ecologist in the Forest Service, in charge of range management research for the Rocky Mountain Region, and is stationed at the Rocky Mountain Forest and Range Experiment Station, Fort Collins, Colo. Dr. Costello is a native of Nebraska and a graduate of the University of Chicago.

James E. Smith has been engaged in extensive grass-seed collection, production, and cleaning work since 1935. A graduate of Kansas State College, he is associate agronomist and nursery manager in the Nursery Division, Soil Conservation Service, in charge of the grass nursery at the station at Woodward.

The Mountain Region

GRASS AND WATER KEEP THE KEYS

GEORGE STEWART

IN THE Mountain Region, which extends from Mexico to Canada and between the Sierra Nevada mountains and the plains, grass and water keep the keys.

It is an arid region, generally. It is rich in resources, but to make the best use of them special methods of irrigation, dry farming, and grazing are needed. Water here has double its usual importance: Save in some broad lowlands, communities are located on alluvial land in front of canyons that have permanent streams; in those lowlands, towns get their water through long canals that lead principally from storage reservoirs.

It is a region of extremes. It includes the entire States of Arizona, Nevada, Utah, Idaho; the parts of California, Oregon, and Washington that lie east of the Sierra Nevada and the Cascade Mountains; the parts of Montana, Wyoming, Colorado, and New Mexico that are west of the Great Plains; and Texas west of the Pecos River.

Mostly it consists of mountains and narrow valleys—except in eastern Washington and Oregon, the Snake River plains, and the Southwest, where lowlands are extensive. Part of southeastern California is below sea level; the Rockies rise to above 14,000 feet in Colorado. Plateaus and mountains constitute 80 percent of the region.

Roughly two-thirds is plateau and high-valley land between 4,000 and 7,000 feet in elevation; considerable flat country in Colorado and Wyoming is 7,000 to 8,000 feet above sea level. Extensive mountainous grazing areas in the central and northeastern part occur from 7,000 to about 9,000 feet, and in Colorado up to 10,000 feet.

Precipitation is around 5 inches in parts of the lower Colorado Basin and the Great Basin; it is more than 50 inches in parts of the Yellowstone Park area at the headquarters of the Columbia-Snake, Missouri, and the Colorado-Green Rivers. A map of rain and snow, could one be made, would resemble a patchwork quilt; the patches in the mountains would be small; in valleys and plateaus they would be larger, but nowhere would they represent a blanket coverage of nearly equal amounts of precipitation such as might occur in regions with a thousand miles or more of nearly uniform topography.

The effects of precipitation and temperature divide the region into three major subdivisions.

First, the low, hot country in southern Nevada, southeastern California, Arizona, New Mexico, and southwestern Texas, where the winters are mild, summer lasts from April to October, and maximum shade temperatures of 105° to 120° F. are common.

Second, the valley and the plateau country north of central Arizona and New Mexico, where winters are cold, summers are dry, and maximum temperatures in July and August are 90° to 100° F. Considerable areas in Washington and Oregon below 2,000 feet have mild, rainy winters.

Third, the mountainous areas above 6,000 feet in the north and 8,000 feet in the south, where winters are long, summers are cool and likely to be rainy, and maximum temperatures in July and early August are 70° to 90° F.

The soils, too, are diverse. In the mountains they are often coarse and poorly developed and tend to have thin topsoils and porous undersoils. In the valley plains near the mountains they may be gravelly or sandy and are usually well drained. Drier soils often bear a lime hardpan, called caliche, a few inches below the surface. Deep, well-drained deposits, generally found near the mouths of canyons and farther out on the extensive flood plains, are the most suitable soils for cultivated crops; generally they are so located that irrigation water, if available, can be brought to them. Near the valley bottoms the soils are usually heavier, often poorly drained and impregnated with excessive amounts of soil salts. In some places only stream-washed soils are free enough from salt to be suitable for cultivation.

Land ownership, except in Washington and Oregon, is predominantly Federal. Vast areas are controlled by the Forest Service, Indian Service, the Bureau of Land Management, Soil Conservation Service, and Bureau of Reclamation.

Of nearly 455 million acres in the region, 6.9 million acres produce harvested forage; 5.4 million acres, farm pasturage; and 142 million acres, forage on private range land. Public range comprises about 300 million acres. The remaining few million acres is State-owned and in nonagricultural use, such as municipal building sites and roads.

Only about 3.3 percent of the total area is cropland; nearly half of that, 1.3 percent, is in hay. An additional 1.2 percent is in tillable pasture. Aside from waste areas, the range lands in all kinds of ownership total about 87 percent and make an important agricultural contribution in range forage.

The region is a livestock province. There are two phases of the livestock industry: First, farm livestock, including the dairy industry, much of it conducted intensively; and, second, the range livestock, an extensive business.

Hay, pasture, and range lands, which provide the forage for this livestock, make up a large part of mountain agriculture. Hay land is cultivated land and produces harvested forage crops. Pasture land is grassland suitable for growing cultivated crops. Grazed land not suitable for cultivated crops is designated as range land. Privately owned range land, about 142 million acres, is largely suitable for spring and fall range. The grazeable part of the 104 million acres of national-forest land is used largely for summer range. The 156 million acres of land in grazing districts and public domain is used primarily as winter range. In New Mexico and Arizona much of the range, public and private, is used the year round.

Throughout the region hay and pasture lands are largely irrigated, and under good management produce high yields. Water is the limiting factor, because more good land is available than there is water to irrigate it. In the cooler parts, considerable areas of forage are grown by dry-farm methods. It is likely that such drought-tolerant grasses as crested wheatgrass will permit the extension of the practice in order to obtain higher pasture yields. Preparation should now be made to seed to grass all submarginal land as soon as the demand for wheat and other products decreases. Prompt seeding would let grass start before weeds occupied such lands as become abandoned to cultivation.

Yields per acre on irrigated lands are high, on dry lands intermediate, and on range lands low, in the ratio of 100:60:4. About one-third of the total forage, therefore, comes from hay and pasture land combined, and two-thirds from range land. About 80 percent of all forage (hay, pasture, and range) is used by range livestock. Only by close integration and management of the sources of forage, however, can the regional welfare now be fully attained.

Important opportunities exist for increasing both the yield and quality of forage by applying the best known principles and treatments. Thereby the whole region will be helped, for, obviously, agriculture in the Mountain Region is chiefly a grassland economy; grass dominates the agriculture; it also gives rise to much of the mercantile, banking, transportation, and professional activities. Income that supports schools, churches, recreation, and the high standard of life has much of its origin in the grassland economy; it takes livestock to utilize grass, and livestock raising is essentially a rural industry.

Many of the livestock graze on the range, and ranching communities are small and far apart. On the other hand, the dependent irrigated communities practice an especially intensive form of agriculture on scattered spots that give rise to compact settlement with highly cooperative and educational activities. Irrigation and domestic water, the lifeblood of the region, comes almost entirely from range watersheds. Since villages, towns, cities, ranches, and specialty farms must all have water, their welfare strongly reflects the conditions of the watersheds on which the water originates.

PASTURES AND NATURAL MEADOWS

GEORGE STEWART

PASTURES are important in the agriculture of the Mountain Region, but only about 10 to 20 percent of pasture land is handled under intensive management. Pastures support farm livestock, including milk cows, which comprise one-third of all cattle over 2 years old in the region, and furnish forage for range livestock for a good part of the year.

Pastures and meadows are of five types: Those on productive, well-drained irrigated land; those on wet or marginal irrigated land; pastures on nonirrigated land; the ones on salty land; and natural meadows used for pastures.

Highly productive irrigated pastures, which naturally accompany intensive agriculture, plus the high-producing dairy herds, compete successfully here with any of the usual farm crops, and may thus become a desirable part of the farm rotation. A few localities have large areas of good pastures but, in the main, irrigated pastures can be greatly improved. Intense pasture development is a new phase of agriculture here, and is developing further. Land and water values and high taxes require maximum production to make this enterprise profitable.

One way to grow better grass on irrigated pastures is to seed mixed species of grasses and legumes. The superiority of mixed species over single species lies in the greater yield, the shorter time needed to get pasturage ready for grazing, the steadier supply of green pasturage throughout the

Acreage of Pasture and Hay Lands, Private Range Land, National-Forest Land, Grazing Districts, Unappropriated Public Domain, and Indian Lands (in Thousands of Acres) by States in Mountain Region, 1945

State	Cropland used only for pasture		Privately owned range land		Federal lands		Indian lands	Total
	Hay	Pasture[1] (1940)	Woodland pastured	Other land pastured	National forest	Grazing districts and unappropriated public domain		
Arizona	209	261	6,007	30,514	11,546	11,280	19,225	78,952
California	145	233	147	951	1,579	4,800	.....	7,855
Colorado	789	715	1,001	9,555	13,697	8,207	551	34,515
Idaho	1,163	779	946	6,230	20,162	12,748	802	42,830
Montana	769	444	637	5,025	15,319	6,959	[2]3,000	32,153
Nevada	434	374	76	5,420	5,053	45,083	697	57,137
New Mexico	115	508	2,822	16,210	7,568	14,749	8,578	50,550
Oregon	698	759	1,529	10,056	8,680	13,211	1,804	36,737
Texas	101	15	5	17,478	.....	.....	.....	17,599
Utah	629	395	173	8,263	7,762	23,907	1,560	42,689
Washington	515	676	1,252	6,427	3,923	557	2,713	16,063
Wyoming	397	258	45	11,741	8,397	16,643	2,250	39,731
Total	5,964	5,417	14,640	127,870	103,596	158,144	41,180	456,811

[1] The acreage reported in 1940 census is thought to represent more truly the correct pasture area than that of 1945.

[2] Estimated for part of Montana in region.

season, and a more varied diet for the animals.

In Colorado, for example, mixed grasses and red clover yielded 1.87 tons of pasturage; mixed grasses and sweetclover, 1.17 tons; and mixed grasses without legumes, 0.76 ton. In Utah, yields of red clover, alfalfa, or Ladino clover mixed with grass gave significantly higher yields than other clovers with grass or grass mixtures, and all of them gave higher yields than one or two grasses without legumes. In Arizona and New Mexico, alfalfa outyields mixtures including grass and is, therefore, the basis of much of the pasturage. Species that start rapidly (such as red clover and Ladino, where they are adapted) shorten the time needed to get new seedings ready for the first grazing. Legumes add to the variety and nutritive value of pasture mixtures.

In Utah, several new mixtures give approximately 50 percent higher yields under rotation grazing than do the standard mixtures widely used for years. The present trend is to replace the two old stand-bys, Kentucky bluegrass and white clover, with taller, higher yielding species like smooth brome, tall oatgrass, orchardgrass, Ladino clover, and alfalfa. Kentucky bluegrass grows little when dry, or in hot weather even when moist. White clover does not yield so well as larger clovers.

In Idaho, bluebunch wheatgrass is a promising species for irrigated pastures. Currently recommended mixtures contain only a few species as compared with the complicated mixtures formerly recommended. Farmers should get current information from their agricultural agent.

In the Southwest the short-season or winter annual crops are often grown for pasturage. In the Salt River Valley, barley or a mixture of oats and barley is often sown for winter pasture. As part of a double-cropping system, barley and oats seeded in September are grazed in December and again in January, and then allowed to mature

grain. Another profitable practice is to seed oats and barley (mixed or alone) in September on alfalfa stubble for winter grazing. Sudangrass and sorghum are planted and pastured after the grain is harvested. Of the perennial plants, alfalfa, Bermuda, and Johnsongrass are most generally used for pasturage. Northern grasses do not thrive in the heat of the Southwest. Johnsongrass is a common weed pest, but infested fields are used for grazing.

Practically no pasture lands in this area require lime to correct soil acidity. Liberal applications of farm manure are recommended for increasing yields; it should be put on before seedbeds are prepared and at yearly intervals after the pasture is established. If it is more convenient to apply commercial nitrogen fertilizer, 100 to 300 pounds an acre usually will increase the growth of grasses but probably will not greatly affect legumes. Farm manure has the advantage of adding organic matter to the soil and, when fortified by 100 to 200 pounds of superphosphate or its equivalent, in annual applications, will build up the yielding power of most soils. Nitrogenous fertilizers help to increase early spring growth.

Pastures on some soils—but not all—respond immediately and strongly to phosphate applications of 100 to 200 pounds an acre. Some deep, productive soils that formerly gave little response to phosphates have, after many years of cropping, responded vigorously. In Cache Valley, Utah, for instance, good soils not formerly responsive to phosphates show yield increases of 45 to 95 percent when fertilized with manure and phosphate. The combination of manure and mineral fertilizers also increased the proportion of legumes. Fertilizers increase the yields and improve the rapidity of growth and prolong the green period.

No part of the region has recorded any outstanding response to potash fertilizers.

Seedbeds should be well prepared—firm beneath, but soft and mellow for ½ to 1 inch on the surface. High-quality, well-chosen seed should be used. The seed should be evenly distributed and covered with about half an inch of soil. Seeding should be done just before the most prolonged period of moist growing weather; new seedings should be kept uniformly but not excessively wet.

Grazing should not begin until the stand is well established and firmly rooted. The intensity of grazing should be moderate, especially during the first year of use. At times it may be desirable to drill the seed in undisturbed grain stubble, especially where soil blowing is a problem. Where it is not practical to use a drill, seed may be broadcast and covered lightly with a harrow. Broadcasting and covering with a cultipacker is often desirable on loose soils.

Sowing pastures with small-grain crops is a questionable procedure. Too heavy stands of grain tend to smother the pasture plants. Thin stands of barley are often successful. Early spring seeding, either with no companion crop or with one that does not produce heavy shade, or with one that is removed early, is favored. On soils that crust badly, nurse crops aid in getting good stands of grass. Properly managed nurse crops are often economically advisable, but the practice should be used with care. In the plateau zone, about one-third the pastures may suitably be seeded in spring with small grain, about one-third in spring alone, and one-fourth in late summer after crops are removed. In southern districts, irrigated pastures are almost always seeded in fall.

In general, pasture stands should be kept moist enough to insure growth continuously during the growing season. Deep-rooted pasture plants should get heavy enough irrigations to wet the root zone while shallow-rooted species, such as white clover and Kentucky bluegrass, need more frequent applications. Overirrigation is likely to damage soil structure and the plant. The ponding of water (either natural or as a result of irrigation) should be corrected

because this favors water-loving grasses or sedges and rushes of low feed value. Leveling the land—or at least grading it to a uniform slope before seeding—is the best way to prevent ponding during irrigation. Where ponding results from waterlogging, drainage is the remedy.

The rotated use of irrigated pastures is recommended, particularly for those sown to tall, deep-rooted species. To do this the pasture is divided into three or four fields. In the spring all animals are placed in one field as soon as the grass is ready to graze. When this field has been closely grazed, the livestock are moved to the second pasture, and so on to the third and fourth fields. Meanwhile, the field that has been grazed can be irrigated and harrowed with a chain drag or a nonrigid harrow to scatter manure droppings. Weeds or coarse grass stalks can be mowed if necessary. Pastures seeded to Kentucky bluegrass and white clover do not respond vigorously to rotation grazing.

Rotation grazing on well-fertilized and well-irrigated pastures keeps the top growth of tall pasture plants active all season long. To aid in maintaining fresh growth, it is wise to graze good irrigated pastures heavily for a time and then give them a rest. The temporary close utilization resulting from rotation grazing corrects uneven utilization and affords some pasturage earlier than can be safely grazed season-long.

In Utah the desirable mixtures have been kept for 7 or 8 years by manuring, harrowing, and heavy close grazing for a time, followed by prompt removal of the livestock to other pastures. Individual pastures were grazed early in spring not oftener than once every fourth year. Pasturing at night as well as by day is also favored; the amount and value of manure deposited on the pasture are thus increased, especially when high-producing dairy cows are fed some grain.

Pastures on good land, well-fertilized, irrigated, and seeded to the most suitable mixture of species and grazed as described, provide as much as 2 to 3 animal units of forage an acre throughout the season, or 6 to 18 animal months a season. More than 12 or 15 tons of green weight (air-dry weight is about 20 to 26 percent as much) often are produced. The better pastures in the Cache Valley have yielded more than 250 pounds of butterfat to the acre. Meat animals on them do correspondingly well.

Marginal Irrigated Land

Perhaps 80 to 90 percent of irrigated pastures are only moderately productive or less. The most common difficulties are waterlogged lands, accumulation of salts, poor management, and poor species of plants. Some waterlogged pastures yield up to 6 or 8 tons an acre, but most of them produce only 2 to 4 tons of green pasturage—about a ton or less of air-dry forage.

A good seedbed is one on which all native or weedy plants are killed before seeding. It is mellow on the surface but firm beneath. Seeding is probably best when done to a depth of less than an inch with a drill, or the seed is broadcast and covered with a harrow or cultipacker, either in early spring or late fall.

In Arizona and New Mexico, fall seeding is best, although summer precipitation makes June or July seeding safe in some places. Fall plowing and the use of farm manure help to provide a good seedbed in the plateau country.

Whether fertilizer is justified without treatments like drainage, leveling, and better irrigation is a local problem about which the county agent has the most reliable information.

Many wet-land pastures support native plants and are not artificially seeded. They consist largely of sedges, rushes, and redtop. Some Kentucky bluegrass occurs on ridges where a few inches of surface soil has natural drainage. Open ditches to drain off excess water improve the pastures. Generally, the topography is somewhat uneven and as the season advances the ridges dry out. All too often "wild" flooding, which further waterlogs the swales and gives the hummocks and ridges too little water, is practiced.

Continuous grazing usually permits some plants to develop seed stalks that become unpalatable to livestock. Grazing thus concentrates on spots grazed early in the season because the young growth is softer and more nutritious. As with intensively farmed pastures, rotation is much more effective when tall grasses and clovers are used.

Coarse, weedy plants like sourdock, wild licorice, and thistles are likely to be common and add to the already unequal forage production and utilization. A survey in Utah estimated this class of pasture to be only 45 percent productive. Pastures on such lands need careful management if they are to be maintained in good condition and the desirable species preserved. Simple drainage ditches, care in irrigation, mowing of weeds and grass bunches, harrowing to scatter manure droppings, and heavy rotation grazing to maintain uniform fresh growth often will increase pasturage production until the land gives good returns on its cost.

Nonirrigated Land

For nonirrigated dry-land pastures the standard grass for the central Mountain States is crested wheatgrass, 6 to 8 pounds an acre.

In cooler, higher areas with more moisture, 4 to 6 pounds of smooth bromegrass is added to the crested wheatgrass.

On heavy soils with some alkali, 4 to 6 pounds of western wheatgrass is mixed with 3 to 4 pounds of crested wheatgrass.

In the northern parts, yellow sweetclover (2 to 4 pounds) is generally mixed with 3 to 4 pounds each of smooth brome and crested wheatgrass.

Throughout the region, 1 to 2 pounds of alfalfa seed may well be added to all recommended mixtures on sites favorable to alfalfa.

Dry-land pastures are not common in the Southwest.

If irrigation water cannot be had, the chief ways to improve the forage yield and prevent surface runoff on these pastures are to maintain as nearly full stands of desirable grasses as possible, avoid overgrazing, and control weeds. Good stands are essential to high yields and, in turn, suppress weeds.

We recommend that at the end of the grazing period 30 to 40 percent of the herbage be left unused and that a reasonably good cover of litter be maintained. Weeds then are largely held in check and the water from heavy rains is absorbed, instead of running off and carrying away a part of the best soils. Grazing closer than this breaks up the litter cover, weakens the forage plants, and increases surface runoff during intense rains.

In the northern part, rabbitbrush and sagebrush are likely to invade dry-land pastures. The most satisfactory remedy now known is complete removal of brush before the areas are seeded to grass and conservative grazing thereafter. Mowing the brush is effective in some cases, but not always, and chemical treatments might help to control undesirable shrubs.

Salty Lands

Besides the large areas of wet-land pastures, smaller areas contain so much salt that the salt itself is a direct difficulty. These lands are seldom cultivated but furnish considerable pasturage. Saltgrass and alkali sacaton are the most common forage species. They furnish moderately good forage when growth is young and palatable. The drier areas bear inkweed, samphire, Salicornia, or greasewood—none of them valuable for forage. When the soils are only slightly salty, redtop, strawberry clover, the reed canarygrass, and white sweetclover can be used. It is well to sow at the rate of 2 pounds of clover and 3 pounds of each of the grasses to the acre.

Natural Meadows

Many natural meadows are pastured for a time in spring, a hay crop is allowed to grow, and after the wild hay is harvested the meadows are again grazed.

In Wyoming, prolonging the spring grazing by 20 to 35 days and cutting at the bloom period produced a total yield of hay plus pasturage 8 percent higher than normal harvesting. The total yield of protein was 20 percent greater. It was found that spring pasturing could be close and the meadows still produce good hay yields provided irrigation water was available late enough to enable the meadow to continue growth.

Scarcity of water in June and July might prevent the prolonged grazing in spring.

CULTIVATED FORAGE CROPS

WESLEY KELLER, H. R. HOCHMUTH

CULTIVATED forage crops harvested as hay or silage occupy 5 or 6 million acres of land in the Mountain Region, more than a third of the harvested cropland. In places where winter feeding of livestock is necessary, half or more of the harvested acreage is generally devoted to cultivated forage crops on which approximately 3 million head of beef cattle are wintered. Large numbers of cattle and sheep are also wintered on irrigated pastures where winter snows are absent.

Cultivated forage, with improved pastures, provides most of the feed for dairy cattle and calves, farm horses, and some beef cattle and sheep kept on farms, all together approximately 1½ million head. Sheep graze on ranges yearlong through most of the region and depend much less on cultivated forage, although in the Salt River Valley of Arizona and some other localities many ewes and lambs are pastured on irrigated alfalfa and small-grain pasture.

The acreage in cultivated forage crops is distributed through the region in a large number of irregular, irrigated areas and in places where soils and precipitation favor dry-farming.

Grazing beef cattle on the range is an extensive enterprise; the production of cultivated forage crops is intensive. Many ranchmen, in order to provide enough winter feed and to balance better their livestock enterprise, might well give attention to increasing the forage production of their cropland. Wherever harvested forage supplements the range, good ways to increase the forage for livestock are through the efficient use of irrigation water and fertilizers and the sowing of the best adapted varieties and species. In the Mountain Region harvested forage is obtained from alfalfa, wild hay, red clover and miscellaneous hay crops, annual and emergency crops, and corn and sorghum silage to provide succulent winter feed.

Alfalfa

Alfalfa is widely adapted to the climate and cultivated soils of the region. It occupies nearly half the acreage devoted to forage crops and produces more than half of all the harvested forage. Alfalfa is a good feed for all classes of livestock.

To meet the climatic extremes here, several types are grown. Ladak and other hardy varieties like Grimm are superior in the northern part and in the high valleys of Colorado. Common alfalfas are widely used in the central portion. In the warmer southern areas the nonhardy alfalfas, chiefly hairy Peruvian, have been grown, but farmers are replacing hairy Peruvian with common alfalfas, which yield less but

better hay. The quality of alfalfa hay depends largely upon leafiness and fineness of stems—characteristics of the hardy types.

Bacterial wilt of alfalfa (*Phytomonas insidiosa*), first described in 1925, has spread to all leading alfalfa-producing areas. The disease has so shortened the life of alfalfa that good stands cannot be maintained more than a few years. Wilt-resistant varieties that are becoming available appear certain to replace the varieties now grown. Accordingly, farmers are advised to consult their county agents for current recommendations on the best varieties for specific conditions.

Thick, uniform stands of alfalfa require a fine, firm, moist, well-worked seedbed. Only on sandy soils are good stands likely if the seed is covered deeper than 1 inch. Shallower coverings are preferable; on heavier soils they are essential. Thin stands of alfalfa mean weedy, inferior hay.

Better stands are usually obtained without a companion crop, except on weedy ground. When a companion crop is used, the rate of seeding should be reduced and the field should be managed so as to meet the needs of the alfalfa. Companion crops are not commonly used with fall plantings and never under conditions where moisture is the limiting factor.

In this region alfalfa is seeded mostly in the spring when moisture is more plentiful. In southern Arizona and adjacent low, hot areas, however, fall seeding is most successful.

Rates of seeding vary from 8 to 25 pounds an acre, the lower rates being ample if good seed is used under favorable conditions. To insure close contact between the seed and moist soil, it is often advisable to cultipack after seeding. Broadcast seed may be covered by a cultipacker or light harrow. Wherever hay is the major objective, alfalfa is never seeded in widely spaced rows.

In Washington, Colorado, Utah, and New Mexico, forage yields have not been increased by seeding perennial forage grasses with alfalfa. It is probable that this holds true wherever in the region alfalfa is well adapted. Some farmers have found, however, that a combination of smooth brome and alfalfa makes a good hay that is easily handled and remains productive longer than either grown alone. Pending the availability of wilt-resistant alfalfas, a combination of alfalfa (8–10 pounds) with smooth bromegrass (6–8 pounds) is to be recommended for irrigated land, and alfalfa (6–8 pounds) with crested wheatgrass (5–7 pounds) for dry-farm lands in Utah. Alfalfa-grass mixtures have also been recommended in Idaho to prevent erosion on sloping irrigated land.

On well-drained soils high in fertility, the yield response of alfalfa is almost directly proportional to available moisture. Heavy annual applications of water should not be attempted except on soils with good natural drainage because any appreciable rise in the water table will shorten the life of the alfalfa and encourage invasion by grasses.

Alfalfa usually responds to applications of barnyard manure and to phosphate fertilizer except on some heavy soils in Arizona.

Because of the widespread occurrence of bacterial wilt, it is generally not advisable to attempt to restore old alfalfa fields by reseeding in thin places to thicken the stand, or by cultivation to destroy weeds or aerate the soil. Before bacterial wilt became widespread, cultivation of alfalfa fields was sometimes advantageous. Stands of alfalfa that thin out and become weedy should be plowed up and the land sown to some other crop.

Through most of the region, the bright summer days have a maximum of sunshine—ideal haying weather. No set schedule for haying operations is possible, but the aim always is to cure the hay as quickly as possible and get it into storage with a minimum of discoloration and loss of leaves.

After mowing, the hay should stay in the swath until it is thoroughly wilted, but not so long that raking into windrows will result in a loss of leaves. Alfalfa mowed in the forenoon often is ready to be windrowed the same day; or, if dews are absent, it may be cut in late afternoon and raked the next morning. Under dry conditions, some farmers prefer to rake immediately after mowing. Additional drying will be accomplished in less time from the loose small windrows made by a side-delivery rake than from the larger ones characteristic of a dump rake. Larger windrows are also more difficult to manage and are more likely to result in musty hay if rained on.

Baling or chopping alfalfa from the windrow takes less work and storage space than loose long hay. But because hay for baling and chopping must be drier than hay handled loose, these methods probably do not shorten the period during which the hay is exposed to storm. Long loose hay can be safely stacked or stored in a barn when the moisture content has been reduced to approximately 25 percent. Alfalfa hay should be dried to 12 to 15 percent moisture before being chopped.

Wild Hay

Much land of low crop value produces wild hay. The yield and management of wild hay meadows varies with local conditions. Most of the hay produced is used to winter beef cattle that graze on range during the summer. Wild hay meadows also provide spring and fall pasturage. One crop of wild hay is generally all that is harvested for winter feeding, and that crop is of variable quality.

Where alsike or other clovers are abundant, together with such grasses as redtop, meadow fescue, timothy, slender wheatgrass, western wheatgrass, or smooth brome, a nutritious hay is obtained if they are cut in the bloom stage. When sedges, wiregrass, or saltgrass predominate, or if the hay is cut in an advanced stage of maturity, it is of low quality.

In high mountain valleys in northern Utah, native meadows are known to respond significantly to manure or phosphate, or both. Desirable species, such as alsike and red clover, established in these native meadows increase their productivity. Meadows plowed and reseeded to such mixtures as timothy and red clover or smooth brome, meadow fescue, and alsike clover, yield almost twice as much as before seeding. Fertilized with manure and phosphate, hay yields were approximately three times the original. The use of fertilizers and of desirable species substantially increases the nutritive value of the hay.

Red Clover

Red clover is extensively grown in the Snake River Valley of Idaho, which is the most concentrated seed-producing region in the United States. The first crop is generally pastured or harvested for hay and the second crop matured for seed. Growing red clover for both hay and seed is also increasing in other parts of Idaho and the irrigated valleys of northern Utah.

Seed is generally drilled in the spring at from 8 to 15 pounds an acre, depending on the condition of the seedbed. The most common causes of poor stands are failure to prepare a fine, firm seedbed, seeding too deeply, and competition from a companion crop.

Red clover should be seeded shallow, usually not more than ½ inch. Under favorable conditions, early spring seedings can be made on the surface and the seed covered with a cultipacker. By careful management good stands of red clover can be obtained with a companion crop of wheat or barley seeded at no more than a bushel an acre. When a companion crop is not used, red clover yields a good hay crop the first season.

It is sometimes seeded in midsummer after a crop of peas or other early crop. When this is done, the ground need not be replowed but merely worked to prepare a seedbed. Ample irrigation water must be available to obtain good stands with midseason planting. Frequent light applications

of water also are essential for highest yields. If seed is to be grown, the hay crop is usually cut in the early-bloom stage, but if only hay is produced, three-fourths to full bloom is preferred.

Red clover hay does not cure so quickly as alfalfa and great care should be used in handling it. Mowing should not begin when the dew is heavy. The crop should be permitted to dry as completely as possible in the swath without losing leaves when windrowing. Small windrows made by a side-delivery rake will cure in less time than larger windrows.

Red clover hay if it is of high quality makes good forage. Good clover straw is an excellent feed for wintering dry livestock; it is regarded as superior to wild hay of average quality for the purpose. Straw molds if it gets wet, and it should be stored where it is dry.

Many small mountain valleys have areas below the well-drained irrigated land where the water table is too near the surface for successful alfalfa production, but the best of this land is adapted to red clover. If hay is the only objective, 6 pounds of red clover with 8 pounds of timothy is recommended, to be cut when red clover is in three-fourths bloom. As the soil approaches the limit of wetness tolerated by red clover, alsike clover is added (3 pounds of red clover to 3 pounds of alsike clover and 8 pounds of timothy). On the wettest lands capable of cultivation, alsike (2 pounds) and reed canary-grass (6 pounds) are recommended.

On a considerable area in the valley bottoms a serious salt problem exists. If salt concentrations are not too great, sweetclover is adapted. In addition to sweetclover, other species such as meadow fescue, tall fescue, smooth brome, reed canary, slender wheatgrass, strawberry clover, and alsike clover will grow on salty land that can be irrigated. On nonirrigated land that is not too salty, species like western and crested wheatgrass are best. Barley, wheat, and oats also can produce satisfactory yields of forage in the presence of moderate amounts of salt.

Acreage Harvested and Yields Per Acre of Alfalfa and Wild Hay for the Four States Wholly Within the Mountain Region [1]

| State | Alfalfa hay | | | | | |
| | Acreage harvested | | | Yield per acre | | |
	1935–44	1945	1946	1935–44	1945	1946
	1,000 acres	1,000 acres	1,000 acres	Tons	Tons	Tons
Arizona......................	178	232	233	2. 63	2. 70	2. 70
Idaho........................	782	812	804	2. 41	2. 40	2. 50
Nevada......................	131	108	108	2. 35	2. 50	2. 70
Utah........................	447	430	408	2. 17	2. 30	2. 20

| State | Wild hay | | | | | |
| | Acreage harvested | | | Yield per acre | | |
	1935–44	1945	1946	1935–44	1945	1946
	1,000 acres	1,000 acres	1,000 acres	Tons	Tons	Tons
Arizona......................	5	3	3	0. 88	0. 90	0. 70
Idaho........................	123	146	146	1. 14	1. 15	1. 10
Nevada......................	217	267	267	1. 04	1. 00	1. 10
Utah........................	70	105	105	1. 20	1. 00	1. 20

[1] From U. S. Department of Agriculture Crop Reporting Board, Crop Production, Annual Summary, Washington, D. C., December 1946.

Emergency Crops and Silage

In the great wheat area of the Palouse, mowing a few swaths around the borders of wheatfields when the grain is in the dough stage gives some hay and, besides, clears an area for the harvester and serves as a fire guard.

Small grains grown alone or with vetch constitute an important source of forage on irrigated land in eastern Oregon and Washington.

In the mountain valleys of Montana and Wyoming, under irrigation, and in the high, cool valleys of northern Utah, either oats or barley mixed with field peas is a productive annual hay crop. Wyoming farmers seed 1 to 1½ bushels of peas an acre and the same amount of oats or barley.

Utah farmers plant 1½ bushels of peas an acre with 1½ to 2 bushels of oats. In warmer parts of Utah, in areas where a large part of the acreage produces feed, oats are seeded with common vetch at 40–50 pounds an acre, giving yields equal to oats and peas in the cooler areas. These mixtures should be seeded early in the spring and cut when the grain is in the soft-dough stage.

Wherever the growing season is not too short, an irrigation after the crop is removed will provide good fall pasture. Vetch should not be seeded on dry-farm or winter-wheat land because it is likely to become a serious weed. Hairy vetch is particularly objectionable under these conditions.

In western Montana, foxtail millet and Sudangrass are recommended as catch crops. They will produce a crop of hay in 2 months from date of seeding. Farther south, barley or other small grains will produce a crop of hay or even mature seed when planted after the failure of an early-spring-seeded crop such as sugar beets. In the southern end of the region, Sudangrass is important for both hay and pasture.

A comparatively small acreage in the region is used for the production of silage; almost everywhere, corn is best adapted. Corn silage can substitute for a third to a half of the alfalfa in the ration for dairy cattle. In the southern part, especially at low elevations, sorghums are more consistent in production than corn, and they produce a satisfactory silage.

Other succulent feeds available, in parts of the region, are sugar-beet tops, either to be consumed while fresh or made into silage, and wet beet pulp. Beet-top silage has a feeding value of about a fourth that of chopped alfalfa hay and about four-fifths that of corn silage. It can replace up to a third of the alfalfa in rations for dairy cows and wet beet pulp up to a fourth.

THE FOUNDATION OF THE RANGE

RAYMOND PRICE, KENNETH W. PARKER, A. C. HULL, JR.

THE MOUNTAIN REGION is the hub of the western-range livestock grazing industry. Here feeder calves and steers are raised for fattening for the Nation's beef supply. Cattle are grass-fattened for the butcher's block, and hides obtained for leather goods. Here are many of the Nation's sheep from which come our lamb, mutton, and wool. Here, also, are goat herds which produce mohair. All depend largely upon natural range forage.

But the range lands do more: When they are in good condition, the range plants protect the watersheds and conserve soil and water. Water is the controlling factor in the arid West; grass and soil are its regulators. Four-fifths of the important water-producing areas are made up of range lands. They constitute important portions of the watersheds of the Colorado, Columbia, Snake, Missouri, Rio Grande, Salt, Gila, and numerous interior-river drainages. Villages and cities, farms and ranches, the great irrigation systems, and hydroelectric plants so vital in the arid West are built upon a stable soil mantle and a regulated stream flow from the water-yielding ranges.

The range lands furnish a home for wildlife. Big game, small game, and upland game birds abound on the range. Fish inhabit the lakes and clear streams that flow from a properly managed range watershed. Range lands also form a setting for camping and other kinds of recreation.

These multiple values and uses of the range give added importance to grass in the Mountain West; we have to improve and use wisely the vegetation that covers its mountains and valleys.

Range vegetation is of many kinds because there are so many variations in elevation, precipitation, temperature, length of growing season, and soil. We recognize several major range types or patterns of natural vegetation—open forests, woodlands, sagebrush-grass, Pacific bunchgrass, salt-desert shrub, southern-desert shrub, semidesert grass, and shortgrass. But even these natural plant formations are not uniform throughout, and minor variations of vegetation are recognized, among them the annual grass of the sagebrush-grass type and the chaparral and mountain brush of the woodland type.

In the Mountain West open forest range types occupy about 70 million acres, an area the size of Nevada, and are the most important summer grazing grounds.

The forest range types vary in elevation from 3,000 to 12,000 feet. In the northern latitudes, the lower limits begin at 3,000 feet; in the southern parts, the lower limits are about 6,000 feet. Precipitation ranges from about 15 to 50 inches. The length of the growing season is about 4 months and becomes shorter at the higher elevations.

In the northern part, commercial timber production overshadows the value of the open-forest type for range use. Dense stands of white pine, larch, hemlock, lodgepole pine, and Douglas-fir have poor forage growth and are relatively unimportant for grazing domestic livestock. But in the open, stands of ponderosa pine and associated meadows are excellent summer grazing areas for both cattle and sheep. The main forage species are tufted hairgrass, Idaho fescue, bluegrasses, wheatgrasses, needlegrasses, pinegrass, and sedges. Mountain meadows and other openings, although small in area, have acre for acre many times the grazing capacity of the open forest proper. These sites, when they are in excellent condition, can graze 1 or 2 cows or 5 to 10 sheep an acre for a month.

In the central Rocky Mountains and the Great Basin, the Douglas-fir-aspen forest is the most important summer grazing grounds. The important forage species include the bluebunch fescue, mountain brome, bluegrasses, wheatgrasses, needlegrasses, aspen, and snowberry. Grazing capacity depends on range condition and topography. On ranges in excellent condition with gentle topography, 2 or 3 acres will maintain a cow for a month.

Open ponderosa pine forests exist throughout central Idaho, Colorado, Arizona, and New Mexico. The important forage plants are Arizona fescue, Idaho fescue, mountain muhly, pine dropseed, blue grama, bluegrasses, and a variety of weed and browse species. On ranges in good to excellent condition with gentle topography, grazing capacity is 2 to 4 acres a cow a month.

Woodlands extend over some 80 million acres on the plateaus and lower fringes of the mountain masses in the Great Basin and Southwest. They are composed chiefly of pinyon pine and junipers, with Gambel oak in Nevada and Utah and evergreen oaks farther south. Included in the woodland range is the chaparral of central Arizona and the mountain brush of the Great Basin, both distinct natural vegetation formations. Woodlands occur between the open forests and lower grasslands and shrub-grass range types. In elevation they lie between 4,000 and 6,500 feet. Annual rainfall is 10 to 20 inches.

The chief forage species in the Great Basin and central Rockies are such browse plants as true mountain mahogany, bitterbrush, snowberry, and cliffrose. Grasses consist mainly of bluebunch wheatgrass, bluestem wheatgrass, needle-and-thread, bluegrasses, and Indian ricegrass. Farther south in Arizona and New Mexico similar forage species occur, but blue grama, sideoats grama, and galleta become predominant.

Before the advent of domestic livestock, much of the pinyon-juniper was confined to rocky ridges and poor, shallow soils. These trees, especially junipers, recently have encroached on the better soils of adjacent grassland areas, and other low-value plants such as big sagebrush, pingue, snakeweed, red three-awn, and ringgrass have also increased in abundance.

In the central part the woodland type forms much of the spring-fall range and is the winter home for large numbers of big game. Farther south it is grazed on a yearlong basis by both cattle and sheep as well as game. In comparison with the higher mountain watersheds, woodlands yield relatively little water but are potential sources of destructive sediment. Grazing capacity is relatively low, even on the ranges in better condition, and varies from 3 to 10 acres a cow a month.

Pacific Bunchgrass

The Pacific bunchgrass type extends over 35 million acres, mostly in eastern Washington and Oregon, Idaho, and western Montana. Originally some of the finest grazing land in the West, much of it is now either cultivated or has been invaded by sagebrush and the annual cheatgrass. The most productive areas are in the Palouse country of Washington and Oregon. Annual rainfall ranges from about 8 to 20 inches, concentrated largely in the winter and early spring.

The most important forage species are bluebunch and beardless wheatgrass, Idaho fescue, bluegrasses, giant wild-rye, needle-and-thread, and balsamroot.

Pacific bunchgrass range is grazed by both cattle and sheep in the fall, early winter, and spring. Grazing capacity is about 2 acres per month per cow on the areas in good condition. On sites where the perennial grasses have been reduced by overgrazing and replaced by cheatgrass or sagebrush, grazing values are much lower.

Sagebrush and Semidesert Grass

Sagebrush-grass range, one of the most extensive range types in the region, covers more than 90 million acres. It occurs chiefly in the Great Basin and central Rocky Mountains and extends into the eastern parts of Oregon and Washington and the northern parts of Arizona and New Mexico, chiefly between 2,000 and 7,500 feet, but also up to 9,000 feet. Annual rainfall, generally scanty, varies from 7 inches to 30 inches in the higher mountains. Most of the cultivated area in the central portion of the region was formerly sagebrush and grass.

Forage species are many because of the extensiveness of the type, marked soil differences, and wide variation in rainfall. The chief perennial grasses are bluebunch and beardless bluebunch wheatgrass, bluestem wheatgrass, giant wild-rye, Idaho fescue, bluegrasses, Indian ricegrass, and arrowleaf balsamroot. In the Southwest, blue grama is characteristic. The annual cheatgrass is now the principal forage on millions of acres of Great Basin range. It is readily eaten by both sheep and cattle when it is green, but

its growing season is short and it forms a severe fire hazard when dry.

Although of low value, the widely distributed big sagebrush is browsed some by sheep during periods when forage is scarce and when other forage is covered with snow. It is often heavily browsed by deer. In open weather the range should always be managed on the basis of the perennial grasses. On sagebrush range in good condition, 4 to 5 acres is required for each cow for a month.

In the northern part of the Mountain Region, sagebrush range is used most extensively by sheep and cattle in the spring and fall although some winter and early summer grazing occurs. In the southwestern part, it is most important as winter range. The portions above 5,000 feet elevation toward the northern limits and above 7,500 feet in the southern part are grazed chiefly in the summer.

Semidesert grass extends over some 50 million acres and is the important grazing area in the southwestern part of the region. It occurs mostly in the zone between the southern-desert shrub and the woodland types. It is grazed yearlong by cattle and sheep in northern Arizona and New Mexico, but it is used mostly by cattle in southern districts and in western Texas. Annual rainfall varies from 8 to about 15 inches a year, concentrated largely in the summer. One year out of five can be expected to be exceptionally dry— a factor always to be reckoned with.

Characteristic forage species are black grama, curly-mesquite, blue grama, dropseeds, galleta, Rothrock grama, bush muhly, and yucca. Some years the perennial forage is temporarily augmented in the spring by annual weeds. Much of the type has deteriorated, with an accompanying increase of low-value range plants such as mesquite, tarbush, burroweed, and snakeweed. On flood flats, playas, and natural catchment basins, tobosa, alkali sacaton, vine mesquite and burrograss are important summer-fall forage.

Although the semidesert grasslands

yield only small amounts of water, they are, when in poor condition, a source of much sediment that is carried into irrigation reservoirs. Semi-desert range in good condition requires from 40 to 80 acres to support a cow yearlong.

Short-grass Type

The short-grass type is confined to the foothills along the eastern fringes of the Rockies in Colorado and northern New Mexico and Arizona. Rainfall ranges from 15 to 20 inches, concentrated mainly in late spring and summer. Elevations range from 4,000 to 6,000 feet.

Principal forage plants are blue and side-oats gramas, galleta, bluestem wheatgrass, black grama, hairy triodia, curly-mesquite, the three-awn grasses, small soapweed, alkali sacaton, and the low-value ringgrass.

Although not extensive in the region, the short-grass range is ideal for year-round production of both cattle and sheep. The grazing capacity of short-grass range in good condition varies from 20 to 60 acres, with an average of about 45 acres per cow yearlong. Considerable areas have deteriorated to snakeweed with only remnant grasses. Such areas are poor in forage production even during years of favorable rainfall.

Southern-Desert Shrub

Southern-desert shrub covers more than 50 million acres in southwestern Arizona, southern New Mexico, and western Texas. The type is dominated by the unpalatable creosotebush. In many areas the southern-desert shrub overlaps and intermingles with semi-desert grassland. Annual rainfall is low and undependable, ranging from 3 to 12 inches.

The principal forage species are black grama, dropseeds, tobosa, big galleta, chamiza, mesquite, and spring annuals such as filaree.

In areas having less than 5 inches

of rainfall, the type is almost valueless for grazing, especially in southeastern California and southwestern Arizona. In other parts of Arizona, in favorable years, annuals form good spring range for sheep and stocker cattle. However, forage crops are not dependable. The most successful operators graze the type only during years of plenty and avoid it in drought. In New Mexico and western Texas where summer annuals are more plentiful, it is grazed on a yearlong basis by cattle. Deteriorated areas of the type located near irrigation projects are the source of much sediment. The most productive areas of the type are those subject to periodic flooding. Here tobosa, alkali sacaton, and Johnsongrass are valuable for summer grazing.

Salt-Desert Shrub

Salt-desert shrub extends over some 40 million acres in the arid parts of Nevada, Utah, eastern Oregon, western Colorado, and southwestern Wyoming. Because of the low rainfall (5 to 10 inches yearly) and saline soils, plant cover is sparse. Despite its low forage yields, this type is the winter home for several million sheep and several hundred thousand cattle.

Important forage species are mostly browse—black sagebrush, shadescale, hopsage, winterfat, and bud sagebrush. Grasses include Indian ricegrass, wild-rye, bluegrasses, sand dropseed, alkali sacaton, and squirreltail. In some areas low-value plants such as little rabbitbrush and snakeweed have increased greatly. On well-vegetated, salt-desert range in good condition, 6 to 8 acres can carry a cow for a month.

[*In addition to the articles in this chapter, readers are referred to tables in the section, Grass in Charts and Tables, that give recommended mixtures for seeding pastures on high-grade, well-drained irrigated land; for seeding waterlogged lands; and for seeding selected sites within broad range types in the Mountain Region.*]

RANGE PRACTICES AND PROBLEMS

RAYMOND PRICE, KENNETH W. PARKER, A. C. HULL, JR.

IN THE DEVELOPMENT of the range livestock-grazing industry in the Mountain West, some distinctive regional differences in range practices have been built up. They result chiefly from differences in climate, topography, range types, market possibilities, and cultural development. No sharp dividing line can be drawn, and practices and problems of one part of the region merge with those of another, but still the major differences justify recognition of three broad provinces.

The first of the three, the northern Rocky Mountains (northwestern Wyoming, western Montana, northern Idaho, eastern Washington, and northeastern Oregon), is characterized by high mountains, lava plateaus, and narrow intermountain valleys. The climate is rugged, with sharp seasonal variations. Range types are predominantly open forest, Pacific bunchgrass, and sagebrush.

Most of the ranches are straight livestock operations with incidental crop farming, although there are a considerable number of livestock-farming units, especially in the irrigated districts. The location of home ranches is governed by land suitable to produce hay, either native or alfalfa, in sufficient quantity to feed livestock during the winter.

Cattle are fed hay on the home ranches about 4 months in the winter. In the spring they are turned out on the foothill and sagebrush ranges and then driven to the higher mountains for summer grazing. In the fall the cattle are moved to the foothill and sagebrush ranges for a month or two. Some are grazed on meadows and croplands following the harvest.

The class of livestock sold varies with the market. Some are marketed as grass-fat off the range. Others are fattened on hay, pasture, or in feed lots. Most ranchers favor marketing steers as 2-year-olds, although selling long yearlings is increasing. Hereford is the prevailing breed; there are a few herds of Aberdeen Angus and Shorthorn.

Sheep are fed part of the winter, although they graze more on the range than cattle, and average about 9 months on the range. In April, May, and June sheep graze the ranges on the lower elevations. During June they are trailed to the mountain summer ranges, where they remain until September. In the fall they again graze the lower ranges, and then are placed on pasture or fields until winter sets in. Some are wintered on the range but are given supplemental feed.

As in other parts of the region, sheep are run in bands of from 1,000 to 1,500 ewes with their lambs. A herder cares for the band night and day, moving from place to place as the need for forage and plan of grazing requires. Rambouillet is the basic breed, but most ewe herds are crossbreeds—Rambouillet crossed with long wools, Lincoln, and Romney. These are then crossed with the medium wools and mutton types, such as Hampshire and Suffolk, to produce market lambs. Shearing and lambing occur on the range and at the home ranches. Considerable shed lambing is practiced in order to reduce losses and produce lambs for early market.

Problems are many and varied. The major one stems chiefly from an unbalanced and inadequate yearlong forage and feed supply for the number of livestock. A general limiting factor is the amount of winter feed available. A critical period is between the first fall snows and the time when new growth is sufficient in the spring for grazing.

Summer range is also inadequate. In eastern Oregon and Washington it is estimated that summer range is 30 percent short of being enough for the livestock population, and potentially productive mountain meadows do not yield up to capacity.

The low-value plants, such as cheat-grass, St. Johnswort, and big sage-brush, are invading the lower ranges.

On overused ranges, grazing capacity is going down steadily and accelerated erosion is increasing. Some contributing factors are too-early and too-late use of seasonal ranges and poor distribution of livestock on the range because of steep slopes, heavy timber, and inadequate water and fencing.

Competition with deer and elk for forage is also a problem in some places. In others, the increase of young trees and brush on timbered areas is reducing the available range. Ranchers also face the threat of a short hay crop during drought years. Winter feeding and the consequent extra handling of livestock results in higher-than-average production costs.

The Intermountain West

Southeastern Oregon, southern Idaho, southwestern Wyoming, western Colorado, Utah, Nevada, and the eastern slope of California, often referred to as the Intermountain West, is a blending of the northern Rocky Mountains and southwestern environments. It embraces high mountains, broad plateaus, deep canyons, extensive alluvial valleys, and barren salt flats. It has wide extremes in temperature and precipitation. Winter snows occur over most of the region. All the major range types found in the Mountain Region are represented, although the semi-desert and short-grass types barely fall within its bounds.

Livestock operations vary. In western Wyoming, Nevada, and western Colorado, ranch operations prevail, while in southern Idaho and Utah, livestock-farming operations are the general practice. In Utah numerous herds are made up of a few cattle or sheep from many farmers and operated on a community basis. The use of the same range by sheep and cattle is general. Home ranches are located mainly where water is available for irrigation.

Cattle are grazed on the mountain summer ranges for 3 to 5 months, pastured during spring and fall, and fed during the winter. A considerable number of cattle, however, remain on the lower ranges in summer. The length of the winter-feeding period depends upon weather conditions and feed supplies. Hereford cattle predominate. The class of livestock marketed includes grass-fat steers, usually 2-year-olds, and long yearlings as feeders.

Sheep are usually grazed on open range throughout the year. They are trailed, often long distances, to the deserts for winter grazing, then back to the foothills for the spring, and to the mountains for the summer. Lambs are removed from the herds for market in late summer or early fall. At the end of the summer-grazing period, late September, the rest of the herd is moved back to the foothills for fall grazing and then to the desert, starting the cycle over again. Some of the smaller herds and most of the community herds are broken up and kept on fields and farm pasture and feed during the winter. In southern Idaho some sheep are fed part of the winter; shed lambing also is common. Most of these lambs are marketed as grass-fat in July. The basic breed is Rambouillet, but crossbreeding with mutton types is increasing in favor in order to obtain bigger, faster-maturing lambs.

For the number of livestock, a lack of balance exists in the supply of year-long forage and feed. The deficiency is general, although the amount of mountain summer and spring-fall range is particularly below demand. The lack of adequate spring-fall range is the crux in sheep grazing operations. Spring range is further reduced by lands placed under cultivation.

The unbalance means that considerable areas of the range are not producing as much as they should. The more palatable plants are waning on the desert winter ranges; sagebrush and cheatgrass are invading the foothills.

On some summer ranges poisonous plants, such as sneezeweed, are prevalent. The thinning of the plant cover on the mountain ranges endangers watershed values. On overgrazed areas topsoil is washing and gullies are forming. Often such conditions cause floods that destroy good agricultural areas and jeopardize city water supplies.

Livestock production on the range is falling off. Costs are increasing. Sheep losses are high during the winter and lamb and wool crops are low because of inadequate forage and feed supplies. The need to trail sheep long distances, often over difficult terrain and deteriorated forage cover, reduces production, increases costs, and further damages range resources. Ranchmen here, as elsewhere in the Mountain Region, have the problem of mixed-land ownerships to complicate their operations.

The Southwest

The third broad province of the Mountain Region is the southwestern part (southeastern California, Arizona, the western two-thirds of New Mexico, and the western tip of Texas). It embraces large areas of low-lying desert and semideserts, broad plateaus, and comparatively isolated mountain ranges. The climate is warm and dry. Winter snows fall in the northern part and on most of the higher peaks, but occur rarely and melt quickly over most of the southern part. Range types are semidesert grass and, southern-desert shrub, woodlands, and open forest, with some extensions of the short-grass and sagebrush-grass types.

Yearlong grazing of sheep and cattle on the range characterizes the Southwest. This is possible because of the mild winters and needful because of the limited crop farming and isolated irrigated areas. Livestock operators are highly dependent on the range-forage resource. Supplemental feeds, usually protein concentrates, are ordinarily purchased and used largely during excessive drought periods when range forage is lacking. Many straight livestock operations with extensive range holdings are common, but numerous small operators live in east-

central Arizona and the northern part of New Mexico.

The lack of adequate feed supplies has fostered the production of feeder cattle and feeder lambs. On the properly stocked and managed cattle ranges, heavy calves and steers that need little additional feeding for fattening are produced. The better sheep outfits commonly market 50 to 80 percent of the lambs as grass-fat. Then, too, the production of finished beef is becoming an established farm enterprise in irrigated areas, such as those in the Salt River Valley. Early milk-fat Easter lambs are also produced.

The southwest part of the region is essentially a cattle-breeding country. Calves and yearlings are the principal source of income, most of the calves being marketed in the fall. Steer grazing is practiced in localities where spring forage is available. Control of cattle on the range is attempted by range riding, water development, salting, and fencing. Nearly all cattle are Herefords. Some ranchmen in the warmer parts of the Southwest are becoming interested in the use of Brahman bulls.

Most of the sheep are of the fine-wool breed, mainly Rambouillet. The Indian flocks—in Arizona they comprise more than half of the sheep population—are a mixed breed that produce medium to coarse, light wool suitable for weaving blankets. In irrigated-pasture areas, crossing is commonly practiced with medium-wool breeds, such as the Hampshire and Suffolk.

Some goats are grazed for mohair production in central Arizona and southern New Mexico.

The problems are like those of the other provinces, but because of the yearlong use on much of the area (some of it dating back to the early Spanish period) and the more delicate balance among climate, soils, and range cover, reduced production of range forage is widespread.

The aspect of many ranges has changed. Mesquite, cacti, and low-value shrubs and half-shrubs are invading large portions of the lower grasslands, brush is claiming many of the lower mountain ranges, and in some places juniper is thickening and spreading onto former grass ranges.

The range has to be used on a seasonal and rotational basis, and more supplemental pastures and feed supplies are needed to speed up range improvement and improve livestock production.

Drought is a constant, continuous

threat in the Southwest: Livestock and range-forest production has to be balanced carefully and conservatively; fencing should be improved to control livestock; permanent stock-watering places should be developed to regulate grazing use and provide water in time of drought; noxious plants must be controlled; ranges need reseeding to improve the forage supply and restore watershed values. Rodents are a problem on many ranges and compete with livestock for the waning forage.

GRASS AS A SAVINGS ACCOUNT

RAYMOND PRICE, KENNETH W. PARKER, A. C. HULL, JR.

THE KEY to range productivity is grass. Sound and effective management of grass as the range resource should be thought of as a long-time business enterprise.

Grass is a crop that renews itself yearly, but if it is grazed too closely each year a grass debt will accumulate that will result in lowered income and an exhausted range resource. On the other hand, leaving some reasonable amount of forage on the ground is putting grass in the bank, a savings account that insures against poor years and pays interest in better livestock production, greater soil fertility, and maximum forage-plant vigor.

Proper range use is the most practical means of keeping grass and soil in good condition. Grass has several uses. Part is harvested, part is returned to the soil, and part is left on the stem. Too often the grass is literally eaten into the ground in an attempt to get the utmost from the total annual production. Such overuse does not pay, although it is often condoned in the hope that the next rains will promote a lush growth of grass and the livestock will again become productive and fat.

Some organic matter in the form of leaves and litter must be returned to the soil each year. A mulch of litter on the ground will increase moisture

penetration as much as 20 percent on well-vegetated areas, which is enough to increase forage production 50 percent. It also provides a good seedbed for the establishment of new grass.

From 40 to 70 percent of the annual herbage production is best left ungrazed (the amount depending on the kind of forage plants, the soil, topography, and condition of the range) in order that the plants may store up sugars and starches within their stem bases and roots to promote and support growth the following year. In the Southwest a reserve of unused herbage has added values: During drought years it furnishes forage for livestock, prevents severe overuse of the plants, and gives added protection to the ranch operator against having to sell short on a poor market or spend excessive amounts for supplemental feed.

An example of the importance of careful adjustment of livestock numbers to the forage supply: On spring-fall sagebrush-wheatgrass range in Idaho the yearly volume of forage has varied from 41 percent above the 9-year average to 33 percent below it, largely as a result of difference in precipitation. Stocking on the basis of the years of high forage production resulted in serious range depletion and adversely affected animal production.

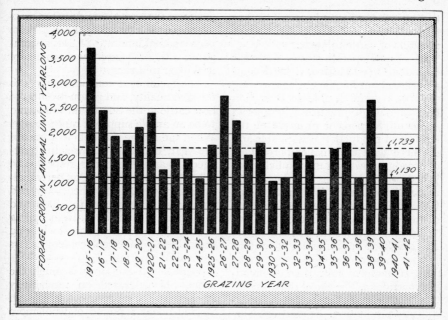

The variations in the forage crop on a southwestern semidesert grassland range are indicated by this chart. The vertical bars, one for each year, express yearlong capacity in animal units. The broken line (marked 1,739) is average of 27 years. The solid line (marked 1,130) is 65 percent of the average. The latter degree of stocking has been found to yield greater returns at less risk and to assure continued range productivity.

Safe utilization of the range was adjudged to be 60 to 65 percent of the average forage production of the bunchgrasses. Forage production in a semidesert grassland range in southern New Mexico fell below the yearly average (1,739 animal units) 13 out of 27 years. If the range had been stocked at 65 percent of the average (1,130 animal units), 24 years of the 27-year period would have had a safe basis of stocking, and this would have provided reserve forage for leaner years.

Sharp fluctuations in the quality of the forage, particularly with respect to protein and phosphorus content, also occur. Whenever deficiencies of materials essential to a well-balanced diet occur, both livestock production and grazing capacity are lower. Browse plants are generally adequate in those nutrients, but deficiencies are common in grasses, especially during winter in the southern districts. Phosphorus may be supplied through mineralized salt or bonemeal, and protein deficiencies can be corrected with such supplements as cottonseed cake.

Whenever animals can eat their fill every day in all seasons, about 70 percent of the digestible nutrients in the forage eaten is required for maintenance of body functions and the remaining 30 percent is available for growth and reproduction. Under such conditions, the mature beef cow will weigh 1,000 pounds or more, produce an 80- to 90-percent or higher calf crop, with calves averaging 400 to 450 pounds or more at 8 months of age. Although these weights may not appear attainable in a few range areas, they still remain a good goal at which to aim. Feed requirements (based on cow with calf as the animal unit) of the different classes of range cattle vary from 45 percent of an animal unit for weanling calves to 65 percent for yearlings, 75 percent for 2-year-olds up to 125 percent for mature bulls. Composition of the herd thus becomes an important item in judging the correct numbers of cattle to graze.

In a cattle operation over a 30-year period in New Mexico, a herd composed of about 55 percent of breeding cows was more flexible in operation than the usual practice where cows made up 70 percent or more of the herd. Beef production was greater and the herd with the smaller percentage of breeding cows was more quickly adjusted to fluctuations in the forage crop. Better distribution on the range was attained because steers tend to scatter and graze out farther.

Keeping part of the herd in steers and dry stock has a further advantage in that these classes of livestock make more economical gains than do breeding cows alone. The age of the breeding cow also bears an important relationship to production. Studies in New Mexico show that the range beef cow reaches peak beef production at 7 years of age and should be culled within the following 2 years in order to realize the greatest returns from the herd.

Similar nutritional relationships can hold true with sheep. A dry ewe requires one-third to one-half less feed than a ewe and her lamb, and produces approximately 10 percent more wool. One rancher near Alpine, Tex., who grazes sheep in common with cattle, has successfully operated on the basis of running a small breeding herd of cattle yearlong and stocking conservatively each fall with wether lambs in numbers varying with the size of the forage crop. The wethers are then sold in the spring before the onset of the summer's growth.

The importance of supplying livestock with adequate forage and feed to obtain top production cannot be overemphasized.

In Colorado two groups of short yearling Herefords were grazed in separate but similar open forest range pastures—one at the rate of 56 head per section, the other at the rate of 43 head per section. The animals on the moderately stocked range gained faster and

more; at the end of the summer grazing season the net return from them per section of land was $1,215, as compared with $919 for those on the more heavily grazed range.

The factor that contributes most to the size, quality, and productiveness of beef cattle in the Southwest was found to be an ample supply of range forage. When the forage was deficient part of the year, cow and calf weights averaged 875 and 347 pounds, respectively. When a greater supply of perennial-grass forage was furnished, cow and calf weights increased to 1,000 and 401 pounds. Good bulls, rigid culling of substandard breeding stock, and critical selection of replacement heifers were also important.

With sheep the story is much the same. Sheep grazed on moderately stocked winter range in western Utah yielded about a pound of wool more per animal, lamb crops were 10 to 12 percent higher, and net returns were $1 to $1.50 more per ewe annually than from sheep on heavily stocked range. Furthermore, the moderately stocked range responded after a few years and produced annually two to three times more forage than the heavily stocked range.

Timely and prompt disposal of all marketable animals is another recommended practice. The most rapid gains in animal weights are made during the "green-feed" period. Grazing marketable animals late in the season in order to bring about slight additional weight gains often wastes forage needed later for the base herd and causes loss of weight and poorer market condition.

Range Management

"The eye of the master fattens his flock" is as true on the range as it is in the feed lot. Constant vigilance and supervision are necessary for care of both the range and livestock. Regular range inspections should be a scheduled part of any ranch operation. The inspection should determine the condition of both range and livestock, the distribution of grazing use, amount and character of stock water supplied, condition of fences, the kind and severity of rodent and insect infestations, the presence of toxic range plants, and the need for management changes.

On many ranges, grazing on parts of the range should be systematically deferred each year, particularly during the growth season. This may be accomplished, with cattle, by subdividing the range with fences. Subdivisions of year-long ranges have an important advantage for better herd management by permitting the segregation of various classes of cattle and the regulation of breeding. With range sheep, which are usually grazed under the herder system, fences, although desirable, are not particularly essential.

Many ranchmen get additional forage from increased plant vigor by practicing some kind of deferred and rotation grazing.

One method is to divide the range into three to five or more units, on one of which grazing use is deferred until the principal perennial grasses mature seed. These units are rotated systematically so that each unit grazed is periodically deferred during the growing season.

On many southwestern ranges a variation of the plan is possible by taking advantage of seasonally palatable forage. For example, tobosa and alkali sacaton are of greatest value to livestock when green and succulent and are easily maintained under moderate grazing use during the growth period; black grama is palatable at any season but for highest production requires periodic protection during growth. In such instances, grazing is best deferred on the black grama areas that are reserved for winter-spring grazing until proper summer-fall use has been made of the tobosa or alkali sacaton areas.

On many high mountain ranges weather limits use to the summer. Proper management of these seasonal ranges is based on the growth requirements of the forage plants and soil moisture conditions. Soils are usually wet and early growth washy, so that ordinarily grazing should not begin until the key forage grasses are 4 to 6 inches high. If the soil is dry, grazing may begin when the grasses are 2 inches high, but should be light and continued for only the fore half of the growing season. The plants are then able to grow and produce seed after the livestock is removed. In the fall, grazing should be moderate or periodically deferred to permit food storage within the plants so that they may make vigorous growth the following year.

The practical implication in animal production of meeting these plant-growth requirements has been demonstrated on the open forest range in California. There it was found that cattle gained best when not placed on the range until the forage plants were ready for grazing and when removed promptly in the fall as gains slackened. Furthermore, cattle gained as well in the timber as on the open meadows. Although meadow forage produced earlier gains, the timber type of forage sustained weights later in the fall.

Uniform distribution of livestock over the range is essential. If properly accomplished, it will increase animal production and relieve congestion of livestock on critical parts of the range. With cattle, the chief means of securing better distribution are fencing, riding, development of stock water, salting away from water, and, in rough terrain, the construction of stock trails.

With sheep under the herder system, proper handling is indicated by open herding, limited use of dogs, the one-night bed-ground system, and close supervision during trailing. A practical means of obtaining better distribution of grazing by sheep, especially on ranges where stock water is scarce, is by hauling the water to the band. A more economical method than herding may be attained (wherever the range is suited) by fencing the range into several pastures, turning the sheep loose, and alternating grazing in accordance with forage conditions. Initial costs of fencing are high and it is necessary to give close attention to control of predatory animals, but over-all labor costs are greatly reduced. Furthermore, more intensive management of the range is possible.

Furnishing adequate forage at all seasons is the most practical means of avoiding death loss from poisonous plants. In general, nearly all toxic range plants are unpalatable or distasteful and are eaten only in times of extreme hunger.

Range improvement often will be enhanced by controlling noxious plants because then the desirable forage plants have full opportunity to utilize the available moisture. These are the areas where the original plant cover has been replaced by low-value plants. In the Southwest, for example, the encroachment into open grasslands by the moisture-robbing mesquite has become a major problem on millions of acres of range. On areas with a fair remnant of perennial grasses, forage yield can be increased twofold and threefold and accelerated erosion arrested by eliminating the mesquite. Comparable results have been obtained with big sagebrush and small rabbitbrush, which present similar problems in much of the Mountain Region.

IMPROVEMENT THROUGH RESEEDING

GEORGE STEWART, WESLEY KELLER

MILLIONS of acres of the potentially productive range lands in the Mountain Region have deteriorated to a point that they produce but little forage. The urgent need for a better plant cover for livestock forage, watershed protection, wildlife, and other values makes it necessary to restore their productivity. Natural recovery through improved management is possible on large areas, and should be used wherever possible. But where natural recovery is too slow or is not practicable, reseeding is needed.

Experimental and large-scale reseeding has been limited in most parts of the West. Most work has been in the Intermountain section where research has furnished the information for successful planting of thousands of acres of range lands, mainly in the sagebrush-grass type.

More information is needed to provide a basis for large plantings in other range types and in other sections, but present knowledge will allow successful planting of many sites within the following range types: Sagebrush-grass and Pacific bunchgrass—chiefly on areas now supporting sagebrush, cheat-grass, and annual weeds; woodlands—chiefly on areas now supporting mountain brush and juniper; open forests—chiefly openings and meadows in pine stands, timber burns, aspen, mountain parks, and openings supporting annual and perennial weeds; and semidesert grasslands—chiefly flooded areas and areas supporting half shrubs or mesquite.

Planting methods must provide conditions favorable for germination and growth of reseeded plants. The chances for success will be increased if attention is given to these principles:

1. Reseed key watershed areas and range sites on which forage is depleted but soils remain intact, and which cannot be improved within a reasonable time through better management.

2. Reseed the better sites where soil, moisture, topography, and related factors are favorable.

3. Remove competing vegetation and encourage germination and plant establishment through the use of proper methods and efficient machinery; also use soil and moisture conservation measures where needed.

4. Plant good seed of adapted spe-

cies or mixtures at recommended rates. Seeding rates should be increased where seed distribution and depth of covering are uneven or where seed is of poor quality or contains chaffy material. Wherever legumes are adapted they should be added to the mixture.

5. Provide even distribution and covering of seed through efficient methods such as drilling. Single-disk drills are generally best for trashy or compact seedbeds; double-disk drills are best for loose or prepared and trash-free seedbeds. Deep-furrow disk and lister drills eliminate considerable weedy plant growth and form deep furrows that hold moisture. Drilled plants at 6- and 12-inch row spacings develop into full stands more quickly and help keep down competing brush and weeds better than do plants at wider row spacings. When seed is distributed by hand or machine broadcasters, the amount of seed should be increased about 25 percent and seed covering provided by harrowing, disking, or some similar method. Scattering seed directly or in pellets by airplane is a rapid method when landing fields are close. The cost of scattering the pellets is high because of the large amount of inert material carried with the seed. We expect further developments in this field, but more experimental work is needed before specific recommendations can be made. The use of seed pellets for drilling or broadcasting also needs further testing; this method might be useful.

6. Plant at the proper depth. Correct depth of seeding is roughly proportional to the size of the seed. Seed of crested wheatgrass and similar species should be covered from $\frac{1}{2}$ to 1 inch deep. Small-seeded species, such as Lehmann lovegrass, should not be covered more than $\frac{1}{4}$ inch deep. In general, deeper covering is desirable on light, sandy soil and a shallower covering on heavy clays.

7. Plant so that newly germinated seedlings will have favorable moisture and temperature for 1 or 2 months of growing weather.

8. Graze the new stand only when the plants are well established and graze moderately to preserve the reseeded stand.

Methods, species, and equipment must be adapted to local conditions of soil, vegetation, topography, rocks, accessibility, the facilities and equipment available for doing the work, and related factors.

Planting Recommendations

The sagebrush-grass and the Pacific bunchgrass types are normally productive, but large areas of them now support plants of low forage value, such as sagebrush, cheatgrass, or annual weeds.

These areas or planting sites may be treated as follows: Sagebrush takes most of the moisture and should be eradicated; the cheapest, most widely adapted, but also the most dangerous way to do so is prescribed or controlled burning. It requires a fair volume of inflammable, evenly distributed vegetation, slight wind, and low relative humidity. Under these conditions, burning leaves a firm, clean seedbed where seed can be drilled the year of burning without further soil preparation. Burning removes all litter and should not be used on areas where wind or water erosion might be serious.

Permits must be obtained before burning and fire must be controlled because the man who does the burning must accept responsibility for control of the fire. Prescribed burning can be safely done on large areas for 30 cents or less an acre.

The wheatland plow (often called disk tiller or one-way disk) kills from 60 to 90 percent of the sagebrush. Where possible, a seeder should be attached to the plow because it allows sagebrush eradication and grass seeding to be done in one operation. Where a seeder attachment is not used, the plowed area may be drilled. Where broadcasting is the only feasible method, it should be done just after plowing so that the seed will be covered by soil sloughing. Seed broadcast ahead of the plow is usually covered too deeply. The Australian "stump-jump" plow with independent disks, which swing up over rocks and piles of brush, is now being tested and is expected to be valuable for sagebrush eradication.

Railing kills 45 to 80 percent of the mature sagebrush but has little effect on the young brush. Improved rails that work at an angle increase the sagebrush kill. Rails can operate on moderately rocky ground, and there is little injury to perennial grasses. Railing provides poor covering for broadcast seed and drilling is recommended.

Pipe harrows cover the broadcast seed effectively and kill much brittle sagebrush in low, open stands. Harrows may be used on weedy and rocky places. Ripping, rolling, scraping, grubbing, mowing, flooding, contour furrows, and disk and moldboard plowing are all useful for sagebrush removal under some conditions.

Cheatgrass, where developed as a full stand, takes nearly all the soil moisture. If cheatgrass can be reduced for one growing season, however, the perennial grasses can become established. The best seasons for eliminating cheatgrass are in the spring before seed forms or in the fall after germination. Moldboard plowing kills most of the cheatgrass and can be used at any season, although it is expensive. Wheatland plowing or shallow cultivation gives good cheatgrass kills. A seeder attachment on the wheatland plow allows for seeding in one operation. When used after cheatgrass has germinated in the fall, deep-furrow drills kill many cheatgrass seedlings and place the seed in a deep furrow where reseeded seedlings have a better chance of survival. Either cropping or summer fallow for a year and fall drilling of perennial grass has given excellent stands. Drilling in the fall, following controlled fire early in the summer, has been a successful method of seeding perennial grass on cheatgrass areas in southern Idaho.

Annual weeds such as Russian-thistle and tumblemustard with summer growth habits do not seriously compete with reseeded grasses for moisture and are often beneficial in protecting the young grass seedlings. Such annual weed areas may be drilled with no soil preparation. Drilling perennial grasses is desirable on those lands before they become covered with cheatgrass, sagebrush, or other species that make reseeding more difficult. Grain-stubble areas are good seedbeds and may also be drilled without soil preparation.

Where fall rainfall is dependable, the sagebrush-grass and Pacific bunchgrass types may be seeded in September or October. Where it is uncertain, seeding should be done in October or November. Where spring rains are certain and early planting is possible, seedings made in March and early April are usually successful.

The standard strain of crested wheatgrass is best for reseeding in these types. In areas with a long, cool, moist spring growing season, bulbous bluegrass is successful as an understory species with crested wheatgrass. Bluestem wheatgrass is a useful addition on heavy saline soils.

Planting Woodlands

The woodlands type covers many sites from the dry juniper to the moist mountain brush areas. Sagebrush, cheatgrass, and annual weeds in this type may be treated as recommended for sagebrush.

Juniper has a natural place in the woodland type. As the result of overgrazing, fire, and possibly other undetermined causes, juniper has invaded former grassland areas and formerly open stands have thickened, reducing the grazing values. It is on these sites that control of juniper together with reseeding is recommended. Where such juniper areas occur in dense stands prescribed burning as outlined for the sagebrush-grass type may be used. In scattered stands, trees may be singed with a torch or burned individually. Afterward a small drill is used to seed among the dead trees. Much work remains to be done in methods of juniper eradication.

Mountain brushlands often contain considerable sagebrush, but plants like oak, snowberry, chokecherry, and maple distingushed these lands from the valley and bottom-land sagebrush type. Most methods used on sagebrush lands apply here, but because precipitation and soils are usually better, the returns from reseeding are greater. Contour plow furrows at 3- to 5-foot intervals open up the brush and allow reseeded grass to become established. Fire should be used with extreme caution on such sites.

Because fall precipitation is usually dependable in northern woodlands, they may be seeded in September and October. On the southern pinyon-juniper site, seedings should be made in early July.

Species adapted to the sagebrush zone do well in the woodland type, crested wheatgrass being the best species. On the moist sites, crested wheatgrass gives way to smooth brome. Either smooth brome or crested wheatgrass should be in all seeding mixtures. Antelope bitterbrush shows some promise as a browse for planting on winter woodland ranges used by deer.

Planting Open Forests

The open forest type extends from the dry, open, pine areas to the moist aspen areas and mountain parks. Seeding treatment should be made according to the vegetation present. The most important planting sites are sagebrush-, cheatgrass-, and aspen-growing lands, (which support annual and perennial weeds), timber burns, logging roads and landings, as well as parks and meadows. Sagebrush, cheatgrass, and summer-growing annual weeds may be treated the same as under the sagebrush type.

Timber burns resulting from forest fires offer excellent reseeding opportunities. They should be seeded immediately after the fire. Seed may be broadcast in the deep, fresh ashes with no further seed covering. A grain nurse crop often is planted to hold the soil and to prevent heat injury to perennial grasses during the first growing season. Logging and skid roads and landings with loose powdery soil can also be planted by broadcasting.

Aspen and similar tree and shrub areas have soil and precipitation which are generally favorable for the growth of grass. The cheapest and most effective way of getting a good stand of grass in aspen is broadcasting just before, during, or after autumn leaf fall. The leaf mat provides a seed covering.

Mountain parks and meadows usually have good soil moisture and offer excellent reseeding opportunities. Spreading of floodwater is often possible; if it is, production will be increased. Where soils are compact, contour furrows or ripping is necessary to open the soil and allow infiltration. Where undesirable brush and perennial weeds and grasses occur, they should be eradicated with the wheatland plow. In inaccessible brushy or weedy areas, pipe harrows may be used. They can be made on the ground with native logs and steel teeth.

Tarweed, common at high elevations, competes for moisture and generally causes failure of the reseeded species. Limited tests indicate that tarweed, an annual, should be eliminated by cultivation early in the spring and the area seeded immediately to desirable grasses.

The open-forest type should be seeded in summer or fall, depending on the time rain is expected—usually July in the southern section, August or September in the central, and October in the northern parts of the region.

In the northern section, crested wheatgrass is best for reseeding, but over the rest of the region smooth brome is the most useful grass. Timothy and orchardgrass do well on most sites; orchardgrass does especially well in the shade. Meadow fescue and white clover are also adapted to moist sites.

Planting Semidesert Areas

Results from the limited research done so far with semidesert grassland indicate that naturally flooded areas and former grassland sites that have been invaded by half-shrubs or mesquite offer good reseeding possibilities. Reseeding also is promising on mixed-grass ranges following mesquite control. Reseeding should not be attempted on those areas where rainfall is less than 10 inches, except on the most favorable sites—those that are naturally flooded, or where moisture-conserving practices, such as water spreading or mulching, can be applied. Floodwater should be spread wherever possible.

Snakeweed, burroweed, and annual grasses should be eliminated before seeding. This is best done by shallow disking. Drilling the seed has given the best results. A tandem cultipacker equipped with special seed hoppers is useful for distributing and covering the extremely small seeds. Broadcasting (followed by cultipacking to firm the soil and cover the seed) is also done.

Mesquite has a widespreading root system and must be eradicated before reseeding. As mesquite sprouts from below the ground, chopping is not successful. Standing trees or stumps resulting from cutting for posts or wood may be killed by application of sodium arsenite or petroleum oils. If the brush resulting from wood- or post-cutting operations is scattered over the treated area, it provides protection against concentration of grazing as well as a more favorable site for seedling establishment. Power grubbers have been successful in tearing out the trees. After eradication, the area may be seeded by drilling or by broadcasting and harrowing.

Where the rainy season comes during the summer, plantings should be made in early July. Lehmann lovegrass and Boer lovegrass have given best results where temperatures seldom go below freezing. Farther north, where there is more precipitation and winters are colder, these species are replaced with weeping lovegrass and side-oats grama. Sand dropseed has a wide range and can be used in mixtures throughout the Southwest. One shrub, fourwing saltbush, often called chamiza, has been successfully seeded for winter forage on calcareous soils up to 7,500 feet elevation.

Grazing Reseeded Areas

Grazing should not commence on newly seeded areas until the plants are well-enough established to resist a vigorous pull and trampling by livestock. This usually occurs during the fall of the second growing season and usually coincides with maturity of the first seed crop. After the stand is established, it should be conservatively grazed.

The amount of grazing that can be had from reseeded stands depends upon the success of the seeding, the productivity of the land, the topography, the kind of plants seeded, and the amount of litter which must be left for soil protection. Usually about 50 percent of the total yearly herbage production may be grazed.

[*For additional information on grass and its use in the Mountain States, readers are referred to the following articles in this book:*

How Range Forage Grows, William G. McGinnies, John L. Retzer; The Major Range Types, E. J. Woolfolk, D. F. Costello, B. W. Allred; Grazing on Range Lands, W. R. Chapline; Planning Range Conservation, W. T. White, W. R. Frandsen, C. V. Jensen; Management That Restores the Range, R. S. Campbell, Lincoln Ellison, F. G. Renner; and other articles appearing in the section, The Range, A Major Resource.

The section, For Further Reference, lists a number of booklets and other published material on this subject.

The two groups of photographs illustrate several aspects of reseeding forest and range lands, range management, conservation, and seed production.]

CONSERVATION PROBLEMS AND PRACTICES

RAYMOND PRICE

GRASS will continue to have great influence on the future welfare of the Mountain West because, in the main, climate, topography, and most soils are best suited for grass.

In this region where the mountains and the valleys are closely linked, a good grass cover is necessary on the mountain and valley reaches for several reasons: Grass serves to improve and hold the soil in place, it aids in safeguarding the watersheds, and provides the forage and other values for a strong mountain-valley agricultural economy. Hence the native forage-producing lands, because of their vast acreage and multiple-use values, will continue in importance. Pastures, meadows, and cultivated forage crops, although small in area, will also increase in value with time.

The growing industrialization of the West and the rapid increase in population bring greater demands on the grassland economy. The need for more water is pyramiding, not only for industrial and domestic use but for irrigation for greater food production. Demands are also mounting for more forage for livestock, wildlife, and game. And, with vacation interest increasing, people are seeking more and varied use of the lands for recreation. It all points to the need for more intensive and skillful use of the natural grasslands and forage-producing lands and a better understanding of the important part these lands play in the mountain-valley relationship in the West.

The foremost problem, from which stem numerous related ones, is how best to handle the range watersheds so as to prevent floods and decrease erosion, insure the delivery of maximum amounts of reasonably sediment-free water, and to improve soil and plant-cover conditions to the end that forage may be fully and properly used.

Floods that come from mountain areas, strewing mud, rocks, and debris over the limited croplands and inundating farms and parts of villages and towns must be prevented.

Witness the flood of July 24, 1946, at Mt. Pleasant, Utah, that descended from an adjacent overgrazed mountain watershed and caused $106,000 damage to this farming community of 2,500 people.

Witness the destructive flood of August 19, 1945, at Salt Lake City that caused an estimated damage of $350,000 that originated on the grass-depleted foothills north of the city.

Witness also the flood of September 1941 at Duncan, Ariz., located on the Upper Gila River, which caused damage to this area conservatively estimated at $500,000.

Witness the flood of May and June 1941 in the Upper Rio Grande Basin in New Mexico where flood waters coming from impaired upstream watersheds inundated 51,000 acres of land and caused damages amounting to $1,293,400 plus another half million spent for emergency measures.

Witness the flood damage to the 35,000 residents of the Boise River Valley in Idaho which amounts to about $700,000 annually.

Sedimentation now taking place at an alarming rate in irrigation reservoirs has to be reduced. Consider the Alamogordo Reservoir on the Pecos River, which has lost water storage capacity at the rate of 2.3 percent a year and it is estimated will lose its effectiveness within another 20 years at the present rate of sedimentation.

Consider the Elephant Butte Reservoir, which is being reduced in capacity at the rate of approximately 20,000 acre-feet annually; it has lost 16 percent of its capacity in 25 years, and every year enough storage capacity is being lost to irrigate between 5,000 and 7,000 acres of land.

Consider the Hoover Dam on the

Colorado and other important reservoirs behind which similar losses are occurring.

Consider the Rio Grande Valley, where productive croplands are being waterlogged because of the upgrading of the stream channels with sediment washed from the upstream parts of the watershed.

And not only these, but in other parts of the region streams are becoming erratic and of less value because of the increased amount of sediment; water tables are lowering because of too heavy drain by pumping; lands in some irrigated sections of the Southwest face the threat of returning to desert because of uncertain water supplies.

Another major problem, how to improve and safeguard the over-all forage and feed supply, has many phases and pertains to ranges, farms, and pastures. Many ranges are in good condition, but on many others the grazing capacity is being reduced and fertile soil is being lost. Forage production on more than half the range area in the region is markedly below potential production—so low and so uncertain that it is difficult or impractical to increase production through management adjustments alone.

More than 600 million acres of western range, a large part of which lies within the Mountain Region, is in need of improvement. Nearly 400 million acres of these lands is in need of major restoration. The aspect of millions of acres of range land has been changed by the invasion of low-value or noxious plants. The production of grass has been proportionately reduced. Many thousands of acres of originally productive native range lands once unwisely plowed for crop production are now abandoned. The problem is twofold—to safeguard the ranges still in good condition and to build up those ranges that have deteriorated. Restoration of these lands would overcome much serious erosion, double forage production, step up livestock production, and materially aid in stabilizing

the western range livestock industry and the many dependent communities.

Adjustments in range and range watershed use may be grouped into three categories: Improvement in systems of management, including proper stocking, better seasonal use, and improved distribution and handling of livestock on the range; forage improvement through range reseeding and noxious plant control; and capital or physical improvements, such as fencing, rodent control, water development, improved stock trails, soil and moisture conservation aids, and other facilities.

As we have seen, much can be accomplished in range and range livestock improvement through better range management, chiefly more conservative stocking and adjusting the season and pattern of grazing use to the plant and soil requirements. Experience and study have shown that no matter how skillful management may be or how much attention may be given to physical range and range watershed improvements, they cannot offset the effects of overstocking.

Too many animals on the range and range watersheds seriously affect the plants and the soil as well as result in reduced livestock returns. Great strides have been made in breeding better classes of animals, but even the best breeding will not increase the weight and condition of the animals if they do not have sufficient forage. The forage crop produced on the range should be viewed as other agricultural crops, and the growth requirements of the principal forage plants recognized and provided for in their harvesting by grazing animals.

Attention should be given to the individual plants and the soil making up the range rather than the general overall appearance of the whole range or watershed unit. Farmers and stockmen should appraise the size of the range forage crop and adjust the numbers of their animals so as to obtain the highest returns per unit on a sustained yield basis of both range and animals.

That conservative stocking and better livestock husbandry is beyond the experimental trial basis and pays dividends in actual range operations is demonstrated by the results of the Victorio Land and Cattle Company in New Mexico. The records of this company show that during the 8-year period 1926 to 1933, inclusive, an average of 18,819 breeding cows were grazed, producing a 47-percent calf crop weighing an average of 244 pounds and a total of 2,158,180 pounds per year. In 1934 a more conservative basis of stocking was practiced and from 1934 to 1937, inclusive, an average of 8,674 breeding cows were grazed, producing a 66-percent calf crop weighing an average of 341 pounds and a total of 1,952,225 pounds per year. During the next 4 years, 1938 to 1941, inclusive, the range was fenced and the stocking reduced to an average of 6,190 breeding cows which produced a 91-percent calf crop weighing an average of 445 pounds and a total of 2,506,685 pounds per year. Range surveys made in 1941 show an average increase of approximately 20 percent in forage production brought about by conservative stocking and better management of the range and livestock.

Similar results on a smaller outfit were obtained by Al Dick, a cattle operator at Peola, Wash. In 1907, as the result of many years of unrestricted grazing use, Al Dick's ranch was so deteriorated that the former owner felt it could never recover. But through a program of more conservative stocking, fencing, and other improvements the ranch has been restored to a point where it now will graze a cow per 3.5 acres per month as compared to 20 acres per cow-month in 1907. The ranch has supported cattle continuously since 1907, has paid all the costs of improvement, paid off all indebtedness, and provided a good living.

Reseeding of adapted grasses and other plants to hold the soil and improve forage production shows much promise as a conservation measure for both the range and the watersheds. Over large areas the stand of desirable plants for forage and soil protection is now so thin, and the loss of fertile topsoil has been so great, that it will take from 20 to 50 years or even longer for the range to recover its former productivity under natural processes and good management. This is too long for economical use of the lands; also on many range watersheds soil movement must be stopped more quickly to save the water values and check floods.

Such conditions require reseeding or other forms of planting to accompany improved management if a satisfactory plant cover is to be established. This is not a simple process, and usually requires 2 to 3 years after seeding before a satisfactory plant cover is established. Nevertheless, by following the recommendations and necessary precautions outlined in the previous article many range lands can be repaired. For example, in central Utah as the result of research, one project of 2,000 acres of range land formerly plowed for crop production and later abandoned were divided into pastures and seeded to crested wheatgrass.

As a result the grazing capacity was increased seven times and eleven times more beef grown on the seeded lands. Moreover, grazing provided on the reseeded lands relieved the grazing pressure on adjacent overgrazed mountain spring range and is aiding in its recovery.

The reseeding of more than 300,000 acres of spring-fall range in Utah, Nevada, and Idaho during the past few years has supplied forage for more than 100,000 cattle or 50,000 sheep for about 2 months in the critical spring period. The soil and forage condition of the range also have been markedly improved.

On range areas now occupied by low-value or noxious range plants such as mesquite and sagebrush, full returns from proper stocking, improved management, and reseeding will not be possible until such soil-moisture-robbing plants are eradicated or controlled. In

Utah the forage on 10 to 15 acres of rough range lands occupied by sagebrush is required to graze one cow for a month. After the sagebrush is removed and the lands seeded to grass, one acre will graze one cow for one month. In Arizona where mesquite has been eliminated on the range, forage production has increased two- to threefold and accelerated erosion has been stopped.

On the high range watershed areas, particularly where soil erosion is advanced, suitable mechanical aids such as contour trenches for holding the soil in place and checking surface runoff aid in checking floods and erosion and help in restoring a suitable plant cover.

On the Davis County watershed in Utah a system of contour trenches was established on the denuded and eroded high range watershed areas from which devastating floods were originating. A number of the contour-trenched areas were also reseeded to adapted grasses. As the result of this treatment the floods have been stopped—rain waters have been allowed to seep into the ground where they fell, thus preventing surface runoff and consequent soil losses, and more favorable moisture conditions have been created in the soil to hasten the restoration of the plant cover.

In general, such mechanical aids should be considered as temporary measures pending the reestablishment of an effective plant cover. However, where erosion is far advanced and sedimentation is a big problem, such as in the lower main stream channels, more permanent mechanical structures may be required.

Control of rodents prior to or in conjunction with other range improvements such as reseeding is often advisable. In every section of the region one or more rodent species can be found.

Jack rabbits and rodents such as ground squirrels, kangaroo rats, prairie dogs, and pocket gophers are the principal range-destroying and forage-consuming animals. Generally the impact of rodent damage is greatest on depleted lands, although the consumption of forage by rodents on land in good condition is startling.

For example, in Arizona 15 antelope jack rabbits eat as much range forage as one sheep; 30 Arizona jack rabbits eat as much as one sheep. Kangaroo rats and ground squirrels draw heavily on seed produced by valuable range grasses. Rodent control programs should be provided for, but the number of most rodents should be reduced only to such an extent that a natural balance is established.

Proper range management is undoubtedly a distinct aid in accomplishing a better rodent balance. Research in New Mexico indicates the heaviest jack rabbit populations are confined largely to the range areas that are continually overused and in poor condition.

Suitable and well-placed capital improvements on the range, such as fencing, water development, trails for stock, and other physical improvements, are essential aids to better management. Such improvements as additional fences and well distributed water developments afford control and distribution of livestock and otherwise aid proper grazing use. The number and character of improvements needed depend on such factors as condition of the range, or range watershed, the amount and character of forage available, the desired seasonal use, and the natural conditions influencing use of the particular area by the kind of livestock grazed.

To facilitate more desirable use of the range and range watersheds in the West, it is estimated that the following improvements are needed: 100,000 miles of new fences, 150,000 spring developments, 250,000 livestock watering reservoirs, 15,000 wells, 20,000 miles of trails, and many other miscellaneous improvements.

Suitable planning is also recognized as a necessary part of the whole program of range and range watershed conservation and development. Surveys and investigations furnish the facts on which effective planning is based. It is estimated that surveys pointed toward the determination of actual range condition on about 700 million acres of range lands in the West should be completed for effective planning and administration.

In many areas within the region range and range watershed lands are being abused because not enough supplemental feed is being produced to round out the year-round forage and feed supply. Lack of sufficient pasture and feed crops has forced too early and too late and even yearlong use of ranges.

More improved pastures and higher yielding forage crops would materially increase the forage base of the region and help to offset the nutritional deficiencies of the native range forage. Pasture production may be increased by controlling soil moisture including proper drainage and leveling, more use of manure and other fertilizers, by seeding higher yielding species, by following recommended grazing practices, and by controlling weeds and old growth of forage plants.

Hay production may be increased by controlling soil moisture, by plowing and seeding neglected tracts and native meadows, and by choosing wilt-resistant strains of alfalfa and higher yielding grasses, and then mowing and handling the forage crop by recommended practices.

Aids to Conservation

Several land-use adjustments and aids are essential in the furtherance of grassland conservation. One important adjustment that will aid conservation is the unraveling of the present mixed-up land ownership. Ownership of range lands in the West is complex. It is not uncommon for a ranch operator, in addition to his own private holdings, to require State leases and national forest and grazing district permits in his yearlong range operations. Moreover, some of these lands may be widely separated, requiring long tedious migration. Such scattered holdings, largely the result of past land disposal policies, have been a contributing factor in the present run-down condition of the range resource.

A related phase of the same problem is the generally inadequate size of ranches. The efficient raising of range livestock in the West hinges on the use of comparatively large areas. For example, a ranching unit of 200 breeding cows may require from 6,000 to 40,000 acres of range. Likewise, a sheep enterprise of 1,000 ewes may require a similarly sized area, including winter, spring, and fall range as well as special ranch property for lambing and shearing. The land disposal policy, based on 640-acre homesteads, contributed too many undersize and uneconomical ranching units. More economical range and ranching units would aid in facilitating the use of better stocking and management practices and increase the economic and social welfare of western rural populations.

Another aid to conservation is the retirement of submarginal croplands and their reconversion to grass. Many thousands of acres of once productive range lands have been plowed and planted to crops. Precipitation is so erratic and irrigation water so limited that the production on many of these lands now is meager, save in years of above-normal rainfall. Many have been abandoned and are sources of serious soil erosion. The general forage base of the region would be materially improved and rural welfare enhanced by returning these lands to production.

Still another important aid to grassland conservation is provision for more adequate extension of information regarding recommended conservation practices. Considerable worth while information about grass and its use, including range and range watershed management and pasture and forage crop production, has been developed. This information needs to be taken to the farms, ranches, and the range and demonstrated and adapted for local use.

Finally, there is need to continue to devise more ways of improving and using grass. The Mountain Region is relatively young and experience with grass comparatively new. Yet, development and use of the lands have been rapid because the grassland resources were needed in the growth of the Nation. As a consequence, problems that have developed are in large part the result of lack of adequate knowledge.

Additional research information is needed in all phases of grassland production and use. For pastures and forage crops, more attention should be given to the development and use of higher yielding forage species, including mixtures; to soil moisture, irrigation, and fertility practices; and to improved grazing and harvesting methods. In range and range-watershed use, major fields of investigation in which more attention is needed include the determination of the influence and evaluation of range watershed conservation practices on water yield, soil movement, and forage production; the determination and evaluation of the degree and systems of management on additional range types in various conditions; the extension of range reseeding studies to include all major range types; the development and evaluation of other improvement practices.

Continued attention should also be given to the development of a fund of basic information on plant growth, soil, and moisture, and their use which is fundamental for continued prosperity.

THE AUTHORS ««« *Raymond Price is a graduate of the University of Utah and Yale University and has been engaged in range research since 1930. Mr. Price is director of the Southwestern Forest and Range Experiment Station at Tucson.*

George Stewart is range ecologist with the Intermountain Forest and Range Experiment Station. Dr. Stewart is coauthor of Principles of Agronomy, and author of Alfalfa Growing in the United States and Canada, and other publications on cultivated forage crops and range management. Prior to joining the Intermountain staff, Dr. Stewart was agronomist with the Utah Agricultural Experiment Station, Utah Agricultural College, at Logan.

Wesley Keller, a native of Utah and a graduate of Utah State Agricultural College and the University of Wisconsin, has been engaged in research on grass improvement since 1936. Dr. Keller, a geneticist in the Bureau of Plant Industry, Soils, and Agricultural Engineering, is stationed at Logan.

H. R. Hochmuth, a native of Colorado and a graduate of the Colorado Agricultural and Mechanical College and the University of California, has been engaged in research on the economics of range and ranch management in the Western States since 1938. Mr. Hochmuth, agricultural economist in the Bureau of Agricultural Economics, is stationed at Logan, Utah.

Kenneth W. Parker, a graduate of the University of California, has been engaged in research in range problems since 1929. Mr. Parker is range ecologist in charge of range research at the Southwestern Forest and Range Experiment Station at Tucson, Ariz.

A. C. Hull, Jr., a native of Idaho and a graduate of the Utah State Agricultural College and Brigham Young University, has been engaged in range management and reseeding research since 1936. Mr. Hull is range ecologist in charge of reseeding research at the Rocky Mountain Forest and Range Experiment Station at Fort Collins, Colo.

The Pacific Coast States

THE RANGE IN CALIFORNIA

M. W. TALBOT, A. W. SAMPSON

ABOUT HALF of the 60 million acres in California that lie west of the Sierra Nevada Divide can be used for grazing. Despite the extent of this forage area, however, more meat and livestock are consumed than produced in the State, and as the population grows and demands on range lands get heavier, the need for sound management of these lands becomes more acute.

The grasslands lying west of the Sierra Nevada differ conspicuously from those in other western regions in climate, vegetation, and utility.

A long, interior trough, the Central Valley, lies between the Sierra Nevada range on the east and the Coast Range on the west. These mountains and the Pacific Ocean contribute to a highly diversified climate. Soil conditions also vary widely and sometimes change abruptly. Precipitation generally is greater and temperature is lower with increase in altitude and latitude. The marine influence moderates temperatures along the coast and intermittently in the Central Valley. Summers are hot and dry. Most of the precipitation occurs from October to June.

Great changes have occurred here since Mission days. Intensive cultivation has replaced much of the grazing. Croplands and city lands now total approximately one-fifth of the Pacific slope. Native perennial bunchgrasses have decreased and introduced annuals have increased over large areas of the lower elevations.

The original cover evidently contained many native annual grasses and forbs; the degree to which these have changed in population is unknown. But the magnitude of the invasion of alien annuals is indicated by surveys that show that these plant immigrants now compose more than half of the herbaceous cover over vast foothill areas— 60 percent, indeed, on the San Joaquin Experimental Range in the central Sierra foothills. Brush fields appear to occupy greater acreage now than formerly because of burnings and other disturbances in forest areas.

On some good timber-growing land, the acreage of available forage in fairly open stands of timber has been considerably reduced, as the thickening new stands of young trees gradually shade out the forage plants. Such forage loss is temporarily offset, at least in part, as timber stands open up with greater age, or as openings are made by logging. Conifers often have invaded mountain meadows.

The cover of vegetation on the Pacific slope comprises four provinces, arranged roughly by altitudinal zones: Open grassland, grass-woodland, chaparral, and timber-grass-brush.

Much of the Central Valley and large sections of the middle and south Coast Ranges are open grasslands, with many local exceptions where tree or shrub areas occur in intermingled patterns. The main body of comparatively treeless grassland, totaling approximately 9¾ million acres, is found from sea level to about 1,500 feet.

Lower elevations receive from 5 to 30 inches of precipitation, mostly in the form of rain, the amount increasing locally to as much as 40 inches in the north coast section. Summer temperatures go up to 105° F.

An unusually rich mixture of annual and perennial grass and forbs is a distinctive feature of the zone. The annual-grass areas are extensively grazed at all seasons, but their greatest value is as winter and spring ranges. Used in conjunction with the lower portion of the adjoining woodland, the open grassland province is the basis for the livestock industry of the State. Proximity to irrigated pastures, to the summer grazing lands of the mountains, to sources of supplemental feeds including crop residues, and to markets, makes it and the grass-woodland province the best situated for maximum flexibility in management.

Grass-Woodland

The increasing abundance of shrubs and trees in the vegetative cover set this zone apart from the adjoining open grasslands. The lower part of this belt has an orchardlike appearance because of the scattered stands of trees and shrubs of which Digger pine, live oak, blue oak, and Califor-

nia buckeye are locally most abundant.

As in the open grassland, hundreds of species of grasses and other herbs are common, but most of the forage comes from comparatively few species. For example, on the San Joaquin Experimental Range of this province, the three most important species—soft chess, foxtail fescue, and broadleaf filaree—provide fully two-thirds of the forage in pastures from which 225 different species have been identified.

Broadly considered, the grazing capacities are greatest along the lower margin. Higher up, the stand of trees and shrubs thickens, the period of availability for grazing shortens, and the acreage requirements per animal increase. The grazing value of the grass-woodland province as a whole is therefore intermediate between that of the lower grassland and the higher chaparral and the timber-grass-brush province.

Chaparral and Brush

From the northern mountains to Mexico, interrupted strips of shrubby growth lie largely below the timber-brush-grass province. The dense, shrubby growth is called "chaparral"; its province is usually termed "brush" land by stockmen.

Chaparral occupies some 11 million acres, or about 18 percent of the Pacific-slope grasslands. It includes also a large acreage of woodland and of cut-over timber that has reverted to various brush species. True chapparal seems chiefly to be limited to areas where the temperature does not exceed 100° F. for long periods and where average annual precipitation is 10 to 35 inches.

Growing on steep, rugged terrain, the denser chaparral stands are found on north and east slopes, and more drought-resistant species occupy the south and west slopes of thinner, drier, and rockier soils. Most of the chaparral species are broadleaved, like manzanita, and ceanothus, but the most common and widely distributed species—chamiza—has narrow, needle-like foliage.

The food plants are primarily important because they supply most of the forage on fresh burns, and on glades within the brush association. Sprout, twig, leaf growth of some of the shrubs is browsed in winter and through the spring. Sprouts are most palatable up to about midsummer.

The limited seasonal pasturage furnished on the average chaparral cover is poor because the brush is of low palatability, and the understory vegetation is sparse and largely inaccessible.

Maximum usefulness of the brushland forage is obtained in late winter, spring, and early summer, when nutritional constituents of the forage are high. After this, feed values decline.

Usually referred to as the coniferous forest zone, the timber-grass-brush province occupies about 28 percent of the area reported upon, and blankets the north Coast Ranges and the Sierra Navada and Cascades. This province also includes in its steep and rugged terrain extensive areas of open, rocky grassland above the timber line in the high Sierra Nevada.

Except in the redwood region, this timber and grass zone lies in the snow belt. Most of the precipitation falls in winter and ranges roughly from 40 to 50 inches on the western slopes of the Sierra to as much as 50 to 80 inches in the redwoods.

Range land on the forested western slopes consists largely of timber and brushland on ridges and steep slopes, interspersed with openings and small bottomlands of open character. Browse and a small amount of grass and forbs furnish the major forage. In the fir stands of the higher elevations and the dense Douglas-fir and redwood forests of the northwestern part of the State, grazing is confined mainly to glades, burns, and small clearings.

In contrast to the three lower provinces, the grasses of this province are nearly all perennial bunchgrasses. The forbs here contribute far less forage than those of the other three prov-

inces. In the lower reaches, deerbrush ceanothus is the most important browse species, whereas in the highest elevations willows are the most important.

Range lands in this coniferous belt of the Sierra Nevada and the timbered areas of the restricted snow belt of the Coast Ranges are grazeable during the summer from May or June until October. Grasslands intermingled with the forests of the rainfall belt in the Coast Ranges are best utilized from February until July, although some are used yearlong. In the highest elevations the grazing season is limited to a few weeks in midsummer.

The hundreds of mountain meadows in this zone are the best of forage types for the summer season. Although comparatively small in acreage, and often overgrazed, these treeless islands of grass often control the use of surrounding lands, because of their high grazing capacity and more abundant water supply. The grazing capacity of the adjoining timber areas is much lower, but the forage is nutritious and the available acreage is much greater.

The major part of the timber range is too rocky, steep, or brushy to graze. In the commercial timber zone, maximum timber and water production is the primary management objective. From a State-wide viewpoint, grazing is comparatively minor; ranges on the national forests, which lie largely in this province, provide scarcely 3 percent of California's total range requirements. In total, however, the grasslands of this belt comprise a locally important grazing resource, particularly since green forage is available when feed is dry over most of the lower ranges.

Principal Uses

The grasslands are the foundation of a large livestock industry. The beef-cattle population of California is more than 1½ million head. There are also more than 2 million sheep, and smaller numbers of horses, pack mules, and goats.

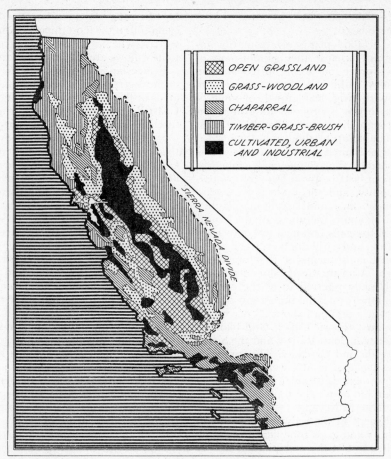

The four grassland areas of the Pacific slope of California. The map is adapted from Forest Survey, California Forest and Range Experiment Station, U. S. Forest Service.

Grass or browse ranges provide food and cover for vast numbers of wildlife, including such important game as antelope, deer, quail, waterfowl, and pheasants.

The grasslands also help meet California's demand for recreational lands and watersheds. Next to soil, water is the important natural resource. It is vital in irrigation agriculture, and it supplies the municipal and industrial needs of a fast-growing population that now numbers more than 9 million.

Vast grassland areas play a major role in the complicated and difficult problem of watershed management to obtain the maximum supply of usable water with the minimum of flood damage, for they extend from the cultivated areas, through the forest zones, and into vast areas above the timber line.

Approximately 4½ million acres of agricultural land are under irrigation. The San Francisco and Los Angeles areas bring water from 100 to 250 miles away. About 85 percent of the electric energy generated in the State comes from hydroelectric plants. Such facts make Federal, State, and private agencies deeply conscious of the importance of water and the need for its more intensive study and management.

In a State having such a variety of conditions—soil, climatic, topographic, vegetative, and economic—it is natural to find a corresponding diversity of practices, patterns, and problems of range management and ranch organization.

Many herds of cattle are kept on the home ranch yearlong, with or without supplemental feed for the dry summer; some remain on the home ranch, but with part of the forage cut green and fed during late summer or fall out of windrow or shock. Others depend only part of the year on the home ranch, obtaining summer feed from national-forest or other high mountain ranges, from irrigated pastures, or from crop residues. Sheep-management practices vary widely, too, between the one extreme of operations involving open-range herding and long trailing between winter lambing grounds and summer grazing grounds, to the other extreme of yearlong grazing in fenced pastures.

These and many other differences in prevailing range practices reflect corresponding differences in such things as operator's objectives, land ownership, and operating conditions.

Prevent Range Deterioration

Even a quick examination of the grasslands of California will reveal lands in all degrees of condition from good to poor, in both private and public ownership. Overgrazing and range depletion have long been recognized; all in all, California range lands are definitely below potential productivity.

Recognition of desirable range condition, direction of range trend, and satisfactory forage utilization are the first setps in preventing deterioration of the range.

If a range is below the desired standard, utilization should be lighter, and the trend should be watched over a period of time to see that more desirable range plants are increasing in abundance and vigor, that litter is accumulating in the topsoil, and that gullies and rills in the soil are healing.

In the annual-forage cover of California, a combination of desirable plants, such as soft chess, and nutritious forbs like the filarees and bur-clover, seems to constitute a good forage mixture. Perennials such as oatgrasses, needlegrasses, and melic grasses are also to be favored, if present in appreciable quantity. If such range is too heavily or, indeed, too lightly grazed, less desirable forage usually develops.

Light grazing results in more annual grass at the expense of palatable forbs and in wasted feed. Too heavy use results in progressively poorer range condition. This may be reflected in less desirable kinds of forage plants, lower vigor in the desirable plants, less protective litter on the soil, or loss of soil because of water or wind erosion. Moderate grazing will maintain satisfactory forage production and allow efficient utilization.

On perennial grass ranges, although the details differ, the same general principles apply. First, the desired standard according to the nutritional qualities and soil protection must be defined for the particular region. Utilization must then be adjusted to maintain this condition, or, if a subcondition exists, to correct it.

A second step in arresting declining soil and forage values is to adjust animal numbers to the year-in, year-out capacity of the forage.

Because of many limiting conditions, including short-term as against long-range objectives of management, satisfactory balancing of livestock numbers with the feed supply is hard. But even more difficult to achieve is control of numbers of big-game animals, chiefly deer, in this region. In some localities adjustment of the grazing requirements of game with those of livestock is still challenging the best thought and effort of public and private groups.

Improving Efficiency

Arresting deterioration of the range is an immediate need. But a continuing need in stable range-livestock production is efficient use of forage from native grasslands year after year—better management facilities over vast areas

Characteristic Range Species and Genera of the Four Major Range Provinces of the Pacific Slope of California

Grasses	Forbs	Shrubs
OPEN GRASSLAND		
Aristiaa, Avena barbata A. fatua, Bromus mollis, B. rigidus, B. rubens, Danthonia californica, Distichlis spicata, Elymus, Festuca, Hordeum gussonianum, Juncus, Koeleria cristata, Lolium, Melica, Poa, Sitanion, Stipa.	*Amsinckia, Baeria, Brodiaea, Cirsium, Erodium, Escholtzia, Gilia, Hemizonia, Lepidium, Lotus, Lupinus, Medicago, Orthocarpus, Plagiobothrys, Plantago, Silybum, Trifolium.*	*Artemisia californica, Atriplex, Salvia, Suaeda.*
GRASS—WOODLAND		
Same genera and many of the same species as in open grassland, particularly over the lower elevations.	Lower elevations similar to open grassland; in upper portion, additional species such as: *Chlorogalum, Cirsium, Clarkia, Collomia, Phacelia.*	*Applopappus, Arctostaphylos, Artemisia californica, Ceanothus, Eriodictyon, Quercus, Rhamnus, Rhus.*
CHAPARRAL		
Same genera and many of same species as in grass-woodland; additional species include: *Aira caryophyllea, Bromus madritensis, Calamagrostis rubescens,* and *Gastridium ventricosum.*	*Chlorogalum, Emenantha penduliflora, Epilobium, Eriophyllum, Fillago gallica, Hieracium, Hypericum concinnum, Lotus, Lupinus.*	*Adenostoma fasciculatum, Arctostaphylos, Ceanothus, Eriogonum fasciculatum, Lotus scoparius, Quercus, Sambucus, Styrax californica.*
TIMBER-BRUSH-GRASS		
Agropyron, Agrostis, Bromus, Carex, Deschampsia, Festuca, Juncus, Muhlenbergia, Phleum alpinum, Poa, Trisetum.	*Aster, Balsamorhiza, Calyptridium, Camassia, Lathyrus, Lupinus, Mimulus, Oxalis, Pentstemon, Polygonum, Ranunculus, Senecio, Vicia.*	*Alnus, Arctostaphylos, Azalea, Ceanothus integerrimus, Ceanothus, Cercocarpus, Cornus, Crossularia, Ribes, Salix.*

for the full utilization of existing forage resources, the timing of grazing use, handling livestock most economically while on the grazing lands or while being moved from one unit to another, and such improvements as fences for controlling grazing and stock watering places. Further, real promise lies in more timely grazing of each range unit when its forage is most nutritious and resting certain parts of each operating unit in turn, and through some form

of deferred and rotation grazing to maintain and increase the vigor of the more valuable forage plants and to insure their reproduction.

Too heavy range use seems also to be associated with increased losses from poisonous plants or plants that under certain conditions might contain toxic elements. Several genera that contain poisonous species are common to all provinces: Milkweed, locoweed, lupine, and deathcamas. In one province or another are St. Johnswort, bracken fern, larkspur, tobacco, rhododendron, kalmia, ledum, leucothoe, skunkbush, wild cherry, and sneezeweed.

Chemical composition of the forage crop is another factor in efficient use. The pattern of organic and mineral constituents of the grassland plants changes markedly with stage of growth, nature of the soils, and seasonal weather. In the grasses and forbs there is a continuous decline in the proportion of crude protein, silica-free ash, calcium, phosphorus, and potassium from the early leaf stage to maturity. The proportion of crude fiber increases as the season advances. The most rapid changes in chemical levels occur from early leaf development to full bloom.

Grass and grasslike species remain green longer in the swales and maintain at least intermediate protein and mineral levels well past the maturity period of the dry-land grasses and forbs. Compared to the annual species, most perennial grasses have a relatively long period of high nutritive levels because of their longer season of succulence.

Chemical studies of the forage have accounted for certain nutritional deficiencies at various seasons. At plant maturity, for instance, the ratio of calcium to phosphorus in many forbs and shrubs greatly exceeds that which favors their satisfactory assimilation by livestock. Likewise, seasonal deficiency of vitamin A, as when the animals are held too long on dry, bleached feed, may occasionally induce nutritional disorders. Provision of ample lush forage, as on irrigated pastures, or supplementing the range pasturage with green cured hay or suitable concentrates provide corrective measures that are economically sound.

Improving Range Forage

Favorable sites in the higher foothills and many mountain meadows can be improved through artificial reseeding, accompanied and followed by good management. Besides increasing yield, successful reseeding may lengthen the period of nutritious green feed.

The California Agricultural Experiment Station has a program for improving range forage plants through selection and hybridization and has made many field reseeding tests on depleted grasslands and on burned chaparral lands. The Extension Service has established row nurseries and other plots in 40 counties. The Forest Service has made nursery and plot tests at the San Joaquin Experimental Range, and has had experimental range plots on six national forests. The Soil Conservation Service has conducted extensive tests in conservation districts.

Preliminary studies at the San Joaquin Experimental Range and elsewhere indicate that the application of commercial fertilizers may have some economic importance on California ranges.

In all the provinces, part of each season's forage growth must be charged to the ravages of rodents and rabbits. Many species of rodents occur on California ranges, each inflicting a different amount and kind of damage. Most species are of minor economic importance. Ground squirrels, kangaroo rats, and gophers are responsible for most of the damage. Their control is a continuing problem.

Control of the chaparral in various foothill localities, long a subject of controversy in California, involves complex considerations of land use. Broadcast burning is the most common control method used. Conflicting viewpoints concern both stockmen and others interested in these marginal lands. There is no single answer to suppression of the brush, for it varies with species, site, climate, and other local factors.

Part of the complexity of brush control arises from the fact that there are two distinctive growth forms of chaparral—sprouting and nonsprouting. Sprouting forms, which predominate, present the greatest difficulties in control by burning. Sprouts provide some additional forage that is palatable to livestock and, incidentally, to deer. The amount of forage varies widely from area to area and in period of availability. Nonsprouting forms of brush may be destroyed in two judicious burnings—preferably 2 years apart. Steeper slopes, characterized by thin soils, should be left unburned because the poor or limited forage which they produce does not offset the erosion losses. The larger part of chaparral lands is of this inferior quality.

Relatively small acreages of level or gently sloping lands in woodland and brush, with deep productive soils, can be improved by fire combined with other methods. Where an additional financial outlay is justified, or on suitable areas of high fire risk, the brush may be removed with a bulldozer, by hand chopping, or by some other me-

chanical method, in combination with burning or with goat grazing, to destroy sprouts and brush seedlings. On the more favorable sites from which brush has been removed, artificial reseeding has a place, but all the possibilities of artificial reseeding have not been fully worked out.

Regardless of the method of brush control employed, careful follow-up management is required to insure maximum forage production and a satisfactory herbaceous cover.

Fitting all phases of management and the needs for grasslands into a long-range pattern of balanced wildland use is a difficult undertaking in any region of the West. It is particularly complex in California, where grasslands are subjected to growing demands from a rapidly increasing population.

FORAGE CROPS IN CALIFORNIA

B. A. MADSEN, R. MERTON LOVE

OF THE 7,500,000-odd acres of land in harvested crops in California, more than a fourth was cropped to hay in 1945.

It is estimated that 200,000 acres are planted to silage and annual pasture crops and about 450,000 acres to perennial irrigated pastures. In addition, livestock are grazed in the fall on most of 2¼ million acres of grain stubble, bean straw, and beet tops—forms of forage that equal a half ton of hay an acre and fill an important gap in the fall from the time cattle and sheep are removed from the mountain ranges until fall rains have started new growths on the lower pasture and range lands.

Alfalfa is the most important cultivated forage crop in California. It is grown in all sections where water and soil conditions permit, and is essentially an irrigated crop. The largest acreage (and the highest production) is centered in the San Joaquin and Im-

perial Valleys, where water, soil, and growing season are the most favorable. In 1943 a total of 945,319 acres of alfalfa was cut for hay.

Alfalfa is grown on many soil types, ranging from light sand to clay loam. The chief essential is that the soil be deep, friable, well drained, and free from excessive amounts of alkali. Practically all the good alfalfa soils are alluvial deposits of valley fills. The soils least suited to the crop, because of poor water penetration, are the heavy clay adobes and hardpan soils.

Fertilizers have been unnecessary on most of the loam soil, but in some areas (particularly the Imperial Valley, the sandy soils of the San Joaquin, and a few others) phosphorus or sulfur, or both, are necessary for maximum yields.

The yields vary with the soil and water supply and the length of the growing seasons. The average for the State is a little more than 4.5 tons an acre, but in the interior valley in the southern half of the State, where 6 to 9 cuttings are obtained for the season, 8 to 10 tons an acre is common.

The most serious problem is the short life of the stand, due mainly to three serious diseases, alfalfa wilt (*Phytomonas insidiosa*) ; alfalfa dwarf, a virus disease peculiar to some sections of California, and crown rot (*Stagonospora meliloti*). Alfalfa wilt and crown rot are prevalent throughout the State, and reduce the life of the stands to about 4 years. The destructive effect of both of these diseases is aggravated by the common practice of frequent irrigation and early cutting in order to obtain the maximum yield of high-quality hay. Where irrigation is less frequent or where the plants are permitted to reach a more advanced stage of growth before cutting, the course of these diseases seems to be less rapid. The alfalfa dwarf (which is caused by the same virus as causes the Pierce disease on grapes) is most prevalent in the San Joaquin Valley and in some sections of southern California. Its effect on the plants and on the life of the stand is essentially the same as that of wilt. Whether the course of the dwarf disease is influenced by irrigation or the stage of cutting has not been determined.

A breeding program has been under way for a number of years to develop a strain of California common alfalfa resistant to wilt. Considerable progress has been made, and we expect that a healthier strain will be available in a few years. Some work also has been started on the development of strains resistant to crown rot and dwarf, but no strain has been found that shows any appreciable resistance to either disease; progress has been slow. It is quite evident that the only cure for these diseases is to develop resistant strains.

Alfalfa hay as grown in California is usually quite clean and free from grasses and weeds, except for the first spring cutting, which often may be so full of weeds as to be practically worthless. Recent experiments have demonstrated that a late-winter spraying before the alfalfa starts rapid growth, with a mixture of oil and a selective weed spray, may eliminate the weedy grasses and weeds.

Because of the rainless summer weather, damage to the hay is not a problem except along the coast, where high humidity and fogs may prolong the curing process and cause bleaching. In the valleys, where most of the alfalfa is grown, the chief problem is to get the hay put up and baled before it becomes so dry that many of the leaves are lost by shattering. Most growers have mechanized and systematized their practices, however, so that this loss is greatly reduced. Generally hay of excellent quality is put up.

During the warmer periods the alfalfa is usually cut in the morning, raked into windrows in the afternoon, and baled the same night. This procedure varies with temperature, humidity, and curing rate, of course. Most of the crop is cut just before the plants begin to bloom. This produces an excellent soft leafy hay with a protein content of 18 to 20 percent, but it does tend to lower the yield and contributes to the short life of the stands.

California common, a nonhardy strain, is the principal variety grown in California. Numerous tests have shown that for most sections it is superior to other varieties and other strains of common alfalfa. Winterkilling is not a problem in California and winter-hardy strains, which go dormant during the winter, yield less as a rule than the nonhardy common.

Most of the 8.5 to 9 million pounds of seed used here is produced in the State or in Arizona. The 10-year average annual production of seed in California is 3.5 million pounds; in 1946 it was 4.5 million pounds. Yields of seed have been low in recent years, mainly because of damage by *Lygus*. Dusting the field with DDT just before blooming has proved effective. Experimental results indicate that seed production can be doubled by proper treatment without increasing the acreage.

Other tame hay consists mostly of cereals or cereals and legume mixtures, with a limited acreage of other annual crops. The acreage and production of other tame hay, according to 1945 census, was: Grain hay, 286,877 acres, 415,914 tons; other tame hay, 245,256 acres, 361,724 tons; clover and timothy, 39,099 acres, 69,712 tons. Besides those, 249,646 acres of oats was cut when ripe, and fed unthreshed. Locally it is considered to be hay and serves the same purpose. The principal cereal seeded for hay is oats either alone or in combination with vetch or some other winter legume. Some oat hay is grown in most counties; it has been particularly popular along the coast from Marin County south, in southern California, and in a few areas of the larger valleys.

The principal variety of oats planted for hay, when grown alone, is California Red, which is preferred for its fine, leafy stems. Rust epidemics frequently reduce the quality of the oat hay in some localities. In southern California, particularly, some farmers are replacing California Red with Ventura, a recent development that is more resistant to rust, yet possesses good hay characteristics.

Growing oats for hay is not essentially different from growing oats for grain. The main difference is in a somewhat heavier rate of seeding to increase the yield and produce a finer product.

Oats and legume mixtures, principally purple or common vetch, have been increasing in popularity as a hay crop. Oats and vetch are particularly favored in the coastal valleys where water is not available for alfalfa. Good crops of oats and vetch can be grown there without irrigation and (if the proper mixture is used) will produce a hay only slightly inferior to alfalfa.

Recognizing the need for a legume hay, farmers for many years attempted to grow mixtures of oats and common vetch, but with poor results. Too often the vetch would fail, and the hay crop would consist mainly of oats. Experiments in the early 1930's showed that the main reason for the poor or uncertain results was the use of seed mixtures that contained too much oat seed and too little vetch.

The most dependable results, it was found, can be had by seeding 15 to 20 pounds of oats and 40 to 50 pounds of vetch. This rate of seeding provided enough oats to support the vetch and produced hay of which approximately half was legume.

This mixture is also grown in some places in the Sacramento and San Joaquin Valleys, especially where, because of disease or some other unfavorable condition, alfalfa cannot be grown. In the Valleys, the mixture is grown mostly on irrigated land. In fact, to be sure of a good crop, irrigation is necessary. In these areas the late fall and winter is somewhat colder than along the coast. If seeding is delayed until the fall rains have moistened the soil, perhaps in late November or early December, the soil may be so cold that the vetch does not germinate and only oats are obtained. Therefore, seeding is on pre-irrigated land, preferably in late October when a good stand of vetch, as well as oats, can be obtained and the plants, once established, survive the winter.

Kanota oats, rather than California Red, are used in mixture with legumes. It has a stiffer straw, is less inclined to lodge, and provides a better support for the legume. Purple vetch is the legume commonly employed in mixture, mainly because of its greater dependability and higher yield. Common vetch, Canadian field peas, and Austrian Winter peas are also used sometimes. Hairy vetch and Tangier peas have given excellent results under a wide variety of conditions, but the scarcity of seed and its high price has kept them from general use.

Some barley and wheat are also cut for hay, for the most part incidentally to the production of grain; if the season is favorable for the grain, the crop is allowed to mature and is harvested for grain. But if conditions for growth and maturity are unfavorable, the crop is cut for hay. As a rule, these crops are allowed to become quite mature before being cut, and the quality of hay is often rather poor.

Other crops grown, to a limited extent, for hay include red clover and alsike clover in mixture with timothy or other grasses, and sorghum or Sudangrass, which is fed on the farm where it is grown and is used mainly to supplement insufficient supplies of alfalfa.

Irrigated Pastures

Both perennial and annual irrigated pastures are important feed crops in California.

The use of perennial irrigated pastures, as known today, dates from the late 1920's, when it was demonstrated that Ladino clover would produce excellent yields of forage on our shallow hardpan soil if properly watered or managed. The use of perennial irrigated pastures since that time has grown rapidly. The present acreage is estimated at about 450,000; it seems likely that within the next score of years it will become our most important forage crop. Irrigated pasture provides forage of high quality at a low cost and produces it on land unsuited to alfalfa.

Ladino clover is still the leading irrigated-pasture plant, but it has limitations: It is shallow rooted; because for continued growth it requires frequent irrigation, especially in summer, it is limited to areas having plenty of water and retentive soil; it cannot stand high temperatures. Ladino is grown on irrigated pastures in a number of districts, but most of the acreage in Ladino is located in the Sacramento and San Joaquin Valleys, where favorable conditions prevail.

We still have much to learn about proper mixtures for the different areas and the best management practices, but now enough experience has been gained to suggest some rather definite procedures.

To get maximum production and a better balanced feed, most of the pasture consists of clover or other legumes with various grasses. In the Sacramento Valley and in other localities in the North, a popular mixture contains Ladino clover, annual and perennial ryegrass, tall fescue, and orchardgrass. In the San Joaquin Valley the same mixture is used, although Dallisgrass is commonly added to it or substituted for the orchardgrass. Some alfalfa is sometimes added to get more legumes during the summer when heat depresses the growth of the clover.

Because the pasture must be irrigated every 10 to 14 days during the warmer months, the field is divided into four or more pastures and grazed in rotation. Opinions differ as to how close the pastures should be grazed, but observation indicates that most pastures are grazed too close, so that recovery is retarded and production lowered.

Ladino clover draws heavily on the mineral nutrients, and many pastures containing it must be fertilized with phosphorus, and sometimes sulfur, for best growth.

The most serious weeds in irrigated pastures are apt to be buckhorn, dock, and various sedges. Partial control may be effected by mowing the pastures after they have been pastured to prevent the plants from seeding and to reduce spreading. Mowing also prevents some of the bunch grasses, particularly orchardgrass and Dallisgrass, from taking over. When pastures become very weedy, the only means of eradication known is rotation with other crops.

Great interest has developed lately in birdsfoot trefoil as a pasture legume. It is a deep-rooted perennial; it is not adapted to the shallow hardpan land, but does well on the deeper, more porous soils. It tolerates more alkali and requires less frequent irrigation than Ladino. It tolerates more heat and is used with excellent results in the Imperial Valley in mixtures with ryegrass, Dallisgrass, Rhodesgrass, and other grasses. Elsewhere it is grown with the same grass mixture as Ladino is. The use of birdsfoot trefoil may greatly extend the area of irrigated pastures, but it should not be considered a substitute for Ladino in areas where the latter can be grown. While no direct comparisons are available, the birdsfoot trefoil does not recover so rapidly after grazing as Ladino, and observation indicates that it produces somewhat less feed.

One-half to two-thirds of the perennial irrigated pasture is grazed by dairy cattle, and provides succulent feed through a large part of the year. The remaining acreage is grazed by beef cattle and sheep. An important use is to finish lambs for market. The general trend appears to be to use ranges primarily to produce feeders to be finished on pasture and concentrates.

The most important annual irrigated-pasture crop, Sudangrass, is used in all of the warmer parts of the State. It is seeded in April or June after a winter hay crop is removed. Sudangrass pasture will produce more feed than any other crop available during the warm summer months. Its principal use is on small dairy farms, where maximum production of feed is required. Some sweet sorghums are used in the same way, but they do not lend themselves so well to pasturing.

Some other forms of forage are produced in limited quantities in some places. For silage, primarily for dairy cattle, various plants are grown in different localities. Corn is the most popular. In the warmer sections the sweet sorghums are grown. On the coast, oats and vetch are used; in some sections farmers put the first cutting of alfalfa, which is usually mixed with foxtail and weeds, in the silo. Silage will continue to be important in some areas, but perennial irrigated pastures, which produce an acceptable substitute at a much lower cost, have reduced its use in other districts.

TREES, GRASS, AND WATER

JOSEPH F. PECHANEC

IN WESTERN OREGON and Washington the question is grass or trees. It is not a problem of coordinating all the uses but of using the type of cover that conduces to soil stability and sustained, timely stream flow.

Here there can be little dual use of the forests because of their nature. Except in the ponderosa pine and sugar pine forests of southern Oregon, the forest cover is dense and the tree canopy almost closed. Shrubs like Oregon-grape, salal, blueberry, vine maple, and salmonberry, with little or no palatability to stock, far outnumber the palatable species in the understory. Grazing values of the forest areas, consequently, are negligible.

Even after logging or accidental fire, native vegetation on these forest lands provides only a temporary forage resource. Succession of vegetation on cut-over and burned-over lands follows a fairly uniform trend. A spectacular growth of annuals and short-lived perennials immediately after logging is almost entirely replaced by a perennial cover in 5 to 12 years. Much of the perennial cover is shrubby, and if the area is not reburned, a coniferous forest gradually will suppress and replace the brush if there is a seed source.

With this trend in the succession, the period is short during which cut-over or burned Douglas-fir lands are grazeable. Only during the first 3 to 7 years is much feed available. Then it can be expected to dwindle because of the encroachment by bracken, shrubs, and tree growth until in 11 to 15 years little grazing use is possible.

Light grazing that removes competing vegetation might be beneficial, but in the past it has been found all but impossible to obtain uniform light grazing use. From the standpoint of forestation, grazing during this early period on newly logged lands may be harmful to the tree seedlings, especially where forests are planted with nursery stock. Severe cropping of the young tree seedlings has occurred in some localities.

Forage Values

Even though an estimated 300,000 acres of the west-side forest lands are logged-over yearly, the temporary forage value of the newly logged-over lands contributes little to the forage resource. Most of the area now being logged-over is on the mountain slopes in the more remote sections of the region. The forage is therefore inaccessible to livestock. Moreover, the temporary nature of the forage resource does not justify the establishment of new livestock enterprises, because most of the areas now being logged provide seasonable forage supplies usable only in spring and summer. There is now little shortage in grassland for use during this period, the critical shortages being in forage for fall, winter, and early spring use.

As a result of the low value of forest lands for grazing, less than one-fifth of the total land area in the northern Pacific coast region is grazed by livestock. Some forested land included in farms is being grazed. But by far the greater part of the grazeable area is formed by the valley and coastal grasslands, the croplands used for pasture, the hill pastures of the oak-madrone type, and the forest lands that have been converted to grassland. In the higher mountains lie subalpine grasslands, numerous small and grassy glades, and hillsides that furnish excellent summer range. To these must be added the grazeable lands of the ponderosa-sugar pine type where it merges with the Douglas-fir type in southern Oregon.

Any further increase of the livestock industry of this region can come about only in two ways—through the improvement in productivity of present grasslands and additional conversion of suitable forest lands. The extent to which the total grassland production can be increased by the former procedure is limited because of the restricted area involved.

The likelihood of further attempts at conversion of forest land to grassland has aroused concern because in the past unwise attempts have laid waste to large acreages in this region. Forest lands were denuded with no thought to the future. Fire protection was inadequate and recurrent fire ran rampant over newly logged areas. Timber operators hastened to liquidate their holdings after logging, and promoted the conversion to grassland.

These speculative efforts recognized no limitations of climate, soil, topography, or economic feasibility. As a result, a militant competing vegetation composed of brush, ferns, moss, and trees marched in and lowered grazing capacities to the point where it was no longer profitable to graze livestock on any except the best soils. Failure was widespread, homesteads and farms were abandoned, and human energies wasted; society was the loser. Natural resources suffered seriously because soils were impoverished and erosion accelerated by the recurrent burning resorted to in an attempt to keep down the encroaching species. Stream courses were scoured out by the silt-laden streams. And finally, the competing ground cover of brush, ferns, or moss that had come in made efforts at rehabilitation either as grassland or forest an extremely costly and difficult task.

During this period both poor grassland and forestry practices have laid waste to large areas. But it is hardly fair to compare these uses on the basis of such history because both the science of grassland management and forest management have made great strides during the past two decades.

Forest conversion to grassland and the grazing of cut-over lands have influenced forest productivity in several ways. Large areas of highly productive forest land have been removed from production, grazing of cut-over lands has in some cases damaged the incoming tree reproduction, and, of major importance, the recurrent and uncontrolled fires used in clearing the land have run over land not intended for conversion and destroyed the tree reproduction and stands of timber.

Grassland in Tree Farming

About the relative effects of grassland and forest on soil stability relatively little knowledge is available. Ample evidence is apparent throughout western Oregon and Washington of the failure of mismanaged forests and mismanaged grasslands to protect the soil and the watershed. It is also clear that in this region of heavy precipitation, from 40 to 100 inches, the undisturbed forest cover provides excellent protection to the soil, retards runoff, lengthens the time required for waters to congregate in streams, and insures continuity of stream flow throughout the dry summer. But there is no evidence on the relative values of well-managed, utilized forests and grasslands on soil stability and water yield.

Because of the nature of the soils and topography in the northern Pacific coast region, grassland and tree farming can go on together on the same farm, and they should. The soils and topography more suitable to grassland can be used for that purpose with the steeper parts, the poorer soils, and the north slopes left to trees. The forests will furnish posts, fuel, and other products essential to farm management. Moreover, with the present high prices for forest products, the forest can furnish cash income supplemental to the income obtained from grassland, and nearby forest industries will afford part-time employment.

Possibilities for successful conversion of forest land to grassland are not widespread. But the conversion can be effected in some places. It requires considerable effort and, since it precludes the alternate use of the land for tree

farming, it should be undertaken only after careful study has assured success.

It is to direct such efforts to the areas where success is likely that five guides are offered.

Conversion to grassland should be confined to areas near established farming enterprises or where some land suitable for production of supplemental feeds and crops is present. This is more important in the northern part of the region than in the southern. Studies reported in Washington Agricultural Experiment Station Bulletin 179, *Grazing on Cut-over Lands of Western Washington,* specify that a ton of hay for a cow or five sheep be provided for a winter feeding period of 3 months.

Soils should be favorable. Because of the highly variable quality of soils throughout western Oregon and Washington, it is important that conversion be considered only on the better soils. It is economically unsound to use costly intensive grassland practices on lands of low potential production. Soils vary widely in their ability to produce grass and in their ability to withstand erosion under a grass cover. Soil survey and land use maps need to be consulted before attempting conversion. Site classification for Douglas-fir production is not a reliable guide to possibilities for grassland production.

The character of competing vegetation should be carefully considered. The character of the vegetation which comes in after a burn varies widely from southern Oregon to northern Washington. Shrubby species that sprout rather readily, such as salal, Pacific poisonoak, and blueblossom ceanothus are formidable competitors. The importance of competing species as indicators of chances of success are emphasized by Washington Agricultural Experiment Station Bulletin 179, which points out that the vine maple areas generally offer much better chances for success than those characterized by western bracken fern.

Slopes should be slight to moderate, not more than 30 percent, and will vary with soil types. Steeper slopes should be left in tree cover to protect the soil surface and to prevent land masses from slipping when saturated by the 60- to 100-inch annual rainfall. South-, southwest-, and southeast-facing slopes generally offer better chances of success than north-facing slopes. The north-facing slopes are more favorable to forest cover and the encroachment by forest cover or undesirable brush species is more likely.

The best practices of grassland establishment and management should be used; the importance of their use cannot be overemphasized.

In converting forest to grassland, man is working against nature. A mili-

tant brush, fern, and moss growth is ever ready to take over the site. Hazards of loss of soil fertility and soil erosion are high under the characteristic high precipitation of the north Pacific coast region. Failure to establish grassland not only is personal loss but it also means loss in soil fertility, probable damage to watersheds, and the creation of a formidable barrier to bringing about either a forest or grassland cover.

Land classification is sorely needed to provide guidance to opportunities for successful conversion of forest to grassland. Facts upon which to classify lands are, however, lacking. Further research bearing on this subject is critically needed.

GRASSLAND IN WESTERN WASHINGTON

E. J. KREIZINGER, ALVIN G. LAW

WESTERN WASHINGTON, that area west of the summit of the Cascades between Canada and the Columbia River, was almost entirely covered with forest when the first settlers arrived. The trees, large and dense, indicated soils of high fertility and an abundance of rainfall. Now the agricultural land is made up of cleared river valleys, tide flats sweet enough to support crops, and a little level upland. Only small areas of potentially good agricultural land remain undeveloped.

The area is approximately 125 miles wide and 325 miles from north to south, embracing 15,894,000 acres; only 2,264,000 acres, or 14.3 percent of this area, is in farms, the average farm having 46 acres. Of the 770,000 acres of cropland, two-thirds is used for hay and pasture; 1,060,000 acres of other land grows pasture and hay. Thus, 67 percent of the land in farms and 67 percent of the cropland produce forage crops.

In 1945 there were 213,000 dairy cows, 170,000 beef cattle, 27,500 sheep, more than 7,000,000 chickens, and approximately 600,000 turkeys in western

Washington. The dairy cows produce about 160,000,000 gallons of milk annually. In 16 of the 19 western Washington counties, dairying is the most important agricultural industry.

The remaining 255,000 acres of cropland produces vegetables, berries, soft fruits, nuts, flower bulbs, and vegetable seed. Several counties grow a fairly large acreage of oats.

Western Washington, like other Pacific coast areas, has a maritime climate. The average January temperature varies from $32°$ to $40°$ F.; the July temperature varies from $54°$ to $66°$. Except during July and August, the relative humidity is high. Approximately 70 percent of the precipitation comes during the fall, winter, and early spring. The average precipitation received during the growing season, April to September, ranges from 6 inches to approximately 18 inches. Rainfall in July and August is insufficient to support grassland vegetation, except in low subirrigated valleys. During the remainder of the growing season enough rainfall is usually received to keep grass and other forage crops growing vigorously. The lowest average annual rainfall is 17 inches at Sequim, on the leeward side of the Olympic Mountains; the highest precipitation, 140 inches, is recorded at Wynoochee Ox Bow on the windward side of the Mountains. The average over the farming area is 35 to 45 inches.

The growing season is about 180 days in the area adjacent to the Cascade Range and more than 260 days in the area close to the Pacific Ocean.

Two groups of soils have developed: The Pedalfers, in which iron compounds accumulate and which are commonly found in the forested regions of the State, and the Interzonal soils.

The representatives of the Pedalfers group west of the Cascades usually do not have a definite sesquioxide accumulation layer, but are characterized by the presence of considerable quantities of iron pellets throughout the entire profile. These "shot" occur both in soils developed from glacial material and in those developed from bedrock. The reaction of the soils west of the Cascades ranges from pH 4.5 to 6.5. The average value for more than 300 samples was found to be pH 5.9. These soils are of intermediate fertility. There is seldom any calcium carbonate present in the parent material and no accumulation of this material occurs in the profile.

Prairie soils occur in western Washington under a variety of rainfall conditions. Two extensive prairies are found on the Olympic Peninsula under an annual rainfall of 120 inches. Others occur in regions with only 17 inches of annual rainfall. Some of these soils, but not all, occur on extremely gravelly substrata. These areas aptly illustrate the power of the vegetative factor in a region of similar rainfall and temperature conditions since the soils produced on the prairies are markedly different from those in the adjacent forested areas.

In the vicinity of Mount St. Helens, extensive areas are covered with pumice. The shallow soils support a heavy forest growth; the soils are only a few inches thick and are light gray in color, with a peculiar fluffy structure. Brown staining along root channels extends to depths of nearly 5 feet, but the material a few inches lower is practically unweathered.

Nearly every major stream flowing from the Cascades contains considerable quantities of gray glacial flour derived from active glaciers on the higher mountain peaks. This material, together with local alluvium, is deposited in the lower river valleys and results in soils of exceptionally high fertility. These gray alluvial soils support some of the most successful farming enterprises in the State. In the southwestern part of the State, several river systems have produced alluvial soils without glacial flour, causing the dominant color in such areas to become dark brown and resulting in soils of somewhat lower fertility. It is a notable fact that the Columbia River, the second largest river system in the United States, has deposited only minor areas of recent alluvium, and soils from this source are of minor importance.

Within these two groups of soils a wide variety of types occurs, varying as to structure, texture, substrata, and conditions of drainage. The inherent fertility of the soils varies markedly and has exerted considerable influence on the crops that can be grown in western Washington.

The use of subterranean clover, alta fescue, orchardgrass, perennial ryegrass, meadow foxtail, Ladino clover, and big trefoil have done much to increase the production of pastures and hay meadows in western Washington. There are still large acreages which can be seeded to these species. Forage crops are much less specific with regard to their response to various soil types than they are to moisture relationships. Experimental evidence and experience of farmers demonstrate that species are distributed through the area on the basis of the water level in the soil when it is at a maximum. Thus it is more important to know the minimum depth to the water table during the year than it is to know the soil type in determining the species to be seeded. The fertility level of the soil will influence the production but has little influence on choice of species.

Establishment of Pastures

The establishment of adapted, high-yielding species and mixtures for hay and pasture production is of primary concern in western Washington. It follows, also, that the maintenance of these stands at high levels of productivity is an essential part of the forage program.

A good seedbed is of primary concern in establishing forage crops. Performance of pastures or hay meadows will depend largely on careful and thorough seedbed preparation. Small-seeded crops, such as alfalfa or the perennial grasses, are best established on a firm, fine-textured, moist seedbed. Packing the seedbed will bring the soil particles into close contact with the small seeds. This will result in good germination because of rapid moisture absorption. A desirable seedbed can best be fitted on land that has been cropped to annual or intertilled crops the year before planting. When permanent pastures or meadows must be reseeded, it is advisable to grow an annual or intertilled crop on the area before attempting reestablishment of the perennial crop.

Early spring seeding is recommended for the perennial grasses and legumes. The most satisfactory method of preparing a seedbed is to plow the area in late summer or early fall, leaving it rough over winter. Cultivation should begin as early as possible the following spring and the soil should be worked sufficiently to destroy any weeds on the area. Two or three cultivations usually will be needed to kill existing weeds; this will leave the seedbed in the proper condition for seeding. Additional cultivations may delay seeding to such an extent that summer drought may reduce stands.

It is recommended that the ferti-lizers be applied before the seeding. If phosphate and potash fertilizers are needed for maximum production, 200 to 300 pounds of treble superphosphate applied before seeding time and worked into the surface of the soil will get the plant food into the root zone where it is absorbed by the plants. The application of 20 pounds of actual nitrogen before seeding is important, particularly on lands of low fertility. Only a few areas have been shown to be deficient in potash; phosphates have been found to give a good response throughout western Washington for maximum production of legume species. Nitrogen fertilizer is necessary for maximum production of the grass species.

It is recommended that most of the species be seeded in the spring while there is sufficient moisture in the soil to insure germination and establishment. The exception to this is on light, sandy soils where drought conditions may develop rapidly. On these soils, early fall seedings may be desirable.

Subterranean clover, likewise, is an exception to the rule of spring seeding. It is a winter annual that does well on the drier sites in western Washington. The most successful stands have been obtained by planting in September or early October, although some farmers have been successful in establishing stands very early in the spring, seeding not later than March 1.

Whenever possible, a drill should be used for seeding the new stands. Drilling insures a uniform depth of planting, prompt emergence, and the development of a smooth, even sward. Less seed is necessary to get a good stand when a drill is used. Broadcasting is still practiced, especially in the smaller fields where the use of a drill or other large farm machinery is not possible. When seed is broadcast, every precaution should be taken to cover the seed very lightly.

New stands should be managed to reduce competition from weeds to a minimum. One or two mowings the first year are usually necessary to control the annual weeds that usually occur in new forage seedings. It is recommended that the new forage seedings be mowed early in the fall to utilize the forage produced. Grazing is not recommended as the young forage plants are not well enough established by the end of the summer growing season to withstand even moderate grazing.

The use of fertilizer is one of the most important factors in good management of older meadows and hayfields. Phosphates are necessary for maximum legume production, while nitrogen stimulates the grasses. Yearly applications of 100 to 200 pounds of treble superphosphate and 40 to 60 pounds of actual nitrogen per acre are recommended. The nitrogen is usually applied in three equal applications, in March, May, and September. Split applications of nitrogen are particularly advisable when irrigation is practiced.

Some soils are slightly acid, and 2 to 4 tons of lime to the acre have given economic returns. Boron is necessary in most of the alfalfa-producing areas of western Washington. Applications of 50 to 60 pounds of borax an acre on heavy soils and 30 to 40 pounds on light soils will supply the needs of the alfalfa plants for boron.

Keeping the perennial pastures in a high state of production in the years following establishment is important. Portions of perennial plants, usually the roots and crown, remain alive over winter. Even during the dormant period these living parts need some food material. The first growth in the spring must come from food stored in the roots. Unless perennial plants are given a chance to store food during the late fall, they may not survive the winter, or, at best, spring recovery will be slow. As a result, yields the following year will be low and in some cases stands may be so reduced that reseeding may be necessary. It usually is necessary for perennial plants to have a month of growing weather without grazing before the first killing frost to store sufficient food in the roots for use during the winter period.

The plant is the only criterion of the time to start the grazing season. Vegetation in the pasture should be at least 5 or 6 inches tall before grazing starts in the spring. If this general rule is followed, there will be little danger of overutilizing the pasture. The date on which the plants will reach this height will depend upon the growing season each year.

The grazing load should be adjusted according to the plan of grazing and the productivity of the pasture species. During the spring when lush, heavy growth occurs, the grazing load can be considerably heavier than during the dry period of the summer. It is desirable to vary the number of animal units according to the productivity of the pasture crop. If such adjustments are impossible, then the excess spring production should be preserved in a silo.

Rotational grazing is recommended for western Washington. The grazing load should be regulated to use the available forage during the length of time that the animals are in each division of the pasture unit. Normally it requires about 30 days from the time animals are removed from a unit before there is sufficient regrowth again to support grazing. This means that with a three-unit pasture, the animals will be on each unit 15 days and each unit will have about 30 days in which to make regrowth. In actual practice the days on each unit should be determined by growth of the herbage and the number of animals on the pasture.

Irrigation

One of the best means of increasing the production of pastures is by irrigation. July and August are dry, and, without irrigation, pasture and meadow vegetation becomes dormant during this period and normally fails to recover until late September. Experimental results and the experience of farmers indicate that forage production can be increased from 25 to 50 percent with irrigation. Sprinkler irrigation is adapted to most of the agricultural area in western Washington. It is admirably suited to the rather rough terrain and the only limiting factor is the water supply. It is necessary to obtain a permit from the department of hydraulics at Olympia to use water from any stream or well for irrigated cropland.

Weeds are a constant problem. The best control is to prevent their entrance into the pasture by using clean seed and by eradicating the weeds from the land before the seeding is made. But if weeds are present, they can be reduced by proper fertilization of the pasture, by regulation of the grazing load to favor the forage species, and by periodic clipping to prevent weed seed production.

Hay and Silage

The safest time for making hay in western Washington is during July and August. High humidity and considerable precipitation during the remaining months of the growing season makes proper curing of hay most difficult. In western Washington, the first hay crop is usually ready to be cut the latter part of May or early June, months of rather high rainfall. To put up hay successfully in May or June, it is necessary to watch weather conditions closely and take advantage of the relatively few days of good drying weather. Progressive farmers in Washington have adopted the plan of utilizing the early, lush growth in the spring as silage or pasture, making hay during July or August.

Barn drying of hay is receiving attention, but results of experiments with it here are not conclusive. Mow drying with forced ventilation, mow drying with natural ventilation, and stack drying with natural ventilation have been suggested as solutions to the problem of curing hay during the spring months when adverse weather conditions are likely to be encountered. These methods are expensive and more nutrients and vitamins are lost than when the forage is preserved as silage.

Research workers are attempting to develop late-maturing types of forage crops that will develop to the hay stage in July. Such crops as Montgomery red clover and late strains of orchardgrass and timothy offer considerable promise of success.

Grass silage is probably the most satisfactory solution to the problem of hay drying. Dairymen are finding that grass silage can replace from 60 to 75 percent of the hay required for feeding milk cows during the dry summer period as well as during the winter. Excellent grass silage can be made during the spring months, thereby utilizing excess forage production that might otherwise be wasted or lost. Early clippings from hay meadows put into the silo make it possible to take off a cutting of hay during August when the hay will dry readily out-of-doors. More feed can be stored in less space and at less expense. The forage is cut when it contains the greatest amount of digestible proteins and minerals. Preservation is thus accomplished without loss in feeding value from rains, shattering of leaves, and bleaching that usually accompany hay making.

Silos of wood staves, plywood, tile, brick, or concrete staves have proved satisfactory. Because grass silage is heavier than corn, silos may require additional strengthening to withstand the pressure developed when they are filled. One important point is that the silo must be airtight. This may mean straightening and tightening the hoops, painting the exterior, and creosoting the interior of wood-stave silos, or pointing up the tile, brick, or concrete silos. The inside of the silo should be checked every year to be sure that weak spots are repaired before they develop into serious structural weaknesses.

Trench silos have been used extensively in western Washington on small farms that cannot afford the more expensive upright or pit silos. Trench silos are quite satisfactory for small farm operators who do not have sufficient livestock to justify a larger silo.

757150°—48——39

A good-quality grass-legume silage can be made without adding a preservative if the wilting method is used to bring the forage to the proper moisture content before ensiling. Freshly cut legumes and grasses usually contain about 80 percent moisture. If this forage material is allowed to wilt in the swaths for a few hours until the moisture content is between 60 and 70 percent, it will make excellent silage. Harvesting should be done with special equipment built for handling the heavy green material. The wilted forage can be raked with a side-delivery rake, picked up with a field chopper, chopped, and blown into wagons.

An alternative method is to use a heavily built hay loader to pick up the green hay and load it on wagons for hauling to the silo, where it is chopped with a stationary cutter. Under farm conditions it is sometimes impossible to wilt the crop to the proper degree. If so, preservatives like molasses or ground cereal grains are recommended; at least 60 pounds of molasses or 200 pounds of ground cereals should be mixed with each ton of material as it is blown into the silo. Grass silage should be chopped in ¼-inch lengths to facilitate uniform packing and insure better preservation. The silage must be thoroughly packed to exclude air pockets and reduce spoilage. A dairy cow can eat up to 75 pounds of this feed a day. Vitamin D may be lacking in grass silage, and it is a good plan to supplement the ration with irradiated yeast during winter months.

There are approximately two million acres of nonrestocking timberland in western Washington. This vast area is not restocking, primarily because of continued burns and the failure to leave seed trees when the logging operation took place. A small part of the land has a suitable soil and satisfactory topography to make it feasible to develop an economic livestock unit. The places that are adjacent to existing farms can be developed for use as a supplementary pasture. Successful development of pastures on cut-over land depends upon the destruction of the existing vegetation. Fall burning to provide a seedbed, followed immediately by a broadcast seeding in the ashes with a recommended mixture, has given successful establishment. Proper management of the new stand insures a supplemental pasture.

THE USE OF LOGGED-OFF LAND

H. B. HOWELL

MILLIONS of acres in the Pacific Coast States are timberlands which man and fire stripped of trees and left desolate. How to use this land well has been a challenge and a problem for a long time—a problem that the Oregon Agricultural Experiment Station and three other agencies started to solve in 1936. To study the seeding, grazing, and management of logged-off and burned-over lands, the station leased a fairly typical area in northwestern Oregon. The methods of procedure and the first findings are of wide application and value.

But before considering them one should know something about logged-off lands and the coastal counties of Oregon and Washington.

Timber once occupied most of this area. In the past 75 years the agricultural land now in production has been cleared of the forest growth with heavy expenditures of time and money. These agricultural lands now consist largely of the valley floors and more accessible low-lying foothills. The proportion of lands cleared of native growth is still low; the rest is in timber or logged-off or burned over.

Along the coast of Oregon and Washington most of the virgin stands of timber have already been logged. The original stands of timber consisted mostly of Douglas-fir, western hemlock, spruce, western red cedar, with smaller amounts of other species. These trees were mostly large, ranging from 3 to 8 feet or more in diameter. The logging methods used on most of the area, until recently, were of the high-lead type, quite destructive of the smaller trees. After the logging of an area was completed, generally the slashing—everything that was left— was burned.

About 95 percent of the agriculture of the coastal area is of the grassland type and is utilized largely by dairy cattle and to a lesser extent by beef cattle and sheep. Some grain, principally oats, is grown for hay but very little for threshing. Farmers are increasing permanent grass seedings for pasture, silage, and hay.

The production of grass and legume seed has been a regular crop for the past 15 years and is increasing in importance. The principal grass seeds grown include Astoria bent, Seaside bent, Chewings fescue, and *Lotus Major* or big trefoil.

Other agricultural activities in the coastal area include poultry raising, bulb growing, cranberry growing, and fur farming.

Practically all of the soils of the coastal area are acid in reaction and of fairly open texture. In their native state they are rather high in organic matter, although on the logged-off lands this organic matter is destroyed many times in the "slashing" burn or subsequent fires. Surface erosion is slight on these open soils but leaching due to the heavy rainfall is serious and maintenance of soil fertility is a major problem. Acidity varies from pH 4.7 to pH 5.5. The principal soil type is Melbourne silt loam, with some Olympic silt loam.

The topography generally is rough and broken, except for the valley floors. In many places the Coast Range reaches almost to the ocean.

The altitude ranges from sea level to about 2,000 feet; a few peaks rise to 3,500 feet. The values for other than grassland agriculture are chiefly for timber production.

The climate favors grassland agriculture. Rainfall on the 800-mile coast line of Oregon and Washington ranges from about 50 inches to 130 inches annually and would average about 75 inches. Most of this comes in winter months; in most areas the average precipitation in July, August, and early September is less than an inch a month—not enough to support maximum production. Temperatures are never extremely high or low. Temperatures seldom exceed 90° F. and generally do not go much below 20°. The frost-free period varies from 200 to 250 days.

. The possible use of logged-off or burned-over lands has attracted farmers from the time of the earliest settlers, who ranged a few head of dairy cows on the native feeds on these lands as they slowly broke or cleared a farm out of the forest and stumps. This was followed in later years by seeding chaff from the haymow, then by various burn mixtures prepared by seedsmen and made up too often mostly of light seeds, weeds, and short-lived grasses. Later, seedings were made of timothy, rye-grasses, and white clover. On the newly burned areas such seedings produced very well for a few years but then fell off, and weeds and brush became the dominant cover.

The real problem of these logged-off lands emerged about 1935, when assessed valuations fell rapidly in many coastal counties in the face of increasing demands for roads, schools, relief, and other purposes. Much of the land paid taxes on an assessed value of $200 to $300 an acre before logging; after logging, it was allowed to become tax-delinquent, and thousands of acres came into the ownership of the counties through tax foreclosures.

These lands for the most part grow another crop of timber in 75 or 100 years—if fire is controlled. Fire is the greatest enemy of the reproduction of trees. It is feared alike by the forester, farmer, soil conservationist, and city dweller. Fire under normal weather conditions is usually stopped by the efficient protection service provided by National, State, and local agencies. But fire under abnormal conditions of low humidity and high wind can be stopped only by changes in weather conditions. The Tillamook fire of 1933, which burned billions of feet of timber, was such a fire. Much of the Tillamook area burned again in 1939, and again in 1945. Very little natural reproduction occurs in areas of repeated burns.

Those who work on the problem of grasses on these logged-off lands feel that one of the major things that can be done to prevent such fires is to have grassland strips or firebreaks 1 to 2 miles wide, fenced, and closely grazed. These grassed areas should run north and south, because the bad fires occur during periods of east winds and low humidities. Such seedings of grass should be made on the lands of better topography and spaced from 10 to 25 miles apart. Besides assisting in fire control, these strips would furnish forage for livestock and develop taxable income. The seedings if properly made would also help control bracken fern, which frequently invades areas repeatedly burned.

Northrup Creek

For its study of these problems, the Oregon Agricultural Experiment Station leased 1,280 acres which had come into the ownership of the Clatsop County Court after it had been logged. The land is in the eastern part of Clatsop County on Northrup Creek in the Nehalem River watershed. The soil, mostly Melbourne silt loam, resembles most of the forest soils. The acidity varies from pH 4.8 to pH 5.4. The contour is rough and broken; two-thirds of the seeded area has a slope of 30 percent or more. The annual precipitation averages about 75 inches, but from June to mid-September rainfall is less than 1 inch a month.

The timber crop, harvested at various times between 1923 and 1936, consisted largely of Douglas-fir and western redcedar 2 to 8 feet in diameter. At the time of seeding to grass, approximately 14 percent of the ground area was covered by logs and stumps, so that mechanical methods of seeding and applications of commercial fertilizers and lime were impractical.

In the fall of 1936 about 500 acres was seeded to various mixtures; some 40 acres was seeded in 1-acre tracts with separate species and mixtures. The Oregon Agricultural Experiment Station, Clatsop County Court, the Oregon State Board of Forestry, and the Soil Conservation Service entered into cooperative arrangements for the experiments. The management of the project is under the experiment station.

The entire area was burned over on September 24, 1936. On approximately two-thirds of the area this was the first fire. The rest had been burned in 1928.

A heavy ash on the ground made the seedbed light and fluffy. Seedings were made from October 20 to November 11, 1936—about a month too late, according to later experience. At the time of seeding it was felt that the principal problem would be to get and maintain a sod cover as rapidly as possible, so four main mixtures were seeded; the sod formers were the only variable. These sod formers were Astoria bentgrass, Highland bentgrass, Kentucky bluegrass, and a mixture of these three.

The general mixture was made up of: Common ryegrass, 4 pounds; perennial ryegrass, 3 pounds; orchardgrass, 2½ pounds; Chewings fescue, 2 pounds; timothy, 2 pounds; white clover, 2 pounds; alsike clover, 1 pound; Highland bent or Astoria bent, 1 pound, or the Kentucky bluegrass, 2 pounds.

This mixture was seeded at the rate of 10 to 12 pounds an acre by hand. The seed cost $1.60 an acre; labor for seeding cost 40 cents an acre. A man seeded 10 acres in 8 hours.

All grasses and legumes in the mixtures were seeded in individual acre plots in the nursery; in addition, acre plantings were made of winter bluegrass, Alta fescue, meadow foxtail, superior reed canarygrass, Akaroa strain New Zealand orchardgrass, creeping red fescue, hop clover, and hairy vetch.

Good stands of all the grasses are obtained, but most of the legumes seeded were killed by frosts.

In 1938 plot seedings were made of broadleaf birdsfoot trefoil, big trefoil, sub clover, and burnet. Many plantings of the legumes have been made since.

About 700 acres were put under fence in 1937, and later divided into fenced pastures of 40 to 80 acres. In 1937 the pastures were grazed by cattle, and since 1938 by cattle, sheep, and goats. Some pastures are grazed exclusively by sheep, others exclusively by cattle, and others by both cattle and sheep at various times. Rotation and deferred grazing is practiced. Goats are used for brush control as needed.

The annual grazing season is about 8 months for cattle and 9 months for sheep; supplemental feeding is necessary the rest of the year. The cattle operation, with grade Herefords, is on the basis of the sale of weaner calves in the fall, with replacement heifer calves retained to maintain the herd. The sheep operation, with grade Romneys, is largely on the basis of the sale of wool and yearlings. We try to utilize most of the forage without overgrazing.

Some pastures are allowed to reseed each year. The number of cattle carried on the 700 fenced acres has averaged 50 to 60 cows and their calves, 20 to 25 yearling heifers, and the necessary bulls. Calf crops have averaged 85 percent weaner calves in the fall. An average of 150 to 175 ewes with lambs are carried, about 100 yearlings, and the necessary rams. Lamb crops average about 90 percent. About 50 head of Angora goats keep brush down.

During the 10 years that have passed since seeding, a number of observations have been made on the ability of the various species to survive under the prevailing high rainfall and the acid soil conditions.

In general, the yield of forage has gradually decreased because of a reduction in soil fertility, due partly to the dying out of some of the shorter lived grasses that originally produced higher yields and partly to failure of the original legume seedings. The legume seeding failed because of the original loose-ash seedbed, fall instead of spring seeding, and lack of adaptability of white and alsike clover.

Results

Of the original seedings some of the grasses and legumes are almost entirely gone, among them common rye, timothy, Kentucky bluegrass, common orchardgrass, tall meadow oatgrass, winter bluegrass, hairy vetch, and alsike clover. Others that are still growing (but not so well as at first) include English ryegrass, Akaroa orchardgrass, meadow foxtail, superior reed canarygrass, and sub clover. The plants that have survived include Astoria bentgrass, Highland bentgrass, Chewings fescue, creeping red fescue, Alta fescue, birdsfoot trefoil, big trefoil, white and hop clover, and burnet.

Big trefoil so far is the outstanding legume in these trials. We got good stands of it in existing grass sods; it thrives in the acid soils and in competition with the vigorous sod-forming bents and fescues. Clip plots of big trefoil and grasses gave nearly three times the yields of adjoining plots of grasses alone. Commercial plantings in the vicinity bear out our observations.

Birdsfoot trefoil also did very well. It was difficult to get started; stands take 4 or 5 years to get into production, but because of the deeper root system it survives drought better than lotus major. The broadleaf, erect-growing type has proved to be better than the narrow-leaf, prostrate type. From research work in progress we hope to get better information on how to establish birdsfoot trefoil.

Subterranean clover, or sub clover, which has shown promise in many parts of Oregon, has not done well under experimental conditions at Northrup Creek, perhaps because of the low amount of available phosphorus. The heavy covering of logs and stumps makes the cost of spreading fertilizer almost prohibitive. We are trying to find better ways to establish this crop.

The bent grasses, Chewings fescue and creeping red fescue, are now the dominant grasses. They maintain a heavy sod that effectively controls the native plants. Their yield is lower than that of the taller growing species, but nitrogen from the legumes might improve the grasses that are on the decline.

Alta fescue is one of the promising newer grasses. It is more palatable than the bents or other fescues; because of its deeper root system it stays green long after the other grasses dry up. Alta fescue also makes more growth in cold weather and makes a quicker regrowth after the livestock have grazed it.

White clover and hop clover have increased slowly on the experimental area under grazing; in pastures where deferred grazing is practiced they have increased more, but they are not nearly so aggressive as lotus.

Burnet, planted in 1938 on established sod, has done fairly well under grazing. It is palatable to livestock. It stays green all summer, and spreads by seeding when grazing is deferred.

Grass and Native Plants

The sod-forming grasses under grazing have effectively controlled native plants common to these lands. This is particularly true of seedings made on the slashing or first burn after logging. On the area seeded after the second burn and where brush had a start of 10 or 12 years over the grasses, there is more brush, but most types are under control. The principal brush plant not kept under control by the grass and grazing is vine maple.

The effect of grasses and grazing on the restocking of coniferous trees seems to depend on the type and intensity of grazing. On the ranges pastured exclusively by cattle very little damage is done to Douglas-fir but cattle browse the cedars and damage them. Ranges pastured by sheep or sheep and cattle together show most small trees damaged unless they are large enough so the livestock cannot reach the growing leader tip. Angora goats damage severely all coniferous types; about the only species not held under control by them are vine maple and red alder.

Bracken fern has been very effectively controlled or reduced by seedings of sod-forming grasses and big trefoil. This control has been of great help in reducing the fire hazard during the summer months.

The effective control of brush plants and the removal by grazing or grass competition of the native plants has clearly shown their value as an effective firebreak to help in controlling the disastrous fires that occasionally sweep these cut-over lands.

For the first 5 or 6 years after seeding, the carrying capacity of these lands was about an animal unit for each 5 acres for an 8 to 9 months' pasture season, or a cow and her calf on 5 acres, or ewe and lamb on 1 acre. With the taller growing short-lived grasses dying out, however, about 7 acres is now needed for an animal unit.

Calves born in March or April average 450 to 475 pounds at weaning time in October. Cattle have uniformly made better gains than sheep and have proved more profitable.

Experience on the Northrup Creek project and elsewhere indicates that proper maintenance and management of grasses seeded on logged-off lands requires fencing. A common rule in this area is that in developing such a range the operator should plan on spending about as much for fencing as is spent for seed and seeding. Only by proper fencing can proper utilization be secured and the native species controlled. The use of bulldozers to remove logs and brush from the fence rows and mechanical post-hole diggers or drivers materially cuts costs. No attempt is made to remove the large stumps from the fence rows. On most areas plenty of cedar for fence posts is available along or near the fence rows. Fencing also reduces costs of herding and gathering livestock, and cuts down losses from straying.

Costs

No attempt will be made here to estimate costs of a home ranch for winter-feed production except to say that 30 to 40 acres of tillable land capable of growing good crops of hay or possibly silage should be available for each section of 640 acres of seeded grazing land.

The costs of range development in the coastal logged-off and burned-over region of western Oregon and Washington would be much higher now than in 1936 to 1938, when most of the Northrup Creek experimental area was developed. The costs of developing a practical commercial operation (aside from the experimental angles) in 1936–38 were approximately these, in dollars per acre: Land, $1.00 to $2.50; seed, 10–12 pounds, $1.60; seeding labor, 1¼ acres per man-hour, $0.40; fencing, $2.00; structures (corrals, cabin, and such), $2.00; livestock for stocking, $20.00.

These costs would vary greatly depending upon the size of the operation, location of the home ranch, shrewdness of operator, and other factors that have a bearing on management.

We cannot make a general recommendation for a seeding mixture that would be adapted to all the varying conditions for an area extending some 800 miles north and south and nearly 100 miles wide. On the basis of experimental work carried on so far and observations of plantings by farmers and nurseries maintained by county agricultural agents in many counties, a few mixtures might be given for areas similar to those near the Columbia River.

For areas of Melbourne or Olympic soils recently logged and not burned more than twice, a mixture of the following grasses and legumes should be used: Perennial ryegrass, 3 pounds; Alta fescue, 3 pounds; orchardgrass (Akaroa strain), 2 pounds; creeping red fescue, 2 pounds; white clover, 1 pound; big trefoil, 1 pound.

Seeding is best at the rate of 10 to 12 pounds an acre, preferably in early spring, from February 15 to March 15 at elevations below 1,500 feet and from March 1 to April 1 for elevations above 1,500 feet.

For lands heavily infested with bracken fern and burned-over three or more times in the past 15 to 20 years, the following mixture has given better results (many of these lands have comparatively few logs and stumps on them and occasionally some have been cultivated at some time): Alta fescue, 4 pounds; creeping red fescue, 3 pounds; big trefoil, 2 pounds; subterranean clover, 2 pounds.

The preferred seeding rate is 12 to 15 pounds an acre, also in early spring. Fertilizers, if ground cover and contour permit distribution, aid in establishing grasses and legumes on these lands. Nitrogen at the rate of 20 to 30 pounds actual nitrogen and phosphorus at the rate of 50 to 60 pounds phosphoric acid per acre pay dividends.

[Although this section, The Pacific Coast States, describes conditions and gives recommendations for this particular area, the reader will also find applicable facts and data in the regional chapters for adjoining areas.

Information of a more general nature is to be found under the headings: Soil: Grass: Conservation; Forage for Livestock; Storage of Forage; Grass and Rotations; The Range, A Major Resource; and others.

Those readers who wish to supplement the information given here on the management and utilization of grass in the Pacific Coast States should refer to the section, For Further Reference, where they will find an extensive list of published pamphlets and other material.]

OUR NEWEST FARMING COUNTRY

H. A. SCHOTH

WESTERN OREGON is part of the newest agricultural region in the United States. Farming there is less than a century old. Before that, it had nature's own grassland agriculture; a wide diversity of plants, used first by game and now largely by domestic animals. The earliest lands to be cultivated were the open prairie or semi-open prairie areas; now the major farm activities are many and varied but still are related to grassland agriculture— the production of general field crops, forage, grain, and seed; dairying; raising sheep, beef cattle, and poultry; horticultural crops; specialty crops, such as ornamentals and flowers, vegetables, hops, condiments, drug- and fiber-producing plants, and, more recently, growing trees in wood and timber lots.

The wide range of soil types can be grouped into five. The tidelands or coastal overflow lands, limited in extent, are subject to either high-ground water level or overflow at various times. They are relatively level and low, and are used most extensively for forage. They are natural grasslands because of usually high fertility and ample moisture, and are considered ideal for dairy farming. Where they can be cultivated, production can be increased. This land is relatively expensive but, for the most part, can be most profitably used for forage for livestock.

River-bottom lands, near larger streams above tidewater, may be subject to occasional overflows. They are usually sandy, silty, or semigravelly, low and level, and considered desirable for practically every type of crop suited to the section.

First benchlands above river bottom vary in composition, fertility, drainage, and crop-producing value. They are relatively level and low, and are used mostly for general farming.

Low-elevation hill lands are generally considered as the first series of low rolling hills above the first benchlands. Nearly all were covered originally with brush and trees, but much has been cleared. Some has remained in continuous cultivation, but some has been allowed to go back to native growth and various introduced plants and weeds. Some has been seeded to improved pasture plants. The soil is generally shallow and low in fertility. It washes badly unless well covered with vegetation. It is primarily pasture land.

High-elevation hill lands vary from 500 to 4,000 or more feet and are quite rough. Much is still covered with brush and timber; some has been cut over or logged off. Only a small part has been cultivated. The soil is mostly shallow and low in fertility for cultivated crops, but reasonably good for timber growth and pasture; it washes badly unless covered with vegetation and gets weedy after timber removal unless occupied by better plants. This land is of primary value for range pasture and reforestation. Some natural meadow areas, free from brush or timber, occur in this type.

Precipitation is mostly as rain—100 or more inches in the coastal area, 35 or 40 inches in the northern inner valleys, and 16 to 25 inches in the southern inner valleys. Eighty percent or more of the precipitation occurs from October 15 to June 1. The remaining period is dry, usually with only occasional, light rains except along the coast. In general, but to a lesser extent for the coastal areas, most forage-type growth occurs during the season of highest precipitation, especially in late fall, late winter, spring, and early summer. Winter growth depends largely on temperature conditions. During the dry period plant growth is checked materially. In recent years the use of new and improved grassland plants has helped to equalize seasonal production where summer irrigation is not available. One grass in particular, Alta fescue, has been of primary value in that respect. Long-lived perennials are of more value for the purpose than short-lived ones or annuals.

In coastal sections and in the northern part of the area between the Coast Range and Cascade Mountains, supplemental irrigation, mostly by sprinkling, is practiced. Farther south irrigation is mostly by furrow or flooding. Many persons find it strange that irrigation is done in sections where the precipitation is from 80 to 100 inches or more annually and still is practical. The practice is increasing in the coastal section because it supplies soil moisture during the summer when precipitation is lowest.

Temperatures in general are mild, seldom above 100° F. Plant growth is fairly continuous, therefore, except during occasional extremes of low and high temperatures, if soil moisture is adequate. Use of field or range is possible during most of the year, although in times when the soil is filled with water the use of the fields is not considered good practice. The growing season generally varies between 150 and 265 days.

Hay—Grass and Legume

Hay is necessary for satisfactory livestock production because it is used when other forms of forage are unavailable or short. Also, there is a good market for hay in places where it is not economical to make hay or it is difficult to cure it satisfactorily. The hay here, however, is of variable quality and composition.

Annual and perennial grasses are extensively used. The annuals are mostly cultivated, with the cereal grains predominating—winter and spring oats, winter and spring wheat, rye, winter barley, and beardless spring barley, Sudangrass, foxtail millet, and cheat. Some uncultivated annual grasses are also harvested for hay, with these being mixtures of species of fescue, bromegrass, hairgrass, oatgrass,

and others. The main cultivated perennials include reed canarygrass, common and perennial rye, Alta fescue, orchardgrass, timothy, tall meadow oat, Tualatin meadow oat, bentgrasses, redtop, sweet vernal, and velvet and meadow foxtail. Some uncultivated perennials harvested for hay are usually in mixture with other grasses and plants, and include quackgrass, blue wild-rye, the German velvetgrass, danthonia, mannagrass, tufted hairgrass, and barnyard grass.

The most common annual legumes are vetches and field peas. Of the vetches, Willamette, common, and Hungarian make up most of the acreage and tonnage. Some hairy vetch is used. Austrian Winter peas and spring peas are used for hay to some extent; the Austrians are grown in the valleys between the Cascade and Coast Range Mountains, and the spring peas are grown in the coastal section. Small amounts of crimson, sub, alsike, and hop clover are harvested for hay.

The perennial legumes used for hay include alfalfa, red clover, Ladino clover, and birdsfoot trefoil and wetland deervetch or big trefoil. Alfalfa is grown mostly in the inner valleys between the Cascade and Coast Range Mountains, without irrigation except in the southern part. Red clover is grown mostly in the northern intermountain area. Ladino is grown wherever soil moisture supplies are plentiful. The acreage of Ladino used for hay is small. The largest acreage of *Lotus,* mostly birdsfoot trefoil, is in the Rogue River Valley of southern Oregon. The wetland deervetch is most common in the northern coastal section.

Hay Mixtures

Approximately 75 percent of the hay in western Oregon is a mixture of grasses and legumes, often with other plants. The most common mixtures of annual hays are vetch and oats and peas and oats. Seedings of perennial legumes, relatively pure to begin with, soon become grassy or weedy; so, many alfalfa seedings are made in combination with desirable grasses for the particular location to reduce low-value grasses and weeds and improve quality and yield.

Separate mixtures of annual grasses and annual legumes for hay are seldom made. Mixtures of perennial grasses are common. The ones generally used are those that develop to the hay stage at about the same time. Perennial legumes are seldom mixed.

The tonnage of tame hay constitutes approximately 95 percent of the hay in western Oregon; only occasionally is any so-called wild hay made. Sometimes volunteer crops used for hay are called wild hay although it may contain 75 percent or more of cultivated plants.

It is said that western Oregon hay is the greatest conglomeration of plants possible to get together and that the quality is the poorest. It is true that a large number of plants are grown and used for hay, and the mixtures of plants, their varying dates of maturity, poor hay-making methods, and adverse weather conditions at times often make for low quality. Most of the hay is naturally cured. Some is artificially cured, but the methods are quite expensive and slow.

Most of the hay produced in western Oregon is used locally. The market demand is primarily for highest quality straight grain (oat), hay, vetch (Willamette or common) and oats, red clover, weed-free alfalfa, and clean grass cut shortly after blooming stage.

Considerable hay, mostly alfalfa, is shipped into the dairying sections from irrigated sections east of the Cascade Mountains in the Pacific Northwest. Such hay is usually of high quality and it costs more, but many dairymen say they have less waste in feeding and better production from it.

Pastures

Many regions consider pastures of primary and increasing importance. Pastures lend themselves to the widest diversification of agricultural possibilities. They are one of man's closest imitations of nature and their values are determined largely by working with nature.

In general, grasses are considered the backbone of pastures. For most of the world, this is probably true. The northern section of the Pacific region is adapted to a wide range of grasses suitable for pasture use, among them annuals, short-lived perennials, and long-lived perennials.

The annuals are both native and introduced. Most of the native species have disappeared, largely as the result of abuse by man-controlled procedures, primarily overgrazing, burning, and land cultivation. Another factor was the introduction of new species, many of which were so aggressive that they crowded out many native species.

The introduced uncultivated annuals are, in general, of little value in comparison to the cultivated ones. The primary cultivated ones include the cereal grains, Sudangrass, and common ryegrass. These are either seeded alone, used as nurse crops for longer-lived plants, or included in mixtures with longer-lived plants to reduce the period from seeding to initial utility.

Short-lived perennials may be called long-lived annuals. The native species are practically nonexistent. Introductions are few. Perennial ryegrass is the most common and most widely used. Timothy is in this category, not by choice altogether, but as the result of its life being shortened by disease infestations. Meadow fescue, while not used extensively, is in this class.

Long-lived perennial grasses are looked upon by most agriculturists as the choicest of pasture grasses. They are of wide adaptability and utility. Some are classed as weeds and are recognized as such.

Sod formers are of special importance in permanent pastures. Several are available for use here. The more common ones include the bents—Seaside, Astoria, Highland, and Colonial; fescues—creeping, red, and Alta; Kentucky bluegrass, German velvetgrass, and quackgrass. Of these, the bents and fescues are most commonly used. Kentucky bluegrass is not widely adapted. German velvetgrass and quackgrass are weeds so their use is discouraged. Some persons feel that the use of Highland bent should be discouraged because of its aggressiveness. Sod formers, which usually grow rather low, are of most value for pasture. Occasionally they are cut for hay. The yields are generally low.

The semi-sod-formers develop a relatively heavy sod but not a complete ground cover. They include redtop, velvetgrass, and timothy.

Bunchgrasses are extensively used for pasture purposes here. They fit in well in mixtures and are comparatively heavy hay producers. They include perennial rye, orchardgrass, tall meadow oat, Tualatin meadow oat, Chewings fescue, Harding, mountain brome, and meadow fescue. Among the grasses that may be considered as either sod formers or bunchy are Alta fescue and Chewings fescue.

Few grasses of primary economic value are adapted to low, wet lands in this section. Two, however, are widely used—meadow foxtail and reed canarygrass which are relatively good sod formers and good pasture producers. They grow under similar conditions, but do not grow well together. Seaside bent is used on occasion.

Legumes in Pastures

Legumes for pasture are always given a high rating for livestock utility. Their usually high palatability, nutritive value, and ability to improve make them valuable.

Legumes for pasture use in this section include annual, biennial, short-lived perennial, as well as the perennial legumes.

All the annual legumes of value for pasture are introduced. They include hop, sub, bur-, and crimson clovers; Willamette, common, hairy, woollypod, and Hungarian vetches; and winter,

rough, and spring field peas. All are cultivated, except hop clover; sub and bur-clover and roughpea are considered as semicultivated or cultivated until established, whereafter they increase without being under cultivated conditions. The others are cultivated except as they volunteer for varying periods.

The main biennial legumes are sweetclover, mostly white-flowered, and alsike clover. The acreage of sweetclover is small, partly because of prejudice against it and partly because of difficulty of production due to stem rot. The development of the Willamette variety, which is highly resistant to stem rot, may result in the increased use of sweetclover for pasture and other forms of forage. Alsike clover is not commonly used for pasture when seeded alone, except as supplemental pasture for short periods in the late fall of the year in which the stand was established, or early the following spring.

Red clover, being the primary one, is the leader of the few short-lived perennial legumes. It is naturally fairly long-lived; however, it is short-lived in this section mostly because of heavy plant damage by insects, particularly root borers.

Perennial legumes used for pasture are both native and introduced. The natives are mostly several species of wild peas and vetches, commonly referred to as wild peavine. Introductions include alfalfa, white and Ladino clover, birdsfoot trefoil, and big trefoil.

The native species have never been under cultivation. They occur most commonly in the higher hill lands in the Coast Range Mountains. Producing areas are usually small, scattered, and materially reduced in plant population by overgrazing. Their spread is slow and largely vegetative because seed production is small and wildlife consumes a large part of the seed.

Of the cultivated legumes, alfalfa, Ladino clover, and the two trefoils are now grown largely for dual-purpose forage use, as pasture, hay, and silage, and for seed. Birdsfoot trefoil is grown most extensively at present in the Rogue River Valley of southern Oregon under irrigation. Big trefoil is grown most extensively in the coastal area in Northwest Oregon and the North Willamette Valley. Both show promise of considerable expansion in production, primarily for pasture. White clover is grown primarily for pasture. Of the locoes, cotton and flexile show most promise and have indicated future possibilities for pasture use. Both are apparently nonpoisonous.

Mixtures for Pastures

Mixtures of plants, grasses and legumes particularly, are considered most satisfactory for pastures. In the northern part of the Pacific Region there are very few conditions or locations where combinations of grasses and legumes cannot be grown.

Because of the wide range of soil and climatic conditions, no one combination or mixture can be prescribed for this part of the Pacific Region. Each area usually requires individual attention; sometimes, even, several recommendations are needed for one farm or range area.

The ideal pasture mixture is a near 50–50 combination—from the production standpoint—of grasses and legumes. But that is seldom possible, particularly with legumes except under irrigation and other special conditions. Fertilization with phosphate is usually a factor in encouraging legumes.

Types of Pastures

Wild or so-called natural pastures occur in the northern part of the Pacific Region. In few cases are the plants native; most are annuals and of short-season utility, with grasses and weeds predominating. Not often have these pastures been improved; weeds and brush are increasing, the result of factors like overgrazing and burning. The improvement that has been made consists of cleaning up brush, spot seeding,

introduction of legumes (especially subterranean clover and hop clover in the area between the Cascades and the Coast Range Mountains, and birdsfoot trefoil, big trefoil, and subterranean, hop, and white clover in the coastal area), and some introduction of good cultivated grasses, including orchardgrass, Alta, Chewings, and red creeping fescue, and Highland and Astoria bentgrasses.

Most pastures are called dry-land pastures even though they are in relatively humid areas—this is because they are not irrigated. The more strictly dry-land pastures are in southern Oregon, where precipitation is relatively low. Fortunately, most pasture plants adapted to this section tolerate the rather dry soil conditions that prevail in summer, and, though production is low, the plants live over and as soon as moisture conditions become more favorable renew growth satisfactorily.

Irrigated pastures are increasing. In some drier areas irrigation is just about necessary for worth-while pasture and other crops, and has been practiced for many years; in other areas, where natural soil moisture is more plentiful except in summer, supplemental irrigation is increasing, particularly on perennial pastures. Irrigation is expensive and quality and quantity must be high to bring the largest possible net returns. Utilization of irrigated pastures by dairy animals has proved most profitable. Irrigated pastures should have a high percentage of legumes in their make-up. Ladino clover is the most commonly used legume; perennial ryegrass, orchardgrass, meadow fescue, Alta fescue, and meadow foxtail are also good.

Good management practices, after establishment of the grass, include: Sufficient plant population of the right kinds to produce maximum production; balance of grasses and legumes; vigorous growth, perhaps encouraged by fertilization; minimum of weeds; rotation or deferred grazing; clipping where utilization is not complete and it can be done; scattering of droppings where feasible; prevention of overgrazing; elimination of poisonous plants or keeping livestock from them; allowing natural reseeding at times on rough or uncultivated lands; prevention of fires unless to burn brush; and economical use of irrigation, where practiced.

The economics of pasture production and use depends on more or less accepted premises in this area as in other parts of the world.

In the past too many farmers considered land that was worthless for anything else usable for pasture—a conclusion perhaps partly true but usually leading to false economy. As a result altogether too much land is below its former productivity and not enough effort is being made to improve it. Fortunately, pasture is being given increased consideration as a regular crop that should produce at a profit commensurate with the values of the land used.

Range

Range here is mostly general uncultivated pasture land near the seat of farming operations, usually hill lands or semimountainous areas either open or timbered. Heavily timbered land may be considered as range; much of its forage being browse.

Nearly all the native range-land grasses and legumes have been replaced by introductions, many of which have adapted themselves and increased quite rapidly where conditions are favorable. Many weedy plants are found on such lands.

The productivity of natural range lands generally is low. Much of it has been badly abused by excessive overgrazing, brush and weeds have taken over, burning has occurred too often, and little effort has been made toward improvement.

Seeding of range lands, other than natural reseeding, is seldom done. Occasionally some spot seeding is done on small cultivated areas or small burns. On large burned-over areas fairly extensive seedlings are made occasionally, particularly where such areas are not too rough, where burns have been relatively clean, and where the areas are reasonably accessible.

Seed Production

The northern section of the Pacific Region, particularly western Oregon, has developed an extensive seed-production business, the result of good soil and climate, favorable financial returns to growers, good production, high-quality seed, and trained growers.

Kinds of grass seeds produced include common and perennial rye; Alta, Chewings, and red creeping fescue; orchardgrass, tall oatgrass, Tualatin meadow oat, bulbous bluegrass, Seaside, colonial, Astoria, Highland, and velvet bent; Harding, redtop, meadow foxtail, reed canarygrass, cheat, and Sudangrass, as well as timothy and the cereal grains. Seed is produced of several legumes—alfalfa; red, white, Ladino, crimson, sweet, hop, sub, and alsike clover; hairy, woollypod, Willamette, Hungarian, common, and purple vetch; Austrian Winter and Dixie Wonder field peas; and birdsfoot and big trefoil.

Seed production is a specialized phase of agriculture and methods vary according to varieties and place of production. Seed production requires suitable soil and climatic conditions for the particular crop; high-quality, clean seed; adequate equipment for growing and harvesting; freedom from weeds; knowledge of production; adequate storage and processing facilities; and satisfactory markets.

Practically all the plants grown for seed production are used for pasture. Their values differ greatly from the standpoints of palatability, nutritive value, and ability to stand pasture. Of the plants indicated, those of least value are purple vetch and winter field peas.

All the plants mentioned are usable for silage, an increasingly popular practice that makes possible relatively cheap feed, saves forage (during wet springs in particular) that otherwise might be lost, and makes most efficient use of many plants other than cultivated crops that are considered of little value as other forms of forage. It is particularly adaptable when combined with pasture programs during the spring flush growing season when there is often more pasture than can be used.

A high proportion of the Nation's seed of cover crops (primarily legumes, including the vetches, field peas, crimson clover, and common ryegrass) is produced in the Willamette Valley of Oregon.

Seed production fits well into rotations. It makes possible both short- and long-time rotations, alternating of grasses and legumes, reduction of pests and undesirable plant populations, increases organic matter, often reduces labor or production costs, makes possible dual use of crops and land, and quite often is a source of feed for livestock in the form of screenings.

The primary markets for field seeds produced in this area are domestic. The Southern States and California use a large part of the seeds of annual legumes and grass. The Middle West and Eastern States use a large part of the seed of the biennial and perennial legumes and perennial grasses. The Pacific Northwest itself uses a large tonnage of all of the seeds. During the war and after it, large shipments went abroad, but those markets for seed are dropping to a prewar basis. The seed-production industry must be kept stabilized; any increase in it should be on the basis primarily of domestic demands or of new and improved crops.

THE AUTHORS«« *H. A. Schoth has been a member of the Bureau of Plant Industry, Soils, and Agricultural Engineering since 1916. Stationed in Corvallis, Oreg., he has spent many years in studies of forage crops and diseases. He is a graduate of Oregon State College.*

M. W. Talbot has been engaged in cultivated-grassland and wildland surveys and research since 1913. He is associate director and in charge of range research at the California Forest and Range Experiment Station, United States Forest Service, and is stationed at Berkeley, Calif. He was educated at the University of Missouri.

A. W. Sampson has been engaged in research on grass since 1907. Dr. Sampson, a graduate of the University of Nebraska, is professor of forestry and plant ecologist in the Agricultural Experiment Station, University of California, at Berkeley.

B. A. Madson is the head of the division of agronomy, University of California, at Davis and Berkeley.

R. Merton Love is associate professor of agronomy in the University of California, at Davis.

Joseph F. Pechanec, a native of Idaho and a graduate of the University of Idaho, has been engaged in grazing and range improvement research since 1932. He is forest ecologist in charge of range research at the Pacific Northwest Forest and Range Experiment Station, Forest Service, Portland, Oreg.

E. J. Kreizinger is extension agronomist, Agricultural Extension Service, State College of Washington in Pullman. He holds degrees from the University of Nebraska and Kansas State College. He has taught in Washington State College, has been in charge of grass breeding there as assistant agronomist in the Bureau of Plant Industry, Soils, and Agricultural Engineering, and has been leader of seed-production work of the Washington Cooperative Farmers' Association in Seattle.

Alvin G. Law is assistant professor of farm crops in State College, Washington; besides teaching, he does research in grass breeding and pasture management. He has degrees in agronomy from Kansas State College and has also studied at the University of Wisconsin.

H. B. Howell has been superintendent of the John Jacob Astor Branch Experiment Station at Astoria, Oreg., since 1934 and in charge of the Northrup Creek Experimental Area since its inception in 1936.

Grasslands in Alaska

ENDLESS STRUGGLE FOR SUPREMACY

O. S. AAMODT, G. W. GASSER

THE AGE-OLD contest of grass can be seen readily in Alaska. Along old trails where horses have fed and where sled runners and wagon wheels have beaten down the moss, grass springs up. On hillsides where fire has destroyed the ground cover, fireweed comes first to flaunt a flaming defiance at all passers-by—then grass, sure and positive; in a few years the cerise of the fireweed is displaced by the quieter shades of green and brown. Other plants find it difficult to send roots through the sod covering of grass into the soil below, but willows and poplars, by an underground line of attack, extend their roots into the sod and send up sprouts, which in time grow into shrubs and trees and, by making shade and usurping water, kill out the grass. Abandoned fields clearly show this struggle for supremacy.

Which type of vegetation, moss, fireweed, grass, or willow will achieve dominance depends on several factors, but chiefly on climate and man. In interior Alaska just now the odds are in favor of grass. The climate is favorable. Grass can take any exigencies imposed by present-day weather, and thrive. To man, the other factor, the value of grass as a feed, as a bulwark against erosion, and as a soil improver is well known and generally appreciated.

In Alaska approximately one-fourth of all phanerograms (flowering plants) consists of grasses. This proportion changes southward, reaching a low of one twenty-fifth at the Cape. There is reason to believe that this proportion and area of grassland in Alaska has increased during the past 50 years, mainly because of fires that have destroyed more or less completely the original plant life. Also noteworthy is that among the species represented are many valuable grasses, such as bluegrasses, bluejoint, and fescues. The most extensive grasslands are made up of the coarser type of grass better suited for use as hay or silage than for grazing.

As a family, the legumes native to Alaska are widely disseminated, but are not so predominant as the grasses. In some small areas they are rather abundant; elsewhere only a few varieties are found in scattered locations. As a whole, they form only a small proportion of the forage plants of the Territory.

In their native habitat the grasses and legumes bear seed and propagate readily, but under cultivated conditions considerable difficulty has been encountered in germinating seed of either the native grasses or legumes. It has been found that close grazing or mowing for hay or silage year after year depletes the stand of the grasses and legumes. Also, the period during which the native grasses may be pastured or cut for hay with maximum yield and nutritive value is short.

Little can be said in favor of the horsetail, which occurs widely in grasslands and in grainfields. Once established, it is difficult to eradicate because of its underground manner of spreading by root stocks. It is not grazed appreciably by preference by cattle or horses. When cut, it is easily cured, becoming light and brittle. There is reason to believe that horsetail, besides having a high silicate content, contains some toxic property.

The extent of the grasslands in Alaska has not been fully determined. Various areas have been investigated and estimates made as to acreage in square miles, the character of the land, and the kinds of grass. These surveys were made by employees of the Alaska Experiment Stations while those stations were operated as insular stations under the direction of the Office of Experiment Stations of the Department of Agriculture. The accounts of these several surveys or investigations were published in the Annual Reports of the Alaska Experiment Stations. A partial list of other reports dealing with the grasslands is given at the end of this article.

The greater part of Alaska consists of high, jagged mountains, many of which are covered with snow, high plateaus, tundra plains, swampy stream valleys, gravelly and cobbly plains and slopes, and other landscapes where either soil or climate, or both, are unsuitable for any kind of crop production. In some of these landscapes, fair to good range could be had for perhaps 3 to 4 months in the year, but mostly these range areas are not associated with land suitable for growing feed crops necessary in the long winter.

Thus, the soil areas where agriculture can be carried out are small and scattered. Perhaps a rather large total of land could be farmed if the United States ever becomes desperate for land. For example, such land occurs along the Yukon, especially within the bend of the Yukon west of Circle, but any reasonable estimate of agricultural needs and prices for agricultural products severely limits the amount of land that can be considered suitable for agriculture within the foreseeable future. The good areas consist largely of young soils developed from stream alluvium or from stream alluvium covered with very fine wind-blown sand.

As early as 1898 investigations of the agricultural possibilities in Alaska were begun along the southern coast and westward along the Aleutian Islands. In the reports of these investigations frequent reference is made to the variety and abundance of the native grasses, whose value for hay and silage in feeding livestock was well known even at that early date. In some districts, as many as 40 varieties and species were found. Letters written in the same year from widely scattered points throughout the Territory indicate that the native grasses were widely disseminated, flourishing as far north as the Yukon River.

In the principal mainland areas, Matanuska, Tanana, and Kenai, agriculture consists chiefly of the production of potatoes and other vegetables and dairying, mostly on a limited scale as judged by standards of production and scope in the States. Some mixed-stock farming, principally in the Matanuska Valley, is in progress with hogs, poultry, sheep, goats, and a few beef cattle. The production of beef and dual-purpose cattle is limited on the Kenai Peninsula, but is slightly more extensive there than elsewhere on the mainland of Alaska.

Straight range livestock production now is limited to three ranches on the Kenai Peninsula, three on Kodiak Island, and one each on the islands of Sitkalidak, Chirokof, Unalaska, and Umnak. The production of range livestock in all parts of Alaska, particularly on the mainland, is restricted by the requirements for winter feed and the many problems involved in producing and preserving such feeds. It is pertinent, however, to note that cattle and sheep are produced on southwestern islands with little if any winter feed except that provided by grazing the narrow fringes of exposed grassland along the beaches during the winter.

The present high cost of land clearance on the mainland limits a more intensive grassland agriculture. Most of the cleared land is necessarily devoted to cash crops (potatoes and vegetables), for which the territorial requirements can be met without greatly expanding present production. Overproduction of those products in the future is destined to direct increased attention to the growing of dairy and beef cattle, sheep, goats, hogs, and poultry. A steady expansion in the acreage of cleared land is also certain to encourage the production of more forage crops and livestock. Diversification in these directions is necessary before a permanently successful system of agri-

culture can be established in Alaska.

The increased production and improved storage of better forage crops for winter feed in all agricultural areas would make it possible to increase greatly the present herds of beef cattle and sheep. This would also enable the livestock farmer to utilize the extensive areas of summer range adjacent to the principal farming areas and accessible by rail from them. Most of the livestock could be fed for a while on valley crops in the fall and then slaughtered for local consumption; only the breeding herd would then be wintered.

Another possibility for utilizing the extensive areas of summer range is to renew the earlier practice of shipping in steers by steamboat from the States, or by trucking them in over the Alaska Highway from Canada. The latter would be a shorter haul and more feasible, but requires special arrangements between Alaska and Canada.

PROBLEMS OF GRASS AND LIVESTOCK

O. S. AAMODT

A CONDITION having a vital bearing on beef production is the long feeding period anywhere in Alaska except in some of the islands of the Aleutian Chain and a coastal band on the western side of the Kenai Peninsula. However, many areas in the interior are as suitable climatically as some of the high ranges of the Western States. There also cattle must be fed from November through to May.

The production and preservation of nutritious forage crops for winter feed would stabilize greatly the grassland program in Alaska. Weather conditions are rarely satisfactory for producing well-cured hay. Native grasses are seldom cut at the proper stage of growth for best results. They are said to be lacking in food value when mature, and become weakened in vigor when cut or grazed annually.

The rough, hummocky nature of the

natural grasslands makes it difficult to mow the grasses for hay or silage. The old growth left on native grasslands hinders mowing, delays thawing, and retards new growth. Surface tillage offers possibilities for leveling hummocky grassland and for adding tame species to the native mixture. Preburning constitutes a practical means of removing old growth, lowering the frost level, and encouraging new growth, but if it is done at the wrong time it may result in a ground fire that will destroy most of the humus in the soil.

Native grasses, principally bluetop, are widely distributed in Alaska. They grow surprisingly fast and tall almost everywhere in the Territory except in the dense shade of forested areas; on extremely wet, swampy land; in the hummocky tundra covering of sedges, moss, and other plants that blankets, insulates, and holds the permanent ice layer near the surface, and in the high, rugged, and perpetually snow-covered mountains. Because most of Alaska falls in one or the other of these negative sites for grass production, extensive areas of open grassland occur only on the southwestern islands, on a part of the Kenai Peninsula, as well as on burned-over areas on the mainland. The native grasses increase rapidly and grow vigorously, however, wherever the better drained lands have their covering of trees cleared or tundra disturbed.

Bluetop, beach wild-rye, and other tall grasses are considered highly nutritious in the early stages of growth, but are reported to be seriously lacking in food value in the matured and cured stages of development. Chemical analysis of the forage collected in 1946, however, indicated that the plants compare favorably with the tall grasses of the States, except that some of the species in Alaska lack calcium and have only border-line values for phosphorus. The tall grasses of Alaska also lack the ability to recover from continuous grazing or cutting. Defects in the taller grasses are overcome somewhat by the presence of palatable legumes in many areas and by the occurrence of superior species of bunchgrasses, chiefly fescues and bluegrasses, at higher altitudes.

Many of the tame grasses and legumes are well adapted to conditions in Alaska and offer possibilities for producing nutritious forage greatly superior to the native plants. The more promising tame species include smooth bromegrass, the fescues, bluegrass, yellow-flowered alfalfa, alsike clover, mammoth red clover, sweetclover, and perennial vetch.

Very little is known about how best to establish, manage, and maintain these plants in Alaska. Most of these forage plants, like those in the States, lose much of their food value in late summer and fall.

The fescues are promising exceptions. Seed supplies of adapted strains are limiting factors for many of these

species, particularly the yellow-flowered alfalfa. Different sources of seed of a given species also vary widely in production and adaptation. The possibility of developing improved strains of the better forage species by intensive plant breeding and testing so far has received scarcely any attention. Little information is available as to the proper mixture of grasses and legumes to use for pastures on various types of soil.

Hardy varieties of wheat, oats, and barley thrive and usually mature in Alaska, and are often used with vetch or peas for bundle feed, hay, or silage. However, the cost of growing and producing these annual crops for feed purposes often greatly exceeds the cost of producing perennial grasses and legumes. Furthermore, the perennials usually complete their growth during the drier part of the season and can then be harvested more readily. It is much harder to harvest the grain-pea-vetch mixtures during the rainy fall season. The grain crops also often become badly infested with weeds, because they have to be planted early and weeds cannot be properly controlled in advance.

Very few plants definitely known to be poisonous occur in Alaska, although a few stock losses, possibly from larkspur and water hemlock, were reported in the Matanuska Valley and on the Kenai Peninsula. The grasses and forage crops of Alaska appear to be comparatively free of diseases. No field bindweed was observed in the Territory; quackgrass was about the only perennial weed difficult to eradicate in cultivated fields.

Mosquitoes, moose flies, and noseeums menace livestock production, especially in early summer. These pests are much less troublesome on extensive wind-swept areas of cleared land or on naturally open grassland than they are near trees and shrubs. The problems of parasite infestations and diseases of livestock and poultry are not nearly so serious as in the States.

The huge brown bear hinders successful livestock production on Kodiak

Island and to a lesser extent on the mainland at the high altitudes. The smaller black bear causes some trouble to livestock on the mainland. Wolves are an ever-present danger to calves and lambs on the higher and wilder ranges of the mainland, especially near Mount McKinley Park, where they are protected from hunters. Beaver that were transplanted on Kodiak Island have increased greatly. Their numerous dams have made sedge marshes of many grass-covered valleys and developed a maze of bogs that are unsuitable for cattle grazing.

Most students of agriculture in Alaska believe that farming is sure to continue and expand as a basic industry and that livestock must take a greater part in farming operations in the future if stability and success are to be achieved. While meat was the livestock product in demand in the early days, prompting the annual importation of beef animals, today the main emphasis is on dairying to supply fluid milk and on poultry to supply eggs.

Matanuska farmers are producing these two products almost to the exclusion of lamb, pork, and beef, except for slaughter of veal calves and discarded milk cows. Beef, pork, butter, cheese, and related products shipped in from the States have appeared to make local competition difficult.

The fact that grass grows abundantly in many areas south of the Arctic Circle lends assurance to the first assumption that cattle ranching could be carried on with a fair chance for success. Many chemical analyses give the lie to the charge that the native grasses of Alaska are not nutritious, that cattle would all but starve on a grass diet. Actual feeding tests from the silo and the haystack and on pasture show that native grasses have good food values comparable to similar grasses in the States.

A wide range exists in protein content of samples obtained from different localities. The contrast between the low values of samples obtained from the Fairbanks and Standard areas and the high values of those from the Circle

Hot Springs and Lignite areas, sampled at about the same time, is probably a reflection of stage of maturity. In other words, the rate of development varies with the area and its climate. The phosphorus content of the material collected at Fairbanks and Standard and of samples from a few other areas, while not showing any very extreme values, does indicate borderline or probably inadequate levels to meet minimum requirements for cattle and sheep. The variations in calcium values are the most remarkable, however, because grasses in the States seldom show deficiencies in that element. Values under 0.2 percent are ordinarily considered inadequate, and in that category were the samples from Fairbanks, Standard, Hurricane, Homer, and Kodiak. The bluetop growing at Circle appeared to be the highest in calcium; it also ranked among the highest in phosphorus and protein.

Cases of rickets in calves and sheep were seen, and it appears that the better informed farmers know that fish-liver oils are effective preventives of this trouble. The occasional deficiency of calcium and phosphorus in forages makes the feeding of vitamin D especially important. No evidence of vitamin A deficiency was obtained. Certainly during the summer there is little reason to suspect it. The hay-curing methods in use, however, probably result in excessive losses in carotene content.

The foremost need in Alaska's grassland development centers around the general winter feed supply—the growing, harvesting, and storing of forages. The making and storing of hay is poorly done in too many instances—it is generally cut too late and becomes weathered. Mow drying and the use of small portable driers require development and study. Silage-making machinery, silos, and silage preservation all need attention, along with choice of crops to be used. Much use has been made of a mixture of oats, field peas, and vetch as a hay and silage crop.

It is desirable to explore other crops,

both annuals and perennials. A beginning has been made in tests of varieties of small grains, peas, and other annuals; also of perennial grasses and legumes. More extensive test plantings of bromegrass, timothy, bluegrasses, fescues, clovers, alfalfas, and vetch are needed for use in summer grazing, hay, and silage experiments. Increased yields as well as increased feeding values should be sought in such studies. Few or no grazing tests have been made.

AGRICULTURE IN VARIOUS LOCALITIES

G. W. GASSER

SOUTHEASTERN ALASKA, or the Panhandle, is the narrow region closest to the States. Although the heaviest concentration of population is in this area, thus insuring a market, the natural conditions do not favor the livestock industry. Rainfall is heavy. It is made up mainly of heavily forested, rugged islands. The mountain meadows are mostly muskeg and moss. Predatory animals make the livestock industry somewhat hazardous. A number of river deltas and salt marshes on the mainland are the most favorable locations for possible livestock operations and limited grassland development.

Southwestern Alaska and the Aleutians include Kodiak Island and environs, the Alaska Peninsula, and the Aleutian Chain. In this area the Russians maintained some livestock during their years of occupation. Using Siberian stock, they apparently gave the stock little care. Winter feeding was usually not necessary, because of favorable weather conditions and the ability of the Siberian cattle to provide for themselves. As late as the turn of the century, strains of the Siberian stock were quite noticeable in some of the cattle in this region.

Perhaps the most romantic chapter in Alaska livestock history is written around Chirikof Island, southwest of Kodiak. In 1886 or 1888 (the records are not clear), a San Francisco company brought to this island one Shorthorn bull, two Shorthorn cows, two Jersey cows, and one Holstein cow. Sometime later, a Jersey bull was brought to this island. The purpose of this importation to isolated Chirikof Island was to establish a fresh-meat supply for the whaling vessels of the company operated in the Bering Sea and the Arctic.

Refrigeration units for ships had not been perfected at that early date, and fresh meat put aboard ship at San Francisco was either consumed or had spoiled by the time sailing craft or steamers had reached Alaskan waters. Scurvy, caused by the lack of fresh meat and fresh vegetables, was a constant problem for shipmasters. Therefore, the San Francisco company believed that by putting ashore enough basic stock to start a herd of cattle, the danger of scurvy, as far as its ships' crews were concerned, would be eliminated, and the Alaskan source of fresh beef would aid materially in its whaling operations.

Within a few years after the cattle were put ashore on wild, uninhabited Chirikof Island, the whaling industry declined and the San Francisco company abandoned the project. They also abandoned the cattle. This livestock roamed Chirikof Island and fared very well on the native bluetop grass and beach rye. The Army contracted with the present lessees of the island for the delivery of a large quantity of beef. At last report, no beef had been delivered. Contributing factors, as stated by Army officers, were the lack of harbor facilities at Chirikof and no protection from weather for a steamer, the lack of an abattoir or cold-storage facilities on the island, and the difficulty of rounding up the wild cattle, due to difficult terrain and lack of facilities. However, as far as raising livestock is concerned, there is concrete evidence that cattle will prosper and increase in this section of the Territory. It should also be stated that Chirikof Island is free of predatory animals.

Local ranchers and farmers brought cattle to Kodiak in 1914, following the eruption of Mount Katmai. The cattle population on the island increased considerably over the next two decades. But the greatest enemy of a successful livestock industry on Kodiak Island is the Kodiak bear, which is protected under the authority of the Alaska Game Commission, a branch of the Fish and Wildlife Service of the Department of the Interior.

The climate of Kodiak Island and nearby islands permits cattle to rustle for themselves throughout the year. Summer range is virtually limitless, but winter feeding of some quantity will be necessary if large cattle herds are to be maintained. Herds are not limited by the amount of beach rye and wild peas available for natural forage in winter, but problems of adequate cold storage, reliable transportation, access to market, and the status of the Kodiak brown bear in relation to livestock await solution before an unqualified endorsement can be given any large-scale projects on the island.

Sheep have been raised for a number of years on Sitkalidak Island, Unimak Island, Unalaska, Umnak Island, and even as far west as Adak Island in the Aleutians. These islands have large natural feeding grounds and a fairly good climate for sheep. Shelters are required during lambing seasons, and some feed and care must be provided when heavy snows cover natural range. Sheep raised in westernmost Alaska produce an excellent grade and quantity of wool and good meat.

The discovery of gold in the Fairbanks area in 1904 marks the beginning of livestock history in the interior of Alaska. Many cattle, sheep, and hogs were brought to the Fairbanks camp and elsewhere in the interior where markets for fresh meat existed. During the summer months, two routes were used for shipment—down the Yukon River by barge to Circle, then 160 miles by trail to Fairbanks, or from Valdez, on the coast, along a trail 370 miles north to Fairbanks. On either route, cattle lived mostly on the plentiful native grasses and forage. At Fairbanks, the stock would be fattened on native hay and such feed as might be available—usually at the cost of $100 or more a ton. The procedure was popular in the interior for a number of years. No attempt was made then to utilize the native grass in the development of a livestock industry near Fairbanks.

A herd of 23 bison was imported in 1927 from Montana and turned loose in the Big Delta country of the Tanana Valley; the herd has been given no attention since it arrived in the Valley. Today at least 400 head are said to be in the area. A small herd of the bison has migrated into the Copper River country and is also reported to be increasing. Natural grass has always been plentiful in the section, and water is ample for cattle operations. Vast swampy areas are a serious problem, though, because they are breeding spots for mosquitoes, which plague cattle in the lowlands in late spring and early summer. Mosquitoes are not so prevalent on hillsides and cleared land.

Because of the cold winters in the interior, most farmers in-feed their cattle from October 15 until May 1. A farm with a good southern exposure can be grazed longer in the fall and a little earlier in the spring than a farm on the valley floor. To insure plenty of feed, stockmen should plan on at least 7½ months of feeding each year; 2½ to 3 tons of hay is needed per head for range cattle, or, if silage is used, 8 or 9 tons per head.

As in the case of southwestern Alaska, the experience with livestock in south-central Alaska and the Kenai dates back to the Russian occupation. Cows of Siberian origin were maintained in the Russian villages on the Kenai Peninsula. Being hardy rustlers, the animals took care of themselves and subsisted on native grasses and hay. In 1906, the United States Department of Agriculture established an experimental station at Kenai. A small herd of Galloway cattle at the station was pastured on native grasses during the open season and fed on native hay during the winter. Although the cattle were transferred to Kodiak after a year, it was observed that the animals maintained themselves in good condition on their diet of native grasses and hay.

Today there are approximately 100 head of cattle in and near the villages on the Kenai Peninsula. Summer feeding is amply taken care of by the luxuriant grasses, but heavy snows made in-feeding necessary in most regions. At Homer, particularly, summer range on the high tableland should be excellent, although the deep snows would drive the cattle to the beach land. The climate at Homer is mild enough for a limited number of cattle to winter out on the beach.

Farther up the Peninsula at Ninilchik, Kasilof, and Kenai, the natural vegetation is favorable for cattle grazing, but winter feeding and shelter are necessary.

The regions mentioned have natural endowments for a grassland agriculture and livestock possibilities, but before much can be accomplished adequate means of transportation must be established.

The Matanuska Valley has the largest developed farm area in the Territory. The cattle are primarily used for dairy purposes, but there have been a few Shorthorns in the Valley; they were established there by the experiment station in 1920. Since the Colony was established, the tide flats have been used occasionally for putting up hay and for summer and winter pasture for cattle and sheep.

West from the Matanuska Valley is the Susitna Valley, which has not been settled. The valley typically has a regular slope, and each tributary to the Susitna River follows in a well-defined drainage from its source to its mouth. The whole valley is alluvial glacial outwash—sand, gravel, or fine silt soil. The Alaska Railroad runs along the east side of the valley as it leaves the Matanuska Valley. Open meadows along the tributaries to the Susitna could be used for hay or silage. Native grass grows abundantly along the river meadows. Successive cuttings would reduce yields, but domesticated grasses might be used after the native grass has run out.

Although these sections have greater precipitation than interior Alaska, the problem of curing hay is less troublesome. The stake method is used mostly to get hay cured so that it can be stored. Limited trials of artificial drying show promise, but for the present the silo may be the best answer to the problem of storing winter feed.

Several small flocks of sheep are maintained in the Matanuska Valley. Summer range pasture on the mountainsides furnishes excellent forage for them for about 4 months of the year. In favorable years, sheep can pasture out in the lowlands until snow is on the ground. Winter feeding and some shelter are needed.

Farming in Alaska involves some specific handicaps not common in the States. For instance, the subsoil is always frozen in most of Alaska; winters usually begin and end abruptly. Wherever green vegetation covers the land, it tends to hold back the water and keep the land wet, which encourages mosquitoes and flies, a constant torment to man and beast during the growing season. Some persons—not all, of course—find the short, dark days of winter intolerable.

We believe grassland agriculture and livestock production is feasible in Alaska. Where grass grows abundantly, beef and sheep can be raised. Where grass flourishes, wheat, oats, and barley will grow and generally ripen. With those feeds available, producing beef and sheep is largely a matter of skill and judgment on the part of the stockman.

In summary, then, we can say that historically there is ample evidence that livestock can survive and prosper in a large part of Alaska.

Old records tell of cows of Siberian origin in many of the Russian settlements along the coast. Cattle have been mentioned in perhaps 10 villages as far west as the Shumagin Islands, as far north as the villages of Cook Inlet, and as far south as Sitka.

In all instances, the cattle seemed to subsist on native hay and forage. It appears that little care was given them, and that the livestock were on their own. Being of hardy Siberian stock, these cattle were endowed naturally with an ability to provide for themselves.

We should bear in mind several pertinent details.

American experience with livestock in Alaksa does not extend much over 50 years. But even the limited and localized case histories of recent years indicate that several natural grassland areas of the Territory can be developed and utilized for livestock raising. The natural conditions favorable to animal husbandry are there—but other phases of the cattle and sheep business have yet to be solved.

There seems to be little difference between Alaska today and the West 75 to 85 years ago—and there seems to be little difference between Alaska's potentialities and those of the West. The westward march of civilization and development has populated the country, and areas thought to be worthless by the pioneers are large producers of food-stuffs and livestock today. A large movement of population to the Territory will advance the agricultural picture greatly.

And with population and industry will come the opportunities in animal husbandry, and the development of a grassland agriculture.

THE AUTHORS≪≪≪ *O. S. Aamodt is head agronomist in charge of the* *Division of Forage Crops and Diseases, Bureau of Plant Industry, Soils, and Agricultural Engineering. He is a native of Minnesota and holds a doctor's degree from the University of Minnesota. Dr. Aamodt was head of the Department of Field Crops, University of Alberta, Canada, for 7 years; there he became familiar with agricultural problems of the far North. He also was chairman of the agronomy department at the University of Wisconsin before entering his present position in 1938. In 1946 he headed a group of eight Department specialists who investigated agricultural problems in Alaska. He was elected President of the American Society of Agronomy in 1947.*

G. W. Gasser went to Alaska in 1907 to take charge of the agricultural experiment station located on the Yukon River at Rampart. In 1921 he was transferred to the experiment station at Fairbanks. He became professor of agriculture at the University of Alaska in 1928 and director of the experiment station in 1932. In 1937 he resigned as director and continued as professor and Dean of Men until 1945, when he was appointed commissioner of agriculture in the newly created Territorial department of agriculture. He was born in Ohio and is a graduate of Kansas State College.

In 1947 Congress appropriated the funds for exploratory investigations of agricultural problems in Alaska to determine the basic problems underlying potential agricultural developments there as a guide to future research. The study was made by eight technical employees of the Department of Agriculture and Mr. Arthur Orr, executive secretary of the Subcommittee on Agricultural Appropriations. They were assisted by other Federal and Territorial employees of stations in Alaska. The men examined various areas to determine their extent, relative productivity, livestock requirements, ability to support population, prospective production, markets, and technical problems of development. The grassland aspects of the agriculture in Alaska were given special attention by D. A. Savage, Charles E. Kellogg, and O. S. Aamodt, of the Bureau of Plant Industry, Soils, and Agricultural Engineering, and N. R. Ellis and H. E. Kemper, of the Bureau of Animal Industry. The Report of the Exploratory Investigations of Agricultural Problems of Alaska, issued in February 1947 by the United States Department of Agriculture, Agricultural Research Administration, makes recommendations for a research program to study, among others, the problems of field and horticultural crops, climate, livestock and dairying, and living conditions. Factors involved in the cost of such a program are also discussed.

Grasslands in Hawaii

SUGAR, PINEAPPLES, AND GRASS

J. C. RIPPERTON [1]

THE TERRITORY of Hawaii consists of seven inhabited islands, which are essentially volcanic domes. The maximum altitudes on the major islands are, roughly, Hawaii, 14,000 feet; Maui, 10,000; Kauai, 5,000; Molokai, 5,000; and Oahu, 4,000. The younger domes are relatively smooth and uneroded; the older ones have deeply desiccated slopes, great gulches, and steep ridges. The more arable lands are the coastal plains, the residual lands on volcanic slopes, and the plateaus on the islands that have two or more mountain domes.

The climate is consistently equable. At sea level the mean air temperature is 74° F. It fluctuates only 5° or 6° from season to season. The temperature decreases an average of 1° per 300 feet of altitude, so that at high elevations the mean temperature is that of the temperate zones. The relative humidity averages about 70 percent.

Hawaii lies in the belt of northeast trades, which prevail about three-fifths of the time during the winter and almost continuously during the summer. Rainfall increases on the windward slopes from about 20 inches to a maximum of 200 inches or more at the crest of the lower ranges. A corresponding

decrease occurs downward on the lee slope to about 20 inches. On Maui and Hawaii the air tends to deflect around the higher mountains and there is less rainfall at higher levels.

The belt of maximum rainfall ranges on the different islands from 2,000 to 6,000 feet. Rainfall from the southwest (or "kona") winds falls principally in winter, and is an important part of the total precipitation in the leeward parts of the islands. The seasonal distribution of trade-wind rainfall is characteristically that of relatively dry summers and wet winters. It is subject to considerable fluctuation, however, in amount and distribution. Uncertainty of rainfall is a major obstacle in non-irrigated agriculture in Hawaii, even in areas with a relatively high average.

The soils are derived almost entirely from volcanic material. Differences in character result from the nature of such material, its age, depth of weathered material, and the rainfall and the temperature under which the soil-forming processes took place. Residual soils derived from lava vary from essentially undecomposed material to deeply weathered Lateritic clays. Soils derived from volcanic ash are common, particularly in the uplands. They range in depth from a shallow covering to deep layers. Such soils are usually friable and are productive when they

---

[1] All articles in this chapter were written by Mr. Ripperton.

have sufficient depth for any kind of use.

Erosion is a serious hazard on most lands used for cultivated annual crops. Rainfall is often torrential, and conservation measures are difficult to apply on steep and irregular slopes. Perennial crops like orchards, sugarcane, and soilage crops provide effective control of erosion. The relatively large areas devoted to forest reserve in the high-rainfall zones are necessary for water conservation and soil conservation. Pastures, however, are the best use for a large proportion of the total land of the Territory.

That such a use is possible in Hawaii arises from several economic factors. Hawaii, with a population of 520,000, is not overpopulated; the more intensive uses of all the land are thus not necessary. The sugar and pineapple industries provide employment at a relatively high economic level for a large part of the total population on only 6.6 percent of the total land area. These two export crops provide a favorable trade balance, which permits the purchase of needed articles of food and feed from other localities at lower cost than they can be produced locally. These industries set wage standards that must be met in general by producers of other crops. Of the major agricultural land uses, sugar uses 5.1 percent, pineapple 1.5 percent, diversified crops 0.35 percent, forest reserve 26.1 percent, and pastures 34.4 percent of the total land area of 4.1 million acres.

One looks almost in vain for fields of corn or cereal grains or legumes, for haystacks or silos, and for the diversified farm with its rotation of cultivated crops and temporary pastures. Corn, wheat, oats, soybeans, and other legumes are fairly well adapted, but their acreage is small. Production costs are high because of difficulties in mechanical operations in small fields and on sloping lands of irregular topography. Rainfall adds uncertainty in the drier zones; in the high-rainfall zones, the problems of disease, good pollination, and curing of the grain are serious.

Haymaking likewise is affected by climate as well as topography. The economy of the silo is an ever-present question where green forage is available throughout the year. All these factors are obstacles to attempts to make Hawaii more self-sufficient as to animal feed and stress the importance of grassland agriculture.

Total livestock products in 1946 were valued at 15.6 million dollars, 11.4 percent of the total agricultural income of the Territory. Of this amount, beef cattle sold for 4.5 millions, dairy cattle and milk for 5.1 millions, swine for 3.4 millions, and poultry and eggs for 2.6 millions of dollars. Beef cattle are grown and fattened almost entirely on pastures and dairy cattle are grazed or fed cut forage, but essentially all concentrates of grain or protein meals are imported. Swine and poultry are raised almost entirely on imported feeds or certain byproduct feeds.

Vegetation Zones

The pattern of rainfall and the uniform temperature gradient produce several strikingly different climates, which are reflected markedly in the distribution of the natural vegetation. This fact has been used as a basis for subdividing—without reference to soil or topography—the entire land mass into a series of broad vegetation zones, each with its characteristic climate and agricultural use or possibilities. The essential purpose is to group together the areas that have similar environments. Statements made regarding the use and the adapted crops for a given zone apply primarily to areas with a moderate slope and soil of sufficient depth to permit normal plant growth and, because of the transition from one zone to another, to average conditions within the zone. Some of the zones have been subdivided into phases based primarily on altitude. The map shows the location of the vegetation zones on the island of Maui and the major land uses.

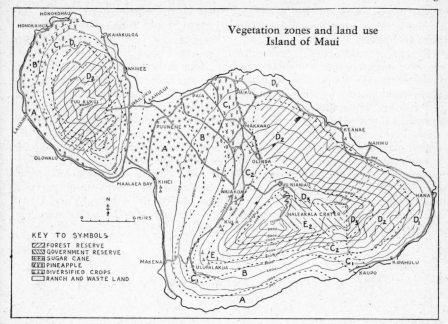

Vegetation zones and land use
Island of Maui

KEY TO SYMBOLS
FOREST RESERVE
GOVERNMENT RESERVE
SUGAR CANE
PINEAPPLE
DIVERSIFIED CROPS
RANCH AND WASTE LAND

Zone A, as shown on the map, has 20 inches or less of rainfall annually. The natural vegetation is a generally sparse coverage of drought-resistant shrubs and a coastal fringe of trees. It is too dry to permit the development of perennial grasses now available. The major forage species are a few deep-rooted shrubs or trees and certain annual grasses and herbs. Pasture development is limited. Only where the coastal fringe with its algaroba trees is extensive is this zone of much value. Grazing is limited largely to summer and fall, when the pods of the algaroba drop.

Zone B has approximate rainfall limits of 20 to 40 inches annually and occurs below 3,000 feet; the natural coverage is xerophytic shrub, with some trees. This zone offers possibilities of considerable pasture development and use. Annual species are still prevalent, but some perennial grasses will persist. Deep-rooted shrubs are important. The better parts can be plowed, and excellent fattening paddocks established. Grazing is restricted largely to the winter months when the kona rains are prevalent.

Zone C has approximate rainfall limits of 40 to 60 inches annually. Natural coverage is mixed open forest and shrubs. It is subdivided into a low or tropical phase and a high or temperate phase at an altitude of about 2,500 feet. It represents the optimum rainfall for the greatest diversity of desirable pasture species, both grasses and legumes, and contains much of the best grazing land in the Territory. The low phase (C_1) contains primarily tropical species. The upper phase (C_2) is adapted to many of the best pasture grasses and legumes of the temperate and subtropical parts of the United States. Grazing can normally be practiced throughout the year.

Zone D receives 60 inches or more of rainfall a year. The natural coverage is mixed forest. It is subdivided into a low, a middle, and a high phase, the latter extending in places to 7,000 feet. This zone has ample rainfall; some parts have too much. The soils of the low and middle phases have been leached excessively and are generally of low fertility. Pasturage is of relatively low quality, and many of the best grazing species are not adapted.

Nevertheless, relatively large areas are available for pasture developments in the lower phase.

Recent mechanical developments for clearing and preparing land offer great promise. It may be possible to maintain certain pasture legumes by the use of fertilizers. The middle phase is used mostly as forest reserve. The pastured areas serve mostly as maintenance or reserve pastures during dry years. The upper phase, lying above the zone of maximum rainfall, has considerable periods of cool, foggy weather. The soils are generally of friable volcanic ash and when they are deep enough, support a pasture mixture similar to

that of the northeastern part of the United States. Some of the finest pastures of the Territory are located in this upper phase.

Zone E lies above 4,000 feet or so, and has about 50 inches of rainfall. It is subdivided into low, medium, and high phases. The natural coverage changes gradually from open forest and shrub in the low phase to mosses and lichens in the high phase. Much of this zone is too high and dry to be of much grazing value. The low phase, containing the drier counterparts of Zone D_3 on the windward and C_2 on the leeward side, has some excellent pastures.

THE RANCHING INDUSTRY IN HAWAII

RANCHING in Hawaii depends solely on grazing to produce and finish its beef. Each ranch functions essentially as an independent unit, there being little sale of feeder cattle. Pen fattening has not proved feasible because of the high cost of imported concentrates. Before the war, many ranchmen hauled molasses to accessible parts of the ranch, but present prices have restricted its use. There are few haystacks, silos, and granaries—fresh grass is fed almost from birth to slaughter. The best ranches market well-finished beef at 2 to 3 years of age that average 550 pounds per dressed carcass. Beef from the poorer ranches is not always well finished, but it is accepted by some of the local markets.

This system of year-round grazing is possible because of the close proximity of zones of markedly different climate. Many of the old royal land grants were in strips of land extending from seashore to mountain top; the pattern persists in present landownership and leases.

Grazing management is largely a matter of moving the animals to where the feed is. The fattening animals are grazed on the best pastures, which may

be in any one of the several zones, depending on the season. Where possible, the animals are kept in one paddock or on the same type of forage during the entire fattening period. The breeding herd is grazed on the less desirable paddocks, often in the zones of relatively high rainfall. The growing stock is generally carried in the least developed open range areas.

The size of the individual paddock varies greatly, according to the ranch, the carrying capacity of the area, and the grazing use.

The poorer range paddocks are sometimes several thousand acres in size, while the fattening paddocks are often as small as a hundred acres. The type of water development and distribution varies with the location. Mostly the collection of surface water is the only feasible method. Where water cannot be had from the public county systems, the rancher must develop his own. In some places, springs can be utilized; in others small dams are constructed in drainage basins and the water piped to the desired locations. Some have a large galvanized-iron roof on a hillside and collect the run-off. Water is stored in wooden or metal tanks and piped to the various paddocks.

In establishing new pastures, the rancher usually has to clear a dense growth of trees and shrubs—formerly accomplished by crude equipment at a cost up to $100 an acre. Now track-layer tractors are commonly used. Bull-dozers are used to break down the larger shrubs; various heavy chain and flexible bar attachments are effective with the smaller shrubs. Probably the most useful tool is the heavy cutaway disk harrow, which breaks down, mac-erates, and finally plows the soil suffi-ciently well for planting. The power mower is used to prevent reinfestation. Weed killers, including Diesel oil and sodium chlorate mixtures and 2,4–D, are sometimes employed. There is evi-dence that the hormone sprays will aid in the control of certain shrubs. Cactus is being partly controlled by a locally developed fungus treatment.

Planting materials and methods vary according to the zone, the use, and the species being planted. A large part of the ranch lands are too broken, rocky, or inaccessible to be handled by ma-chinery. Considerable improvement can be made by scattering seed on the undisturbed soil although progress is often slow and uncertain. Koa haole, guineagrass, molassesgrass, and a number of the temperate species of grasses and legumes have thus been successfully established. Where the area can be plowed the seed is usually broad-cast and disked in.

Kikuyugrass, Napiergrass, and Para-grass are planted by stem cuttings, but Dallisgrass and guineagrass are planted sometimes with stool or crown divisions. The Napiergrass stems are planted with a home-made sled device or hand-placed in furrows and covered. The runners or stems of kikuyugrass and Paragrass are usually spread over the plowed field and disked in. The crowns of guineagrass and Dallisgrass are plowed out, broken up by hand, and planted in furrows.

A serious difficulty with respect to tropical forage species is the lack of reliable sources of seed. Seed of many species is not produced at all for com-mercial distribution; some others are below the specifications of the Federal seed law. Some ranchers collect their own seed, a tedious and costly hand process. The development of equip-ment adapted to local conditions and species, for harvesting, threshing, and drying local seed would be a marked contribution.

With few exceptions, all pastures are of the permanent type, and, once established, pasture management con-sists primarily in preventing the rein-festation by plant pests and keeping production up. Plowing every 5 to 10 years is common on many ranches; the practice destroys many perennial shrubs, reduces stands of undesirable grasses, and permits the development of desirable annuals like ryegrass, bromegrass, bur-clover, black medic, Indian yellow sweetclover, and vetch, which are largely repressed by a dense sod of Bermuda-grass.

Planting corn for one crop is an ex-cellent practice; even a partial crop helps defray the costs of plowing. Lit-tle cultivation is practiced, and by the time the crop is mature there is a lux-uriant growth of pasture species.

Use of nitrogen fertilizers in beef pastures is not yet an accepted prac-tice, but under certain conditions it may be feasible. Among the reasons that may justify its use for beef pro-duction is that by applying the nitro-gen in late spring and fall the addi-tional forage can be carried over into the dry summer and the colder months when growth in most localities is at a minimum. Most soils here are low in available nitrogen, and the response to it is pronounced. Increases of 2 or 3 tons an acre of harvested forage per 100 pounds of ammonium sulfate are common. Besides, good fattening pas-tures are the limiting factor in pro-duction of most ranches, and increased forage would permit larger herds.

Preliminary trials indicate that lime and phosphate give a marked response to most legumes in zone D_1. In zone C, the major response is to phosphates. It is doubtful if fertilizers of any sort are justified in the dry zones A and B without irrigation. There is some evidence of response of grasses to both phosphates and potash in parts of zone D_1, especially when nitrogen is also applied. Many problems connected with liming and fertilizing remain to be answered, but the practice seems to offer a good possibility for more productive and nutritious pastures.

Actual data are fragmentary as to mineral deficiencies or the presence of toxic elements in pasture forage. Forage from the high-rainfall zones tends to be deficient in calcium and phosphorus, and many ranchmen include a lime-phosphate mixture in the salt licks, but there are no mineral deficiencies so widespread or aggravated as to cause any manifest deficiency diseases among grazing animals in any part of the islands.

SPECIES OF PASTURE GRASSES

SINCE about 1850, when trade increased with the outside world, plant introductions of many sorts began to make vast changes in the native vegetation. Clearings of land for cultivated crops, forest fires, and grazing aided in its destruction.

One of the characteristics of an isolated insular vegetation is that existing plant associations are easily upset by exotic species. And, except for the forest reserves and land in the higher elevations where the native vegetation has been subjected to the least disturbance, Hawaii is a land of exotic species; the grazing industry depends almost solely on them.

Not all introductions, whether deliberate or accidental, have been desirable; some have become serious pests because the natural vegetation cannot hold them in check. But the result has been the gradual development of a varied series of desirable pasture swards, each adapted to its particular climatic zone. The Hawaii Agricultural Experiment Station, established in 1901, and other Government institutions and private agencies have made thousands of introductions from all parts of the world. The station maintains a series of testing plots at varying altitudes to determine the value and specific zonal adaptability of each species.

Many of the better known forage species have been introduced into Hawaii, but all the possibilities have by no means been exhausted. Forage plant exploration in the Tropics is essentially a virgin field; even the more advanced parts of the Tropics have not completely evaluated the forage possibilities of the species occurring there. Few concerted attempts have been made through selection and breeding to improve the species in common use. Since most tropical forage crops are perennial and are commonly propagated vegetatively, there has been little attempt to purify them.

Our experience has been that seed introductions from various sources, especially those in which the plant is endemic, segregate into greatly varied forms. These in themselves, or through hybridization, should make possible advances in greater production or development of strains for specific uses or qualities.

The Hawaiian rancher, because of the diversity of climates and soil types, especially if his ranch extends over several vegetation zones, has to vary his methods of developing, using, and managing his pastures and the species he plants. In the nonarable range lands, he depends primarily on the natural forage and employs only the cheapest methods of establishing more desirable species. His improved paddocks, however, call for careful consideration of what species to plant.

Beef Production, Total Area of Pastures, Total Number of Cattle, Number and Weights of Marketed Animals in Hawaii, 1946

Name of island	Total area	Total grazing	Ranches [1]	Total cattle	Pasture per head	Cattle marketed	Dressed weight of marketed animals
	1,000 acres	*1,000 acres*	*Number*	*Number*	*Acres*	*Number*	*1,000 pounds*
Hawaii..............	2,570	962	110	82,730	11.6	26,260	11,817
Maui..............	466	141	52	24,600	5.7	6,780	3,051
Oahu..............	384	17	14	3,760	4.4	1,405	635
Kauai and Niihau ...	397	135	38	13,860	9.8	2,490	1,120
Molokai and Lanai..	256	77	14	5,360	14.3	1,900	855
Territory total.....	4,073	1,332	228	130,310	10.2	38,835	17,478

[1] Ranches that carry 20 head or more.

First to consider, of course, is adaptability, which in the ecological sense means the ability of the plant to persist in a given zone under the environmental conditions existing in the pasture.

Species for Grazing

Dallisgrass is one of the most important of tropical grazing species in Hawaii. It is adapted to a wide range of conditions throughout zones C and D from sea level to 6,000 feet. It will stand hard and continuous grazing and has a high carrying capacity. Some pastures carry as much as one animal to an acre throughout the year. It has the further advantage that other species of grasses and legumes will grow in association with it, especially if the sod is plowed every 5 years or so.

Kikuyugrass is the most maligned and the most praised of grasses. Its proponents point to its advantages of ease and speed of establishment, its ability to hold many pasture pests like guava partly in check, the protection it gives against soil erosion, its wide adaptability, its high carrying capacity and ability to withstand heavy and continuous grazing, and its apparently satisfactory nutritive value as measured by beef gains. Its opponents object primarily to the very characteristic that gives it virtue—it tends to

sweep everything before it, good and bad, and become a one-species pasture. Probably its greatest value is in zone D, where its quick ground coverage and ability to hold pests in check are important.

Paragrass has value in the poorly drained, heavy soils of the coastal flats and river valleys of zone D. It grows fairly well at elevations up to 2,000 feet. It will not persist under heavy, continuous grazing, but with rotational grazing and on fertile soils and ample moisture it has a high carrying capacity. It is not extensively used for grazing beef cattle.

Molassesgrass is not liked at first by animals, but many ranchers consider it an acceptable forage. An advantage is that seed of excellent quality can be purchased. The seedlings develop rapidly into a semibunchgrass, often 3 feet high; the trailing stems tend to grow over taller shrubs. It seeds in the fall, and in the dryer zones it regenerates itself by natural seeding. Grazing experiments at the Haleakala Branch Station on Maui, 2,200 feet elevation, indicate that it cannot withstand excessive trampling or hard continuous grazing, but it will maintain itself indefinitely either as clumps or, when there is sufficient rainfall, as closely cropped crowns.

Napiergrass, generally regarded as a cut forage crop, is used in intensively managed grazing paddocks. An experiment at the Haleakala Farm has shown it to have a yearly carrying capacity of $1\frac{1}{2}$ animals an acre. Our practice has been to fertilize it with at least 450 pounds of ammonium sulfate a year, applied in two or three applications. Napier succumbs if it is grazed continuously; a desirable practice is to graze 40 to 50 percent of the time, by using enough animals to consume all the leaves in about 2 months and allowing about 2 months of rest. Normally, the animals eat only the green leaves and the succulent top part of the stem. During the resting period, nodal buds develop a fine leafy growth on these stems. New basal shoots replace them mostly during the spring months. Mowing or disking down these productive stems reduces the carrying capacity. If it is necessary to mow or disk in order to destroy volunteer pests, it is best to do it in the early spring just before the major development of basal shoots.

Guineagrass is a widely used grazing species. It will grow satisfactorily in the more moist locations, but its main value is in the drier zones, especially zone B. It is somewhat sensitive to low temperatures and is not commonly planted above 1,500 feet. Once established, it is remarkably drought-resistant. In the dry zones it spreads by natural seeding. The fresh growth is palatable; even the dry leaves are well eaten in the low rainfall areas. It will withstand hard grazing. Planted in combination with koa haole, it comprises some of the best dry-zone fattening paddocks.

Temperate or cool-weather grasses include Kentucky bluegrass, which is common in zone D_3 and bordering parts of zones E_1 and C_2; cocksfoot, which is extensively planted in the same zones as Kentucky bluegrass; canarygrass, of much less importance; ryegrass, of which both perennial and annual types are valuable, but of restricted adaptability to the best parts of zones D_3 and E_1; bromegrass, which is important only in restricted parts of zone C_2; Yorkshire fog, which is not generally recommended in other parts of the world but is invaluable in zones D_3 and E_1.

Of the legumes, algaroba is important in the coastal parts of zones A and B as shade and as a source of nutritious beans. Occasional thinning of the stand where it becomes too dense results in a greater bean crop and more forage growth. Koa haole is an important leguminous shrub in zones A and B; the forage is palatable and nutritious. In past years locally gathered koa haole seed has been extensively planted on the range. The seed has hard seed coats, these may be scarified by strong acid, hot water, or mechanical scarifiers.

Pigeonpeas, once extensively planted in Hawaii for beef fattening, have a productive life under grazing conditions of only 3 to 5 years. Certain of the ranchers insist, however, that the pigeonpea is worth the trouble and expense of maintaining a stand. Our experiments indicate that a light grazing or topping when the plant is one-half or two-thirds grown is a desirable practice, which reduces the final height of the plant and produces more numerous and more pliable branches. It is customary to interplant grasses or allow volunteer species to grow with the pigeonpeas; those include Rhodes, molasses, Dallis, and kikuyu grasses. The pigeonpea cannot stand heavy, continuous grazing; rotational grazing is preferred. It should be planted only on productive, well-prepared soils. Its optimum environment is from about 500 to 2,500 feet in zone C.

Spanish clover is a well-naturalized, perennial, herbaceous shrub of especial importance in zone C. It is not exceptionally palatable, but it grows the entire year and is of undoubted forage value.

Kaimi clover holds especial promise for zone D_1, where so few desirable legumes are adapted. This perennial legume has creeping stems, which root at the nodes. It will stand hard grazing and grows well with kikuyu, Dallis, or any other sod grasses if they are grazed short enough to prevent shading out of the clover.

Sensitiveplant is naturalized in most of zone D_1 and, when kept under control by careful grazing or periodic mowing, is a valuable grazing legume. Uncontrolled, it forms a thorny bramble, which assumes the proportions of a pest.

Two other tropical legumes show promise—creeping Indigo and tropical kudzu. The former has persisted 8 years in one pasture trial and is well eaten by animals.

Temperate zone legumes have been extensively planted in past years and their zonal adaptability seems well established. White clover does its best in zone D_3 and extends into the wetter parts of the adjacent zones. Seldom is it of importance below 2,500 feet. Hop clover is still more localized in D_3. Vetch extends throughout much of D_3 and C_2. Red, alsike, and Ladino clovers will persist over a period in D_3, but have never spread or become important. Birdsfoot trefoil makes a robust growth in D_3 in protected areas, but seldom persists under grazing conditions. Three annual legumes, burclover, black medic, and Indian yellow sweetclover, are particularly well adapted to the seasonal rainfall of C_2. They are valuable additions to the pastures in spring and early summer.

The Dairy Industry

Like the beef industry, dairying conforms to a relatively simple pattern. Primarily it is a matter of the daily cutting and feeding of roughage from a nearby field of a perennial crop like Napiergrass. The remainder of the ration is made up of purchased concentrates, most of which are imported.

This procedure is desirable in that it requires only simple equipment and facilities and uniform daily labor for harvesting the forage and care of the fields. It has its disadvantages, however: This daily piecemeal harvesting of 4 or 5 tons of forage for the average

dairy precludes the effective use of machinery. The current procedure is to cut it by hand, carry the forage to a nearby truck, and unload and handfeed the coarse forage into the chopper. These operations take perhaps 5 manhours a ton; at the present high prices that means $5 to $6 a ton of green forage.

The production costs of this procedure added to the costs of harvest mean that the dairyman is not getting cheap forage regardless of high yields. Other difficulties are the seasonal periods of rapid and of slow growth, present even in Hawaii, and, with them, the possibility of alternate surplus and shortage of forage. Also, it is difficult to harvest forage during rainy periods. Silos of various sorts have been tried from time to time; there has been a recent renewal of interest in them, and several dairies use them. The use of silos means added facilities and some loss of nutrients in the ensiling process, but they have much to commend them in any attempt to modernize the procedure of forage production.

The need to cut forage costs has become acute lately because of increases in labor costs. Revised field layouts that would permit more efficient irrigation and cultural operations and the mechanizing of all operations, particularly harvesting, should permit marked reductions in labor requirements.

While most dairies, particularly those on Oahu, depend primarily on cut forage, a number of dairies practice grazing, at least in part. Many establishments which feed soilage crops to the milking herd carry the dry cows and young stock on pastures, sometimes located on another part of the same island and even on another island. A few dairies graze the milking herd, but find that concentrate supplements are necessary for satisfactory milk production.

The greater economy of grazing (where enough land and good pasturage are available), over the use of cut forage has been proved and is being stressed on the mainland as a means of offsetting present high costs of labor and purchased feed. The extent to which it is applicable in Hawaii depends primarily on the development of more nutritious pasture swards. Zone C offers the best possibilities of high quality grazing of a mixed grass-legume sward, but even here uncertain rainfall is an obstacle. Irrigated pastures offer possibilities for zones A and B, but since two or three times as many animals can be carried on an acre from cut roughage as from pasturage, present land limitations generally preclude grazing on irrigated lands. The high rainfall of zone D_1 presents special problems with respect to the development of nutritious pasturage and perhaps with respect to the direct effect on the animal itself. However, this phase has the largest area of accessible land available.

SOME CROPS FOR FODDER

OF THE soilage crops, Napiergrass is most commonly used because of its long life, ease of production, and remarkably high yields. It is grown as cut forage almost entirely in zones A, B, and C_1 under irrigation. The average yield at the University Farm in Honolulu through 3 years was 71 tons of green forage to the acre each year.

Yields of 50 tons for a single crop have been recorded; one dairy, which had 500 cows and produced most of its roughage requirements on 35 acres of Napiergrass, reported 150 tons. This grass requires ample water and fertilizer for heavy yields. A 75-ton yield would remove from the soil the equivalent of 1,200 pounds of ammonium sulfate, 500 pounds of superphosphate, and 1,500 pounds of potassium sulfate. Many soils will provide sufficient available phosphorus and potassium for a long period, but nitrogen soon becomes the limiting factor in production on most soils.

Napiergrass is not a high-quality forage; it commonly contains about 4 percent protein on a dry basis. Cut at an immature stage, it may contain as much as 15 percent protein. At this stage, however, the dry matter content drops from the normal of about 20 percent to 10 or 12 percent; while the palatability as well as total production of protein increases, the production of dry matter per acre per year drops. Hence, it becomes a question between lower production of better and more palatable forage, or higher production of less desirable feed with a greater annual total of dry matter and total digestible nutrients. Digestibility trials show that 59 percent of the dry matter even of mature Napier is digestible.

Paragrass is grown for cut forage in zone D_1 without irrigation. When grown on good soil and adequately fertilized, it can be cut as often as every 8 weeks. At the University Farm it produced 46 percent more digestible crude protein than Napier, with essentially the same yield of total digestible nutrients. It is palatable, and some dairymen believe it is a better milk producer than Napiergrass. It can be readily cut with a power mower, and gathering and feeding the cut forage is somewhat easier than with the coarse Napiergrass. Para and Napier make up probably 90 percent of the grass roughage cut for the dairy herd.

Sudangrass once was extensively planted, but now it is of little importance. Its rather rapid decline in yields of successive ratoon crops and susceptibility to rust during the winter months are its principal weaknesses. The crop has much to commend it: It is readily established by seed, and produces its first crop about 2 months after planting. It recovers rapidly, and as many as 8 cuttings during the first year, with a total annual yield of 49 tons an acre of green forage, have been obtained at the University Farm. Tests at the University showed that Sudangrass was the only one of several grasses that gave significantly higher milk production.

Sugarcane tops—or the entire plant if it is cut at an immature stage—make excellent roughage. One dairy that grows sugarcane for the purpose reported increased milk yield over that produced by Napiergrass. Strip cane and pineapple pulp, byproducts of the sugar and pineapple industries, are also fed as fresh roughage.

The only legume grown widely for soilage is koa haole. Many dairymen were reluctant to use it because of its depilatory effect on nonruminants; they feared also that it might affect reproduction and produce off-flavors in milk. Investigations at the Hawaii Agricultural Experiment Station showed that the depilatory effect is due to the compound mimosine and not to selenium, as was supposed. The experience of several dairies seems to justify the conclusion that koa haole is a safe and nutritious feed for dairy cows. Milk production trials at the University Farm have shown that 55 pounds of fresh koa haole a day for each cow provided enough digestible protein to replace all the soybean meal in the supplemental feed, with no significant lowering of production.

Since the plant normally grows as a woody, treelike, stemmed shrub, the Hawaii Agricultural Experiment Station undertook experiments to determine aspects of establishment, culture, frequency of cutting, height of cutting above ground levels, and moisture requirements. We found that in most respects it is hardy and adaptable and can be handled much like any other perennial row crop. It grows slowly at first, and from 6 to 9 months are required before the first cutting can be made. The optimum yields are at about 4-month intervals when the new growth is about waist high. Cutting at 2 to 4 inches above ground level gives yields essentially the same as at higher levels.

Forage yields have not been exceptionally high, however. At the Pensacola Station in Honolulu, 25 tons an acre a year of green forage and 2,700 pounds of protein per acre were produced. At Poamoho Farm, at an elevation of 700 feet, only 18 tons were obtained. Probably that is the maximum altitude for its practical use as a soilage crop. One of its most valuable characteristics is its ability to produce good forage yields without irrigation, where the natural rainfall is as little as 3 to 4 inches a month. Under similar conditions Napiergrass requires irrigation every 10 to 12 days.

The power-driven corn binder can be used without change to cut koa haole. In fact, hand cutting of the crop is so laborious and expensive that its production would not be feasible without the corn binder.

Alfalfa used to be planted rather extensively as a cut forage crop. Yields for the first year of 60 tons of green forage have been had with a cutting interval of 4 to 5 weeks. An average of 37.5 tons was obtained from eight plantings at the University Farm. Despite such yields, the crop is grown on a limited acreage now, primarily because of its relatively short productive life and the high labor cost of removing noxious grasses from the stand. It is possible that use of tractor-mounted disk cultivators and selective weed sprays may solve the weed problem economically. With proper equipment, a field can be plowed and planted to alfalfa and harvesting begun on the new field in about 5 months. Alfalfa would be a welcome addition to the dairy ration in Hawaii.

The total area devoted to soilage legumes is small, probably less than 5 percent of that in soilage grasses. The main reason is that grasses like Napier will produce a much greater annual yield of dry matter and total digestible nutrients an acre than will legumes. For example, a yield of 80 tons an acre of Napiergrass contains about 20,000 pounds of total digestible nutrients, with a nutritive ratio of 13.3, while a 25-ton yield of koa haole contains only 8,590 pounds of total digestible nutrients, with a nutritive ratio of 3.3. This higher production is important, because most dairies here have available only a limited amount of good, arable land. The use of these grasses with such a wide nutritive ratio requires relatively large amounts of costly imported concentrates to balance the ration.

THE AUTHOR≪← *J. C. Ripperton, a graduate of Kansas State Agricultural College, has lived in Hawaii since 1920. He has investigated many tropical crops and their relationship to the general problem of diversified agriculture in Hawaii. He has been associated with tropical forage crop and pasture research since 1930. He is the agronomist of the Hawaii Agricultural Experiment Station, University of Hawaii.*

E. Y. Hosaka, assistant agronomist, and M. Takahashi, junior agronomist, of the Hawaii station, provided data and helped prepare the manuscript.

Grasslands in Puerto Rico

FARMING ON A TROPICAL ISLAND

RAY C. ROBERTS [1]

PUERTO RICO viewed from the air looms up like a big deflated balloon. The wrinkled mountainous interior of this tiny tropical island has been faulted and tilted by earthquakes, serrated and dissected by thousands of rivulets, and scarred by hurricanes—a striking contrast with the level alluvial flood plains along the coast and the rounded grass-covered hills of the arid southwestern part.

Puerto Rico, which is a little smaller than Connecticut, is about 1,200 miles north of the Equator and nearly 1,400 miles southeast of New York City. Its tropical, uniform temperature, which ranges from a mean of about 68° F. in the mountains in the winter to a mean of about 82° in the lowlands in the summer, gives it a yearlong growing season. Nearly ideal conditions exist for a heavy rainfall over most of its surface, because the moisture-laden northeast trade winds from the warm waters of the Atlantic fan the island almost all day. The annual rainfall, however, ranges from about 25 inches along the southwestern coast to more than 200 inches in the high mountains. The sudden change in rainfall is reflected so much in the native vegetation that in a distance of a few miles and a

descent of a few hundred feet one may pass from the luxuriant tropical rain forest to desert shrubs.

According to *El Libro de Puerto Rico,* the first introduction of livestock into Puerto Rico was in 1502 when Yáñez, one of Columbus' captains, brought in a few goats and some hogs. About 10 years later Ponce de Leon brought a few head of cattle and horses from Santo Domingo. In 1534, stallions descended from Arabian stock were imported from Andalucia. Sometime during the 15th century guineagrass was introduced from Africa. This droughtresistant, nutritious grass, an exceedingly important one in Puerto Rico, is planted mostly in the more arid regions; the malojillo grass, which was imported from South America, grows in the wet sites. These palatable grasses insured an abundant, nutritious forage all year long, and the numbers of livestock increased rapidly.

The *Soil Survey of Puerto Rico* states that during the middle of the 18th century some of the fine horses from Yabucoa Valley were sold for $1,000 each. Most of the horses at that time were similar to the ones now used in the island. They are small, wiry, hackney-gaited, sure-footed. They are used principally for carrying large packs of bananas, charcoal, coffee, and other products down the steep, rocky,

[1] *All articles in this chapter were written by Mr. Roberts.*

narrow, mountain trails and slippery, muddy roads to town—to return laden with beans, fish, rice, and other articles of food for the numerous small stores along the trails and roads of the interior. Very seldom are horses used for draft purposes, although hundreds may be seen that have two large wicker baskets fastened to a harnesslike saddle. Livestock, such as pigs, chickens, and turkeys, and all kinds of crops, are transported to market in the baskets. The number of horses has declined since 1910—to 16,239 in 1940.

Cattle are the most important livestock raised. There were 299,734 head in the island in 1940. R. P. Steddom in *A Report Concerning the Cattle of Porto Rico* estimated the number at 500,000 in 1899. Since 1906 few cattle have been exported, chiefly because the island has had increasing demands for cattle from the expansion of the sugarcane industry, which requires many work oxen, and the increasing population, which needs more beef animals for food. The number of cattle produced has declined, partly because hundreds of acres of level, fertile grassland along the arid and the semiarid southern coast formerly all in cattle ranches are now in sugarcane.

Grass still occupies most of the hills along the arid south coast, as well as many of the steep hills, which have very shallow soils. The cattle of Puerto Rico have been selected for draft purposes for such a long time that they are docile, powerful, large-boned, thick-skinned animals with short hair, wide-spreading horns, and thick polls. Practically all have horns and nearly all the oxen used on the main roads are shod. They pull heavy, two-wheeled carts, plows, and other implements. The cattle are either native or crosses of Brahman, or zebu, on native stock. Most of the ranchers have some zebu and some native stock. For draft purposes, many of the progressive ranchers recommend crosses of one-third zebu and two-thirds native stock.

THE TYPES OF GRASSLAND FARMING

THE TYPES of grassland agriculture in Puerto Rico are linked closely with the rainfall belts. The driest belt, the extreme southwestern part, receives from 25 to 35 inches annually of rainfall. This is about the same range of precipitation as between Nebraska City and Grand Island, Nebr. But the similarity ends there: Instead of luxuriant, level Nebraska fields, rich grass, rounded haystacks, groves, dark soil, and sectionized roads, with two or four large homes at the crossroads, there are here brown, highly calcareous soils, cacti and spiny shrub-covered hills, valleys of guineagrass pastures for the hundreds of native oxen, and a few ranch houses along oxcart roads. This is the "Great Plains" of Puerto Rico.

A typical ranch here reminds one somewhat of Arizona and New Mexico and some other Western States. It consists of a small group of ranch buildings surrounded by several thousand acres of fenced and cross-fenced, undulating, hilly grass and cactus pastures. One rancher may own 2,000 to 3,000 head of cattle and hire 30 or more hands.

The irrigated lands, with green, succulent sugarcane on all land that is not charged with alkali and saline salts, are in sharp contrast with the arid hills nearby. The soils in this area are mostly high in calcium and other plant nutrients, and the grass appears to be fairly high in phosphorus, calcium, carotene, and crude protein, as indicated by the healthy appearance of the livestock during an average season.

In this area and in the belt that gets about 10 inches more of precipitation, the common practice is to put about 60 head of cattle in a 60- or 70-acre pasture for several days, then change them to another pasture. The yearly carrying capacity of the land ranges from about 2 acres a head on the nearly level alluvial fans to about 5 or 6 acres a head on the rolling uplands. The carrying capacity varies considerably from year to year and from place to place, depending upon the rainfall, the care of the pasture, and the kind of grazing. About 20 inches more of rain a year would nearly double the carrying capacity in districts receiving from 25 to 50 inches of precipitation.

Pastures that have been freed of weeds such as cacti, zarzarilla, and guayacan blanco have a much higher carrying capacity than the weed-infested pastures. Zarzarilla spreads rapidly, and several stockmen report that the animals that eat it may lose some of their hair and manes. Guayacan blanco grows mostly on the shallow soils derived from limestone in both the arid and subhumid districts. The pollen from this plant seems to irritate the eyes of the animals and some ranchers report that it causes blindness in cattle.

The carrying capacity of the range depends somewhat on the management of the livestock. Cattle that are badly infested with ticks require more grass and a larger area to graze in order to be in as good a condition as the nearly tick-free animals. Most of the so-called native cattle and the zebu strains are more or less immune to tick fever, but if they are infested with ticks their strength is sapped, a point of vital importance during the dry periods when pastures are overgrazed. In places along the arid southern coast, hundreds of cattle die of starvation during a long drought like the one in the winter of 1930–31. Generally speaking, the first to die are those most heavily infested with ticks.

The approximate acreage of pasture land in this area (25 to 45 inches of precipitation), according to the 1940 Federal census, is 143,000 acres. Many of the pastures have been planted with guineagrass, which grows 1 to 6 feet high and seems to be much more nutritious than grass grown in the humid sections. Cattle born and raised on grass from the neutral or calcareous soils in this district are generally in better condition than animals born and raised on the coarse, less nutritious grass from acid soils of the humid districts.

Bermuda-grass is another important grass in this district. It is tolerant to alkali and saline salts and is grown largely on the level lands near the coast. Bermuda-grass and horquetilla morada, or Mexican bluegrass, a fine-leaved grass, are propagated naturally over the arid and semiarid districts.

Mexican bluegrass is fairly nutritious, but good stands of it often are plowed under, and guineagrass is planted. The general procedure is to plant bunches of guineagrass in rows. It is often interplanted with corn during the rainy season (summer), but in some places the seed is planted. The seeds, however, may lie dormant in the soils for some time before they receive enough moisture for germination. In a few years after planting, the guineagrass will spread if the soils are deep and well drained and the area receives considerable moisture, but in the shallow soils or on dry hillsides the guineagrass bunches do not readily stool. During drought periods, this grass becomes brown and dry, but it still has enough strength to keep the cattle alive. Within a few days after a rain the grass in the previously brown, baked pastures becomes green and fresh. Cattle may be completely hidden by the tall, dense guineagrass in some pastures. Fertilizers would probably not greatly increase the yields here.

In the 45- to 55-inch rainfall belt the type of agriculture is quite different from that in the more arid, thinly populated regions. The ever-increasing population pressure in Puerto Rico (there are nearly 600 persons to the square mile) forces the cultivation of steep hillsides, so steep in places that it is dangerous to walk. In this rainfall belt the population is dense, and the precipitation is sufficient to tempt the small farmer or jibaro to plant clean-cultivated crops such as corn, beans, tobacco, and pigeonpeas. Generally, rainfall is insufficient for rapid plant growth. When the rainy season starts, the intense showers wash the soil down the hillside before any vegetation has a chance to retard the flow of the water. The amount of erosion is not so great as in the clean-cultivated mountain areas of some of the tobacco districts, but the harm resulting from the erosion is more lasting. Evenutally much of this land becomes unproductive for cultivation, it is abandoned, and grass takes over. Small gullies form before the slowly growing pasture grasses can become established well enough to withstand the lashing rains. This land erodes severely for a year or two, but finally the grass thickens and erosion is arrested.

The management of the approximately 63,000 acres of grass pastures in this zone is difficult. The fields are small, and the owners cannot afford to buy fertilizers and take care properly of the pasture land. The pastures are used for goats, hogs, and local work oxen and dairy cows. As soon as erosion scars are healed, the chances are that the land will be plowed again and used for subsistence crops; erosion starts, and the circle repeats.

The 55- to 75-inch rainfall belt has approximately 184,000 acres of pasture. Proper fertilizer and better grasses would improve the pastures greatly. Many farms are planted to cultivated crops year after year on slopes of 60, 80, and 100 percent. Erosion is rapid, but vegetation grows so quickly and densely that the force of the running water is checked before it does destructive washing. In fact, some washing is desirable, because it keeps the soil young and more plant nutrients are available.

Under a heavy vegetation the soil granules are bound together by the millions of plant roots. Then, too, most of the soils of the island are derived from tuffs and shales, which contain a small amount of quartz. Therefore the weathering of these rocks produces a soil that is high in permeable clay, medium low in silt, and low in sand. Because the soils are without either a high content of silt, which may melt away like sugar under a tropical shower, or the abrasive effect of tons of sand plowing down the hillside, erosion in many places only keeps pace with the rapid decomposition and disintegration of the rocks. The moist, hot climate makes an ideal condition for the rapid weathering of rocks; also, the runoff water on most farms on Puerto Rico has a steep but short course before it empties into grass-covered, healed-over ravines or rock-bottomed small streams.

The Puerto Rican farmer has prevented soil loss by building brush and rock terraces along the contours of the steep slopes and by planting guinea-grass in hedgelike strips at irregular intervals on the steep hillsides. In the tobacco area, the farmers dig short checkerboard ditches along the hillsides. The bottoms of the ditches often rest on solid rock, thus eliminating conditions favorable for gully erosion. If any soil reaches the ditches, it flows to the ocean, but because of the many small squares surrounded by ditches, the water does not have a chance to collect much soil before it runs into a ditch. When sheet erosion has reduced the depth of the surface soil to such an extent that only unprofitable yields can be obtained, the land is usually abandoned. Grass, weeds, and brush start growing and the soil washing stops; the fast soil-forming process soon builds a new soil, to be cultivated again within 2 or 3 years.

The belt that has more than 75 inches of rainfall includes a larger portion of Puerto Rico than any other. It has approximately 228,000 acres of pasture land. It produces a great diversity of crops—nearly every type of product grown on the island: Corn, beans, yucca, yautia, sweetpotatoes, pigeonpeas, ñames, oranges, bananas, plantain, mangoes, breadfruit, papaya, alligator-pears, coffee, grapefruit, pineapples, sugarcane, tobacco.

The rainfall here is sufficient for all crops—but the high precipitation so necessary for the existence of the plants has had a destructive effect on soil, people, and stock. In the high rainfall areas, most of the soils have been leached to the extent that they want calcium, phosphorus, and magnesium. The calcium-phosphorus deficiency is critical in part of this rainfall belt. Only a few of the small landowners use fertilizer or manure to offset the loss of these mineral elements, and the plants produced, whether grains or grasses, do not have the food values necessary for the development of bones, teeth, and the physical well-being of the animals and people who eat them. Rickets and poor teeth are common in the mountains. The stock that graze on grasses of the neutral or alkaline soils of the arid regions have larger bones, smoother hair, and better general appearance than those pastured in the moist mountains, where acid-leached soils are dominant and the grass is tall and dense. Calcium-phosphorus deficiency is becoming serious in this area. Phosphorus fertilizer should be beneficial, especially on the red Lateritic soils.

In places the tall, thick grass is so low in nutritive value that cows do not produce sufficient nutritive milk to produce normal calves. In contrast to these sites of leached Lateritic soils, nearby Rendzina soils, black, calcareous, productive, and developed from soft limestone, produce nutritive grass, and the cattle pastured on these productive soils have the same appearance of health as those in the arid regions. Naturally, the boundary between these two contrasting soil sites is sharp, as is also land use and vegetation. The jibaros say the grass from the limestone areas is "sweet" and the stock like it much better than the grass produced on the red soils. They also say that pigeonpeas produced on the black soils and on the shallow brown soils are better and yield much more than those planted on the deep, red, acid soils.

THE GRASSES IN THE INTERIOR

THE GRASSES planted in the interior of the island for livestock are molassesgrass, a prostrate, twining, fine, hairy, sweet-smelling grass that is relished fairly well by livestock after they become accustomed to it; Guatemala grass, a rank-growing nutritious grass well adapted to acid soil in humid sections; and the Napiergrass (elephant grass), which somewhat resembles Uba sugarcane.

All the molassesgrass is pastured; after it becomes established, it is excellent for the prevention of soil erosion. It would be exceedingly difficult for water passing across a field of this grass to have sufficient force to wash soil particles from the intricately woven lower leaves and roots.

The Guatemala and Napier grasses generally are cut by hand, made into bundles, and carried to the stables or corrals. In this way enough hay can be gathered from an acre of most soil types to feed four or five oxen or dairy cows throughout the year.

Other grasses of importance for livestock in the humid districts are grama or St. Augustinegrass, cerillo, and matojo. The St. Augustinegrass, superior to the other two, is exceedingly good when grown on the alkaline soils. It also is good for the control of erosion, as its long runners securely anchor themselves to the soil and extend over gullies and on both sides of ditchbanks, thus binding the soil in place. Cerrillo grows mostly in the subhumid districts, but it grows to some extent in the humid areas. It is considered a good grass for cattle or horses. Matojo grows in humid areas or on poorly drained soils. It is a rank-growing, coarse grass of doubtful value for livestock. The animals eat it, but it does not seem to keep them in good condition. It is also used in thatching houses.

The grass with the highest carrying capacity on the island is the malojillo grass, which grows on wet sites, which generally are recent alluvial soils subject to overflow. It is a tall, coarse grass that is always green. It is palatable and a heavy producer. Yields ranging between 7 and 8 tons to the acre are the average, and some fields have been said to produce 40 tons an acre during one year. This grass grows only on poorly drained soils or in humid districts. It would grow in the arid districts if the land were irrigated. It is generally cut by hand and fed in bundles, but it is also pastured. Most of the poorly drained soils of the flood plains are neutral or alkaline in reaction, and apparently the quality of the feed pro-

duced is high. Dairymen report that cows do very well on malojillo grass.

In Puerto Rico, as in other parts of the world, there appears to be a close correlation between the quality of the forage, the fertility of the soils, and the health of man and animals. In general, the more fertile the soil, the better the forage, and therefore the healthier the animals.

THE AUTHOR«← *Ray C. Roberts, soil scientist in the Division of Soil Survey, Bureau of Plant Industry, Soils, and Agricultural Engineering, is principal soil correlator for the Far Western Region and is stationed in Berkeley, Calif. He was in charge of the soil survey of Puerto Rico, which was started in 1928 and finished in 1936. Because of his previous experience on ranches and farms in Wyoming and Nebraska, as well as soil survey work in Nebraska, Montana, New York, and Rhode Island, he readily recognized the relationship in Puerto Rico between the low fertility of the soils and the poor quality of crops and animals.*

Grass in a Plant Round-up

Grass: Green, Grain, Grow

THE FAMILY TREE OF GRAMINEAE

WILLIAM A. DAYTON

THE WORD *grass* supposedly evolved from an old Aryan root, *ghra-*, to grow. It is related to *grain, green, grow,* and the Latin *gramen,* grass.

The Oxford Dictionary gives the primary definition of grass as "herbage in general, the blades or leaves and stalks of which are eaten by horses, cattle, sheep, etc." This elemental usage is reflected, for example, in the Bible (. . . *all flesh is as grass, and all the glory of man as the flower of grass*). Now, however, *grass* primarily refers to the natural botanical family of grasses (*Gramineae* or *Poaceae*).

Grasses belong to the seedplant subkingdom (*Spermatophyta*) and thereunder (1) to the subdivision of angiosperms (*Angiospermae*) with rudimentary seeds (ovules) enclosed in an ovary, and (2) to the class monocotyledons (*Monocotyledones*), the embryos of which have one seedleaf, or cotyledon.

Grasses are herbaceous and, sometimes, woody plants. Their stems, or culms, are jointed and the joints (nodes) are closed and solid; otherwise the stems mostly are hollow, although the number of solid-stemmed grasses, especially in the more arid sites, is considerable.

The leaves, alternate in two ranks, are parallel-veined, consisting of a basal portion (sheath) enveloping the stem, ligule (marked *G* in the drawing), and blade. Ligule is derived from the Latin word *ligula* (literally, "little tongue"), a narrow strap as in a shoe latchet. The ligule, a characteristic feature of the grass family, is quite constant in a given species and is often an important means of distinguishing grasses, especially when not in flower or fruit. It is a projecting, often tonguelike, membranous end of the lining of the leaf-sheath, seen at the base of the leaf-blade, between it and the stalk; sometimes it is reduced to a mere fringe of hairs or to a hardened ring.

The flowers of grasses are mostly perfect (*i. e.*, with both male and female floral organs), although occasionally they are one-sexed, mostly rather small, arranged primarily in small clusters (spikelets) on a central axis (rachilla), and containing (besides the floral organs themselves) two to many two-ranked bracts (*A*). The two lowest and empty bracts are termed glumes, although occasionally one or both of these may be absent; above the glumes are one to many lemmas, or "flowering glumes" and opposite each of these is often a second, two-nerved bract called the palea (*A, B*).

The stamens, or male floral organs, are usually three but vary from one to

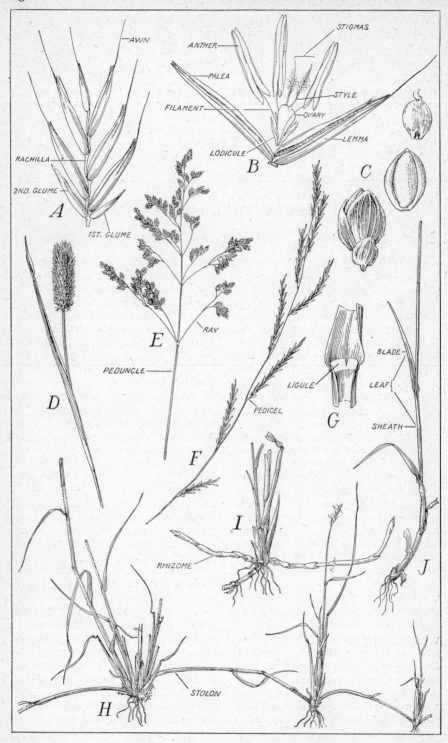

six in number and have two-celled anthers. The pistil, or female floral organ, is solitary, with a one-celled ovary and usually two (rarely one or three) styles and stigmas; the latter are usually feathery (plumose). The perianth or corolla of more showy flowers is often represented in grasses by some rudimentary appendages known as lodicules, usually two (sometimes three) in number, which are small, thin, more or less translucent scales (*B*). These help to force open the lemma and palea, at the time of anthesis, to aid in fertilization.

The spikelets are usually themselves aggregated into terminal spikes, panicles, and racemes (*D, E, F*).

The fruit of grasses is a caryopsis, the seed and fruit being united, the seed adhering throughout to the thin outer fruit-covering, or pericarp (*C*). The caryopsis may be free, as in wheat and dropseeds (*Sporobolus*), or tightly invested, as in three-awns (*Aristida*) and gramas (*Bouteloua*).

Grasses form a large natural family comprising about 600 genera. Of these about 150 genera and 1,500 species occur in the United States.

Our species represent 14 tribes, which are differentiated primarily on spikelet characters.

Use has been made in grass taxonomy by some modern investigators of the basic number, size, and changes in "arm"-length of the chromosomes. W. M. Myers, in The Botanical Review for June 1947, writes that, despite certain limitations, "chromosome numbers, size and morphology provide critical information regarding phytogenetic relationships when used in conjunction with morphological, geographical, and ecological studies."

Grasses, widely distributed and among the most numerous individually of all plants, often form savannas or pure grass types, of which the buffalo-grass-grama "shortgrass" areas known as the Great Plains of our Middle West are familiar examples. Grasses range in height from less than an inch to more than 100 feet. The greatest number of species is in the Tropics, but the greatest number of individuals is in cooler climates.

For those interested in studying grasses, an admirable introduction is Mrs. Agnes Chase's *First Book of Grasses*. Though long officially retired, Mrs. Chase works every day in her office in the Smithsonian Institution and maintains her world-wide interest in systematic agrostology.

THE AUTHOR ≪← *William A. Dayton is in charge of dendrology and range forage investigations of the United States Forest Service. He is probably best known for his publications on native range plants and is joint author, with Harlan P. Kelsey, of Standardized Plant Names. Mr. Dayton has been connected with the Forest Service since 1911, and has been chief of the dendrology and range forage investigations since 1942.*

THE MAIN GRASSES FOR FARM AND HOME

MAX M. HOOVER, M. A. HEIN, WILLIAM A. DAYTON, C. O. ERLANSON

WHEATGRASSES (*Agropyron* species) are hardy, drought-resistant, and versatile. They produce abundant forage that is acceptable to all classes of livestock. Most of them are perennial, with or without running rootstocks. Usually the culms (stems) grow erect. The spikes resemble wheat, hence the scientific name, *Agropyron*, which is derived from *agrios*, wild, and *pyros*, wheat. In the United States, wheatgrasses have great value in the Northern Great Plains, the Intermountain region, and the higher altitudes of the Rocky Mountain States.

Some wheatgrasses form sod; others

grow in bunches. The sod-forming species are particularly valuable for erosion control. Germination of the seed, which usually is produced in abundance, is rapid and the young seedlings may become established in competition with weeds and other grasses. This seedling vigor permits the sowing of wheatgrasses with a minimum of seedbed preparation. Often good stands have resulted when the seed was drilled in weeds or small grain stubble. Their ease of establishment and adaptation to many kinds of soils, moisture conditions, and extremes of climate make the wheatgrasses of first rank for use in plantings that are intended to protect the soil.

Early spring growth, with high production of lush forage at the season when most needed by overwintering livestock, is another good characteristic of these grasses.

The wheatgrasses have been used extensively for revegetating depleted range and abandoned farm lands. They are unexcelled for this purpose in the areas to which they are adapted. Seed is generally available, and successful methods of stand establishment are generally known and readily applicable. Many thousands of acres of previously cropped farm land in the Great Plains owe their present economic usefulness for grazing to these hardy, nutritious grasses.

The genus *Agropyron* contains approximately 150 species widely distributed in temperate regions of the world. About 100 species occur in Eurasia, 30 in North America, and most of the remaining in South America. The species probably familiar to most of us is *A. repens,* commonly called quackgrass, which invades our cultivated fields and gardens with such aggressive persistence that it has fully earned its place in the category of weeds. Its aggressiveness, however, has been put to good use in holding soil in conservation practices.

A few of the species are annuals for which no particular use has as yet been found.

None of the group has any long period of domestication behind it—the first cultivation reported dates no further back than 1895—although several of the species have long been recognized as valuable range grasses, both here and abroad. Others may furnish valuable breeding materials.

It has been demonstrated that two introduced species, *A. elongatum* and *A. intermedium,* will hybridize with common and durum wheats. Many promising possibilities are thus opened. Russian plant breeders say they have produced a perennial wheat from such crosses, but we have been unable to obtain material for trial.

CRESTED WHEATGRASS
(*Agropyron cristatum*)

Crested wheatgrass is a hardy perennial bunchgrass that produces an abundance of both basal and stem leaves. The leaves, about one-fourth inch wide and 6 to 10 inches long, are flat, somewhat lax, and slightly hairy on the upper surface. The stems are fine and develop dense tufts about 2 to 3 feet high. The dense spikes are 2 to 3 inches long; the spikelets are closely crowded and tend to form comblike crescents.

Crested wheatgrass is well adapted to the cool, dry areas of the Northern Great Plains, the Intermountain Region, and the higher elevations of the Rocky Mountain States. It has a widespreading, deeply penetrating root system. Partly for this reason, it can survive cold and drought, withstand grazing, and compete with weeds and associated grasses.

Crested wheatgrass usually begins growth in early spring. It ceases to grow during long, hot, dry periods of summer, but it again makes growth when moist, cool weather returns. By producing forage in early spring and early fall, when the normal growth of native grasses has not yet begun or has ended, this grass provides succulent feed when it is most needed. High palatability, good quality, and good volume of forage, combined with hardiness, drought resistance, and adaptation to widely different soil types, make crested wheatgrass one of the most valuable of forage grasses in this country.

Hay of excellent quality is obtained by cutting the plants early, just after heading and before blooming. If cutting is delayed the forage quickly becomes stemmy and less palatable. The better quality and greater feeding value of hay produced by early cutting more than offset its lesser quantity. Forage yields of crested wheatgrass are comparable to those of brome in the more moist parts of its range in the United States and are greater than those of brome in the drier parts.

Consistently good seed crops can be expected except when limited by drought. Average yields of 200 pounds of seed an acre on dry land—when planted in rows and cultivated—and about half that amount from solid stands on dry land have been reported.

The grain binder, combine, and swather have been used satisfactorily for seed harvest. The ordinary small grain thresher or combine with proper screen and air adjustments may be used for threshing the seed.

The normal time between seed ripening and seed shattering is about 2 weeks. When seed harvesting equipment (such as binders or swathers) is used, field harvesting operations can be started several days before the seed has ripened sufficiently for the most efficient operation of a combine.

Threshed material as it comes from the combine or thresher separator often contains large amounts of dirt, chaff, broken straw, and clusters of seed spikelets. Spikelet clusters can be broken up by processing the seed with a hammer mill. Clean seed of good quality may be obtained by removing all foreign material with an ordinary fanning mill. The number of clean seed per pound varies from 165,000 to 200,000. A bushel of clean seed with a purity of more than 90 percent and germination of 88 percent weighs about 22 pounds.

757150°—48——42

Crested wheatgrass seedlings resist drought and withstand competition from weeds and grasses if given sufficient protection during the first 2 years of their establishment. Time of seeding varies with locality and with purpose of seeding. If sufficient moisture is present in early fall, seeding can be started in September and continued until field operations are stopped by cold weather. In the southern range of this species, spring seeding is satisfactory.

Seedbeds may be well prepared or the seed may be drilled or broadcast directly in small grain stubble, weeds, or depleted native range cover. However, when the latter methods of seeding are used, one or more additional seasons of protection are often needed for the newly established seedlings to overcome the competition of associated vegetation and arrive at the stage of readiness for use by livestock. Hence, if it is urgent that the newly seeded area be available for use in the shortest possible time, it often pays to make the additional effort needed for preparing a clean, firm seedbed.

Satisfactory stands have been obtained from solid drilling or broadcast seeding at rates of 4 to 8 pounds of clean seed per acre, depending on the density of plant stand desired. Where seed production is the major purpose of the seeding, the most satisfactory results are obtained by seeding in rows, spaced to permit cultivation. Seeding rates of 2 to 4 pounds an acre are satisfactory in making these seedings.

Since the introduction of crested wheatgrass, many hundreds of successful seedings have been made and the area of adaptation of this grass is well established. Perhaps no other forage grass has filled such an important place in our revegetation program.

Crested wheatgrass was first obtained by the Federal Government in 1898 from an experiment station in Russian Turkestan, where it was already under test. Seed of the first introduction made little impression because most of it was dissipated in trials where the conditions were unfavorable.

A second and larger introduction from the same place in 1906 afforded a wider distribution of seed and, during the dry years between 1916 and 1921, the species began to attract attention in North Dakota for planting on abandoned wheat land. Commercial seed has been available since 1929.

It is long-lived; sometimes a stand is utilized as long as 25 years. Slender wheatgrass, by comparison, does poorly after about 5 years or so in permanent pastures.

Another species, *A. desertorum*, was apparently brought in with the seed of crested wheatgrass in 1906 and was for a long time thought to be only a strain of that species. The history of *A. desertorum* is similar to *A. cristatum* in the United States, the variety called Fairway being from *A. cristatum*, while the variety Standard is said to be derived from *A. desertorum*.

INTERMEDIATE WHEATGRASS
(*Agropyron intermedium*)

Intermediate wheatgrass is a perennial sod-forming wheatgrass. In the few years since it was introduced by the Department of Agriculture from the Soviet Union, it has been tested extensively in the northern and central parts of the Great Plains and the Pacific Northwest. Under a wide variety of soil and climatic conditions, it shows great promise for use as a pasture and forage species throughout those regions. The species is more drought-resistant than smooth brome and somewhat less hardy and drought-resistant than crested wheatgrass.

The plants begin growth in early spring and reach a height of 3 to 4 feet before growth ceases in midsummer because of scarcity of moisture. The return of moisture and cool temperatures in the late summer brings good growth recovery.

The abundant leafy foliage is relished by all classes of livestock. Plant growth is vigorous. Established seedlings tend to form a full sod somewhat less rapidly than those of smooth brome

or western wheatgrass grown under like conditions of soil and moisture.

Seed production is dependable, particularly when plants are grown in rows to permit interrow cultivation. Seed yields of 300 pounds an acre have been had from row plantings. Seed may be harvested with standard farm equipment such as a binder, combine, or swather. As with other wheatgrass species, the quality of seed is improved by processing with a hammer mill and cleaning with a fanning mill.

Excellent seedling vigor permits relatively low seeding rates. This species has greatest promise for seeding in mixture with other adapted long-lived species for range and forage uses; its seed-producing qualities are so promising that the amount of seed needed for revegetation will no doubt become available in commercial quantities within the next few years.

WESTERN WHEATGRASS
(*Agropyron smithii*)

Western wheatgrass (a drawing of which appears on the next page) is a native, perennial, sod-forming grass distributed generally throughout the United States except in the humid Southeastern States. It is most abundant in the northern and central parts of the Great Plains, where it frequently occurs as the dominant species in native plant associations. Plant growth is vigorous, with seed heads at a height of 2 to 3 feet and with leaves 8 to 12 inches long and less than one-fourth inch wide. The leaf blades do not droop but are more or less stiff and erect. The entire plant is usually covered with a grayish bloom, which gives it a distinctive coloration.

The seed heads are 2 to 6 inches long. Usually there is but one spikelet at each node of the rachis.

Although western wheatgrass is adapted to a wide range of soils (including alkaline soils), it seems to prefer the heavy soils characteristic of shallow lake beds or along intermittent swales and water courses that receive

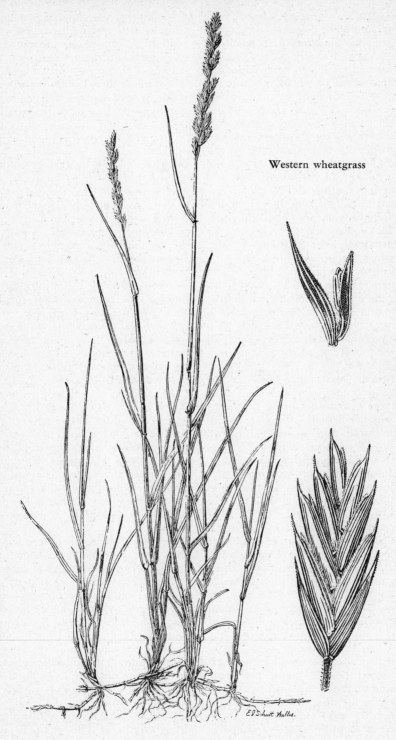

Western wheatgrass

excess surface drainage water. Under these conditions, western wheatgrass may be found in almost pure stands. It also occurs in nearly pure stands on abandoned cultivated fields where the original stand of wheatgrass was not entirely eliminated by cultivation. These "go back" fields are dependable for the production of hay or seed.

Western wheatgrass has several characteristics that make it exceedingly valuable for use in revegetation and erosion control. Its hardiness and drought resistance and its capacity to spread rapidly by means of underground rhizomes are outstanding values for conservation. It is excellent for terrace waterways and contour strip plantings for erosion control. The extent of its underground rhizomes and roots depends on availability of moisture and on the soil fertility. Ordinarily these underground plant parts make a profuse, dense growth, resulting in a tough, fibrous sod that effectively binds the soil and offers protection from erosion.

Growth starts fairly early in the spring and continues until limited by shortage of moisture or by continued hot summer periods. Abundant forage is produced and is relished by all classes of livestock until it becomes harsh and woody during late summer.

Mature plants cure well into a palatable, nutritious forage that provides excellent winter grazing. Leafy, high-quality hay also may be produced if proper precautions are taken to cut the grass while it is still succulent, not after the leaves and stems become harsh and woody. Yield of hay depends upon moisture, particularly that available during the early part of the growing season. It is not uncommon to obtain yields of three-fourths ton per acre of nearly pure western wheatgrass hay from "go back" fields. Native undisturbed areas seldom produce this much hay unless they have especially fertile soil and abundant moisture.

Seed yields are variable. They are influenced by soil fertility and by abundance of moisture and cool temperatures during the flowering stage of plant growth. Seed yields are more dependable if the plants are grown in rows and cultivated. Yields of 200 pounds of seed per acre have been obtained under these conditions, whereas yields of seed harvested from native stands are seldom more than half as great.

The seed may be harvested with a binder, a combine, or a swather. As in the case of crested wheatgrass, it is often found advantageous to use the binder or swather for the early stages of seed harvest and increase the normal 2- to 3-week harvest period.

Threshed material as it comes from the combine may contain excessive amounts of dirt, chaff, spikelet clumps, broken straw, and weed seeds. These may be removed by use of the ordinary fanning mill. In some instances it may be necessary to process the seed with a hammer mill to break up the clumps of spikelets. When the mill is properly adjusted as to screen size, air volume, and speed, seed of very high quality and purity should be obtained.

The number of clean seed per pound ranges from 100,000 to 125,000. Clean seed weighs about 20 pounds a bushel and has an average purity of 88 percent and a germination of 80 percent. Seed of the western wheatgrass, like that of many other native grasses, has low germination immediately after harvest. Its dormancy can ordinarily be overcome by 6 months to 1 year of dry storage.

Very good stands of western wheatgrass have been obtained from solid drill or broadcast seedings at the rate of 6 to 12 pounds of clean seed per acre. Best results have been obtained when seedings were made on well-prepared, clean seedbeds. Because the young seedlings are small and inconspicuous, the new stand often appears disappointing; but with full protection from grazing until the second growing season, the stand improves rapidly in vigor and density.

Western wheatgrass seedlings are drought-resistant. They compete fairly well with weeds and other grasses, although not so well as crested wheatgrass. The plants spread rapidly by means of underground rhizomes. Thus, if seeding results in a relatively thin stand, the spread will soon provide the density of cover desired. The sod-forming habit of western wheatgrass also provides a means of vegetative propagation on desired areas. The usual procedure is to start the new planting by use of sod pieces 3 or 4 inches square. This is an effective method of establishing a dense sod cover for a diversion channel, terrace, water outlet, or contour strip.

Its growth characteristics, drought resistance, hardiness, and wide adaptation to soil and climatic conditions make western wheatgrass one of the best grasses for revegetation and general farm use. Many acres of range and previously cropped farm lands have been seeded to this grass alone or in combination with other adapted forage grasses. Shortage of seed supplies has often limited the use of this grass.

Bluebunch Wheatgrass
(*Agropyron spicatum*)

Bluebunch wheatgrass, a native, perennial, drought-resistant bunchgrass is found chiefly in the dry, open areas of the western United States. It is the climax herbaceous species of the native vegetation of the Pacific Northwest and Intermountain States where it forms as much as 60 percent of the vegetative cover in many localities. Its abundance, general distribution, drought resistance, and dependability as range forage make it important in the two regions.

The vigorous plant growth starts rather early in the spring if enough moisture is available. The leaves are flat, rather lax, about 1/4 to 1/2 inch wide and 6 to 10 inches long. The volume of forage produced is usually high and dependable. The leafage remains green throughout the growing season and is nutritious and palatable even after growth ceases, although the stems become wiry late in the season. Plants may reach a height of 4 feet. Seed heads are about 6 inches long; the fairly dense spikelets have prominent divergent awns.

Agropyron inerme, beardless bluebunch wheatgrass, is closely related to bluebunch wheatgrass and differs only in that it lacks the awned spikelets. Many stockmen prefer it for the reason that lack of awns makes the plants more palatable, especially during the late stages of growth.

Both of these wheatgrasses are propagated only from seed. Deferring grazing until seed maturity, thus utilizing livestock for scattering the seed and trampling them into the ground, has been practiced to good advantage in some places. Many successful plantings have been made in revegetation work on range and farm lands in the Pacific Northwest.

Seed production from native stands is erratic. It depends upon moisture conditions during the spring months and upon cool temperatures during the critical period of blooming. These species produce seed satisfactorily when grown under cultivation; yields of more than 250 pounds per acre have been reported.

Seed may be harvested with a binder, a combine, or a swather, equipment that is most effective when the seed crop is grown under cultivation in rows. Native stands frequently occur on sites that are too rough, stony, and uneven for use of machinery; under such circumstances seed heads may be collected by means of a hand stripper or sickle. Mowing mature seed hay and subsequently scattering this seed material on a prepared seedbed has been practiced satisfactorily on areas that are not too extensive.

As seed material comes from the thresher or combine it often contains excessive amounts of dirt, chaff, straw, and other inert material. The divergent awns of bluebunch wheatgrass often are a great hindrance to the handling of this seed in drills of standard make. Processing the seed material with a hammer mill to remove the awns results in a clean seed product that can readily be drilled with standard seeding equipment. This processing is not costly, and the improved quality of seed more than pays for the small additional cost of time as well as labor.

Considerable progress has also been made in breeding and selecting improved strains of these species. Adequate and dependable sources of seed have not been developed, however; therefore, field plantings remain on a relatively small scale. Farmer seed producers and commercial seedsmen are endeavoring to produce seed of improved adapted strains under seed certification.

SLENDER WHEATGRASS
(*Agropyron trachycaulum*)

Slender wheatgrass is a native perennial bunchgrass distributed throughout the United States except in the Southeast and South Central States. It is most prevalent throughout the Northern Great Plains and the Rocky Mountain States. It commonly grows to a height of 3 feet, and the dense, leafy bunches may reach a foot or more in diameter. The leaves are from 3 to 13 inches long and about ¼ inch to ½ inch wide. Most of the leaves are basal, although there are quite a few stem leaves. The bunches enlarge by tillering, and propagation is entirely by seed. It is native to the Northern States and Canada. It was the first species to be cultivated and is one of the few native grasses that have become of commercial importance.

Although slender wheatgrass occurs on most soil types, it prefers the lighter soils, the sandy loams. It is less drought-resistant than either crested wheatgrass or western wheatgrass.

The flowering stems, erect and coarse, are numerous. The spikelets are usually not awned; this gives the seed head a characteristic slender appearance that distinguishes this grass from the other wheatgrasses.

Slender wheatgrass begins growth rather early in the spring and provides an abundance of palatable forage that is well liked by all classes of livestock. The forage cures well on the ground and furnishes considerable quantities of nutritious feed for winter grazing. The plants are not so resistant to close grazing as sod-forming species such as western wheatgrass, and careful management is required for most satisfactory grazing returns.

Good yields of high-quality hay are obtained if the plants are cut before the foliage becomes harsh and woody. The plants are relatively short-lived, and stand density decreases rapidly after the fourth production year. On the other hand, seedling vigor is exceptionally good and excellent vegetative cover is provided a few weeks after planting. These characteristics, combined with the relatively short life of the plants, suggest using this grass in mixture with other adapted grasses that are slow to become established but persist once they have done so.

Good crops of high-quality seed are usually obtained, particularly when this grass is grown in rows and cultivated. Seed yields of 200 to 300 pounds an acre have been produced under these conditions. Seed harvested from native stands seldom amounts to more than half this yield. There are between 140,000 and 160,000 clean seeds per pound, and a bushel weighs approximately 18 pounds.

Seed may be harvested with a binder, a combine, or a swather. Since seed heads shatter when fully ripe, it is often advantageous to make use of the binder or swather to lengthen the normal period of harvest. Combine-run seed usually contains excessive amounts of dirt, chaff, straw, and weed seeds; therefore, it is desirable to improve the quality of harvested seed by careful cleaning with a fanning mill.

Seeding at rates of 8 to 12 pounds per acre has resulted in good stands. The amount of seed should be adjusted in accordance with the kinds of species when mixtures are seeded.

When it is seeded with mixtures of other adapted species, particularly those having greater permanency of stand, this native species has a leading place in the revegetation of range and abandoned farm land. It is adapted to a wide range of soils and climates, and the forage is palatable to all classes of livestock. These desirable characteristics should encourage its more extensive use.

THE BENTGRASSES
(*Agrostis* species)

The name *Agrostis* is assigned to the genus that includes the bentgrasses and redtop. It is an ancient Greek name for a forage grass, from *agros,* a field. To all but one of the subdivisions or species the common name bent is applied, the exception being the species known as redtop. The creeping habit of growth is more or less characteristic of all species, including redtop. All are low to moderately tall annuals or (more usually) perennials.

Redtop is a perennial with a creeping habit that makes a coarse, loose, turf. It matures about the same time as timothy. The leaves are about one-fourth inch wide. The stems are slender. The panicle is loose, pyramidal, and usually reddish. Redtop is widespread in the United States; it grows from Canada to the Gulf of Mexico and from New York to California.

Many common names other than redtop have been assigned to it—whitetop, fiorin, white bent, Herd's grass, and others. Because all these names belong more properly to other grasses, they should not be used for redtop.

Of the many grasses of the genus *Agrostis,* redtop is the only one of much prominence for hay. It is used in pasture mixtures under humid conditions, as a soil binder, and as a winter lawn and golf-green grass in the Southeast. It ranks among the lowest of our standard northern pasture grasses in palatability, but it is valued in pasture mixtures because it comes

Creeping bent

quickly and vigorously and helps to form a compact turf that protects the soil until the slower growing grasses become established.

Redtop has outstanding ability to grow under a variety of conditions. It is one of the best wet-land grasses, but it also resists drought and will grow on soils so low in lime that most other grasses fail. The strength and the rhizomatous character of the roots make it useful for holding banks to prevent erosion. It will add to the yield of timothy and clover hay, but buyers of market hay find it objectionable.

Because the seeds are small, the best results are obtained from planting on a compact, well-prepared seedbed. Redtop is usually sown broadcast, 8 to 15 pounds to the acre when seeded alone. In a mixture, 2 to 4 pounds are commonly used. Fall is considered the best time for seeding.

The crop will persist for several years, depending upon the fertility of the soil and the management. It is ideal for use in lawn mixtures where quick establishment is desired because

Colonial bent

ductive longer and produce more seed. Grazing keeps them from becoming infested with weeds. Seed yields vary from season to season, but the average is about 55 pounds an acre. There are approximately 5,740,000 seeds in a pound; 14 pounds is the average weight of a bushel. Redtop seed will maintain viability for about 2 years.

The fine bentgrasses—colonial bent (*Agrostis tenuis*), creeping bent (*A. palustris*), and velvet bent (*A. canina*)—have been found well adapted for putting greens and, in mixtures with other grasses, for lawns over much of the northern half of the United States. For many years they have made beautiful lawn turf in New England.

Of the many strains of creeping bentgrass, most must be started by planting pieces of the stolons or runners because no seed is available. Washington creeping bent and Metropolitan creeping bent were the first named strains; many different strains now available are being used on putting greens. Seed of Seaside bent, also classed as creeping bent, is commercially available.

Velvet bentgrass (*A. canina*) is a fine-leaf type commonly found in rather limited districts in old turf. It is propagated from stolons, as are some varieties of creeping bent. Seed also is commercially available.

The bentgrass most generally used in lawn mixtures is commonly known as colonial bent (*A. tenuis*). It does not creep extensively; partly for that reason it needs less attention than the creeping bents. Astoria bent is essentially the same as the common colonial bent. Highland bent is classed as a variety of colonial bent but has a slightly different color and growth habit than the common colonial bent. All the colonial bents have given good results in lawn mixtures. They are affected by large brown patch, a fungus disease, and where they are grown alone they are likely to be injured by the disease.

The seeds of the bentgrasses run about 8 million to the pound.

it germinates rapidly but does not offer extreme competition to the slower growing, more permanent grasses. Redtop is seldom seeded alone.

Practically all the seed is produced in southern Illinois and parts of Missouri. The seed-producing fields remain for several years, depending upon management; the average duration in Illinois is 6 years. Seed fields that are pastured intermittently remain pro-

MEADOW FOXTAIL
(*Alopecurus pratensis*)

Meadow foxtail, a native of the temperate parts of Europe and Asia, has been cultivated since about 1750. Some of the earliest records indicate that it was recommended by Kalm in Sweden and Schreber in Germany in the middle of the 18th century, about 100 years before it was introduced into the United States.

A long-lived perennial, meadow foxtail resembles timothy in head so closely that it is often mistaken for it. The rootstocks are short (2 to 4 inches) and are comparatively few, as are the underground branches. The individual plants are generally in loose tufts, however, and old, heavy stands will produce medium dense sods. The flowering stems are erect and usually about 3 feet high; rarely they grow to 6 feet. The leaves are dark green, medium broad, and numerous.

The seeds are usually light in color. Occasional plants produce brown or black seeds. The caryopsis is enclosed in a light, fluffy, membranous covering.

Meadow foxtail is one of our earliest cultivated grasses. Growth begins in early spring. Flowering stems vary with climatic conditions. In places where winters and early springs are mild, a succession of flowering stems is produced from late in the winter to early summer. That is one of several characteristics that make this grass outstanding and versatile.

Cool, moist, climates are conducive to best growth of meadow foxtail. It is not sensitive to heat or cold, and succeeds in areas where summer temperatures occasionally reach 100° F. and where winter temperatures drop below zero for relatively long periods. Continuous winter growth often occurs where mean minimum temperatures are 40°. Soil moisture is the limiting factor during periods of high mean maximum temperatures, and usually growth is checked at these times. It is definitely not a southern grass but is adapted to the moist, cool climates of southern Canada and the Pacific Northwest. It also appears to have possibilities as a forage grass in several sections of the northern half of the United States.

Meadow foxtail is naturally a wet- or moist-land grass and makes its best growth on fertile or swampy soils. It is used extensively on diked lands near the coast in the Pacific Northwest. The occasional overflow of brackish water does little or no damage to established stands. It is quite tolerant to saline soils, but that tolerance depends largely on soil moisture. It responds to irrigation in cool climates and is adapted to irrigated pastures when seeded alone or in mixtures of other grasses and legumes.

Both fall and spring seedings are successful in the Pacific Northwest. Generally, in most sections where it is adapted, spring seeding is the most satisfactory on cultivated lands.

When it is seeded in combination with other grasses and legumes, 3 to 5 pounds of seed of meadow foxtail is usually used per acre. But allowances should be made for its extreme variability in germination; when only low-quality seed can be had, the rate of seeding should be increased.

Meadow foxtail is primarily a pasture grass. Its long life, long grazing season, winter hardiness, and succulent forage make it a valuable pasture grass where it is adapted. It is seldom used for hay, but the hay is leafy and palatable to all kinds of livestock. In Oregon its hay yields sometimes average about 1½ tons an acre for one cutting.

In the coastal sections of the Pacific Northwest for a number of years, meadow foxtail, in combination with various grasses and legumes, has been made into silage. We have no reports of silage made from pure stands of meadow foxtail.

Most of the seed is imported or produced in Oregon. Seed supplies have generally been ample despite low yields and difficulty in cleaning. Yields of seed vary from 25 to 300 pounds an acre, with an average of approximately 100 pounds. A bushel of seed weighs from 6 to 12 pounds. The seeds vary considerably in size, depending on quality; a pound contains 500,000 to 1,000,000 seeds.

Only to a limited extent do insects attack meadow foxtail in the humid climates. Slugs and cutworms cause some damage. In dry climates, especially late in the growing season when grasshoppers are numerous, considerable damage is caused. Occasionally aphids attack the green heads. No troublesome diseases have been noted, but ergot (*Claviceps purpurea*), scald (*Rhynchosporium orthosporum*), and stem rust (*Puccinia graminis*) have been observed on this plant.

THE BEACHGRASSES
(*Ammophila* species)

The grasses of the genus *Ammophila* provide protection for sandy coastal areas. They derive their name from the Greek, *ammos*, sand, and *philos*, loving. They are tough, coarse, erect perennials with hard, scaly, creeping rhizomes and dense, spikelike panicles. They produce heavy growth on unstable beach sand of low fertility.

The normal spread of plants from rhizomes is rapid, and the young plants are well able to withstand the cutting effect of wind-driven sand particles without serious injury.

Beachgrass should be considered primarily for the special purpose of erosion control on eroding sandy areas. Such planting sites should be completely protected from livestock because the trails formed by grazing animals frequently are the first cause of serious blow-outs. The capacity of beachgrasses to provide initial stabilization on shifting dune areas and the rapid accumulation of organic matter from their leafy foliage are outstanding qualities.

European beachgrass, *Ammophila arenaria*, is a robust perennial with deep, extensively creeping rhizomes. It is native to the coastal sands of northern Europe. The species has become well established at points along our Atlantic and Pacific coasts. The plants normally grow 5 feet high and produce large amounts of harsh, tough basal foliage. The root system is deep, with extensive rhizomes. The spikelike panicles are about 12 inches long, but viable seed are seldom produced.

American beachgrass, *Ammophila breviligulata*, occurs on the shores of the Great Lakes, along the Atlantic coast from Newfoundland to North Carolina, and sparingly along the Pacific coast. It resembles European beachgrass except for the smaller size of its ligule.

Both species have been used extensively for initial stabilization of moving sand on coastal areas. The most effective method of revegetation is by transplanting parts or clones of established plants. Clones for new planting are obtained by undercutting the old plants and separating the stems into convenient sizes for transplanting. Small buds, hidden by the lower leaf sheaths and occurring at the base of the stems, can form new plants and are an essential part of any vegetative material used to reproduce new plants.

Planting stock should be collected during the cool, wet months from late fall through early spring at a time when the plant is most nearly dormant. For convenience in handling, the culms are cut back to an over-all length of about 20 inches. These are set in hills on the new site, usually 3 to 5 culms per hill spaced at 2- to 3-foot intervals, with about 12 inches of the culms left standing above the surface.

The success of beachgrasses as sand stillers is due to the mechanical effect of the coarse stems that are allowed to project above the surface and give it protection against scouring; their rapid growth—2 feet or more in a single season—through heavy deposits of sand; the rapid multiplication of the stems from underground buds, so that large clumps soon are formed; the development of an extensive root system; and, in some cases, the production of horizontal underground stems capable of growing into unvegetated areas and producing new clumps.

Permanent grass or woody species should be the ultimate vegetative goal, but the beachgrasses are unexcelled for the special purpose of initial sand stabilization.

THE BLUESTEMS
(*Andropogon* species)

The *Andropogon* genus comprises a large group of species and is well represented throughout the world's warmer regions. The name, from the Greek *andros,* man's, and *pogon,* beard, alludes to the villous sterile pedicels.

Stems of *Andropogon* species are solid or pithy, differing in this respect from those of most other grasses, which are hollow. Two spikelets are produced at each node of the rachis. One spikelet is sessile and produces seed; the other is stalked but infertile.

Several species are regarded as good forage grasses because of their wide natural occurrence and dependability. Big bluestem, *A. gerardi,* and little bluestem, *A. scoparius,* are perhaps the most prevalent constituents of the wild hay of the prairie States. They are valued highly for grazing, although they are much less palatable as they mature.

Broomsedge, *A. virginicus,* also has a wide natural distribution and produces vegetative cover on soils of very low fertility. The palatability of broom sedge is poor; therefore it ranks low as a livestock forage. But its wide occurrence and persistence on worn-out, unproductive, sterile soils contributes materially to the protection of these sites.

Big Bluestem
(*Andropogon gerardi*)

Big bluestem is a vigorous, coarse, perennial native bunchgrass that occurs widely over most of the United States. Its major distribution is in the region of the tall-grass prairie in the Central States and along the eastern edge of the Great Plains.

Big bluestem

Plants usually grow 6 feet tall under favorable conditions of soil and moisture. Although short rhizomes are present, it usually makes a bunch type of growth. Leaf blades are about 12 inches long and from one-fourth to about one-half inch wide.

The leaves may be hairy near the base, and the sheaths are usually hairy. The flowering stalks are stout, coarse, and solid; the stalks of most other grasses are hollow. The extensive root system penetrates deeply. The grass grows well on most soil types but is most abundant on moist, well-drained loams of relatively high fertility.

Growth starts in late spring and continues throughout the summer. The abundant, leafy forage is palatable to all classes of livestock. It makes good-quality hay if mowed before the stemmy seed heads have formed. Much of the native hay marketed in the Midwest consists of big bluestem and associated species.

Successful plantings of big bluestem have been made on many soil types. The species may be seeded alone or in mixture with other adapted grasses. It has been planted chiefly to retire cropped land for permanent meadow or pasture use. The vegetative cover offers good surface protection. Seedings should be made on a well-prepared, firm seedbed free from weeds. Seeding rates of 15 pounds of good seed an acre have given excellent results. Full protection during the period of establishment is necessary; weeds should be mowed to lessen the competition for water and nutrients.

Big bluestem seldom produces seed every year, because the combination of plentiful moisture and moderate temperatures at the critical time of blooming does not occur regularly. When it is grown in rows and cultivated, however, it consistently produces 150 to 200 pounds of seed an acre. The seed normally matures in late September and October.

Ordinary binders and small-grain combines have been used satisfactorily to harvest the seed. Seed material as it comes from the combine or thresher usually contains excessive amounts of stems, chaff, and other inert matter. The material should be cleaned with a fanning mill. If cleaning is done satisfactorily, the seed should have a purity of at least 40 percent and a germination of about 60 percent.

LITTLE BLUESTEM
(Andropogon scoparius)

Little bluestem is a vigorous, long-lived, native bunchgrass of wide distribution over the United States. It is most prevalent in the Great Plains, particularly in the Flint Hill sections of Kansas and Oklahoma, where it supplies dependable grazing and cured forage. But in many areas it is not considered of major economic value because of low palatability and poor quality of its forage as the plants mature.

Little bluestem

Little bluestem is smaller than big bluestem. The two usually are found in close association, but little bluestem is more drought-resistant and is better adapted therefore to sites that receive limited moisture.

Growth begins late in the spring and continues through the summer. Plants usually grow 1 to 3 feet tall. The leaf blades are less than $\frac{1}{4}$ inch wide and from 4 to 8 inches long. The leaves, flattened at the base, are light green until the plants reach maturity, when they develop the distinctive reddish-brown color.

Because of its habit of growth and the wide range of soils on which it thrives, little bluestem has great value for erosion control. It is suitable for use in crop rotations and in mixtures for regrassing abandoned cultivated land. Seedings should be made on a well-prepared, firm seedbed free from weeds. A seeding rate of 15 pounds an acre has given good results.

Seed matures in late September and

October. The amount of seed produced in native stands depends on timely rainfall during the growing season, the reserve moisture, and favorable temperatures during the period of seed development. Because of these requirements, dependable seed harvests seldom occur in any area in successive years. If it is grown in rows and cultivated, however, it sometimes yields 200 pounds or even more of seed to the acre.

Seed can be harvested with a binder, combine, or swather. The seed units of little bluestem are light and chaffy, with awned appendages, and the seed material as it comes from the combine or thresher requires additional cleaning before it can be seeded with farm drills. The ordinary farm hammer mill has been found useful in processing the seed material.

By processing it with a hammer mill and cleaning it with a fanning mill to remove seed appendages and break up excessive stems and straw, a seed product of satisfactory quality can be obtained.

Seed purity of at least 40 percent and germination of 60 percent should be obtained by properly processing and cleaning the thresher-run seed material. A pound of clean seed contains 254,000 to 263,000 seed units.

TALL OATGRASS
(*Arrhenatherum elatius*)

Tall oatgrass, a standard grass in parts of Europe, is grown quite generally in the Central and Northern States. Kalm advocated its culture in Sweden in 1747. The genus name is from the Greek word *arren,* meaning masculine, and *ather,* meaning awn, which refers to the awned staminate florets. It was cultivated in Massachusetts as early as 1807 and in South Carolina in 1821.

A hardy and upright perennial, tall oatgrass grows to 30 to 60 inches and produces many leaves. It does not propagate by rootstocks. It tends to be bunchy. It produces seed in open heads

Tall oatgrass

or panicles resembling those of cultivated oats, although the seed is smaller and much more chaffy.

Tall oatgrass prefers well-drained soil and seems to be especially adapted to light sandy or gravelly land. It does not grow well in shade. It has never attained great importance in any locality, but it does have many desirable forage qualities. It can be used for pasture or meadow; it gives a heavy yield of hay, which is quite palatable. Although it does not produce a very good sod, it seems to stand pasturing well and furnishes abundant grazing.

It comes on early in the spring and remains green until late in the autumn. Best results are obtained if it is grazed in rotation and given controlled grazing. Under continuous, close grazing the stand is easily reduced. It is becoming a common practice in the Pacific Northwest to use a mixture of tall oatgrass and sweetclover for a short-rotation hay or pasture combination. Mixtures of tall oatgrass, orchardgrass, and red clover have been used. For the best hay the mixture should be cut at about the time that it begins blooming.

Its poor seed habit is a drawback. It produces abundant seed, but harvesting is difficult because the seed shatters before fully mature. The seed is often of low viability. The seed weighs 10 to 16 pounds a bushel. Approximately 150,000 seeds weigh a pound. The usual rate of seeding is 30 to 40 pounds to the acre.

In sections where there is a reasonable amount of moisture in autumn or late summer and where winters are not severe, best results will probably be obtained by seeding in September or early October; otherwise, spring seedings are best. Broadcasting is best, because the coarse, fluffy seed does not feed evenly through a drill. A well-fitted seedbed is essential. After sowing, the seed should be covered by cultipacking or harrowing lightly.

An improved strain, developed in Oregon, is being increased under the name Tualatin. Its seed shatters less readily than that of common tall oatgrass; in the East it is somewhat shorter in growth and has narrower leaves.

CARPETGRASS
(*Axonopus affinis*)

Carpetgrass, a native of Central America and the West Indies, was introduced into the United States before

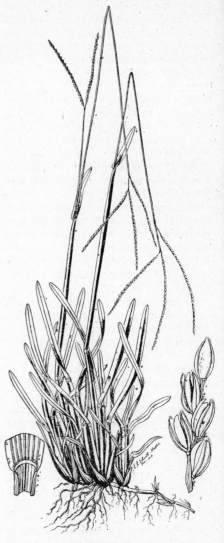

Carpetgrass

1832. A specimen collected near New Orleans that year is still preserved.

Carpetgrass has now spread over the Coastal Plain from Virginia to Texas and inland to Arkansas. It now grows in the Tropics of both hemispheres.

A perennial creeping grass, it makes a dense sod and is distinguished by its compressed, two-edged, creeping stems, which root at each joint, and by its blunt leaf tips. The slender flower stems grow a foot high—rarely 2 feet if the soil is fertile. Because it has no underground stems, it never has become a pest in cultivated fields.

Carpetgrass is especially adapted to sandy or sandy loam soils, particularly where the moisture is near the surface most of the year. It grows well in the low, flat woods in the Coastal Plains region. It is moisture loving, but it does poorly in swamps or where seepage is continuous. Over much of the area where it is grown, carpetgrass is probably most valuable for permanent pasture. It also has value for firebreaks in forests, lawns and turf, for use along roads, and for open areas in the pine forests. The cheapness and abundance of seed and ease of establishment make it popular in the South.

Because its sod is dense and its habit of growth is aggressive, legumes are maintained with difficulty in a cultivated pasture when carpetgrass is used. On fertile soils it makes a good growth, but generally it is not high enough in feed nutrients to furnish a balanced diet. Consequently, it is not generally recommended for the improved, high-producing pastures.

Seed is harvested mainly in Mississippi and Louisiana. Seed harvested with a combine (the general practice now), if properly handled, is usually superior in color, purity, and germination to that cut with a mower, shocked in field, and threshed later. A pound contains about 1,350,000 seeds; a bushel of seed weighs 18 to 36 pounds.

The usual rate of seeding is 5 to 10 pounds to the acre. Seed can be sown on a well-prepared seedbed or broadcast on burned-over open areas in timberland. It is spread quite easily by grazing animals and by natural reseeding. Seeding is best done in spring, early summer, or even midsummer.

THE GRAMA GRASSES
(*Bouteloua* species)

All species of *Bouteloua* are native to the Western Hemisphere. About 18 species occur in the United States. They are well represented throughout the Great Plains and Western States. They are reliable producers of good forage on range and pasture land and are prized therefore in various sections.

The gramas are summer growers, and the amount of forage they produce depends upon the moisture available during the growing season. In years of extreme drought they make little or no new top growth. Most species cure naturally, however, and standing growth from previous seasons makes very satisfactory and palatable forage for most classes of livestock.

Individual spikelets are small and single-flowered, a characteristic that greatly simplifies the identification of species of *Bouteloua*.

SIDE-OATS GRAMA
(*Bouteloua curtipendula*)

Side-oats grama is a long-lived, native grass with an exceptionally wide, natural distribution. It is most abundant in the Great Plains. It has short, scaly rhizomes; usually it makes a bunch-type growth and seldom forms a dense sod.

The flowering stalks are 2 to 3 feet tall. The leaves are about 6 inches long and nearly ¼ inch wide. The seed head consists of a large number of spikes set on a slender, zigzag rachis about 6 to 8 inches long. The stalks of the spikes are twisted, so that the spikes all extend, like a banner, on one side of the central axis. The root system is fairly deep and well branched; thus the plants can effectively utilize all available moisture.

Side-oats grama produces an abundance of leafy forage, which is well liked by all classes of livestock. Good hay can be had if the plants are mowed at the proper stage of growth.

Ordinarily this species is seeded in mixtures with other adapted grasses. A seeding rate of 15 to 25 pounds an acre is generally recommended. The desirable rate depends upon the quality of seed and upon the other grasses, if any, used in mixture. Seed matures about midsummer. The plants reach sufficient height to be harvested with a binder. They can be combined with ordinary small-grain equipment.

Yields of 100 pounds or more of seed an acre are not uncommon from a native stand. If plants are grown in rows and cultivated, seed yields of more than 400 pounds an acre have been obtained.

Throughout the threshing operation, the seeds tend to remain in clusters, which usually require some mechanical treatment to break them into individual units. After it is cleaned with a fanning mill, the seed should have a purity of 30 percent and a germination of 65 percent. A pound of pure seed contains about 125,000 seed clusters or about 500,000 separate seed units.

Side-oats grama is considered excellent for conservation use. It produces a good volume of leafy forage and is adapted to a wide range of soil and climatic conditions. Seedling vigor is good, and failure to obtain a satisfactory stand seldom occurs if minimum care is used in seedbed preparation and drilling.

Elreno side-oats grama, a new variety developed through plant selection, is now being grown and certified by the Kansas Agricultural Experiment Station.

BLUE GRAMA
(*Bouteloua gracilis*)

Blue grama is a low-growing, long-lived, native perennial that grows throughout the Great Plains. The leaves are 3 to 6 inches long and less than ⅛ inch wide. The flowering stems are 12 to 18 inches tall. Each stem usually has two purplish spikes that extend at a sharp angle from the main stem.

Blue grama is found on all soil types, including alkaline soils, but is most abundant on the heavier rolling upland soils. Its capacity to resist drought permits it to occupy the drier sites throughout its range of adaptation.

Growth begins fairly late in the season and depends on how much moisture is available. The forage is relished by all the classes of livestock. Growth ceases during long droughts but begins again upon the return of favorable moisture and temperature. Because of its wide distribution, high quality, hardiness, and growth habits, it is one of our most important range species.

Under heavy grazing, blue grama often persists in nearly pure stands after the associated grasses disappear.

Blue grama is readily established from seed. Excellent stands have been obtained by broadcast or solid-drill seedings. The usual seeding rate is 8 to 12 pounds of clean seed to the acre. For most satisfactory results, the seedbed should be well prepared and be free of weeds, but the seedlings are relatively persistent and compete with weeds and other grasses if they are not grazed until they become well established.

The seed usually matures in August. The amount of seed produced depends on whether moisture is plentiful and temperatures are cool during the period of blossoming and seed formation. Seed heads of blue grama ripen rapidly as they near maturity, and utmost care must be used to harvest the seed before the seed heads shatter. Direct combining and swathing followed by pick-up combining are the most effective methods of seed harvest. Seed yields of 100 to 180 pounds an acre have been obtained from good natural stands.

After being cleaned in a fanning mill, the seed should have a purity of at least 40 percent and a germination of 75 percent. A pound of pure seed contains about 800,000 units.

Because of its wide adaptation, ease of establishment, and economic value, blue grama is used extensively for conservation purposes. Although its erosion-control properties are effective when blue grama is seeded alone, the general practice is to make plantings with mixtures of other adapted grasses. Most revegetation seedings have been made on range land and abandoned cropland.

As a general rule, seed should be used near its point of origin. Experi-

In the grass nursery at Woodward, Okla., J. R. Harlan examines strains of buffalo-grass—female plants on the right and male on the left. He compares them as to the sex ratios in different progenies, germination, seedling vigor, rate of growth, the quality and quantity of vegetation, probable seeding habits, and so on. Below, to obtain pollen, technicians at Woodward select male plants from one of the plots. Besides the new strains from plant breeders, collections from native vegetation and introductions from abroad provide material for ultimate use on farms, ranches, and eroded areas—if they survive the thorough research studies and observations.

The pollen from the selected male strain is carefully brushed on the flower of a promising female plant. The resulting seed is planted, for increase, in nurseries—as in the picture below, which shows rows of Russian wild-rye at the Northern Great Plains Field Station at Mandan, N. Dak. In the nurseries, supplemental observation in conservation problem areas, and in research studies by several units of the Department, new grasses are tested at this stage for influence on the soil structure and the fertility, resistance to diseases and insects, response to acid or alkali soils, value for forage and conservation, season of use, and the rate of development.

Among the many new grasses that are being developed or tested in the Great Plains nurseries are (top, left) a typical plant of the standard crested wheatgrass; (top, right) a new wheatgrass, stiffhair wheatgrass or *Agropyron trichophorum,* that is well adapted to the Plains region; (below, left) Siberian wheatgrass, which was introduced from Russia and resembles the crested wheatgrass but is inferior to it; and (below, right) Mandan wild-rye, an improved strain of the Canada wild-rye that was released to American farmers in 1946. Whatever laymen think of grass, to plant breeders a grass is a living individual with its own specific uses, habits, place, and needs.

The work of getting new and better grasses and legumes is big and complex. As A. L. Hafenrichter and A. D. Stoesz put it, one has to find, assemble, test, and improve new materials and then grow large amounts of seed. Sometimes one has to devise special machines to harvest and plant the new grasses. One such is the seed harvester (above). The fluffy, chaffy seed, as harvested, is usually threshed and treated in a hammer mill. Below are pictures of unprocessed (top) and processed seed of grama, bluestem, and wild-rye. Many farmers have their own seed plots; from several hundred production fields other farmers can obtain seed.

Agricultural workers have had to perfect special drills and drill attachments to make it easier to seed in stubble mulches, reseed ranges and abandoned lands, and plant the new grass-legume mixtures. A rotary hoe (above) and a double drill box were combined so that mixtures of a large-seeded grass, a small-seeded grass, and a legume could be planted in stubble mulches. Drill box attachments were made to handle tiny seeds (below, left) like those of lovegrass. Depth bands were fastened to double-disk drills (below, right) to plant the seeds uniformly at shallow depth. Sometimes grass grows like Topsy; sometimes it needs special techniques.

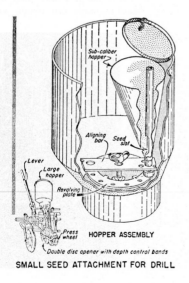

SMALL SEED ATTACHMENT FOR DRILL

Fertilization is a major item in grassland agriculture. A test plot of wild-rye at Mandan got no fertilizer; on another acre (below) 90 pounds of nitrogen was used. Soil fertility regulates the amount of crop growth and influences its quality. As J. T. Sullivan and H. L. Wilkins point out, fertilization may favor the growth of some plants rather than others. Fertilizers also change the chemical composition of the individual plant. Plants take up any element present in soluble form in the soil and may take up more when more is present. The response to fertilizers depends upon the fertility of the soil and upon the age and condition of the plant.

Sand dunes in the United States cover an area a tenth as large as the area of farm land. Along the coasts, around the Great Lakes, and in nearly all inland States, dunes menace forests, destroy agricultural lands, and leave waste behind. In the words of Charles J. Whitfield and Robert L. Brown, sand dunes have been a problem for centuries; most of the active dunes in the United States are caused by man's abuse of the protective cover of vegetation; their permanent control can be achieved only by establishing on them a vegetative cover by natural succession or by seeding. Mechanical structures stop sand movement only temporarily.

A coastal dune in Oregon (preceding page, top) was out of hand. First, to stabilize it, the sand was stilled temporarily with beachgrass (preceding page, bottom; and above). A year later (below), the dune is permanently fixed by the perennial plants like Clatsop red fescue, tall fescue, hairy vetch, and purple beachpea. In the Midwest and Great Plains the hard areas around individual dunes are often deep-listed to catch sand blown from the dunes and scatter it; sometimes a drag pole is used to break down the crests. The area is then mulched and seeded to switchgrass, the bluestems, Indiangrass, big sandreed grass, the lovegrasses, or others.

The picture above was taken in 1903. It shows an open, productive grassland in the Southwest, the kind that made the pioneers stop and marvel at the bounty of nature, at the luxuriant grass that grew belly-high to a horse and fed cattle like no other. Forty years later the picture below was made from the same spot. What has happened here has happened on millions of acres in Arizona, Texas, and New Mexico: Mesquite, a low-value forage plant, has invaded the range after grazing by domestic livestock—and grazing capacity is lowered, erosion is accelerated, the costs of handling livestock are up. The remedy: Kill the noxious plants, reseed, then graze conservatively.

A burned brush range in central Utah supported mainly big sagebrush, snowberry, shrub oak, and chokecherry. Seed of 17 promising species of range plants was broadcast and harrowed in (above). In September of the following year grass nearly waist-high (below) was growing on the place, and the grazing capacity was 15 times greater than before burning. Men in the Forest Service estimate that 80 million acres of range land need reseeding. To be successful and as inexpensive as possible, reseeding must be done carefully: Sites must be chosen wisely; low-value competing vegetation must be removed; and proved species seeded according to tested practices.

At Woodward, Okla., mowing in two successive Junes and keeping livestock off the range from June to September killed many sagebrush plants, weakened the rest, improved the pastures, and made surviving shrubs more palatable. Almost any heavy-duty power take-off mower, properly equipped, can be used to mow heavy brush (above). Tests in 1947 near Woodward and in Texas showed that 2,4–D, which can be applied from airplanes for as little as $2 an acre, killed sand sagebrush, skunkbush, plum thicket, and many other range weeds. Below, E. H. McIlvain, ecologist at the Southern Great Plains Field Station at Woodward, inspects results of the mowing and the weed killer.

Many types of implements have been used to control noxious plants. A specially designed bit (above) is used to uproot a late species of juniper, or cedar, on thousands of acres in Texas. A one-way disk plow, of the wheatland type, is commonly used for eradicating sagebrush in Utah, Idaho, and Nevada (below). Other tools used with varying success in the Southern Great Plains to remove brush include brush beaters, which do a good job if properly built; rolling cutters, which are satisfactory in brush too heavy to handle otherwise; and railroad rails. To fight mesquite, sodium arsenite, oils, grubbing, or power machinery are recommended.

Of many ways to put up hay, no one method seems best for all farms. As R. B. Gray says, kind and quantity of hay, its use, growing conditions, equipment, and so on determine the choice. But regardless of method, the grass must first be cut—by the familiar mower or a newer machine. The field grass chopper (above) cuts and chops the green crop for silage as it stands in the field. Or, after cutting, the hay is raked into windrows to facilitate handling. Dump rakes handle widths up to 24 feet. Below is a tractor-powered side-delivery rake on rubber, designed for fast raking and raking heavy crops. Its four-bar reels are said to shatter the leaves less.

After the hay is cut and windrowed, it is loaded or baled. The raker-bar loader (above) has reciprocating bars with flexible teeth that rake the hay up the sloping deck and drop it on the rack. It has a folding foretruck for easier storing. For loading green crops, loaders built more ruggedly are often used. Of several types of balers, a one-man baler (below) makes a roll 36 inches long, 14–22 inches thick, and 40–100 pounds in weight. Its pick-up feeds the hay into a series of belts. When the desired diameter of bale is attained, a device ties it with twine. Other types of balers are operated by one, two, or three men and use wire or twine. Some make rectangular bales.

A mower-crusher (above) is available to make it easier to cure coarse-stemmed hay. It cuts the hay in the usual way and passes it through crushing rolls to crack the stems. Then the hay is windrowed. On the Group Brothers farm in southeastern Pennsylvania (below), field-chopped grass is unloaded from a truck into the trough of the elevator that blows the material into the silo. The motor at the right operates a shaft that rolls back a canvas floor in the truck to speed up unloading. The Group Brothers use a 4-1-1-1 rotation of grass-legumes, corn, oats, barley. Two-thirds of their farm is in grassland, primarily orchardgrass and Ladino.

To see whether his legume hay is ready for ensiling, a Pennsylvania farmer uses a moisture tester (above), a flat-bottomed plunger in a steel pipe. A hay sample in the pipe is too wet if juice oozes from small holes in the pipe when 32 pounds of sand is put in the pail. If no juice comes when twice that weight is applied, the hay is too dry. Scientists in the Bureau of Dairy Industry, who devised the tester, set up baby silos (below) at Beltsville to help in their extensive tests of silage mixtures and treatments. Later in full-size silos they conduct further experiments with processes that look promising in the pilot silos, which measure 4 feet by 8 feet.

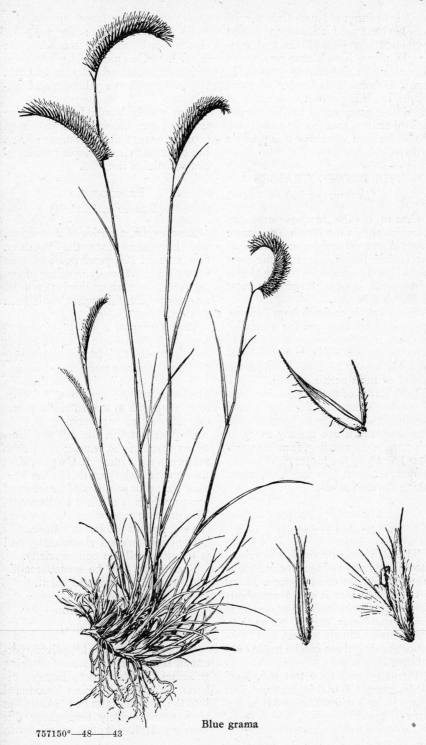

Blue grama

mental plantings of North Dakota seed have not been productive when planted in the Southern Great Plains and, conversely, plants from Texas-grown seed do not make satisfactory growth in North Dakota. This matter of plant adaptation is important with many of the native grasses and has led to the general caution that locally grown seed should be used whenever it is possible to do so.

THE BROME GRASSES
(*Bromus* species)

Grasses of the brome genus are found mostly in the North Temperate Zone. About 43 species are native to the United States. Some of our most important forage species belong to this genus—and also some of our most troublesome weeds.

The name is derived from *bromos,* an ancient Greek name for a kind of oat, and is cognate with *broma,* food. Most bromes are highly palatable— even the weedy bromes, during their period of most active growth.

Leaf blades of the bromes are characteristically flat, and the edges of the sheath grow together to form a tube. The seed heads are usually more or less open and spreading, forming panicles. The tip of the rather rigid lemma is notched into two teeth, between which the awn arises.

CALIFORNIA BROME
(*Bromus carinatus*)

The California brome is a vigorous, short-lived native of the Rocky Mountain and Pacific coast regions. Many botanists consider it a polymorphous species that includes *Bromus marginatus, B. maritimus,* and *B. polyanthus.* All forms are closely related, and separations among them can be made only arbitrarily.

Plants grow 3 to 4 feet tall. Leaf blades are flat, 6 to 8 inches long, and about ½ inch wide. The seed is rather strongly awned.

The species is characterized by ca-

pacity to produce large quantities of leafy forage that is relished by all classes of livestock. The mature foliage is harsh and less palatable, a condition that is offset somewhat by the fact that the seed heads are palatable and nutritious.

This species would have extensive use for revegetation if adequate seed supplies were available. Some progress has been made in developing commercial supplies of the seed.

RESCUEGRASS
(*Bromus catharticus*)

Rescuegrass, a native of Argentina, was introduced into the Southern States about 100 years ago and now appears spontaneously in many places there. It is a short-lived perennial adapted to humid regions with mild winters.

Plants grow to a height of 2 to 3 feet. Leaf blades are 8 to 12 inches long and about ¼ inch wide. Young plants are usually pubescent, but mature plants are only slightly so. Panicles are branched and are about 6 inches long, with two to five spikelets at the extremity of each branch.

Growth starts in the fall and continues through the winter; the plants mature in early summer. On poor land they make little growth but on rich soils they produce a good amount of forage, which is relished by livestock. The growing vegetation also protects the soil against erosion in winter.

Seed is produced abundantly, and is usually available commercially. Rescuegrass can be seeded readily with available farm equipment.

SMOOTH BROME
(*Bromus inermis*)

Smooth brome is a long-lived, perennial sod grass with strong creeping rhizomes. It is native to Europe, Siberia, and China. It was introduced into the United States in 1884 and has been grown widely throughout this country. It is adapted especially to

Smooth brome

regions of moderate rainfall and low to moderate summer temperatures.

Plants grow to a height of 3 to 4 feet and produce an abundance of basal and stem leaves. Leaf blades vary from 8 to 12 inches in length and from $\frac{1}{4}$ to $\frac{1}{2}$ inch in width. The leaf sheaths are smooth and closed, forming a tube. The inflorescence is a panicle from 6 to 8 inches long. The root system is extensive, with strong rootstocks. The interlaced roots and rootstocks form a coarse but dense sod, which resists grazing and trampling and, by binding the soil, protects it against wind and water erosion.

Two distinct types of smooth brome, differing in growth behavior, are generally recognized.

The "southern type" came originally from central Europe and is best adapted to the Corn Belt States and to the parts of the central Great Plains that have protracted dry periods and high summer temperatures. Improved varieties include Achenbach, Lincoln, and Fischer.

The "northern type" was introduced from Siberia and has been found well adapted to Canada and the Northern Great Plains, where long periods of hot weather seldom occur.

Smooth brome makes its best growth on moist, well-drained clay loam soils of relatively high fertility. Although more drought-hardy than most cultivated species, it does not withstand the extremes of low moisture and low winter temperatures so well as crested wheatgrass or many of the native grasses of the Great Plains.

As a pasture or hay grass, smooth brome scarcely has an equal in the area of its best adaptation. Growth begins early in the spring and continues through the summer if enough moisture is available. Its good volume of leafy forage is relished by all classes of livestock.

Satisfactory stands have been obtained in the Great Plains, where this grass has been seeded at rates of 12 to 15 pounds an acre on well-prepared, weed-free seedbeds. Smooth brome fits well into a grass-legume seeding, and many acres are now in brome-alfalfa mixture that formerly were devoted to legumes alone.

Such grass-legume seedings have special conservation and economic values. They give greater forage yield and protection to the soil than either the brome or the alfalfa would have given if seeded alone, and the danger of bloat to grazing animals is less. The presence of a legume in the mixture also prolongs the useful life of the stand, presumably because it increases the amount of nitrogen available in the soil and thereby keeps the grass stand from becoming sod-bound.

Seed matures in midsummer. Under normal conditions about 75 percent of the seeds are well filled. Yields often average 300 to 500 pounds of seed an acre—more, if the grass is grown in rows on fertile soil and cultivated.

Seed may be harvested with a binder or with a small-grain combine. Combine- or thresher-run seed, if cleaned with a fanning mill, should have a purity of 85 percent and a germination of 90 percent. Approximately 175,000 pure seeds weigh a pound.

MOUNTAIN BROME
(*Bromus marginatus*)

Mountain brome is a short-lived grass that is native to the Rocky Mountain and Pacific coast regions. It is closely related to California brome and similar to it in soil and climatic adaptation.

Plants usually grow to a height of 3 to 4 feet, with leaves 6 to 12 inches long, and about $\frac{1}{4}$ inch wide. The flat leaf blades are usually hairy on their lower parts. Leaf sheaths are closed and form tubes.

Growth starts in early spring and continues with the production of large amounts of leafy forage that is liked by livestock. Rapid growth, vigor of seedlings, and a well-branched and deeply penetrating root system, the outstanding characteristics of mountain brome, make it one of the most valuable grasses for use where vegetative cover is required immediately to protect erodible sloping land.

Seed matures in midsummer and can be harvested with a binder or with a small-grain combine. Good-quality seed can be obtained by cleaning the combine-run seed material with a fanning mill. Seed yields are heavy and the quality and the amount produced from cultivated rows are significantly greater than from solid seedings. Seed yields of 400 to 500 pounds an acre have sometimes been obtained where the grass is grown primarily for seed. The forage remaining after removal of the seed crop is of fair quality and may be grazed or cut and cured for roughage.

One of the important uses of this grass in the agriculture of the Pacific Northwest is for seeding in mixture with alfalfa or sweetclover. In such a mixture, the grass adds materially to both root and top growth. The combination offers greater soil protection than legumes alone because of greater density of plants and greater volume of roots. It is said also that the mixture of grass with the legumes, which are high in protein content, lessens the danger of bloat and provides a better-balanced forage.

Bromar, an improved variety, has recently been released by State experiment stations of the Pacific Northwest and is being produced as certified seed in commercial quantities by members of the several crop-improvement associations.

BUFFALOGRASS
(*Buchloë dactyloides*)

Buffalograss is a fine-leaved, native, sod-forming perennial. It is the dominant species on large areas of upland on the short-grass region of the central part of the Great Plains. Generally it grows 4 to 6 inches high and produces leaves less than 1/8 inch wide and 3 to 6 inches long. It spreads rapidly by surface runners and forms a dense, matted turf. During the growing sea-

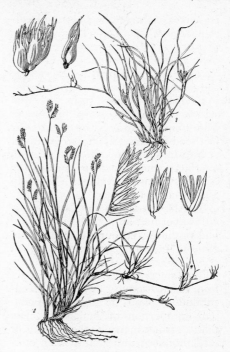

Buffalograss

son the foliage is grayish green, which turns to a light straw color when the plants cease growth.

Growth begins in late spring and continues through the summer. Livestock like its forage. Its palatability, prevalence, and adaptation to a wide range of soil and climatic conditions make it an important forage species of the Great Plains.

It withstands long, heavy grazing better than any other grass native to that region; on ranges consistently subjected to severe use it often survives as a nearly pure stand. Because of its excellent ground cover, aggressive spread under use, wide climatic adaptation, and relative ease of establishment, buffalograss is ideally suited for erosion control on range and pasture lands where the soil does not contain too much sand.

The seed of the grass is enclosed in hard burs, one or more grains in a bur. The burs normally have a low germination. Soaking and chilling, processing with a hammer mill, or some other such treatment of the burs is usually required to insure good stands from planting at moderate rates.

Small-grain combines altered so that the sickle can be run very close to the ground are satisfactory for harvesting buffalograss burs from ungrazed stands. Suction machines, brooms, or beater equipment must be used to collect seed from closely grazed stands.

Natural stands have yielded as much as 100 pounds of clean burs to the acre. A pound averages 40,000 to 55,000 clean burs.

The buffalograss plants are unisexual; about half are female in function and produce seed burs; the others are male in function and produce pollen only. When plants are grown under cultivation primarily for seed production, it is customary to grow 10 seed-producing plants to 1 pollen plant. This proportion of female to male plants greatly increases the amount of seed produced under cultivation on a given acreage over that possible under natural conditions.

Revegetation by use of sod pieces is effective. Sod pieces about 4 inches in diameter are placed at 3- to 4-foot intervals on a well-conditioned seedbed. Usually this results in a complete sod cover by the end of the second growing season.

Buffalograss seed is available from commercial sources, although not in abundance.

RHODESGRASS
(*Chloris gayana*)

Rhodesgrass was first brought to the attention of the agricultural world by the late Cecil Rhodes, after whom it is named. It is a perennial grass native to South Africa and was first introduced into this country in 1902.

It is fine-stemmed and very leafy and grows approximately 3 feet high. The spreading, clustered spikes of the flowering head number from 10 to 15, and seed is produced in abundance. The plant also spreads by running branches, or stolons, that are 2 to 6

Rhodesgrass

feet long and root and produce a plant at every node. That factor suggests that the Rhodesgrass might become a troublesome weed, but such has not been the case. Tests show that it can be easily controlled.

Rhodesgrass is not winter-hardy and rarely withstands temperatures below 15° or 18° F. Its adaptation therefore is limited. However, it is winter-hardy and perennates in a narrow strip along the Gulf Coast from Florida to southern Texas and in southern Arizona and California. Farther north it must be treated as an annual, but as yet its use in that way is not recommended.

It does best on fairly moist soil, although it will make growth during several months of drought. It grows well on sandy soils in south Texas, well-drained peaty soils in Florida, and on soils too alkaline for alfalfa, cotton, and other crops in southern California.

Rhodesgrass can be sown any time during warm weather, but early spring usually is preferred. The seed is usually broadcast at rates of 5 to 7 pounds per acre. In regions of abundant rainfall or in irrigation fields, rates of 10 to 12 pounds may be advisable. The quantity also varies with quality of the seed and condition of the land. A well-prepared seedbed will help insure a good stand, although stands have been established on rather loose, rough ground.

Rhodesgrass was first cultivated for pasture. It withstands trampling, recovers quickly, and is relished by livestock. Rotation grazing is the best method of management to insure greater production and maintenance of stand. It will also yield a leafy hay of high quality. The production for pasture or hay varies greatly, depending on soil fertility and the season. Yields of 5 to 7 tons of hay an acre have been reported.

Rhodesgrass will produce three or four crops of seed a year, but the seed development lacks uniformity. The first crop is generally the most productive, with annual yields of 400 to 500 pounds an acre not uncommon. Seed is harvested with combine, binder, or, sometimes, with seed strippers. Because of lack of uniformity in maturity, great care is necessary to obtain seed of good quality. The seeds vary greatly in size but average approximately 2 million to the pound.

BERMUDA-GRASS
(*Cynodon dactylon*)

Bermuda-grass is a native of the Old World, probably of India, but is now common in all tropical and subtropical parts of the world. We do not know when it was introduced into the United States, but reports published in 1807 mentioned it as an important grass in the Southern States. Now it is found in all parts of the southern half of the United States from Virginia to Florida and westward to Arizona and California. It is also called wiregrass, dog's tooth grass, and devil grass.

Bermuda-grass is a long-lived perennial with a spreading habit of growth. It propagates by runners, underground rootstocks, and seed. The runners vary from a few inches to 3 or 4 feet in length, and under favorable conditions they may grow 15 to 20 feet in a season. The rootstocks, which may become stolons (runners) on hard soils, are thick and white. The erect, flowering branches are usually 6 to 12 inches high, depending on the fertility and moisture of the soil. The leaves are short, flat, bluish-green, and 1 to 4 inches long. At the base of each leaf is a fringe of white hairs; the leaf sheath is compressed and slightly hairy. The flowers are in slender spikes, three to six in a cluster, similar in appearance to crabgrass.

Bermuda-grass will grow well on almost any soil that is fertile and not too wet but better on heavy soils rather than those that are light and sandy. It thrives in warm or hot weather. It usually does not survive heavy freezes, although it has lived through temperatures of 10° F. in the vicinity of the District of Columbia. For that reason it is often considered as a weedy pest in the lawns in parts of Virginia and Maryland.

Bermuda-grass may be propagated by seed or by vegetative cuttings or stolons. Because the seeds are small and light, a well-prepared seedbed is desirable for best establishment. Spring seedings, 5 to 7 pounds to the acre, are generally best. The seed should be covered with a cultipacker or a light harrow.

Many methods are used in planting stolons. The common practice is to plow furrows 4 to 6 feet apart, drop stolons 2 or 3 feet apart in the furrow, and cover them by plowing or with the foot. Deep planting is important if the stolons are not watered when set, because the stolons might dry out. Rolling or cultipacking the soil after plantings is also desirable. A complete fertilizer, such as 4–8–4 or 6–6–6, should be applied at 400 to 600 pounds per acre just ahead of planting or seeding. For rapid establishment, nitrogen fertilizer should be applied in midsummer at rates of 100 to 200 pounds of nitrate of soda or its equivalent.

The principal use of Bermuda-grass

Bermuda-grass

is for pasture and lawns, but it is also used for hay. It is palatable and nutritious even after frost in the fall. Many farmers hesitate to use it because it is difficult to control in row or cultivated crops.

Bermuda-grass responds to cultivation and old undisturbed pasture sods soon become weedy and unproductive. The best method of maintaining a productive pasture with it is by shallow plowing every 3 to 5 years or so, fertilizing, and maintaining the stands of legumes in it.

Improved varieties are more vigorous in growth than common Bermuda, more disease-resistant, and superior in other characters. These new varieties produce seed sparsely and must be planted vegetatively. Of the two varieties most widely used now, Coastal Bermuda is more productive over the region than Suwannee, but Suwannee shows promise in Florida. Fine-leaved, compact, sod-forming strains also are

now being developed for lawn and turf purposes, but are not ready yet for distribution.

Commercial seed supplies of common Bermuda-grass are harvested in Arizona and southern California. Seed is harvested from volunteer stands of grass in old abandoned cultivated crop fields and alfalfa plantings. Seed yields vary from 100 to 200 pounds an acre. One or two seed crops are harvested annually with an ordinary field mower and then threshed soon after harvest.

Insects and disease have caused some injury. In Florida mole crickets have been known to kill out large areas; a scale insect is widely distributed, but it has not caused serious damage. Diseases that attack Bermuda-grass are *Rhizoctonia, Helminthosporium,* and *Sclerotium.*

ORCHARDGRASS
(*Dactylis glomerata*)

Orchardgrass has been in cultivation in North America since 1760. It is a native of Europe, where it is known as cocksfoot. It is a long-lived perennial, a distinctly bunch-type grass with folded leaf blades and compressed sheaths. It grows in large contiguous masses. This tussock-forming habit is lessened somewhat by careful grazing management and by seeding with a legume, such as Ladino clover, lespedeza, or alfalfa. It does not produce stolons or underground rhizomes and, therefore, never forms a dense sod. The peculiar cluster formation of the inflorescence is characteristic and cannot be mistaken for that of any other cultivated grass.

Orchardgrass was first cultivated in Virginia. Now it is widely distributed over the United States. Its persistency, leafiness, and ability to withstand relatively adverse soil and climatic conditions in the humid temperate regions of the United States make it a desirable pasture grass. The most extensive acreage is in the southern half of the timothy-bluegrass region, which extends from southern New York State to southern Virginia and westward from the Atlantic coast to eastern Kansas and southeastern Nebraska.

Orchardgrass flourishes on rich soil, but it also succeeds on light soil of medium fertility and on moist, heavy land. Sometimes it does well where Kentucky bluegrass is unsuccessful. It is one of the best cultivated grasses for shade. Where it is adapted it is generally dominant in orchards, woodland pastures, and similar areas. It is quite cold-resistant and continues growth until the first severe frosts. Orchardgrass is more productive and better adapted in the southern range of the timothy-growing region than timothy or smooth brome because it will tolerate more heat, drought, and lower soil fertility. It can be seeded in early spring with or without a nurse crop. It is one of the first grasses to start growth in the spring. Smooth brome and timothy are more resistant to winterkilling, but neither can equal orchardgrass in summer production of leafy pasturage.

Livestock graze orchardgrass early in the spring, and since it starts growth early it is necessary that the animals be turned on before seed heads form; otherwise the early spring growth becomes unpalatable for pasturage.

Good results have been obtained with a combination of orchardgrass and Korean lespedeza in regions where lespedeza is adapted. Both the grass and the legume thrive on soils of medium fertility although both, of course, respond to improved fertilizing practices. The bunch type of growth, once considered objectionable, makes orchardgrass an ideal companion for Korean lespedeza. Both thrive in summer and therefore extend the pasture season on land that would not maintain a growth of clover or alfalfa.

The practice of making grass silage has further demonstrated the value and usefulness of orchardgrass. When it is grown in combination with legumes such as red clover and Ladino clover, orchardgrass is able to produce the maximum tonnage of high-quality

Orchardgrass

silage early in the season. If this early growth is removed, the orchardgrass will not crowd the legume, and its rapid recovery will produce an abundant, high-quality summer pasturage at a time when permanent pastures are dormant. This production during the summer months, when permanent pastures are unproductive, is an important factor in favor of this grass. Although other grass-legume combinations may give equal or higher total forage yields for the season, orchardgrass has a definite place in pasture management because livestock must have continuous pasture of good production throughout the growing season.

Grown alone, orchardgrass will average 1 to 2 tons of field-cured hay to the acre. From a combination of orchardgrass and clover or alfalfa, yields of 2 to 3 tons can be expected. In the seed-producing areas of Kentucky and Virginia, the growth remaining after seed harvest is used to good advantage for pasture or hay.

In Virginia the northern counties produce most of the seed. In Kentucky the central section and Oldham and Henry Counties in the north are among the high seed producers.

A common practice for establishment of orchardgrass for seed production is to sow 1 bushel (about 14 pounds) with red clover and take a hay crop the first year. Seed is harvested in succeeding years and the aftermath pastured or removed as hay. Some growers successfully use sweet-clover or alfalfa in combination with orchardgrass. Yields of 350 pounds of seed per acre have been reported from orchardgrass in 3-year-old stands with alfalfa; afterward, 1 ton of high-quality hay was obtained per acre.

Nitrogen is probably the most effective fertilizer in increasing seed yields and quality. On soils of medium to good fertility, nitrogen appears to give the most effective results. Approximately 20 to 30 pounds of nitrogen are usually sufficient, except on poorer soils or on old established fields of orchardgrass in which 40 to 50 pounds of nitrogen may be necessary. Heavier applications often cause the grass to lodge and sometimes cause the heads to fail to fill out.

Orchardgrass is not seriously troubled by insect pests. Diseases have been less severe in grazed fields than when the grass is allowed to grow to hay stage. The most serious diseases are anthracnose, leaf stripe, leaf blotch, and stripe smut.

It is estimated that about 1 million acres of orchardgrass are grown each year; 40,000 acres or more are harvested for seed. The harvesting season is usually in June. A small quantity of seed is occasionally imported, but most of the seed used in this country is grown here.

WILD-RYE
(*Elymus* species)

The genus *Elymus* is well represented in the native grass species of the Western States. Most wild-rye species are perennial and many are bunchgrasses; a few, however, form sod.

The scientific name is derived from the Greek *elumos,* an ancient name for a kind of grain.

These grasses have coarse and rough foliage and are relatively unpalatable, but they are most useful for revegetation because of their good seed habits, high forage production, wide adaptation to a variety of soils, and relative ease of establishment.

The wild-rye grasses are susceptible to ergot, a fungus disease that replaces the kernel of the seed head. If livestock eat large quantities of ergot, losses may be serious.

Canada Wild-rye
(*Elymus canadensis*)

Canada wild-rye is a vigorous, widely distributed, perennial bunchgrass. It is most abundant in the Great Plains, the Pacific Northwest, and the Rocky Mountain States.

The seed heads grow to 3 to 5 feet and may be green or green-blue. The leaf blades are broad, flat, and rough. They are 6 to 12 inches long and usually ½ inch or more wide. The mature spikes, dark purple in color, average nearly 6 inches in length and have sharp awns that emerge from the spikelet parts.

Wild-rye begins growth about a week later in the spring than brome or crested wheatgrass. It usually continues to grow through the summer if

Canada wild-rye

moisture conditions are favorable, and may resume growth in the fall after a summer drought if enough moisture is available then.

The palatability of the forage is fair but becomes less as the plants become harsh and woody at maturity. The young seedlings are exceptionally vigorous and quickly form a good protective cover; Canada wild-rye therefore is useful in mixtures, especially with grasses that do not produce ground cover rapidly.

Seeding rates should vary with the number and kinds of other grasses in the mixture. Ordinarily 6 to 8 pounds of Canada wild-rye to the acre produces a good stand.

Hay of good quality may be had if the wild-rye is harvested just as the seed heads are emerging from the boot.

Seed matures in late summer and can be harvested most satisfactorily with a binder. Seed may also be harvested directly with a small-grain combine, but if this is done, the product is likely to include an excessive quantity of immature seed, which lowers germination and the general vigor of the seedlings.

Seed yields of 300 to 400 pounds an acre have been obtained from natural stands; yields from grass grown in rows and cultivated are higher.

The combine- or thresher-run seed should have an average purity of 65 percent and a germination of 90 percent. Processed pure seed contains 110,000 to 120,000 seeds to the pound.

The awns present on Canada wild-rye seed make seeding with ordinary farm drills difficult. The awns, like the seed appendages on many other species of native grass seed, can be removed readily by processing the seed with a hammer mill. The additional time and effort required for processing and seed cleaning is more than offset by the improved quality of the seed.

Mandan wild-rye, an improved variety developed through selection and breeding at the Northern Great Plains Field Station in North Dakota, produces more forage and seed. Its seed is now being produced under certification by members of the North Dakota Crop Improvement Association.

GIANT WILD-RYE
(Elymus condensatus)

Giant wild-rye is a coarse, robust, perennial with thick, short rootstocks. It occurs in all the Western States. It is the largest of the native ryegrasses. Individual plants often grow 10 feet high and form clumps several feet thick. The erect flower spikes may grow 1 foot long. Leaves are flat and coarse, nearly ¾ inch wide and 2 feet long. The extensive root system has short, thick, perennial rootstocks.

This bunchgrass is abundant on moist or wet saline soils; it occurs also on moderately dry fertile soils, but moderate grazing, especially during early spring, is essential to good stands.

During the early settlement of the Western States, it was a primary source of spring grazing and winter feed for livestock. Excessive use, particularly while the plants were young and succulent, has depleted the natural stands.

Giant wild-rye is grazed readily while young. Later the foliage becomes coarse and harsh, and livestock leave it if they can get more palatable forage. If it is left standing, the grass provides a considerable amount of winter feed for cattle and horses. Fairly good hay can be had from the young growth.

Good stands of giant wild-rye have been obtained by drilling the seed about an inch deep. It is valuable for range reseeding on flood plains. Seed of native stands can be harvested by combine.

Scarcity of seed has limited the use of giant wild-rye for revegetation of range lands in the West.

BLUE WILD-RYE
(Elymus glaucus)

Blue wild-rye is a native perennial bunchgrass that grows throughout the Western States, particularly on old burns and cut-over areas in the North-

Blue wild-rye

made optimum growth in plantings with various grasses and legumes as ground cover. Blue wild-rye was shade-tolerant, provided excellent ground protection, and gave the highest forage yields of the several grasses under test. When planted with alfalfa under these conditions, the forage yield of alfalfa-grass was good, but the grass-legume mixture seeding depressed tree growth.

When grown under cultivation, seed yields of 300 to 400 pounds an acre have been obtained. The threshed seed had a purity of 80 percent as it came from the thresher; when it was cleaned, its purity was 97 percent and the germination was 81 percent. The test weight is about 23 pounds per bushel.

Blue wild-rye has not been used extensively in reseeding, primarily because of inadequate seed supplies.

THE LOVEGRASSES
(*Eragrostis* species)

The genus lovegrass, *Eragrostis,* comprises 250-odd species and is represented in all temperate regions. Only a few species, some native and some recently introduced, have been recognized as of agricultural value in the United States. Several native species are considered weeds.

The name comes from the Greek *eros,* love, and *agrostis,* a kind of grass. Several species are recognized for their capacity to produce an abundance of seed and forage on soils of low fertility; hence they are used to provide vegetative cover on eroding sites.

The best known species is *E. abyssinica,* called Tef in Ethiopia, where it is cultivated as a cereal. It is cultivated also in India and Australia but usually as a forage plant. Although introduced at various times, it has never found a place in American agriculture.

In the United States where about 40 species occur naturally, only 4 have been noted as of much value. *E. obtusiflora,* ranging from New Mexico and Arizona southward into Mexico, is a hard and rigid perennial that spreads by rhizomes and thrives on alkaline

west. It commonly grows in small tufts and rarely forms dense, pure stands. It is the most widely distributed and common species of wild-rye in the Western States.

Seedstalks may grow to 5 feet high, with broad, flat, smooth leaves nearly 12 inches long. Roots are vigorous and penetrate deeply. The plant derives its name from the bluish bloom on leaves and stems.

It is most abundant on moist soils, but it stands considerable drought. The foliage, although rather coarse, is grazed by cattle and horses, especially during the early part of the season, when they seem to relish it.

Blue wild-rye produces good growth during the cool season in parts of California; it also persists very well there under limited rainfall and shows promise for use as dry-land pasture, hay, or range.

Experimental plantings as a vegetative cover in wood lots in Washington have been successful; black locust trees

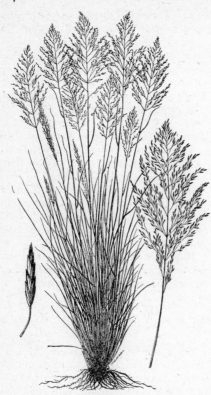

Weeping lovegrass

to the soils and climate of the Southern Great Plains.

Weeping lovegrass plants produce seedstalks 2 to 5 feet tall and numerous slender, curving basal leaves 10 to 20 inches long. The heavy forage is eaten readily by cattle in early spring but sparingly in summer. The normal presence of green shoots in the bases of the plants often induces cattle to eat old growth in winter.

The plants resist summer heat and drought and survive temperatures as low as −11° F. if the soil has adequate moisture at the time of the first killing frost.

Weeping lovegrass is easily established from seed. Its vigorous young seedlings quickly make an effective ground cover. The seed ripens in late June and thus escapes the hazards of the dry, hot midsummer. Seed yield per acre has amounted to 200 pounds under dry-land farming conditions and 600 pounds under irrigation.

Binders, headers, and combines have been used in harvesting seed. Recleaned seed should have a purity of 98 percent and germination of 85 percent. About 1,500,000 clean seed weigh a pound.

SAND LOVEGRASS
(*Eragrostis trichodes*)

Sand lovegrass, a vigorous, long-lived, native bunchgrass, occurs on sandy soils of the central and southern parts of the Great Plains. Plants normally grow to 3 to 6 feet. The elongated panicles are sometimes half as tall as the plant and have a distinctive purple color. The slightly hairy leaf blades are ¼ inch wide and about 12 inches long. Leafy foliage, primarily basal, is abundant. Roots are vigorous, spreading, and deeply penetrating, and therefore of value in conservation.

Plants begin growth very early in the spring and remain green until late fall. It is generally considered one of the most palatable and nutritious of the range grasses, and frequently it suffers from continuous overuse.

soil. It furnishes a great deal of forage in areas where it grows naturally.

Plains lovegrass, which grows on dry or sandy prairies in the Southern States, also has some value in New Mexico and Arizona as range forage and ground cover.

WEEPING LOVEGRASS
(*Eragrostis curvula*)

Weeping lovegrass is a vigorous, perennial bunchgrass native to South Africa. It was introduced by plant explorers from the mountainous part of Tanganyika in 1927. Several importations of it have been made in the past 20 years; the most promising importation, from which the present seed stocks were obtained, was brought into the United States in 1934 and first tested and grown in the Southwest. This grass is particularly well adapted

Sand lovegrass is easily established from seed and volunteers aggressively. It makes excellent growth when seeded either alone or in mixture on sandy soils but does not thrive on heavy soils, except in pure stands.

Native stands are seldom suitable for seed harvest because of the presence of brushy plants such as sand sagebrush (*Artemisia filifolia*), shinnery oak (*Quercus* spp.), or the skunkbush (*Rhus trilobata*). Seed yields have exceeded 400 pounds an acre under irrigation and 150 pounds on dry land.

Binders and combines have been used for seed harvest. Cleaning the seed with a fanning mill should result in a purity of 98 percent and a germination of 75 percent.

CENTIPEDEGRASS
(*Eremochloa ophiuroides*)

Centipedegrass is a native of southeastern Asia. It was first introduced into the United States in 1919 from China. It has been distributed in the Southern States and as far west as the Pacific coast. A low-growing perennial, it spreads by stolons. In appearance it is intermediate between carpetgrass and Bermuda-grass; it has shorter nodes than the latter and makes a dense mat of creeping stems and leaves.

Centipedegrass is adapted to a wide range of soils, especially on the Coastal Plains of North Carolina to eastern Texas. It will grow on clay soils and the poorest Norfolk sand if enough moisture and plant food are available for it to get started. It has withstood temperatures of 12° F. or slightly lower, but it is not adapted to conditions in the North.

Because of its low nutritive value, its best use is for lawns and erosion control. It is not suitable for heavy or intensive use, such as on airport runways. In pastures it generally has given poor livestock gains. Because of its dense and aggressive growth it crowds out desirable legumes. Chemical analysis of grass samples, even in young vegetative growth, resembles (with

Centipedegrass (vertical)

some variations) the analysis of cereal straws. The crude fiber is higher in centipede than in straw, but the fat- and nitrogen-free extract is lower.

Centipedegrass will grow well on poor soils, but a complete fertilizer will encourage a more rapid spread and dense turf. Nitrogen fertilizer gives a most noticeable effect; there is no specific need for limestone. Because of its low fertility requirements, it is a desirable lawn or turf grass on low-fertility soils when costs of maintenance must be kept low.

Seed is unavailable in commercial quantities, and plants or stolons must be used. To establish new stands, a seedbed should be prepared as for any crop; then furrows, 2 to 3 inches deep

Meadow fescue

Spring-planted stolons have spread as much as 8 to 10 feet in a season. Approximately 15 to 20 pounds of stolons should set about 1,000 square feet of lawn at the rates given.

Its vigorous growth habit and ability to produce some seed make eradication rather difficult. It is therefore not recommended in places where it might become a pest.

THE FESCUES
(*Festuca* species)

The fescues compose a large genus of which there are about 100 species in temperate or cool zones. They vary in texture and growth. Some are annuals, some perennials; some are low and others are rather tall; different ones are fine, coarse, tufted, creeping, erect, and so on. Thus they comprise a versatile group of varying uses.

The annual species are weedy, but the perennials are excellent for forage and turf. The several species that are cultivated as pasture grasses can be classified as the broad-leaf and the fine-leaf species.

Of the broad-leaf species that currently are most widely used, meadow fescue (*Festuca elatior*) and tall fescue (*F. elatior* var. *arundinacea*) are outstanding. Of the fine-leaf species, red fescue (*F. rubra*), Chewings fescue (*F. rubra* var. *commutata*), and sheep fescue (*F. ovina*) are perhaps the most useful.

MEADOW FESCUE
(*Festuca elatior*)

Meadow fescue, a hardy perennial, is believed to have been introduced into the United States from Europe, probably England, where it is a standard grass.

It flourishes in deep, rich soils; where it is adapted it will usually grow to 15 to 30 inches. The leaves are bright green and rather succulent. The leaf sheaths are smooth and reddish purple at the base, and the young leaves involute in the bud. The blade

and about 10 to 18 inches apart, should be opened. The plants or stolons are placed about 6 inches apart in the furrows and covered immediately to prevent drying, with an inch or more of the plant left protruding above the surface. A closer spacing of rows and plants in the row gives a quicker establishment and cover. If the stolons are well watered and top-dressed with nitrogen, growth will be more rapid.

is glossy on the under surface. The panicles are open, similar in appearance to those of Kentucky bluegrass, although much larger and coarser. It flowers in June and July.

It does not propagate itself by rootstocks or form a dense sod. It produces comparatively few culms, and produces an abundance of highly germinable seed. The seed, which is easily harvested and cleaned, weighs 22 to 27 pounds to the bushel; there are 225,000 seeds in a pound. The usual rate of seeding is approximately 25 or 30 pounds to the acre.

Some years ago all seed of meadow fescue was imported, but now most of it (1,235,000 pounds a year between 1940 and 1946) is produced in the United States. The seed yield fluctuates considerably. Fields 2 or 3 years old are the most productive, but some that have been in for 8 or 10 years average 300 pounds of seed an acre.

Weeds that make it hard to maintain stands of meadow fescue include chess or cheat (*Bromus secalinus*) and whitetop fleabane (*Erigeron strigosus*). Cheat has always caused trouble in meadow fescue stands because its seeds closely resemble those of the fescue.

Meadow fescue can be grown well throughout the timothy region and also farther south and west because it can withstand more heat and drought than timothy. In regions where it is adapted it is grown to a limited extent for pasture and hay. In the past it was commonly used in pasture mixtures, especially on soils that tend to be wet, but it is being used less and less for hay and pasture because of the improvement and increase in the production of tall fescue.

TALL FESCUE
(*Festuca elatior* var. *arundinacea*)

Tall fescue is a deeply rooted and strongly tufted perennial with stems 3 to 4 feet high, erect and smooth. The numerous dark-green basal leaves are broad and flat, the sheath is smooth, and the ligule is short. The nodding

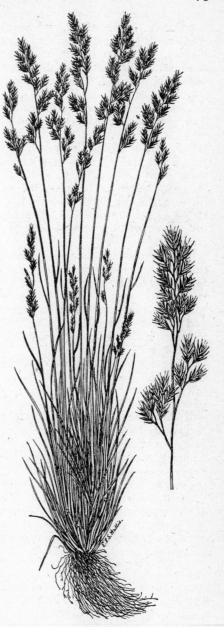

Sheep fescue

panicle head is 4 to 12 inches long and has lanceolate spikelets that are ½ inch or more long and many-flowered. This variety, like the species, flowers in June and July.

Tall fescue is found growing in

damp pastures and wet places throughout Europe, North Africa, and North
America. It can be distinguished from
meadow fescue by height, its broad
leaf, and the deep green of the upper
surface of the leaf, which is prominently ribbed and rough.

Tall fescue was introduced from Europe probably about the same time as
meadow fescue. Two strains, Alta and
Ky. 31, are receiving the most attention now. Alta fescue is a selection
made from a 4-year-old stand of tall
fescue in Oregon in 1923; Ky. 31 is an
increase from tall fescue found in 1931
on a Kentucky farm, where apparently
it had been growing for something like
50 years.

Tall fescue is adapted to a variety of
soils and in general to the same region
as meadow fescue. Like meadow fescue,
it does best on heavy soils that have
considerable humus. Somewhat coarser
and taller than meadow fescue, tall
fescue is higher in forage yield and
longer-lived.

The exact forage and pasture value
of tall fescue has not been determined,
but it will grow well in wet as well as
in dry situations. In the Pacific Northwest, Alta fescue is rather widely used
for pasture for cattle and sheep. Indications are that it may be desirable for
winter pasture in the South. Farther
north it may serve well for pastures of
somewhat low fertility. It is quite
drought-resistant and aggressive; it
competes strongly with the legumes
and sometimes wins out over them.
It is less palatable than bromegrass,
orchardgrass, or timothy.

SHEEP FESCUE
(*Festuca ovina*)

Sheep fescue, probably a native of
the Northern Hemisphere, is a bunchgrass that forms dense tufts with numerous stiff, rather sharp, bluish-gray
leaves. It is adapted to about the same
climate as bluegrass and can be grown
in the most northern agricultural
areas. It succeeds better than most
grasses on sandy or gravelly soils. Cat-

Red fescue

tle and sheep will graze sheep fescue
but it is not generally recommended

for pastures—its greatest use is for making a durable turf on sandy soils. The commercial seed comes from Europe. The seed weighs 10 to 15 pounds per bushel. The usual rate of seeding is 25 to 30 pounds to the acre.

RED FESCUE
(*Festuca rubra*)

Red fescue resembles sheep fescue, but its leaves are bright green and it does not grow in tufts. It creeps by underground stems.

From the commercial standpoint, there are two distinct forms, red fescue and Chewings fescue.

The first is a creeping grass, although this characteristic is rather variable, for some strains are more creeping than others. This may account for the use of the common name creeping red fescue in an attempt to make a distinction between strains.

Chewings fescue is cespitose or tufted and does not creep. It has been assumed by some that Chewings and red fescue had a common origin; that can hardly be true because both occurred in Europe and were described before they were of commercial importance.

Like sheep fescue, they are hardy, robust plants. They are used mainly for lawns and good turf and are especially adapted to shaded, dry sites.

Much of the seed of both red and Chewings fescue used in the United States is produced here or in Canada. Large amounts used to be imported from Europe, Australia, and New Zealand. Several new strains have been produced, but their general regions of adaptation have not been determined. These include the Illahee and Rainier strains from Oregon and the Olds strain from Canada.

THE RYEGRASSES
(*Lolium* species)

The common name, ryegrass, is applied to a group of plants comprising two species of the genus *Lolium*. One, *L. multiflorum*, is known as Ital-

Italian ryegrass

ian ryegrass, and the other, *L. perenne,* as perennial ryegrass. The two species are closely related morphologically and their cultural practices are practically the same.

Italian ryegrass, usually an annual, is generally distinguished from perennial ryegrass by the awned lemma and stem characters and by the arrangement of the leaf in the bud. Awns are present on seed of Italian ryegrass and

Perennial ryegrass

Mediterranean region, apparently was first cultivated in northern Italy; it was known in Switzerland in 1820 and in France in 1818.

Perennial ryegrass was the first of all perennial grasses to be grown in pure stands for forages. It was mentioned in agricultural literature in England in 1611. It occurs naturally in all of temperate Asia and in north Africa. It succeeds best in cool, moist regions that have mild winters.

In this country best results have been had with it on the Pacific coast and in the central and southern parts of the Atlantic States. The hot, dry weather of July and August affects the growth; if drought continues into September, the recovery is slow. Like Italian ryegrass, it has a wide range of adaptability to soils, but it prefers medium to high fertility. In some sections the grasses are considered wet-land grasses, although production usually declines as the drainage gets poorer.

Italian ryegrass is more valuable as a hay plant on the Pacific coast than anywhere else in the United States. It makes an excellent temporary pasture and gives a quick cover for early grazing in permanent pastures. When sown in combination with winter grains for temporary pasture, it makes a desirable bottom grass and increases the length of the grazing season. Italian ryegrass is a most desirable annual grass for temporary poultry range. In the South it is used extensively for fall seeding on permanent lawns in order to furnish a green cover in winter. It also makes a good temporary lawn because it produces a turf quickly.

The principal use for perennial ryegrass in this country is for permanent pasture seedings. It starts growth early in the spring and affords grazing while the more permanent or longer-lived grasses are becoming established. Because of the toughness of its leaves, which makes it hard to mow, perennial ryegrass is not usually considered desirable for lawns—nor will it give a good turf in the summer months.

The ryegrasses can be seeded in the

are usually absent on perennial ryegrass. The culm or stem of Italian ryegrass is cylindrical but that of perennial ryegrass is slightly flattened. The leaves of Italian ryegrass are rolled in the bud. In perennial ryegrass the leaves are folded in the bud. The plants of Italian ryegrass are yellowish green at the base. Those of perennial ryegrass are commonly reddish.

Italian ryegrass, a native of the

fall or early spring. Spring seedings are preferable where winters are severe. Fall seedings are more successful in more temperate regions. Seed may be broadcast by hand or with an endgate seeder and covered with a smoothing harrow, or it can be sown with a grain or grass-seed drill. The seed should be covered with approximately one-half inch of soil. When the grain drill is used it may be necessary to reduce the size of the seed outlets to prevent sowing too much seed.

When seeded alone for forage or seed production, 20 to 25 pounds of seed per acre is sufficient. When seeded with small grain or a legume for annual pasture, 8 to 10 pounds per acre will give a satisfactory stand. When it is seeded on established grasses to furnish green lawns for winter, or when it is seeded alone in spring or fall for a temporary lawn, 3 to 5 pounds per 1,000 square feet is used.

Very little seed of pure Italian ryegrass is produced in the United States. Domestic-grown seed sold as such is a mixture of annual and perennial types; many intermediate types have resulted from field crossing. Such types are generally called common ryegrass, although they are classified as *Lolium multiflorum*.

Practically all the seed of common ryegrass and perennial ryegrass is produced in the Pacific Northwest. Harvesting practices are the same as for small grains. Because the seed shatters easily, larger yields are obtained by cutting with a header or binder when the seed is in the hard-dough stage. Average seed yields are from 600 to 700 pounds an acre. Approximately 275,-000 seeds make a pound of Italian ryegrass; seed of perennial ryegrass is slightly smaller.

Improved strains of the ryegrasses are not in commercial production in the United States. Some seed is imported from Great Britain, other parts of Europe, Australia, and New Zealand. Limited amounts of varieties like Westerwold and Wimmera ryegrass are imported; both are true annuals.

INDIAN RICEGRASS
(*Oryzopsis hymenoides*)

Indian ricegrass, a densely tufted, native, perennial bunchgrass, is widely distributed over the Western States. The genus name *Oryzopsis* is derived from the Greek words *oruza*, rice, and *opsis*, appearance.

The plump, milletlike seeds are nearly round, black, tipped with a short awn, and densely covered with conspicuous white hairs. Once they were a food staple of the Indians; particularly when the corn crop failed, seed of ricegrass was gathered in quantity, ground into meal or flour, and made into bread.

The plants grow from 1 to 2 feet tall. The slender leaves are nearly as long as the stems. The delicate spreading panicle has long pediceled spikelets and lemmas with hairs that are conspicuous and silky.

Indian ricegrass occurs mainly on dry sandy soils and frequently is important on sand dune areas. It is drought-resistant and somewhat tolerant of alkali. Once it was widely distributed over the western ranges, particularly in semidesert areas, but overgrazing on much of the land there has almost eliminated it. Now it grows in abundance in some places that have been ungrazed or conservatively grazed—places, for example, that are inaccessible to livestock or remote from watering places. Stockmen regard the grass highly as a winter feed for animals and prize the areas where it grows.

Seed formation in native stands is erratic, but when seasonal rainfall is plentiful, a good crop of seed can be expected. The seed can be harvested satisfactorily with a combine and cleaned by processing with a hammer mill to remove the silky hairs from the seed coats. About 140,000 clean seeds make a pound.

Seeding rates of 8 to 10 pounds of clean seed to the acre give satisfactory stands. Initial thin stands will increase in density if natural reseeding is per-

Floret   Spikelet

Indian ricegrass

range reseeding because of its drought resistance, palatability, and capacity to grow and spread by natural reseeding on areas where practically no other grasses can be established.

THE PANICGRASSES
(*Panicum* species)

The *Panicum* genus includes approximately 500 species that grow chiefly in warm regions of the world. The species native to the United States occur primarily in the Southeast but are well represented also in the warmer parts of the West.

Panicgrasses belong to the millet tribe, *Panicum* being the Latin name for millet. Proso (*Panicum miliaceum*) is believed to have been the first cereal cultivated by man.

Vine-Mesquite
(*Panicum obtusum*)

Vine-mesquite is a vigorous, long-lived, native perennial of the Southwestern States. The stiff, erect culms are 1 to 2 feet tall; leaves are 4 to 6 inches long and about ¼ inch wide. Stolons are numerous, often several feet long, with swollen hairy or woolly nodes. The seed panicle is 2 to 5 inches long with a few racemelike branches.

This grass grows where rainfall is scant but is generally most abundant where additional water is received in occasional floods.

It produces a fair amount of forage, which livestock relish when it is green and succulent. Ranchers differ in their opinion as to the feeding value of the forage as it approaches maturity, however; some maintain that stock will not eat the mature plants if other feed is available.

Seed is rather hard to get and is generally of low quality, an undesirable feature that is offset somewhat by the ability of the plants to spread rapidly by stolons, which may grow 15 feet in a single season. The plants therefore can well be propagated by transplanting sod pieces. Vine-mesquite hay, cut after

mitted by careful management. Seed can be produced economically from cultivated row plantings.

The low germination of newly harvested seed is due partly to the hard, moisture-resistant seed coat. To break the natural dormancy and permit good germination, the seed should be scarified, treated with acid, or held a year in dry storage. Good germination may also occur if the newly harvested seed is planted in the fall, so that natural changes in soil temperature can soften the seed coat.

Indian ricegrass is important for

the seed heads mature, can be used as another means of establishing new seedings.

SWITCHGRASS
(*Panicum virgatum*)

Switchgrass is a vigorous, native, perennial, sod-forming grass that occurs throughout most of the United States. It is most abundant and important as a forage and pasture grass in the central and southern parts of the Great Plains. It usually grows 3 to 5 feet high, with short, vigorous rhizomes. The stand looks like a colony rather than a sod. The flowering head is a widely branching open panicle. The leaves are usually from one-fourth to one-half inch wide and 6 to 18 inches long. Leaves are green to bluish-green. Switchgrass occurs on nearly all soil types but is most abundant and thrives best on moist low areas of relatively high fertility.

Heavy, vigorous roots and underground stems make the species excellent for conservation use. Seedling growth is aggressive. Usually switchgrass is seeded with the species with which it occurs naturally. Best seedling stands have been obtained where plantings were made on a clean, firm, well-prepared seedbed.

Growth begins in late spring and continues through the summer if there is enough moisture. Forage is produced in abundance and—especially during the period of early rapid growth—is acceptable to livestock. Hay of good quality can be had by mowing the grass when seed heads begin to form.

The seed matures in September. The amount produced depends on moisture and cool temperatures during the period of blooming and seed formation.

Binders and combines have been used for seed harvesting. Native stands commonly yield more than 100 pounds of seed per acre; this yield can be increased to 300 pounds by growing the plants in rows under cultivation.

Recleaning the seed with a fanning mill should give a purity of 95 percent

Switchgrass

and a germination of 30 percent. Germination improves during storage and may be twice as high if the seed is held in dry storage for a year after harvest.

A pound of pure seed contains 370,-000 to 420,000 seeds.

Blackwell, a new and improved variety developed through plant selection and breeding work at the Kansas Agricultural Experiment Station, yields excellent forage and shows considerable resistance to stem rust, a disease that is injurious to most native switchgrass plants. Seed of Blackwell is being produced by seed growers of the Kansas Crop Improvement Association under field inspection and certification.

THE PASPALUM GRASSES
(*Paspalum* species)

Of the 400-odd species of *Paspalum*, few have economic importance in the United States. The most important are

Dallisgrass

Bahiagrass (*Paspalum notatum*) and Dallisgrass (*P. dilatatum*). Vaseygrass (*P. urvillei*) and ribbed paspalum (*P. malacophyllum*) are of minor value.

Dallisgrass is an upright-growing bunching grass, and is the most winter-hardy and most widely adapted of the four species. It can be grown as far north as the Carolinas and thrives in the irrigated sections of the milder parts of the Southwestern States. It was first introduced into the United States about 1875, probably from South America.

Dallisgrass requires a moist but not wet soil; growth is best where organic matter is abundant. It requires a higher fertility than carpet or Bahia-grass. Because it seldom forms a dense sod, it is an excellent grass to mix with legumes and other grasses.

Seeded alone, it often fails to make a perfect stand. Dallisgrass produces abundant seed, but the germination is often poor because of the fungus disease ergot (*Claviceps paspali*), which attacks or destroys the seed.

Most of the domestic-grown seed is produced in Louisiana, Mississippi, and Alabama. Because the seed is produced throughout the summer, it is possible to harvest two crops or more in a season.

Vaseygrass resembles Dallisgrass but it is taller and more erect. It is best adapted to fertile soils and is common in the South along highways or railroads where it has not been heavily grazed. Because of its erect growth it can be easily eradicated by close, continuous grazing.

Ribbed paspalum, a more recent introduction from Brazil, also resembles Dallisgrass but is finer-stemmed and has more erect growth. It produces an abundance of seed, but the seed rapidly loses its vitality. Like Vaseygrass, it requires careful management because it is injured by heavy grazing.

Bahiagrass is a low-growing perennial that was also introduced from South America. It differs from Dallisgrass in that it spreads by short, heavy runners and forms a dense, tough sod even on droughty, sandy soils. Common Bahia is less winter-hardy than Dallisgrass but survives the winter in the Southern Coastal Plains when temperatures are not too severe.

Two new varieties of Bahiagrass, Paraguay and Pensacola, are now being increased in the United States. They are more winter-hardy and have narrower and more hairy leaves than the common Bahiagrass. Paraguay and Pensacola produce a good seed crop of excellent quality.

Seed of common Bahia is imported mostly from Cuba and Costa Rica. It does not germinate well unless treated in some manner, as with sulfuric acid, so as to make the seed coat more permeable to water.

Paspalum grasses are primarily pasture grasses. Some are short-lived, but Dallis and Bahia maintain good stands and remain productive for a long time if properly fertilized and managed. To establish new stands, seedings should be made in the spring after corn-planting time—the latter part of April or early May. A good seedbed is essential. Lime and fertilizer should be applied ahead of planting and also in later years. Dallisgrass requires greater amounts of plant food than Bahiagrass for equal growth.

The main center of variability of these grasses appears to be in Brazil, where some of the species form the dominant cover over large areas.

Some 10 other species, native to southern Brazil, Uruguay, Paraguay, and adjacent Argentina, have been reported as valuable native forage in those countries. Efforts to obtain them and additional strains of Dallisgrass and Bahiagrass have met with only slight success. Exploration in temperate South America for *Paspalum* and other forage plants should give us other species of value for the South.

PEARLMILLET and NAPIERGRASS
(*Pennisetum* species)

Of the many species of *Pennisetum*, only two are important for forage. Their common names are pearlmillet and Napiergrass; their respective botanical names are *P. glaucum* and *P. purpureum.*

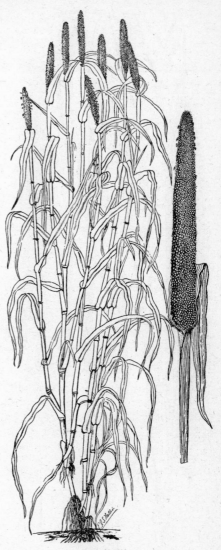

Pearlmillet

They are large, upright plants that grow 6 to 10 or more feet tall. The coarse stems grow in thick clumps. The leaves are about an inch wide, 2 to 3 feet long, and quite numerous in both species. The flowers are borne in terminal spikes 6 to 12 inches long. Pearlmillet is an annual; Napiergrass is a perennial. Both have come to us from Africa.

Pearlmillet was introduced into the United States many years ago; we do

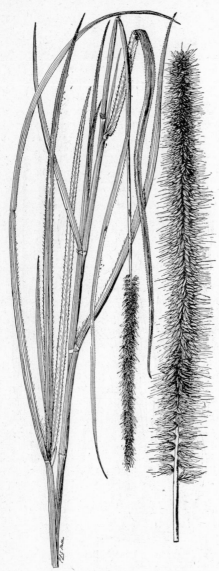

Napiergrass

Both grasses require a rich soil for best growth. Under favorable conditions they produce enormous amounts of green fodder and can be cut several times a season. They are warm-climate crops and grow only in the warmer part of the year. Napier, being slow in establishment and perennial, cannot be grown except in regions having but little or no frost. Pearlmillet, a summer annual, will mature seed as far north as Maryland, but it can be used economically only farther south.

Pearlmillet seed is planted directly in the field where the crop is to be grown. It is commonly planted in 4-foot rows; 4 pounds of seed to the acre give good results.

When Napiergrass is grown from seed, the seeding is made in greenhouse flats or a nursery; the plants are transplanted to the field. The more common practice with Napiergrass, however, is to grow the crop from planted canes. The mature stocks or canes are cut into short lengths that contain one to three nodes, which are planted in rows and covered as one would cover potatoes or other crops that are reproduced vegetatively. Plantings of Napiergrass will continue to produce for a number of years, but old stands decline in productive value and should occasionally be renewed.

A fine-stemmed strain of Napier has been called Merker grass; actually, it is only a selected variant. Other names, such as elephant grass and Carter grass, also are used for this.

Pearlmillet is sometimes known as cattail millet.

Improved strains of Napiergrass that are more disease-resistant and furnish superior grazing and production have been developed in Florida and Georgia.

CANARYGRASSES
(*Phalaris* species)

The canary grasses, both the native and introduced species, are widely distributed throughout the world, although those in the United States are not so numerous as most other genera.

not know the exact date. It came by way of the West Indies from India, where it is considered an important forage plant. Napiergrass, introduced in 1913, is grown in several countries, particularly Africa and Australia, but in no place is it used extensively. Both grasses now are considered of importance in sections of the South, where they are used for grazing and silage.

Reed canarygrass

The canarygrasses are annuals or perennials. Most of the ones found in the South are winter annuals; some of them occur in the North as summer annuals. The common name, canarygrass, probably had its origin from the fact that the seed of *Phalaris canariensis* has long been used as canary bird feed. Reed canarygrass, *P. arundinacea,* is a leafy perennial of wide agricultural importance in this country as a wet-land grass.

Hardinggrass, *Phalaris tuberosa* var. *stenoptera,* a perennial of recent introduction, has given good yields of forage in places where winter weather is relatively mild and soils are fertile. Hardinggrass is an outstanding forage grass in Australia. Most of the canarygrasses are nutritious and palatable to livestock. They grow most rapidly during the cool seasons.

Reed canarygrass was recognized as a good forage plant in Sweden about 1750. Its use in southwestern Oregon about 1885 has been reported. It is adapted to the northern half of the United States; the largest acreages now are in Oregon, Washington, northern California, Minnesota, Wisconsin, and Iowa. It is being used more and more for waterways and for seeding on wet pastures.

Reed canarygrass grows in clumps that often are 3 feet across. The dense heads are 2 to 8 inches long and become whitish as the seed matures. It makes its best growth in fertile and moist or wet soils, and is one of the best grasses for swamplands of a muck and peat nature. Contrary to earlier opinion, it is adapted and makes excellent growth on upland soils that are frequently dry for long periods in summer. It is winter-hardy and grows most rapidly during the cool spring months. Its long life, long grazing season, and large yields of nutritious, palatable forage make it a valuable pasture plant.

It will not survive under continuous, close grazing. Its use as a silage crop is increasing. Yields of 3 to 4 tons of hay in a season are not at all uncommon. Early cutting of the hay crop improves the quality; otherwise it may be somewhat coarse.

Seed is harvested in all the regions where the grass is grown. The mature seed shatters so readily that it is frequently hand harvested. Grain binders are sometimes used for harvesting, but seed losses are high. Seed yields are from 30 to 150 pounds an acre.

Hardinggrass resembles reed canarygrass in general appearance, growth, and cultural practices. The principal differences are the more compact seed head of the Hardinggrass and its less spreading rootstocks. Also, the seed of Hardinggrass shatters less freely and harvesting is easier. The annual species, *Phalaris canariensis,* makes an upright growth, with little stooling. It can be seeded and harvested like wheat and other small grains.

TIMOTHY
(*Phleum pratense*)

Timothy is of European origin but it was first cultivated in the United States. It was once called Herd's grass after the man who found it growing along the Piscataqua River near Portsmouth, N. H. The earliest record of the name timothy is from a letter dated July 16, 1747, to Jared Eliot from Benjamin Franklin, who states that the Herd's grass seed received proved to be "mere timothy." The designation "timothy" may be derived from the name of Timothy Hansen, who apparently brought the grass from New England to Maryland. In 1807 timothy was the most important hay grass in the United States; for many years its supremacy in this country was never threatened.

The stems or culms are 20 to 40 inches tall. They emerge from a swollen, or bulb-like, base and form large clumps. Timothy differs in one respect from most other grasses in that one (sometimes two) of the lower internodes is swollen into an ovoid body, which is referred to as a "bulb" or "corm" although it really is only a thickened internode. Each one of these "corms" is annual in duration, forming in early summer and dying the next year when seed matures. The leaves are elongate. The panicle is cylindrical and commonly 2 to 4 inches long and often longer.

Timothy grows better on clay loams than on light-textured, sandy soils. It is well adapted to the cool humid climate of the Northeastern and North Central States and also to the valleys of the Rocky Mountains and to the coastal region of the Pacific Northwest.

Fall seedings are best when seeding alone or with winter wheat; seedlings started then are less likely to be injured by dry weather in late spring or early summer than are seedlings from spring seedings. Less seed is required for fall than for spring seeding.

From 3 to 5 pounds an acre is recommended for fall; 10 pounds is recommended for spring seeding. It is commonly sown with clover—medium red, mammoth, or alsike—or with alfalfa in order to get a hay with higher protein content and to maintain a better soil productivity.

A change in the quality of hay occurs as the season advances. The percentage of nitrogen-free extract, fat, and protein gradually decreases while the less digestible and less valuable crude fiber increases with maturity. Therefore, timothy should be cut when it is in early bloom in order to get the greatest value per acre of high-quality hay.

About 6 percent of the timothy acreage of the United States is harvested for seed each year. Most of the domestic seed is harvested in a few Western States. The acreage cut for hay is estimated at more than 6 million in the United States.

The genus *Phleum* contains about 10 species. Half of them are annuals. All are native to Eurasia except *P. alpinum,* which is spread throughout the cold and mountainous parts of the Northern Hemisphere and as far south as the mountains of South America. Most of the species have been intro-

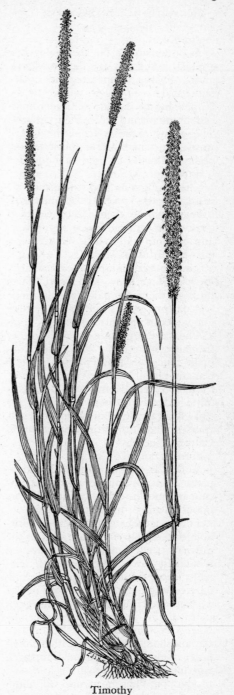

Timothy

duced into the United States, but only timothy is cultivated.

THE BLUEGRASSES
(*Poa* species)

Approximately 200 species of *Poa* are distributed through the world, primarily in the temperate and cooler regions. The 65 species native to the United States include some commercially important cultivated grasses. The genus name is from the Greek word *poa,* which was applied to any plant that could be used as fodder for livestock.

The *Poa* genus is distinguished by small, awnless spikelets; lemmas with a heavy midnerve like the keel of a boat; glumes, one- to three-nerved; and flat or folded leaf blades, with boat-shaped tips.

The bluegrasses are valued primarily for pasturage, hay, and lawn. They rank as the most palatable of range and pasture grasses and are suited for many special agricultural uses.

The most important are *Poa pratensis,* more commonly known as Kentucky bluegrass, and *P. compressa,* or Canada bluegrass. They are natives of the Old World. Kentucky bluegrass is quite extensively used for lawns, for turf on fairways and tees of golf courses, and for permanent pastures. Canada bluegrass is most useful as a pasture grass.

Generally, the bluegrasses should be planted in autumn because temperature and moisture then conduce to germination and promote good growth.

For a vigorous growth and a desirable dark-green color, nitrogen is the nutrient needed most where bluegrass is used for lawns. Nitrogen is the element most frequently found lacking where the grass has indications of underfeeding. However, when bluegrass is used for pastures and especially where seed production is the aim, attention should be given to other nutrients as well, because too much nitrogen will tend to delay flowering and seed production. Phosphorus also stimulates growth. For best growth and seed production, then, phosphorus, potassium, and nitrogen must be plentiful. Unless

Kentucky bluegrass

the soil is quite deficient in calcium, lime is not necessary.

Other species of bluegrass that are well known and have their place in agriculture are the *Poa arachnifera* (Texas bluegrass); *P. trivialis* (roughstalk bluegrass); *P. bulbosa* (bulbous bluegrass); *P. annua* (annual bluegrass); *P. ecunda* (Sandberg bluegrass); and *P. ampla* (big bluegrass).

KENTUCKY BLUEGRASS
(*Poa pratensis*)

The Kentucky bluegrass (sometimes called junegrass) is used principally for lawn and turf purposes but is also extensively used for pasture.

The definite date of its introduction into the United States is not known. It is believed to be a native of the Old World; it occurs over much of Europe and Asia. Probably the early colonists brought seed of Kentucky bluegrass to

Texas bluegrass

CANADA BLUEGRASS
(*Poa compressa*)

Canada bluegrass resembles Kentucky bluegrass but is different from it because of its blue-green foliage, distinctly flat culms, and short and much contracted panicles. It also is rhizomatous and spreads by these underground rootstalks. It is a native of Europe. It is extensively naturalized in this country. It is adapted to open, rather poor, dry soils, and in such situations competes with Kentucky bluegrass as a pasture grass. For lawns and golf links and similar purposes it can be used to advantage under conditions too dry or otherwise not entirely favorable to Kentucky bluegrass. Seed is produced quite abundantly and is easily harvested and threshed.

ROUGHSTALK BLUEGRASS
(*Poa trivialis*)

Roughstalk bluegrass, known also as roughstalk, resembles Kentucky bluegrass but differs from it in that it has no creeping rootstocks. The branches of the panicle are more slender and spreading. It also is a native of Europe, where it is a prominent pasture grass in many districts. It is used to some extent in this country as a wet-pasture grass, but it is used most often as a grass for seeding mixture for shady lawns.

BULBOUS BLUEGRASS
(*Poa bulbosa*)

Bulbous bluegrass is thought to be a native of southern Asia, Europe, and north Africa. It grows in nearly all temperate and subtropical regions. It was probably inadvertently brought into the United States in seed of other grasses and clovers. It is grown most extensively in southern Oregon and northern California.

Bulbous bluegrass forms true bulbs at the base and bulblets or bulbils in the panicle. Only rarely do the plants produce perfect flowers on the culms

this country in mixtures with the other grasses. Apparently the climate and soil of the Northern States and the mountainous and cooler localities farther south were hospitable, for it is so widely distributed throughout those regions that its origin is often questioned.

Kentucky bluegrass grows 18 to 24 inches tall and under exceptionally favorable conditions often reaches 36 inches. It is easily identified by its boat-shaped leaf tip. It is a long-lived perennial. Some fields of it are known to be more than 60 years old. It spreads by underground rhizomes and thus makes a dense sod. The open, pyramidal panicle produces much seed.

It is dormant during exceptionally hot, dry periods of summer and turns brown unless ample water is applied. It is quite attractive, however, in the fall and spring and is more or less green in winter when it is properly managed and fertilized—an important factor in lawns.

Canada bluegrass

ANNUAL BLUEGRASS
(*Poa annua*)

Annual bluegrass, as the name implies, is an annual. It normally begins growth in late summer or early fall from seed produced earlier the same year. It is more dwarfed in growth than Kentucky bluegrass and lacks creeping rhizomes. It also has shorter, broader leaves than the other bluegrasses and the color, a considerably lighter green than that of Kentucky bluegrass or the others, is distinctive. The entire plant is smooth. The leaves are shiny on the dorsal side. No other turf species can produce seedstalks under regular mowing, but this grass can reproduce seeds even when mowed regularly at a height of one-fourth inch.

It is of little economic importance and under most conditions is considered a weedy pest, especially on lawns and golf courses.

BIG BLUEGRASS
(*Poa ampla*)

Big bluegrass is a robust, perennial, native bunchgrass that grows in all parts of the West. Plants are tufted and vigorous, about 2 to 4 feet tall, and have numerous basal leaves. Leaf blades are pale green, flat, and about ⅜ inch wide and 8 to 16 inches long. Panicles are erect, dense, and from 4 to 10 inches long. The fibrous roots penetrate deeply.

Although seldom found in dense stands, big bluegrass is an important range species because of its heavy forage production, palatability, and tendency to begin growth in early spring and continue into the fall. Because of its wide distribution, extensive root system, and adaptation to adverse sites and climates, it is useful for regrassing abandoned farm land and depleted range land. For this purpose it is one of the most useful of the bluegrasses.

Heavy, continuous grazing and severe trampling are injurious to native stands, but if it is grazed in moderation it responds satisfactorily.

or the seedstalks, and even these fail to develop a caryopsis or true seed. Growth usually begins about October 1 and ceases May 1 to May 15 when the bulblets formed in the panicle are mature. The seedstalks reach a height of 10 to 18 inches, depending on the fertility of the soil.

Bulbous bluegrass is best adapted to sections that have a dry summer, a mild winter, and winter rainfall. It grows during fall, winter, and early spring.

The production of seed (bulblets) on a commercial basis is confined largely to southwestern Oregon. Harvesting is done with a mowing machine with a swather.

The seeds are large and ordinarily are produced in abundance. When grown in rows and cultivated for seed production, big bluegrass has given excellent yields of good seed. Mixed field plantings of big bluegrass and legumes have produced high forage yields of good to excellent quality. This is particularly true of grass-alfalfa mixtures adapted to areas receiving limited rainfall.

Plant-selection work at Moro, Oreg., has resulted in development of an improved variety of big bluegrass named Sherman, which is now being grown for seed increase under State seed certification procedure. It should be ready for distribution before long.

TEXAS BLUEGRASS
(Poa arachnifera)

Texas bluegrass is a vigorous, sod-forming, native perennial that occurs in the Southeastern States and the warmer parts of the Southern Great Plains. This bluegrass is dioecious—a plant that produces pollen does not produce seed, and vice versa. The most characteristic difference in the appearance of the two kinds of plants is that the female plants have a mass of fine cobwebby hairs on their spikelets; the spikelets of the male plants are smooth and hairless.

Plants grow to a height of 1 to 3 feet, with numerous leaves ¼ inch wide and from 6 to 12 inches long. Seed panicles are about 6 inches long, light greenish in color, and dense and somewhat spikelike in form. Long, webby hairs at the base of the lemma are very prominent.

Texas bluegrass grows through the winter, producing an abundance of leafy, nutritious forage at the season when most range forage is harsh and least palatable to livestock.

Because of the palatability and abundance of the forage it yields, this species is valuable for range and pasture in the area to which it is adapted, but its use for reseeding at present is limited by the paucity of the seed it

produces. Breeding work has been in progress for some time to increase its seed production, but no new varieties are yet available.

Processing the seed to remove the woolly, hairlike seed covering has been only partly effective.

SANDBERG BLUEGRASS
(Poa secunda)

The most common native bluegrass is Sandberg bluegrass. It is a glabrous, tufted perennial that occurs generally throughout the Northern Great Plains and the Western States.

Plants may grow to a height of 8 to 24 inches. The inflorescence is a panicle only about a half inch wide. The forage is scanty but palatable. Since Sandberg bluegrass begins growth early in the spring, it supplies green, succulent forage at a time when it is most beneficial to grazing animals. It usually matures and dries by the first part of July. It is considered highly drought-resistant—partly because of its habit of making early growth and then going into dormancy as available moisture becomes scant.

Fair crops of seed are produced, but viability is usually low. Seed can be harvested readily with small-grain harvesting combines.

When used for revegetation, this bluegrass is ordinarily seeded in mixtures with other adapted grasses. The first species of the mixture to begin growth, it is dominant in spring but yields dominance to other species of the mixture as the season advances.

MUTTON BLUEGRASS
(Poa fendleriana)

Mutton bluegrass (Poa fendleriana, syns. P. brevipaniculata, P. longepedunculata, and P. scabriuscula), also known as Fendler bluegrass and muttongrass, occurs from northern Michigan and northern Wisconsin to southeastern British Columbia, eastern Washington, California (east of the Sierra Nevada), east to the Chisos

Mountains of western Texas and south into the mountains of Sonora, Chihuahua, and Baja California.

It is a perennial bunchgrass, tillering from the base, characteristically without rootstocks although, very rarely, small rootstocks, or rhizomes, are produced. The erect, tufted stems, varying in height from 6 to 24 inches, are roughened below the flower cluster—the panicle. The tufts range up to about a foot in diameter. The leaves are mostly basal. The firm and rather stiff blades are folded or inrolled, rarely flat. The leaf sheaths are somewhat roughened. The ligule, the tonguelike appendage in the collar of the leaf sheath and an important identification mark in grasses, is very small and scarcely noticeable. The oblong, contracted, usually green or pale bluish-purple flower head is long-exserted from the top leaf sheath and up to about 3 inches long. The individual spikelets are 4- to 7- (mostly 5- or 6-) flowered, flattened, and about $\frac{1}{3}$ inch long; the 2 glumes (the lowest and empty scales of a grass flower) are broad and $\frac{1}{8}$ inch long. The lemmas, or flowering scales, lack the cobwebby hairs at the base so often found in the bluegrass genus, but have fine hairs on the lower part of the midrib and on the marginal nerves, the intermediate nerves being obscure.

Mutton bluegrass occurs in grasslands, in open stands of aspen and coniferous timber, on rocky slopes, and mesas. Its altitudinal range in the Far West is considerable, ranging from sagebrush types at around 4,000 feet to timber line at about 11,500 or 12,000 feet in the Rocky Mountains. It occurs on all slopes but especially on dry, southern exposures, chiefly inhabiting rich, well-drained clay loams, especially those of limestone origin, but it is also found in sandy and gravelly soils. In the northern parts of its range, this grass often occurs in the foothills and on lower slopes, but in the Southwest it characteristically grows at higher elevations, the lower slopes and mesas ordinarily being too hot and dry

in summer for bluegrass. In fact, this tufted perennial is probably the only native bluegrass sufficiently abundant in the Southwest to be of more than purely local importance.

Mutton bluegrass is resistant to drought and, to a considerable extent, fire—often it is found on burns. The flowering period varies from March to early June; seed dissemination varies from July to November. Frequent associates (among grasses) are species of brome, fescue, needlegrass, redtop, trisetum, and wild-rye, and (among range weeds) aster, cinquefoil, lupine, penstemon, senecio, and yarrow; also, sedges, sagebrush, and shrubby cinquefoil.

Mutton bluegrass is one of the more important native range grasses, due to its high palatability, nutritiousness, wide distribution, fair abundance, and the fact that it starts growth very early in the spring and consequently is available when there is little other forage. For example, on the Colorado Plateau its density is light and it furnishes not over 5 percent of the total forage, as contrasted with the far greater bulk of Arizona fescue (*Festuca arizonica*), but because of its exceptionally early growth and the fact that its flowering period immediately follows the melting of the snow when there is but little other green vegetation, the species is conspicuous and is one of few generally recognized by local stockmen, who often call it "wintergrass" or "winter bluegrass."

It rates as excellent forage for cattle and horses and very good or good for sheep, elk, and deer, especially in early spring. The foliage becomes rather harsh and dry with increasing maturity, and the palatability decreases somewhat as the season advances, although it is grazed well throughout the summer. In fall, when more tender and succulent forage is scarce, cattle and horses readily eat the air-cured herbage. The common name "muttongrass" reflects the reputation of this species held by sheepmen for fattening sheep and lambs, especially in spring.

FOXTAIL MILLET
(*Setaria italica*)

Foxtail millet has erect or ascending stems that mostly are simple but are sometimes branching. It grows 2½ to 5 feet high under cultivation and bears broad, flat leaves. The seeds are borne in a rather dense, cylindrical spike. Foxtail millet, an annual, was cultivated in China as early as 2700 B. C. and later introduced into Europe. In 1849 seed was distributed by the United States Patent Office and by 1899 it had become a rather important crop in the Central States. The grassy weed known as foxtail is a rather close relative.

Foxtail millet is grown throughout the Great Plains, as far south as northern Texas, east through Missouri, southern Iowa, and northern Arkansas, and across Tennessee, Kentucky, and southern Illinois and Indiana. It can be grown in almost any area that has warm weather during the growing season and enough rain for any other crop. In fact, it has a lower requirement than most other crops but is seriously damaged by severe drought.

A number of varieties are recognized, the better known being Common, German, Hungarian, Siberian, and Kursk. The German and Common are the ones most generally grown.

Foxtail millet is used as hay, pasture, and green fodder; the seed is used for bird feed. It is useful as a catch crop to supply supplemental feed when pastures fail or the hay crop is short.

The seed deteriorates rapidly, and fresh seed should be used. Seed 2 years old will have deteriorated but little if kept in good storage, but seed older than that usually has low germination. The weight of seed is from 48 to 60 pounds per bushel.

Fertilizers are not used with foxtail millet in the Great Plains. Farther east, nitrogen and phosphate particularly have given increased yields, but as a general rule fertilizer should be applied to other crops in the rotation rather than to the millet.

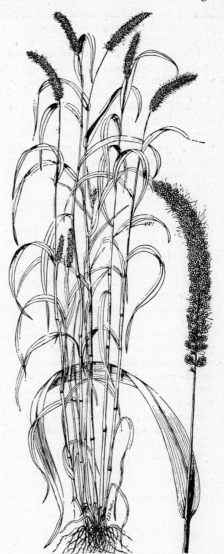

Foxtail millet

A good seedbed should be prepared by plowing, harrowing, and cultipacking or otherwise firming the seedbed. The seed is sown from shortly after corn-planting time to the middle of summer.

From 25 to 30 pounds of seed an acre should be used in places of ample rainfall and 15 to 20 pounds in drier localities. A grain drill should be used when foxtail millet is seeded alone. A mixture of the millet and soybeans or cow-peas should be broadcast by hand or drilled separately.

Foxtail millet hay is fed to horses and cattle, but opinions differ as to its value. The feeding value is greatest from the time of the first bloom until the seed reaches the milk stage. The crop is cut with an ordinary mower, windrowed, shocked, or handled otherwise as one would any ordinary hay crop. Hay yields are from 1 to 3 tons, depending on fertility, moisture, and like conditions of growth.

Foxtail millet hay is usually considered inferior to timothy and some of the other tame grasses. It is less palatable and does harm to horses if it is fed as the sole roughage. Some farmers think it makes fairly good hay for cattle and sheep; and as roughage for growing stock, it is about equal to prairie hay but inferior to alfalfa and clover.

The seed crop is usually harvested with a grain binder and placed in shocks and handled like wheat or other small grain. Ordinary threshers are used in threshing by adjusting to proper screens and making other minor adjustments. Yields of seed up to 20 bushels an acre are obtained under favorable conditions.

Foxtail millet is often used as a cash crop in a regular rotation and as a catch crop following small grain or other late-spring- or early-summer-maturing crops.

SORGHUMS and CONGENERS
(*Sorghum* species)

The forage sorghums, Sudangrass, and Johnsongrass are among our most important forage resources. The sorghums and Sudangrass are summer annuals that tolerate long, hot, dry periods of weather; thus they are particularly adapted to the Great Plains and valuable as emergency forage in the more humid areas. Johnsongrass, a rapidly spreading perennial where winter temperatures are not severe, is considered a serious weed in cultivated fields, but it is valuable for hay and pasture in many parts of the Southern States.

All are of foreign origin. The sorghums were cultivated during ancient times throughout Africa and southern Asia. Johnsongrass is a native of the Mediterranean. Sudangrass was introduced from Africa.

FORAGE SORGHUMS
(*Sorghum vulgare* and vars.)

On the basis of uses, the sorghums can be divided into four kinds: Grain, forage, sirup, and those for industrial brooms, wallboard, and so on. No clear distinction can be made between grain and forage sorghums, but those that have sweet or slightly sweet and juicy stems and the more leafy ones usually are classified generally as forage sorghums.

Sorghum generally is grown like corn; during the early stages of growth corn and sorghum look somewhat alike. The leaves are broad; the coarse stems grow from 2 to 15 feet high, depending on variety and growing conditions.

The seed is borne in heads composed of loose branches or panicles sometimes 8 inches thick and more than a foot long.

Because sorghums probably were cultivated in prehistoric periods in many parts of Asia and Africa, under widely different conditions of environment, hundreds of varieties have developed through natural selection. The sweet sorghums were introduced into the United States about 1850. Since then large numbers of varieties have been developed through selection and breeding.

Many of the sorghums used as forage are cut and fed later as fodder or silage.

The feeding of green sorghum to livestock, either by pasturing or soiling, is not widely practiced because of the risk of prussic acid poisoning. Losses in livestock from such poisoning is greatest when the second growth or a stunted growth is pastured. Practically all of the prussic acid disappears as the fodder is being cured. Varieties having a low, nontoxic level of prussic acid are being developed to overcome the hazard.

In the Southeastern States the sorghums are susceptible to several leaf diseases which reduce their feed value.

Sudangrass
(*Sorghum vulgare* var. *sudanense*)

Sudangrass was introduced into the United States in 1909 from Africa. Its widespread adaptation to many regions here have made it one of the most valuable of summer annual forage grasses. Like the sorghums, it tolerates droughty conditions and its rapid growth from late seedings makes it an ideal emergency forage for pasture, hay, or silage.

Sudangrass grows 4 to 7 feet tall, depending on method of planting and fertility. The stems, of which many arise from a single clump, are relatively fine but erect; they seldom become much larger than a lead pencil. The numerous leaves are long and narrow; the heads are composed of loose-bending branches 6 to 18 inches long.

Sudangrass usually is grown alone in places that have limited soil moisture; where rainfall is adequate it is frequently grown with soybeans. Yields of forage, depending upon rainfall and soil fertility, range from 1 to 7 tons an acre; likewise, yields of seed may vary from 250 up to 2,000 pounds.

Sudangrass occasionally may contain enough prussic acid to be toxic to livestock, although the risk is not so great as in the sorghums, particularly in northern latitudes. Short, stunted growth usually contains more prussic acid than normal growth.

If humidity and temperatures are high, Sudangrass is attacked by several leaf diseases that reduce its value.

There are several varieties of Sudangrass—one is resistant to certain leaf diseases, another combines the sweet-stem characteristic of sweet sorghum with the fine stems and leaves of com-

Sudangrass

mon sudan, and still another, now being developed, is nearly free from prussic acid.

Johnsongrass
(*Sorghum halepense*)

Johnsongrass is different from all other species of sorghum in that it is a perennial that spreads by vigorous

Alkali sacaton

livestock poisoned by it. Johnsongrass is condemned by many people, but it does have a profitable place in livestock production in many sections of the South.

DROPSEEDS
(*Sporobolus* species)

The *Sporobolus* genus is large and widely distributed. The species native to the United States number 36 and are most abundant in the Southern Great Plains and the Southwest. The scientific name is derived from the Greek *spora*, seed, and *ballein*, to cast forth; the common name, dropseed, refers to the prompt casting of seed as it nears maturity.

Spikelets of *Sporobolus* are single-flowered. In most species the stems are solid or pithy, rather than hollow. Most of the perennial species are palatable to animals.

Practically all the dropseeds produce an abundance of viable, long-lived seed that—because of a hard, impervious seed coat—may lie dormant many years before germinating under natural conditions; that characteristic is sometimes an advantage and accounts for the appearance of seedlings after long periods of drought.

ALKALI SACATON
(*Sporobolus airoides*)

Alkali sacaton is a densely tufted, long-lived, native bunchgrass that occurs generally throughout the western and southwestern sections.

The seed stalks are erect, smooth, solid, and about 3 feet tall. The seed heads are open panicles that terminate in single florets.

The foliage is basal and abundant; the leaves are about one-fourth inch wide and 8 to 18 inches long. The roots are coarse and fibrous and penetrate the soil to good depths. The grass is commonly found on moist alkaline soils but it occurs also on other types of soil. Normally the stand has a distinctive tufted or bunchy appearance.

rootstocks. The stems, leaves, and heads of Johnsongrass resemble those of Sudangrass, although it seldom grows so tall. It was brought from Turkey about 1830, and has spread throughout the South.

Johnsongrass grows wherever cotton is produced and thrives where moisture is abundant. Its seed fertility is high. Two and three crops of hay are frequently harvested a season; yields of more than 15 tons are common. It is valuable for pasture and is grown with several winter annual legumes. Yields of seed may reach 8 to 10 bushels an acre.

Johnsongrass may contain small quantities of prussic acid, but rarely are

Alkali sacaton produces much forage, which is eaten freely by cattle and horses during the growing season. As the plants mature, however, the foliage becomes coarse, tough, and unpalatable and does not cure into nutritious winter feed. Grass that is kept closely cropped affords good grazing. It produces hay of fair quality if cut at the proper stage of development.

Seed is ordinarily obtained from native stands, no doubt because of the general abundance of the species over wide areas. Nearly always a satisfactory seed crop matures at some place each season. Seed can be harvested with a combine or by threshing mature seed hay. Seed of excellent quality has been produced under cultivation, but the procedure seems unnecessary as long as native stands are a dependable source.

SAND DROPSEED
(*Sporobolus cryptandrus*)

Sand dropseed is a tufted, widely distributed, native grass. It occurs most abundantly in the Southern Great Plains and the Southwest. It is a pioneer or invader species on raw, denuded soil and is most prevalent on sandy soil.

Plants grow about 2 to 3 feet tall, with solid stems and fairly numerous leaves about one-fourth inch wide and 4 to 12 inches long. Seed heads are open, the finely branched panicles average 8 to 12 inches in length and terminate in single spikelets. Characteristically, many of the seed heads remain within the upper portion of the surrounding sheath, so that the plants tend to retain large portions of their seeds. Roots are coarse, fibrous, and penetrating—a characteristic that accounts partly for the wide adaptation of the species.

Sand dropseed produces a fairly large amount of foliage, which is taken readily by livestock while green but only sparingly after the plants reach maturity.

It is a prolific seeder and, when protected or properly grazed, tends to in-

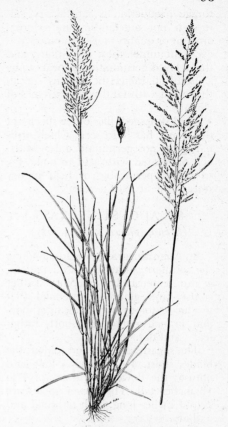

Sand dropseed

crease in density on the depleted range.

Seed matures in late summer and is readily harvested with a small grain combine. When the grass has been grown in rows and cultivated or grown under irrigation, exceptionally high yields have been obtained exceeding 1,000 pounds an acre.

Its widespread occurrence has encouraged its use for revegetation. It is generally recommended for seeding in mixtures with adapted species at about 1 pound per acre. Because of the small size of the seed (usually more than 5 million in a pound), planting should be shallow and the new seeding should be protected during the period of seedling establishment.

Many excellent characteristics make it valuable for revegetation use. It is widely adapted as to soils and climate;

forage production is satisfactory (although not outstanding in its total amount or quality) ; seed production is excellent under most conditions; and the delayed germination appears to be a useful characteristic for any species that must withstand wide extremes of climate.

Sand dropseed, like other species of the genus, has hard seed, which ordinarily do not germinate unless scarified or treated with acid to make the seed coat permeable or held in dry storage for at least a year.

ST. AUGUSTINEGRASS
(*Stenotaphrum secundatum*)

St. Augustinegrass, now found along the southern Atlantic coastal regions, is an extensively creeping, rather coarse, and glabrous perennial that produces stolons with long internodes and branches that are short, rather leafy, and flat.

The sheaths are flat and folded; the blades short, 4 or 6 inches long and obtuse; the flowering culms are 4 to 12 inches tall. The flower spikes are 2 to 4 inches long, both terminal and axillary.

In the region where it is adapted, it thrives in shaded areas so it is especially useful for lawns. On many golf courses in the South it is used on fairways. It is naturally a seashore plant and will withstand salt spray.

It is native to the West Indies. In Cuba it is called *camalote, gramon de costa,* and *canamazo amargo.* It is also found in Upper and Lower Guinea, Africa, and in South Africa from Cape Town to Natal. In the Pacific area, from southern Mexico to Australia, it is also native. It has been introduced into southern France and Italy. In the Hawaiian Islands it was formerly called *Manienie,* a native name that is now applied to Bermuda-grass there. In British Guiana it is sometimes called sheep grass.

St. Augustinegrass affords good pasturage but it has not been used extensively for that purpose. It is used for

St. Augustinegrass

grazing on muck soils in the Everglades in Florida, where it furnishes more grazing than such grasses as Para, which is commonly used there. The creeping, flat stems of St. Augustinegrass root to form dense sods which stand trampling.

Because practically no seed is produced, vegetative material must be used in making new plantings. Rooted runners, used for this purpose, are planted in rows or disked into the soil during moist periods, and subsequently packed. Establishment is not difficult, and good stands are usually had.

St. Augustinegrass should be well fertilized. Nitrogen is especially essential; on sandy land it will require annual applications. Ample moisture is also necessary for best growth and development.

This grass is subject to brown patch fungus, which does most damage in warm weather when there is undue moisture. The disease is controlled rather easily by stimulating growth of the plant with nitrogen fertilizers or by using calomel and corrosive sublimate. (Care should be exercised by anyone who uses corrosive sublimate, a virulent poison.) But so far the disease has not been a serious factor in growing the grass.

Chinch bugs also may do damage. Small brown areas that soon widen indicate their presence. Known remedial measures consist of blowing tobacco dust down between the stems of the grass by means of a dusting machine or spraying with nicotine sulfate (a poison!), using 1 part of nicotine sulfate to 500 parts of water.

STIPAS OR NEEDLEGRASSES
(*Stipa* species)

The *Stipa* genus is distributed through the temperate zones. About 30 species grow in the Western States. The scientific name *Stipa* is from the Greek word *stupe,* tow, referring to the feathery awns of some species. Each spikelet has one flower and terminates in a prominent awn that accounts for the common name "needlegrass," that often is used for the various species of this genus.

Stipa grasses rank fairly high as forage grasses on the western ranges because of their abundance, wide distribution, long growing period, and capacity to cure well on the ground.

The injuries that the long, sharp awns cause on grazing animals are a serious objection to these grasses regardless of their other virtues.

NEEDLE-AND-THREAD
(*Stipa comata*)

Needle-and-thread is a deep-rooted, long-lived, native bunchgrass that occurs generally on the western ranges and most abundantly on the sandy soils of the Northern Great Plains. It grows in almost pure stands as an invader on some of the abandoned croplands of the Plains. It derives its name from the appearance of the seed, which is sharp-pointed and has a long, bent, twisted, threadlike awn that looks like a threaded sewing needle.

Seedstalks grow 1 to 4 feet high, with leaves less than one-eighth inch wide and 8 to 12 inches long. Leaf auricles are absent, but the ligule is membranous, notched, and prominent. Seed awns, also prominent, usually average 6 inches or more in length.

Growth starts in early spring, usually before associated native grasses green up, and continues throughout the summer if enough moisture is available. Growth is resumed after a drought if favorable moisture and temperatures are present in the fall.

Flowering of this species usually begins early in June, and the seed matures and is shed in July. Livestock graze the plants sparingly during this period. Palatability is reduced by the sharp points of the seeds, which injure livestock by working into the mouth parts and the hide. Except for the period when seeds are present, livestock eat the forage readily. They make good use of the standing cured forage for winter grazing.

Seed is produced in abundance most years, but the heavy awns and sharp points on the seed make it difficult to handle. Seeding is almost impossible with an ordinary grain drill, because the long awns cause the seed to mat into large clumps that clog the seeding spouts. Processing the seed with a hammer mill to remove awns improves its quality.

Although this grass has wide adaptation in the Plains, it has been used only sparingly for reseeding, mostly because

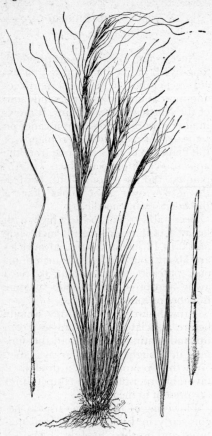

Needle-and-thread

Green needlegrass grows to a height of 3 feet. Its leaves, mostly basal, vary in width from one-fourth to one-half inch, and in length from about 8 to 12 inches. The seed heads are compact panicles about 4 to 8 inches long. Seed spikelets have short, bent awns about an inch long that are conspicuous, but not nearly so troublesome to grazing animals or in seed handling as the awns of needle-and-thread grass. The green needlegrass has rather deep, fibrous, penetrating roots, which fact accounts for its wide adaptation.

Growth starts early in the spring and continues into the fall when enough moisture is available. It makes excellent recovery after grazing or clipping and provides good pasture forage for all classes of livestock. Hay of excellent quality may be produced. If the plants are permitted to stand, fairly good winter grazing is furnished.

Seed of green needlegrass matures in early July. For seed production the grass can be harvested with a binder, header, or swather, then cured and threshed. Seed heads are indeterminate in ripening; hence these methods of harvesting will give the smallest amount of undeveloped seed in the threshed seed material. Seed yields of 150 pounds an acre have been obtained from natural stands. Yields of 300 to 500 pounds have been obtained from plants in rows and cultivated.

The seed awns of green needlegrass are not so large or troublesome as those of other *Stipa* species and can be removed readily by processing the seed with a hammer mill and cleaning it in a fanning mill. The seed should then have a purity of 98 percent. The low germination of freshly harvested seed is due to a high percentage of dormant seed. Dormancy may be overcome by mechanical scarification, treatment with acid, or dry storage for a year.

Green needlegrass is a good native species for use in revegetation. The young seedlings are vigorous and fairly resistant to drought and insects. Customarily this grass is seeded in mixture

of objections to it for grazing and difficulties in handling the seed during seeding operations.

Green Needlegrass
(*Stipa viridula*)

Green needlegrass, known also as feather bunchgrass, is a rather coarse, leafy, native perennial adapted to the Western States. It is most abundant on the upland prairie and ranges of the Northern Great Plains. It is seldom found as the major constituent in the native association except where it receives additional moisture from flooding or where it invades abandoned cropland. It seems to be well adapted to most soil types but makes its best growth on the sandier soils.

with one or another adapted species.

Plant selection and breeding with this species at the Mandan Field Station in North Dakota has resulted in development of a new variety named Green Stipa grass; it has excellent seedling vigor, a high degree of disease resistance, and good yields of forage and seed.

THE ZOYSIA GRASSES
(*Zoysia* species)

There are three species of *Zoysia* in the United States, Manilagrass (*Z. matrella*), Japanese lawngrass (*Z. japonica*), and Mascarenegrass (*Z. tenuifolia*). All are natives of tropical or eastern Asia.

Mascarenegrass, the smallest, finest, and least hardy of the *Zoysia* species, is of least importance. It seldom grows more than 2 inches high and the plants have a shallow root system. It has been grown somewhat in the South and as far west as California.

Japanese lawngrass has a broad, coarse leaf similar to that of redtop. It does not grow so tall as redtop but makes a dense cover. It is the most winter-hardy of the three species and has been grown successfully as far north as Boston. Because seed is not available, it has to be established vegetatively. Therefore, it is not now being recommended generally; it is of value for lawn or turf purposes only. It is tough, harsh, and unpalatable, and, once established, extremely hardy and persistent.

Manilagrass is the most important and widely used of the *Zoysias*. It turns brown with the first heavy frost in the fall and does not renew growth until after the last heavy frost in the spring. Near the District of Columbia, it remains green from mid-April to late October. It has survived the winter as far north as Rhode Island, but its general limit of northern adaptation is approximately 40° latitude. It will tolerate some shade, especially in the South.

Manilagrass is not very exacting in its

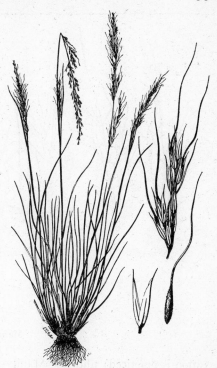

Green needlegrass

soil requirements, but it appears better adapted to the heavier-textured soils. Complete fertilizers in regular applications are necessary to establish and maintain good turf. The same methods of seedbed preparation are recommended as for other lawn grasses.

Seed is not available in commercial quantities, and vegetative planting is necessary. One square yard of thick sod is sufficient to sprig-plant 750 to 1,000 square feet, with rows 8 to 10 inches apart and sprigs 3 inches apart in the row. Because the plants are sensitive to cold, it is best to establish Manilagrass in the spring as soon as the soil is warm.

One of its principal weaknesses is its slow growth. It usually requires at least 2 years to obtain a good cover at the rate of planting recommended. Kentucky bluegrass, redtop, or similar grasses may be seeded between the rows of Manilagrass sprigs to control weeds (unless hand weeding or culti-

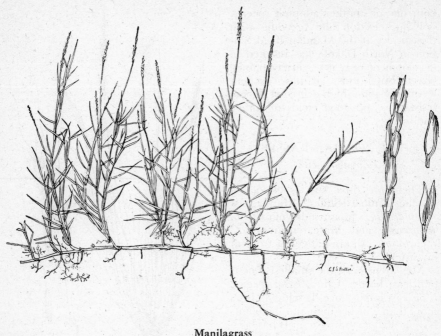

Manilagrass

vation is practiced) until the Manila-grass is established.

Considerable selection and improvement work is being conducted with Manila and Japanese lawngrass to develop superior turf strains, and it is likely that good seed-producing strains can be obtained. With seed available, the establishment of stands will be much less of a problem.

THE AUTHORS ‹‹‹ *Max M. Hoover, as assistant chief of the Soil Conservation Service, Nursery Division, gave impetus to conservation work in developing the use of native grasses under field conditions, provided a seed source through nursery cultivation, and demonstrated the feasibility of large-scale seed harvest. Dr. Hoover recently transferred to the Bureau of Plant Industry, Soils, and Agricultural Engineering and continues research work with headquarters at Ames, Iowa. He received his first two degrees at Kansas State College and his doctor of philosophy degree at Cornell. He is author of several widely used bulletins and coauthor of others.*

M. A. Hein is an agronomist in the Division of Forage Crops and Diseases in the Bureau of Plant Industry, Soils, and Agricultural Engineering. He is engaged in experimental work with native and introduced grasses for hay, pasture, and silage; adaptation studies; breeding for improvement; cultural practices, and other factors relating to grass. Mr. Hein received the degree of master of science in agronomy from the University of Illinois.

William A. Dayton is in charge of dendrology and range forage investigations of the United States Forest Service.

C. O. Erlanson is principal ecologist in the Division of Plant Exploration and Introduction, Bureau of Plant Industry, Soils, and Agricultural Engineering. He has been engaged in research on the origin and utilization of economic plant materials since 1930.

The Legumes of Many Uses

A GENERAL VIEW OF THE LEGUMINOSAE

ROLAND MCKEE [1]

A LEGUME is a plant that bears pods as do beans, peas, soybeans, and cowpeas. In more technical terms, a legume is a superior one-celled, monocarpellary fruit, usually dehiscent into two valves, and having the seed attached along the ventral suture. The fruit is called a pod.

All plants conforming to this definition are grouped together in one large family called the legume family, or *Leguminosae*. In a listing or classification of flowering plants based on the stage or complexity of development, legumes are intermediate in the list.

Considered in its broadest sense, the legume family contains three divisions, or subfamilies. These are known as *Mimosoideae, Caesalpinioideae,* and *Faboideae*. In flower structure these subfamilies differ quite widely and it is this difference that is usually used in classifying or identifying the groups.

In *Mimosoideae* the flowers are regular and usually in dense heads; in *Caesalpinioideae* and *Faboideae* they are irregular and fewer in a cluster or raceme. In *Caesalpinioideae* the flowers do not have the papilionate or butterfly shape that is characteristic of the *Faboideae*. It is the *Faboideae* that is most commonly associated with the

term legume. All the economic legumes of agriculture come under this group.

The flowers in the *Fabiodeae* are distinctive. The petals of an individual flower vary in shape. The largest and most showy petal is known as a banner or standard. It is usually nearly flat and somewhat circular and is the outer one of the petals. The two inner petals, which are folded together, are usually bent or curved and enclose the stamens. These are known as the keel. On either side of the keel are two petals known as wings. When the petals are in normal position and the banner extended, the resulting flower has somewhat the appearance of a butterfly and the flower, accordingly, has been called papilionaceous (*papilio,* a butterfly, + *aceous*). Some have called this subfamily the *Papilionoideae* rather than the *Faboideae*. Inside the petals, or showy part of the flower, are concealed the stamens and pistil. These are the essential parts of the flower since they are the organs involved in seed production.

Legumes have been known to man from the time of earliest records. Tares, as referred to in the Bible, are thought to be the common vetch. Alfalfa was among the earliest of cultivated crops, as indicated by early historical writings. Its native habitat is presumed to be Persia. In China the soybean dates

[1] *All articles in this chapter were written by Mr. McKee.*

back to the earliest of preserved writings and probably long antedates written records. Alfalfa can thus be considered the earliest cultivated forage crop and soybeans probably the earliest legume food crop. This early use of these crops suggests that even in the first period of recorded history the superiority of legumes was recognized. Their early use in pastures and crop rotations suggests this conclusion.

The legumes today are universally thought of as having higher feeding value than nonlegumes and this, for the most part, is true. One of the main reasons why they are superior is the fact that in general they contain a higher percentage of protein than nonlegumes, and protein is an essential food constituent. The seeds of legumes are particularly high in protein, but the leaves and stems also contain a relatively higher amount than is contained in other plants when they are harvested at a like stage of maturity.

It is true that seeds of some nonlegumes have a high protein content and the leaves and stems of some are comparatively high in this constituent, but for the most part, legumes can be considered decidedly superior. Legumes not only have a higher percentage of protein, they also have high-quality protein. This is of prime importance and helps greatly in obtaining high nutritive value in feeds for animals as well as food for human consumption. The quality of the protein of legumes is such as to make them especially valuable as feed to supplement the cereal grains, which do not have the proper protein for a balanced livestock feed.

Legumes are also valuable because they contain a comparatively large amount of calcium and have a fair amount of phosphorus, which is necessary in proper nutrition. Likewise, legumes are recognized as the best source of vitamins A and D for livestock feed and are largely depended upon for supplying these constituents.

Besides being of special value for feed and food, legumes are superior for soil improvement. This is due to the large amount of nitrogen they are able to supply the soil for the use of subsequent crops. It is not, however, merely that they return a large amount of nitrogen to the soil that makes them superior for soil improvement; it is the fact that much of the nitrogen contained in a legume is taken from the air rather than from the soil, as is the case with other plants, and in this way new and additional nitrogen is added to the already existing soil supply. Legumes thus add to the soil nitrogen that it did not previously contain. Nonlegumes merely take nitrogen from the soil and return it again.

The total amount of nitrogen that legumes take from the air cannot be known with any exactness since the condition under which they are grown influences the relative amounts taken from the air and soil. In a soil that is low in nitrogen, much more of the element is taken from the air than is the case when there is a large soil supply of nitrogen. It also is probable that the relative amount taken from the air and soil varies with the different legumes. It is generally assumed, however, that at least half the nitrogen in legumes comes from the air.

The total acreage of legumes in the United States, both in cultivated and pastured areas, can only be estimated. Data are available covering acreage cut for hay and seed of the major legume crops but are lacking for acreage used for pasturage and cover crops. From the general information that is available, however, it is estimated, in round numbers, that the acreage of all legumes cut for hay is 40 million acres; cut for seed, 15 million acres; used for cover crop, 5 million acres; and pastured, 40 million acres.

Assuming that this acreage averaged a ton per acre dry weight of tops and roots and that this growth averaged 2 percent nitrogen, the total nitrogen produced would be 2 million-odd tons.

Studies that have been made on roots of legumes indicate that the weight of the roots generally is about one-third that of the tops and that the percentage of nitrogen in the roots is slightly less than that in the tops. The percentage of nitrogen in roots of a number of legumes that have been analyzed ranges from 1.40 percent to 2.30 percent and in tops from 2.10 percent to 2.80 percent.

As previously stated, it is generally assumed that more than half the nitrogen in legumes is taken from the air. This means then that more than a million tons of nitrogen is taken by legumes each year from the air. Of course, all that amount would not be returned to the soil because the hay, pasturage, and seed fed to animals would only be returned in part and mostly as manure. As has been indicated, about one-third of the total nitrogen of most legumes is in the root; this, with the amount returned to the soil would no doubt be well over half of the amount taken from the air.

The nitrogen taken from the soil by legumes, of course, does not add to the total nitrogen of the soil, but such nitrogen, when again returned to the soil, is usually considered to be more readily available for use in plant growth and in this way adds to the nitrogen supply. The total nitrogen in the form of commercial fertilizer used annually in the United States has been less than 500,000 tons. It is thus seen that the nitrogen supplied by the legume crops is greater than the amount used in commercial fertilizers.

Getting nitrogen from the air usually is considered a special function of legumes, although it is known that a few other plants can do so, too. In the case of legumes, taking nitrogen from the air is accomplished through symbiotic bacteria (*Rhizobia*) that develop in

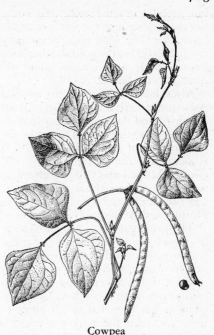

Cowpea

nodules on the roots of the legumes. The bacteria take nitrogen direct from the air as they grow and multiply in the nodule. The nitrogen in turn becomes available to the legume plant and aids in its nourishment and growth. It is this symbiotic association of legumes and *Rhizobia* that gives legumes a distinct advantage over non-legume plants.

In order to attain the advantage of symbiosis it is necessary to bring the *Rhizobia* in contact with the young growing rootlets of the legume. In agricultural operations this is a common practice and is referred to as inoculation. Inoculation is accomplished by mixing a liquid or humus culture of the *Rhizobia* inoculum with the seed just before seeding.

THE MAIN SPECIES OF LEGUMES

ALYCECLOVER (*Alysicarpus vaginalis*) is a summer annual. In thin stands it tends to spread and be moderately branched but in thick stands it is ascending and little branched. It attains a height of about 3 feet on moderately fertile soil. The stems are rather coarse but fairly leafy. The leaves are unifoliolate, broadly oval, and borne the entire length of the stems on short leafstalks. The seed, which is quite small, 275,000 to the pound, is borne in jointed pods and weighs about 60 pounds to the bushel.

Alyceclover is native to tropical Asia from where it has spread to parts of Africa and America. It was first introduced into the United States by the Department of Agriculture in 1910. It is adapted to the area adjacent to the Gulf of Mexico and is being grown in many places throughout that area. It has been most extensively planted in Florida and Mississippi.

The principal use of alyceclover has been for hay and soil improvement but it also makes good pasturage. In limited feeding trials by State experiment stations it has given good results in comparison with other hay. Commercially it has been fed to all kinds of livestock and in the market commands about the same price as other legume hays.

The fertilizer requirements of alyceclover are about the same as for most other legumes of the South. It does not tolerate wet lands and makes poor growth on soils of low fertility. It should be seeded about the first of May or later at the rate of 15 to 20 pounds of seed per acre. When the crop is harvested for seed or when the plants are allowed to mature and shatter seed, a volunteer crop is assured for the following year. When used for green manure, the crop is volunteered several years.

Inoculation has not been needed in sections where alyceclover has been grown to date.

For hay or green manure, the crop can be handled with ordinary farm machinery. The cut hay dries readily and in good weather can be stacked or baled the day after it is cut.

When the crop is to be harvested for seed, it can be allowed to grow the entire season, or an early crop may be cut for hay and the second growth allowed to produce seed. In this latter case, the seed crop may be reduced.

Alyceclover seed shatters or drops from the plant when ripe and for this reason harvesting seed is somewhat difficult. Combines have been used but with considerable loss of seed. Although yields up to 600 pounds per acre have been obtained, 300 pounds would be a high average.

On land that has grown alyceclover continuously for several years, or has grown other crops harboring the root knot nematode, damage by this pest becomes serious. This can be overcome to some extent by proper crop rotations, but the more satisfactory way is to make plantings, as far as possible, on new land. On account of its susceptibility to nematode, alyceclover should not be seeded on fields to be used subsequently for crops that are susceptible to this pest.

PEANUT
(*Arachis hypogaea*)

The peanut is a strong low-growing, spreading, summer annual having odd-pinnate leaves and broad, oval leaflets. The flowers, which are inconspicuous, are borne in the axis of the leaves. After the flowers fall the end of the flower stalk bends downward, elongates, and forces the fruit into the ground. The pod, which contains from one to three seed, thus develops and ripens underground.

The center of origin of the peanut is presumed to be Brazil. Several closely related species occur in that country. The Nambyquare peanut, which is grown by the Nambyquare Indians of Brazil, is equal in size to any varieties that have been in commercial production. Peanuts were unknown to white men until after the discovery of America. At that time the American Indian used them for food. The early colonists in the Carolinas and Virginia brought peanuts under cultivation; later peanuts were spread to widely scattered tropical regions.

The countries of largest production today are India, Bengal, China, Nigeria, Gambia, and the United States.

In this country more than 2 million pounds of seed have been produced annually in recent years. While peanuts are used largely for human consumption, they also furnish a large amount of forage and the seed is fed to hogs in limited amounts.

Sandy loam soils of good fertility and good drainage are best suited for peanut production. Sandy soils of lower fertility will produce good crops if properly fertilized. The use of 300 to 500 pounds of a 2–8–2 or a 2–8–3 fertilizer is recommended for most southern areas of the United States. Growing and turning under a winter green manure crop of lupines or other winter legume in rotation with peanuts will give increased yields; this practice recently has been greatly extended. Inoculation of the peanut is not needed, but a seed disinfectant used before seeding will help good stands.

Peanuts are seeded from April 10 to May 10 or even later in the extreme South. The rate of seeding is 32 to 48 pounds per acre of unhulled seed or 20 to 30 pounds of hulled. The seed should be hulled by hand or special machinery to avoid injury.

Planting and cultivation of peanuts is similar to most row-grown crops, but harvesting of the seed is quite different since the seed is produced underground. Plows or diggers are used to remove the plants from the soil and then the plants, with roots and nuts attached, are stacked, with nuts to the center, around an upright pole 6 or 8 feet high, which has a cross bar about 12 inches above the ground to keep the peanuts off the ground.

When dry, the peanuts are threshed and the straw, or hay, as it is called, is fed to livestock. Peanut straw has high feeding value and brings a good market price. Seldom are peanuts grown to be used exclusively for hay. The so-called runner varieties are planted to be used exclusively for hog pasture in which case both the nuts and tops of the plant are consumed.

Many commercial uses are made of the harvested seed, the ordinary

Peanut

roasted peanut probably commanding first importance. Peanut oil, candy, and peanut butter are other common commodities. In the tropical countries where they are grown, peanuts are one of the chief sources of food; not only are they easily grown—they are among the most nutritious of all foods.

CROTALARIA
(*Crotalaria* species)

Of the 400 to 600 species of *crotalaria* only a few have been brought under cultivation. These are upright summer annuals or short-lived perennials. The stems are coarse; the central stem is upright and branches quite freely, except in very thick stands. The leaflets are borne singly or in threes in the axis of the leaf and vary in shape from linear to broad ovate. The plants in general are leafy, bloom freely, and set seed in abundance. The yellow flowers are showy and the seed

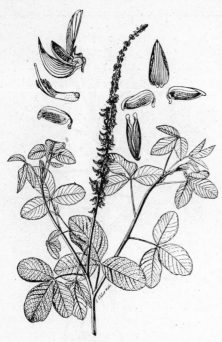

Striped crotalaria

The two outstanding characteristics of crotalaria are its resistance to root knot nematode and its ability to grow on poor acid soils. In addition, however, it produces good crops of seed that can be readily harvested and by reason of its high percentage of hard seed, it can, with proper management, be volunteered for an indefinite term of years. For sandy soils in the South no crop is better adapted; while there are plants that are better liked by livestock than crotalaria, the fact that it will grow and afford reasonably good feed makes it highly desirable for many of the poorer situations.

Crotalaria should be seeded about corn-planting time or later. When volunteering crotalaria in corn, the original seeding should be made several weeks before the last cultivation of the corn.

Since the organism that inoculates crotalaria seems to be present in all our soils, artificial inoculation is not considered necessary.

The use of commercial fertilizer will increase the yield but the growth without fertilizer is sufficiently large to make its use profitable.

Crotalaria can be harvested with ordinary farm machinery but it has not been used commercially for hay.

In harvesting for seed, care should be taken to dry the seed after harvest and store it in a dry place in order to insure germination after storage.

Crotalaria is largely tropical and warm-temperate in its requirements. The preponderance of species appears to be in equatorial Africa. Although there has been no special program of introduction for the group, about 70 species have been introduced in an effort to find some of value for poor, sandy soils in the Southeast. The presence in some species of substances toxic to stock is a deterring factor in a more general use of these species.

It is possible that among the many species not yet introduced there may be some that do not contain these toxic substances and would be of greater value than the ones now in cultivation.

pods as a rule are quite conspicuous. The seed color varies from straw-yellow through brown to black.

The first crotalaria introduced into the United States came from Brazil in 1899, but it was 30 years later before the crop was recognized as having agricultural importance.

Being summer-growing plants and of tropical origin, the crotalaria are adapted only in the Cotton Belt. There are no statistics regarding the acreage of crotalaria in the United States but it is estimated at several hundred thousand acres.

The species having forage value are *C. intermedia, C. mucronata,* and *C. lanceolata.* These are also used as cover crops. Another, a poisonous species, *C. spectabilis,* is used for cover.

In seeding crotalaria, it is desirable to use scarified seed to insure germination. When seeding broadcast or in close drills, from 10 to 20 pounds of seed per acre is sufficient, the amount varying with the species and thoroughness of seedbed preparation.

SOYBEAN
(*Glycine max*)

The soybean, an annual, summer legume, came originally from southeastern Asia. It is an erect, branching plant resembling in its early growth the ordinary field or navy bean. The pods, stems, and leaves are covered with fine, brown or gray hairs. The leaves vary widely in shape, size, color, and degree of persistence. They usually fall before the pods are mature.

The small, inconspicuous, self-fertile flowers are borne in the axil of the leaf and are either white or purple. The pods usually contain two or three seeds and occasionally four. Most varieties have unicolored seeds of straw yellow, greenish-yellow, green, brown, or black.

Soybeans are grown more intensively in Manchuria than in any other country. China, Korea, and Japan are large producers. The crop is also grown in the Philippines, Siam, India, and the East Indies. A small amount is grown in the Soviet Union, Rumania, Austria, and Czechoslovakia.

We do not know the early history of the soybean. Ancient Chinese records of methods of culture, varieties for different purposes, and numerous uses indicate that the soybean is one of the oldest crops grown by man.

Like maize and some other crops of long domestication, the relationship of the soybean to wild-growing species can no longer be traced with any degree of definiteness. It is a cultigen—a cultural variety—with an infinity of cultivated forms.

Soybeans were probably brought into the United States from China and Japan as early as the Colonial period, but serious investigations as to their possibilities under our conditions did not begin until about 1890. The first mention of soybeans in American literature was made in 1804. The Department of Agriculture introduced a number of varieties in 1898, and by 1910 about 50,000 acres were under cultivation.

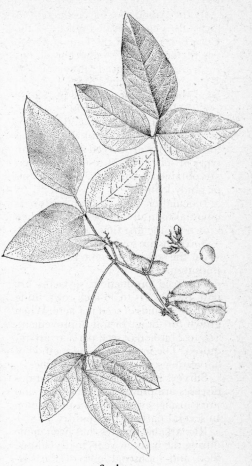

Soybean

Success with some of the varieties and the eagerness with which growers accepted the new plant immigrant caused an early demand for types adaptable throughout the Central States. Federal plant explorers combed the soybean areas of northern China, Manchuria, and Japan from 1929 to 1931, bringing hundreds of forms to the United States. Many of these soon found their way into commercial cultivation. Worth 14 million dollars in 1929, the soybean industry by 1944 increased in value to 395 million dollars. This spectacular development would not have been possible without the patient, fundamental exploration and introduction which preceded it.

In the Americas, the production of soybeans is concentrated chiefly in the Corn Belt region of the United States, where more than 90 percent of our soybeans are produced. Production of soybeans in the United States has risen from about 3 million bushels in 1920 to 201,275,000 bushels in 1946.

In general, the climatic adaptations of the soybean are about the same as for corn. It will succeed on nearly all types of soil; the best results, however, are obtained on mellow, fertile loams or sandy loams.

Inoculation with soybean culture is essential to insure the best results when grown for the first time.

Soybeans are sown from early spring, when the soil has become warm, until midsummer.

For seed production, soybeans are best sown in 21- to 36-inch rows, using 45 to 60 pounds of seed per acre. When grown for forage or soil improvement, 1½ to 2 bushels of seed per acre are required. The most successful method of harvesting seed is with the combine.

Surveys indicate that several serious diseases are prevalent in soybeans and are causing severe losses in production in several parts of the country.

Remarkable progress has been made during the past few years in developing food and industrial uses of the soybean, the oil, and oil meal. Soybean foods receiving most attention are soy flour, grits, and flakes. There are more than 150 soybean-processing plants, which have an annual capacity of 172,-000,000 bushels. Soybean oil has a wide variety of food and industrial uses, the principal food use being for shortening. The oil meal, a highly concentrated feed, is used largely for all kinds of livestock.

ROUGHPEA

(*Lathyrus hirsutus*)

Roughpea is a winter annual with weak stems and decumbent growth except in thick stands, when it is ascending. In general it has the appearance of sweet peas, the leaves having one pair of long, narrow leaflets and terminating with a coiled tendril. The lavender flowers are usually borne in pairs on a long stem and are fairly conspicuous. The seed pods are rough or hirsute and the seed is round and characteristically tuberculate. There are about 14,000 seed in a pound and a bushel weighs about 55 pounds.

Roughpea is native to the Mediterranean region. The date of its introduction into the United States is not known but it has long been established as an escape. In recent years it has been brought under cultivation as a cover and pasture plant. The common name, roughpea, has been given to the crop, but other names also are in current use, the best known being wild winter pea, Caley-pea, and Singletary pea.

Roughpea is adapted to the southern third of the United States wherever moisture conditions are favorable. It prefers lime soils but will grow on the average acid soil of the South. Although it does best on well-drained soils, it will grow on soils too wet for clover or small grain. There are no statistics as to the acreage but it has been estimated that 100,000 acres in mixtures are pastured in Alabama, with lesser acreages in others of the Gulf States.

The principal uses of roughpea are for pasturage, winter cover crop, and hay. It is a weed in grain fields. In most parts of the South it makes much less growth than Austrian Winter field peas or hairy vetch, and is, accordingly, inferior to these crops as green manure to precede cotton or early planted corn. When it can be allowed to stand until late in spring it makes a good soil-improving crop.

Injury to livestock from grazing roughpea nearing maturity has been observed in Alabama and Louisiana and, therefore, caution is advised when grazing maturing plants or feeding hay containing plants with well-developed seed. It can be pastured safely through April, however, and later if the plants are grazed rather closely and are kept from forming seed.

Roughpea should be seeded in the fall, the best time being from September 15 to October 15. Twenty pounds of scarified seed, either drilled or broadcasted, should give a good stand. Once it is established, further seeding is not necessary since plants can be volunteered almost indefinitely.

Roughpeas do quite well in most parts of the South, indicating that their lime requirements are comparatively low. In most places, however, the use of 200 pounds of lime is beneficial. The use of 200 pounds or more of 20-percent superphosphate will give greatly increased yields in most soils of the South; in some cases the use of potash is also beneficial.

Inoculation has not been found necessary in any section.

In harvesting roughpeas, an ordinary mower with windrow attachment can be used for either hay or seed. The seed crop is usually ready to harvest in the latter part of May or early June in the extreme South and correspondingly later farther north. When the crop is cut for seed it is either left in the windrow or shocked. For threshing, a pick-up combine or stationary thresher can be used.

Roughpeas seed heavily and produce up to 1,000 pounds or more per acre. Average yields are much less, probably about 600 pounds.

LESPEDEZA

(*Lespedeza* species)

The genus *Lespedeza* includes about 125 species of leguminous shrubs and herbs often called bushclovers. Their native range is divided between temperate eastern Asia and eastern United States; of the species all but 17 are found in Asia. As far as known, only two of the species are annuals, and these, both introduced from Asia, have revolutionized the agriculture over some 20 million acres of lime-deficient, sandy land in the southern and eastern parts of the United States.

Common lespedeza had become established in the fields and roadsides of Georgia by 1850. The circumstances of its actual introduction from Asia are not known, but its subsequent spread was rapid as far west as Missouri. Commercial seed was available in the early 1900's. Korean lespedeza, the other annual, grows wild over most of Manchuria and Korea. First introduced in 1919, its excellent showing and hardiness soon made it a valuable addition and extended the use of lespedeza as far north as the Great Lakes region.

About 35 of the perennial oriental species have been imported for study along with our native species. The most promising of these is *L. cuneata*, introduced from Japan at various times from as early as 1896. Extensive trials are still being made to ascertain its range of adaptability and use.

Known only as wild plants until their cultivation in the United States, the lespedezas offer an excellent example of the early stages of crop domestication.

More than two-thirds of the perennial species are woody or semiwoody, upright plants. The rest are herbaceous or semiherbaceous. In all species the leaves are trifoliolate but vary in shape from linear to ovate. The lavender flowers are conspicuous in the shrubby species but are inconspicuous in most of the herbaceous perennials and annuals.

The species used commercially are all of Asiatic origin. These are common lespedeza, *Lespedeza striata;* Korean lespedeza, *L. stipulacea;* and sericea lespedeza, *L. cuneata*. Sericea lespedeza is perennial, the others annual. The first recorded planting of sericea lespedeza was in 1896 and of Korean lespedeza in 1921.

Lespedezas are adapted to most of the eastern half of the United States, being especially serviceable in the area roughly defined as from south of the Ohio River to central Georgia and Mississippi and west to eastern Kansas and Oklahoma.

Korean lespedeza is the species most

Common lespedeza

extensively used. It is estimated that there are about 40 million acres of this species in cultivated and pasture lands in the United States.

Common lespedeza, of which Kobe is the most used variety, is especially adapted to the southern third of the lespedeza area, while Korean is especially suited to the more northern part.

Sericea lespedeza is being used as a crop only in the south central part of the lespedeza area.

Lespedezas are especially useful on acid soils of low fertility and it is under such conditions that their use has been extended.

The most extensive use of lespedeza is for pasturage. It supplies, however, a large amount of hay, and more than 100 million pounds of seed are harvested annually. It also is recognized as an excellent soil-improving cover crop.

Seedings are made in early spring, either broadcast or in close drills, using 20 to 25 pounds of seed per acre.

In no section has inoculation of the seed been found necessary.

Fertilizers, especially phosphates, give increased yields and 200 or more pounds of 20-percent superphosphate per acre or a complete fertilizer often can be used to advantage.

For hay and seed crops, the lespedezas are handled with ordinary farm machinery, the combine being most commonly used in harvesting for seed. The usual seed yields for common lespedeza, as harvested commercially, range from 100 to 150 pounds per acre; Korean and sericea lespedeza average from 200 to 250 pounds. Much higher yields are obtained in the more favorable situations. Hay yields of lespedeza are about the same as for clover, a ton from an acre being near the average in commercial production.

THE TREFOILS
(*Lotus* species)

In the genus *Lotus* there are two species of agricultural importance: *L. uliginosus* and the *L. corniculatus*. These go under the common names of the big trefoil and birdsfoot trefoil, respectively.

They are perennial, fine-stemmed, leafy plants that are somewhat decumbent when grown as single plants but are fairly upright in thick stands. Both species have taproots with fibrous, branching laterals. Big trefoil, however, also has underground rootstocks, or rhizomes.

The leaves are sessile along the stems and have 5 leaflets, which vary in shape from linear to oval. The yellow flowers, which are quite showy, are borne on long flower stalks, which carry several or more characteristically spreading seed pods that resemble a bird's foot. This has given rise to the common name, birdsfoot trefoil, for the species having the lesser number of pods.

Both big trefoil and birdsfoot trefoil are native to the Old World. The date of their introduction into the United States is not known but it probably was within the past century that they were established as escape plants. It is within the past 20 years that their commercial planting and use has assumed importance.

Birdsfoot trefoil is grown in eastern New York. Both big trefoil and birdsfoot trefoil are grown in western Oregon and northern California, although birdsfoot trefoil occupies a larger acreage. Big trefoil is less winter-hardy than birdsfoot trefoil and has succeeded only in regions with comparatively mild climate. Birdsfoot trefoil, however, has succeeded well in northern sections as well as farther south.

The primary use of trefoils is for pasturage, both alone and in mixtures, but they also make good hay.

The establishment of stands of trefoil has been somewhat difficult. Since the seed is very small, good seedbed preparation is essential. In the North seeding is done in the spring. Farther south, seedings can be made either in the spring or fall. A very firm seedbed is one of the prime essentials. Five pounds of birdsfoot trefoil seed and 3 pounds of big trefoil is enough for an

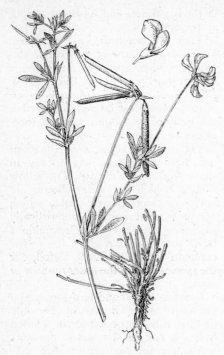

Birdsfoot trefoil

acre when seeded alone. Less can be used when seeded in mixtures.

Both big trefoil and birdsfoot trefoil require a special inoculant, which must be supplied at time of planting.

As with most other legumes, a fertilizer high in phosphate will increase yields and often can be used to advantage.

The harvesting of trefoils for hay offers no special difficulties, but harvesting for seed is not so easily accomplished. This is because the seed ripens unevenly and shatters easily when ripe. To help offset this difficulty, the seed crop should be cut before fully ripe and handled as rapidly as possible.

Yields of 50 to 100 pounds of seed per acre are about all that can be expected. In comparison with other legumes, the trefoils have high feeding value both for hay and pasturage. They are especially useful for furnishing late summer feed.

Trefoils are of special value because they are deep-rooted, make growth in late summer, and will grow in situations where alfalfa and clover cannot be grown to advantage.

THE LUPINES
(*Lupinus* species)

The lupines (*Lupinus*) are almost all American. The center of variability appears to be in western North America, but South America is also well represented. In the Old World a small series of annual species centers about the Mediterranean. Recent studies indicate that the total number of species may be several hundred. Their ability to produce an abundance of herbage and seed on sandy, acid soils makes them worthy of consideration as potential forage and green-manure crops for our Southeast. The presence of toxic alkaloids in some species has been a deterrent in the exploitation of the group.

In Europe some of the Mediterranean annuals have been cultivated for years, the large seeds being used as food and the herbage as fodder and green manure. Sweet strains, without alkaloids, were developed from two of the species, blue lupine and yellow lupine. Although introduced into the United States many times during the past 50 years, the European species have found little favor here until the last few years. The blue lupine is now commercially grown in the South; in Georgia alone, 27 million pounds of seed were produced in 1946. As a winter annual, it fits nicely between fall harvest and spring planting of other crops.

Twenty-five annual species, some of which are locally abundant and valuable in native pasture, occur in the western United States. Exploration and tests of the New World annuals may yield better material than anything introduced from Europe.

Most of the lupines are herbaceous plants but shrubby types are not uncommon. No species native to the United States has ever been brought under cultivation. Three European species have been cultivated in Europe for many years and recently have been brought under cultivation in the United States. These are coarse, herbaceous, upright annuals that branch quite freely when grown in thin stands and usually attain a height of from 2 to 3½ feet. The leaves are palmate, with 6 to 8 leaflets and the flowers are borne in large, showy, terminal and lateral racemes.

In the United States lupines have been grown only in the Gulf coast area of the Southeastern States. Whether or not they can be grown successfully elsewhere remains to be determined. They will grow on more acid soils than many crops and will stand temperatures around freezing. Lower temperatures usually will do serious damage.

The principal use of lupines has been as a cover and soil-improving crop. The yields of blue lupine for green manure are high, 40,000 pounds of green weight per acre being not uncommon.

As feed and food their use has been limited, largely on account of a poisonous alkaloid contained in all parts of the plant. In recent years strains free of this poison have been developed, so that extended use for feed will probably follow. The lupines that are under cultivation now are all winter annuals.

Seedings are made in the fall, broadcast or close drilled, using from 50 to 80 pounds of seed per acre.

Inoculation of seed at time of planting is essential on land that has not previously grown lupine. The use of stable manure before seeding will help insure inoculation and reduces the requirement for mineral fertilizer. When stable manure is not used, an application of up to 400 pounds of 20-percent superphosphate or a similar amount of superphosphate plus 100 pounds of muriate of potash will usually be beneficial.

Since lupines are not used for hay, harvesting operations consist of handling the acreage cut for seed. The

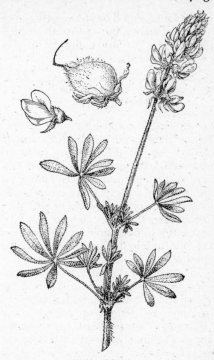

Yellow lupine

seed crop can be cut with an ordinary mower and bunched and threshed with an ordinary thresher. If the seed is allowed to become fairly ripe it can be harvested directly with a combine. The greater part of the acreage harvested for seed today is taken care of by this method.

Seed yields are high, ranging up to 2,000 pounds per acre—with about 1,000 pounds an average. The total seed production for the United States in 1946 was more than 37,000,000 pounds. The value of this seed would be about $2,000,000—one reason for the upsurge of interest in lupines.

Immediately after harvest, lupine seed contains a high proportion of moisture, which must be reduced at once in order to insure good seed. The use of artificial driers for the purpose probably is the most satisfactory procedure. Small lots of seed are sometimes spread 2 or 3 inches deep on a dry floor and turned frequently to insure drying and to prevent any heating. This method has been satisfactory in a dry season, but in seasons of high humidity it has been difficult to preserve seed in that way.

ALFALFA AND MEDIC
(*Medicago* species)

Medicago, comprising some 50 species of herbs and small shrubs, spread from the Mediterranean eastward through Asia Minor, Turkestan, northern India, and into western China. As some of its species have been cultivated since prehistoric times and have been carried from place to place by man, it is difficult now to be definite as to the original distribution of the group.

It is certain that none of the species occurred in the New World before the Spanish Conquest. They are sun lovers, adapted to periods of drought, and tolerant to most soils except those deficient in lime. More than half of the species known to exist have been introduced into the United States—some of them, such as alfalfa, hundreds of times—to supply the needs of investigators.

Medicago sativa, commonly called alfalfa (or Common alfalfa or purple alfalfa) in the New World and lucerne in Europe, is by far the most important species. It is probably native to Asia Minor and the Caucasus Mountains, but the beginning of its domestication and subsequent spread go back into antiquity. We now find what appear to be wild plants over most of the range of the genus. Its first introduction into the United States is not known, but the earliest date recorded is 1736 when it was presumably introduced into what is now Georgia.

The establishment of alfalfa in the United States as a crop began about 1850, when seed was brought to the Pacific coast by gold seekers from Chile, where it had been established by the Spaniards, and where the 49'ers had stopped on their way to California. Conditions in southern California being almost identical to those of Chile, the Chilean strain of the species rapidly became one of the most important hay and forage crops in the Southwest. By 1900 its cultivation had spread to the Mississippi Valley, locally adapted types segregating from the polymorphic material first introduced. Having been grown many generations under different climatic conditions, the original "Common alfalfa" has differentiated into regional strains which are generally adapted in the latitudes where they have been growing for a long period of time. These regional strains are distinguished by the name of the State where grown, such as Kansas Common, Montana Common, and so on.

As early as 1793 alfalfa had been grown in several Eastern States, but because of lack of knowledge about its needs as to fertility and inoculation it was not successful. Consequently, the growing of alfalfa in the United States spread from the West rather than from the East—from the irrigated sections of the West where it was particularly adapted, to Utah, Kansas, Nebraska, and eastward. In recent years the center of production of alfalfa has shifted from the drier Western States to the more humid Central States, such as Minnesota, Wisconsin, and Michigan. Pennsylvania, New York, and other Eastern States now have a substantial acreage of alfalfa, and will probably have more when better adapted varieties are developed by plant breeders for them.

About the time that Chilean seed was catching hold in California, another strain, which had long been cultivated in his native region of Baden, was brought in by a German settler. This German, Wendelin Grimm, settled in Minnesota and through the years persistently selected from his original stock seed of the hardiest types. Almost 50 years later this beginning gave us our hardy Grimm alfalfas and extended the utilization of this crop over the Northern States.

Spurred by the possibilities shown within the few strains introduced and by the recurring appearance of diseases, a program of intensive introduction began about the turn of the present century. The first federally sponsored plant exploration trip in 1897 had as one of its main objectives the procurement of hardy native strains from central Asia.

From this and subsequent explorations have come our hardy Turkestan alfalfas from Russian Turkestan, as well as other species. From northern India has come Ladak alfalfa, one of the hardiest and most drought-resistant; recently from Turkey came a creeping type that promises to be invaluable for inclusion in pasture mixtures. Perhaps as many as 1,000 strains of this one species are being scrutinized at experiment stations throughout the United States—and we have hardly scratched the surface of plant introduction possibilities for this crop, which now is worth annually 250 million dollars.

There are four other perennial species of *Medicago* which might be called alfalfas for lack of a better name. None of them is commercially important now in the United States, perhaps because of lack of investigation into their possibilities for improvement. These are *M. falcata, M. ruthenica, M. platycarpa,* and *M. tunetana.* The first three originated in Siberia, ranging farther north and west than *M. sativa.* They are cold- and drought-resistant and may contain important characteristics for the breeder.

Hybrids between *M. falcata* (found growing wild in Siberia) and *M. sativa,* that is sometimes identified as *M. media,* already have yielded the hardy strains now being cultivated under the general name of variegated alfalfas. *M. tunetana* comes from the Mediterranean region. Because it spreads readily by rhizomes, it may have possibilities for use with grass mixtures on permanent pastures in the South and Southwest.

Alfalfa is one of the most important forage crops in the United States, and exceeds in acreage any of the perennial crops grown for that purpose. Of the perennial species, *Medicago sativa* and *Medicago media* are the only ones grown commercially. *M. sativa* has purple flowers; a number of important varieties (most of which are relatively cold-resistant and have variegated flower colors) belong to *M. media. M. falcata* successfully overwinters in Alaska, where most of the other alfalfas winterkill. It is used in a number of breeding programs to obtain cold resistance in the resulting hybrids. It is difficult to obtain seed of this species because the pods shatter easily.

Alfalfa now is grown on approximately 15 million acres in the United States. Some is grown in every State, although there is relatively little in the Southeastern States and the greatest acreage is in the Central and Northern States. In recent years, California, Kansas, Nebraska, Minnesota, Wisconsin, and Michigan have each had more than a million acres in alfalfa. Its wide distribution shows its remarkable adaptability, but it prefers deep loams with open, porous, well-drained subsoil; as a rule it does not thrive on acid soils.

A heavy feeder, alfalfa requires an abundance of available plant nutrients for the best growth. Lime, phosphate, and potash should be applied where needed; in many Eastern areas boron has been found to increase greatly yields and longevity. Farmers should take care to get the varieties adapted to their own localities before they attempt to grow the crop.

Alfalfa makes a good hay crop for almost all farm animals, good pasture, and good silage. It is an excellent soil improver. In combination with grasses it helps stop soil erosion. Alfalfa meal, dehydrated alfalfa, and other similar products are becoming increasingly important.

For hay and seed crops, alfalfa is handled with the ordinary farm machinery. An ordinary mower or rake, with or without side delivery attachments, are used in all parts of the country for harvesting the hay crop. The combine is used most generally for har-

Purple alfalfa

vesting seed. The production of seed is most dependable in places where the climate is relatively dry, as in parts of the West.

Destructive insects, such as the lygus, hinder seed production. DDT gives good control of lygus. On the other hand, beneficial insects, such as wild bees and honeybees, are necessary to trip the alfalfa flowers before seed can be produced.

Average yields of seed range from 50 pounds to 200 pounds an acre—even more if the site, season, and pollinating insects are particularly favorable.

Alfalfa hay averages about 2 tons an acre throughout the country, ranging from 1½ tons in less favorable locations to more than 5 tons an acre under favorable irrigation conditions.

The ordinary methods of harvesting the hay are wasteful. A loss of 20 percent in dry matter and protein and more than 90 percent in the carotene content is usual even in good haying weather; in bad weather the losses can be even higher. Great care should be exercised to retain the leaves and thereby the quality in the final product. Well-cured and well-preserved alfalfa hay is one of the best forages because its high protein content means that the farmer will not have to buy protein in costlier concentrates.

A number of diseases attack alfalfa. The most serious is bacterial wilt, caused by the organism *Corynebacterium insidiosum*. Plant breeders of the Department and State agricultural experiment stations have been able to breed varieties resistant to the disease by crossing resistant types from Turkestan with domestically adapted varieties. These are now being increased for commercial use.

Attention is also being given to crown and root rots and leaf and stem diseases. Resistance to leafhopper yellows, caused by the potato leafhopper, *Empoasca fabae,* may be obtained from a cross with an introduction from Saudi Arabia.

Progress is being made in producing an alfalfa with rhizomes. Such a type would be especially valuable in pasture mixtures and in resisting soil erosion.

Black medic (*M. lupulina*), though it has been frequently introduced, has found no distinctive place in our agriculture. It has become widely naturalized; in the southern United States it grows well with some of the better pasture grasses. Apparently there are both annual and perennial strains. In the warmer regions, such as Argentina and Hawaii, it is relatively more important, and seed is available commercially for the improvement of pastures.

BUR-CLOVER
(*Medicago* species)

The annual species of *Medicago* are called bur-clover, because most of them bear spiny, coiled pods. The plants have weak stems that ascend only with support. They attain a stem length of a few inches up to three feet or more. In general appearance the plants resemble white clover but lack the conspicuous flower heads of that plant. The leaves are trifoliolate as in clover, but the small, yellow flowers are rather inconspicuous. Bur-clover is adapted for growing only in regions where temperatures seldom go much below freezing. Of the two important species in the United States, *Medicago hispida* is more abundant in the far Western States and is generally known by the common name California bur-clover.

The other (*M. arabica*) is most abundant in the Southeastern States. It is known by the common name spotted bur-clover.

Both were introduced as escapes from the Mediterranean region and have become extensively established in range and pasture lands in the South and West. Their major role is in mixtures with grasses, such as Bermuda-grass, to furnish winter forage to complement the summer forage of the grasses.

Bur-clover volunteers from year to year from seed that develops and escapes grazing. When used as a green-manure crop for turning under early—before seed matures—it is necessary after a few years to allow the crop to mature seed before turning under in order to insure volunteer stands. The rate of seeding recommended for new stands is 20 pounds of hulled seed, or 100 pounds in the bur. Bur-clover is always fall-seeded. Inoculation is needed on lands on which alfalfa, clover, or bur-clover have never been grown.

While bur-clover will succeed on practically all types of soils, loams are most suitable. A soil rich in lime is especially favorable, although it will grow on soils poor in this substance. On soils of low fertility it is necessary to use liberal quantities of stable manure or commercial fertilizer. Usually, superphosphate is the most essential fertilizer ingredient; often as much as 400 pounds of it is needed.

Bur-clover is seldom used for hay. Harvesting of seed is accomplished by

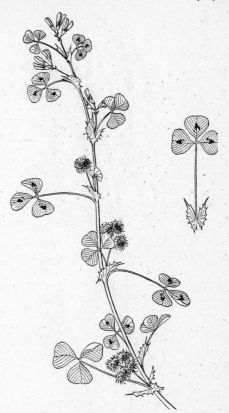

Spotted bur-clover

allowing the burs or pods to ripen thoroughly and fall to the ground. The burs then are swept into heaps by barn brooms or they are collected by the use of large, specially constructed suction machines. Bur-clover sets seed abundantly and several hundred pounds of hulled seed is not an uncommon yield. On average good land the hay or green manure yield will be about 12,000 pounds green weight or 2,000 pounds dry.

Bur-clover is recognized as having good nutritive value for both hay and pasturage, although it is not eaten so readily as alfalfa or clover. An objection to its use for sheep pasture arises from the spiny pods, which collect in the wool of the sheep and do considerable damage. The burs or pods taken from the sheep wool are one of the sources of seed, however.

White sweetclover

SWEETCLOVER
(*Melilotus* species)

The sweetclovers, of which there are approximately 20 species, appear to be natives of southwestern Asia Minor. The plants are upright, with few to many branches. The leaflets are linear oval and the flowers yellow or white. None is indigenous to the United States, even though plants may be found widely scattered along roadsides and waste places. The date of the chance introduction into this country is not known, but available records indicate that it was early in the eighteenth century. For many years it was considered to be a weed, and its great value in maintaining soil productivity was not recognized until about 1900. Its value for grazing was appreciated even later.

The three species of agricultural importance are white sweetclover, *Melilotus alba;* yellow sweetclover, *M. officinalis;* and sourclover, *M. indica.* White and yellow sweetclovers are principally biennial in growth habit, but annual forms occur, some of which have considerable agricultural value. Sourclover is a winter annual that makes its best growth along the Gulf coast, southern New Mexico, Arizona, and California regions. The species *M. suaveolens,* which has both annual and biennial forms, has a limited use; plants called *M. altissima* have been collected in the Northeastern States.

Sweetclover will make good growth in regions of the United States where the effective rainfall is 17 inches or more if the soil reaction is neutral or if limestone and other needed minerals are applied. Within those limits, it is particularly adapted to conditions of the Western States.

Sweetclover is also widely used in the Corn Belt in rotations with corn and small grains for temporary grazing and green manure. After stand establishment, it is more tolerant of summer drought than other agricultural legumes. In the Great Plains it is widely used for hay, although its stems are large and woody in the second year of growth. The species grown in this country contain coumarin, a substance that has a vanillalike odor.

Spoiled sweetclover hay and poorly preserved sweetclover silage is frequently toxic to animals, causing both external and internal bleeding. A decomposition product of the coumarin occurring during spoilage is the toxic principle.

The many varieties and strains of white and yellow sweetclovers differ in maturity, productivity, tolerance to frost, leafiness, seedling vigor, disease resistance, and other agronomic characteristics.

Biennial yellow sweetclover is better adapted to the Great Plains conditions than biennial white, because of greater tolerance to drought and unfavorable climatic conditions during the seedling year. Because of early maturity, seed production is more reliable than biennial white sweetclover. On the other hand, biennial white sweetclover produces higher yields of forage for green manure and gives longer grazing during the second year.

FIELD PEA
(*Pisum arvense*)

The common name, field pea, is generally used to designate the group of pea varieties that are used as forage for livestock rather than for human consumption. The essential difference is the inferior taste to humans of the field peas. Unlike garden peas, they are seldom wrinkled, mostly smooth and round, and often are dark-colored. The plants are weak-stemmed and half-viny. The leaves are borne throughout the length of the stem; usually they have three pairs of broad, ovate leaflets and terminate with a tendril. The flowers are large, white or lavender, and usually in pairs on a long flower stalk; the pods look somewhat inflated before maturity.

Peas are of ancient origin. They are native to the eastern Mediterranean region. The early Colonists brought them from England to America. In more recent times their planting has been extended until today they are almost universal.

For livestock feed in the United States their use is largely confined to the Northern States from New York west to Washington and Oregon. Farther south, their use is mostly for green manure or, in rotation with cotton and corn, for a winter cover crop.

Field peas are seeded either broadcast or in close drills. From 40 to 60 pounds or more per acre is needed, the larger amount being used in more northern latitudes.

In most sections inoculation of the seed at time of planting is beneficial. In the Southeastern States, where field peas are used as a cover crop, the use of 200 pounds or more of 20-percent superphosphate at time of planting is usually recommended unless the previous crop has been well fertilized.

When field peas are grown for green manure, the crop should be worked into the soil with a disk harrow or an ordinary plow. When grown for a seed crop, field peas are cut with a mower with swather attachment, put into windrows, and then threshed with a pick-up combine. Yields of seed are heavy, averaging between 800 and 1,000 pounds per acre in commercial production. In the South, when used for green manure, a yield of from 15,000 to 20,000 pounds of green weight per acre can usually be depended upon for March 15 turning. The total acreage seeded to field peas for cover crops is estimated at about a million acres. The acreage seeded for seed production is about 50,000 acres and the total seed production has been about 50 million pounds.

The variety most extensively grown in the United States is the Austrian Winter, the most winter-hardy of all pea varieties. Seed production of the variety is confined largely to the Pacific Northwest; Oregon has the largest acreage.

The most serious insect enemy of the pea is the seed weevil (*Bruchus pisorum*). DDT should be dusted on the fields and sanitary methods used to combat the weevil.

In the South, there are several diseases that reduce yields, but never entirely destroy the crop. To control the diseases, the peas should be rotated with other crops. Seed production in the South is not practical because of high spring temperatures, diseases, and possible insect damage.

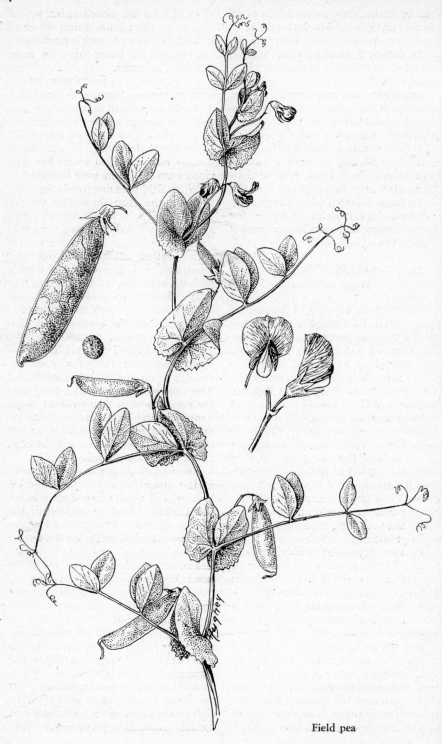

Field pea

KUDZU
(*Pueraria thunbergiana*)

Kudzu is a long-lived perennial; it is a coarse-growing vine, with long runners or stems that become woody in regions where they are not killed by frost. It has large trifoliolate leaves. Sometimes the leaflets are coarsely lobed. The flowers, which are borne in long racemes, are purple and quite large. The pods are flat, papery, and covered with a tawny pubescence. Seed is set very sparingly and often plants do not even bloom.

Kudzu is adapted as a crop to only the southern half of the United States. It will grow somewhat farther north, but under northern conditions it makes much less growth and cannot compete with such plants as clover and alfalfa.

Kudzu was introduced from Japan in 1876 but not until 1905 was its value for forage recognized. Commercial plantings were established by 1910 and slowly expanded. It is estimated that in 1946 there were about 300,000 acres planted to this crop.

Kudzu is used for hay, pasturage, and control of soil erosion.

For hay it is considered equal to alfalfa when the two crops are grown under the same conditions and it will give equally as large yields. The viny nature of kudzu makes it somewhat difficult to harvest for hay. This is especially true in the first cutting of a thick stand. The use of a special lifter guard and divider attachment that is available for use on an ordinary mower will greatly facilitate the mowing. In the heavy stands it is sometimes necessary to have two men with pitchforks roll the kudzu back from the cut swath.

Kudzu hay cures relatively fast but does not keep well if it is left unprotected in the field. In order to preserve the hay it should be baled as soon as sufficiently dry and then stored under cover.

As pasturage kudzu is recognized as having high feeding value and it serves well as a pasture plant. In order to maintain good stands, heavy pasturing should be avoided and ample fertilizer used. Since kudzu does not mature until late fall, it is available for pasturage at any time during the year and can often be used as an emergency reserve feed.

On land rough or otherwise hard to work, kudzu will reduce erosion while furnishing an abundance of good feed. On tillable land kudzu increases soil fertility in long rotations, as shown by increased yields of crops following it in rotations—but kudzu is not a crop to be grown on poor land without fertilizer. Ample use of fertilizer at time of planting is necessary to assure a good stand.

Kudzu plants are increased vegetatively. The long runners root at the nodes and form new plants and these rooted plants are taken from old fields and used for establishing new plantings. The digging and the planting of kudzu crowns must be done while the plants are dormant.

If dug before the planting time, the crowns should be stored in a cool, dry storage room with the roots in moist (not wet) sphagnum moss or sand. In new plantings the plants are set in rows 20 to 30 feet apart and spaced so as to use about 500 plants per acre. For the first year after planting and sometimes during the second year, the kudzu field should be cultivated. Row plantings of corn or other row crops can be grown between the kudzu rows during this period. When once established the stand will last many years if properly managed.

VELVETBEAN
(*Stizolobium* species).

The velvetbean is a vigorous-growing summer annual legume. Its vines (except those of the bush varieties) attain a length of 25 feet or more. The leaves are trifoliolate with large, ovate leaflets.

The flowers of the different species and varieties are white to dark purple and are borne singly or in twos and threes in long pendant clusters. The

Deering velvetbean

pods are of two distinct types; one has a dense, black, velvety pubescence and the other has white or grayish hairs. The pods of the different species range from 2 to 6 inches long with 3 to 6 seeds per pod.

The velvetbean is apparently a native of India. It is said to have been introduced into Florida nearly a century ago. It was grown for many years as an ornamental vine for porches and trellises. As early as 1890, the variety known as the Florida velvetbean was used somewhat for green manure in citrus orchards in Florida.

Through the introduction of new species, hybridization, and selection, several promising early varieties have been developed, so the successful production of the velvetbean has been extended northward until it is now grown in nearly all sections of the Cotton Belt States.

Mostly the early-maturing varieties are grown—Georgia (or Ninety-Day Speckled) and Alabama (or Hundred-Day Speckled). Other less widely used varieties or species are Florida velvetbean and Bush or Bunch, Lyon, and Tracy Black. The greater acreage of velvetbeans is in the well-drained sandy Coastal Plain soils of the South Atlantic and Gulf States, where conditions are especially adapted to the crop.

Although the velvetbean is easy to raise, the best results are obtained on a well-prepared seedbed. It is sometimes advisable to apply a small amount of fertilizer on poor soils. Velvetbeans will not germinate well in cold or wet soils and planting should be delayed until all danger of frost is past.

The seed (except the Bush variety) should be planted with a supporting crop. Corn, pearlmillet, the Japanese sugarcane, sorghum, and other strong-growing plants are used for the purpose. If planted with corn and the beans are a secondary consideration, 2 to 3 quarts of beans will be enough. If a heavy crop of beans is desired, twice as many beans should be used. For green manure or a smother crop, 30 to 60 pounds of beans are used to the acre.

Handpicking is about the best way to harvest them. The pods may be threshed with a flail or with one of several threshing machines.

The velvetbean has been an important factor in the development of the livestock industry and as a soil-improving crop in the Southern States. The seeds have a high feeding value and are important as a concentrated feed; the leaves and vines afford good roughage. For soil improvement, especially on sandy soils, the velvetbean is one of the best crops.

THE TRUE CLOVERS
(*Trifolium* species)

Throughout the world there are approximately 250 species of the genus *Trifolium*. More than 80 species indigenous to the United States have been described, although more detailed study may prove that many of them are only variants of other species. Nine species are now of regional or national importance in agriculture. None of the native species has proved to be of agricultural value in this country, although they contribute to grazing and to the wild hay crop and supply the associated grass with needed nitrogen.

The origin of the true clovers is believed to be southwestern Asia Minor and southeastern Europe, for it is in this general location that the greatest number of species, with wide diversity of forms, is found. The genus is one of the most widely distributed of the legumes. Its wild species are found on all continents except Australia. All are herbaceous.

The clovers are perennial or annual. For the most part, except at high latitudes, the growth period of the annual species is confined to the fall, winter, and spring months. In general, they thrive in a cool, moist climate on soils where there is an available supply of phosphorus, potassium, and calcium.

Many of the perennial species may behave as biennials and annuals because of the action of unfavorable climatic conditions and attacks of diseases and insect pests which shorten their life cycle.

Photoperiodism is important in the adaptation of species and varieties. Generally speaking, most of the species are long-day plants, although many continue to flower into early fall.

Wide differences exist in the ability of different species to tolerate unfavorable environments and in habit of growth, flowering, and reproduction.

Red clover, alsike clover, and crimson clover form crowns, zigzag clover (*T. medium*) and Kura clover (*T. ambiguum*) produce underground root stocks. White clover and strawberry clover spread by creeping stems that root at the nodes. The growth of sub clover is decumbent with the stems lying on the soil, while Hungarian clover (*T. pannonicum*) produces stiff, woody stems.

The flowers of all species are borne on heads, with the number of florets or individual flowers varying from as low as 5, in sub clover, to as many as 200 per head, in red clover and white clover. Seeds per pod vary from 1 to 8, depending upon the species. Sub clover gets its name from the fact that it buries its seed as they are maturing. Individual plants of the species *T. amphianthum* produce both aerial and underground seed heads. The

Red clover

flowers of some species are self-sterile, requiring cross-pollination. Others are self-fertile but must be tripped or shaken to insure pollination; still others are self-fertile and self-pollinating.

The nine species that are of agricultural importance are red clover, (*T. pratense*), white clover (*T. repens*), crimson clover (*T. incarnatum*), alsike clover (*T. hybridum*), small hop clover (*T. dubium*), large hop clover (*T. procumbens*), strawberry clover (*T. fragiferum*), Persian clover (*T. resupinatum*), and sub clover (*T. subterraneum*).

Red clover, an upright perennial, is composed of two forms—medium red (or double cut) and mammoth (or single cut).

A large number of regional and local strains (in addition to improved varieties) have been developed by breeding programs. While red clover culture is principally confined to the Northern States, recent experiments indicate that it is rather promising in the Southern States when it is properly fertilized and managed. It is grown alone and in mixture with grasses and is used for hay, pasturage, and soil improvement.

White clover, a decumbent perennial, is of three general types as related to size of growth—large, intermediate, and small. These types are represented by Ladino as the large type, Louisiana white, New Zealand and certain Corn Belt strains as the intermediate type, and English wild white and New York wild white as the low-growing types.

Common white clover (most frequently but still meaninglessly called White Dutch clover) is of the intermediate or small type or a mixture of the two. White clover is omnipresent in all States, wherever there is plenty of moisture and soil minerals. It is one of our most important pasture plants and is used extensively in seeding lawns.

Crimson clover, an upright, winter annual, is principally adapted to the Southern States, although it may be successfully grown in the Pacific Northwest. In the northern part of Maine it behaves as a summer annual. It is used for hay, pasturage, and soil improvement.

Alsike clover, also an upright perennial, is principally adapted to the Northern States and is particularly suitable for soils that have a tendency to be wet. Alsike is used for hay and pasture.

Sub clover, used mainly for grazing, is a decumbent, winter annual adapted to the Pacific Northwest; it gives promise in several places in the Southern States. There are many varieties of sub clover; successful production depends on the selection of the right one.

Small hop clover is a winter annual widely scattered throughout the Southern States and Pacific Northwest and is a species that tolerates unfavorable soil and climatic conditions.

Large hop clover is a winter annual similar to small hop clover except that it is more productive. For stand establishment and good growth, it requires a greater supply of mineral elements than small hop clover. The hop clovers are particularly valuable for early spring pasturage.

Strawberry clover is a perennial, particularly adapted to low-lying, wet soils throughout the Western States, where it is used for pasturage. It is tolerant of soil salinity and makes a decumbent growth similar to white clover.

Persian clover is a winter annual principally adapted to the heavy, low-lying soils of the Southern States. It is most valuable for pasture and hay.

Besides the above-mentioned winter annual species, the following form productive stands under local restricted conditions: Cluster clover (*T. glomeratum*), striata clover (*T. striatum*), rose clover (*T. hirtum*), ball clover (*T. nigrescens*), lappa clover (*T. lappaceum*), and Carolina clover (*T. carolinianum*).

Some of the productive native species of the West are fendler clover (*T. fendleri*), seaside clover (*T. wormskjoldii*), and white tip clover (*T. variegatum*).

Beekeepers say that kura clover (*T. ambiguum*) is an excellent nectar-producing plant. As yet, a symbiotic form of the organism giving successful inoculation on kura clover has not been found.

VETCH
(*Vicia* species)

Only a few of the many species of vetch are of commercial importance. The vetches are weak-stemmed or semivining plants. The leaves are pinnate, terminating in tendrils. The flowers are light to dark lavender with few or many in a raceme. The pods are linear, never inflated, and burst open readily when ripe.

Hairy vetch has the smallest seed, about 18,000 to a pound; common vetch has the largest, about 8,000 seed to a pound. The weight per bushel (60 pounds) is nearly the same for all the species.

The vetches grown commercially are all annuals and of European origin. They require a cool climate for their best development. In regions with mild winters they are fall-planted; in regions with very cold winters they must be planted in the spring. Hairy vetch (*Vicia villosa*) is the most winter-hardy of those commercially grown. Other species of importance in the United States in the order of their decreasing winter hardiness are Hungarian vetch (*V. pannonica*), common vetch (*V. sativa*), monantha vetch (*V. articulata*), and purple vetch (*V. atropurpurea*).

On poor soils fertilizer is needed to insure good growth. Phosphorus is the most essential. From 200 to 400 pounds of superphosphate or 500 pounds of basic slag can usually be used to advantage. On sandy and sandy-loam soils hairy vetch is the best adapted. Common and purple vetch require soils of higher fertility, such as clay loams or sandy loams. Hungarian vetch does best on heavier soils or soils with more clay.

The approximate acreages of vetch in the United States for different purposes are:

	Cover crop	Hay	Seed
Hairy vetch_	800,000	10,000	125,000
Hungarian__	50,000	200,000	23,000
Common ___	300,000	200,000	60,000
Monantha __	1,000	1,000	1,000
Purple _____	1,000	50,000	10,000

The seeding rates and seed yields are:

	Pounds of seed planted per acre	Range in seed yield (pounds per acre)	Average commercial seed yield (pounds per acre)
Hairy vetch_	30–40	100–800	260
Hungarian__	50–80	300–1,500	700
Common ___	50–80	300–1,500	600
Monantha __	40–70	300–1,500	600
Purple _____	40–70	300–1,500	600

Vetches are also used for pasturage and silage. Most of the seed is produced in the Pacific Coast States. The largest acreage for cover crops is in

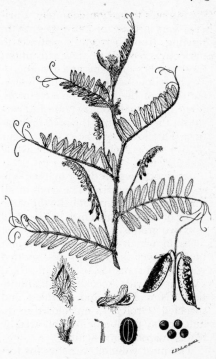

Hairy vetch

the Southeastern States. For pasturage, hay, and silage they are used to some extent in all regions in which they are grown.

The yield of hay for all species ranges from 1 to 3 tons per acre. For hay of best quality vetches should be cut when in early bloom. An ordinary mower with swather attachment can be used in harvesting.

COWPEA
(*Vigna* species)

The cowpea, an annual summer legume, came from central Africa. The cultivated cowpea consists of three main groups—the asparagus or yard-long bean with much elongated inflated pods; the catjang, with small erect pods and small subcylindric seeds; and the cowpea, with pendent, rather long pods.

The cowpea is indeterminate in growth; that is, under favorable conditions of moisture and temperature, it continues to grow indefinitely. Varieties vary greatly in habit of growth, ranging from perfectly prostrate to perfectly erect. With few exceptions the branches are viny and twining.

The trifoliolate leaves, which resemble those of the garden or navy bean, range from small to very large and persist on the vines until the pods are mature. The flowers of the cowpea occur in two colors, white or nearly white and violet.

Seeds of cowpeas differ markedly in color, shape, and size. The seeds of all three species have practically the same range of colors, which may be classified into two groups. One group consists of seeds in which the coloration is not uniform over the whole seed—spotted with round spots (Blackeye), marbled (Whippoorwill), speckled with minute dots (New Era), and marbled and speckled (Groit). In unicolored seeds, buff or clay predominates, followed by black, maroon, and white.

The most valuable varieties for forage are Whippoorwill, Iron, and New Era, and their hybrids, the Brabham, Groit, and Victor. Important but of secondary value are such indefinite groups of varieties as the Unknown, Clay, Red Ripper, and Black. For table use, the white-seeded varieties (such as Conch and Cream), the Blackeye sorts (the California Blackeye and Virginia Blackeye), and the crowder types (Sugar Crowder and Brown Crowder) are preferable.

The large number and great diversity of cultivated varieties throughout Africa and over the southern half of Asia and the adjacent islands, as well as the Mediterranean region of Europe, indicate that the cowpea is of ancient cultivation for food. It was early introduced into the Spanish settlements of the West Indies and was grown in North Carolina in 1714. Its culture in Virginia was reported about 1775 and no doubt was quite general in the Colonies early in the nineteenth century. Now the cowpea is one of the best known and most extensively grown leguminous crops in the Southern States.

The cowpea is adapted generally to about the same climatic conditions as corn, but it requires somewhat more heat. The cowpea succeeds on practically all types of soil. Soils that are naturally unproductive or badly run down by continuous cropping should be fertilized to obtain the best results.

The seedbed should receive as careful preparation as that for corn to obtain the best results. Cowpeas should not be sown until all danger of cold weather is past. The best method for seed production is to sow in rows about 3 feet apart, using about 45 pounds of seed to the acre. For forage or green manure, the seeds are sown broadcast or in drill rows 6 to 8 inches apart, using 1½ to 2 bushels to the acre. The cowpea is especially valuable as a catch crop and for hay or seed production in almost any system of rotation. Root-knot, wilt, and root canker are the most serious diseases.

THE AUTHOR≪ *Roland McKee, a senior agronomist in the Bureau of Plant Industry, Soils, and Agricultural Engineering, has been with the Department of Agriculture since 1905. As director of investigations on miscellaneous legumes, he has seen the now well-known cover crops like Austrian Winter peas, Willamette vetch, purple vetch, Hungarian vetch, monantha vetch, blue lupine, Crotalaria spectabilis, C. intermedia, C. mucronata and alyceclover come into use. He has also instigated the development of nonpoisonous strains of lupines in both the blue- and yellow-flowered species, and the development of high-yielding late strains of annual lespedezas.*

Cousins and Companions

WEEDS ARE PLANTS OUT OF PLACE

WILLIAM A. DAYTON

TO THE FARMER a weed is a plant out of place, especially if it is herbaceous, aggressive, and pestiferous.

The Oxford Dictionary gives as the first definition of weed: "A herbaceous plant not valued for use or beauty, growing wild and rank, and regarded as cumbering the ground or hindering the growth of superior vegetation."

To the stockman in the West, a weed is a nongrasslike range herb—or what the ecologist calls a forb.

A considerable number of the plants that the farmer considers weeds actually are fair or good range forage plants, especially on ranges where, under unfavorable conditions of growth, the same aggressiveness and vitality that makes a species a pest in agricultural land clothe it with utility if it possesses palatability.

The late Dr. Adrian J. Pieters of the Department of Agriculture considered it unfair to brand with the stigma of "weed" plants so useful as, say, Kentucky bluegrass or red clover, which might be undesirable invaders of gardens. So he defined weed thus: "A plant that does more harm than good and has the habit of intruding where not wanted."

The suffix -*weed* is a familiar one in the English names of noxious plants as, for example, bitterweed, crazyweed, snakeweed, and sneezeweed, but it also appears as a suffix in the names of harmless herbaceous plants, such as beeweed, cudweed, duckweed, gumweed, and ironweed.

The 1942 edition of *Standardized Plant Names* contains a list—admittedly not exhaustive—that includes 57 families of "weeds," 244 genera, and 518 species. Of these, the enormous composite (or "daisy") family easily ranks first, with 52 genera and 123 species. Grasses are second, with 26 genera and 52 species. Crucifers (or "mustards") are in third place, with 22 genera and 50 species.

Weeds can take it. As a class they are tolerant of drought, of extremes of heat and cold, of fire and high wind. They possess vigorous reproductive powers. Many have highly developed underground and persistent rootstocks, tubers, and the like. Frequently they produce fruits or seeds with prickles, barbs, or other prominences that fasten themselves to passing objects; some have wings, feathery parachutes, or similar items that greatly facilitate their distribution.

Weeds, as such, have far-reaching economic significance. In Iowa alone the amount of loss by weeds is conservatively estimated to be about 50 million dollars a year.

Some of the commonest weeds in

agricultural grounds are not without economic value in their own right. For example, bigseed falseflax (*Camelina sativa*), horseweed (*Erigeron canadensis*), and wormseed (*Chenopodium ambrosioides*) yield commercial oils.

Black mustard (*Brassica nigra*) is the source of a familiar condiment. A considerable number are official drug plants, among them boneset (*Eupatorium perfoliatum*), gumweed (*Grindelia squarrosa*), the black henbane (*Hyoscyamus niger*), butter-and-eggs (*Linaria vulgaris*), hoarhound (*Marrubium vulgare*), and biting stonecrop or goldmoss (*Sedum acre*).

Some are occasionally cultivated as vegetables or for potherb greens, including Jerusalem-artichoke (*Helianthus tuberosus*), gardencress (*Lepidium sativum*), common sowthistle (*Sonchus oleraceus*), and common dandelion (*Taraxacum officinale*).

Moreover, some appear in horticultural catalogs as ornamentals: Pricklepoppies (*Argemone* spp.), centaureas or starthistle (*Centaurea* spp.), flowering spurge (*Euphorbia corollata*), common sunflower (*Helianthus annuus*), and star-of-Bethlehem (*Ornithogalum* spp.), for example.

Grasses are a prominent constituent of the weed population. The worst of these is a naturalized citizen, quackgrass (*Agropyron repens*), a poor relation of wheat. Of this egregious pest L. W. Kephart says: "With the possible exception of the Canada thistle, quackgrass is the most notorious of all weeds and probably causes a greater monetary loss than any other single species of plant."

Some native grasses, such as foxtail barley (*Hordeum jubatum*) and bottlebrush squirreltail (*Sitanion hystrix*), with long-bearded heads, are often troublesome to livestock, the long, often minutely barbed awns working into the animals' mouths, noses, and eyes. The value of sheep's wool, too, may be diminished by these awns, as well as by the prickly fruits of such plants as avens (*Geum* spp.) and beggarticks (*Bidens* spp.).

Some weeds are of especial annoyance to particular groups, such as puncturevine (*Tribulus terrestris*) to the motorist, sandburs (*Cenchrus* spp.) to the barefoot child, and poisonivy (*Toxicodendron radicans*) to the recreationist in the woods.

Some weeds pose interesting problems in land management. For example, cheatgrass brome or cheatgrass (*Bromus tectorum*), an introduced weedy annual grass, has heavily invaded many overgrazed areas (as in southern Idaho) in the Far West. In many places it furnishes the bulk of spring range forage, it quickly forms a ground cover on partially denuded soils, and it replaces plants that are hosts to the beet leafhopper—thus being "of tremendous importance to sugar-beet, bean, and tomato growers." On the other hand, its life is short, its awns cause stock injuries, and it is a fire hazard when it is dry.

In the vegetative cover of range lands are a vast array of herbs other than grasses and grasslike plants—sedges and rushes—which the stockman calls weeds. These plants belong to upwards of 600 genera and 8,000 species and run the gamut from "ice-cream plants" of highest palatability, such as cowparsnip (*Heracleum lanatum*), to worthless pests, such as tarweeds (*Madia* spp.), and highly poisonous plants, such as waterhemlock (*Cicuta* spp.).

The broad vegetative types or formations in this country are tree, shrub, grass, or grasslike in character. There is no true "range weed" type unless, perhaps, it be the curious glasswort (*Salicornia*)—incorrectly called samphire—association such as occurs on the saline flats near Great Salt Lake. Rather, these "range weeds" occur in open forests—such as ponderosa pine and aspen—in shrub, grass, and sedgerush associations, above timber line, in mountain meadows, associated with grasses, and the like. These "range weeds" are a highly important component of the range forage crop, especially on sheep range, and their values to watersheds and wildlife are great.

The literature on weeds and their eradication or control is extensive, particularly on individual species. Their control is, of course, intimately tied in with such factors as their life history, reproduction, location, and abundance. With annuals, control is established merely by preventing them from seeding.

Tests carried on in all parts of the country since 1944 indicate that in lawns, parks, cemeteries, meadows, and pastures where grass is the only desired vegetation, 2,4–D is superior to other herbicides for the control (and perhaps eventual eradication) of biennial and perennial weeds. The chemical may be applied as a spray or a dust. The size of the area, the nature of the terrain, and the nearness to sensitive crops determine the type of treatment and the method of applying it.

Many valuable crops are sensitive to 2,4–D. Most garden plantings, trees and ornamentals, tobacco, and cotton are injured by 2,4–D, even in small amounts. The utmost care must be used in applying the herbicide. Slight winds will carry the dust or fine spray to sensitive plants. Fumes may also affect sensitive plants some distance away. Suitable shields of canvas, oilcloth, light wood, or metal will help keep the chemicals from drifting. Spray planes can be equipped with check valves at each nozzle to eliminate dribble when pressure is shut off. Special precautions may be needed to prevent accidental discharge of the finely divided dust through minute crevices during flights to and from the area to be treated.

Generally, good pasture management will control weeds more surely and at lower cost than treatment with the herbicide. Investigations show that liberal applications of fertilizer, proper mowing, and regulated grazing will keep weeds under control. An infestation of wild garlic on a dairy pasture, however, may call for the quick work of 2,4–D, even though it injures the clover. Spray applied before the first of March is recommended.

POISONOUS PLANTS

WILLIAM A. DAYTON

PRACTICAL knowledge of the identity and actions of poisonous plants has been the possession of primitive peoples since time immemorial. Aboriginal folk everywhere are familiar with fish poisons, and the use of vegetable poisons on arrows by unlettered peoples is so general and widespread that it has given the modern science of toxicology (derived from the Greek *toxon,* bow, and its plural, *toxa,* bow and arrow) its technical name.

Published references to poisonous plants are of great antiquity. The ancient Egyptians were familiar with the toxic properties of aconite (*Aconitum*), henbane (*Hyoscyamus niger*) and poisonhemlock (*Conium maculatum*). About 900 B. C., in the fourth chapter of 2d Kings, we read that the famished "sons of the prophet," after partaking of a puree of "wild gourds" at Gilgal, cried out to Elisha "there is death in the pot!" Scholars are agreed that what these unfortunate gentlemen ate was the colocynth (*Citrullus colocynthis*), the colocynthis, or "colocynth apple," of our present-day drug trade. The prophet Amos complains that his countrymen "have turned the fruit of righteousness into hemlock." Xenophon, in the Anabasis, refers to the poisonous properties of an Asiatic rhododendron. The execution of Socrates (399 B. C.) with a cup of poisonhemlock, is a familiar incident both of bigotry and ancient toxicological lore. Probably the oldest extant treatise on poisonous plants is the poem Alexipharmica, by the Lydian priest-poet-physician, Nicander of Colophon (2d century B. C.), after whom the poisonous ornamental apple-of-Peru genus (*Nicandra*) is named. The celebrated Greek herbalist, Dioscorides Pedanius (1st century A. D.) was familiar with the poisonous properties of ergot (*Claviceps*), autumn-crocus (*Colchicum*), the opium poppy (*Papaver somniferum*), and a number of other plants. Claudius Caesar, the Roman emperor mentioned in Acts 18: 2 as having banished the Jews from Rome, was poisoned A. D. 54 by his niece and wife, Agrippina, with a dish of toadstools (*Amanita*) in order to put her son Nero, by a former marriage, on the throne and, from this fact, *Amanita caesarea* is thought to have derived its scientific name. Shakespeare has many references to poisonous plants: Hamlet's father's ghost tells his son that he was murdered with a vial of henbane; the witches in Macbeth add "root of hemlock digg'd i' the dark" to their "hell-broth"—apparently alluding to European waterhemlock (*Cicuta virosa*), and darnel (*Lolium temulentum*), poisonhemlock, and fumitory (*Fumaria officinalis*) are referred to as noxious in the plays King Lear and Henry V.

Poisonous plants are an important consideration in livestock management, especially on range and native pastures. Annual losses in Colorado alone from this source are reported to average about a million dollars, and losses in the range country as a whole from poisonous plants average about 4 percent annually. In addition, there is a considerable annual loss of human life from poisonous plants, particularly toxic fungi, and children are often tempted to eat elderberry (*Sambucus*) roots, raw horsechestnuts

(*Aesculus hippocastanum*), waterhemlock tubers and the like, sometimes with fatal results. In this catalog of bad actors, the microscopic plants, particularly the bacteria, will not here be considered because of the lack of space.

A conservative estimate of the plants in this country known to poison domestic livestock or man is 62 families, 182 genera, and about 525 species. This list would easily run into four figures if every plant were considered about which some suspicion has been raised or which somebody somewhere has questioned. It disregards such plants as the potato, which, at certain stages, may contain toxic compounds, and ignores the numerous plants (such as species of *Ceanothus* and *Cercocarpus*) which are known to be important and valuable browse plants, but which, theoretically, are sometimes listed among poisonous plants because some chemical analysis has demonstrated some glucoside or other allegedly poisonous compound in some part. Admittedly, however, the list is still incomplete and scarcely a year goes by without adding some new culprit. The families with the greatest number of genera involved are, in order: Composites (daisy family), Liliaceae (lily family), legumes, spurges, heaths, crowfoots (buttercup family), umbellifers (parsnip family), milkweeds, grasses, and figworts. The four families with the greatest number of species involved are, in order: Legumes (easily first, with 102 species), crowfoots, composites, and spurges. Some families, such as the dogbane, milkweed, and spurge families, are notorious for their general possession of toxic properties, which are largely, in the families named, resident in their milky juices. In the case of some families, such as the lily and legume families,

→

Some common range stock-poisoning plants: *A*, Pingue (*Actinea richardsonii*); *B*, crazyweed (*Oxytropis lambertii*); *C*, Douglas waterhemlock (*Cicuta douglasii*); *D*, grassy deathcamas (*Zigadenus gramineus*); *E*, Menzies larkspur (*Delphinium menziessi*); *F*, tailcup lupine (*Lupinus caudatus*).

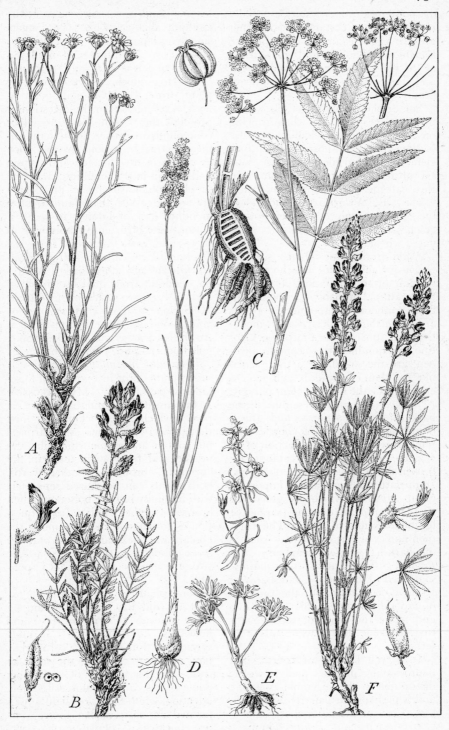

the poisonous properties are especially characteristic of certain tribes or other groups, as, for example, the asphodel, bunchflower, nolina and scilla tribes of the lily family, and the andromeda and rhododendron tribes of the heath family.

Some plants, harmless elsewhere, may become poisonous when growing on soils containing selenium because of their ability to substitute this toxic element for a harmless substance, such as sulfur, in their metabolism. In this category are the woody asters (*Aster,* sec. *Xylorrhiza*) crucifers of the genus *Stanleya,* timber poison-vetch (*Astragalus convallarius*), culti-vated wheat, etc.

Aside from those plants, such as poison-ivy and nettles, which cause ir-ritation or inflammation of the skin (dermatitis), probably the most com-mon poisonous compounds in plants are (1) *alkaloids,* such as andromedo-toxin, cicutin, cocaine, morphine, nico-tine, and quinine—these contain nitro-gen, are the so-called "active princi-ples" of plant compounds, and, in gen-eral, include the most virulent poisons; (2) *glucosides,* such as esculin (in the bark of horsechestnuts), and amyg-dalin (in the kernels of cherries and plums), which, under the action of an enzyme, acid, or other catalyst are broken down into sugars, alcohols, etc. In the latter category are an important group *saponins,* which are glucosides that have a soaplike action (saponify) in the presence of water. The com-mon names of certain genera—such as soapbark (*Quillaja*), soapberry (*Sa-pindus*), soapplant (*Chlorogalum*), soapweed (*Yucca* spp.), and soapwort (*Saponaria*)—testify to the presence of saponin in certain of their tissues and make the parts of those plants toxic to some degree when taken in-ternally.

It is well known, of course, that hydrocyanic (prussic) acid is widely distributed in the vegetable kingdom, and is perhaps particularly familiar in the species of the plum-cherry-choke-cherry-peach genus (*Prunus*), in many

legumes, and in certain grasses of the sorghum alliance. This very danger-ous, toxic liquid occurs in plants in a "locked-up" condition and needs an enzyme or ferment of some kind as a "key" to unlock it—otherwise the plant, from the HCN standpoint at least, is harmless. In the digestion of proteins these complex nitrogenous compounds are broken down in the ali-mentary tract by various enzymes, such as pepsin in the stomach and trypsin and erepsin in the small intestine, into simpler, soluble substances principally amino acids. With these familiar facts in mind, it is of interest to recall a curious case of extensive poisoning of sheep and cattle reported from the Georgina River valley of extreme west-ern Queensland, northeastern Austra-lia, resultant from dual use by sheep and cattle of two shrubs or small trees, "Georgina gidgee" (*Acacia geor-gina*)—one of those curious leafless Australian acacias with leaflike petioles (phyllodia)—and "spotted berrigan" (*Stenochilus maculatus*), which is a showy plant of the myoporum, or false-sandalwood family (Myoporaceae). In this case it was found that the acacia pods (which the stockmen at first thought were poisonous), are harmless but contain an enzyme which liberates prussic acid from a glucoside in the "berrigan" browse. In other words, both plants can be grazed separately with impunity but are poisonous when browsed together. This raises a ques-tion as to whether or not, among the obscure and unexplained cases of range stock-poisoning in this country, a toxic twosome may occasionally be respon-sible.

Some plants seldom give trouble ex-cept in wild hay, familiar examples being brackens (*Pteridium* spp.) and horsetails (*Equisetum* spp.). In some species as, for example, corncockle, flax, and horsechestnut, the seeds or fruits are the source of poisoning. Some plants cause photosensitivation, affecting white-faced or lightly pig-mented animals; among these, some are buckwheat (*Fagopyrum*), flax

(*Linum* spp.), the lechuguilla (*Agave* spp.), and St. Johnswort (*Hypericum* spp.).

As a general rule, poisonous plants are not eaten extensively by livestock when other and more palatable and harmless plants are available. There are, however, important exceptions. At least one case is on record where cattle went out of their way to eat waterhemlock which had been grubbed out of a "poison" area and hung on a rack to dry prior to burning. Poisoning is particularly likely to occur on overgrazed areas, along streams and in meadows where stock like to congregate, in the spring (when plants like low larkspur and deathcamas make their appearance) and, when snow is on the ground, and leaves of evergreen poisonous plants (such as mountain-laurel and rhododendron) are in evidence and tempt hungry animals. Some plants, such as lupines, are particularly toxic to sheep and other plants, such as larkspur, are especially dangerous to cattle. Rhododendron, dangerous for domestic livestock, is an important deer browse.

Perhaps the most important range stock-poisoning plants of this country are species of the following genera: pingue (*Actinea*), burroweed and jimmyweed (*Aplopappus*), locos and poisonvetches (*Astragalus*), waterhemlocks (*Cicuta*), larkspurs (*Delphinium*), sneezeweeds (*Helenium*), lupines (*Lupinus*), crazyweeds (*Oxytropis*), podgrasses and arrowgrasses (*Triglochin*), and deathcamases (*Zigadenus*). The drawing on page 731 illustrates six of these plants, brief accounts of which follow.

Pingue (*Actinea richardsonii*) occurs on dry, sandy or gravelly soils, from sagebrush to the spruce types, from Saskatchewan and Alberta to Texas, Arizona, eastern California, and eastern Oregon. Losses usually occur in early spring or late summer or on heavily overgrazed range, as its palatability, under normal conditions, is zero to poor. It is definitely poisonous to sheep, losses occurring chiefly in the Southwest. It is known also as "Colorado rubberweed" and at one time it received much publicity as a possible source of commercial rubber. A related species, bitterweed, or bitter rubberweed (*Actinea odorata*) has caused heavy sheep losses in the Edwards Plateau region of western Texas.

Douglas waterhemlock (*Cicuta douglasii*, syn. *C. occidentalis*), a marsh herb, perennial from a cluster of elongated fleshy roots, and ranging from Alaska to California, New Mexico, and South Dakota, belongs to a genus of what are probably the most virulently poisonous flowering plants in North America. All parts of the plant, but especially the roots, are toxic. A small piece of the root, which is easily pulled out of moist ground by a cow, horse, or sheep, is likely, if eaten, to prove speedily fatal. The species was discovered by and is a namesake of David Douglas (1799–1834), the famous Scotch botanical explorer.

Menzies larkspur (*Delphinium menziesii*), perhaps the commonest and most widely distributed of the low, or "spring," larkspur, ranges from British Columbia to northern California, New Mexico, and Montana. This species is especially characteristic of open grass-weed-brush areas, at altitudes from about 1,000 feet in northwestern California up to as high as 10,500 feet in the southern portions of the Rocky Mountains. It is readily grazed and causes heavy losses of cattle on spring and early-summer ranges. Later the above-ground portions dry up and blow away. The species bears the name of its discoverer, Dr. Archibald Menzies (1754–1842), surgeon-naturalist on the Vancouver voyages.

Tailcup lupine (*Lupinus caudatus*), named from the backward prolongation of the floral cup (calyx), is distributed from Washington and Oregon (east of the Cascades) to California (east of the Sierra Nevada), Nevada, Colorado, and Idaho, chiefly between 3,000 and 8,500 feet. It is one of the common lupines in the ponderosa pine type and is often locally abundant.

Unfortunately it is one of the more palatable lupines and is particularly poisonous to cattle and horses and somewhat so to sheep. This makes it remarkable among native range lupines, which are commonly poisonous only to sheep and, as a rule, only the pods and seeds are notably toxic.

Crazyweed (*Oxytropis lambertii*) is representative of a group related to the locoweeds (*Astragalus* spp.) that cause locoism. Because of its confusion in poisonous plant literature with other related species, its precise status is somewhat uncertain, but there is no doubt that it is one of the important sources of locoism in domestic livestock. It has a wide altitudinal variation, from plains to the Engelmann spruce-lodgepole pine belt, and occurs from Minnesota to Montana and southward to Arizona and Texas. Attempts to isolate and determine the chemical identity of the toxic principles of crazyweed have thus far failed.

Grassy deathcamas (*Zigadenus gramineus*) belongs to the bunchflower tribe of the lily family and ranges from South Dakota to Saskatchewan, Idaho, Utah, and Colorado, occurring on hills and meadows between about 4,000 and 7,000 feet, usually in sandy or gravelly loams. It is the most toxic member of this poisonous genus—all parts are injurious—and is especially dangerous in early spring (when other feed is relatively scarce) and at fruiting time, the seed being especially virulent. It affects all classes of livestock.

THE AUTHOR≪ *William A. Dayton is in charge of dendrology and range forage investigations of the United States Forest Service.*

GRASSES CAN BE ORNAMENTAL

ROLAND McKEE

GRASSES hold a prominent place as ornamentals and their value for this purpose is generally recognized. Any list of plants commonly used in home gardens and public parks will include a number of grass species. When set against ornamentals with large and showy flowers grasses afford a pleasing contrast. Although small and inconspicuous, the flowers of grasses are produced in abundance and, when massed in large plumose or gracefully drooping panicles, they are delightfully beautiful. Grasses are attractive, not only for their tiny flowers in graceful panicles, but also for the graceful display in clumps of upright leaves.

The large grasses lend themselves admirably for use in spacious parks or in large home lawns. The species of importance in this class are pampasgrass (*Cortaderia selloana*), Uvagrass (*Gynerium sagittatum*), and Chinese silvergrass (*Miscanthus sinensis*) usually known by the misnomer "eulalia."

The smaller grasses can be used everywhere in lawns and gardens as bedding plants, background plants, or for borders. The most important for such uses are West Indies pennisetum (*Pennisetum setaceum*), feathertop (*P. villosum*), weeping lovegrass (*Eragrostis curvula*), flarescale lovegrass (*E. amabilis*), Japanese lovegrass (*E. tenella*), big quakinggrass (*Briza maxima*), little quakinggrass (*B. minor*), and desmazeria (*Desmazeria sicula*).

Although the greatest use of grass ornamentals is for outdoor planting, their use for cut flowers is of importance. The flowering panicles of many grasses, when arranged in tall vases or low bowls, make a beautiful display.

The flowering panicles of a number of grasses can be dried and used through a long period of time. Among the grasses that can be used in this way are winter bent (*Agrostis hiem-*

alis), cloud bent (*A. nebulosa*), harestail (*Lagurus ovatus*), and the quaking grasses (*Briza maxima, B. minor,* and *B. media*).

THE AUTHOR«« Roland McKee is an agronomist in the Bureau of Plant Industry, Soils, and Agricultural Engineering.

BAMBOOS FOR FARM AND HOME

F. A. McCLURE

THE BAMBOOS are set off from the more familiar grasses by certain technical characters, such as the woody stems and the petiolate, or stalked, leaf blades. They comprise a highly varied array of plants that range in size and habit from tiny dwarfs a few inches high to long and slender climbers and giants a foot in diameter and more than 100 feet tall. Among them are individual kinds with properties that suit them, in aggregate, to a thousand functions. Many of the uses, although of basic importance in the areas where industry remains largely in the handicraft stage, are looked upon in this mechanized world only as curiosities. Other uses have come closer to our everyday lives than most of us know.

The most successful of Thomas A. Edison's early incandescent electric lamps had for its light-giving element a carbonized filament of bamboo—a slender, wirelike element made from a single fibro-vasular bundle from an internode of a bamboo culm, or stem. Bamboo fibers were still used in carbon-filament lamps for special purposes as late as 1910.

Apparently—we are not sure—Edison used fibers from a species of bamboo growing wild in the jungle at an elevation of about 5,000 feet on the slopes of Volcan Chiriquí, Panama. I have collected botanical specimens and fibers from this bamboo, which is said by local witnesses to have been the source of some of Edison's experimental material. It is *Chusquea pittieri* Hackel, a plant that appears to the casual observer to be of little interest or technical promise.

There have been many changes since the carbon-filament lamp revolutionized illumination, but bamboo now promises to offer to the technical world another fundamental raw material, cellulose. That the bulk of China's vast paper requirements has been supplied, for hundreds of years, by hand-dipped bamboo pulp is common knowledge. It may be news to many, however, that paper is already being made by machine, on a commercial scale, from bamboo pulp in Trinidad, Siam, Burma, India, and France, as well as in China. The Forest Research Institute at Dehra Dun, India, publishes its annual reports on machine-made bamboo paper, which seems to me to be the equal of the best book paper made from wood pulp.

The promise of bamboo is great. This is in terms of yearly per-acre production of cellulose and of possible increase of digester capacity.

Estimates based on carefully documented records of the United States Forest Service indicate that plantations of slash pine managed on a 35-year rotation gave, at a time when most of the trees were under 20 years of age, an average annual yield of 1.13 tons of oven-dry, sulphate, kraft pulp per acre. *Bambusa vulgaris,* on the other hand, according to records of the Trinidad Paper Pulp Co., Ltd., mentioned by the general manager, C. T. B. Ezard, in an interview, has produced more than 4 tons of pure, dry, cellulose pulp a year on a 3-year cutting cycle, at St. Augustine, Trinidad. On a 4-year cutting cycle it produced up to 4.5 tons.

As for digester capacity, the capacity of a given digester, in terms of yield per charge, has been increased as much as 20 percent by using some species of bamboo instead of southern pine. This increase, with the use of bamboo, is due to the greater density and better loading properties of bamboo chips.

Only by actual experiment can we find whether existing wild stands of bamboo will meet the ultimate need. In any case, we cannot afford to ignore what has happened to our wild stands of pulp-producing forest trees. The great reservoirs of one species after another have been depleted to an alarming extent by the axe of the pulpwood gatherer, and it remains to be seen whether scientific management of the remnants will succeed in raising the production of pulpwood to levels at which our skyrocketing consumption of pulp can be supplied.

The rapidly mounting requirements of the rayon industry are now added to those of the paper industry. The combined consumption of pulpwood by the paper and rayon industries of the United States increased more than 60 percent in the past decade, according to statistics supplied by the Forest Service—from 10,349,000 cords in 1937 to 17,816,000 cords in 1946.

For the rayon industry, also, certain bamboos have been found well suited by virtue of superior technical properties, including a high alpha-cellulose content. That the use of bamboo for cellulose is no longer in the experimental stage is suggested by the fact, as we find in *Fibres*, for March 1947, that a company has been organized in Travancore, India, for the commercial production of rayon from bamboo. Such use of bamboo may well be extended as the demand for rayon continues. *Forest Resources of Chile*, issued by the Forest Service, reported that "World production of rayon has been going up rapidly, from about 20 million pounds in 1912 to almost 2,000 million pounds in 1938."

Building upon the fundamental research carried out by William Raitt through many years of patient labor, our great paper research laboratories have been refining the methods and perfecting the techniques of using bamboo in the making of paper. Now it is possible on a commercial basis to make any desired quality of paper from a large number of different bamboos. Among the principal remaining problems are to find the best, most productive, and most easily harvested bamboos and to mechanize the processes of cutting and preparing them for the mill.

During the recent war, unseasoned, home-grown, bamboo culms sold at wholesale for as much as 25 cents a running foot. The acute shortage of bamboos suitable for our strategic needs, which developed soon after our supply from the Far East was cut off, emphasized the importance of establishing numerous plantings of superior bamboos in the Western Hemisphere. From these plantings, supplies adequate for our needs might be drawn should a similar emergency arise.

Through its program of technical collaboration with Latin American countries, the Office of Foreign Agricultural Relations of the Department of Agriculture is fostering the development of such a reservoir of superior bamboo material.

As a part of the program of its Tropical Forest Experiment Station at Rio Piedras, P. R., the Forest Service is conducting extensive experimental plantings of several species of bamboo. Because of their excellent soil-binding properties and heavy mulch production, bamboo plantings are particularly appropriate for trial on wasteland too steep for cultivation. In the experiments at Rio Piedras, bamboos are being tested as a possible crop for such lands.

The Federal Agricultural Experiment Station at Mayaguez, P. R., experimenting with bamboos introduced from abroad, has brought to light a great deal of basic information concerning methods of propagation, seasoning, utilization, protection against the attacks of wood-eating insects, and so on.

The Forest Products Laboratory at Madison, Wis., has carried out preliminary studies on several species of bamboo. The studies include tests of strength, gluing tests, and impregnation for the modification of the physical properties of the culms and for protecting them against insects and fungi.

A large collection of living bamboos from abroad has been built up at the Barbour Lathrop Plant Introduction Garden, near Savannah, Ga., and at the Coconut Grove Garden, near Miami, Fla., by the Department of Agriculture through its Division of Plant Exploration and Introduction.

Uses on the Farm

Besides the commercial importance of products obtained from bamboo, its use as a supplementary crop and source of material for farm and home use is interesting. The development of bamboo for such uses has only just begun.

Propagation material of bamboos of excellent technical properties is available in the United States. They can be grown in a large part of the United States. Groves of bamboo on the farm can be useful as chicken runs and bird refuges. They can also supply edible shoots, supplemental winter forage for livestock, and poles for a hundred other uses: Tree props, poles for harvesting nuts and Spanish moss, fishing poles, fish-net handles, chicken fences, garden stakes, lining-out poles for fence building, and for staking off lands in plowing—to name only a few.

Once a grove is established, boys and girls can soon learn to supplement their incomes by selling poles in town for use in window displays, for interior decoration, vaulting poles, javelins, musical instruments, handles for insect-collecting nets, and material for basketry and other manual training and handicraft needs.

On the basis of documented material, government and private agencies are making tests and analyses of introduced bamboos, to ascertain the relative excellence of individual kinds for specific purposes. On the basis of our present knowledge, certain species from India of the genus *Ochlandra,* not yet introduced, appear to be better suited for the production of cellulose pulp for paper and rayon than anything now available in the Western Hemisphere.

All the continents except Europe have bamboos in their native flora. It is estimated that the total number of distinct kinds of bamboo that have been described is between 600 and 700. These comprise about 60 genera. Nine genera, with about 200 species, have been described from the Western Hemisphere.

Of these nine American genera, only one, *Arundinaria,* has been found outside this Hemisphere—in Asia and Africa. The known native bamboo flora of the United States comprises two species and several varieties of the genus *Arundinaria. A. gigantea,* the Giant Southern Cane, occurs in southern Ohio, Indiana, Illinois, Missouri, Oklahoma, and other States to the south; the switch cane (*A. tecta*) is confined to the Atlantic and Gulf coastal region from Maryland southward. Once more abundant and more utilized than now, our native canes have gradually been eliminated by the plow from most of the fertile valley lands where they flourished in extensive groves, or canebrakes, which served as refuges for birds, bear, and deer, and provided winter protection and forage for domestic animals.

Other genera of the Western Hemisphere are:

Arthrostylidium (mostly climbers);

Aulonemia (the thin-walled culms are often used for weaving, thatch, and shepherds' pipes and the leaves for forage);

Chusquea (mostly climbers with solid, largely pithy, stems used locally in basketry and in house construction; and with abundant foliage which often furnishes grazing for cattle and green fodder for guinea pigs in the highlands of Ecuador and Peru);

Elytrostachys (the type species, with

climbing, thin-walled culms; it flowers frequently and bears abundant, edible grains);

Glaziophyton (known by a single species whose small, smooth, and thin-walled culms with chambered pith are branched only near the tip);

Guadua (closely related to the Asian genus *Bambusa;* mostly thorny species, the giant, 80–90 foot culms of *G. angustifolia* constitute the principal building material in parts of Colombia and Ecuador);

Merostachys (chiefly Brazilian; all the known species have thin-walled culms); and two, *Athroostachys* and *Brasilocalamus,* or *Rettbergia,* (of which little is known).

The natural distribution of bamboos in the Western Hemisphere extends from the southern part of the United States southward to Argentina and Chile, and from sea level to elevations of more than 12,000 feet in the tropics. Gaps occur principally in relatively arid regions or in places where agriculture has destroyed the natural forest cover. Species of *Arundinaria* and *Chusquea* are the most cold-resistant of the western bamboos; the former extends farthest north and the latter farthest south and highest above sea level.

It is well known that in parts of the Far East the utilization of various species of bamboo has been highly developed and greatly diversified. Perhaps less familiar are the facts relating to the importance of bamboo in the local economies of the countries to the south of us, where species of *Guadua, Chusquea, Arthrostylidium, Autonemia,* and *Merostachys* are found. These, according to their natural occurrence and technical properties, supply the principal or preferred material for houses, fences, bridges, basketry, and so on. Many of the Old World species introduced into the Western Hemisphere provide superior material for these and other purposes.

During the past 50 years or so, many bamboos have been introduced into the United States, principally from China,

Japan, Java, and India. The introduction and subsequent trial of these bamboos have been the work of many individuals, and of private and governmental agencies. At Mayaguez, major attention has been given the tropical species. The agronomic and industrial experimentation carried out there has high-lighted several species of noteworthy promise for structural and industrial purposes and for erosion control. *Bambusa tulda* and *B. longispiculata,* two closely related species from India, have proved to be outstanding for making furniture and split-bamboo fishing rods, especially heavy-duty salt-water rods.

They are also especially suited for use as structural elements in low-cost houses for tropical conditions. *Bambusa tuldoides,* a Chinese species, is also well suited for these uses, but its wood is not so strong as that of the two already mentioned. (According to unpublished data from tests made by George Merritt, the tensile strength of the wood of the internodes of *B. tuldoides* is about 40,000 pounds to the square inch, whereas according to tests carried out at the College of Agriculture of the University of Puerto Rico, the tensile strength of *B. tulda* is 60,000 pounds to the square inch.) *B. tuldoides* has, however, the advantage of being somewhat more cold-resistant, easier to propagate, and more prolific. All three of these species are suitable for the control of erosion.

Bambusa textilis, a Chinese species, has special promise as material for woven ware, such as basketry and matting, and for durable garden stakes. *Dendrocalamus strictus,* from India, a species with thick-walled, strong culms, has found special use in the bamboo furniture industry in Puerto Rico.

Bambusa vulgaris, probably native to Madagascar, was one of the first bamboos to be introduced into the Western Hemisphere. For that reason, and because of the ease with which it is propagated and its high productivity, it has long been the most common bamboo in cultivation in the American tropics. It is utilized in many areas in the absence of more suitable species for general farm purposes, including house construction, fences, and shades and pots for nursery plants. The extreme susceptibility of its wood to invasion by powder-post beetles, however, sometimes means severe losses to its users. This species has been used successfully by the Trinidad Paper Pulp Company, which maintains a plantation of more than 800 acres as a source of paper pulp. It is not the best bamboo for paper pulp but it is a heavy producer.

Bambusa multiplex and several of its horticultural forms, all apparently of Chinese origin, are less tender than the other tropical species mentioned and are suitable for landscaping; they have therefore become perhaps the most familiar bamboos of the warmer parts of the United States. They thrive as far north as Savannah on the Atlantic seaboard. The culms of the so-called parent species, which attain a height of 30 feet and a diameter above 1 inch, provide structural elements for low-cost houses in Jamaica. They also make a good paper pulp.

Sinocalamus oldhami (*Dendrocalamus latiflorus* of California gardens), from Formosa, is frequently cultivated as an ornamental in the United States, from San Francisco southward and in the warmer parts of the Gulf States. Its freedom from pests and its stately form give this bamboo a special place in the hearts of many plant lovers. Its culms grow tall and erect and in compact, slowly spreading clumps.

Trials of the hardier group of introduced bamboos have been largely carried out by private growers. The results to date comprise principally data on the adaptation of the various species to the areas where they have been tried, although E. A. McIlhenny, in articles in the National Horticultural Magazine for January and April, 1945, has given valuable information on cultural methods and yields of several species at Avery Island, La.

These hardier bamboos are represented—among the introductions of superior promise—principally by species of *Arundinaria* and *Phyllostachys*. There are a good many introductions of relatively minor importance, except as ornamentals, from other genera, such as *Pseudosasa, Sasa, Semiarundinaria, Shibataea,* and *Sinarundinaria.*

Bamboos of the genus *Sinarundinaria* (rarely seen in this country outside of California) are exceptional in the hardy group in that they have certain structural features characteristic of most tropical bamboos—a caespitose (compact) clump habit, determinate (nonrunning) rhizomes (underground stems), and lack of visible tessellation (cross-veins) in the leaf blades. All of the other hardy bamboos are characterized by tessellate-veined leaf blades (with cross-veins forming little rectangles) and by slender "running" rhizomes that are responsible for their spreading, aggressive growth habit.

Arundinaria amabilis was only recently introduced, at least as living plants, from China. Its industrial importance in this country is a matter of history, however, for since the turn of the century its culms have been the most highly satisfactory and most universally used source of material for split-bamboo fishing rods. Curiously, although our supply of this bamboo comes from China, where it is cultivated and processed for export, it is known in the trade as Tonkin Cane.

Arundinaria simoni, another Chinese species introduced here by way of Europe, has become rather common in cultivation, chiefly as an ornamental. During the recent war, an industrial concern in Florida built up a considerable trade in the culms, using them chiefly as handles for shuffleboard mallets.

Pseudosasa japonica (more popularly called *Arundinaria japonica*), which comes from Japan, where it is known as the arrow bamboo, is perhaps the most widely distributed exotic bamboo in cultivation in the United States. It thrives all the way from Florida to New York City and in corresponding climates westward.

Semiarundinaria fastuosa, introduced early in the century from Japan, where it is known as the Narihiri bamboo, is one of the hardiest; in that respect it approaches *Pseudosasa japonica,* which it rivals in distribution, if not in abundance, in the United States. The plant has an erect habit and good foliage and is considered one of the best of the hardy introduced bamboos for ornamental purposes.

Of the genus *Phyllostachys,* some 30 kinds have been introduced from China and Japan. Of these, the following species and varieties have been established to some extent in general cultivation: *P. aurea, aureosulcata, bambusoides, bambusoides* var. *castilloni, congesta, dulcis, edulis, meyeri, nidularia, nigra, nigra* var. *henonis, nuda, purpurata, sulphurea* var. *viridis, viridiglaucescens,* and *vivax.* The young shoots of all known species of this genus are good to eat, perhaps the most highly esteemed being those of *P. dulcis* and *P. sulphurea* var. *viridis.*

Bamboos of the genus *Phyllostachys* constitute the principal source of paper pulp, and of raw material for hundreds of other industrial needs in China. Several species have become widespread or locally abundant in cultivation in this country.

Phyllostachys bambusoides, one of the so-called Giant Timber Bamboos and perhaps the best known of the group, apparently was introduced first from Japan (where it is known as Madake), and later from China, its native home. At the Barbour Lathrop Plant Introduction Garden and at the old Tevis estate near Bakersfield, Calif., it produces culms 75 feet tall and 6 inches in diameter. These are used in this country chiefly for interior decoration (paneling, for example), merchandising kiosks, split-bamboo fishing rods, staving-off poles, garden fences, shade houses, flag poles, and poles for collecting Spanish-moss. The slender stems of a horticultural form, Slender Crook-stem, are said to make the best poles for harvesting pecans.

Phyllostachys aureosulcata (*P. ne-*

vinni of some of the earlier records), a Chinese species, was extensively distributed some years ago for trial as the stake and forage bamboo. Its culms are used to a considerable extent locally for fishing poles and garden stakes, but aside from its graceful habit and its relative hardiness (it thrives in Washington, D. C., and good examples of it may be seen in the outdoor aviary at the National Zoological Park), it has less to recommend it from a utilitarian point of view than many other species of the genus.

Phyllostachys aurea, also a native of China, produces a high percentage of culms with shortened basal internodes, the character by which it is most readily recognized. This is an excellent bamboo for fishing poles, and important quantities of the culms were imported from Japan for the purpose.

Phyllostachys meyeri, similar to *P. aurea* in size and general appearance but lacking the shortened basal culm internodes, was introduced from China by Frank N. Meyer early in the century. It is good for general farm purposes and for fishing poles.

THE AUTHOR⋘ *F. A. McClure is a native of Shelby County, Ohio. He holds four degrees from Ohio State University. As agricultural explorer with the United States Department of Agriculture and Lingnan University at Canton, he has done botanical work on four trips to China. He has carried on research on bamboo for more than 20 years under the auspices of those two institutions and with grants in aid from Rockefeller Foundation, China Foundation, the National Research Council, and the Guggenheim Foundation. His work with bamboo has taken him to China, the Philippine Islands, Indochina, Central America, and South America. He is field service consultant on bamboo for the Technical Collaboration Branch, Office of Foreign Agricultural Relations and research associate in botany under the Smithsonian Institution, whose National Herbarium extends facilities for his work.*

Grass in Charts and Tables

DATA ON THE SEED AND CULTURE OF COMMON GRASSES AND LEGUMES

The information given in the following tables (pages 744–752) is intended as a guide to scientific and common names, certain seed statistics, and regions of adaptation of various grasses and legumes.

The purity, germination, and viability of seed are affected by many factors. The percentages shown are for average good lots of seed. In the case of legumes with a purity below 99 percent, this is to allow for other crop seeds and inert matter that are not objectionable. The number of seeds per pound and weight per bushel are an approximation, as these vary greatly from lot to lot and depend on seasonal and other environmental conditions under which the plants are grown and the seed is harvested.

The longevity of seed also varies greatly, depending on conditions of harvest and storage. For that reason only relative classes of longevity are given. These classes indicate the relative period of time the seed can be expected to remain viable enough for general use. Since harvest and storage conditions have a marked influence on loss of viability, the purchaser of seed should not depend on the longevity figures but should insist on current germination figures of the material he buys.

Rate of seeding is influenced by local weather conditions, thoroughness of seedbed preparation, and method of seeding, so that only a general range of seeding rates can be given. The figures, however, indicate in general the amount of seed required.

The designations (e. g., 3a, 4a) in the right-hand column ("Where adapted") refer to similar numbers on the map below.

In the case of regions of adaptation, the designations are necessarily general. They are suggestive only, as local requirements cannot be given in detail. Tables on later pages give such information more precisely for the Corn Belt and Lake States, the Southern States, the Northern and Southern Great Plains, the Mountain Region, and Hawaii. Recommendations for seedings in the Northeastern States are given on page 409.

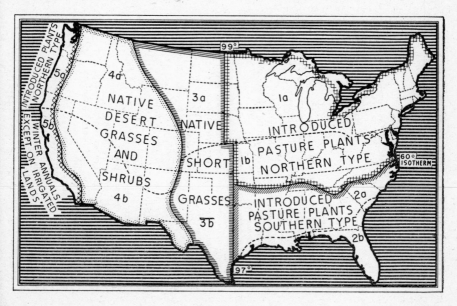

GRASSES

Scientific and common name	Seed information				Cultural information	
	Purity	Germination	Seed per pound	Longevity class (xx)	Seeding rate per acre	Where adapted
	Percent	*Percent*	*Number*		*Pounds*	
Agropyron cristatum, crested wheatgrass	95	85	175,000	2	6-12	3a, 4a.
Agropyron dasystachyum, thickspike wheatgrass			154,000	2	6-12	3a, 4a.
Agropyron desertorum, desert wheatgrass	95	85	175,000	2	6-12	3a, 4a.
Agropyron elongatum, tall wheatgrass	94	90	79,000	2	8-12	3a, 4a, 4b.
Agropyron inerme, beardless wheatgrass			150,000	2	6-12	3a, 4a.
Agropyron intermedium, intermediate wheatgrass	89	91	88,000	2	8-12	3a, north 3b, 4a.
Agropyron michnoi	95	85	162,000	2	6-12	3a, 4a.
Agropyron repens, quackgrass (w)			110,000	2	6-12	1a.
Agropyron riparium, streambank wheatgrass	88	87	156,000	2	6-12	3a, 4a.
Agropyron semicostatum, drooping wheatgrass	76	89	59,000	2	6-12	3a, 4a.
Agropyron sibiricum, Siberian wheatgrass	80	80	170,000	2	6-12	3a, 4a.
Agropyron smithii, western wheatgrass			110,000	2	5-15	3a, north 3b, 4a.
Agropyron spicatum, bluebunch wheatgrass			95,000	2	6-12	3a, 4a.
Agropyron subsecundum, bearded wheatgrass	95	85	117,000	2	6-12	3a, 4a.
Agropyron trachycaulum, slender wheatgrass	93	85	159,000	2	6-12	3a, 4a.
Agropyron trichophorum, stiffhair wheatgrass	92	90	100,000	2	8-12	3a, north 3b, 4a.
Agrostis alba, redtop	95	90	4,990,000	1	5-10	1a, 1b, 5a.
Agrostis canina, velvet bent	95	90	10,800,000	3	40-60	1a, 5a.
Agrostis palustris, creeping bent	95	90	7,800,000	3	40-60	1a, 5a.
Agrostis tenuis, colonial bent	90	80	8,723,000	3	40-60	1a, 1b, 5a.
Alopecurus pratensis, meadow foxtail			576,000	2	15-25	1a, 4a, 5a.
Ammophila arenaria, European beachgrass			114,000		Vegetative	1a, 5a.
Ammophila breiligulata, American beachgrass					Vegetative	1a, 5a.
Andropogon furcatus, big bluestem	40	60	165,000	2	10-15	West 1a, w. 1b, 3a, 3b.
Andropogon hallii, sand bluestem	40	60	113,000	2	10-20	West 1a, w. 1b, 3a, 3b.
Andropogon intermedius var. *caucasius*, Caucasian bluestem	15	39	1,072,000	2	10-15	2a, 2b, 3b.
Andropogon ischaemum, yellow bluestem	25	57	1,409,000	2	10-15	3b.
Andropogon scoparius, little bluestem	55	60	260,000	2	10-15	West 1a, w. 1b, 2, 2b.
Andropogon virginicus, broomsedge						

Anthoxanthum odoratum, sweet vernalgrass	98	80	726,000	3	15–25	1a, 1b, 2a, 5a.
Aristida longiseta, red three-awn					40–50	3a, 3b, 4a, 4b.
Arrhenatherum elatius, tall oatgrass	85	80	150,000	1	40–50	1a, 1b, 4a, 5a.
Astrebla pectinata, Mitchellgrass	49	59	82,000	2		3b.
Avena sativa, oats	98	90	13,000	1	60–90	General.
Axonopus affinis, carpetgrass	92	90	1,222,000	3	5–12	2a, 2b.
Bouteloua curtipendula, side-oats grama	30	65	191,000	2	10–15	3a, 3b.
Bouteloua eriopoda, black grama	37	22	1,335,000	2	10–15	West 3b, 4b.
Bouteloua filiformis, slender grama	55	55	1,428,000		10–15	3b, 4b.
Bouteloua gracilis, blue grama	45	75	825,000	2	10–15	3b, 4b.
Bouteloua hirsuta, hairy grama	26	39	980,000	1	10–15	West 3b, 4b, South 4a.
Bouteloua rothrockii, Rothrock grama	56	34	4,095,000		10–15	4b.
Briza maxima, big quakinggrass (o)						5b.
Briza minor, little quakinggrass (o)						2a, 2b, 5b.
Bromus arvensis, field brome	98	81	280,000	2	15–30	1a, 1b.
Bromus catharticus, rescuegrass	95	85	62,000	2	15–25	2a, 2b, 3b, 4b, 5b.
Bromus erectus, meadow brome			71,000	2	10–20	3a, 4a.
Bromus inermis, smooth brome	92	85	136,000	2	10–20	1a, north 1b, 3a, 4a.
Bromus marginatus, mountain brome	98	85	71,000	2	10–20	4a.
Bromus secalinus, chess (w)			71,000	3		General.
Bromus tectorum, cheatgrass brome (w)	85	95	208,000	3	*4–8	West 1a, 3a, 4a.
Buchloë dactyloides, buffalograss		95	*56,000			3a, 3b.
Calamagrostis canadensis, bluejoint reedgrass		70				1a, 3a, 4a.
Calamovilfa gigantea, big sandreed	89	74	88,000	2	8–12	3b.
Calamovilfa longifolia, prairie sandreed	85	75	273,700	2	8–12	3a.
Chloris distichophylla, weeping chloris	92	30	1,770,000		8–15	2b, South 5b.
Chloris gayana, Rhodesgrass	60	60	2,143,000	2	8–15	2b, South 3b, 4b, 5b.
Cynodon dactylon, Bermuda-grass	97	85	1,787,000	1	6–8	2a, 2b, 5b.
Cynosurus cristatus, crested dogtail	98	80	722,000	1	15–25	1a, 5a.
Dactylis glomerata, orchardgrass	85	85	654,000		6–15	1a, 1b, 4a, 5a.
Digitaria decumbens, pangolagrass				3	Vegetative	2b.
Digitaria sanguinalis, hairy crabgrass (w)			825,000			1a, 1b, 2a.
Distichlis stricta, inland saltgrass						3a, 3b, 4a, 4b.
Echinochloa crusgalli var. *frumentacea*, Japanese millet	97	90	155,000	2	20–25	1a.
Elymus canadensis, Canada wild-rye	85	85	115,000	2	10–15	3a, 4a.
Elymus condensatus, giant wild-rye	78	83	166,000	2	10–15	3a, 4a.
Elymus giganteus, Siberian wild-rye			100,000	2	10–15	3a, 4a.
Elymus glaucus, blue wild-rye	91	85	137,000	2	10–15	4a.
Elymus junceus, Russian wild-rye	88	85	175,000	2	8–10	3a, 4a.
Elymus triticoides, creeping wild-rye		90	51,000	2	5–15	4a.
Elymus virginicus, Virginia wild-rye	70	84	73,000	2	10–15	3a, 4a.

See footnotes at end of table.

GRASSES—Continued

Scientific and common name	Seed information				Cultural information	
	Purity	Germination	Seed per pound	Longevity class (xx)	Seeding rate per acre	Where adapted
	Percent	*Percent*	*Number*		*Pounds*	
Eragrostis chloromelas, Boer lovegrass	96	71	2,922,000	2	1–3	4b.
Eragrostis curvula, weeping lovegrass	95	87	1,463,000	2	1–3	3b, 4b.
Eragrostis lehmanniana, Lehmann lovegrass	84	66	4,245,000	2	1–3	4b.
Eragrostis trichodes, sand lovegrass	92	69	1,300,000	2	1–3	3a, 3b.
Eremochloa ophiuroides, centipedegrass	43	70	408,000	1	15–25	2a, 2b.
Euchlaena mexicana, teosinte			6,930		3–5	2b, south 3b.
Festuca elatior, meadow fescue	97	90	230,000	2	10–25	1a, 1b, 4a, 5a.
Festuca elatior, var. *arundinacea*, reed fescue	97	90	227,000	2	10–25	1a, 1b, 4a, 5a.
Festuca idahoensis, Idaho fescue						4a.
Festuca myuros, rattail fescue (w)			412,000			4a.
Festuca octoflora, sixweeks fescue (w)			965,000			4a.
Festuca ovina, sheep fescue	96	85	680,000	2	15–25	1a, 5a.
Festuca rubra, red fescue	97	80	615,000	2	15–40	1a, 1b, 5a.
Festuca rubra, var. *commutata*, Chewings fescue	97	80	615,000	2	15–40	1a, 1b, 5a.
Hilaria belangeri, curly-mesquite	28	19	269,000	3	4–8	South 3b, 4b.
Hilaria jamesii, galleta	21		159,000		4–8	4b.
Hilaria mutica, tobosa	6	55	267,000	1	4–8	South 3b, 4b.
Hilaria rigida, big galleta	12	30	33,000	3		4b.
Holcus lanatus, velvetgrass	95	85	1,524,000	3	10–25	1a, 1b, 2a, 5a.
Hordeum bulbosum, bulbous barley	71	48	50,000	2	8–12	4a.
Hordeum jubatum, foxtail barley (w)	93			2		3a, 4a.
Hordeum nodosum, meadow barley (w)	99	76				3a, 4a.
Hordeum vulgare, barley		90	14,000	2	60–90	General, (3b, 4b, 5b).
Hyparrhenia hirta	35		614,000		5–10	2b, south (3b, 4b, 5b).
Hyparrhenia rufa, jaragua		80	707,000		5–10	2b, south (3b, 4b, 5b).
Imperata cylindrica, cogongrass		90			Vegetative	2b.
Koeleria cristata, junegrass	50	43			8–12	3a.
Lolium multiflorum, Italian ryegrass	98	90	227,000	2	25–35	1a, 1b, 2a, 5a.
Lolium perenne, perennial ryegrass	98	90	227,000	2	25–35	1a, 1b, 5a.

Species						
Muhlenbergia porteri, bush muhly	41	30	2,424,000	3		3b, 4b.
Oryzopsis hymenoides, Indian ricegrass	94	11	141,000	3	8–10	3a, 4a.
Oryzopsis miliacea, smilograss	91	69	884,000	2		5a.
Panicum antidotale, blue panic	79	70	657,000	1	2–6	2a, 2b, 3b, 4b, 5b.
Panicum maximum, Guinea-grass	30	35	1,106,000	1	Vegetative	2b.
Panicum miliaceum, proso	98	85	82,000	2	15–25	3a, 3b.
Panicum obtusum, vine-mesquite	50	65	143,000		5–10	3b, 4b.
Panicum purpurascens, Paragrass					Vegetative	2b.
Panicum repens, torpedograss	36	96	510,000	1	Vegetative	2a, 2b.
Panicum virgatum, switchgrass	95	75	389,000	2	5–8	West 1a, w. 1b, 3a, 3b.
Paspalum dilatatum, Dallisgrass	70	70	220,000	1	8–20	2a, 2b, 5b.
Paspalum laeve, field paspalum (w)	9	29	156,000	1		1b, 2a, 2b.
Paspalum malacophyllum, ribbed paspalum	50	39	1,059,000	1	10–20	2a, 2b.
Paspalum notatum, Bahiagrass	72	70	166,000	2	10–15	2a, 2b.
Paspalum plicatulum, brownseed paspalum	55		317,000		10–15	2b.
Paspalum stramineum, sand paspalum	72	64	258,000	2	5–10	3b, 4b.
Paspalum urvillei, Vaseygrass	69	59	440,000		10–20	2a, 2b.
Pennisetum glaucum, pearlmillet	98	85	88,000	1	20–30	2a, 2b.
Pennisetum purpureum, Napiergrass			1,402,000		Vegetative	2a, 2b, 5b.
Phalaris arundinacea, reed canarygrass	96	80	533,000	1	5–10	1a, 1b, 5a.
Phalaris canariensis, canarygrass		80	68,000	2	25–30	General.
Phalaris caroliniana, Carolina canarygrass	89	92	429,000		10–15	2a, 2b.
Phalaris tuberosa var. *stenoptera*, Hardinggrass	90	60	355,000		25–30	5b.
Phleum pratense, timothy	99	90	1,230,000	1	6–12	1a, 1b, 4a, 5a.
Poa ampla, big bluegrass	81	49	882,000	2	6–10	4a.
Poa annua, annual bluegrass	80	80	1,196,000	2	15–25	1a, 5a.
Poa arachnifera, Texas bluegrass	71	78	1,874,000	2	4–6	3b.
Poa bulbosa, bulbous bluegrass	97	86	463,000	2	20–25	5a.
Poa compressa, Canada bluegrass	80	80	2,495,000	2	15–25	1a.
Poa nevadensis, Nevada bluegrass	86	64	1,082,000	2	6–10	3a, 4a.
Poa pratensis, Kentucky bluegrass	85	80	2,177,000	2	15–25	1a, 1b, 5a.
Poa secunda, Sandberg bluegrass	89	66	925,000	2	6–10	4a.
Poa trivialis, rough bluegrass	85	80	2,540,000	2	15–25	1a, 5a.
Puccinellia nuttaliana, Nuttall alkali-grass	74	62	2,108,000	2	6–10	4a.
Redfieldia flexuosa, blowoutgrass	88	23	263,000	2	Vegetative	3a, 3b.
Saccharum officinarum, sugarcane					Vegetative	2b.
Secale cereale, rye	97	85	18,000	1	90–160	General.
Setaria italica, foxtail millet	98	90	220,000	1	20–30	3a, 3b.
Setaria macrostachya, plains bristlegrass	39	23	305,000	2	4–6	3b.
Sorghastrum nutans, yellow Indiangrass	68	63	175,000	1	10–15	West 1a, w.1 b, 3a, 3b.

See footnotes at end of table.

GRASSES—Continued

Scientific and common name	Seed information				Cultural information	
	Purity	Germination	Seed per pound	Longevity class (xx)	Seeding rate per acre	Where adapted
	Percent	*Percent*	*Number*		*Pounds*	
Sorghum halepense, Johnsongrass	98	85	118,000	2	10–25	2a, 2b.
Sorghum vulgare, sorghum	98	85	28,000	1	15–75	3a, 3b, 4a, 4b.
Sorghum vulgare var. *sudanense*, Sudangrass	98	80	55,000	1	20–25	General.
Sporobolus airoides, alkali sacaton	85	80	1,758,000	2	4–6	4a, 4b.
Sporobolus asper, tall dropseed	64	80	503,000	1	4–6	1a, 1b.
Sporobolus asper var. *hookeri*, meadow dropseed		76	823,000		4–6	1a, 1b, 3a, 3b.
Sporobolus cryptandrus, sand dropseed	93	80	5,298,000	2	2–4	West 1a, w. 1b, 3a, 3b
Sporobolus giganteus, giant dropseed	87	30	1,723,000	2	2–4	4b.
Sporobolus wrightii, sacaton	87	70	1,965,000	1	2–4	4b.
Stenotaphrum secundatum, St. Augustinegrass					Vegetative	2b.
Stipa comata, needle-and-thread	29	13	115,000	3	8–12	3a, 4a.
Stipa pulchra, California needlegrass						4b, 5b.
Stipa viridula, green needlegrass	95	24	181,000	3	8–12	3a, 4a.
Trichachne californica, Arizona cottontop	32	44	718,000	2		4b.
Tricholaena repens, Natalgrass	26	71	501,000	1	4–8	2b.
Tridens flavus, purpletop	83	88	465,000	1	4–6	1a, 1b, 2a.
Tripsacum dactyloides, eastern gamagrass			7,280		Vegetative	1a, 2a, 2b.
Trisetum flavescens, yellow trisetum						1a, 1b.
Triticum aestivum, wheat	99	90	15,000	1	60–150	General.
Uniola latifolia, broadleaf uniola (o)	81	60	94,000	1		1b, 2a.
Uniola paniculata, sea-oats (o)						2a, 2b.
Zea mays, corn	99	90	1,118	2	6–10	General.
Zizania aquatica, annual wildrice			11,340		50–100	1a, 1b, 2a, 2b.
Zoysia japonica, Japanese lawngrass		24	1,300,000	2	Vegetative	1a, 1b, 2a.
Zoysia matrella, Manilagrass	97	50	681,000	2	Vegetative	1b, 2a.
Zoysia tenuifolia, Mascarenegrass					Vegetative	5b.

w = weedy in character.   o = ornamentals.   * = in burs.

xx = 1 represents short-lived seed, 2 represents intermediate, and 3 represents long-lived seed.

LEGUMES

Scientific and common name	Seed information					Cultural information	
	Purity	Viable seed	Seed per pound	Weight per bushel	Longevity class [1]	Seeding rate per acre (broadcast)	Where adapted
	Percent	*Percent*	*Number*	*Pounds*		*Pounds*	
Alysicarpus vaginalis, alyceclover	98	85	300,000	60	3	10-12	2b.
Anthyllis vulneraria, kidneyvetch	98	[2]85	180,000	60	3	15-20	1a.
Arachis hypogaea, peanut	99	80	1,000	[3]22	1	[4]40	2a, 2b, and east 1b and 5b.
Astragalus cicer, cicer milkvetch	98	[2]90	130,000	60	3	20-25	1a, 3a, 4a, northern 3b.
Astragalus falcatus, sicklepod milkvetch	98	[2]90	130,000	60	3	20-25	Do.
Astragalus rubyi, Ruby milkvetch	98	[2]85	240,000	60	3	10-12	Do.
Cajanus indicus, pigeonpea	99	90	8,000	60	2	[4]8-10	2b.
Cassia tora, sickle senna	98	[5]90	22,000	60	2	40-45	1b, 2a, and 2b.
Chamaecrista fasciculata, showy partridge-pea	98	[5]90	64,000	57	2	20-30	1a, 1b, 2a, 2b.
Cicer arietinum, garbanzo	99	90	1,000	54	2	[4]20-30	5b.
Coronilla varia, varia crownvetch	98	[2]90	110,000	55	2	15-20	1a, 1b, 3a, 4a, 5a.
Crotalaria incana, shak crotalaria	98	[6]90	85,000	60	3	15-18	2a, 2b, southern 1b, and Irrigated 3b, 4b, 5b.
Crotalaria intermedia, slenderleaf crotalaria	98	[6]90	100,000	60	3	10-15	Do.
Crotalaria juncea, sunn crotalaria	99	[6]80	15,000	60	3	35-40	Do.
Crotalaria lanceolata, lance crotalaria	98	[6]90	170,000	60	3	7-10	Do.
Crotalaria mucronata, striped crotalaria	98	[6]90	75,000	60	3	10-15	Do.
Crotalaria spectabilis, showy crotalaria	99	[6]75	30,000	60	3	25-30	Do.
Cyamopsis tetragonoloba, guar	99	[2]90	20,000	60	1	30-40	3b, 4b, 5b.
Dalea alopecuroides, foxtail dalea	80	[2]80	150,000	60	1	10-15	3a, 3b, and adjacent areas.
Desmodium purpureum, tall tickclover	95	[2]85	200,000	60	2	8-10	2a, 2b, 5b.
Dolichos lablab, hyacinth-bean	99	90	1,400	60	2	[4]20-25	1b, 2a, 2b, irrigated 4b, 5b.
Glottidium vesicarium, bagpod	99	[5]90	1,500	56	3	[4]20-30	2a, 2b.
Glycine soja, soybean	98	80	5,000	60	1	45-60	All regions.
Hedysarum coronarium, sulla	98	85	100,000	60	1	20-25	5a, 5b.
Indigofera hirsuta, hairy indigo	98	[2]70	200,000	55	1	8-10	2a, 2b, irrigated 4b, 5b.
Lathyrus cicer, flatpod peavine	99	90	8,000	60	2	60-70	All regions.

See footnotes at end of table.

L E G U M E S—Continued

| Scientific and common name | Seed information | | | | Longevity class [1] | Seeding rate per acre (broadcast) | Cultural information |
	Purity	Viable seed	Seed per pound	Weight per bushel			Where adapted
	Percent	Percent	Number	Pounds		Pounds	
Lathyrus hirsutus, roughpea	98	90	15,000	55	2	50–60	2a, 2b.
Lathyrus sativus, grasspea	99	90	5,000	60	2	70–80	All regions.
Lathyrus sylvestris, flatpea	99	85	8,000	60	2	60–70	Do.
Lathyrus tingitanus, Tangier-pea	99	90	5,000	60	2	70–80	2a, 2b, 5a, 5b.
Lens esculenta, lentil	99	90	9,000	60	2	[4] 12–15	5a, 5b, and Palouse 4a.
Lespedeza bicolor, bicolor lespedeza	98	[2] 80	82,000	60	2	[4] 1–2	1b, 2a, 2b, 5b.
Lespedeza cuneata, sericea lespedeza	98	[2] 90	350,000	60	2	10–15	1b, 2a, 5b.
Lespedeza cyrtobotrya, bush lespedeza	97	[2] 80	65,000	60	2	[4] 1–2	1b, 2a, 2b, 5b.
Lespedeza hedysaroides, rush lespedeza	98	[2] 90	300,000	60	2	10–15	1b, 2a, 5b.
Lespedeza latissima, decumbent lespedeza	98	[2] 90	300,000	60	2	10–15	1b, 2a, 5b.
Lespedeza stipulacea, Korean lespedeza	97	90	[3] 225,000	[3] 40	1	[3] 10–15	1b, 2a, and southern 1a.
Lespedeza striata, common lespedeza var. Kobe	97	90	[3] 190,000	[3] 25	1	[3] 10–15	1b, 2a, and 2b.
Lespedeza striata, common lespedeza var. Tennessee #76.	96	90	[3] 310,000	[3] 25	1	[3] 8–10	1b, 2a, and 2b.
Lotus corniculatus var. arvensis, broadleaf birdsfoot trefoil.	96	[2] 90	375,000	60	2	5–8	1a, 1b, 5a, irrigated west.
Lotus corniculatus var. tenuifolius, narrowleaf birdsfoot trefoil.	96	[2] 90	400,000	60	2	5–8	5a, irrigated 5b, 4a, 4b, heavy; wet lands in East.
Lotus uliginosus, big trefoil	96	[2] 85	1,000,000	60	2	3–5	Low, wet in 5a, 5b, 2a, 2b.
Lupinus albus, white lupine	99	90	1,500	60	1	100–120	2b.
Lupinus angustifolius, blue lupine	99	90	2,500	60	1	70–100	2b, lower part 2a.
Lupinus luteus yellow lupine	99	90	4,000	60	1	50–80	Do.
Lupinus subcarnosus, bluebonnet	99	[2] 90	14,000	60	1	40–45	2a, 2b.
Medicago arabica, spotted bur-clover	[6] 80	[5] [6] 90	210,000	[3] 10	3	[3] 100	2a, 2b, and 5b in shade.
Medicago falcata, yellow alfalfa	98	[2] 90	208,000	60	3	15–20	1a, 3a, 4a.
Medicago hispida, California bur-clover	98	[2] 90	140,000	60	3	20–25	2a, 2b, 3b, 4b, 5b.
Medicago lupulina, black medic	98	[2] 90	300,000	60	3	10–15	All regions.
Medicago minima, little bur-clover	[6] 80	[5] [6] 90	400,000	[3] 10	3	[3] 60	2a, 2b, 4b and 5b.
Medicago orbicularis, buttonclover	98	[2] 90	150,000	60	3	15–20	Do.

Medicago sativa, purple alfalfa	98	[2]90	200,000	60	3	15–20	All regions except 2b.
Medicago scutellata, snail medic	98	[2]90	43,000	[3]15	3	[3]100	2a, 2b, 4b, and 5b.
Melilotus alba, white sweetclover	98	[2]90	260,000	60	3	10–15	All regions except 2b.
Melilotus indica, sourclover	98	[2]90	275,000	60	3	10–15	5b, 4b, 3b, west 2a and 2b.
Melilotus officinalis, yellow sweetclover	98	[2]90	260,000	60	3	10–15	All regions except 2b.
Melilotus suaveolens, Daghestan sweetclover	98	[2]90	250,000	60	3	10–15	3a.
Onobrychis viciaefolia, sainfoin	98	70	30,000	55	1	30–35	3a, 4a with irrigation.
Ornithopus sativus, serradella	98	85	[3]160,000	[3]36	1	[3]15–20	2a, 2b, and eastern 1b.
Phaseolus aconitifolius, mat bean	99	90	20,000	60	1	35–40	5b.
Phaseolus acutifolius, Texas bean	99	90	25,000	60	2	25–30	3a, 3b, 4a, 4b, and 5b.
Phaseolus angularis, adsuki bean	99	90	4,000	60	1	[4]20–25	1b, 2a, 2b.
Phaseolus aureus, mung bean	99	90	10,000	60	1	60–70	1b, 2a, 2b, 5b.
Phaseolus calcaratus, rice bean	99	90	10,000	60	1	70–80	1b, 2a, 5b.
Pisum arvense, field pea	99	90	3,000	60	1	70–90	All regions.
Pueraria phaseoloides, tropical kudzu	98	[2]80	37,000	54	2	[4]6–10	Tropics only.
Pueraria thunbergiana, Thunberg kudzu	99	[5]70	40,000	54	2	20–25	1b, 2a, 2b, and 5b.
Sesbania exaltata, hemp sesbania	99	[2]90	40,000	60	2	20–25	2a, 3b, 4b, 5b, 2b.
Stizolobium deeringianum, Deering velvetbean	99		1,000	60	2	30–40	2a, 2b.
Strophostyles helvola, trailing wildbean	99	[5]90	9,000	50	3	50–60	1a, 1b, 2a, 2b.
Trifolium agrarium, hop clover	98	[2]90	1,000,000	60	3	4–5	1a, northern 4a.
Trifolium alexandrinum, berseem	98	[2]85	200,000	60	3	15–20	Warm parts of 4b and 5b.
Trifolium dubium, small hop clover	90	[2]90	1,000,000	60	3	4–5	1b, 2a, 2b, 5a, 5b.
Trifolium fragiferum, strawberry clover	97	[2]85	300,000	60	3	6–10	4a, 4b, 5a, 5b.
Trifolium glomeratum, cluster clover	95	[2]90	1,000,000	60	3	3–4	West part of 2a.
Trifolium hirtum, rose clover	98	[2]90	140,000	60	3	15–20	1a, 2a, 2b, 5a, 5b.
Trifolium hybridum, alsike clover	97	[2]90	700,000	60	3	6–8	1a, 1b, 3a, 4a, 5a.
Trifolium incarnatum, crimson clover	98	[2]85	140,000	60	2	15–20	1b, 2a, 2b, 5a, 5b.
Trifolium lappaceum, lappa clover	96	[2]70	680,000	60	3	4–5	2a.
Trifolium nigrescens, ball clover	96	[5]90	1,000,000	60	3	2–4	2a, 2b.
Trifolium pratense, red clover	98	[2]90	275,000	60	3	8–12	All regions except 2b.
Trifolium procumbens, large hop clover	96	[2]90	2,000,000	60	3	3–4	1b, 2a, 2b, 5a, 5b.
Trifolium repens, white clover	96	[2]90	800,000	60	3	1–4	All regions.
Trifolium resupinatum, Persian clover	95	[2]85	675,000	60	3	4–6	2a, 2b.
Trifolium striatum, knotted clover	95	[2]90	231,000	60	3	8–12	Do.
Trifolium subterraneum, sub clover	99	[2]90	65,000	60	2	20–25	2a, 2b, 5a, 5b.
Trigonella foenum-graecum, fenugreek	99	[2]90	23,000	60	3	25–35	5b.
Vicia angustifolia, narrowleaf vetch	97	[2]90	30,000	60	3	30–40	1a, 2a, 2b, 5a, 5b.
Vicia articulata, one-flower (monantha) vetch	97	90	12,000	60	2	50–60	5a, 5b, 2a, 2b.
Vicia atropurpurea, purple vetch	97	90	10,000	60	2	50–60	5a, 5b, 2b.
Vicia cracca, bird vetch	99	[5]85	40,000	60	3	30–35	1a, 3a, 4a, 5a.

See footnotes at end of table.

LEGUMES—Continued

Scientific and common name	Seed information					Cultural information	
	Purity	Viable seed	Seed per pound	Weight per bushel	Longevity class [1]	Seeding rate per acre (broadcast)	Where adapted
	Percent	*Percent*	*Number*	*Pounds*		*Pounds*	
Vicia dasycarpa, woollypod vetch	90	[2] 90	10,000	60	3	50–60	1b, 2a, 2b, 5a, 5b.
Vicia faba var major, broadbean	99	90	500	60	3	[4] 70–80	5b, 2a, 2b.
Vicia faba, horsebean	99	90	3,000	60	3	80–100	Do.
Vicia grandiflora, bigflower vetch	95	[5] 90	32,000	60	3	35–40	2a, 2b.
Vicia pannonica, Hungarian vetch	97	90	10,000	60	3	70–80	5a, 5b, 2a.
Vicia sativa, common vetch	97	90	7,000	60	2	70–80	Do.
Vicia villosa, hairy vetch	97	[2] 90	20,000	60	3	40–45	All regions.
Vigna sinensis, cowpea	98	85	3,000	60	1	[4] 20–30	1b, 2a, 2b, 5b.

[1] 1 represents comparatively short-lived seed, 2 represents intermediate, and 3 represents long-lived seed.
[2] Medium percent of hard seed.
[3] Unhulled.
[4] Planted in rows 3 to 4 feet apart.
[5] High percent of hard seed.
[6] In the bur.

Native and Adventive Grasses That Have Been Domesticated and Improved for Conservation Uses [1]

Name, strain, and origin	Conservation uses and land classes [1]	Area of use	Remarks
Beardless wheatgrass (*Agropyron inerme*), "Whitmar" strain. Native vegetation.	Seeding wind-eroded cropland; reseeding range land. Classes III, IV, VI. (See footnote.)	Intermountain Pacific Northwest; Great Basin; light-textured soils.	Fine, erect stems; leafy; good production; drought-resistant. Good seeder; easy to handle.
Slender wheatgrass (*Agropyron trachycaulum*), "Primar" strain. Native vegetation.	Sweetclover-grass mixtures for green manure. Classes II, III, IV.	Intermountain Pacific Northwest.	Growth stages same as Spanish sweetclover; production high. Excellent seeder; easy to handle and easy to establish.
American beachgrass (*Ammophila breviligulata*), "Talriza" strain. Native vegetation.	Initial stabilization of eroding coastal sand dunes. Class VIII.	Seacoasts; inland dunes in Maine and New York.	Rapid tillering rate; strong rhizomes; tall coarse stems; broad leaves. Planted as clones.
Little bluestem (*Andropogon scoparius*), "E–17" strain. Native vegetation.	Regrassing range land; seeding wind-eroded cropland; eroded slopes, sandy land. Classes IV, VI, VII.	Oklahoma and Texas......	Slender stems; long narrow leaves; good seedling vigor; early maturity. Process seed; erratic seeder.
Side-oats grama (*Bouteloua curtipendula*), "Elreno" strain. Native vegetation.	Native grass mixtures for wind-erosion control on shallow sandy and gravelly soils. Classes IV, VI.	Kansas and Oklahoma......	Resistant to rust; good production; tenacious roots. Good seeder under irrigation; process seed.
Slender grama (*Bouteloua filiformis*), "T–901" strain. Native vegetation.	Reseeding eroded range lands, especially on alkaline soils. Class VI.	Southern and southwest Texas.	Long basal leaves; long season of use; ability to grow on adverse sites. Good seeder; process seed; volunteers readily on dry ranges.
Mountain brome (*Bromus marginatus*), "Bromar" strain. Native vegetation.	Sweetclover-grass mixtures for green manure; seeding burned-over timberland. Classes II, III, IV.	Intermountain Pacific Northwest.	Smut-resistant; leafy; late; growth stages same as Spanish sweetclover. Good seeder; process seed; rapid developing and easy to establish.

See footnote at end of table.

757150°—48——49

Native and Adventive Grasses That Have Been Domesticated and Improved for Conservation Uses—Continued

Name, strain, and origin	Conservation uses and land classes [1]	Area of use	Remarks
Canada wild-rye (*Elymus canadensis*), "Mandan" strain. Native vegetation.	Sweetclover-grass mixtures on sandy soils subject to wind erosion. Classes III, IV.	Northern Great Plains.....	Fine-stemmed; leafy; short; long-lived. Good seeder; process seed; rapid developing; easy to establish.
Red fescue (*Festuca rubra*), "Clatsop" strain. Native vegetation.	Permanent cover for coastal sand dunes. Classes VI, VIII.	Northern seacoasts..........	Grows in cool weather; remains green in summer. Good seeder; seed easy to handle.
Switchgrass (*Panicum virgatum*), "Blackwell" strain. Native vegetation.	Seeding drainage ways, terrace outlets; in grass mixtures on sandy and poorly drained land. Classes I to VI.	Kansas and Oklahoma......	Leafy; fine-stemmed; rust-resistant. Good seeder under irrigation; easy to handle.
Bahiagrass (*Paspalum notatum*), "Pensacola" strain. Adventive stand.	Erosion control on sloping sandy land; in pasture. Classes II, III, IV, VI.	Florida to southern parts of South Carolina, Georgia, Alabama, and Mississippi.	Narrow leaves; frost-resistant; tall stems. Good seeder..
Big bluegrass (*Poa ampla*), "Sherman" strain. Native vegetation.	Grass and grass-legume mixtures for hay, soil improvement, and dryland pastures; seeding burned-over timberlands. Classes III, IV, VI.	Intermountain Pacific Northwest; Great Basins; light-textured soils.	Wide range of use; good producer under difficult conditions; excellent root producer. Excellent seeder; easy to harvest; seed small.
Feather bunchgrass (*Stipa viridula*), "Green stipagrass" strain. Native vegetation..	Seeding abandoned wind-eroded farm land and wet-land hay mixture. Classes II, III, IV, VI.	Northern Great Plains......	Good producer; makes excellent regrowth; withstands flooding. Good seeder; process seed.

[1] Land capability classes denote the suitability of land for cultivation, grazing, and forestry. Classes I, II, and III are suited for cultivation with slight to intensive corrective measures; Class IV is suited only for limited or intermittent cultivation; Classes V, VI, VII, and VIII are not suited for any cultivation but may be used for grazing or forestry.

Much of the data for the tables on grasses for conservation were supplied by E. B. Coffman, M. E. Heath, C. B. Marshall, L. B. Scott, A. D. Slavin, and C. B. Webster, of the Nursery Division, Soil Conservation Service.

This table and the two following were prepared by A. L. Hafenrichter and A. D. Stoesz, whose article "Domesticated Grasses in Conservation," begins on page 354.

Introductions of Grasses and Legumes That Have Been Domesticated for Conservation Uses

Name, strain, and origin	Conservation uses and land classes	Area of use	Remarks
Tall wheatgrass (*Agropyron elongatum*). Asia Minor.	Seeding range and abandoned lands at high elevations, wet alkaline meadows and irrigation canal seeps. Class VI.	Intermountain Pacific Northwest; Great Basin; Northern Great Plains; Pacific Southwest.	Tall, robust; coarse but palatable; long season of use. Easy to establish; good seeder; seed easy to handle.
Intermediate wheatgrass (*Agropyron intermedium*). Asia Minor.	Alfalfa-grass mixtures in conservation rotations; hay or pasture; seeding waterways and terrace outlets; requires good soils. Classes II, III, IV.	Northern Great Plains; Intermountain Pacific Northwest; Great Basin; Pacific Southwest.	Sod former; good ground cover; high production and good quality feed. Easy to establish; seed easy to handle; sod-binds unless grown with alfalfa.
Pubescent wheatgrass (*Agropyron trichophorum*).	Alfalfa-grass or grass mixtures for pasture; adapted to eroded soils and wind-blown areas; seeding waterways. Class VI.	Intermountain Pacific Northwest; Great Basin; Northern Great Plains; Pacific Southwest.	Palatable sod former; low fertility requirement; long season of use. Easy to establish; seed easy to handle; should be grown with legume in subhumid areas.
Caucasian bluestem (*Andropogon intermedius*). Caucasius.	Seeding abandoned cropland and sandy areas subject to wind erosion. Class VI.	Northern portion of Southern Great Plains.	Fine-stemmed; leafy; good ground cover. Seed small; process seed; volunteers from shattering; requires careful planting.
Yellow bluestem (*Andropogon ischaemum*), "King Ranch" strain. Asia.	Seeding eroded range and cropland, and faces of stock dams. Classes II, III, IV, VI, VII.	Central Oklahoma and central Texas to Rio Grande River.	Good ground cover; withstands grazing pressure; adapted to eroded soils; aggressive. Seed small; process seed; easy to establish; volunteers from shattering.
Field brome (*Bromus arvensis*). Sweden.	Winter cover crop for erosion control in vineyards, orchards, row crops. Classes II, III, IV.	New England States; Northeastern States.	Rapid growth; good annual winter ground cover. Easy to establish; self seeder.
Rhodesgrass (*Chloris gayana*). Cold-resistant strain. South Africa.	Erosion control on clay and loam soils of medium to high fertility. Classes I, IV.	Central and southern Texas.	Cold-resistant; vigorous; leafy. Good seed producer.

Introductions of Grasses and Legumes That Have Been Domesticated for Conservation Uses—Continued

Name, strain, and origin	Conservation uses and land classes	Area of use	Remarks
Russian wild-rye (*Elymus junceus*). Omsk, U. S. S. R.	An auxiliary to crested wheatgrass; seeding abandoned cropland. Classes III, IV, VI.	Northern Great Plains, especially medium to high elevations.	Remains green and palatable in late summer and early fall; good ground cover from dense basal leaves; good root producer. Erratic seed producer; seed shatters; process seed; easy to establish on soils of medium fertility.
Weeping lovegrass (*Eragrostis curvula*), "A–67" strain. East Africa.	Range revegetation; seeding abandoned land and eroded slopes; strip cropping; wind erosion. Classes III, IV, VI, VIII.	Pacific Southwest; Southern Great Plains to Arkansas and Louisiana; northward to Massachusetts.	Rapid, uniform growth, produces dense masses of vegetative cover; quick regrowth. Easy to establish; good seeder; seed easy to handle; volunteers readily.
Lehmann lovegrass (*Eragrostis lehmanniana*), "A–68" strain. South Africa.	Reseeding of denuded desert ranges and burned-over land. Class VI.	Southern Arizona, New Mexico, and western Texas.	Drought-resistant; ability to self-seed under adverse conditions; otherwise same as weeping lovegrass.
Blue panicum (*Panicum antidotale*), "A–130" strain. Australia.	Supplements other pastures; streambank protection; flood plains and desilting areas. Classes I, II, III, VI.	East central Oklahoma and south; southern part of Pacific Southwest; southern California.	Tall; broad leaves; heavy basal growth and root system; vigorous. Good seeder; tends to shatter but seed easy to handle; requires good soil and moisture.
Crotalaria (*Crotalaria spectabilis*), "T–1099" strain. India.	Strip cropping on sandy soils subject to wind erosion; peanuts and early crotalaria alternating. Classes III, IV.	Peanut land, Texas and Oklahoma.	Early maturing; drought-resistant; no woody; unpalatable; prolific seeder; seed hard to harvest; volunteers from shattering.
Sericea lespedeza (*Lespedeza sericea*). Asia.	Planting severely eroded slopes, gullies, road embankments and cuts and depleted pastures; wildlife borders. Classes III, IV, VII.	Southeastern States; eastern Texas and Oklahoma.	Thick-growing; ability to grow on hard, badly eroded soils. Good seeder; high seed yields; easy to establish.
Kudzu (*Pueraria thunbergiana*), "Foreman" strain. Japan.	Planting eroded slopes, gullies, road cuts; depleted pastures; soil improvement. Classes III, IV, VI, VII.	Northern Arkansas; eastern Oklahoma and eastward.	Dark-green foliage; good seed producer, cold resistant. Can be grown from seed.

Improved Commercial Grasses and Legumes for Conservation Uses

Name and strain	Conservation uses	Area of use	Remarks
Smooth brome (*Bromus inermis*): Southern strains: "Achenbach" "Fischer" "Lincoln" "Martin" "Elsberry" Northern strain: "Manchar"	Alfalfa-grass and clover-grass mixtures in soil-conserving and improving rotations; improved pastures and meadows; terrace outlets; seeded waterways and ditch banks; requires good soil. Classes I, II, III, IV.	Corn Belt, eastern portion of Great Plains, irrigated lands; "Manchar" for northern portion of Western States.	Southern types are strongly rhizomatous; have early season use with leaves near base of culms; northern type carries leaves high on stem, is weakly rhizomatous, has purple seeds. Strains and types have no essential differences as to culture. *Origin:* Southern types from old field strains; Northern named strain from Manchurian introduction.
Creeping red fescue (*Festuca rubra*) "Columbia Co." strain.	Orchard cover crop; grassing terrace outlets, diversion ditches, road cuts and fills; widely adapted to poor and good soils. Classes III, VII.	New York, Michigan, West Virginia, Pennsylvania, and Northeastern States.	Strongly rhizomatous; dense growing; tough and resilient; summer active with sufficient moisture. Easy to establish; seed easy to handle. *Origin:* An old field strain.
Caley-pea (*Lathyrus hirsutus*) "Vetchfree" strain.	Soil-improving winter cover crop; pasture improvement. Classes I, II, III, IV.	Southern States............	Pure as to species. Self seeder, seed easy to handle. *Origin:* Purified from adventive stands.
Reed canarygrass (*Phalaris arundinacea*) "Ioreed" strain.	Gullies, sodded waterways and sod flumes; water lines on farm ponds; pastures on overflow creek bottoms. Classes I, IV.	Southern Iowa; northern Missouri and eastward.	Best established from sod for waterways; field plantings from seed. *Origin:* A composite of 10 selected lines supplied by Iowa Agricultural Experiment Station.
Hardinggrass (*Phalaris stenoptera*).	Grass and grass-legume pasture mixtures; supplements annual range in early winter and early summer. Classes III, IV.	Subhumid areas of California.	Pure as to species and quite uniform. Good seed producer; seed shatters and must be harvested carefully. *Origin:* Developed from old field strains and purified to eliminate annual and other *Phalaris* species.

Improved Commercial Grasses and Legumes for Conservation Uses—Continued

Name and strain	Conservation uses	Area of use	Remarks
Tall fescue (*Festuca arundinacea* "Ky. 31" and "Alta" strains).	Grass-legume mixtures under subhumid conditions or irrigation; pasture. Classes I, II, III, IV.	Pacific Coast States; Southern States; southern part of Corn Belt.	Adaptation to southern States (Ky. 31) and to northern States (Alta); good seeder; easy to handle; long season of use; wide adaptation to soil reaction. *Origin:* Developed from old field strains.
Birdsfoot trefoil (*Lotus corniculatus*).	Seeding in renovated pastures; wet areas. Classes III, VI.	Pacific Northwest; southern part of Corn Belt; Northeast.	Only broadleaf type in general use. Seed shatters; can be established in renovated bluegrass pastures. *Origin:* Developed from old field strains.

DATA ON GRASSLANDS IN THE CORN BELT AND LAKE STATES

Acreages in Pastures and Field Crops

[In thousands of acres]

State	Corn, 1945	All small grains, 1945	All tame hay, 1945	Pasture lands in 1930			
				Plowable	Woodland	Other	Total
	Acres	*Acres*	*Acres*	*Acres*	*Acres*	*Acres*	*Acres*
Illinois.............	8, 130	4, 789	2, 652	4, 092	2, 010	1, 505	7, 607
Indiana.	4, 364	3, 040	1, 765	2, 810	1, 834	1, 312	5, 956
Iowa...............	10, 706	5, 477	3, 277	4, 982	1, 969	2, 558	9, 509
Michigan...........	1, 769	2, 661	2, 859	2, 064	2, 410	1, 418	5, 892
Minnesota.	5, 926	7, 046	4, 329	2, 249	3, 656	2, 342	8, 247
Missouri............	3, 873	2, 922	3, 914	7, 018	5, 262	2, 017	14, 297
Ohio...............	3, 468	3, 341	2, 578	3, 763	1, 854	2, 421	8, 038
Wisconsin...........	2, 679	3, 232	4, 207	1, 900	4, 440	2, 483	8, 823
Total..........	40, 915	32, 508	25, 581	28, 878	23, 435	16, 056	68, 369

Numbers of Livestock on Farms in 1945

State	All cattle and calves	Swine	Sheep and lambs	Chickens	Horses and mules
	Number	*Number*	*Number*	*Number*	*Number*
Illinois..............................	3, 244	5, 709	769	25, 332	428
Indiana.............................	1, 893	3, 992	644	17, 588	265
Iowa................................	5, 528	10, 693	1, 800	38, 598	597
Michigan............................	2, 016	978	793	13, 343	258
Minnesota...........................	3, 680	3, 760	1, 322	29, 209	499
Missouri............................	3, 347	4, 000	1, 522	26, 426	691
Ohio................................	2, 283	3, 267	1, 791	23, 062	326
Wisconsin...........................	3, 947	1, 736	420	18, 096	422
Total........................	25, 938	34, 135	8, 361	191, 654	3, 486

All figures are from census figures of the U. S. Department of Commerce or the crops and market reports of the U. S. Department of Agriculture.

MINNESOTA: Recommended Hay and Pasture Mixtures and Quantity of Seed per Acre

[1] Seeding No.

Kind of seed	1	2	3	4	5	6	7	8	9	10	11
	Pounds	Pounds	Pounds	Pounds	Pounds	Pounds	Pounds	Pounds	Pounds	Pounds	Pounds
Alfalfa	8–12	5	5	6–8	6–8	2	6	6–8	5	5	
Alsike clover						2					
Medium red clover			4								2
Common biennial sweetclover			5			2			5	5	4
Smooth bromegrass		6			6–8		8	6–8		6–8	
Timothy		4			2–4	3	2			5–6	
Meadow fescue			5	6–8							6–8
Redtop						3					

[1] Seeding No.

Kind of seed	12	13	14	15	16	17	18	19	20	21
	Pounds	Pounds	Pounds	Pounds	Pounds	Pounds	Pounds	Pounds	Pounds	Pounds
Alsike clover	2	2	2	2						
Medium red clover	4	4	3–5	3–5						
Common biennial sweetclover			5	5	10–12	10–12	6	6	10–12	
White clover	1–2	1								
Kentucky bluegrass		2					1			
Smooth bromegrass	6	6		6–8		6–8	8	12		
Reed canarygrass										6–8
Timothy		2		5–6		5–6			6	

[1] Seedings Nos. 9, 10, 14, 15, 16, and 17 are used in pasture renovation. All others are seeded in short or long rotations for hay and pasturage.

MISSOURI: Recommended Hay and Pasture Mixtures and Quantity of Seed per Acre

¹Seeding No.

Kind of seed	1	2	3	4	5	6	7	8	9
	Pounds	Pounds	Pounds	Pounds	Pounds	Pounds	Pounds	Pounds	Pounds
Alfalfa	12-20								
Alsike clover				3-5	3-5	3-5			
Medium red clover							8		
Crimson clover								12-15	
Korean lespedeza									10
Kentucky bluegrass		10	10						10
Smooth bromegrass									
Reed canarygrass				10					
Redtop					5	10			
Timothy		5			5		5-10		5

¹Seeding No.

Kind of seed	10	11	12	13	14	15	16	17
	Pounds	Pounds	Pounds	Pounds	Pounds	Pounds	Pounds	Pounds
Korean lespedeza	10	10	10	10	10-25	10		
Common biennial sweetclover							10	12-25
Canada bluegrass		1-5	1-3					
Kentucky bluegrass		10-15						
Orchardgrass	10-14		10				10	
Redtop	1-5							
Tall fescue				10-15				
Timothy						5-10	5	

¹ Seedings Nos. 1, 2, 3, 7, 8, 14, 15, and 17 are used in rotations for hay and pasture. All others are used for establishing permanent pastures. Seedings Nos. 1, 2, 3, 7, 9, 16, and 17 are grown under conditions of high soil fertility; all others are used on soils of moderate or low fertility. Seedings Nos. 4, 5, and 6 are recommended for use on wet, poorly drained soils.

IOWA: Recommended Hay and Pasture Mixtures and Quantity of Seed per Acre[1]

Kind of seed	[2] Seeding No.											
	1	2	3	4	5	6	7	8	9	10	11	12
	Pounds	Pounds	Pounds	Pounds	Pounds	Pounds	Pounds	Pounds	Pounds	Pounds	Pounds	Pounds
Alfalfa	12–15	10–12	6–8	5	3	4	3	4				
Alsike clover					1	2						
Medium red clover				3	2	4	4		8–10	6–8	2–3	1
Common biennial sweetclover					4			5			5–6	3
Smooth bromegrass		4–6	8–10	10			8	10				4
Timothy						5	4			6	4	6

Kind of seed	[2] Seeding No.											
	13	14	15	16	17	18	19	20	21	22	23	24
	Pounds	Pounds	Pounds	Pounds	Pounds	Pounds	Pounds	Pounds	Pounds	Pounds	Pounds	Pounds
Alfalfa	1											
Alsike clover		2	2	2	2			3				
Medium red clover	3	4	6	6	3	3	3					
Common biennial sweetclover	4				5	7	5		8			
Lespedeza										20		
Kentucky bluegrass				4								
Smooth bromegrass		10							10			
Reed canarygrass								3				
Timothy	6		6	5		5	5	3			6–8	6
Redtop								3				4

[1] On infertile acid soils in southern Iowa, Korean lespedeza may be added to advantage to commonly used mixtures at the rate of 5 to 10 pounds per acre.

[2] Seedings Nos. 8, 16, 20, 23, and 24 are used for establishing areas to be maintained permanently in hay or pasturage. All other mixtures are seeded in rotations for hay and pasturage.

WISCONSIN: Recommended Hay and Pasture Mixtures and Quantity of Seed per Acre

Kind of seed	¹Seeding No.								
	1	2	3	4	5	6	7	8	9
	Pounds	Pounds	Pounds	Pounds	Pounds	Pounds	Pounds	Pounds	Pounds
Alfalfa	6–8	8–10	6–8	6–8					
Alsike clover					3	3	2	2	5
Medium red clover	3–4		3–4		5	5			
Ladino clover	½–1	½–1					1–2	1–2	
Smooth bromegrass				6–8		6		6	
Timothy	6–8	6–8	3–4		4		4		4

Kind of seed	¹Seeding No.							
	10	11	12	13	14	15	16	17
	Pounds	Pounds	Pounds	Pounds	Pounds	Pounds	Pounds	Pounds
Alsike clover	2	3	3					
Medium red clover		3	3	4	4	6	1–2	
Ladino clover				2	2			
White clover		2	2					
Common biennial sweetclovers								10–15
Smooth bromegrass				6–8	3–4			
Timothy	2	5	5			8	2	
Kentucky bluegrass	6	7	7					
Reed canarygrass							4	
Redtop		2	2					

¹ Seedings Nos. 1, 2, 3, 4, 13, 14, and 15 are used in rotations or renovations to provide hay and pasturage on well-drained, fertile upland soils; seeding No. 4 is used in rotations on fertile sandy soils, and seedings Nos. 5, 6, 7, 8, 9, 10, and 16 are grown in rotations on poorly drained soils. Seedings Nos. 11 and 12 are used in establishing permanent pastures.

OHIO: Recommended Hay and Pasture Mixtures and Quantity of Seed per Acre

[1][2] Seeding No.

Kind of seed	1	2	3	4	5	6	7	8	9	10
	Pounds	Pounds	Pounds	Pounds	Pounds	Pounds	Pounds	Pounds	Pounds	Pounds
Alfalfa	7	5	4			10	10	7	10	7
Alsike clover			2							
Korean lespedeza					4					
Mammoth red clover								3		3
Medium red clover	3	5	4	6–8						
Common biennial sweetclover										
Smooth bromegrass					2–4				5–10	5–10
Orchardgrass							6	6		
Redtop										
Perennial or domestic ryegrass										
Domestic ryegrass						3–6				
Timothy	3–6	3–6	3–6	3–6	2–4	3–6				

[1][2] Seeding No.

Kind of seed	11	12	13	14	15	16	17	18	19
	Pounds	Pounds	Pounds	Pounds	Pounds	Pounds	Pounds	Pounds	Pounds
Alfalfa	10–12								
Alsike clover									
Korean lespedeza				4–6			20–30		
Mammoth red clover			8–10						
Medium red clover		8–10							
Common biennial sweetclover					10–12	10			15
Smooth bromegrass									
Orchardgrass						6			

Redtop . . . .
Perennial or domestic ryegrass . . . .
Domestic ryegrass 20
Timothy 8

¹ 1½ to 2 pounds of Ladino clover may be added to seedings Nos. 1 to 10, inclusive, or alsike clover may be replaced in seedings 3 and 5 with 1 to 2 pounds of Ladino clover.

² Mixtures or seedings primarily for permanent pasture:
a. Add 3 to 5 pounds of Kentucky bluegrass and ½ to 1 pound each of Ladino and Louisiana white clover to any hay mixture commonly grown.
b. Medium red clover 4 or alfalfa 5, or a mixture of the two, alsike clover 0 to 2, Louisiana white clover ½ to 1, Ladino clover ½ to 1, redtop 2 to 4 (on wet land only), timothy 3 to 6 and Kentucky bluegrass 4 to 6.
c. Korean lespedeza 15, orchardgrass 6.
d. Korean lespedeza 6 to 12.
e. Ladino and Louisiana white clovers ½ to 1 each.
f. Reed canarygrass 5 to 10.

MICHIGAN: Recommended Hay and Pasture Mixtures and Quantity of Seed per Acre

Kind of seed	¹Seeding No.										
	1	2	3	4	5	6	7	8	9	10	11
	Pounds	Pounds	Pounds	Pounds	Pounds	Pounds	Pounds	Pounds	Pounds	Pounds	Pounds
Alfalfa	8	8	8	5							
Alsike clover				2	2						
Medium red clover				3	7						
Common biennial sweetclover						12–15	12	10			
Kentucky bluegrass		5								15	
Smooth bromegrass											
Reed canarygrass											
Timothy			2	1	2				5		
Orchardgrass							5		2		
Chewings fescue											15
Domestic ryegrass								10			

¹ Seeding No. 8 is seeded in the last cultivation of corn and is intended primarily for green manure. Seedings Nos. 10 and 11 are used to establish permanent cover in orchards. All others are seeded in rotations for hay and pasturage.

INDIANA: Recommended Hay and Pasture Mixtures and Quantity of Seed per Acre

[1] Seeding No.

Kind of seed	1	2	3	4	5	6	7	8	9	10	11	12
	Pounds	Pounds	Pounds	Pounds	Pounds	Pounds	Pounds	Pounds	Pounds	Pounds	Pounds	Pounds
Alfalfa	8–12	8	8	8								
Alsike clover					1–2	4	4			2	2	2
Korean lespedeza						1–2	5				3–5	4–8
Medium red clover					4	3	4			6	6	4
Mammoth red clover			4	5–8		4			8–10			
Smooth bromegrass								8–10				
Timothy		1–6	1–3		2–3	2–3	2–3			2–5	2–5	2–5
Domestic ryegrass												

[1] Seeding No.

Kind of seed	13	14	15	16	[2]17	[2]18	[2]19	20	21	22	23	24
	Pounds	Pounds	Pounds	Pounds	Pounds	Pounds	Pounds	Pounds	Pounds	Pounds	Pounds	Pounds
Alfalfa	4–6											
Alsike clover		4–6										
Korean lespedeza					8–10	8–10	8–10	10–12	12–15	10–20		
Common biennial sweetclover				10–12								
White clover												
Ladino clover			1–1½									
Reed canarygrass												5–10
Meadow fescue							6					
Orchardgrass						6			6			
Redtop		2–4						3–5				
Timothy		1–2			3–5							
Domestic ryegrass											15–30	

[1] Ladino clover may be added to seedings Nos. 1 to 21 inclusive at the rate of ¼ pound of seed per acre if intended primarily for hay and ½ pound where intended primarily for pasture.

Seedings Nos. 1, 2, 3, and 4 are for highly productive soils having good drainage; 5, 6, 7, 8, and 9 for soils having fair to good drainage and productivity; 10 and 11 for soils having fair to good drainage but with a pH of 5.4 or less; 12 for soils having fair drainage and productivity and a pH of 5 to 5.4; 13 and 14, for soils having poor drainage and a pH of 5 to 5.4; 20 and 21 for well drained soils of low productivity; 22 for unlimed droughty soils, and 24 wet poorly drained soils on which water may stand for a portion of the year.

Seedings Nos. 14, 20, 21, 22, and 24 may be continued as permanent pasture. The addition of 3 to 5 pounds of Kentucky bluegrass and ½ pound of Ladino clover to seedings numbered 2, 3, 4, 5, 6, 7, 10, 11, and 12 make them suitable for permanent pasture.

[2] 4 pounds of Korean lespedeza should be added to these mixtures in the northern one-third of the State.

Average Annual Production and Consumption in Thousands of Pounds of Certain Forage Grass and Legume Seeds in 1940–42

State	Consumption					Production				
	Red clover	Alsike clover	Sweet-clover	Alfalfa	Timothy	Red clover	Alsike clover	Sweet-clover	Alfalfa	Timothy
	1,000 pounds	1,000 pounds	1,000 pounds	1,000 pounds	1,000 pounds	1,000 pounds	1,000 pounds	1,000 pounds	1,000 pounds	1,000 pounds
Illinois	11,765	1,753	10,403	3,918	5,652	12,279	1,300	3,675	....	5,343
Indiana	7,304	999	2,780	2,871	3,320	12,259	578	901	717	2,863
Iowa	11,465	1,779	8,529	6,156	10,038	8,194	459	4,230	1,019	25,500
Michigan	5,579	949	1,384	5,666	1,966	7,700	1,093	1,303	3,709	....
Minnesota	2,778	1,329	5,176	3,954	2,227	3,374	2,746	19,544	5,597	2,970
Missouri	3,750	266	1,943	1,126	3,153	5,473	134	2,048	....	6,860
Ohio	8,045	....	2,206	3,995	4,704	11,127	....	1,274	1,174	7,928
Wisconsin	7,524	1,634	2,081	8,333	6,127	8,763	1,787	634	1,848	1,796
United States	77,952	14,712	49,771	67,722	52,674	86,415	16,380	49,293	65,733	53,750

ILLINOIS: Recommended Hay and Pasture Mixtures and Quantity of Seed per Acre

Kind of seed	[1] Seeding No.											
	1	2	3	4	5	6	7	8	9	10	11	12
	Pounds	Pounds	Pounds	Pounds	Pounds	Pounds	Pounds	Pounds	Pounds	Pounds	Pounds	Pounds
Alfalfa	6	8	2	8–10	3	4	4	4	2	4		1
Alsike clover	2		2						1			
Lespedeza						5						
Ladino clover					2			4	2	1–2	4	
Medium red clover	6		2		4	4	4	4			6	2
Common biennial sweetclover												
White clover			2						1			1
Kentucky bluegrass			4						5			5
Smooth bromegrass			4	7–8			8	4		7		5
Reed canarygrass												
Meadow fescue												
Redtop			3			4			4			
Timothy		6	3			5	3		4	5	4	4
Orchardgrass				4	4							

Kind of seed	[1] Seeding No.											
	13	14	15	16	17	18	19	20	21	22	23	24
	Pounds	Pounds	Pounds	Pounds	Pounds	Pounds	Pounds	Pounds	Pounds	Pounds	Pounds	Pounds
Alfalfa	2							2				
Alsike clover		4	4									
Lespedeza					5	3	2	2	3	12	8	1
Ladino clover									5			
Medium red clover	2	4	2	6–8	4							
Common biennial sweetclover	2				4				4	3		
White clover							1					
Kentucky bluegrass			5				4					

Smooth bromegrass	....	....	....	5	....	....	....	....
Reed canarygrass	....	....	....	....	....	....	....	....
Meadow fescue	....	....	....	....	....	8	2	2
Redtop	2	3	4	5	3	....	....	2
Timothy	2	4	5	4–8	5	3	....	4
Orchardgrass	6	4	6–8	5	....	5	....	....

¹ Seedings Nos. 7, 8, 9, 10, 12, 15, 18, 19, 20, and 21 are used to establish permanent pastures. The remaining mixtures are seeded in rotations for hay and pasturage.

Recommendations Relative to the Use of Lime, Phosphate, and Potash for (a) Establishing New Seedings and (b) Maintaining the Production of areas Utilized for Hay, Grass Silage, and Rotation and Permanent Pastures in the Corn Belt and Lake States Region

State	Lime per acre	Phosphate and potash per acre—	
		For establishment	For maintenance following establishment
	Tons	*Pounds*	*Pounds*
Illinois	2–4	100 to 500 of 0–14–7, 0–12–12, 0–14–14, 0–20–20, or 0–20–0. 500 to 2,000 of raw rock phosphate may be substituted for the 0–20–0.	100 to 200 of 0–20–0 and 100 to 300 of 0–0–60 (where needed). Every 3 years.
Indiana	1–5	General: 200 to 400 of 0–14–7, 0–10–20, 0–12–12, 2–12–6, 3–12–12, 2–18–9, or 3–9–18. Light sands: 300 of 0–9–27, 0–10–20, 0–12–12, 3–12–12, or 3–9–18. Black sands: 300 of 0–10–20 or 0–9–27.	General: 400 of 0–20–0 or 400 to 600 of 0–14–7. Light sands: 400 to 600 of 0–14–7. Black sands: 400 of 0–10–20. Every 3 to 4 years.
Iowa	2–4	Typical well-drained soils excepting those high in lime and sandy soils: 200 to 300 of 0–20–0 or 5–20–0. High lime soils: 200 to 300 of 0–20–20. Slowly drained and sandy soils: 200 to 300 of 0–20–10 or 0–20–20. 250 to 350 of 4–16–8.	Typical well-drained soils excepting those high in lime and sandy soils: 300 of 0–20–0 (every 2 to 3 years). High lime soils: 300 of 0–20–20 (every 2 to 3 years). Slowly drained and sandy soils: 300 of 0–20–10 or 0–20–20 (every 2 to 3 years).
Michigan	1–3	Acid muck: 200 to 350 of 0–9–27 or 3–9–18+2½ $CuSO_4$. Alkaline: 300 to 350 of 0–9–27 or 3–9–18+15 $MnSO_4$. Loams: 300 of 0–20–0, 0–14–7, or 0–20–10. Sands: 300 of 0–12–12 or 0–10–20.	Acid muck: 100 to 150 of 0–9–27+5 $CuSO_4$. Alkaline: 100 to 150 of 0–9–27. Loams: 200 to 300 of 0–20–0, 0–14–7, or 0–20–10. Sands: 200 to 300 of 0–12–12, 0–20–20, or 0–10–20. Annually or every 2 years.

Recommendations Relative to the Use of Lime, Phosphate, and Potash for (a) Establishing New Seedings and (b) Maintaining the Production of areas Utilized for Hay, Grass Silage, and Rotation and Permanent Pastures in the Corn Belt and Lake States Region—Continued

State	Lime per acre	Phosphate and potash per acre—	
		For establishment	For maintenance following establishment
	Tons	*Pounds*	*Pounds*
Minnesota	1–3	General: 250 of 0–20–0, 0–20–10, or 0–20–20; 300 of 0–16–8; 350 of 0–14–7 or 0–12–12. Peat: 350 of 0–10–20.	General: 300 of 0–20–0, 0–20–10, or 0–20–20; 350 of 0–14–7 or 0–12–12; 150 of 0–47–0. Peat: 250 of 0–10–20 or 200 of 0–12–24. Every 3 to 4 years.
Missouri	1½–3	No manure: 200 to 500 of 0–20–10, or 0–20–20; 300 to 500 of 0–14–7 or 0–12–12; 150 of 3–18–9, 200 of 2–12–6, 3–12–12, 4–12–4, 4–12–8, 4–16–4, or 5–10–10; 250 of 8–8–8. Manured: 200 to 300 of 0–20–10, 0–20–20, 0–14–7, or 0–12–12.	No manure: 300 of 0–20–10 or 400 of 0–14–7. Manured: 300 to 500 of 0–20–0 or 150 to 200 of 0–45–0. Biennially with alfalfa or every 3 to 5 years with other crops; 1,000 of raw rock phosphate every 4 to 8 years.
Ohio	According to need	No manure: Sands: 400 of 3–12–12, or 4–12–8; Loams: 350 of 0–12–12, 2–12–6, or 3–12–12; Muck: 350 of 0–10–20, or 3–9–18. Manured: Sands: 350 of 0–14–7, 2–12–6, or 4–12–8; Loams: 300 of 0–12–12 or 0–14–7; Muck: 300 of 0–12–12 or 0–10–20.	No manure: Sands: 500 of 0–14–7. Loams: 400 of 0–14–7. Muck: 400 of 0–12–12. Manured: Sands: 400 of 0–20–0. Loams: 300 of 0–20–10. Muck: 400 of 0–14–7. Every 4 years.
Wisconsin	1–5	Mucks and peats: 250 to 500 of 0–20–20, 0–10–20, or 0–9–27. Silts and clay loams: 200 to 500 of 0–20–0, 0–20–20, or 3–12–12. Sands and sandy loams: 200 to 500 of 3–12–12, 3–9–18, or 0–9–27.	Mucks and peats: 200 to 500 of 0–20–20, 0–10–20, or 0–9–27. Silt and clay loams: 200 to 500 of 0–20–10, 0–20–20, or 0–10–20. Sands and sandy loams: 200 to 500 of 0–20–20, 0–10–20, or 0–9–27. Every 3 or 4 years.

Important Insects Injurious to Forage Grasses and Legumes in the Lake States and Corn Belt

Common Name	Scientific name	Principal host plants	Plant parts injured	Principal practical controls
Lesser clover weevil	Hypera nigrirostris (F.)	Clovers, legumes	Foliage	Crop rotation, burning, insecticides.
Clover-leaf weevil	Hypera punctata (F.)	Clovers, alfalfa	do.	Do.
Sweetclover weevil	Sitonia cylindricollis (Fahr.)	Sweetclover	do.	Crop rotation, insecticides.
Clover-root curculio	Sitonia hispidula (F.)	Clovers, alfalfa	Root	Do.
Blister beetles	Epicauta sp.	Legumes, many plants	Foliage	Insecticides.
White grub	Phyllophaga fusca (Froh.)	Grasses	Underground parts	Crop rotation, tillage, renovation.
Do.	Phyllophaga hirticula (Knoch.)	do.	do.	Do.
Do.	Phyllophaga rugosa (Melsh.)	do.	do.	Do.
Do.	Phyllophaga tristis (Fab.)	do.	do.	Do.
Clover-root borer	Hylastinus obscurus (Marsh.)	Clovers	Root	Crop rotation, tillage.
Clover-seed midge	Dasyneura leguminicola (Lint.)	do.	Seed	Time of cutting.
Alfalfa plant bug	Adelphocoris lineolatus (Gocze)	Legumes, alfalfa	do.	Burning stubble, insecticides.
Tarnished plant bug	Lygus oblineatus (Say)	do.	do.	Do.
Pea aphid	Macrosiphum pisi (Kltb.)	Legumes, especially peas	Systematic	Mechanical drags, insecticides.
Meadow spittle bug	Philaenus leucophthalmus (L.)	Alfalfa, many plants	do.	Burning stubble, insecticides.
Potato leafhopper	Empoasca fabae (Harr.)	Legumes, many plants	do.	Time of cutting, insecticides.
Clover seed chalcid	Bruchophagus gibbus (Boh.)	Clovers, alfalfa	Seed	Time of cutting, clean culture.
Sod webworms	Crambus sp.	Grasses	Foliage	Tillage.
Army worm	Cirphis unipuncta (Haw.)	Grasses, legumes	do.	Poison-bran bait, clean culture.
Army cutworm	Chorizagrostis auxiliaris (Grote)	Legumes, many plants	do.	Do.
Corn earworm	Heliothis armigera (Hbn.)	Corn, many plants	do.	Do.
Fall webworm	Laphygma frugiperda (A. & S.)	Grasses, many plants	do.	Do.
Variegated cutworm	Peridroma margaritosa (Haw.)	Many plants	do.	Do.
Green clover worm	Plathypena scabra (F.)	Clovers, alfalfa	do.	Time of cutting, insecticides.
Clover head caterpillar	Grapholitha interstinctana (Clem.)	Clovers	Seed	Time of cutting.
Clear-winged grasshopper	Camnula pellucida (Scudd.)	Grasses, legumes	Foliage	Poison-bran bait, tillage.
Two-striped grasshopper	Melanoplus bivittatus (Say)	Legumes, many plants	do.	Do
Red-legged grasshopper	Melanoplus femur - rubrum (Deg.)	Alfalfa, many plants	do.	Do.
Lesser migratory grasshopper	Melanoplus mexicanus mexicanus (Sauss.)	Legumes, many plants	do.	Do.

Chart of Important Diseases of Alfalfa, the Clovers, and Sweetclovers in the Lake States and Corn Belt, With the Causal Agent in Each Plant Listed Under the More Common Suspect

Disease	Alfalfa	Medium red clover	White, alsike, and other perennial clovers	Sweetclover
Mosaic	Several viruses	Several viruses	Several viruses	Several viruses.
Bacterial wilt	Corynebacterium insidiosum	None	None	None.
Pythium blight	Pythium debaryanum and other species	Same	Same	Same.
Phytophthora root rot	None	None	None	Phytophthora cactorum.
Downy mildew	Peronospora trifoliorum	...do	...do	Rare.
Powdery mildew	Rare	Erysiphe poligoni	Rare	Do.
Spring blackstem	Ascochyta imperfecta	Phoma trifolii	Limited	Mycosphaerella lethalis.
Summer blackstem	Cercospora zebrina	Less common	Less common excepting in southern portion.	Mycosphaerella davisii.
Stem hypertrophy	None	None	None	Ascochyta caulicola.
Leaf spot and root rot	Leptosphaeria pratensis	...do	Causes damage in southern portion.	Same.
Zonate leaf spot	Pleospora herbarium	Stemphylium sarcinaeforme	Same	Uncommon.
Sooty blotch	None	Uncommon	Cymadothea trifolii	None.
Pseudoplea leaf spot	Uncommon	...do	Pseudoplea trifolii	Uncommon.
Common leaf spot	Pseudopeziza medicaginis	Pseudopeziza trifolii	Same	Do.
Yellow leaf spot	Pyrenopeziza medicaginis	None	None	None.
Sclerotinia root rot	Same	Sclerotinia trifoliorum	Same	Same.
Fusarian cylindrocarpon root rots	Fusarian and Cylindrocarpon species	Same	...do	Do.
Southern anthracnose	Uncommon	Colletotrichum trifolii	...do	Rare.
Northern anthracnose	Rare	Kabatiella caulivora	Uncommon	None.
Rusts	Uromyces striatus medicaginis	Uromyces trifolii	Same	Rare.
Rhizoctonia root rot	Rhizoctonia sp	Uncommon	Uncommon	Do.

PASTURE AND FORAGE CROPS RECOMMENDED FOR THE SOUTHERN STATES

VIRGINIA: Recommended Pasture and Forage Crops
{Rate per acre}

Crop	Fertilization	
	Initial	Maintenance
Alfalfa...............	1,000-1,200 pounds 2–12–12 or 0–12–12.	600–800 pounds 0–12–12 or 2–12–12.
Clovers (alone).........	400–500 pounds 0–14–7 or 0–12–12.	
Grass hays.............	300–400 pounds 4–12–4 or 3–12–6.	
Lespedeza.............	300–400 pounds 0–14–7 or 0–12–12.	
Ladino clover..........	600–800 pounds 0–14–7, 0–12–12, or 2–12–12.	
Timothy..............	300–400 pounds 4–12–4 or 3–12–6.	
Pasture (new).........	500–800 pounds 4–12–4, 3–12–6, 0–14–7, or 0–20–0.	
Pasture (temporary).....	500–800 pounds 4–12–4 or 0–14–7.	

Data from H. L. Dunton.

SOUTH CAROLINA: Recommended Pasture and Forage Crops
{Rate per acre}

Crops or mixtures	Use	Fertilizer (initial and maintenance)
Grain sorghum (Caprock, Plainsman, and Martin's).	Grain or forage..	500 pounds 4–10–6 and 16 to 32 pounds N as side application.
Alfalfa (common)...........	Hay...........	500 pounds 3–12–12 plus 15 to 25 pounds borax and 500 pounds 0–12–12 annually.
Soybeans (C. N. S., Palmetto).	.....do.........	400 pounds 4–10–6.
Lespedeza (Kobe).............	.....do.........	Responds to phosphate and potash after preceding crop.
Bermuda-grass and Ladino clover or white clover.	Pasture.........	500 pounds 3–12–12, 500 pounds superphosphate, and 200 pounds muriate of potash annually.
Bermuda and sub clover......	.....do.........	(Same as for Ladino and white.)
Fescue (Alta or Ky. 31)......	.....do.........	300 to 500 pounds 4–10–6 with 24 to 32 pounds N as top dressing in spring.
Ryegrass and crimson clover..	.....do.........	500 pounds 3–12–12 and 16 to 32 pounds N as top dressing in spring.
Corn.....................	Silage.........	500 pounds 4–10–6 and 32 to 48 pounds N as side dressing.
Corn and soybeans (Biloxi)...	.....do.........	500 pounds 4–10–6 and 16 to 32 pounds N as side-dressing.
Oats.....................	.....do	400 to 600 pounds 4–12–4 or 3–12–6 and 16 to 32 pounds N as top dressing.

Data from W. K. Paden.

GEORGIA: Recommended Pasture and Forage Crops
[Rate per acre]
PIEDMONT AND MOUNTAINS

Crop and variety	Uses	Fertilizer per acre
Soybeans (Gatan, Volstate, Otootan).	Hay, grazing, silage....	350 pounds 4–8–6.
Sorghum (Hegari, Texas seeded ribbon).	Silage, fodder.........	350 pounds 4–8–6 plus 24 pounds nitrogen top dressing.
Alfalfa (Kansas common)....	Hay, grazing, silage....	Lime as needed—½ to 3 tons, and 96 pounds P_2O_5 before seeding; 100 pounds K_2O and 20 pounds borax after first cutting.
Annual lespedeza (Kobe, Korean).	Hay, grazing, soil improvement.	1 ton of lime; P and K residual from grain or 60 pounds P_2O_5 with K depending on soil.
Lespedeza, sericea............	....do.............	1 ton of lime; 60 pounds P_2O_5.
Kudzu.....................	....do.............	1 ton of lime; 60 pounds P_2O_5.
Pearlmillet................	Grazing.............	350 pounds 6–8–6 plus 32 pounds nitrogen top dressing.
Sudangrass (Tift, Sweet)......	Grazing, hay.........	350 pounds 6–8–6 plus 32 pounds nitrogen top dressing.
Johnsongrass with a legume..	....do.............	1 ton of lime; 60 pounds P_2O_5 for the associated legume.
Cowpeas (Iron, Groit, Clay, New Era).	Hay, soil improvement..	1 ton of lime; 60 pounds P_2O_5.
Oats, ryegrass, crimson clover. (Red rust-proof type of oats).	Fall and winter pasture.	1 ton of lime; 400 pounds 6–8–6; 48 pounds nitrogen top dressing.
Bermuda-grass, crimson clover.	Late winter and summer pasture.	1½ tons lime; 72 pounds P_2O_5; K and boron where soil requires.
Dallisgrass-Ladino clover, Bermuda-grass, and white clover.	Permanent pasture.....	2 tons of lime; 90 to 140 pounds P_2O_5; K where needed.
Bluegrass-orchardgrass, white or Ladino clover.	....do.............	Do.

COASTAL PLAIN

Cattail millet................	Grazing.............	
Oats and vetch..............	....do.............	500 pounds 4–8–6.
Abruzzi rye................	....do.............	Do.
Bermuda-grass and/or lespedeza, hop and crimson clover (upland pasture).	....do.............	400–600 pounds 4–8–6 every 2–3 years; top-dress with nitrogen annually.
Carpetgrass, Dallisgrass, lespedeza, and white clover (lowland pasture).	....do.............	Do.
Kudzu.....................	Hay.............	
Coastal Bermuda-grass.......	....do.............	
Peanuts...................	....do.............	

Data from O. E. Sell and J. L. Stephens.

NORTH CAROLINA: Recommended Pasture and Forage Crops
[Rate per acre]

| Crop or mixture | Use | Fertilization [1] | |
		Initial	Maintenance
Alfalfa.............	Hay...........	700–1,000 pounds 2–12–12; 35 pounds borax.	500 pounds 0–9–27 or 0–12–12; borax if needed.
Lespedeza..........	Hay and grazing..	200 pounds 0–12–12 (Coastal Plain); 200 pounds 0–14–7 (Piedmont and Mountains).	Annually.
Soybeans...........	Hay and grazing..	400 pounds 0–10–20...	Do.
Cowpeas...........	Hay...............	.....do.............	Do.
Kudzu.............	Grazing and hay..	300 pounds 0–14–7....	2-year intervals.
Sericea lespedeza.....	Hay and grazing..	....do.............	Do.
Meadow (grasses and legumes).	Hay and grazing..	.....do.............	Do.
Permanent pasture.... Piedmont and Mountains. Orchardgrass. White clover. Lespedeza. Orchardgrass. Redtop. White clover. Lespedeza. Coastal Plain. Dallisgrass. Orchardgrass. White clover. Lespedeza. Dallisgrass. Redtop. White clover. Lespedeza.	Grazing..........	650 pounds 0–12–12...	200 pounds 0–12–12.
Rotational pasture.... Orchardgrass. Ladino clover. Tall fescue. Ladino clover.	Grazing..........	800 pounds 2–12–12...	500 pounds 0–12–12.
Small grain..........	Grazing..........	300 pounds 6–8–6 (Coastal Plain); 300 pounds 5–10–5 (Piedmont and Mountains); 16–32 pounds nitrogen top dressing.	Annually.
Small grain and crimson clover.	.....do............	.....do.............	Do.
Ryegrass and crimson clover.	.....do............	.....do.............	Do.
Small grain and vetch.	Hay.............	300 pounds 6–8–6 (Coastal Plain); 300 pounds 5–10–5 (Piedmont and Mountains)	Do.

[1] Lime is necessary for all legumes. Amount to be determined by soil test.

Data from R. L. Lovvorn.

LOUISIANA: Recommended Pasture and Forage Crops

[Rate per acre]

Crops and mixtures	Use	Fertilization
Alfalfa....................	Hay...............	None or only phosphates in bottom areas.
Soybeans..................	.....do.............	None in bottoms; 400 pounds an acre 3–12–12 or 0–14–7 in terrace and coastal plain areas.
Lespedeza (Kobe and common).	.....do.............	400 pounds an acre 3–12–12 in terrace, prairie, and coastal plain areas.
Lespedeza (Korean).........	.....do.............	None in bottom areas.
Alyceclover................	.....do.............	None in bottoms; 400 pounds an acre 3–12–12 or 0–14–7 in terrace and prairie areas.
Red clover.................	.....do.............	None in bottom areas; lime and 400 pounds an acre 3–12–12 or 9–14–7 in terrace and prairie areas.
Johnsongrass and Bermuda-grass are cut for hay in bottom lands where they have dominated.		
Vaseygrass and bluestems are cut for hay on native meadows.		
Corn....................	Silage.............	60 pounds an acre of nitrogen in bottom areas; 400 pounds an acre 6–8–8 under and 32 pounds nitrogen as side dressing in other areas.
Sorghums (sweet)..........	.....do.............	48 pounds an acre of nitrogen in bottoms; 600 pounds an acre 8–8–8 or 6–8–8 in other areas.
White clover, Bermuda-grass and Dallisgrass.	.....do.............	None in bottom areas.
Oats....................	Temporary pasture..	32 pounds of nitrogen an acre in bottom areas; 300 pounds 6–8–8 or 4–8–8 at planting and 32 pounds of nitrogen as top dressing in terrace, prairie, and coastal plain areas.
Sudangrass................	.....do.............	Same as for oats pasture.
Ryegrass.................	.....do.............	Do.
Lespedeza (common).......	.....do.............	400 pounds an acre 3–12–12 or 0–14–7 in terrace, prairie, and coastal plain areas.
Alyceclover................	.....do.............	None in bottom areas and same as lespedeza in other areas.
Oats and vetch............	.....do.............	Same as for oats pasture.
Dallisgrass and white clover.	.....do.............	None in bottom areas; 400 to 600 pounds of 3–12–12 and lime in other areas.
Bermuda-grass and white clover.	.....do.............	None in bottom areas.
Dallisgrass, white clover, and lespedeza.	.....do.............	Lime and 400 to 600 pounds an acre of 3–12–12 or 4–12–8 in terrace, prairie, and coastal plain areas; 200 to 300 pounds of 0–12–12 or 0–14–7 for second and later applications.
Bermuda-grass, carpet-grass, white or hop clover, and lespedeza.	.....do.............	Same as above for terrace and coastal plain areas.

Data from M. B. Sturgis.

FLORIDA: Recommended Pasture and Forage Crops
[Rate per acre]

Crop	Use	Fertilization		Lime
		Initial	Maintenance	
Bahiagrass (common or Pensacola)	Pasture	200–500 pounds 6–6–6	500 pounds 6–6–6	1 ton if strongly acid.
Bahiagrass and lespedeza (common and Kobe)	do	200–400 pounds 0–10–10	400 pounds 0–10–10	1 ton if acid.
Bahiagrass and white clover	do	500 pounds 0–10–10	500 pounds 0–10–10	1 to 2 tons.
Pangolagrass	Pasture and/or hay	500 pounds 6–6–6	500 pounds 6–6–6	1 ton if acid.
Pangolagrass and lespedeza (common and Kobe)	do	400 pounds 0–10–10	400 pounds 0–10–10	1 ton.
Pangolagrass and white clover	do	500 pounds 0–10–10	500 pounds 0–10–10	1 to 2 tons.
Bermuda-grass (Coastal or Suwannee)	do	500 pounds 6–6–6	500 pounds 6–6–6	Do.
Bermuda-grass and Lespedeza (common and Kobe)	do	400 pounds 0–10–10	400 pounds 0–10–10	Do.
Bermuda-grass and white clover	do	500 pounds 0–10–10	500 pounds 0–10–10	Do.
Carpetgrass	Pasture	200–500 pounds 6–6–6	500 pounds 6–6–6	1 ton if strongly acid.
Carpetgrass and lespedeza (common and Kobe)	Pasture and/or hay	200–400 pounds 0–10–10	400 pounds 0–10–10	1 to 2 tons.
Carpetgrass and white clover	do	500 pounds 0–10–10	500 pounds 0–10–10	2 tons.
Bahia, Pangola, Bermuda, and carpet grasses with black medic and/or sweetclover (Hubam)	do	do	do	Do.
Crimson clover	Pasture or hay	300 pounds 5–7–5	300 pounds 0–10–10	1 ton if acid.
Crimson clover and oats or rye	Pasture and/or hay	200–500 pounds 5–7–5	30 pounds nitrogen	Do.
Oats or rye	do	0–200 pounds 0–10–10	0–200 pounds 0–10–10	Do.
Hairy indigo	do	400 pounds 0–10–10	400 pounds 0–10–10	Do.
Kudzu	do	400–1,000 pounds 5–7–5	30–60 pounds nitrogen	Do.
Napiergrass	Pasture and/or silage	500–1,000 pounds 5–7–5	do	
Sugarcane	do		do	
Sweet sorghum	Silage	500 pounds 5–7–5	30 pounds nitrogen	
Grain sorghum	Pasture or grain	do	do	

Data from G. B. Killinger.

KENTUCKY: Recommended Pasture and Forage Crops

[Rate per acre]

Crop [1]	Use	Fertilization per acre [2]	
		Initial	Maintenance
Alfalfa, timothy, orchardgrass, or redtop.	Hay, silage	3–4 tons limestone; 500–1,000 pounds 0–20–0.	After 5 years, 500 pounds 0–20–0.
Alfalfa, red clover, timothy, orchardgrass, or redtop, Korean lespedeza.	....do	....do... 0–20–0.	Do.
Red clover, timothy, or orchardgrass, or redtop, Korean lespedeza.	....do	2 tons limestone; 250–500 pounds 0–20–0.	
Orchardgrass or redtop, Korean lespedeza.	Hay or pasture	2 tons limestone; 250–500 pounds 0–20–0.	300–500 pounds 0–20–0 biennially.
Kentucky bluegrass, red clover, white clover.	Permanent pasture	2 tons limestone; 500–1,000 pounds 0–20–0.	1 ton limestone each 10 years; 200–300 pounds 0–20–0 biennially.
Kentucky bluegrass, red clover, Korean lespedeza.	....do	....do...	Do.
Redtop, Canada bluegrass, Korean lespedeza, hop clover.	....do	....do...	Do.
Kentucky 31 fescue, Ladino clover, or white clover.	....do	....do...	Do.
Alfalfa or biennial sweetclover, or Ladino clover, Korean lespedeza, orchardgrass.	....do	3–4 tons limestone; 500–1,000 pounds 0–20–0.	1 ton limestone each 10 years; 300 pounds 0–20–0 biennially.
Sudangrass	Emergency and supplemental pasture.	1 ton limestone; 500 pounds 6–8–6....	
Winter small grain alone or with crimson clover.	Winter pasture.	1 ton limestone; 300–500 pounds 0–20–0 or 4–12–4.	
Corn or sorghum.	Silage.	300–500 pounds 4–12–4.	

[1] Crops and mixture listings are for general use and do not include those recommended for limited use. Mixtures of grasses often recommended for hay as well as pasture. Varieties recommended—Red clover: Kenland, Kentucky 215, and Cumberland; alfalfa: Atlantic, Hardigan, Buffalo, Ranger, Kansas Common, Oklahoma Common; white clover: Kentucky, Louisiana, and Mississippi grown; small grain: Balbo rye, Kentucky No. 1 barley, Thorne, Clarkan, Currell's Prolific, and Fulcaster wheat; Sudangrass: Tift, sweet, and ordinary; timothy: Marietta and ordinary; corn: Kentucky 102, Kentucky 203, U. S. 13; sorghum: Williams sorgo.

[2] Fertilizer and liming recommendations are very general. They should be modified for much of the soil of the State in accordance with natural fertility and recent liming and fertilizing. Potash will be needed in some fields, particularly for hay. Apply 40–80 pounds K_2O an acre. Field tests and quick soil tests are recommended as guides to treatment.

Data from E. N. Fergus.

ARKANSAS: Recommended Pasture and Forage Crops
[Rate per acre]

Crops or mixtures	Use	Fertilization	
		Initial	Maintenance
Permanent pastures:			
Bermuda-grass, hop clover, bur-clover, white clover, lespedeza.	Pasture	300 pounds 0–20–0 or 0–14–7 or 3–12–6	Same as initial.
Redtop (northern Arkansas)	do	do	Do.
Bluegrass (northern Arkansas)	do	do	Do.
Orchardgrass (northern Arkansas)	do	do	Do.
Dallisgrass (southern Arkansas)	do	do	Do.
Carpetgrass (southern Arkansas)	do	do	Do.
Temporary pastures:			
Sudangrass	Hay and pasture	300 pounds 3–12–6	
Lespedeza (mixture of varieties)	Pasture	300 pounds 0–20–0 or 0–14–7	
Oats or rye (Traveler, DeSoto, Ferguson 922, oats, or Balbo rye).	do	300 pounds 4–12–4 or 4–16–0	
Hay:			
Lespedeza (Korean, Kobe, Climax)	Hay	300 pounds 0–20–0 or 0–14–7	
Red clover (Cumberland)	do	Lime and 300 pounds 0–20–0 or 0–14–7	
Alsike clover	do	300 pounds 0–20–0 or 0–14–7	
Alfalfa	do	Lime and 500 pounds 0–20–0 or 0–14–7	
Soybeans (Laredo, Otootan, Red Tanner, Arksoy, or Ogden).	do	300 pounds 0–20–0 or 0–14–7	
Mung beans	do	do	
Cowpeas	do	do	
Silage: Atlas sorgo	Silage	200 pounds 4–12–4 plus side-dressing of 100 pounds 16–0–0.	

Data furnished by R. P. Bartholomew.

OKLAHOMA: Recommended Pasture and Forage Crops for the Eastern Half
[Rate per acre]

Crops or mixtures	Use	Fertilization [1]	
		Initial	Maintenance
Native grass mixture (bluestems, Indiangrass and switchgrass).	Pasture and hay.......	....	P.
Bermuda-grass..............	Pasture.............	N and P......	N and P.
Bermuda+annual lespedeza+ hop clover, white clover, and other winter legumes.	.....do.............	N and P.......	N and P.
Ryegrass (annual)............	.....do.............	N and P.......	N and P.
Annual lespedezas (Korean and Kobe).	Pasture and hay.......	P.............	P.
Lespedeza, sericea...........	Hay................	P.............	P.
Annual ryegrass+annual lespedeza+hop clover.	Pasture.............	N and P.......	N and P.
Winter oats (Wintok)+annual lespedeza.	.....do.............	P.............	P.
Winter small grains, oats, wheat, barley, rye.	.....do.............	N and P.......	N and P.
Hairy vetch..................	.....do.............	P.............	P.
Hairy vetch+rye (Balbo or Abruzzi).	.....do.............	P.............	P.
Sweetclover (Hubam, Madrid, bi-white or Evergreen).	.....do.............	P.............	P.
Alfalfa (Oklahoma Common)+ smooth brome.	Pasture and hay.......	N and P.......	N and P.
Sudan (common or Sweet).....	.....do.............		
Johnsongrass	.....do.............		
Kudzu......................	.....do.............	P.............	P.
Weeping lovegrass+sweetclover or annual lespedeza.	.....do.............	N and P.......	N and P.
Cowpeas—all varieties........	Hay................		
Soybeans (Ogden, Arksoy).....	.....do.............	P.............	P.
Sweet sorghums (redtop, Orange, and Atlas).	.....do.............		
Grain sorghums (10 to 12 varieties).	Bundles or silage.......	....	
Dallisgrass	Pasture.............	N and P.......	N and P.
Red clover, alsike, Ladino, white, perennial rye, Alta fescue, redtop, bur clover, black medic—used in many combinations.	Pasture and hay.......	N and/or P....	N and/or P.
Mung beans (green or golden).	Hay................	P.............	P.

[1] Limestone and phosphate used with all legumes if the soil needs either or both.

Data from Hi W. Staten.

EAST TEXAS: Recommended Pasture and Forage Crops [1]
[Rate per acre]
TIMBER AREA

Forage and pasture crops	Use	Fertilizer (initial and maintenance)
Hairy or Willamette vetch....	Pasture...............	300 pounds 0–14–7 on sandy soils; 200 pounds 20 percent superphosphate on other soils.
Vetch and small grain.......	Pasture, hay.........	300 pounds 4–12–8.
Austrian Winter peas........	Pasture...............	300 pounds 0–14–7 on sandy soils; 200 pounds 20 percent superphosphate on other soils.
Austrian Winter peas and small grain.	Pasture, hay.........	300 pounds 4–12–8.
Peanuts...................	Hay.................	400 pounds 4–12–4.
Alfalfa (common)...........	Pasture...............	1 to 2 tons limestone and 400 pounds 4–12–4 to establish a stand on acid soils; 400 pounds 0–14–7 on established stand on acid soils annually.[2]
Sweetclover................	.....do...............	Same fertilizing practices as alfalfa.
Soybeans (Laredo, Otootan, Avoyelles).	Hay.................	400 pounds 4–12–4.
Velvetbeans (Early Speckle, Osceola, Bunch).	Pasture...............	Do.
Kudzu.....................	Pasture, hay.........	400 pounds 4–12–4 to establish stand; 300 pounds 0–14–7 on established stands annually.
Sericea lespedeza...........	Hay.................	Do.
Cowpeas (Brabham, Iron)....	.:...do..............	400 pounds 4–12–4.
Small grains...............	Pasture, hay.........	300 pounds 5–10–5 at seeding; top-dress with 100 pounds ammonium nitrate[3] when 3 inches high; do not graze until 3 inches high.
Forage sorghums...........	Hay, silage, bundle feed, some grazing.	300 pounds 5–10–5.
Little bluestem.............	Hay.................	300 pounds 5–10–5 on established stands annually.
Upland: Bermuda-grass, Kobe or common lespedeza.	Permanent pasture....	400 pounds 5–10–5 to establish pasture. For maintenance: 300 pounds 0–14–7 on sandy soils; 200 pounds 20 percent superphosphate on other soils annually.
Bermuda-grass, Dallisgrass, hop clover, burclover, and Kobe or common lespedeza.	.....do...............	Do.
Bottom land: Bermuda-grass, Dallisgrass, white clover, hop clover, Persian clover, and Kobe or common lespedeza.	.....do...............	200 pounds 5–10–5 plus 200 pounds 20 percent superphosphate to establish pasture. For maintenance: 200 pounds 20 percent superphosphate annually.
Carpetgrass, Dallisgrass, white clover, hop clover, Persian clover, and Kobe or common lespedeza.	.....do...............	Do.

See footnotes at end of table.

BLACKLAND PRAIRIE AREA

Forage and pasture crops	Use	Fertilizer (initial and maintenance)
Sweetclover [4] (Hubam, White biennial, Yellow biennial, Madrid, *Melilotus indica*).	Hay and pasture.......	300–400 pounds 0–14–7 on sandy loam soils; 200–400 pounds 20 percent superphosphate on other soils annually.
Bur-clover in permanent pasture.	Pasture..............	Do.
Black medic in permanent pasture.	.....do..............	Do.
Alfalfa (common)...........	Hay and pasture.......	Do.
Hairy vetch................	Pasture..............	Do.
Small grain and hairy vetch..	Pasture and hay.......	Do.
Austrian Winter peas........	Pasture..............	Do.
Austrian Winter peas with small grain.	Pasture and hay.......	Do.
Forage sorghums............	Hay, silage, bundle feed, some grazing.	100 pounds ammonium nitrate.[3]
Sudan or Sweet Sudan.......	Pasture and hay.......	Do.[3]
Johnsongrass overseeded with Hubam or Madrid sweetclover.	....	300–400 pounds 0–14–7 on sandy loam soils; 200–400 pounds 20 percent superphosphate on other soils.
Small grains................	Pasture and hay......	200 pounds 5–10–5 at seeding; top-dress with 100 pounds ammonium nitrate [3] in early spring on sandy loam soils; 100 pounds ammonium nitrate [3] on other soils.
Italian ryegrass.............	Pasture..............	
Rescuegrass	.....do..............	
Small grains................	Pasture and grain......	200 pounds 5–10–5 at seeding; top-dress with 100 pounds ammonium nitrate [3] in January or early February on sandy loam soils; 50 pounds ammonium nitrate [3] in January or early February on other soils.
Bermuda-grass..............	Pasture..............	300–400 pounds 5–10–5 on sandy loam soils; 100 pounds ammonium nitrate [3] on other soils to establish pasture. For maintenance: 150–200 pounds 5–10–5 on sandy loam soils; 100 pounds ammonium nitrate [3] on other soils annually.
Buffalograss	.....do..............	
Yellow beardgrass............	.....do..............	
Dallisgrass	.....do..............	
Little bluestem..............	Hay or pasture.......	
Bermuda-grass, Dallisgrass, black medic or bur-clover, buffalograss.	Pasture..............	300 pounds 5–10–5 to establish pasture. For maintenance: 300 pounds 0–14–7 on sandy loam soils; 200 pounds 20 percent superphosphate on other soils annually.

See footnotes at end of table.

GULF COAST PRAIRIE AREA

Forage and pasture crops	Use	Fertilizer (initial and maintenance)
Sweetclover (Hubam and *Melilotus indica*).	Pasture and hay pasture.	200–400 pounds 0–14–7 on sandy soils; 200–400 pounds 20 percent superphosphate on other soils.
Soybeans (Laredo, Otootan, Avoyelles).	Hay................	Do.
Cowpeas (Brabham, Iron, Clay, Chinese Red, New Era, Whippoorwill).	....do..............	Do.
Forage sorghums............	Hay, silage, bundle feed, some grazing.	300 pounds 5–10–5 on sandy soils; 200 pounds 6–12–0 on other soils.
Sudan and Sweet Sudan.....	Pasture, hay..........	Do.
Small grains: Wheat (Austin).......... Oats (Ranger, Rustler, Camellia).	....do..............	200 pounds 5–10–5 on sandy soils; 100 pounds ammonium nitrate [3] on other soils.
Dallisgrass, white clover, hop clover, Persian clover, Kobe or common lespedeza.	....	600 pounds 0–14–7 on sandy soils; 500 pounds 20 percent superphosphate on other soils. For maintenance, one-half initial rate.
Bermuda-grass, white clover, Kobe or common lespedeza.	Permanent pasture.....	Do.
Carpetgrass, white clover, hop clover, Persian clover, Kobe or common lespedeza.	....do..............	Do.

[1] For purpose of these recommendations, east Texas is considered that area of the State east of 97° longitude.

[2] 400 pounds 20 percent superphosphate to establish stand on neutral soils; 400 pounds 20 percent superphosphate on established stand on neutral soils annually.

[3] Ammonium nitrate or its equivalent in nitrogen from other inorganic carriers.

[4] Sweetclovers usually seeded in fall in southern half and spring-seeded in northern half of the area.

Data from R. D. Lewis.

TENNESSEE: Recommended Pasture and Forage Crops
{Rate per acre}

Crop	Use	Fertilizer-amount per acre [1]	
		Initial	Maintenance
Pasture mixtures:			
Mixture A—productive upland.	Permanent pasture..	Lime, 2–4 tons; superphosphate 20 percent, 400–800 pounds.	Lime, phosphate, and potash as needed.
Orchardgrass or Ky. 31 or Alta fescue. Kentucky bluegrass. Alfalfa. Red or alsike clover. White clover. Lespedeza.			
Mixture B—shallow upland. Redtop. Lespedeza. Bermuda.	.....do.............	.....do............	Do.
Mixture C—bottom land. Ky. 31 or Alta fescue. Redtop. Alsike. Ladino or Louisiana white clover. Bermuda-grass (optional).	.....do.............	.....do............	Do.
Alfalfa............. Kansas Common. Oklahoma Common. Buffalo.	Hay or pasture.....	Lime, 2–4 tons; ..... 0–14–7 or 0–12–12, 400–800 pounds; borax, 20 pounds.	Do. Also borax 20 pounds annually.
Red clover.......... Tennessee Anthracnose Resistant. Cumberland. Kenland.	.....do............	Lime, 2 tons; 0–14–7 or 0–12–12, 300–600 pounds.	
Lespedeza........... Korean. Kobe. Sericea.	.....do............	Lime, 2 tons; superphosphate 20 percent, 200–400 pounds.	Lime, phosphate, and potash as needed.
Lespedeza........... Korean. Kobe.	Supplementary summer pasture.	.....do............	
Lespedeza and Bermuda-grass.	Supplementary summer pasture.	.....do............	Do.
Sudangrass .... Common. Tift. Sweet.	.......do.........	4–12–4, 400–600 pounds.	

See footnotes at end of table.

TENNESSEE: Recommended Pasture and Forage Crops—Continued

| Crop | Use | Fertilizer-amount per acre [1] | |
		Initial	Maintenance
Soybeans........... Ogden. Volstate. Laredo.	Hay or pasture.....	Lime, 1 ton; 0–14–7 or 0–12–12, 200– 300 pounds.	
Italian ryegrass........ Common.	Supplementary win- ter pasture.	Lime, 2 tons; 4–12– 4, 200–400 pounds.	
Small grains (fall seeded). Forkedeer oats. Jackson No. 1 bar- ley. Thorne or Ful- caster wheat. Balbo rye.	.....do............	4–12–4, 400–600 pounds.	Top dressing: 16–32 pounds nitrogen in February or March.
Winter annual leg- umes. Crimson clover: Common. Dixie. Hairy vetch. Austrian Winter peas.	.....do............	Lime, 2 tons; super- phosphate 20 per- cent, 200 pounds, or 0–14–7 or 0–12– 12, 200–400 pounds.	

[1] Recommendations are general. Specific recommendations based on soil tests are preferable.

Data from O. H. Long.

ALABAMA: Average Number of Grazing Days per Year Provided by Crops, 1942–46 [1]

| Month | Average number of days by months | | | |
	Perma- nent pasture	Alfalfa	Crimson clover and ryegrass	Winter oats
March................................	11	....	24	....
April.................................	4	....	28	....
May..................................	21	....	12	....
June..................................	22	8	....	....
July..................................	14	24	....	....
August...............................	15	22	....	....
September............................	18	1	....	....
October..............................	7	....	13	7
November............................	7	5	24	16
December............................	4	....	14	12
January..............................	....	....	10	13
February.............................	....	....	15	8
Total............................	123	60	140	56

[1] Alabama Agricultural Experiment Station Progress Report Series No. 9, revised April 1947.

MISSISSIPPI: Recommended Pasture and Forage Crops
[Rate per acre]

Crop	Use	Fertilization (Initial and maintenance)	
Permanent pasture....	Grazing..........	80 pounds P_2O_5 every 4 years; potash and lime as indicated by test for Delta area; 40–60 pounds P_2O_5 annually and 500–1,000 pounds lime every 5 years on hill area; add 50 pounds K_2O every 3 years on sandy land.	
Temporary pasture...	Grazing:		
	Grass.........	30–60 pounds nitrogen in Delta area; 32 pounds nitrogen at planting plus 32 pounds later in hill area.	
	Legumes......	60 pounds P_2O_5 and 25 pounds K_2O or 400 pounds 0–14–7 at planting.	
		Initial	**Maintenance**
Alfalfa..............	Hay		
	Prairie........	500 pounds 20 percent P_2O_5; 100 pounds 50 percent K_2O.	3 tons stable manure plus 40 pounds P_2O_5 20 pounds borax where needed.
	Delta.........	Surface drainage.....	Surface drainage.
Alyceclover..........	Hay, seed, supplemental grazing.	60 pounds P_2O_5.....	Do.
Lespedeza...........	Hay, seed, grazing.	60 pounds P_2O_5; 50 pounds K_2O.	Annual.
Johnsongrass.........	Hay, grazing......	60 pounds P_2O_5 every 3rd year; 32 pounds nitrogen annually.	Annual—32 pounds nitrogen.
Winter legumes, all clovers (white, Persian, Lappa, etc.), medic.	.....do...........	60 pounds P_2O_5, 25 pounds K_2O; lime to pH 6.5.	Annual.
Summer legumes.....	Hay or grazing....	.....do............	Do.

Data from H. W. Bennett.

Frequency of Drought Periods of Specified Lengths During Critical Periods for Use of Nitrogen Fertilizer by the Corn Crop

Place and period	Number of years 1889–1942 with droughts during specified periods longer than—		
	14 days	21 days	28 days
Raleigh, N. C. (June and last part of July)..........	17	3	2
Montgomery, Ala. (June and last part of July).......	21	6	4
Indianapolis, Ind. (July and last part of August)......	40	21	9

ALABAMA: Recommended Pasture and Forage Crops
[Rate per acre]

Crop	Use	Fertilizer	
		Initial [1]	Maintenance
General [2] for entire State except Black Belt: White clover.... Annual lespedeza. Dallisgrass......	Permanent pasture...	1 to 3 tons lime; 100 to 140 pounds P_2O_5; and 80 to 100 pounds K_2O.	Apply annually 54 to 72 pounds P_2O_5 and 40 to 50 pounds K_2O.
Black Belt: Lime soil: White clover.... Black medic .... Dallisgrass......	....do.............	100 to 140 pounds P_2O_5 and 80 to 100 pounds K_2O.	Apply annually 54 to 72 pounds P_2O_5 and 40 to 50 pounds K_2O.
Acid soil: White clover.... Black medic .... Dallisgrass......	....do.............	2 to 3 tons lime; 100 to 140 pounds P_2O_5; and 80 to 100 pounds K_2O.	Apply annually 54 to 72 pounds P_2O_5 and 40 to 50 pounds K_2O.
Oats..............	Supplementary grazing and hay.	12 pounds N; 30 pounds P_2O_5; and 20 pounds K_2O.	Top-dress with 24 to 30 pounds N.
Oats and vetch, or oats and crimson clover, or crimson clover and Italian ryegrass.	.....do.............	1 to 3 tons lime; 20 pounds N; 50 pounds P_2O_5; and 35 pounds K_2O.	Top-dress with 24 to 30 pounds N.
Crimson clover.....	Supplementary grazing.	1 to 3 tons lime; 40 to 50 pounds P_2O_5; and 30 to 40 pounds K_2O.	
Bur-clover..........	.....do.............	1 to 3 tons lime; 40 to 50 pounds P_2O_5; and 30 to 40 pounds K_2O.	
Caley-peas (Lathyrus hirsutus).	.....do.............	1 to 3 tons lime; 40 to 50 pounds P_2O_5; and 30 to 40 pounds K_2O.	
Sericea lespedeza...	Supplementary grazing and hay.	40 to 50 pounds P_2O_5 and 30 to 40 pounds K_2O.	40 to 50 pounds P_2O_5 and 30 to 40 pounds K_2O.
Kudzu..............	.....do.............	40 to 50 pounds P_2O_5 and 30 to 40 pounds K_2O.	40 to 50 pounds P_2O_5 and 30 to 40 pounds K_2O.
Peanuts...........	Supplementary grazing.	30 to 40 pounds P_2O_5 and 25 to 30 pounds K_2O.	
Johnsongrass and Sudangrass.	Hay and supplementary grazing.	30 to 40 pounds N; 20 to 30 pounds P_2O_5; and 15 to 20 pounds K_2O.	

See footnotes at end of table.

ALABAMA: Recommended Pasture and Forage Crops—Continued

Crop	Use	Fertilizer	
		Initial [1]	Maintenance
Alfalfa............	Hay and supplementary grazing.	2 to 3 tons lime; 80 to 100 pounds P_2O_5; 120 to 180 pounds K_2O; and 20 pounds borax.	54 to 72 pounds P_2O_5; 120 to 240 pounds K_2O; and 15 pounds borax.
Soybeans..........	Hay...............	40 to 50 pounds P_2O_5 and 30 to 40 pounds K_2O.	
Cowpeas...........	....do...........	40 to 50 pounds P_2O_5 and 30 to 40 pounds K_2O.	
Annual lespedeza...	Hay and supplementary grazing.	40 to 50 pounds P_2O_5 and 30 to 40 pounds K_2O.	
Sorghum..........	Silage..............	30 to 40 pounds N; 20 to 30 pounds P_2O_5; and 15 to 20 pounds K_2O.	

[1] Lime applications should be repeated every 6 to 8 years.
[2] In northern Alabama add Kentucky bluegrass and orchardgrass.

Data furnished by T. H. Rogers.

THE GREAT PLAINS: TABLES OF SEEDING AND OTHER INFORMATION

Suggested Mixtures and Seeding Rates for General Pasture Seedings in the Eastern and in the Central and Western Parts of the Northern Great Plains Region

Species	Pounds to seed per acre							
	Eastern				Central and western			
Crested wheatgrass............	5	6	4	6	8	4	4	.....
Western wheatgrass...........	.....	.....	.....	.....	.....	1	.....	.....
Intermediate wheatgrass......	.....	.....	.....	4	.....	.....	.....	.....
Bromegrass..................	5	2	2	.....	.....	.....	.....	.....
Russian wild-rye.............	.....	.....	2	.....	.....	3	1	.....
Canada wild-rye..............	.....	2	.....	.....	.....	.....	.....	.....
Feather bunchgrass...........	.....	.....	2	.....	.....	.....	3	.....
Blue grama...................	.....	.....	.....	.....	.....	.....	.....	5
Side-oats grama..............	.....	.....	.....	.....	.....	.....	.....	3
Buffalograss.................	.....	.....	.....	.....	.....	.....	.....	2
Alfalfa......................	2	2	2	2	1	.....	.....	.....
Sweetclover.................	.....	.....	.....	.....	1	2	2	.....
Total.................	12	12	12	12	10	10	10	10

Range Land Compared to Cropland, Irrigated and Nonirrigated, in 210 Northern Great Plains Counties of 6 States
[1940 Census Data]

Number of counties by States	Total land area	Cropland [1]			Range, including farm pastures, waste, water surface, townsites, etc.	
		Irrigated	Non-irrigated	Total	Area	Percent of total
	1,000 acres	*1,000 acres*	*1,000 acres*	*1,000 acres*	*1,000 acres*	*Percent*
37......eastern Montana	62,812	781	8,036	8,817	53,996	85.9
18......eastern Wyoming	44,941	1,082	658	1,740	43,202	96.1
9 ......northeastern Colorado .	10,058	1,075	1,905	2,980	7,078	70.4
56......western Nebraska	36,244	610	12,271	12,881	23,414	64.5
46......western North Dakota .	38,219	22	18,781	18,803	19,267	50.6
44......western South Dakota..	38,984	60	10,060	10,120	28,864	70.0
210 counties.............	231,258	3,630	51,711	55,341	175,821	76.1

[1] Includes land used for crops (harvested and failed) and cropland, idle or fallow.

Land Use, Livestock, and Income in the Northern Great Plains by Type of Farming Areas, 1944

MAJOR LAND USE

Item	Spring wheat area	Corn area	Wheat range area	Range area	Northern Great Plains region
	1,000 acres	*1,000 acres*	*1,000 acres*	*1,000 acres*	*1,000 acres*
Total land area..............	42, 804	27, 418	44, 541	121, 705	236, 468
Land unusable for farming or grazing......................	2, 956	1, 015	2, 701	4, 834	11, 506
Cropland.......................	24, 190	15, 648	10, 525	11, 171	61, 534
Land pastured:					
Within farms.................	11, 701	9, 833	23, 348	77, 631	122, 515
Outside of farms..............	3, 957	920	7, 967	28, 069	40, 913

ALL LIVESTOCK BY CLASSES

	Spring wheat area	Corn area	Wheat range area	Range area	Northern Great Plains region
	1,000 animal units	*1,000 animal units*	*1,000 animal units*	*1,000 animal units*	*1,000 animal units*
Total livestock..................	2, 343	2, 929	1, 370	4, 129	10, 771
Horses and mules.................	281	293	152	365	1, 091
All cattle and calves..............	1, 661	2, 079	913	2, 718	7, 371
Kept for milk.................	852	768	245	365	2, 230
Not kept for milk.............	809	1, 311	668	2, 353	5, 141
All sheep and lambs..............	170	59	239	937	1, 405
Stock sheep..................	164	49	231	910	1, 354
Sheep and lambs on feed.......	6	10	8	27	51
All hogs and pigs................	163	367	45	72	647
All chickens.....................	69	131	22	37	259

SALES OF FARM PRODUCTS BY SOURCE

	Spring wheat area	Corn area	Wheat range area	Range area	Northern Great Plains region
	1,000 dollars	*1,000 dollars*	*1,000 dollars*	*1,000 dollars*	*1,000 dollars*
All farm products sold [1]...........	328, 377	323, 301	166, 544	241, 350	1, 059, 572
All crops sold....................	214, 769	119, 005	104, 919	66, 598	505, 291
All livestock and livestock products sold........................	113, 539	204, 268	61, 597	173, 925	553, 329
Dairy products..............	23, 014	21, 398	7, 015	10, 059	61, 486
Poultry and poultry products....	13, 915	31, 490	2, 943	7, 648	55, 996
Other livestock and livestock products..................	76, 610	151, 381	51, 639	156, 217	435, 847

[1] Figures may not add up because "Forest products sold" is not included.

U. S. Census of Agriculture, 1945. Livestock on Farms January 1, Bureau of Agricultural Economics, also Geographic Differences in Production from Agricultural Land, Northern Great Plains.

Suggested Native-Grass Mixtures and Rates of Seeding in the Southern Great Plains

Site and mixture	Rate of seeding		Germinable seeds per pound	
	Rough material	Processed or re-cleaned	Rough material	Processed or re-cleaned
Medium rainfall areas:				
Sandy upland:	*Pounds*	*Pounds*	*Number*	*Number*
Sand lovegrass....................	0.5	0.5	([1])	800,000
Side-oats grama....................	5.0	.5	50,000	650,000
Blue grama........................	3.0	.5	180,000	950,000
Sand bluestem....................	5.0	1.0	30,000	150,000
Switchgrass.......................	2.0	.5	60,000	250,000
Total..........................	15.5	3.0	....	....
Heavy upland:				
Buffalograss	3.0	.5	[2] 5,000	180,000
Blue grama.......................	5.0	1.0	180,000	950,000
Side-oats grama...................	5.0	1.0	50,000	650,000
Total..........................	13.0	2.5	....	....
Lowlands:				
Switchgrass.......................	2.0	1.0	60,000	250,000
Indiangrass	5.0	2.0	50,000	130,000
Sand bluestem....................	6.0	2.0	30,000	150,000
Side-oats grama...................	5.0	1.0	50,000	650,000
Total..........................	18.0	6.0	....	....
Low rainfall areas:				
Sandy upland:				
Blue grama.......................	4.0	.5	180,000	950,000
Side-oats grama...................	5.0	1.0	50,000	650,000
Sand lovegrass....................	.5	.5	([1])	800,000
Total..........................	9.5	2.0	....	....
Heavy upland:				
Buffalograss	3.0	1.0	[2] 5,000	180,000
Blue grama.......................	6.0	1.0	180,000	950,000
Total..........................	9.0	2.0	....	....
High rainfall areas or moist bottom land:				
Sand bluestem....................	6.0	1.0	30,000	150,000
Little bluestem....................	5.0	2.0	40,000	160,000
Indiangrass	5.0	2.0	50,000	130,000
Switchgrass.......................	3.0	1.0	60,000	250,000
Total..........................	19.0	6.0	....	....

[1] Normally handled as recleaned grain.
[2] Untreated burs.

Grasses of the Southern Great Plains, Their Adaptation, Value, Growth

	Class and species of grass	Common name	Use for irrigation or dry land
	NATIVE GRASSES *Warm-season*		
1	Andropogon furcatus............	Big bluestem................	Both........
2	Andropogon hallii...............	Sand bluestem...............	....do.....
3	Andropogon saccharoides.........	Silver beardgrass...........	Neither.....
4	Andropogon scoparius...........	Little bluestem.............	Both........
5	Aristida longiseta.............	Red three-awn..............	Neither.....
6	Aristida purpurea..............	Purple three-awn...........	....do.....
7	Bouteloua curtipendula.........	Side-oats grama............	Both........
8	Bouteloua eriopoda............	Black grama................	Dry land....
9	Bouteloua gracilis.............	Blue grama.................	....do.....
10	Bouteloua hirsuta.............	Hairy grama................	....do.....
11	Buchloë dactyloides...........	Buffalograss...............	....do.....
12	Calamovilfa gigantea..........	Giant reedgrass............	....do.....
13	Calamovilfa longifolia.........	Long-leaved reedgrass.......	....do.....
14	Distichlis stricta.............	Inland saltgrass...........	Neither.....
15	Eragrostis trichodes..........	Sand lovegrass.............	Dry land....
16	Hilaria jamesii...............	Galleta...................	....do.....
17	Hilaria mutica...............	Tobosa....................	....do.....
18	Panicum obtusum.............	Vine-mesquite.............	....do.....
19	Panicum virgatum............	Switchgrass................	Both........
20	Paspalum stramineum.........	Sand paspalum.............	Dry land....
21	Redfieldia flexuosa............	Blowoutgrass...............	....do.....
22	Sorghastrum nutans...........	Yellow Indiangrass.........	Both........
23	Sporobolus airoides...........	Alkali sacaton.............	Neither.....
24	Sporobolus cryptandrus........	Sand dropseed.............	Dry land....
	Cool-season		
25	Agropyron smithii.............	Western wheatgrass.........	Both........
26	Elymus canadensis............	Canada wild-rye...........	....do.....
27	Koeleria cristata.............	Junegrass.................	Irrigation.....
28	Phalaris arundinacea..........	Reed canarygrass...........	....do.....
29	Phleum pratense.............	Timothy...................	....do.....
30	Poa arachnifera.............	Texas bluegrass............	Both........
31	Stipa comata................	Needle-and-thread..........	Neither.......
	INTRODUCED GRASSES *Warm-season*		
32	Andropogon intermedius var. caucasius.	Caucasian bluestem.........	Dry land....
33	Andropogon ischaemum..........	Turkestan bluestem..........	....do.....
34	Chloris gayana................	Rhodesgrass................	....do.....
35	Cynodon dactylon.............	Bermuda-grass.............	Irrigation.....
36	Eragrostis chloremalas.........	Boer lovegrass.............	Dry land....
37	Eragrostis curvula............	Weeping lovegrass..........	Neither.....
38	Eragrostis lehmanniana.........	Lehmann lovegrass..........	Dry land....
39	Panicum antidotale...........	Blue panic................	....do.....
40	Paspalum dilatatum............	Dallisgrass................	....do.....
41	Sorghum halepense............	Johnsongrass...............	Both........
	Cool-season		
42	Agropyron cristatum...........	Crested wheatgrass.........	....do.....
43	Agropyron trachycaulum.........	Slender wheatgrass.........	....do.....
44	Agrostis alba.................	Redtop....................	Irrigation.....
45	Bromus inermis...............	Smooth brome..............	Both........
46	Dactylis glomerata............	Orchardgrass...............	Irrigation.....
47	Festuca elatior...............	Meadow fescue.............	....do.....
48	Lolium perenne...............	Perennial ryegrass.........	....do.....
49	Poa pratensis.................	Kentucky bluegrass.........	....do.....

Habits, Seed Qualities, and Cultural Recommendations

Adaptation			Grazing value			
General soil preference	Part of region	Relative abundance	General	Palatability		
				Growing	Dormant	
Rich loam	Humid E	Scarce	Good	Medium	Low	1
Deep sand	Entire	Medium	...do	...do	...do	2
Loam	Waste land	Scarce	Poor	Low	...do	3
Rocky-sandy loam	Entire	Medium	Fair	...do	Very low	4
Sandy loam	...do	Scarce	Poor	Very low	..do	5
Sand	...do	..do	..do	..do	...do	6
Rocky-sandy loam	...do	Medium	Very good	High	Medium	7
Fine sandy loam	W. & SW	Scarce	...do	...do	...do	8
Loam-clay	Entire	Much	...do	...do	High	9
Rocky-sandy loam	...do	Scarce	Fair	Low	Very low	10
Clay-loam	...do	Much	Very good	High	High	11
Sand	S. half	Scarce	Poor	Very low	Very low	12
Sand-sandy loam	N. half	...do	Fair	Low	...do	13
Wet alkaline	Entire	...do	Poor	Very low	...do	14
Sand	...do	Medium	Very good	High	Medium	15
Clay loam	West	Scarce	Fair	Low	Very low	16
...do	SW	...do	Poor	Very low	..do	17
Loam	Entire	..do	...do	Low	...do	18
Sandy loam	...do	Medium	Good	Medium	Low	19
Sand	...do	Scarce	...do	High	..do	20
...do	...do	..do	Poor	Very low	Very low	21
Sandy loam	E. half	..do	Good	Medium	Low	22
Wet alkaline	Entire	..do	Poor	Low	Very low	23
Sand-sandy loam	...do	Much	Fair	Medium	Low	24
Loam-clay	N. & W	Medium	Good	High	Medium	25
Sand-sandy loam	Entire	Scarce	Fair	...do	Low	26
Loam	NW	..do	...do	Medium	...do	27
...do	North	..do	Good	...do	...do	28
...do	NW	..do	...do	...do	...do	29
Sandy loam	S. half	..do	Very good	High	Medium	30
Loam	North	..do	Poor	Very low	Very low	31
...do	Entire	..do	Good	Medium	Low	32
...do	...do	..do	...do	...do	...do	33
...do	S. edge	..do	Fair	...do	...do	34
Sandy loam	SE	..do	...do	Low	Very low	35
Loam	SW	..do	...do	Medium	Low	36
...do	S. half	Medium	Poor	Low	Very low	37
...do	SW	Scarce	Fair	Medium	Low	38
...do	South	..do	Good	...do	Medium	39
...do	S. edge	..do	...do	...do	Low	40
Sandy loam	S. half	Medium	Fair	...do	...do	41
Clay-loam	N. & NW	..do	Good	High	Medium	42
...do	NW	Scarce	Fair	...do	Low	43
Loam	...do	..do	Good	Medium	...do	44
...do	North	..do	Very good	High	Medium	45
...do	...do	..do	Good	Medium	Low	46
...do	...do	..do	...do	...do	...do	47
...do	...do	..do	...do	...do	...do	48
...do	...do	..do	...do	High	Medium	49

Grasses of the Southern Great Plains, Their Adaptation, Value, Growth

	Class and species of grass	Common name	Grazing value	
			Nutritive	
			Growing	Dormant
	NATIVE GRASSES *Warm-season*			
1	Andropogon furcatus.......	Big bluestem............	Medium....	Low.......
2	Andropogon hallii.........	Sand bluestem.........	...do......	...do......
3	Andropogon saccharoides...	Silver beardgrass........	...do......	...do......
4	Andropogon scoparius.....	Little bluestem...........	...do......	Very low...
5	Aristida longiseta..........	Red three-awn..........	Very low....	...do......
6	Aristida purpurea.........	Purple three-awn.......	...do......	...do......
7	Bouteloua curtipendula....	Side-oats grama........	Medium....	Low.......
8	Bouteloua eriopoda.......	Black grama............	High......	Medium....
9	Bouteloua gracilis.........	Blue grama.............	...do......	...do......
10	Bouteloua hirsuta........	Hairy grama...........	Medium....	Low.......
11	Buchloë dactyloides........	Buffalograss............	High......	Medium....
12	Calamovilfa gigantea......	Giant reedgrass.........	Medium....	Low.......
13	Calamovilfa longifolia.....	Long-leaved reedgrass....	...do......	...do......
14	Distichlis stricta...........	Inland saltgrass........	...do......	...do......
15	Eragrostis trichodes........	Sand lovegrass.........	High......	Medium....
16	Hilaria jamesii............	Galleta.................	Medium....	Very low...
17	Hilaria mutica............	Tobosa................	...do......	...do......
18	Panicum obtusum..........	Vine-mesquite..........	...do......	Low.......
19	Panicum virgatum.........	Switchgrass............	...do......	...do......
20	Paspalum stramineum.....	Sand paspalum.........	...do......	Medium....
21	Redfieldia flexuosa........	Blowoutgrass..........	...do......	Low.......
22	Sorghastrum nutans........	Yellow Indiangrass......	...do......	...do......
23	Sporobolus airoides.......	Alkali sacaton.........	...do......	Very low...
24	Sporobolus cryptandrus.....	Sand dropseed..........	High......	Medium....
	Cool-season			
25	Agropyron smithii.........	Western wheatgrass.....	...do......	...do......
26	Elymus canadensis........	Canada wild-rye.......	...do......	...do......
27	Koeleria cristata..........	Junegrass..............	...do......	Low.......
28	Phalaris arundinacea.......	Reed canarygrass.......	...do......	...do......
29	Phleum pratense...........	Timothy...............	...do......	...do......
30	Poa arachnifera............	Texas bluegrass........	...do......	Medium....
31	Stipa comata..............	Needle-and-thread.......	...do......	Low.......
	INTRODUCED GRASSES *Warm-season*			
32	Andropogon intermedius var. caucasius.	Caucasian bluestem......	...do......	Medium....
33	Andropogon ischaemum....	Turkestan bluestem......	...do......	...do......
34	Chloris gayana............	Rhodesgrass............	Medium....	Low.......
35	Cynodon dactylon........	Bermuda-grass.........	...do......	...do......
36	Eragrostis chloromelas......	Boer lovegrass..........	High......	...do......
37	Eragrostis curvula.........	Weeping lovegrass......	...do......	...do......
38	Eragrostis lehmanniana.....	Lehmann lovegrass.......	...do......	...do......
39	Panicum antidotale........	Blue panic.............	Medium....	...do......
40	Paspalum dilatatum........	Dallisgrass.............	...do......	...do......
41	Sorghum halepense........	Johnsongrass...........	...do......	...do......
	Cool-season			
42	Agropyron cristatum.......	Crested wheatgrass.......	High......	Medium....
43	Agropyron trachycaulum...	Slender wheatgrass......	Medium....	Low.......
44	Agrostis alba..............	Redtop................	...do......	...do......
45	Bromus inermis............	Smooth brome.........	...do......	...do......
46	Dactylis glomerata.........	Orchardgrass..........	...do......	...do......
47	Festuca elatior............	Meadow fescue........	...do......	...do......
48	Lolium perenne...........	Perennial ryegrass......	...do......	...do......
49	Poa pratensis.............	Kentucky bluegrass......	...do......	...do......

Habits, Seed Qualities, and Cultural Recommendations—Continued

Season of growth	Time of maturity	Market seed supplies	Source of seed	Adapted for re-seeding	
Apr.-Oct.	Oct.	Low	Culti. & range	Medium	1
....do	....do	None	....do	..do	2
....do	Sept.	..do	Range	None	3
....do	Oct.	Low	Culti. & range	Medium	4
....do		None		None	5
....do		..do		..do	6
....do	Aug.–Sept.	Low	Culti. & range	High	7
....do	Sept.	None	Range	Low	8
....do	July–Sept.	Medium	....do	High	9
....do	July	None	Cultivation	Low	10
....do	June–Sept.	Low	Culti. & range	High	11
....do		None	Cultivation	Low	12
....do		..do	....do	..do	13
....do		..do	....do	None	14
Mar.–Nov.	Sept.–Oct.	Low	Cultivation	High	15
Apr.–Oct.	Aug.	None	Range	Low	16
....do	....do	..do	....do	..do	17
....do	Sept.	..do	Cultivation	..do	18
....do	Oct.	Low	Culti. & range	High	19
....do	Aug.	None	Cultivation	Medium	20
....do	....do	..do	....do	Low	21
....do	Oct.	Low	....do	Medium	22
....do	Aug.	None	....do	Low	23
....do	Sept.–Oct.	Low	Culti. & range	..do	24
Sept.–June	July–Aug.	..do	....do	High	25
....do	....do	..do	....do	Medium	26
Oct.-May			Cultivation	Low	27
....do		Low	....do	Medium	28
....do		High	....do	..do	29
Sept.–June	July–Aug.	None	....do	..do	30
Oct.-May		..do		None	31
Apr.–Oct.	Oct.	..do	Cultivation	Medium	32
....do	....do	Low	....do	..do	33
....do		Medium	....do	..do	34
....do		High	....do	Low	35
....do	July	Low	....do	Medium	36
Mar.–Nov.	....do	Medium	....do	Low	37
Apr.–Oct.		Low	....do	Medium	38
....do	Aug. and Oct.	Medium	....do	..do	39
....do		High	....do	High	40
....do	Sept.	Medium	....do	Medium	41
Sept.–June	July–Aug.	High	....do	High	42
....do	....do	Low	....do	Medium	43
Oct.-May		Medium	....do	Low	44
Sept.–Oct.		..do	....do	High	45
Oct.-May		..do	....do	Low	46
....do		..do	....do	..do	47
....do		High	....do	..do	48
Sept.–Oct.		..do	....do	..do	49

Grasses of the Southern Great Plains, Their Adaptation, Value, Growth

	Class and species of grass	Common name	Seed as usually threshed and partly cleaned		
			Usual condition	Purity	Germination
	NATIVE GRASSES				
	Warm-season			*Pct.*	*Pct.*
1	Andropogon furcatus...	Big bluestem..........	Chaffy florets....	40	54
2	Andropogon hallii......	Sand bluestem.........	.....do.........	20	59
3	Andropogon saccharoides	Silver beardgrass.....			
4	Andropogon scoparius...	Little bluestem........	Chaffy florets....	38	47
5	Aristida longiseta.......	Red three-awn........			
6	Aristida purpurea......	Purple three-awn......			
7	Bouteloua curtipendula.	Side-oats grama......	Smooth florets...	25	64
8	Bouteloua eriopoda.....	Black grama..........	Chaffy florets....	37	22
9	Bouteloua gracilis......	Blue grama...........	.....do.........	35	66
10	Bouteloua hirsuta.......	Hairy grama..........			
11	Buchloë dactyloides.....	Buffalograss..........	Clean burs......	85	54
12	Calamovilfa gigantea....	Giant reedgrass......			
13	Calamovilfa longifolia...	Long-leaved reedgrass..			
14	Distichlis stricta........	Inland saltgrass.......			
15	Eragrostis trichodes.....	Sand lovegrass........	Free grain......	92	59
16	Hilaria jamesii..........	Galleta..............			
17	Hilaria mutica.........	Tobosa..............			
18	Panicum obtusum......	Vine-mesquite........			
19	Panicum virgatum......	Switchgrass...........	Smooth florets...	85	63
20	Paspalum stramineum...	Sand paspalum........	.....do.........	72	15
21	Redfieldia flexuosa.....	Blowoutgrass.........			
22	Sorghastrum nutans....	Yellow Indiangrass.....	Chaffy florets....	68	67
23	Sporobolus airoides.....	Alkali sacaton........			
24	Sporobolus cryptandrus.	Sand dropseed........	Free grain......	91	77
	Cool-season				
25	Agropyron smithii......	Western wheatgrass....	Smooth florets...	78	78
26	Elymus canadensis......	Canada wild-rye.......	Chaffy florets....	77	79
27	Koeleria cristata.......	Junegrass............			
28	Phalaris arundinacea....	Reed canarygrass.....			
29	Phleum pratense.......	Timothy.............			
30	Poa arachnifera........	Texas bluegrass........	Chaffy florets....	Not usable before processing	
31	Stipa comata..........	Needle-and-thread.....			
	INTRODUCED GRASSES				
	Warm-season				
32	Andropogon intermedius var. caucasius.	Caucasian bluestem....	Chaffy florets....	36	57
33	Andropogon ischaemum.	Turkestan bluestem....	.....do.........	25	57
34	Chloris gayana.........	Rhodesgrass...........	Clean florets....	25	70
35	Cynodon dactylon......	Bermuda-grass........			
36	Eragrostis chloremalas ..	Boer lovegrass........	Free grain......	96	71
37	Eragrostis curvula......	Weeping lovegrass.....	.....do.........	93	83
38	Eragrostis lehmanniana.	Lehmann lovegrass.....	.....do.........	87	75
39	Panicum antidotale.....	Blue panic...........	Smooth florets...	71	64
40	Paspalum dilatatum....	Dallisgrass...........			
41	Sorghum halepense.....	Johnsongrass.........			
	Cool-season				
42	Agropyron cristatum....	Crested wheatgrass.....	Smooth florets...	87	86
43	Agropyron trachycaulum	Slender wheatgrass.....	.....do.........	93	93
44	Agrostis alba..........	Redtop...............			
45	Bromus inermis........	Smooth brome........			
46	Dactylis glomerata.....	Orchardgrass.........			
47	Festuca elatior.........	Meadow fescue.......			
48	Lolium perenne........	Perennial ryegrass.....			
49	Poa pratensis..........	Kentucky bluegrass....			

Habits, Seed Qualities, and Cultural Recommendations—Continued

Seed as usually threshed and partly cleaned—Continued				Seed as hulled or further cleaned			
Seeds per pound	Rate sown			Usual condition	Purity	Germination	
	Pure stands		Mixture				
	Drills	Rows					
No.	*Lbs.*	*Lbs.*	*Lbs.*		*Pct.*	*Pct.*	
30,000	15–20	5–8	5–6	Chaffy florets.....................	....	....	1
20,000	15–30	8–10	6–8	Clean grain......................	90	82	2
......	......	......	......	....	....	....	3
102,600	15–20	6–8	5–6	Chaffy florets.....................	75	65	4
......	......	......	......	....	....	....	5
......	......	......	......	....	....	....	6
30,000	12–15	5–8	3–5	Clean grain......................	....	....	7
300,000	5–8	3–4	2–3	.....do.........................	90	65	8
240,000	6–10	2–3	4–6	.....do.........................	91	75	9
......	......	......	......	....	....	....	10
45,000	10–12	3–4	1–2	Clean grain......................	95	70	11
......	......	......	......	....	....	....	12
......	......	......	......	....	....	....	13
......	......	......	......	....	....	....	14
700,000	1–2	1	$\frac{1}{4}$–$\frac{1}{2}$	Free grain........................	98	70	15
......	......	......	......	....	....	....	16
......	......	......	......	....	....	....	17
......	......	......	......	....	....	....	18
250,000	3–4	2	1–2	Smooth florets....................	95	75	19
100,000	6–8	3	2–3	.....do.........................	90	50	20
......	......	......	......	....	....	....	21
80,000	8–10	3–4	2	....	93	75	22
......	......	......	......	....	....	....	23
3,500,000	1–2	1	......	Free grain........................	98	80	24
80,000	10–12	3–4	2–3	Trimmed florets....................	90	85	25
60,000	12–15	5–6	......	.....do.........................	90	80	26
......	......	......	......	....	....	....	27
......	......	......	......	....	....	....	28
......	......	......	......	....	....	....	29
Not usable before processing				Clean grain......................	71	78	30
......	......	......	......	....	....	....	31
400,000	5–8	1	......	Clean grain......................	92	60	32
150,000	5–8	2	......	.......do........................	85	75	33
400,000	5–6	3–4	......	.......do........................	62	75	34
......	......	......	......	....	....	....	35
1,500,000	1	$\frac{1}{2}$	......	Free grain........................	98	90	36
1,000,000	$\frac{3}{4}$–1	$\frac{1}{2}$	......	.....do.........................	98	92	37
4,000,000	$\frac{1}{2}$	$\frac{1}{3}$	......	.....do.........................	98	85	38
500,000	1	$\frac{1}{3}$	......	Smooth florets....................	95	80	39
......	......	......	......	....	....	....	40
......	......	......	......	....	....	....	41
160,000	6–8	3–4	......	Smooth florets....................	92	90	42
100,000	8–10	4–5	3–4	.....do.........................	90	85	43
......	......	......	......	....	....	....	44
......	......	......	......	....	....	....	45
......	......	......	......	....	....	....	46
......	......	......	......	....	....	....	47
......	......	......	......	....	....	....	48
......	......	......	......	....	....	....	49

Grasses of the Southern Great Plains, Their Adaptation, Value, Growth

	Class and species of grass	Common name	Seeds per pound	Rate sown — Pure stands Drills	Rate sown — Pure stands Rows	Mixture
	NATIVE GRASSES		*No.*	*Lbs.*	*Lbs.*	*Lbs.*
	Warm-season					
1	Andropogon furcatus....	Big bluestem..........	60,000	8–12	4–5	3–4
2	Andropogon hallii......	Sand bluestem.........	45,000	3–5	2	1–2
3	Andropogon saccharoides.	Silver beardgrass......	......	......	......	......
4	Andropogon scoparius...	Little bluestem........	220,000	2–2½	2	1
5	Aristida longiseta.......	Red three-awn.........	......	......	......	......
6	Aristida purpurea.......	Purple three-awn......	......	......	......	......
7	Bouteloua curtipendula.	Side-oats grama.......	540,000	2–2½	1	½
8	Bouteloua eriopoda.....	Black grama..........	500,000	2	¾	½
9	Bouteloua gracilis.......	Blue grama...........	700,000	1	½	¼
10	Bouteloua hirsuta.......	Hairy grama..........	......	......	......	......
11	Buchloë dactyloides.....	Buffalograss..........	280,000	1–2	½	¼–½
12	Calamovilfa gigantea....	Giant reedgrass.......	......	......	......	......
13	Calamovilfa longifolia...	Long-leaved reedgrass...	......	......	......	......
14	Distichlis stricta........	Inland saltgrass.......	......	......	......	......
15	Eragrostis trichodes......	Sand lovegrass........	1,300,000	1	½	¼
16	Hilaria jamesii.........	Galleta..............	......	......	......	......
17	Hilaria mutica.........	Tobosa..............	......	......	......	......
18	Panicum obtusum.......	Vine-mesquite........	......	......	......	......
19	Panicum virgatum......	Switchgrass..........	380,000	2–3	1½	1
20	Paspalum stramineum...	Sand paspalum.......	260,000	3–4	1–2	1
21	Redfieldia flexuosa......	Blowoutgrass.........	......	......	......	......
22	Sorghastrum nutans.....	Yellow Indiangrass.....	120,000	2–3	1	1
23	Sporobolus airoides.....	Alkali sacaton........	......	......	......	......
24	Sporobolus cryptandrus..	Sand dropseed........	5,000,000	1–2	1	......
	Cool-season					
25	Agropyron smithii.......	Western wheatgrass....	100,000	5–6	2–3	......
26	Elymus canadensis......	Canada wild-rye.......	100,000	5–6	3	......
27	Koeleria cristata........	Junegrass............	......	......	......	......
28	Phalaris arundinacea....	Reed canarygrass......	......	......	......	......
29	Phleum pratense........	Timothy.............	......	......	......	......
30	Poa arachnifera.........	Texas bluegrass........	1,260,000	1¼	⅓	......
31	Stipa comata...........	Needle-and-thread.....	......	......	......	......
	INTRODUCED GRASSES					
	Warm-season					
32	Andropogon intermedius var. caucasius.	Caucasian bluestem....	2,000,000	1	½–¾	......
33	Andropogon ischaemum.	Turkestan bluestem....	1,350,000	1–2	½–¾	......
34	Chloris gayana.........	Rhodesgrass..........	1,300,000	1	½	......
35	Cynodon dactylon......	Bermuda-grass........	......	......	......	......
36	Eragrostis chloromelas...	Boer lovegrass........	2,600,000	⅓	¼	......
37	Eragrostis curvula......	Weeping lovegrass.....	1,500,000	½	¼	......
38	Eragrostis lehmanniana..	Lehmann lovegrass.....	6,800,000	¼	⅛	......
39	Panicum antidotale.....	Blue panic...........	650,000	¾	¼	......
40	Paspalum dilatatum.....	Dallisgrass...........	......	......	......	......
41	Sorghum halepense......	Johnsongrass.........	......	......	......	......
	Cool-season					
42	Agropyron cristatum....	Crested wheatgrass.....	190,000	5–7	2–3	......
43	Agropyron trachycaulum	Slender wheatgrass.....	135,000	6–7	3–4	2–3
44	Agrostis alba...........	Redtop..............	......	......	......	......
45	Bromus inermis........	Smooth brome........	......	......	......	......
46	Dactylis glomerata......	Orchardgrass.........	......	......	......	......
47	Festuca elatior.........	Meadow fescue.......	......	......	......	......
48	Lolium perenne........	Perennial ryegrass.....	......	......	......	......
49	Poa pratensis..........	Kentucky bluegrass....	......	......	......	......

Habits, Seed Qualities, and Cultural Recommendations—Continued

Time sown	Depth	Method	Seedbed	Generally seeded	
	In.				
Mar.–Apr...........	½–1	Drills or rows...	Sorghum stubble....	Mixtures.	1
.....do.............	½–1	.....do...........	.....do...........	...do.....	2
					3
Mar.–Apr...........	½–1	Drills or rows...	Sorghum stubble....	Mixtures.	4
					5
					6
Mar.–Apr...........	½–1	Drills or rows...	Sorghum stubble....	Mixtures.	7
.....do.............	½	.....do...........	.....do...........	...do.....	8
.....do.............	½	.....do...........	.....do...........	...do.....	9
					10
Mar.–Apr...........	½–1	Drills or rows...	Sorghum stubble....	Mixtures.	11
					12
					13
					14
Mar.–Apr...........	½	Drill-broadcast-rows	Sorghum stubble	Mixtures.	15
					16
					17
					18
Mar.–Apr...........	½–1	Drills or rows...	Sorghum stubble....	Mixtures.	19
Feb.–Apr............	½–1	.....do...........	.....do...........	...do.....	20
					21
Mar.–Apr...........	½–1	Drills or rows...	Sorghum stubble....	Mixtures.	22
					23
Mar.–Apr...........	½	Drill-broadcast..	Sorghum stubble....	Alone....	24
Sept.–Oct., Feb.–Mar.	1	Drills or rows...	Wheat or sorghum stubble.	...do.....	25
.....do.............	1	.....do...........	.....do...........	...do.....	26
					27
					28
					29
Sept.–Oct., Feb.–Mar.	½	Drills or rows...	Millet or wheat stubble.	Alone....	30
					31
Mar.–Apr...........	½	Drills or rows...	Sorghum stubble....	Alone....	32
.....do.............	½	.....do...........	.....do...........	...do.....	33
Feb.–Apr............	½–1	.....do...........	.....do...........	...do.....	34
					35
Mar.–Apr...........	½	Drills or rows...	Sorghum stubble....	Alone....	36
.....do.............	½	.....do...........	.....do...........	...do.....	37
.....do.............	½	.....do...........	.....do...........	...do.....	38
Feb.–Apr............	½	.....do...........	.....do...........	...do.....	39
					40
					41
Sept.–Oct., Feb.–Mar.	1	Drills or rows...	Wheat or sorghum stubble.	Alone....	42
.....do.............	½–1	.....do...........	.....do...........	Mixtures.	43
					44
					45
					46
					47
					48
					49

HAWAII: Important Pasture Species, Their Forage Value, and Zonal Distribution (See map, page 619)

GRASSES

Scientific name [1]	Common name	Forage value [2]	Zonal adaptability [3]							
			A	B	C_1	C_2	D_1	D_2	D_3	E_1
*Andropogon barbinodis	Fuzzytop	Medium	+	++						++
Anthoxanthum odoratum	Sweet vernalgrass	Fair			++	++		+	+	
Avena fatua	Wild oat	Medium		+						++
Axonopus affinis	Carpetgrass	Fair			+	+		++	+++	++
*Bromus catharticus	Bromegrass	Good			+	+++				
Bromus mollis	Soft chess	do.			+	+				
Cenchrus echinatus	Sandbur	Medium				+				
*Chloris gayana	Rhodesgrass	Good		+						+
Chloris inflata	Swollen fingergrass	Fair	++	+++	+					+++
*Chloris virgata	Feather fingergrass	Medium		+	++					+++
Cynodon dactylon	Bermuda-grass	Good								
*Dactylis glomerata	Cocksfoot	do.			+	++			+	
*Danthonia pilosa	Hairy oatgrass	do.			+				++	
Danthonia semiannularis	Wallaby grass	do.								
Deschampsia nubigena	Kalamaloa	Medium								
Digitaria henryi	Henry's crabgrass	Good				++	+			
Digitaria sanguinalis	Kukaipuaa	do.			+	++	++			
Digitaria violascens	Kukaipuaa	do.								
Eragrostis brownei	Sheep grass	Medium								
Festuca dertonensis	Brome fescue	do.								
*Heteropogon contortus	Pili grass	do.		+						+
*Holcus lanatus	Yorkshire fog	do.								
*Lolium multiflorum	Italian ryegrass	Good		+				+	+++	+++
Lolium perenne	Perennial ryegrass	do.			+			+	+++	++
*Melinis minutiflora	Molassesgrass	do.	+	+	+	++++				
*Microlaena stipoides	Puu lehua	do.		+	++					
*Panicum maximum	Guineagrass	do.					+	+	++	+
Panicum purpurascens	Paragrass	do.								
Panicum tenuifolium	Mountain pili	Medium					+	+		+

Scientific name	Common name	Palatability
Panicum torridum	Kakonakona	do.
Panicum xerophilum		Good
Paspalum conjugatum	Hilograss	Fair
Paspalum dilatatum	Dallisgrass	Good
Paspalum orbiculare	Ricegrass	Fair
*Pennisetum clandestinum	Kikuyugrass	do.
*Pennisetum purpureum	Napiergrass	Good
Pennisetum setosum	Feathery pennisetum	Fair
Phalaris tuberosa	Canarygrass	Good
*Poa pratensis	Kentucky bluegrass	do.
Sacciolepis contracta	Glenwoodgrass	do.
Setaria geniculata	Yellow foxtail	Fair
Setaria verticillata	Bristly foxtail	Medium
Sporobolus capensis	Rattail	Fair
Stenotaphrum secundatum	Buffalograss	do.
*Tricholaena repens	Natal redtop	Medium

FORBS

Scientific name	Common name	Palatability
*Atriplex semibaccata	Australian saltbush	Medium
Bidens pilosa	Pilipili	do.
Commelina diffusa	Honohono	do.
*Desmodium canum	Kaimi Spanish clover	Good
*Desmodium uncinatum	Spanish clover	do.
Erodium cicutarium	Filaree	do.
Geranium carolinianum var. australe	Wild geranium	Medium
Hypochaeris glabra	Smooth gosmore	do.
Hypochaeris radicata	Gosmore	do.
Malvastrum coromandelianum	False mallow	do.
*Medicago hispida	Bur-clover	Good
*Medicago lupulina	Black medic	do.
*Melilotus indica	Indian yellow sweetclover	do.
Modiola caroliniana	Bristly-fruited mallow	do.
*Trifolium procumbens	Hop clover	do.
*Trifolium repens	White clover	do.
*Vicia sativa	Common vetch	do.

See footnotes at end of table.

HAWAII: Important Pasture Species, Their Forage Value, and Zonal Distribution (See map, page 619)—Continued

SHRUBS AND TREES

Scientific name [1]	Common name	Forage value [2]	Zonal adaptability [3]							
			A	B	C₁	C₂	D₁	D₂	D₃	E₁
*Cajanus cajan.	Pigeonpea.	Good.		+	+	++				
*Desmanthus virgatus.	Desmanthus.	do.		++	++					
*Leucaena glauca.	Koa haole.	do.	++	++						
Prosopis chilensis.	Algaroba.	do.	++	+	+					
Sida fallax.	Ilima.	Fair.								

[1] Species with asterisks (*) are recommended for planting. Those without asterisks are not recommended for planting, either because they occur naturally, are unimportant from a forage standpoint or have low palatability.

[2] Forage value means palatability or animal acceptance.

[3] + Means adapted but does not assume appreciable importance.
++ Means well adapted; it is, or is capable of becoming, an important part of pasture sward.

THE MOUNTAIN REGION: RECOMMENDATIONS FOR SEEDING AND OTHER DATA

Land Area, Land in Farms, and Land in Acres Producing Forage in 1944, Mountain Region (U. S. Census of Agriculture, 1945)

Item	Arizona	California [1]	Colorado [1]	Idaho	Montana [1]	Nevada
	1,000 acres	*1,000 acres*	*1,000 acres*	*1,000 acres*	*1,000 acres*	*1,000 acres*
Land area....................	79, 691	14, 097	32, 193	52, 997	29, 152	70, 273
Land in farm.................	37, 856	1, 313	10, 622	12, 503	9, 572	6, 178
Cropland harvested............	652	203	1, 295	3, 442	1, 167	487
Forage:						
Alfalfa cut for hay...........	165	38	277	799	250	107
Wild hay cut................	2	74	335	135	323	267
Clover and timothy..........	4	6	106	122	96	31
Small grains for hay..........	15	5	15	49	13	3
Corn for forage..............	8	0	8	11	([2])	1
Sorghums for forage..........	8	0	1	0	0	([2])
Other tame hay..............	7	22	47	47	87	25
Total acres forage........	209	145	789	1, 163	769	434

Item	New Mexico [1]	Oregon [1]	Utah	Washington [1]	Wyoming [1]	Total by crops
	1,000 acres	*1,000 acres*	*1,000 acres*	*1,000 acres*	*1,000 acres*	*1,000 acres*
Land area....................	40, 659	42, 439	52, 701	21, 913	26, 136	462, 251
Land in farm.................	19, 913	15, 036	10, 309	12, 797	6, 631	142, 730
Cropland harvested............	381	1, 938	1, 248	3, 579	526	14, 918
Forage:						
Alfalfa cut for hay...........	72	214	442	280	134	2, 778
Wild hay cut................	8	258	103	23	91	1, 619
Clover and timothy..........	6	46	34	50	36	537
Small grains for hay..........	4	135	13	116	9	377
Corn for forage..............	11	1	18	4	1	63
Sorghums for forage..........	7	0	([2])	0	([2])	16
Other tame hay..............	7	44	19	42	126	473
Total acres forage........	115	698	629	515	397	5, 863

[1] Part of State lying in the Mountain Region.
[2] Less than 500 acres.

Commonly Recommended Mixtures for Seeding Pastures on High-Grade, Well-Drained, Irrigated Land in the Mountain Region
[Pounds per acre]

Species in mixture [1]	Nevada	Utah — New [2] (1)	Utah — New [2] (2)	Utah — Standard	Southern Idaho	Montana	Wyoming	Colorado	New Mexico	Arizona Plateau	Arizona Hot country
	Pounds	*Pounds*	*Pounds*	*Pounds*	*Pounds*	*Pounds*	*Pounds*	*Pounds*	*Pounds*	*Pounds*	*Pounds*
Smooth brome (*Bromus inermis*)		7–10	7	4	4	3–4	6	8	4	5	
Meadow fescue (*Festuca elatior*)	5			4	4	3–4	6	6	4–8	3	[6]
Tall fescue (*Festuca elatior* var. *arundinacea*)											5[3]
Orchardgrass (*Dactylis glomerata*)	3	6–8	7	3	4	4–6	2	8[2]	4–8		4
Tall oatgrass (*Arrhenatherum elatius*)					[4]						
Kentucky bluegrass (*Poa pratensis*)	5		4	4		4–6				2	
Perennial ryegrass (*Lolium perenne*)				3					4	4	4
Timothy (*Phleum pratense*)	3									5	
Crested wheatgrass (*Agropyron cristatum*)							4	[4]			
Slender wheatgrass (*Agropyron trachycaulum*)							4	[4]			
White clover (*Trifolium repens*)	4			2	[2]	1–2		[2]			
Alsike clover (*Trifolium hybridum*)				2	[2]	1–2					
Ladino clover (*Trifolium repens*)		1–2	2		4[3]				3–4	2[3]	
Yellow sweetclover (*Melilotus officinalis*)							2	2[2]	2		
Red clover (*Trifolium pratense*)		2–3	2					[2]		[2]	
Alfalfa (*Medicago sativa*)		2					2		Some	2	[2]
Bur-clover (*Medicago hispida*)											2[3]
Hubam sweetclover (*Melilotus alba annua*)											2
Dallisgrass (*Paspalum dilatatum*)											6
Total	20	18–25	22	22	20	16–24	20	24	21–28	25	23

[1] Mixture consists of all plant species recommended in the State.   [2] Mixtures now being used for first time.

[3] Alternate with figure in [ ]. For example, in Idaho white or alsike clover may be used in place of Ladino clover, or tall oatgrass for orchardgrass on sandy soil.

Commonly Recommended Mixtures of Species for Seeding on Waterlogged Lands and on Waterlogged Land with Considerable Soil Salt in the Mountain Region

[Pounds per acre]

Species	Waterlogged land in—								Waterlogged land-alkali salts [1] — Utah	
	Nevada	Utah	Idaho	Montana	Wyoming	Colorado	New Mexico	Montana	1	2
	Pounds	Pounds	Pounds	Pounds	Pounds	Pounds	Pounds	Pounds	Pounds	Pounds
Smooth brome (*Bromus inermis*)		3				3				
Meadow fescue (*Festuca elatior*)		3	4			3	6–8			6
Tall fescue (*Festuca elatior var. arundinacea*) [2]		[4]	[4]							[6]
Perennial ryegrass (*Lolium perenne*)	6	3				4	4			
Redtop (*Agrostis alba*)			8	5–6	6					
Reed canarygrass (*Phalaris arundinacea*)	6	3		4–5		4	6–8			
Timothy (*Phleum pratense*)			6	5–8	6					
Western wheatgrass (*Agropyron smithii*)	4							10–14		6
Alsike clover (*Trifolium hybridum*)			2	2–3	3	2				
Yellow sweetclover (*Melilotus officinalis*)		3				2	2		8–10	
Strawberry clover (*Trifolium fragiferum*)		2				2	3–4	5–6		2–4
Total	16	17	20	16–22	15	20	15–26	15–20	8–10	2–16

[1] More alkali than 2,000 parts per million (p. p. m.) is damaging to ordinary pasture plants. When more than 3,500 to 4,000 p. p. m. is present, salt-tolerant species as here listed must be used instead of the ordinary ones listed in the previous table.

[2] Tall fescue is a high-yielding substitute for meadow fescue. It is rather low in palatability. It is moderately salt-tolerant.

Species, Mixtures, and Rate Per Acre for Seeding Selected Sites Within Broad Range Types of Mountain Region

[x = species adapted for reseeding certain sites]

Species	Amount of seed if seeded alone (Pounds per acre)	Semidesert grassland with rainfall below 14 inches; no serious freezing (Pounds per acre)	Semidesert grassland with rainfall 15 inches or above (Pounds per acre)	Southern woodland (pinyon-juniper); annual precipitation between 13 and 18 inches (Pounds per acre)	Sagebrush-grass and Pacific bunchgrass; annual precipitation 8 to 14 inches in the north and 10 to 16 inches in south (Pounds per acre)	Mountain brush, Pacific bunchgrass, and upper sagebrush-grass; annual precipitation 15 to 19 inches (Pounds per acre)	Open pine and mountain brush and Pacific bunchgrass; annual precipitation 20 to 24 inches (Pounds per acre)	Mountain parks and aspen; annual precipitation 22 inches and above [1] (Pounds per acre)
Recommended species for mixtures: [2]								
Lehmann lovegrass	1–2	1						
Sand dropseed	2–3	½	½	½				
Weeping lovegrass	1–2		½	2				
Side-oats grama	10–20		2					
Blue grama	8–10		4	x	x	x		
Bluestem wheatgrass	8–15			2	6	5		
Crested wheatgrass	5–8			4		3	3	
Tall oatgrass	7–10						3	3
Smooth brome	8–15					2	4	5
Slender wheatgrass	8–12						x	2
Orchardgrass	4–8						x	2
Timothy	2–8							1
Total		1½	7	8½	6	10	10	13
Species useful for reseeding:								
Giant panicgrass [3]	6–8	x						
Alkali sacaton [3]	2–3	x						
Boer lovegrass [3]	1–2	x	x					
Rothrock grama [3]	10–15	x	x					
Fourwing saltbush [3] (chamiza)	10–15	x	x	x				
Galleta [3]	10–15	x			x			
Indian ricegrass [3]	10–15		x	x	x			

Species	Seeding rate
Bulbous bluegrass	6–10
Bluebunch wheatgrass	7–10
Siberian wheatgrass [3]	5–8
Michel's hybrid rye	10–40
Mountain rye [3]	8–20
Antelope bitterbrush [3]	10–20
Big bluegrass	5–8
Blue wild-rye [3]	7–10
Alfalfa	6–14
Yellow sweetclover	6–12
Chewings fescue	5–8
Mountain brome	10–16
Bearded wheatgrass [3]	8–12
Kentucky bluegrass	4–10
Reed canarygrass	6–10
Meadow fescue	7–12
White clover	4–8
Promising species which need further study:	
Arizona cottongrass [3]	8–12
Slender grama [3]	10–20
Stiffhair wheatgrass [3]	7–10
Russian wild-rye [3]	5–8
Intermediate wheatgrass [3]	6–9
Tall wheatgrass [3]	6–9
Alta fescue	7–12

[1] Where there is good moisture during the growing season or where water spreading and irrigation are possible, increase the amount of timothy and add white or Ladino clover.

[2] These mixtures are recommended for large areas, and it may be necessary to adjust them to local soil and moisture conditions.

[3] Seed is not always commercially available; however, seed can often be collected from native stands and it is sometimes available on the market or from ranchers who have collected seed.

Recommended Pasture and Hay Mixtures for Western Washington

[Number in parentheses = pounds per acre]

Adaptation area	Pasture mixtures	Hay mixtures
I. Well-drained uplands (depth to hardpan, 30 inches or more).	1. Perennial ryegrass (3), Alta fescue (6), orchardgrass (4), white clover (2), and alsike clover (2). 2. For dry sites: creeping red fescue (4), orchardgrass (4) or tall oatgrass (4), and sub clover (5).	1. Alfalfa (15). 2. Oats (70) and vetch (30). 3. Alta fescue (6) and alfalfa (10) orchardgrass (6). 4. Alta fescue (6) or orchardgrass (6) and birdsfoot trefoil (4). 5. Perennial (8) and red clover (10) or alsike clover (4) or Italian ryegrass (8).
II. Well-drained valley soils (minimum depth to water table at any time of year, 30 inches or more).	1. Perennial ryegrass (3), orchardgrass (4), Alta fescue (6), white clover (2) (or Ladino clover (2) under irrigation), and alsike clover (2) (Kentucky bluegrass may be added).	1. Alfalfa (15). 2. Oats (70) and vetch (30). 3. Alta fescue (6) or orchardgrass (6) and alfalfa (10). 4. Alta fescue (6) or orchardgrass (6) and birdsfoot trefoil (4). 5. Perennial ryegrass (3), orchardgrass (4), Alta fescue (6), alsike clover (2), and white clover (2). 6. Perennial (8) or Italian ryegrass (8) and red clover (10) or alsike clover (4).
III. Poorly drained uplands (depth to hardpan, 12 inches to 30 inches). IV. Poorly drained valley soils (minimum depth to water table at any time of year, 12 inches to 30 inches).	1. Perennial ryegrass (3) or Italian ryegrass (3), Alta fescue (6) or orchardgrass (6), Kentucky bluegrass (2), alsike clover (2), and Ladino clover (2) or white clover (2). 2. Meadow foxtail (6) or Alta fescue (6), and big trefoil (2) or birdsfoot trefoil (4). 3. Reed canarygrass (10) and big trefoil (2) or birdsfoot trefoil (4).	1. Italian ryegrass (8) and alsike clover (4) or birdsfoot trefoil (4). 2. Meadow foxtail (6) and alsike clover (4), or birdsfoot trefoil (4) or big trefoil (2). 3. Alta fescue (6) or orchardgrass (6) and alsike clover (4) or birdsfoot trefoil (4) or big trefoil (2).
V. Tidelands (or lands where minimum depth of water table at any time of year is less than 12 inches).	1. Meadow foxtail (6), Alta fescue (6), and big trefoil (2). 2. Redtop (4), meadow foxtail (6), alsike clover (2), and white clover (2). 3. Reed canarygrass (10) (on extremely wet sites).	

VI. Prairies and droughty soils............

1. Creeping red fescue (4) or Chewings fescue(4), orchardgrass (4), and alsike clover (3) or sub clover (5).
2. Orchardgrass (4) or tall oatgrass (4), Alta fescue (6), and alsike clover (3) or sub clover (5).

1. Winter oats and vetch.

Effect of Cow Manure¹ on Grazed Grass-Clover Pasture Coverage, Grass, Clover, Weeds, and Yield Per Acre (See "Manure and Grass-Farming," by Firman E. Bear and Carl B. Bender, page 289)

GRASS-WHITE CLOVER

Annual tons of manure per acre	Coverage	Grass	Clover	Weeds	Coverage	Grass	Clover	Weeds	Coverage	Grass	Clover	Weeds	Coverage	Grass	Clover	Weeds	Dry matter per acre, 1941–45 average
	Percent	Percent	Percent	Percent	Percent	Percent	Percent	Percent	Percent	Percent	Percent	Percent	Percent	Percent	Percent	Percent	Pounds
0.............	93	52	27	14	96	52	31	21	95	45	22	28	96	52	35	9	2,900
2½............	97	55	29	13	96	55	32	9	95	44	35	16	98	37	48	13	3,406
5.............	91	46	25	20	96	45	44	7	90	34	41	15	97	39	54	4	3,820
10............	91	46	29	16	96	43	45	8	92	41	33	18	97	44	42	11	3,190

GRASS-LADINO CLOVER

Annual tons of manure per acre	Coverage	Grass	Clover	Weeds	Coverage	Grass	Clover	Weeds	Coverage	Grass	Clover	Weeds	Coverage	Grass	Clover	Weeds	Dry matter per acre, 1941–45 average
0.............	98	60	30	8	100	60	28	12	96	52	23	21	98	56	25	17	2,046
2½............	98	68	26	7	97	60	33	4	98	45	27	18	99	41	51	7	4,349
5.............	100	64	29	7	99	53	41	5	98	39	47	12	99	34	56	9	5,185
10............	100	62	31	7	100	65	32	3	100	55	34	11	97	55	30	12	5,490

¹ 250 pounds 20-percent superphosphate per acre applied separately.

Numbers of Livestock, Total Value, and the Value Per Head of Various Classes in the States and Parts of States Included in the Mountain Region

[Census figures for 1945, except milk cows which is the 1946 figure]

State	Livestock (thousands)					
	All cattle	2 years and over	Milk cows	Sheep	Goats	Horses
Arizona....................	750	382	49	511	90	72
California..................	252	....	107	118	3	15
Colorado [1]...............	680	359	[2] 97	1, 403	10	93
Idaho......................	949	465	244	1, 336	5	144
Montana [1]................	412	197	[2] 33	456	2	50
Nevada....................	479	266	20	534	3	38
New Mexico [1].............	347	214	[2] 22	813	99	58
Oregon [1].................	710	363	[2] 158	606	2	73
Texas.....................	294	....	173	1, 301	243	20
Utah......................	562	304	122	1, 672	9	73
Washington [1].............	527	268	[2] 188	419	6	71
Wyoming [1]...............	348	196	[2] 25	1, 414	1	50
Total.................	6, 310	3, 014	1, 238	10, 583	473	757

State	Total value ($1,000)					
Arizona....................	$44, 785	$25, 931	$5, 684	$3, 873	$361	$4, 663
California..................	18, 334	....	9, 373	1, 307	17	1, 371
Colorado...................	42, 110	27, 987	10, 185	14, 271	32	3, 845
Idaho......................	67, 923	44, 398	26, 108	14, 938	27	7, 121
Montana...................	30, 855	18, 254	3, 894	3, 904	8	1, 588
Nevada....................	32, 852	21, 794	2, 600	5, 461	16	2, 518
New Mexico................	20, 048	13, 879	1, 848	7, 134	345	2, 179
Oregon....................	46, 157	28, 433	15, 168	5, 365	5	4, 068
Texas.....................	18, 001	....	12, 461	9, 292	1, 004	995
Utah......................	42, 542	29, 890	14, 884	17, 017	43	4, 470
Washington................	35, 265	22, 553	20, 304	3, 887	29	4, 366
Wyoming..................	23, 100	16, 259	2, 850	13, 322	3	1, 656
Total ($937,210).........	$421,972	$249,378	$125,359	$99, 771	$1, 890	$38, 840

State	Value per head (dollars)					
Arizona....................	$59. 73	$67. 84	$116. 00	$7. 58	$4. 00	$64. 85
California..................	80. 00	....	113. 00	10. 20	....	96. 00
Colorado...................	61. 97	77. 93	105. 00	10. 17	3. 21	41. 36
Idaho......................	71. 55	95. 50	107. 00	11. 18	5. 00	49. 60
Montana...................	74. 91	92. 61	118. 00	8. 56	4. 91	31. 95
Nevada....................	68. 54	81. 88	130. 00	10. 23	4. 95	65. 68
New Mexico................	57. 71	64. 87	84. 00	8. 78	3. 50	37. 29
Oregon....................	64. 98	78. 40	96. 00	8. 85	3. 08	55. 93
Texas.....................	49. 00	....	65. 00	6. 00	....	55. 00
Utah......................	75. 68	98. 19	122. 00	. 10. 17	5. 00	61. 20
Washington................	66. 90	84. 10	108. 00	9. 27	5. 00	61. 12
Wyoming..................	69. 05	83. 05	114. 00	9. 42	4. 05	33. 10

[1] That part of the State in the Mountain Region.
[2] Estimated number of milk cows in that part of the State included in Mountain Region.

SOME FACTORS THAT AFFECT THE FUTURE OF GRASSLAND FARMING

Average Quantity of Food Products Consumed at Home Per Household Per Week by Nonfarm Families, by Annual Net Money Income Class, United States, Spring 1942

Food products	Under $1,000	$1,000–$1,999	$2,000–$2,999	$3,000 or over
Major food groups:	*Pounds*	*Pounds*	*Pounds*	*Pounds*
Milk (total equivalent, excluding butter).......	18.6	27.2	29.3	33.6
Eggs..	1.5	2.2	2.4	2.5
Meat, poultry, and fish......................	4.1	7.0	9.7	12.1
Fats and oils (including butter and fat cuts)....	3.2	3.8	3.8	4.2
Grain products..............................	11.3	10.8	10.7	11.1
Dry beans, peas, and nuts....................	1.2	1.2	1.0	.8
Potatoes and sweetpotatoes..................	7.1	9.3	9.3	9.9
Citrus fruit and tomatoes....................	4.8	7.9	11.6	15.0
Green and yellow vegetables.................	4.9	6.6	8.1	9.4
Other vegetables and fruit...................	6.5	9.6	11.7	13.7
Sugar and sweets...........................	2.6	3.1	3.3	3.4
Selected products:				
Whole milk.................................	10.7	17.3	20.7	23.0
Butter.....................................	0.7	1.1	1.3	1.7
Beef.......................................	1.3	2.4	3.4	4.2
Pork and lard..............................	2.8	3.0	3.2	3.5

Family Food Consumption in the United States, U. S. Department of Agriculture, Misc. Pub. 550.   Appendix A, Tables.   1944.

Potential Crop and Livestock Requirements as Related to National Agricultural Resources, 1947

Commodity	U.S. human consumption potential [1]		Industrial uses [2]	Feed, seed and other uses	Exports	Total
	Per capita	For total population				
	Pounds	*Million*	*Million*	*Million*	*Million*	*Million*
Intertilled crops:						
Corn..................bushels	68.1	175	80	2,970	25	3,250
Soybeans for beans.........do....	3.2	8	131	36	.....	175
Peanuts, picked and threshed....pounds	6.0	1,360	200	200	.....	1,760
Sugarcane, raw [5].............tons	108.0	8.2	.....	.....	.....	8.2
Sugar beets, raw [5].............do....						
Potatoes, white............bushels	125.0	296	5	63	4	368
Beans, dry edible, clean [5]...100-lb. bags	6.5	9.2	.....	.9	.6	10.7
Truck crops, fresh, farm weight....tons	119.7	8.5	.....	.....	.....	8.5
Truck crops, processed, farm weight....do....	51.4	7.7	.....	.....	.2	7.9
Cotton [5]................bales	33.7	10.0	.....	.....	3.5	13.5
Tobacco................pounds	10.9	1,550	.....	.....	525	2,075
Sorghums, all (except sirup) [6]....bushels	.....	.....	.....	135	.....	135
Other intertilled crops...........	.....	.....	.....	.....	.....	.....
Close-growing crops and summer fallow:						
Oats and barley............bushels	8.9	37	61	1,652	.....	1,750
Wheat..................do....	218.7	520	.....	275	100	895
Flaxseed................do....	.....	.....	38	3	.....	41
Rice, rough..............do....	5.8	28.1	2.0	7.0	20	57.1
Other close-growing crops.........	.....	.....	.....	.....	.....	.....
Summer fallow...............	.....	.....	.....	.....	.....	.....
Tame hay, seeds, and cover crops.......	.....	.....	.....	.....	.....	.....
Rotation pasture.............	.....	.....	.....	.....	.....	.....
Total cropland, excluding idle and orchards..	.....	.....	.....	.....	.....	.....
Fruits:						
Citrus, fresh equivalent.........pounds	112.2	15,930	.....	.....	800	16,730
Other (deciduous trees, vines, berries)....do....	215.0	30,530	.....	.....	3,000	33,530

	Unit						
Edible fats and oils: [8]							
Vegetable	do	14.9	} 7,510				7,510
Animal fats	do	38.0					
Other pasture in farms [9]							
Other grazing lands [11]							
Forest products (forest land)	cubic feet	20,000	20,000				20,000
Livestock and products:							
Beef and veal, [13] (all cattle and calves)	pounds	81.8	11,610		3,200	60	11,670
Milk and products [14] (dairy cows)	do	1,013.5	143,920			500	147,620
Lamb and mutton [13] (sheep and lambs)	do	5.8	825			5	830
Pork (excluding lard) [13] (sows)	do	85.7	12,190			340	12,530
Wool, grease basis	do	6.0	850				850
Eggs (hens and pullets)	dozen	43.0	4,070		140	20	4,230
Chickens (including broilers) [13]	pounds	27.3	3,880				3,880
Turkeys [13]	do	4.8	680				680

See footnotes at end of table.

Potential Crop and Livestock Requirements as Related to National Agriculture Resources, 1947—Continued

Commodity	Source of supply		U. S. acreage needed[3]			Acreage available[4]	
	Imports and shipments	U. S. production	Yield per acre	By crop	Group total	Usable without impairment	Subject to impairment
	Million	*Million*		*1,000 acres*	*1,000 acres*	*1,000 acres*	*1,000 acres*
Intertilled crops:							
Corn........................bushels		3,250	36	90,280			
Soybeans for beans........do		175	21	8,330			
Peanuts, picked and threshed..pounds		1,760	800	2,200			
Sugarcane, raw[5]..........tons	5.9	2.3	24	300			
Sugar beets, raw[5]........do			14	900			
Potatoes, white...........bushels		368	165	2,230			
Beans, dry edible, clean[5].100-lb. bags		10.7	900	1,280			
Truck crops, fresh, farm weight..tons		8.5		2,010			
Truck crops, processed, farm weight..do		7.9		2,740	156,440	67,700	88,740
Cotton[5]..................bales	.2	13.3	285	22,300			
Tobacco...................pounds	75	2,000	1,100	1,810			
Sorghums, all (except sirup)[6]..bushels		135	18	16,000			
Other intertilled crops......				6,060			
Close-growing crops and summer fallow:							
Oats and barley...........bushels		1,750	31	56,450			
Wheat.....................do		895	14.5	61,720			
Flaxseed..................do	15.5	25.5	9.5	2,680	143,880	52,000	91,880
Rice, rough...............do		57.1	51	1,120			
Other close-growing crops....				1,910			
Summer fallow.............				20,000			
Tame hay, seeds, and cover crops....		[7]			65,000		
Rotation pasture...........		[7]			50,000		
Total cropland, excluding idle and orchards....					415,320		
Fruits:							
Citrus, fresh equivalent......pounds	4,400	16,730		1,050	8,050		
Other (deciduous trees, vines, berries)..do		29,130		7,000			

Item	Unit			Livestock needed	Feeding units
				Millions	*Millions*
Edible fats and oils:[8]					
Vegetable	do	} 700			
Animal fats	do				
Other pasture in farms[9]			6,810	(7)	[10]576,000 239,000 337,000
Other grazing lands[11]				(7)	[10]375,000 196,000 179,000
Forest products (forest land)	cubic feet				[10]461,000 [12]164,000 [12]297,000
Livestock and products:					
Beef and veal[13] (all cattle and calves)	pounds	250	11,420	88.9	
Milk and products[14] (dairy cows)	do	750	146,870	28.8	
Lamb and mutton[13] (sheep and lambs)	do		830	47.2	} 183.3 grain-consuming animal units.
Pork (excluding lard)[13] (sows)	do		12,530	16.0	
Wool, grease basis	do	450	400		
Eggs (hens and pullets)	dozen	5	4,225	422.5	} 76.4 roughage-consuming animal units.
Chickens (including broilers)[13]	pounds		3,880	1,118	
Turkeys[13]	do		680	45.3	

[1] Based upon an assumed food consumption per capita equal to consumption in 1941 of those persons having an income of $2,000 or more per family or per unattached individual. For nonfood items (cotton, flaxseed, tobacco, wool) high-level consumption is assumed to be the same percentage increase over 1935–39 as the average for all foods. Total meat consumed is indicated by 1941 statistics, but consumption of each kind of meat is taken as a normal percentage of the total. U. S. population used is 142 million, the same as estimated for July 1, 1946.

[2] Use of grains and potatoes for nonfood purposes, brewing and distillation and of oilseeds for oil.

[3] Acreages of corn, oats, barley, sorghums and hay are to provide feed for livestock production shown.

[4] Estimates based on the acreage of land adequately protected and the acreage used without protection in 1946.

[5] Yield of sugarcane is in tons of cane; of sugar beets in tons of beets; of beans, uncleaned beans; and of cotton in pounds. Sugar production shown is continental U. S. production. The "Imports" column includes shipments from Hawaii and Puerto Rico and other imports.

[6] Production is shown for only the 7,500,000 acres of grain sorghums.

[7] Combined hay, forage, and pasture production is sufficient for the 76,400,000 roughage-consuming animal units.

[8] Figures are shown for consumption, imports, and production of all edible fats and oils. Quantities required are included in acreages of soybeans, cotton and other crops and in milk production and livestock numbers.

[9] Includes other plowable pasture, nonplowable, woodland pasture, and range in farms.

[10] There is some duplication between "Other pasture in farm", "Other grazing land" and forest acreage.

[11] Both forest and untimbered public and private lands other than in farms.

[12] Includes both timber and land resources.

[13] Dressed weight.

[14] Fluid-milk equivalent.

(From: USDA Testimony Proposing Long-Range Agricultural Policy and Programs Before Congressional Committees on Agriculture, April 21, October 6, 7, 8, 1947, at Washington, D. C.)

Typical Haymaking Crews, Average Rate of Handling Hay From Windrow, and the Cost of Using Haying Machines and Equipment for Common Methods of Haymaking, 1945 (See "The Costs and Ways of Making Hay," by Albert P. Brodell and Martin R. Cooper, page 173)

Haymaking crew and method	Hay handled		Average tonnage handled per year with specified equipment	Cost per ton for use of haying machines and equipment[1]		
	Per crew hour	Per hour of labor		Average tonnage	One-half of average tonnage	Two times average tonnage
	Tons	*Tons*	*Tons*	*Dollars*	*Dollars*	*Dollars*
Long loose hay, hauled from windrow and stored in barn:						
3 men, 2 horses, wagon, load and unload by hand[2]	0.7	0.23	15	0.11	0.12	0.10
3 men, 2 horses, wagon, usual power forks or slings, load by hand[3]	.8	.27	25	.35	.50	.25
3 men, wagon, 2 horses or tractor, hay loader, power forks or slings	1.0	.33	50	.65	1.05	.45
7 men, 3 wagons, 6 horses, hay loader, power forks or slings, and hoist	3.0	.40	100	.45	.70	.35
3 men, tractor, buck rake, power slings, and hoist	1.5	.50	30	.90	1.65	.50
Long loose hay, hauled from windrow and stored in stack:						
3 men, 2 horses or tractor, wagon, load and unload by hand	.8	.27	15	.11	.12	.10
5 men, 6 horses, 2 buck rakes, mechanical stacker	3.0	.60	100	.50	.80	.30
4 men, tractor, buck rake, 2 horses, mechanical stacker	2.8	.70	100	.50	.80	.30
3 men, tractor, hydraulic buck-stacker	2.5	.83	100	.40	.70	.25
Baled hay, baled from windrow, hauled, and stored in barn:						
6 men, pick-up baler (automatic tie), 2 tractors, wagon, load and unload by hand	2.5	.41	300	1.90	2.65	1.50
7 men, pick-up baler (hand-tie), 2 tractors, wagon, load and unload by hand	2.5	.36	100	1.45	1.95	1.15
7 men, stationary power baler, tractor, 4 horses, buck rake, wagon, load and unload by hand	1.5	.21	100	1.10	1.50	.90

See footnotes at end of table.

Chopped hay, hauled from windrows and stored in barn:

3 men, 2 horses, wagon, loader, tractor, stationary ensilage cutter, and blower............	1.2	.40	[5] 50	.55	.85	.35
2 men, 2 tractors, buck rake, stationary ensilage cutter, and blower......	1.5	.75	[5] 50	.50	.75	.30
4 men, field chopper with power take-off, 4 tractors, 2 wagons, stationary blower...............	2.5	.62	[6] 100	1.30	2.30	.75

[1] Includes cost of using hay-harvesting equipment only, such as wagons, racks, slings, forks, cable and track, buck rakes, stackers, choppers, cutters' blowers, and balers, including wire and twine. Hay stored principally in low mows or small barns.

[2] Includes some labor for cocking and bunching. Hay stored principally in large barns.

[3] Includes some labor for cocking and bunching.

[4] Crew and equipment shown in next item may be more suitable with 100 or more tons of hay.

[5] In computing the equipment costs, it was assumed that the ensilage cutter and blower was used one-third of the time on the tonnage of hay shown, with the remaining use on silage and other roughage. Costs of the silage cutter and blower are therefore based on their use in handling 150 tons of hay or equivalent use for silage and other materials under average conditions.

[6] Computations handled as shown in footnote 4, with the exception that one-half of the annual use of the cutter and blower was assumed to be for chopping 100 tons of hay, with one-half of the annual use for silage crops and other roughages.

Average Daily Quantities of Hay or Grass Silage Consumed, Dry Matter Consumed, and Percentage of Required Nutrients Consumed, by Months in Lactation (See "Dairy Cattle Must Have Good Forage," by L. A. Moore, page 120)

HAY OR GRASS SILAGE CONSUMED (FRESH BASIS), POUNDS

Feed	Months in lactation											
	1	2	3	4	5	6	7	8	9	10	11	12
Hay	34.9	40.9	41.3	44.2	47.2	45.5	44.4	44.4	43.1	45.2	43.3	39.4
Silage	82.8	104.6	95.0	100.5	103.4	101.6	102.8	86.5	92.1	92.6	88.7	102.6

HAY OR GRASS SILAGE CONSUMED (DRY BASIS), POUNDS

Feed	1	2	3	4	5	6	7	8	9	10	11	12
Hay	31.9	37.4	37.7	40.4	43.1	41.6	40.8	40.6	39.4	41.3	39.6	36.0
Silage	27.6	34.8	31.6	33.5	34.4	34.2	34.4	32.0	33.2	30.3	29.6	34.2

NUTRIENT REQUIREMENTS CONSUMED, PERCENT

Feed	1	2	3	4	5	6	7	8	9	10	11	12
Hay	81.5	96.9	105.1	118.7	125.9	124.8	125.8	129.6	123.3	134.8	134.7	141.5
Silage	82.2	102.1	97.3	106.4	112.4	107.9	113.9	107.3	114.7	112.1	119.5	132.6

General Recommendations for Planting and Grazing Pasture Crops for Swine (See "The Use of Forage in Feeding Hogs," by John H. Zeller, page 99)

Crop	Seed per acre	Method of planting	Time to seed [1]	Ready to pasture	Carrying capacity per acre of 50–100 pound hogs
	Pounds			*Months*	*Number*
Bluegrass [2]	6–10	In mixture	Fall	12–18	5–10
Alfalfa	15–20	Broadcast or drill	Spring or fall	4–5	15–20
Red clover	10–15	....do	....do	4	10–15
Sweetclover	20–30	....do	Early spring	3–4	15–20
Ladino	3–4	....do	Spring or early fall	6	20–25
Rape	4–8	Rows or broadcast	March to June	1½–2	20–25
Soybeans [3]	60–120	Rows or drill	May to July	1½–2	12–15
Cowpeas	60–180	....do	....do	1½–2	12–15
Sudangrass [3]	20–30	Broadcast or drill	....do	1–1½	15–20
Rye	85–170	....do	Spring or fall	2–3	15–20
Barley	75–100	....do	....do	2–3	10–12
Wheat	90–120	....do	....do	2–3	10–15
Oats	65–130	....do	....do	2–3	10–15
Italian ryegrass [4]	10–25	....do	....do	2–3	10–15
Oats and field peas	{ 50	....do	March to May	1½–2	10–15
	60	....do	....do	1½–2	10–15
MIXED-GRASS PASTURES					
Orchardgrass	⌠ 6–8	....do	Spring or early fall	5–6	20–25
Red clover	⎰ 3–4	....do	....do	5–6	20–25
Ladino clover	⌡ 1	....do	....do	5–6	20–25
Bromegrass	⌠ 10	....do	....do	5–6	20–25
Alfalfa	⌡10–15	....do	....do	5–6	20–25

[1] For information as to best pastures for locality, as well as for time and rate of seeding, consult local county agent.

[2] Usually sown in grass mixtures for hay. Grazed second or third year.

[3] Often seeded together at rate of Sudangrass 10 pounds, soybeans 1 bushel, per acre.

[4] Frequently seeded with grain crops to give solid turf. Also furnishes succulent grazing after grain crops mature.

Composition of Dry Matter and Gross Losses of Dry Matter and Nutrients From Two Lots of Chopped Forage of Different Moisture Content and Dried on Barn Hay Finishers (See "Principles of Making Hay," by R. E. Hodgson, R. E. Davis, W. H. Hosterman, and T. E. Hienton, page 161)

Kinds of chopped forage	Dry matter	Pro-tein	Fiber	Ether extract	N–free extract		Ash	Caro-tene
					Sugar	Total		
Contents:								Micro-grams
High moisture:	Percent	Percent	Percent	Percent	Percent	Percent	Percent	per gram
Put on...........	60. 8	18. 6	27. 9	1. 8	5. 4	45. 1	6. 7	113
Taken off........	85. 8	18. 4	27. 9	1. 9	4. 7	44. 9	6. 9	41
Low moisture:								
Put on...........	67. 1	18. 4	28. 8	1. 7	5. 4	44. 5	6. 6	100
Taken off........	89. 4	18. 4	27. 6	1. 7	5. 0	45. 5	6. 8	47
Losses:								
High moisture......	9. 9	11. 1	9. 8	3. 3	22. 4	10. 3	6. 4	67. 3
Low moisture......	5. 7	5. 7	9. 6	9. 5	11. 0	3. 5	2. 9	55. 7

Rail Rates in Cents Per 100 Pounds of Livestock, Fresh Meat, and Packing-House Products, May 1, 1947 (See "Marketing and Transportation," by Knute Bjorka and W. F. Finner, page 376)

From—	To—	Live-stock [1]	Fresh meat	Packing-house products
Chicago................	New York..............	64	100	68
Columbus..............	.....do..............	49	78	55
Des Moines.............	.....do..............	93	128	94
Austin.................	.....do..............	94	128	94
St. Paul...............	.....do..............	97	134	97
Sioux City.............	.....do..............	106	145	107
Omaha................	.....do..............	103	145	106
Atlanta...............	.....do..............	64	108	77
Nashville.............	.....do..............	69	118	83
Des Moines.............	Chicago.............	41	35	35
Austin................	.....do..............	41	38	34
St. Paul...............	.....do..............	45	35	34
Sioux City.............	.....do..............	49	48	48
Omaha................	.....do..............	48	48	48
Des Moines.............	Los Angeles.............	124	196	163
Fort Dodge.............	.....do..............	127	196	163
Omaha................	.....do..............	118	187	156
Scottsbluff.............	.....do..............	104	175	146
Kansas City............	.....do..............	118	181	151
Denver................	.....do..............	95	167	139
Ogden................	.....do..............	71	130	130
Chicago...............	.....do..............	136	211	176
Do...............	Atlanta................	69	115	86
Do...............	New Orleans.............	81	130	97

[1] Rates apply to double-deck cars for calves, hogs, and sheep, and single-deck cars for cattle.

WHERE TO WRITE FOR INFORMATION ON ACTIVITIES RELATING TO GRASSLANDS

First see your county agricultural agent, who may be able to refer you to a local representative of these agencies

Department of Agriculture, Washington 25, D. C.

Bureau of Plant Industry, Soils, and Agricultural Engineering.—Plant breeding and selection; methods of growing, harvesting, transporting, and storing crop plants. Soil classification and determination of best systems of soil management. Engineering problems of farm machinery, equipment, and structures.

Bureau of Animal Industry.—Research on breeding, feeding, and care of all domestic animals except dairy cattle.

Bureau of Dairy Industry.—Research on the breeding, feeding, and care of dairy cattle, and problems in handling and manufacturing dairy products.

Bureau of Agricultural Economics.—Economic problems in farm organization and operation, prices, costs. Statistics on crop and livestock production. Market outlook.

Extension Service.—Adapting results of research to local needs of farmers. Acquainting farmers with the types of assistance available from State and Federal agencies.

Farm Credit Administration.—Short- and long-term credit on a sound basis to farmers, stockmen, and their cooperatives.

Farmers Home Administration.—Supervised loans on a sound basis to low-income farmers for farm ownership, production, and subsistence and water facilities.

Agricultural Conservation Programs Branch.—Working through State and local committees makes payments to farmers for performance of soil-building and soil-conserving practices.

Forest Service.—Research on grazing management, artificial revegetation, range forage investigations, and range watershed studies. Administers grazing privileges on national forests.

Soil Conservation Service.—Research on methods of handling farm and range land to minimize soil and water losses. Provides technical assistance in planning farms for erosion control and in establishing conservation practices.

Department of the Interior, Washington 25, D. C.

Fish and Wildlife Service, 222 North Bank Drive, Chicago 54, Ill.—Research in conservation, restoration, and control of wildlife on forage crop and grazing areas, including that on rodents and predators.

Bureau of Land Management.—Administers grazing on about 180 million acres of Federal range lands in Western States. Range improvement and soil and water conservation projects on these lands.

Office of Indian Affairs.—Provides guidance for conservation and improvement of Indian lands through planned use, irrigation, erosion control, forest and range management, and development of natural resources.

Office of Land Utilization.—Coordinates range-management programs and directs the soil and moisture programs of all land administering bureaus in the Department.

Tennessee Valley Authority, New Sprankle Building, Knoxville, Tenn.

Produces and distributes fertilizers and in cooperation with the land-grant colleges, through test demonstration farms and areas, indicates how they can be used to rebuild soil and control erosion as a foundation for desirable farm adjustments.

LIST OF AGRICULTURAL EXPERIMENT STATIONS
IN THE UNITED STATES

State	Location
ALABAMA	Auburn.
ALASKA	Palmer.
ARIZONA	Tucson.
ARKANSAS	Fayetteville.
CALIFORNIA	Berkeley 4.
COLORADO	Fort Collins.
CONNECTICUT	New Haven 4 (State station).
	Storrs (Storrs station).
DELAWARE	Newark.
FLORIDA	Gainesville.
GEORGIA	Experiment (State station).
	Tifton (Coastal Plain station).
HAWAII	Honolulu 10.
IDAHO	Moscow.
ILLINOIS	Urbana.
INDIANA	La Fayette.
IOWA	Ames.
KANSAS	Manhattan.
KENTUCKY	Lexington 29.
LOUISIANA	University Station, Baton Rouge 3.
MAINE	Orono.
MARYLAND	College Park.
MASSACHUSETTS	Amherst.
MICHIGAN	East Lansing.
MINNESOTA	University Farm, St. Paul 1.
MISSISSIPPI	State College.
MISSOURI	Columbia.
MONTANA	Bozeman.
NEBRASKA	Lincoln 1.
NEVADA	Reno.
NEW HAMPSHIRE	Durham.
NEW JERSEY	New Brunswick.
NEW MEXICO	State College.
NEW YORK	Geneva (State station).
	Ithaca (Cornell station).
NORTH CAROLINA	State College Station, Raleigh.
NORTH DAKOTA	State College Station, Fargo.
OHIO	Wooster.
OKLAHOMA	Stillwater.
OREGON	Corvallis.
PENNSYLVANIA	State College.
PUERTO RICO	Rio Piedras.
RHODE ISLAND	Kingston.
SOUTH CAROLINA	Clemson.
SOUTH DAKOTA	Brookings.
TENNESSEE	Knoxville 16.
TEXAS	College Station.
UTAH	Logan.
VERMONT	Burlington.
VIRGINIA	Blacksburg (College station).
	Norfolk 1 (Truck station).
WASHINGTON	Pullman (College station).
	Puyallup (Western Washington sta.).
WEST VIRGINIA	Morgantown.
WISCONSIN	Madison 6.
WYOMING	Laramie.

Lists of Plant Names

THESE LISTS, prepared under the supervision of William A. Dayton, M. A. Hein, and Roland McKee, give the scientific and common names of grassland plants mentioned in this volume. The purpose is to help the reader identify the plants, especially since many are known by different names in different parts of the United States.

The lists have the general approval of botanists and others who have contributed to this Yearbook of Agriculture, but the reader is advised that it is difficult permanently to fix botanical nomenclature because (for one reason)

names change as new facts are obtained about structure and habits of plants.

First, the scientific names are given in alphabetic order, followed by the common names. The second table alphabetizes the common names, which are followed by the scientific forms.

In each, the genus is given in capital letters (ACACIA); species and varieties listed under a generic name are designated by lower-case letters (greggii); approved common names are printed in small capital letters (CATCLAW ACACIA); synonyms—that is, forms in use but not approved—are in italics (*catclaw*).

SCIENTIFIC NAMES

SCIENTIFIC NAMES	COMMON NAMES
ACACIA	ACACIA
greggii	CATCLAW ACACIA (*catclaw*)
ACER	MAPLE
circinatum	VINE MAPLE
ACTINEA richardsoni	PINGUE (*Colorado rubberweed*)
AESCULUS	BUCKEYE
californica	CALIFORNIA BUCKEYE
glabra	OHIO BUCKEYE
hippocastanum	HORSECHESTNUT
AGROPYRON	WHEATGRASS
cristatum	CRESTED WHEATGRASS
Hort. var.[1] FAIRWAY	
dasystachyum	THICKSPIKE WHEATGRASS
desertorum	DESERT WHEATGRASS

[1] "Hort. var." and "Hort. vars." are abbreviations for "horticultural variety" and "horticultural varieties," respectively.   "Sp." stands for "Spanish."   In a few instances "grass" has been shortened to "gr."

SCIENTIFIC NAMES	COMMON NAMES
elongatum	TALL WHEATGRASS
inerme (*A. spicatum* var. *inerme*)	BEARDLESS WHEATGRASS (*beardless blue-bunch wheatgrass*)
intermedium	INTERMEDIATE WHEATGRASS
michnoi	
repens	QUACKGRASS
riparium	STREAMBANK WHEATGRASS
saundersii	SAUNDERS WHEATGRASS
semicostatum	DROOPING WHEATGRASS
sibiricum	SIBERIAN WHEATGRASS
smithii	BLUESTEM WHEATGRASS; WESTERN WHEAT-GRASS
spicatum	BLUEBUNCH WHEATGRASS; BEARDED BLUE-BUNCH WHEATGRASS
subsecundum	BEARDED WHEATGRASS
trachycaulum (*A. pauciflorum*)	SLENDER WHEATGRASS
trichophorum	STIFFHAIR WHEATGRASS (*pubescent wheat-gr.*)
AGROSTEMMA githago	CORNCOCKLE
AGROSTIS	BENT (*bentgrass*)
alba	REDTOP (*herdsgrass*)
canina	VELVET BENT
Hort. vars. of velvet bent	
KERNWOOD	
PIPER	
RARITAN	
hiemalis	WINTER BENT (*ticklegrass*)
nebulosa	CLOUD BENT (*cloudgrass*)
palustris	CREEPING BENT
Hort. vars. of creeping bent	
ARLINGTON	
COHANSEY	
COLLINS	
CONGRESSIONAL	
METROPOLITAN	
NORBECK	
SEASIDE	
TORONTO	
WASHINGTON	
tenuis	COLONIAL BENT
Hort. vars. of colonial bent	
ASTORIA	
HIGHLAND	
AIRA	HAIRGRASS (*silver hairgrass*)
ALLENROLFEA occidentalis	PICKLEWEED
ALOPECURUS pratensis	MEADOW FOXTAIL
ALYSICARPUS vaginalis	ALYCECLOVER
AMELANCHIER	SERVICEBERRY
AMMOPHILA	BEACHGRASS
arenaria	EUROPEAN BEACHGRASS
breviligulata	AMERICAN BEACHGRASS
ANANAS comosus	PINEAPPLE
ANDROMEDA	ANDROMEDA
ANDROPOGON	BLUESTEM (*beardgrass*)
divergens	PINEWOODS BLUESTEM
gerardi (*A. furcatus*)	BIG BLUESTEM (*big bluejoint; bluejoint turkeyfoot*)
hallii	SAND BLUESTEM (*turkeyfoot*)
intermedius	AUSTRALIAN BLUESTEM
var. caucasius	CAUCASIAN BLUESTEM
ischaemum	TURKESTAN BLUESTEM (*yellow beardgrass; yellow bluestem*)
littoralis	SEACOAST BLUESTEM
saccharoides	SILVER BLUESTEM (*silver beardgrass*)
scoparius	LITTLE BLUESTEM (*prairie beardgrass*)
tener	SLENDER BLUESTEM

SCIENTIFIC NAMES   COMMON NAMES

SCIENTIFIC NAMES	COMMON NAMES
virginicus	BROOMSEDGE (*yellowsedge bluestem*)
ANEMONE patens (*Pulsatilla patens*)	SPREADING PASQUEFLOWER
ANTHOXANTHUM odoratum	SWEET VERNALGRASS (*sweet vernal*)
ANTHYLLIS vulneraria	KIDNEYVETCH
AULOPAPPUS	GOLDENWEED
heterophyllus	JIMMYWEED
tenuisectus (*A. fruticosus*)	BURROWEED
APOCYNUM	DOGBANE
ARACHIS hypogaea	PEANUT (*groundnut*)
N. B. "Runner" and "Spanish" represent large groups of peanut, rather than horticultural varieties.	
ARCTOSTAPHYLOS	MANZANITA
ARGEMONE	PRICKLEPOPPY
ARISAEMA triphyllum	JACK-IN-THE-PULPIT (*Indian-turnip*)
ARISTIDA	THREE-AWN (*wiregrass*)
longiseta	RED THREE-AWN
purpurea	PURPLE THREE-AWN
stricta	PINELAND THREE-AWN
ARRHENATHERUM elatius	TALL OATGRASS
Hort. var. TUALATIN	
ARTEMISIA	SAGEBRUSH (*wormwood*)
cana	SILVER SAGEBRUSH
dracunculoides	FALSE-TARRAGON SAGEBRUSH (*green sagebrush*)
filifolia	SAND SAGEBRUSH
frigida	FRINGED SAGEBRUSH (*estafiata; silver sage*)
gnaphalodes	CUDWEED SAGEBRUSH
nova	BLACK SAGEBRUSH
spinescens	BUD SAGEBRUSH
tridentata	BIG SAGEBRUSH
tripartita	THREETIP SAGEBRUSH
ARTOCARPUS altilis	BREADFRUIT
ARUNDINARIA tecta	SWITCH CANE (*small cane*)
ASCLEPIAS	MILKWEED
incarnata	SWAMP MILKWEED
tuberosa	BUTTERFLY MILKWEED
verticillata	WHORLED MILKWEED
Aspidium filixmas (*See* DRYOPTERIS filixmas)	
ASTRAGALUS	LOCO; MILKVETCH; POISONVETCH
cicer	CHICKPEA MILKVETCH (*cicer milkvetch*)
coltoni	COLTON LOCO
falcatus	SICKLEPOD MILKVETCH (*sickle milkvetch*)
rubyi	RUBY MILKVETCH
ASTREBLA pectinata	MITCHELLGRASS
ATRIPLEX	SALTBUSH
canescens	FOURWING SALTBUSH (*chamiza*)
confertifolia	SHADSCALE SALTBUSH (*shadscale*)
AVENA sativa	OATS
Hort. vars. of oats	
CALIFORNIA RED	
KANATA	
VENTURA	
AXONOPUS affinis	COMMON CARPETGRASS
Azalea (*See* RHODODENDRON)	AZALEA (*honeysuckle*)
BALSAMORHIZA sagittata	ARROWLEAF BALSAMROOT
BECKMANNIA syzigachne	AMERICAN SLOUGHGRASS
BIDENS	BEGGARTICK
BLEPHARONEURON tricholepis	PINE DROPSEED
BOUTELOUA	GRAMA
curtipendula	SIDE-OATS GRAMA
Hort. var. TUCSON	
eriopoda	BLACK GRAMA
filiformis	SLENDER GRAMA

SCIENTIFIC NAMES	COMMON NAMES
gracilis	BLUE GRAMA
hirsuta	HAIRY GRAMA
rothrockii	ROTHROCK GRAMA
BRACHIARIA ciliatissima	PERENNIAL SIGNALGRASS
BRASSICA	
napus	RAPE (*winter rape*)
Hort. var. DWARF ESSEX	
nigra	BLACK MUSTARD
oleracea var. gongylodes (*B. caulorapa*)	KOHLRABI
BRIZA	QUAKINGGRASS
maxima	BIG QUAKINGGRASS
media	PERENNIAL QUAKINGGRASS
minor	LITTLE QUAKINGGRASS
BROMUS	BROME
arvensis	FIELD BROME
carinatus (incl. *B. marginatus*)[2]	MOUNTAIN BROME (*California brome*)
catharticus	RESCUEGRASS (*rescue brome*)
erectus	MEADOW BROME
inermis	SMOOTH BROME
Hort. vars. of smooth brome	
ACHENBACH	
ELSBERRY	
FISCHER	
LINCOLN	
MARTIN	
marginatus (*See* B. carinatus)[2]	
mollis	SOFT BROME (*soft chess*)
secalinus	CHESS BROME (*chess; cheat*)
tectorum	CHEATGRASS BROME; CHEATGRASS (*downy brome; downy cheat*)
BUCHLOË DACTYLOIDES	BUFFALOGRASS
CACTACEAE	CACTI (any plant of the cactus family)
CAJANUS cajan (*C. indicus*)	PIGEONPEA
CALAMAGROSTIS	REEDGRASS
canadensis	BLUEJOINT REEDGRASS (*bluejoint; bluetop*)
rubescens	PINEGRASS
CALAMOVILFA	SANDREED
gigantea	BIG SANDREED (*giant reedgrass*)
longifolia	PRAIRIE SANDREED (*prairie reedgrass; prairie sandgrass*)
CAMELINA sativa	BIGSEED FALSEFLAX
CANNABIS SATIVA	HEMP
CARDARIA	WHITETOP
CAREX	SEDGE
filifolia	THREADLEAF SEDGE; NIGGERWOOL
CARICA papaya	PAPAYA
CASSIA tora	SICKLE SENNA
CEANOTHUS	CEANOTHUS
americanus	JERSEYTEA CEANOTHUS (*redroot*)
integerrimus	DEERBRUSH CEANOTHUS
thyrsiflorus	BLUEBLOSSOM CEANOTHUS
CELTIS	HACKBERRY
CENCHRUS	SANDBUR
CENTAUREA	CENTAUREA
solstitialis	STARTHISTLE
CERASTIUM	CHICKWEED
CERCOCARPUS	MOUNTAIN-MAHOGANY
betuloides	BIRCHLEAF MOUNTAIN-MAHOGANY (*birchleaf mahogany*)
montanus	TRUE MOUNTAIN-MAHOGANY
CHAMAECRISTA fasciculata	SHOWY PARTRIDGE-PEA
CHENOPODIUM	GOOSEFOOT

[2] This synonym is controversial. If *B. marginatus* is regarded as a distinct species it should be called mountain brome and *B. carinatus,* California brome.

SCIENTIFIC NAMES   COMMON NAMES

album	LAMBSQUARTERS
ambrosioides	WORMSEED
CHLORIS	CHLORIS
distichophylla	WEEPING CHLORIS
gayana	RHODESGRASS
inflata	FLATSTEM CHLORIS (*Mexican bluegrass*) HORQUETILLA MORADA (Sp.)
CHRYSOTHAMNUS	RABBITBRUSH
nauseosus	RUBBER RABBITBRUSH
stenophyllus	SMALL RABBITBRUSH
CICER arietinum	GARBANZO; CHICKPEA
CICUTA	WATERHEMLOCK
douglasii (*C. occidentalis*)	DOUGLAS WATERHEMLOCK
maculata	SPOTTED WATERHEMLOCK
CITRUS paradisi	GRAPEFRUIT
CITRUS sinensis	SWEET ORANGE
COFFEA arabica	COFFEE
CONIUM maculatum	POISONHEMLOCK
CONVOLVULUS arvensis	BINDWEED
CORONILLA varia	CREEPING CROWNVETCH; VARIA CROWN-VETCH
CORTADERIA selloana	PAMPASGRASS
COWANIA stansburiana	STANSBURY CLIFFROSE (*cliffrose*)
CREPIS acuminata	TAPERTIP HAWKSBEARD
CROTALARIA	CROTALARIA (*rattlebox*)
incana	SHAK CROTALARIA
intermedia	SLENDERLEAF CROTALARIA
juncea	SUNN CROTALARIA
lanceolata	LANCE CROTALARIA
mucronata (*C. striata*)	STRIPED CROTALARIA
spectabilis	SHOWY CROTALARIA
CYAMOPSIS tetragonoloba	GUAR
CYNODON dactylon	BERMUDA-GRASS (*wiregrass*)
Hort. vars. of Bermuda-grass	
COASTAL	
TIFT	
CYNOSURUS cristatus	CRESTED DOGTAIL
DACTYLIS glomerata	ORCHARDGRASS (*cocksfoot*)
Hort. var. AKAROA	
DALEA alopecuroides	FOXTAIL DALEA
DANTHONIA	DANTHONIA (*oatgrass*)
spicata	POVERTY DANTHONIA; POVERTYGRASS
DATURA stramonium	JIMSONWEED
DELPHINIUM	LARKSPUR
menziesii	MENZIES LARKSPUR
tricorne	ROCK LARKSPUR (*dwarf larkspur*)
DESCHAMPSIA caespitosa	TUFTED HAIRGRASS
DESMAZERIA sicula	DESMAZERIA
DESMODIUM	TICKCLOVER; BEGGARWEED (*beggar-lice*)
arenicola	SAND TICKCLOVER
canum	KAIMI-CLOVER
purpureum	TALL TICKCLOVER (*Florida beggarweed*)
uncinatum	SPANISH-CLOVER
DICENTRA cucullaria	DUTCHMANS-BREECHES (*staggerweed*)
DIGITARIA	CRABGRASS; FINGERGRASS
decumbens	PANGOLAGRASS (*spreading c r a b g r a s s; spreading fingergrass*)
pentzii	PENTZ FINGERGRASS (*woollyfinger*)
runyoni	DUNE FINGERGRASS
sanguinalis	HAIRY CRABGRASS
stolonifera	WOOLLYFINGER
DISTICHLIS	SALTGRASS
stricta	INLAND SALTGRASS (*desert saltgrass*)
DOLICHOS lablab	HYACINTH-BEAN
DRYOPTERIS filixmas (*Aspidium filixmas*)	MALEFERN

SCIENTIFIC NAMES	COMMON NAMES
ECHINOCHLOA crusgalli	BARNYARDGRASS
var. frumentacea	JAPANESE-MILLET
ELEUSINE indica	GOOSEGRASS
ELYMUS	WILD-RYE (*ryegrass*)
canadensis	CANADA WILD-RYE
Hort. var. MANDAN	
chinensis (*E. pseudoagropyron*)	CHINESE WILD-RYE
condensatus	GIANT WILD-RYE
flavescens	YELLOW WILD-RYE
giganteus	SIBERIAN WILD-RYE (*mammoth wild-rye*)
glaucus	BLUE WILD-RYE
junceus	RUSSIAN WILD-RYE
macounii	MACOUN WILD-RYE
mollis	COMMON DUNE WILD-RYE (*American dune-grass; beach wild-rye*)
triticoides	CREEPING WILD-RYE (*beardless wild-rye*)
virginicus	VIRGINIA WILD-RYE
ELYONURUS tripsacoides	FALSE-GAMA; BALSAMSCALE
EPILOBIUM angustifolium	FIREWEED
EQUISETUM arvense	FIELD HORSETAIL
ERAGROSTIS	LOVEGRASS
amabilis	FEATHER LOVEGRASS
chloromelas	BOER LOVEGRASS
curvula	WEEPING LOVEGRASS
intermedia	PLAINS LOVEGRASS
lehmanniana	LEHMANN LOVEGRASS
obtusa	FLARESCALE LOVEGRASS
obtusiflora	ALKALI LOVEGRASS
spectabilis	PURPLE LOVEGRASS
tef (*E. abyssinica*)	TEFF LOVEGRASS
tenella	JAPANESE LOVEGRASS
trichodes	SAND LOVEGRASS
EREMOCHLOA ophiuroides	CENTIPEDEGRASS
ERIANTHUS	PLUMEGRASS
ERIGERON	FLEABANE
canadensis	HORSEWEED
strigosus	WHITETOP FLEABANE
ERIOGONUM	ERIOGONUM
ERODIUM	HERONBILL
cicutarium	ALFILERIA; FILAREE
EUCHLAENA mexicana	TEOSINTE
Eugenia cumini (See SYZYGIUM cumini)	
EUPATORIUM	EUPATORIUM
adenophorum	PAMAKANI
perfoliatum	BONESET
rugosum (*E. urticaefolium*)	WHITE SNAKEROOT
EUPHORBIA	EUPHORBIA
corollata	FLOWERING EUPHORBIA (*flowering spurge*)
esula	LEAFY EUPHORBIA (*leafy spurge*)
EUROTIA	WINTERFAT
lanata	COMMON WINTERFAT (*winterfat*)
FESTUCA	FESCUE
arizonica	ARIZONA FESCUE
capillata	HAIR FESCUE (*fine-leaved fescue; various-leaved fescue*)
elatior	MEADOW FESCUE
var. arundinacea	TALL FESCUE (*reed fescue*)
Hort. vars. of tall fescue	
ALTA	
KY. 31 (*Suiter's grass*)	
idahoensis	IDAHO FESCUE (*bluebunch fescue*)
megalura	FOXTAIL FESCUE
myuros	RATTAIL FESCUE
octoflora	SIXWEEKS FESCUE

SCIENTIFIC NAMES	COMMON NAMES
ovina	SHEEP FESCUE
var. duriuscula	HARD FESCUE
rubra	RED FESCUE
Hort. vars. of red fescue	
ILLAHEE	
RAINIER	
var. commutata	CHEWINGS FESCUE
var. heterophylla	SHADE FESCUE
FLOURENSIA cernua	TARBUSH
FRANSERIA dumosa	WHITE BUR-SAGE
GAULTHERIA shallon	SALAL
GERANIUM	GERANIUM; CRANESBILL
GEUM	AVENS
GLOTTIDIUM vesicarium	BAGPOD
GLYCERIA	MANNAGRASS
GLYCINE max (*G. soja; Soja max*)	SOYBEAN
GLYCYRRHIZA lepidota	AMERICAN LICORICE (*wild licorice*)
GRAMINEAE	GRASSES; THE GRASS FAMILY
GRAYIA	HOPSAGE
GRINDELIA squarrosa	CURLYCUP GUMWEED
GUAIACUM sanctum	GUAYACAN BLANCO; GUAYACANILLO (Spanish names); ROUGHBARK LIGNUMVITAE
GUTIERREZIA	SNAKEWEED
dracunculoides	TARRAGON SNAKEWEED (*annual broomweed*)
sarothrae	BROOM SNAKEWEED (*snakeweed*)
GYMNOCLADUS dioicus	KENTUCKY COFFEETREE
GYNERIUM sagittatum	UVAGRASS
HEDYSARUM	SWEETVETCH
boreale	NORTHERN SWEETVETCH
coronarium	SULLA; SULLA SWEETVETCH
HELENIUM	SNEEZEWEED
autumnale	COMMON SNEEZEWEED
hoopesii	ORANGE SNEEZEWEED (*western sneezeweed*)
tenuifolium	BITTERWEED (*bitter sneezeweed*)
HELIANTHUS	SUNFLOWER
angustifolius	SWAMP SUNFLOWER
annuus	COMMON SUNFLOWER
tuberosus	JERUSALEM-ARTICHOKE
HERACLEUM lanatum	COMMON COWPARSNIP
HILARIA	HILARIA
belangeri	CURLY-MESQUITE
jamesii	GALLETA
mutica	TOBOSA
rigida	BIG GALLETA
HOLCUS	VELVETGRASS
lanatus	COMMON VELVETGRASS (*Yorkshire fog*)
mollis	GERMAN VELVETGRASS
HORDEUM	BARLEY
bulbosum	BULBOUS BARLEY
jubatum	FOXTAIL BARLEY (*squirreltail barley*)
nodosum	MEADOW BARLEY
vulgare	BARLEY
HYOSCYAMUS niger	BLACK HENBANE
HYPARRHENIA	
hirta	
rufa	JARAGUA (*jaragua grass*)
HYPERICUM perforatum	COMMON ST. JOHNSWORT
ILEX glabra	GALLBERRY; INKBERRY
IMPERATA cylindrica	COGONGRASS (*cogon satintail*)
INDIGOFERA	INDIGO
endecaphylla	CREEPING INDIGO
hirsuta	HAIRY INDIGO
IPOMOEA batatas	SWEETPOTATO

SCIENTIFIC NAMES

COMMON NAMES

JUNCUS	RUSH
balticus	BALTIC RUSH
roemerianus	BLACK RUSH; NEEDLEGRASS RUSH
JUNIPERUS	JUNIPER
KALMIA	KALMIA (*laurel*)
latifolia	MOUNTAIN-LAUREL
KOELERIA cristata	PRAIRIE JUNEGRASS; JUNEGRASS
KRAMERIA	RATANY
LAGURUS ovatus	HARESTAIL
LANTANA camara	COMMON LANTANA
LAPPULA redowskii (*L. occidentalis*)	WESTERN STICKSEED
LARREA tridentata	CREOSOTEBUSH
LATHYRUS	PEAVINE
cicer	FLATPOD PEAVINE (*falcon-pea*)
hirsutus	ROUGHPEA (*Caley-pea; singletary pea*)
japonicus	MARITIME PEAVINE (*purple beachpea*)
leucanthus	ASPEN PEAVINE
sativus	GRASSPEA
sylvestris	FLATPEA
tingitanus	TANGIER-PEA; TANGIER PEAVINE
LEDUM	LEDUM
LEGUMINOSAE	LEGUMES; THE LEGUME, OR PEA FAMILY
LENS culinaris (*L. esculenta*)	COMMON LENTIL
LEPIDIUM	PEPPERWEED
densiflorum	PRAIRIE PEPPERWEED
sativum	GARDENCRESS
Leptoglottis portoricensis (See SCHRAN-KIA)	PUERTO RICO SENSITIVEBRIER; ZARZARILLA (Spanish name)
LEPTOLOMA cognatum	FALL WITCHGRASS
LEPTOTAENIA	LEPTOTAENIA (*wild carrot*) [3]
LESPEDEZA	LESPEDEZA
bicolor	BICOLOR LESPEDEZA (*shrub lespedeza*)
cuneata (*L. sericea*)	SERICEA LESPEDEZA (*Chinese lespedeza*)
cyrtobotrya	CYRTO LESPEDEZA (*bush lespedeza*)
hedysaroides	RUSH LESPEDEZA
latissima	DECUMBENT LESPEDEZA
sericea (See L. cuneata)	
stipulacea	KOREAN LESPEDEZA
Hort. var. CLIMAX	
striata	COMMON LESPEDEZA
Hort. vars. of common lespedeza	
KOBE	
TENNESSEE 76	
thunbergii	THUNBERG LESPEDEZA
LEUCAENA glauca	WHITE-POPINAC; KOA HAOLE (Hawaiian name)
LEUCOTHOE	LEUCOTHOE
LINARIA vulgaris	BUTTER-AND-EGGS
LOBELIA inflata	INDIAN-TOBACCO
LOLIUM	RYEGRASS
multiflorum	ITALIAN RYEGRASS; COMMON RYEGRASS
perenne	PERENNIAL RYEGRASS
rigidum (*L. subulatum*)	WIMMERA RYEGRASS
LOTUS	DEERVETCH; TREFOIL
corniculatus	BIRDSFOOT TREFOIL; BIRDSFOOT DEERVETCH
var. arvensis	BROADLEAF BIRDSFOOT TREFOIL
var. tenuifolius	NARROWLEAF BIRDSFOOT TREFOIL
uliginosus (*L. major*)	BIG TREFOIL; WETLAND DEERVETCH (*marsh birdsfoot trefoil*)
wrightii	WRIGHT DEERVETCH (*red-and-yellow-pea*)
LUPINUS	LUPINE
albus	WHITE LUPINE

[3] "Wild carrot" is properly applicable only to wild spp. of Daucus.

SCIENTIFIC NAMES	COMMON NAMES
angustifolius	BLUE LUPINE
caudatus	TAILCUP LUPINE
luteus	YELLOW LUPINE
perennis	SUNDIAL LUPINE
subcarnosus	BLUEBONNET; TEXAS LUPINE
MACLURA pomifera	OSAGE-ORANGE
MADIA	TARWEED
glomerata	CLUSTER TARWEED
MAHONIA	MAHONIA
aquifolium	OREGON-GRAPE
MANGIFERA indica	MANGO
MARISCUS	SAWGRASS
MARRUBIUM vulgare	COMMON HOARHOUND
MEDICAGO	MEDIC; BUR-CLOVER; LUCERNE
arabica	SPOTTED MEDIC; SPOTTED BUR-CLOVER
Hort. vars. of spotted medic	
GIANT	
MANGANESE	
falcata	YELLOW ALFALFA (*sickle alfalfa*)
gaetula	LIBYAN MEDIC
hispida	CALIFORNIA BUR-CLOVER
lupulina	BLACK MEDIC (*yellow trefoil*)
minima	LITTLE BUR-CLOVER; LITTLE MEDIC
orbicularis	BUTTONCLOVER; BUTTON MEDIC
platycarpa	BROADPOD MEDIC
ruthenica	RUTHENIAN MEDIC
sativa	PURPLE ALFALFA
Hort. vars. of purple alfalfa	
BUFFALO	
HARDISTAN	
KANSAS COMMON	
NEMASTAN	
NORTHERN COMMON	
ORESTAN	
PERUVIAN	
SOUTHERN COMMON	
sativa var. media	VARIEGATED ALFALFA
ATLANTIC	
BALTIC	
CANADIAN VARIEGATED	
COSSACK	
GRIMM	
HARDIGAN	
LADAK	
RANGER	
scutellata	SNAIL MEDIC (*snailclover*)
MELICA	MELIC
MELILOTUS	SWEETCLOVER
alba	WHITE SWEETCLOVER
Hort. vars. of white sweetclover	
EMERALD	
EVERGREEN	
HUBAM	
SANGAMON	
SPANISH	
WILLAMETTE	
dentata	BANAT SWEETCLOVER
indica	SOURCLOVER (*annual yellow sweetclover; sour sweetclover*)
officinalis	YELLOW SWEETCLOVER
Hort. vars. of yellow sweetclover	
ERECTOR	
MADRID	
suaveolens	DAGHESTAN SWEETCLOVER

SCIENTIFIC NAMES	COMMON NAMES
MELINIS minutiflora	MOLASSESGRASS
MELIOSMA obtusifolia	CERRILLO (Sp.); PUERTO RICO MELIOSMA
MENZIESIA	MENZIESIA (skunkbush)
MESEMBRYANTHEMUM	MESEMBRYANTHEMUM
crystallinum	ICEPLANT
MIMOSA	MIMOSA
pudica	SENSITIVEPLANT
MISCANTHUS sinensis	CHINESE SILVERGRASS (swordgrass; eulalia)
MUHLENBERGIA	MUHLY
capillaris	HAIRAWN MUHLY
expansa	CUTOVER MUHLY
montana	MOUNTAIN MUHLY
monticola	MESA MUHLY
porteri	BUSH MUHLY
pungens	SANDHILL MUHLY
torreyi	RING MUHLY (ringgrass)
MUSA paradisiaca var. sapientum	COMMON BANANA
ONOBRYCHIS viciaefolia	SAINFOIN; COMMON SAINFOIN
OPUNTIA	PRICKLYPEAR
megacantha	MISSION PRICKLYPEAR (panini)
ORNITHOGALUM	STAR-OF-BETHLEHEM
ORNITHOPUS sativus	SERRADELLA
ORYZOPSIS	RICEGRASS
bloomeri	BLOOMER RICEGRASS
hymenoides	INDIAN RICEGRASS
miliacea	SMILOGRASS
OSMORHIZA occidentalis	SWEET-ANISE
OSMUNDA cinnamomea	CINNAMONFERN
OXYTROPIS lambertii	CRAZYWEED
PACHYSANDRA	PACHYSANDRA
PANICUM	PANICUM; PANICGRASS
antidotale	BLUE PANIC (giant panicgrass)
hemitomon	MAIDENCANE
maximum	GUINEAGRASS
miliaceum	PROSO (broomcorn millet; hog millet)
obtusum	VINE-MESQUITE
purpurascens	PARAGRASS
repens	TORPEDOGRASS; TORPEDO PANICUM
virgatum	SWITCHGRASS
Hort. var. BLACKWELL	
PASPALUM	PASPALUM
conjugatum	HILOGRASS
dilatatum	DALLISGRASS
laeve	FIELD PASPALUM
malacophyllum	RIBBED PASPALUM
monostachyum	GULF DUNE PASPALUM (dune paspalum)
notatum	BAHIAGRASS
Hort. var. of Bahiagrass	
PARAGUAY	
PENSACOLA	
plicatulum	BROWNSEED PASPALUM
stramineum	SAND PASPALUM
urvillei	VASEYGRASS
vaginatum	SEASHORE PASPALUM
PENNISETUM	PENNISETUM
clandestinum	KIKUYUGRASS
glaucum	PEARLMILLET (cattail millet)
purpureum	NAPIERGRASS
ruppelii	FOUNTAINGRASS
setaceum	WEST INDIES PENNISETUM
villosum	FEATHERTOP
PENSTEMON	PENSTEMON
PERSEA americana	AVOCADO (alligator-pear)

SCIENTIFIC NAMES	COMMON NAMES
PHALARIS	CANARYGRASS
arundinacea	REED CANARYGRASS
Hort. vars. of reed canarygrass	
IOREED	
SUPERIOR	
canariensis	CANARYGRASS
caroliniana	CAROLINA CANARYGRASS
tuberosa	LARGE CANARYGRASS
var. stenoptera	HARDINGGRASS
PHASEOLUS	BEAN
aconitifolius	MAT BEAN (*moth bean*)
acutifolius	TEXAS BEAN
var. latifolius	TEPARY BEAN
angularis	ADSUKI BEAN
aureus	MUNG BEAN
calcaratus	RICE BEAN
PHLEUM	TIMOTHY (*Herd's grass*)
alpinum	ALPINE TIMOTHY
pratense	TIMOTHY
Hort. vars. of timothy	
ITASCA	
LORAIN	
MARIETTA	
PHRAGMITES communis	COMMON REED
PHYTOLACCA americana (*P. decandra*)	COMMON POKEBERRY (*garget; pigeonberry; scoke*)
PICEA engelmanni	ENGELMANN SPRUCE
PINUS	PINE
caribaea	SLASH PINE
contorta var. latifolia	LODGEPOLE PINE
echinata	SHORTLEAF PINE
edulis	PINYON; COLORADO PINYON PINE
monophylla	SINGLELEAF PINYON
ponderosa	PONDEROSA PINE
sabiniana	DIGGER PINE
taeda	LOBLOLLY PINE
PISUM	PEA
sativum var. arvense (*P. arvense*)	FIELD PEA
Hort. vars. of field pea	
AUSTRIAN WINTER	
CANADIAN	
DIXIE WONDER	
PLANTAGO	PLANTAIN
lanceolata	BUCKHORN PLANTAIN
purshii	WOOLLY INDIANWHEAT
PLEUROPOGON	SEMAPHOREGRASS
PLUCHEA camphorata	CAMPHORWEED
POA	BLUEGRASS
ampla	BIG BLUEGRASS
annua	ANNUAL BLUEGRASS
arachnifera	TEXAS BLUEGRASS
bulbosa	BULBOUS BLUEGRASS (*winter bluegrass*)
compressa	CANADA BLUEGRASS
nevadensis	NEVADA BLUEGRASS
pratensis	KENTUCKY BLUEGRASS
secunda (*P. sandbergii*)	SANDBERG BLUEGRASS
trivialis	ROUGHSTALK BLUEGRASS (*rough bluegrass*)
POLYGONUM	KNOTWEED
POPULUS	POPLAR
tremuloides	QUAKING ASPEN (*aspen*)
POTENTILLA	CINQUEFOIL
PROSOPIS	MESQUITE
chilensis	CHILEAN MESQUITE (ALGAROBA and KIAWE, Hawaiian names)
juliflora	COMMON MESQUITE

SCIENTIFIC NAMES	COMMON NAMES
PRUNUS	CHERRY; CHOKECHERRY; PLUM
augustifolia	CHICKASAW PLUM
var. watsonii (*P. watsonii*)	SAND PLUM; CHICKASAW SAND PLUM
serotina	BLACK CHERRY
PSEUDOTSUGA taxifolia	DOUGLAS-FIR
PSIDIUM guajava	GUAVA
PTERIDIUM aquilinum	BRACKEN
PUCCINELLIA nuttalliana	NUTTALL ALKALI-GRASS (*salt meadow grass*)
PUERARIA	KUDZU (*kudzubean*)
phaseoloides	TROPICAL KUDZU
thunbergiana	THUNBERG KUDZU; KUDZU
PURSHIA tridentata	BITTERBRUSH; ANTELOPE BITTERBRUSH
QUERCUS	OAK
alba	WHITE OAK
douglasii	BLUE OAK
gambelii	GAMBEL OAK
havardi	SHINNERY OAK
virginiana	LIVE OAK
wislizeni	INTERIOR LIVE OAK (*Wislizenus oak*)
RANUNCULUS	BUTTERCUP
acris	TALL BUTTERCUP (*tall crowfoot*)
sceleratus	BLISTER BUTTERCUP (*bitter buttercup*)
REDFIELDIA flexuosa	BLOWOUTGRASS
RHODODENDRON (incl. *Azalea*)	RHODODENDRON; AZALEA
RHUS	SUMAC
diversiloba (*See* **TOXICODENDRON** *diversilobum*)	
trilobata	SKUNKBUSH SUMAC (*skunkbush; skunkbrush; lemonade sumac*)
RHYNCHOSPORA	BEAKRUSH
ROBINIA pseudoacacia	BLACK LOCUST
RUBUS spectabilis	SALMONBERRY
RUMEX	DOCK
acetosa	SOUR DOCK
SABAL	PALMETTO
SACCHARUM officinarum	SUGARCANE
SALICORNIA	GLASSWORT (*samphire*)[4]
SALSOLA kali var. tenuifolia	RUSSIAN-THISTLE
SALVIA	SAGE
SANGUISORBA minor	SMALL BURNET; SALAD BURNET
SARCOBATUS	GREASEWOOD
vermiculatus	BLACK GREASEWOOD
SCHRANKIA portoricensis (*Leptoglottis portoricensis*)	PUERTO RICO SENSITIVEBRIER (ZARZARILLA, Spanish name)
SCIRPUS	BULRUSH
SCLEROPOGON brevifolius	BURROGRASS
SECALE cereale	RYE
Hort. vars. of rye	
ABRUZZI (*Abruzzes*)	
BALBO	
montanum	MOUNTAIN RYE
SEDUM acre	GOLDMOSS STONECROP (*biting stonecrop; goldmoss*)
SENECIO	GROUNDSEL
SEQUOIA sempervirens	REDWOOD
SERENOA	SAWPALMETTO
SESBANIA exaltata	HEMP SESBANIA
SETARIA	BRISTLEGRASS MILLET (*foxtail*)
faberii	CHINESE MILLET
italica	FOXTAIL MILLET

---

[4] The name samphire should be restricted to the Old World genus *Crithmum*.

SCIENTIFIC NAMES	COMMON NAMES
Hort. vars. of foxtail millet	
COMMON	
GERMAN	
HUNGARIAN	
SIBERIAN	
WHITE WONDER	
macrostachya	PLAINS BRISTLEGRASS
SIMMONDSIA chinensis (*S. californica*)	JOJOBA
SISYMBRIUM altissimum	TUMBLEMUSTARD (*Jim Hill mustard*)
SITANION	SQUIRRELTAIL
hystrix	BOTTLEBRUSH SQUIRRELTAIL
jubatum	BIG SQUIRRELTAIL
SMILAX	GREENBRIER
Soja max (*See* GLYCINE max)	
SOLANUM	NIGHTSHADE
carolinense	CAROLINA HORSENETTLE (*horsenettle; sand briar*)
nigrum	BLACK NIGHTSHADE
SONCHUS oleraceus	COMMON SOWTHISTLE
SORGHASTRUM nutans	YELLOW INDIANGRASS (*Indiangrass*)
SORGHUM	SORGHUM
halepense	JOHNSONGRASS
vulgare	SORGHUM
Hort. vars. of sorghum	
ATLAS	
AXTEL	
BLACK AMBER	
DAKOTA AMBER	
FREMONT	
LEOTI	
RANCHER	
ROX	
vulgare var. technicum	BROOMCORN
vulgare var. sudanense	SUDANGRASS
Hort. var. TIFT	
SPARTINA	CORDGRASS
alterniflora	SMOOTH CORDGRASS
leiantha (*S. foliosa*)	SPIKE CORDGRASS (*California cordgrass*)
pectinata	PRAIRIE CORDGRASS (*sloughgrass*)
townsendi	TOWNSEND CORDGRASS (*ricegrass*)
SPHAERALCEA coccinea	SCARLET GLOBEMALLOW
SPOROBOLUS	DROPSEED
airoides	ALKALI SACATON
asper	TALL DROPSEED (*longleaf rushgrass; rough rushgrass*)
var. hookeri	MEADOW DROPSEED (*meadow tall dropseed*)
cryptandrus	SAND DROPSEED
curtissii	CURTISS DROPSEED
giganteus	GIANT DROPSEED
gracilis (*S. junceus*)	BLUE DROPSEED (*pineywoods dropseed*)
heterolepis	PRAIRIE DROPSEED
indicus	WEST INDIES SMUTGRASS; MATOJO (Sp.)
junceus (*See* S. gracilis)	
wrightii	SACATON
STENOTAPHRUM *secundatum*	ST. AUGUSTINEGRASS
STIPA	NEEDLEGRASS; STIPA
cernua	NODDING NEEDLEGRASS
comata	NEEDLE-AND-THREAD
lepida	FOOTHILL NEEDLEGRASS
occidentalis	WESTERN NEEDLEGRASS
pulchra	CALIFORNIA NEEDLEGRASS (*purple needlegr.*)
spartea	PORCUPINEGRASS
speciosa	DESERT NEEDLEGRASS
viridula	GREEN NEEDLEGRASS (*feather bunchgrass; green stipa*)

SCIENTIFIC NAMES	COMMON NAMES
STIZOLOBIUM	VELVETBEAN
deeringianum	DEERING VELVETBEAN
STROPHOSTYLES helvola	TRAILING WILDBEAN
SUAEDA	SEEPWEED (*inkweed*)
SYMPHORICARPOS	SNOWBERRY
SYZYGIUM cumini (*Eugenia cumini*)	JAMBOLAN (*Java-plum*)
TARAXACUM	DANDELION
officinale (*T. vulgare*)	COMMON DANDELION
TETRADYMIA	HORSEBRUSH
THYMUS	THYME
vulgaris	COMMON THYME
TILLANDSIA usneoides	SPANISHMOSS
TOXICODENDRON	
diversilobum (*Rhus diversiloba*)	PACIFIC POISON-OAK
radicans (*Rhus toxicodendron* Auth., not L.)	COMMON POISON-IVY
TRACHYPOGON montufari	CRINKLE-AWN
TRIBULUS terrestris	PUNCTUREVINE
TRICHACHNE californica (*Valota saccharata*)	ARIZONA COTTONTOP
TRICHOLAENA repens	NATALGRASS
TRIDENS	TRIDENS (*triodia*)
flavus	PURPLETOP
pilosus	HAIRY TRIDENS
TRIFOLIUM	CLOVER
agrarium	HOP CLOVER
alexandrinum	BERSEEM (*Egyptian clover*)
ambiguum	KURA CLOVER (*Caucasian clover; Pellett clover*)
amphianthum	
carolinianum	CAROLINA CLOVER
dubium	SMALL HOP CLOVER (*least hop clover*)
fendleri	FENDLER CLOVER
fragiferum	STRAWBERRY CLOVER
glomeratum	CLUSTER CLOVER
hirtum	ROSE CLOVER
hybridum	ALSIKE CLOVER
incarnatum	CRIMSON CLOVER
Hort. vars. of crimson clover	
AUBURN	
DIXIE	
lappaceum	LAPPA CLOVER
medium	ZIGZAG CLOVER (*red clover*)
nigrescens	BALL CLOVER
pannonicum	HUNGARIAN CLOVER
pratense	RED CLOVER
Hort. vars. of red clover	
CUMBERLAND	
DOLLARD	
KENLAND	
KY. 215	
MAMMOTH	
MIDLAND	
MONTGOMERY	
TENNESSEE ANTHRACNOSE-RESISTANT	
procumbens	LARGE HOP CLOVER (*low hop clover; big hop*)
reflexum	BUFFALO CLOVER
repens	WHITE CLOVER (*White Dutch clover*)
Hort. vars. of white clover	
COMMON	
KENT WILD	
LADINO	
LOUISIANA	
NEW YORK WILD	
NEW ZEALAND	

SCIENTIFIC NAMES	COMMON NAMES
resupinatum	PERSIAN CLOVER (*shaftal clover*)
striatum	STRIATA CLOVER (*knotted clover*)
subterraneum	SUB CLOVER
Hort. vars. of sub clover	
BACCHUS MARSH	
DWALGANUP	
MT. BARKER	
TALLAROOK	
variegatum	WHITETIP CLOVER
willdenovii (*T. wormskjoldii*)	SIERRA CLOVER; SEASIDE CLOVER
TRIGLOCHIN palustris	ARROW PODGRASS; MARSH ARROWGRASS
TRIGONELLA foenum-graecum	FENUGREEK; FENUGREEK TRIGONELLA
TRIPLASIS purpurea	PURPLE SANDGRASS
TRIPSACUM	GAMAGRASS
dactyloides	EASTERN GAMAGRASS
laxum	GUATEMALA GAMAGRASS (YERBA GUATE-MALA, Spanish name)
TRISETUM flavescens	YELLOW TRISETUM (*yellow oatgrass*)
TRITICUM aestivum	WHEAT
TYPHA	CATTAIL
UNIOLA	UNIOLA
latifolia	BROADLEAF UNIOLA
paniculata	SEA-OATS
VACCINIUM	BLUEBERRY
Valota saccharata (*See* TRICHACHNE californica)	
VICIA	VETCH
angustifolia	NARROWLEAF VETCH
articulata	MONANTHA VETCH (*one-flower vetch*)
atropurpurea	PURPLE VETCH
cracca	BIRD VETCH
dasycarpa	WOOLLYPOD VETCH
faba	HORSEBEAN
var. equina	TICKBEAN
var. major	BROADBEAN
grandiflora	SHOWY VETCH; BIGFLOWER VETCH; GRANDI-FLORA VETCH
pannonica	HUNGARIAN VETCH
sativa	COMMON VETCH
villosa	HAIRY VETCH
var. glabrescens	SMOOTH VETCH
VIGNA sinensis	COWPEA
VINCA	PERIWINKLE; VINCA
XANTHIUM	COCKLEBUR
echinatum	BEACH COCKLEBUR
orientale (*X. canadense*)	ORIENTAL COCKLEBUR
YUCCA	YUCCA
glauca	SMALL SOAPWEED
ZEA mays	CORN; MAIZE
ZIGADENUS	DEATHCAMAS
gramineus	GRASSY DEATHCAMAS
ZIZANIA aquatica	ANNUAL WILDRICE
ZOYSIA	
japonica	JAPANESE LAWNGRASS (*Korean lawngrass*)
matrella	MANILAGRASS
tenuifolia	MASCARENEGRASS

COMMON NAMES

COMMON NAMES	SCIENTIFIC NAMES
ACACIA	ACACIA
ACACIA, CATCLAW	greggii
ALFALFA	MEDICAGO sativa
Hort. vars. of alfalfa	
BALTIC	
BUFFALO	
CANADIAN VARIEGATED	
COSSACK	
GRIMM	
HARDISTAN	
LADAK	
NEMASTAN	
NORTHERN COMMON	
ORESTAN	
PERUVIAN	
RANGER	
SOUTHERN COMMON	
TURKESTAN	
ALFALFA, VARIEGATED	MEDICAGO sativa var. media
ALFALFA, YELLOW	MEDICAGO falcata
ALFILERIA	ERODIUM cicutarium
algaroba (CHILEAN MESQUITE)	PROSOPSIS chilensis
ALKALI-GRASS, NUTTALL	PUCCINELLIA nuttalliana
alligator-pear (AVOCADO)	PERSEA americana
ALYCECLOVER	ALYSICARPUS vaginalis
ANDROMEDA	ANDROMEDA
ARROWGRASS, MARSH; ARROW PODGRASS	TRIGLOCHIN palustris
ASPEN, QUAKING	POPULUS tremuloides
ASPHODELS	ASPHODELEAE, the poisonous Asphodel tribe of the lily family and especially its type genus ASPHODELUS
ASTER	ASTER
AVENS	GEUM
AVOCADO	PERSEA americana
AZALEA (*honeysuckle*)	RHODODENDRON
BAGPOD	GLOTTIDIUM vesicarium
BAHIAGRASS	PASPALUM notatum
Hort. vars. of Bahiagrass	
PARAGUAY	
PENSACOLA	
BALSAMSCALE; FALSE-GAMA	ELYONURUS tripsacoides
BALSAMROOT, ARROWLEAF	BALSAMORHIZA sagittata
BAMBOO	A grass of the BAMBUSEAE, or bamboo tribe of the grass family, and particularly of the type genus Bambusa and closely related genera.
BANANA, COMMON	MUSA paradisiaca var. sapientum
BARLEY	HORDEUM; H. vulgare
BULBOUS	bulbosum
FOXTAIL (*squirreltail barley*)	jubatum
MEADOW	nodosum
BARNYARDGRASS	ECHINOCHLOA crusgalli
BEACHGRASS	AMMOPHILA
AMERICAN	breviligulata
EUROPEAN	arenaria
beachpea, purple (MARITIME PEAVINE)	LATHYRUS japonicus
BEAKRUSH	RHYNCHOSPORA
BEAN	PHASEOLUS
ADSUKI	angularis
MAT (*moth*)	aconitifolius
MUNG	aureus
RICE	calcaratus

COMMON NAMES	SCIENTIFIC NAMES
TEPARY	acutifolius var. latifolius
TEXAS	acutifolius
beardgrass (BLUESTEM)	ANDROPOGON
beardgrass, prairie (LITTLE BLUESTEM)	scoparius
beardgrass, silver (SILVER BLUESTEM)	saccharoides
beardgrass, yellow (TURKESTAN BLUESTEM)	ischaemum
BEGGARTICK	BIDENS
BEGGARWEED; TICKCLOVER	DESMODIUM
beggarweed, Florida (TALL TICKCLOVER)	purpureum
BENT (including "South German mixed bent")	AGROSTIS
CLOUD	nebulosa
COLONIAL	tenuis
Hort. vars. of colonial bent	
ASTORIA	
HIGHLAND	
CREEPING	palustris
Hort. vars. of creeping bent	
ARLINGTON	
COHANSEY	
COLLINS	
CONGRESSIONAL	
METROPOLITAN	
NORBECK	
SEASIDE	
TORONTO	
WASHINGTON	
VELVET	canina
Hort. vars. of velvet bent	
KERNWOOD	
PIPER	
RARITAN	
WINTER	hiemalis
bentgrass (BENT)	AGROSTIS
BERMUDA-GRASS	CYNODON dactylon
Hort. vars. of Bermuda-grass	
COASTAL	
TIFT	
BINDWEED	CONVOLVULUS arvensis
BITTERBRUSH	PURSHIA; P. tridentata
BITTERBRUSH, ANTELOPE; BITTERBRUSH	PURSHIA tridentata
BITTERWEED	HELENIUM tenuifolium
BLOWOUTGRASS	REDFIELDIA flexuosa
BLUEBERRY	VACCINIUM
BLUEBONNET; TEXAS LUPINE	LUPINUS subcarnosus
BLUEGRASS	POA
ANNUAL	annua
BIG	ampla
BULBOUS (*winter*)	bulbosa
CANADA	compressa
KENTUCKY	pratensis
NEVADA	nevadensis
ROUGH; ROUGHSTALK	trivialis
SANDBERG	secunda (*P. sandbergii*)
TEXAS	arachnifera
winter (BULBOUS)	bulbosa
big bluejoint (BIG BLUESTEM)	ANDROPOGON gerardi (*A. furcatus*)
bluejoint (BLUEJOINT REEDGRASS)	CALAMAGROSTIS CANADENSIS
bluejoint turkeyfoot (BIG BLUESTEM)	ANDROPOGON gerardi (*A. furcatus*)
BLUESTEM	ANDROPOGON
BIG	furcatus (*A. gerardi*)
CAUCASIAN	intermedius var. caucasius
LITTLE	scoparius
PINEWOODS	divergens
SAND	hallii
SEACOAST	littoralis

COMMON NAMES	SCIENTIFIC NAMES
SILVER	saccharoides
SLENDER	tener
TURKESTAN BLUESTEM (*yellow bluestem*)	ischaemum
yellowsedge (BROOMSEDGE)	virginicus
bluetop (BLUEJOINT REEDGRASS)	CALAMAGROSTIS canadensis
BONESET	EUPATORIUM perfoliatum
BRACKEN	PTERIDIUM aquilinum
BREADFRUIT	ARTOCARPUS altilis
briar, sand (CAROLINA HORSENETTLE)	SOLANUM carolinense
BRISTLEGRASS; MILLET	SETARIA
PLAINS	macrostachya
BROADBEAN	VICIA faba var. major
BROME	BROMUS
California (MOUNTAIN)	carinatus (*B. marginatus*)[1]
CHEATGRASS	tectorum
CHESS	secalinus
downy (CHEATGRASS)	tectorum
FIELD	arvensis
MEADOW	erectus
MOUNTAIN (*California*)	carinatus (*B. marginatus*)[1]
SMOOTH	inermis
Hort. vars. of smooth brome	
ACHENBACH	
ELSBERRY	
FISCHER	
LINCOLN	
MARTIN	
SOFT	mollis
BROOMCORN	SORGHUM vulgare var. technicum
BROOMSEDGE (*yellow bluestem*)	ANDROPOGON virginicus
broomweed, annual (TARRAGON SNAKE-WEED)	GUTIERREZIA dracunculoides
BUCKEYE	AESCULUS
CALIFORNIA	californica
OHIO	glabra
BUFFALOGRASS	BUCHLOË dactyloides
BULRUSH	SCIRPUS
BUNCHFLOWER	MELANTHIUM [2]
bunchgrass, feather (GREEN NEEDLEGRASS)	STIPA viridula
BUR-CLOVER; LUCERNE; MEDIC	MEDICAGO
CALIFORNIA	hispida
LITTLE; LITTLE MEDIC	minima
southern (SPOTTED)	arabica
SPOTTED (*spotted medic*)	arabica
Hort. vars. of spotted bur-clover	
GIANT	
MANGANESE	
BURNET, SMALL; SALAD BURNET	SANGUISORBA minor
BURROGRASS	SCLEROPOGON brevifolius
BUR-SAGE, WHITE	FRANSERIA dumosa
BUTTER-AND-EGGS	LINARIA vulgaris
BUTTERCUP	RANUNCULUS
BLISTER (*bitter*)	sceleratus
TALL	acris
BUTTONCLOVER; BUTTON MEDIC	MEDICAGO orbicularis
CACTI; CACTUS	CACTACEAE; a member or members of the cactus family
Caley-pea (ROUGHPEA)	LATHYRUS hirsutus
CAMPHORWEED	PLUCHEA camphorata
CANARYGRASS	PHALARIS; P. canariensis
CAROLINA	caroliniana

[1] This synonym is controversial. If *B. marginatus* is regarded as a distinct species it should be called mountain brome and *B. carinatus,* California brome.

[2] The type genus of the bunchflower tribe (*Melianthieae*), a poisonous group of herbs of the lily family.

COMMON NAMES	SCIENTIFIC NAMES
LARGE	tuberosa
REED	arundinacea
Hort. vars. of reed canarygrass	
IOREED	
SUPERIOR	
cane, small (SWITCH CANE)	ARUNDINARIA tecta
CANE, SWITCH	ARUNDINARIA tecta
CARPETGRASS, COMMON	AXONOPUS affinis
carrot, wild (LEPTOTAENIA)	LEPTOTAENIA
catclaw (CATCLAW ACACIA)	ACACIA greggii
CATTAIL	TYPHA
CENTAUREA	CENTAUREA
CEANOTHUS	CEANOTHUS
BLUEBLOSSOM	thyrsiflorus
DEERBRUSH	integerrimus
JERSEYTEA	americanus
CENTIPEDEGRASS	EREMOCHLOA ophiuroides
CERRILLO (Sp.) ; PUERTO RICO MELIOSMA	MELIOSMA obtusifolia
chamiza (FOURWING SALTBUSH)	ATRIPLEX canescens
cheat, downy (CHEATGRASS BROME ; CHEAT- GRASS)	BROMUS tectorum
CHEATGRASS ; CHEATGRASS BROME	BROMUS tectorum
CHERRY ; CHOKEBERRY ; PLUM	PRUNUS
CHERRY, BLACK	PRUNUS serotina
CHESS	BROMUS secalinus
CHICKPEA ; GARBANZO	CICER arietinum
CHICKWEED	CERASTIUM
CHLORIS	CHLORIS
WEEPING	distichophylla
CHOKECHERRY	PRUNUS
CINNAMONFERN	OSMUNDA cinnamomea
CINQUEFOIL	POTENTILLA
CLIFFROSE	COWANIA
CLIFFROSE, STANSBURY	COWANIA stansburiana
CLOVER	TRIFOLIUM
ALSIKE	hybridum
BALL	nigrescens
BERSEEM (*Egyptian*)	alexandrinum
BUFFALO	reflexum
CAROLINA	carolinianum
Caucasian (KURA)	ambiguum
CLUSTER	glomeratum
CRIMSON	incarnatum
Hort. vars. of crimson clover	
AUBURN	
DIXIE	
Egyptian (BERSEEM)	alexandrinum
FENDLER	fendleri
HOP	agrarium
HUNGARIAN	pannonicum
KURA	ambiguum
STRIATA (*knotted*)	striatum
LAPPA	lappaceum
LARGE HOP (*low hop*)	procumbens
least hop (SMALL HOP)	dubium
Pellett (KURA)	ambiguum
PERSIAN	resupinatum
red (ZIGZAG)	medium
RED	pratense
Hort. vars. of red clover	
CUMBERLAND	
DOLLARD	
KENLAND	
KY. 215	
MAMMOTH	
MIDLAND	

COMMON NAMES   SCIENTIFIC NAMES

MONTGOMERY
TENNESSEE   ANTHRACNOSE-
   RESISTANT
ROSE   hirtum
  seaside (SIERRA)   willdenovii (*T. wormskjoldii*)
  shaftal (PERSIAN)   resupinatum
  SIERRA (*seaside*)   willdenovii (*T. wormskjoldii*)
  SMALL HOP (*least hop*)   dubium
  STRAWBERRY   TRIFOLIUM fragiferum
  STRIATA (*knotted*)   striatum
  SUB   subterraneum
     Hort. vars. of sub clover
        BACCHUS MARSH
        DWALGANUP
        MT. BARKER
        TALLAROOK
  WHITE (*White Dutch*)   repens
     Hort. vars. of white clover
        COMMON
        KENT WILD
        LADINO
        LOUISIANA
        NEW YORK WILD
        NEW ZEALAND
  WHITETIP   variegatum
  ZIGZAG   medium .
COCKLEBUR   XANTHIUM
  BEACH   echinatum
  ORIENTAL   orientale (*X. canadense*)
cocksfoot (ORCHARDGRASS)   DACTYLIS glomerata
COFFEE   COFFEA arabica
COFFEETREE, KENTUCKY   GYMNOCLADUS dioicus
COGONGRASS; COGON SATINTAIL   IMPERATA cylindrica
COMPOSITE   A plant of the composite family (COM-
                                            POSITAE or ASTERACEAE)
CORDGRASS   SPARTINA
  California (SPIKE)   leiantha (*S. foliosa*)
  PRAIRIE   pectinata
  SMOOTH   alterniflora
  SPIKE (*California*)   leiantha (*S. foliosa*)
  TOWNSEND   townsendi
CORN; MAIZE   ZEA mays
CORNCOCKLE   AGROSTEMMA githago
COTTONTOP, ARIZONA   TRICHACHNE california (*Valota
                                            saccharata*)
COWPARSNIP, COMMON   HERACLEUM lanatum
COWPEA   VIGNA sinensis
CRABGRASS, HAIRY   DIGITARIA sanguinalis
crabgrass, spreading (PANGOLAGRASS)   DIGITARIA decumbens
CRANESBILL; GERANIUM   GERANIUM
CRAZYWEED   OXYTROPIS lambertii
CREOSOTEBUSH   LARREA tridentata
CRINKLE-AWN   TRACHYPOGON montufari
CROTALARIA   CROTALARIA
  LANCE   lanceolata
  SHAK   incana
  SHOWY   spectabilis
  SLENDERLEAF   intermedia
  STRIPED   mucronata (*C. striata*)
  SUNN   juncea
crowfoot, tall (TALL BUTTERCUP)   RANUNCULUS acris
CROWNVETCH, VARIA (*creeping crownvetch*) CORONILLA varia
CRUCIFER   A plant of the mustard family (CRUCI-
                                            FERAE)
CURLY-MESQUITE   HILARIA belangeri
DALEA, FOXTAIL   DALEA alopecuroides

COMMON NAMES	SCIENTIFIC NAMES
DALLISGRASS	PASPALUM dilatatum
DANDELION	TARAXACUM
COMMON	officinale
DANTHONIA	DANTHONIA
POVERTY; POVERTYGRASS	spicata
DEATHCAMAS	ZIGADENUS
DEATHCAMAS, GRASSY	ZIGADENUS gramineus
DEERVETCH	LOTUS
WETLAND; BIG TREFOIL	uliginosus (*L. major*)
WRIGHT	wrightii
DESMAZERIA	DESMAZERIA sicula
DOCK	RUMEX
SOUR	acetosa
DOGBANE	APOCYNUM
DOGTAIL, CRESTED	CYNOSURUS cristatus
DOUGLAS-FIR	PSEUDOTSUGA taxifolia
DROPSEED	SPOROBOLUS
BLUE; PINEYWOODS	gracilis (*S. junceus*)
CURTISS	curtissii
GIANT	giganteus
MEADOW (*meadow tall*)	asper var. hookeri
PINE	BLEPHARONEURON tricholepis
PINEYWOODS; BLUE	SPOROBOLUS gracilis (*S. junceus*)
PRAIRIE	heterolepis
SAND	cryptandrus
TALL	asper
dunegrass, American (COMMON DUNE WILD-RYE)	ELYMUS mollis
DUTCHMANS-BREECHES	DICENTRA cucullaria
ERIOGONUM	ERIOGONUM
estafiata (FRINGED SAGEBRUSH)	ARTEMISIA frigida
eulalia (CHINESE SILVERGRASS)	MISCANTHUS sinensis
EUPATORIUM	EUPATORIUM
EUPHORBIA	EUPHORBIA
FLOWERING	corollata
LEAFY	esula
falcon-pea (FLATPOD PEAVINE)	LATHYRUS cicer
FALSEFLAX, BIGSEED	CAMELINA sativa
FALSE-GAMA; BALSAMSCALE	ELYONURUS tripsacoides
FEATHERTOP	PENNISETUM villosum
FENUGREEK; FENUGREEK TRIGONELLA	TRIGONELLA foenum-graecum
FESCUE	FESTUCA
ARIZONA	arizonica
bluebunch (IDAHO)	idahoensis
CHEWINGS	rubra var. commutata
fine-leaved (HAIR)	capillata
FOXTAIL	megalura
HAIR (*various-leaved*)	capillata
HARD	ovina var. duriuscula
IDAHO	idahoensis
MEADOW	elatior
Hort. vars. of meadow fescue	
ALTA	
KY. 31	
RATTAIL	myuros
RED	rubra
Hort. vars. of red fescue	
ILLAHEE	
RAINIER	
reed (TALL)	elatior var. arundinacea
SHADE	rubra var. heterophylla
SHEEP	ovina
SIXWEEKS	octoflora
TALL (*reed*)	elatior var. arundinacea

COMMON NAMES	SCIENTIFIC NAMES
FIGWORTS	SCROPHULARIACEAE, and especially the type genus SCROPHULARIA
FILAREE; HERONBILL	ERODIUM
FINGERGRASS	DIGITARIA
DUNE	runyoni
PENTZ	pentzii
spreading (PANGOLAGRASS)	decumbens
FIREWEED	EPILOBIUM angustifolium
FLATPEA	LATHYRUS sylvestris
FLATSTEM CHLORIS (*Mexican bluegrass*)	CHLORIS inflata
FLAX	LINUM
FLEABANE	ERIGERON
WHITETOP	strigosus
FOUNTAINGRASS	PENNISETUM ruppelii
foxtail (MILLET; BRISTLEGRASS)	SETARIA
FOXTAIL, MEADOW	ALOPECURUS pratensis
GALLBERRY; INKBERRY	ILEX glabra
GALLETA	HILARIA jamesii
BIG	rigida
GAMAGRASS, EASTERN	TRIPSACUM dactyloides
GAMAGRASS, GUATEMALA; YERBA GUATEMALA (Spanish name)	TRIPSACUM laxum
GARBANZO	CICER arietinum
GARDENCRESS	LEPIDIUM sativum
garget (COMMON POKEBERRY)	PHYTOLACCA americana (*P. decandra*)
GERANIUM; CRANESBILL	GERANIUM
GLASSWORT	SALICORNIA
GLOBEMALLOW, SCARLET	SPHAERALCEA coccinea
GOOSEFOOT	CHENOPODIUM
GOOSEGRASS	ELEUSINE indica
GRAMA	BOUTELOUA
BLACK	eriopoda
BLUE	gracilis
HAIRY	hirsuta
ROTHROCK	rothrockii
SIDE-OATS	curtipendula
Hort. var. TUCSON	
SLENDER	filiformis
GRAPEFRUIT	CITRUS paradisi
GRASSES	GRAMINEAE
GRASSPEA	LATHYRUS sativus
GREASEWOOD	SARCOBATUS
BLACK	vermiculatus
GREENBRIER	SMILAX
groundnut (PEANUT)	ARACHIS hypogaea
GROUNDSEL	SENECIO
GUAR	CYAMOPSIS tetragonoloba
GUAVA	PSIDIUM guajava
GUAYAN BLANCO (Spanish name); ROUGHBARK LIGNUMVITAE	GUAIACUM sanctum
GUAYACANILLO (Spanish name); ROUGHBARK LIGNUMVITAE	GUAIACUM sanctum
GUINEAGRASS	PANICUM maximum
GUMWEED, CURLYCUP	GRINDELIA squarrosa
HACKBERRY	CELTIS
HAIRGRASS	DESCHAMPSIA
TUFTED	caespitosa
HARDINGGRASS	PHALARIS tuberosa var. stenoptera
HARESTAIL	LAGURUS ovatus
HAWKSBEARD, TAPERTIP	CREPIS acuminata
HEATHS	ERICACEAE, the heath family, and especially the type genus ERICA
HEMP	CANNABIS sativa

COMMON NAMES	SCIENTIFIC NAMES
HENBANE, BLACK	HYOSCYAMUS niger
Herd's grass (TIMOTHY)	PHLEUM pratense
herdsgrass (REDTOP)	AGROSTIS alba
HERONBILL; FILAREE	ERODIUM
HILOGRASS	PASPALUM conjugatum
HOARHOUND, COMMON	MARRUBIUM vulgare
HOLLY	ILEX
honeysuckle (AZALEA)	RHODODENDRON
HOPSAGE	GRAYIA
HORQUETILLA MORADA (Spanish name); FLATSTEM CHLORIS (*Mexican bluegrass*)	CHLORIS inflata
HORSEBEAN	VICIA faba var. equina
HORSEBRUSH	TETRADYMIA
HORSECHESTNUT	AESCULUS hippocastanum
HORSENETTLE, CAROLINA (*horsenettle*)	SOLANUM carolinense
HORSETAIL, FIELD	EQUISETUM arvense
HORSEWEED	ERIGERON canadensis
HYACINTH-BEAN	DOLICHOS lablab
ICEPLANT	MESEMBRYANTHEMUM crystallinum
INDIANGRASS, YELLOW (*Indiangrass*)	SORGHASTRUM nutans
INDIAN-TOBACCO	LOBELIA inflata
Indian-turnip (JACK-IN-THE-PULPIT)	ARISAEMA triphyllum
INDIANWHEAT, WOOLLY	PLANTAGO purshii
INDIGO	INDIGOFERA
CREEPING	endecaphylla
HAIRY	hirsuta
INKBERRY; GALLBERRY	ILEX glabra
inkweed (SEEPWEED)	SUAEDA
JACK-IN-THE-PULPIT	ARISAEMA triphyllum
JAMBOLAN (*Java-plum*)	SYZYGIUM cumini (*Eugenia cumini*)
JAPANESE-MILLET	ECHINOCHLOA crusgalli var. frumentacea
JARAGUA	HYPARRHENIA rufa
Java-plum (JAMBOLAN)	SYZYGIUM cumini (*Eugenia cumini*)
JERUSALEM-ARTICHOKE	HELIANTHUS tuberosus
JIMMYWEED	APLOPAPPUS heterophyllus
JIMSONWEED	DATURA stramonium
JOHNSONGRASS	SORGHUM halepense
JOJOBA	SIMMONDSIA chinensis (*S. californica*)
JUNEGRASS; PRAIRIE JUNEGRASS	KOELERIA cristata
JUNIPER	JUNIPERUS
KAIMI-CLOVER	DESMODIUM canum
KALMIA	KALMIA
KIAWE (Hawaiian name)	PROSOPIS chilensis
KIDNEYVETCH	ANTHYLLIS vulneraria
KIKUYUGRASS	PENNISETUM clandestinum
KNOTWEED	POLYGONUM
KOA HAOLE (Hawaiian name)	LEUCAENA glauca
KOHLRABI	BRASSICA oleracea var. gongylodes
KUDZU (*kudzubean*)	PUERARIA
THUNBERG	thunbergiana
TROPICAL	phaseoloides
LAMBSQUARTERS	CHENOPODIUM album
LANTANA, COMMON	LANTANA camara
LARKSPUR	DELPHINIUM
MENZIES	menziesii
ROCK	tricorne
laurel (KALMIA)	KALMIA
LAWNGRASS, JAPANESE	ZOYSIA japonica
lawngrass, Korean (JAPANESE LAWNGRASS)	ZOYSIA japonica
LEDUM	LEDUM
LEGUMES	LEGUMINOSAE
LENTIL, COMMON	LENS culinaris (*L. esculenta*)

COMMON NAMES	SCIENTIFIC NAMES
LEPTOTAENIA	**LEPTOTAENIA**
LESPEDEZA	**LESPEDEZA**
BICOLOR (*shrub*)	bicolor
bush (CYRTO)	cyrtobotrya
COMMON	striata
Hort. vars. of common lespedeza	
KOBE	
TENNESSEE 76	
CYRTO (*bush*)	cyrtobotrya
DECUMBENT	latissima
KOREAN	stipulacea
Hort. var. CLIMAX	
RUSH	hedysaroides
SERICEA	cuneata (*L. sericea*)
shrub (BICOLOR)	bicolor
THUNBERG	thunbergii
LEUCOTHOE	**LEUCOTHOË**
LICORICE, AMERICAN (*licorice, wild*)	**GLYCYRRHIZA** lepidota
LOCO; MILKVETCH; POISONWEED	**ASTRAGALUS**
LOCO, COLTON	**ASTRAGALUS** coltoni
LOCUST, BLACK	**ROBINIA** pseudoacacia
LOVEGRASS	**ERAGROSTIS**
ALKALI	obtusiflora
BOER	chloromelas
FEATHER	amabilis
FLARESCALE	obtusa
JAPANESE	tenella
LEHMANN	lehmanniana
PLAINS	intermedia
PURPLE	spectabilis
SAND	trichodes
TEFF	tef
WEEPING	curvula
LUCERNE; MEDIC; BUR-CLOVER	**MEDICAGO**
LUPINE	**LUPINUS**
BLUE	angustifolius
SUNDIAL	perennis
TAILCUP	caudatus
TEXAS	subcarnosus
WHITE	albus
wild (SUNDIAL)	perennis
YELLOW	luteus
mahogany, birchleaf (BIRCHLEAF MOUNTAIN-MAHOGANY)	**CERCOCARPUS** betuloides
MAHONIA	**MAHONIA**
MAIDENCANE	**PANICUM** hemitomon
MAIZE; CORN	**ZEA MAYS**
MALEFERN	**DRYOPTERIS** filixmas (*Aspidium filixmas*)
MANGO	**MANGIFERA** indica
MANILAGRASS	**ZOYSIA** matrella
MANNAGRASS	**GLYCERIA**
MANZANITA	**ARCTOSTAPHYLOS**
MAPLE	**ACER**
VINE	**ACER** circinatum
MASCARENEGRASS	**ZOYSIA** tenuifolia
MATOJO (Sp.); WEST INDIES SMUTGRASS	**SPOROBOLUS** indicus
meadow grass, salt (NUTTALL ALKALIGRASS)	**PUCCINELLIA** nuttalliana
MEDIC; BUR-CLOVER; LUCERNE	**MEDICAGO**
BLACK	lupulina
BROADPOD	platycarpa
BUTTON; BUTTONCLOVER	orbicularis
LIBYAN	gaetula
LITTLE; LITTLE BUR-CLOVER	minima

COMMON NAMES | SCIENTIFIC NAMES

COMMON NAMES	SCIENTIFIC NAMES
RUTHENIAN	ruthenica
SNAIL	scutellata
SPOTTED; SPOTTED BUR-CLOVER	arabica
MELIC	MELICA
MENZIESIA	MENZIESIA
MESEMBRYANTHEMUM	MESEMBRYANTHEMUM
MESQUITE	PROSOPIS
CHILEAN	chilensis
COMMON	juliflora
Mexican bluegrass (FLATSTEM CHLORIS)	CHLORIS inflata
MILKVETCH	ASTRAGALUS
CHICKPEA	cicer
CICER	cicer
RUBY	rubyi
SICKLEPOD (*sickle*)	falcatus
MILKWEED	ASCLEPIAS
BUTTERFLY	tuberosa
SWAMP	incarnata
WHORLED	verticillata
MILLET	SETARIA
BROOMCORN	PANICUM miliaceum
CHINESE	SETARIA faberii
FOXTAIL	SETARIA italica

Hort vars. of foxtail millet
COMMON
GERMAN
HUNGARIAN
SIBERIAN
WHITE WONDER

hog (BROOMCORN; PROSO)	PANICUM miliaceum
MIMOSA	MIMOSA
MITCHELLGRASS	ASTREBLA pectinata
MOLASSESGRASS	MELINIS minutiflora
MOUNTAIN-MAHOGANY, BIRCHLEAF	CERCOCARPUS betuloides
MOUNTAIN-MAHOGANY, TRUE	CERCOCARPUS montanus
MUHLY	MUHLENBERGIA
BUSH	porteri
CUTOVER	expansa
HAIRAWN	capillaris
MESA	montana
MOUNTAIN	montana
RING	torreyi
ringgrass (RING)	torreyi
SANDHILL	pungens
MUSTARD, BLACK	BRASSICA nigra
mustard, Jim Hill (TUMBLEMUSTARD)	SISYMBRIUM altissimum
NAPIERGRASS	PENNISETUM purpureum
NATALGRASS	TRICHOLAENA repens
NEEDLE-AND-THREAD	STIPA comata
NEEDLEGRASS	STIPA
CALIFORNIA	pulchra
DESERT	speciosa
FOOTHILL	lepida
GREEN	viridula
needlegrass (NEEDLE-AND-THREAD)	comata
NODDING	cernua
purple (CALIFORNIA)	pulchra
WESTERN	occidentalis
NIGGERWOOL; THREADLEAF SEDGE	CAREX filifolia
NIGHTSHADE, BLACK	SOLANUM nigrum
OAK	QUERCUS
BLUE	douglasii
GAMBEL	gambelii
INTERIOR LIVE (*Wislizenus*)	wislizeni
LIVE	virginiana
SHINNERY	havardii

COMMON NAMES	SCIENTIFIC NAMES

WHITE   alba
Wislizenus (INTERIOR LIVE)   wislizeni
OATGRASS   ARRHENATHERUM
  TALL   elatius
  yellow (YELLOW TRISETUM)   TRISETUM flavescens
OATS   AVENA sativa
  Hort. vars. of oats
    CALIFORNIA RED
    KANATA
    VENTURA
ORANGE, SWEET   CITRUS sinensis
ORCHARDGRASS   DACTYLIS glomerata
  Hort. var. AKAROA
OREGON-GRAPE   MAHONIA aquifolium
OSAGE-ORANGE   MACLURA pomifera

PACHYSANDRA   PACHYSANDRA
PALMETTO   SABAL
PAMAKANI   EUPATORIUM adenophorum
PAMPASGRASS   CORTADERIA selloana
PANGOLAGRASS   DIGITARIA decumbens
PANIC, BLUE   PANICUM antidotale
PANICUM; PANICGRASS   PANICUM
  blue (BLUE PANIC)   antidotale
  giant panicgrass (BLUE PANIC)   antidotale
  TORPEDO   repens
panini (MISSION PRICKLYPEAR)   OPUNTIA megacantha
PAPAYA   CARICA papaya
PARAGRASS   PANICUM purpurascens
PARTRIDGE-PEA, SHOWY   CHAMAECRISTA fasciculata
PASPALUM   PASPALUM
  BROWNSEED   plicatulum
  dune (GULF DUNE)   monostachyum
  FIELD   laeve
  GULF DUNE   monostachyum
  RIBBED   malacophyllum
  SAND   stramineum
  SEASHORE   vaginatum
PASQUEFLOWER, SPREADING   ANEMONE patens (PULSATILLA
      patens)
pea, Caley- (ROUGHPEA)   LATHYRUS hirsutus
PEA, FIELD   PISUM sativum var. arvense (*P. arvense*)
  Hort. vars. of field pea
    AUSTRIAN WINTER (*Austrian*)
    DIXIE WONDER
pea, red-and-yellow (WRIGHT DEERVETCH)   LOTUS wrightii
pea, Singletary (ROUGHPEA)   LATHYRUS hirsutus
PEA, TANGIER; TANGIER PEAVINE   LATHYRUS tingitanus
PEANUT   ARACHIS hypogaea
PEARLMILLET   PENNISETUM glaucum
PEAVINE   LATHYRUS
  ASPEN   leucanthus
  FLATPOD   cicer
  MARITIME   japonicus
  TANGIER; TANGIER-PEA   tingitanus
PENNISETUM   PENNISETUM
  WEST INDIES   setaceum
PENSTEMON   PENSTEMON
PEPPERWEED, PRAIRIE   LEPIDIUM densiflorum
PERIWINKLE   VINCA
PICKLEWEED   ALLENROLFEA occidentalis
pigeonberry (COMMON POKEBERRY)   PHYTOLACCA americana (*P. decandra*)
PIGEONPEA   CAJANUS CAJAN (*C. indicus*)
PINE   PINUS
  COLORADO PINYON; PINYON   edulis
  DIGGER   sabiniana

COMMON NAMES

LOBLOLLY	taeda
LODGEPOLE	contorta var. latifolia
LONGLEAF	palustris
PONDEROSA	ponderosa
SHORTLEAF	echinata
SLASH	caribaea
PINEAPPLE	ANANAS comosus
PINEGRASS	CALAMAGROSTIS rubescens
PINGUE	ACTINEA richardsoni
PINYON; COLORADO PINYON PINE	PINUS edulis
PINYON, SINGLELEAF	PINUS monophylla
PLANTAIN	PLANTAGO
BUCKHORN	lanceolata
PLUM	PRUNUS
CHICKASAW	angustifolia
CHICKASAW SAND	angustifolia var. watsonii (*P. watsonii*)
Java-plum (JAMBOLAN)	SYZYGIUM cumini (*Eugenia cumini*)
SAND	PRUNUS angustifolia var. watsonii (*P. watsonii*)
PLUMEGRASS	ERIANTHUS
PODGRASS	TRIGLOCHIN palustris
POISONHEMLOCK	CONIUM maculatum
POISON-IVY, COMMON	TOXICODENDRON radicans
POISON-OAK, PACIFIC	TOXICONDENDRON diversilobum (*Rhus diversiloba*)
POISONVETCH	ASTRAGALUS
timber	convallarius
POKEBERRY, COMMON	PHYTOLACCA americana (*P. decandra*)
POPLAR	POPULUS
PORCUPINEGRASS	STIPA spartea
POVERTYGRASS	DANTHONIA spicata
PRICKLEPOPPY	ARGEMONE
PRICKLYPEAR	OPUNTIA
PROSO	PANICUM miliaceum
PUNCTUREVINE	TRIBULUS terrestris
PURPLETOP	TRIDENS flavus
QUACKGRASS	AGROPYRON repens
QUAKINGGRASS	BRIZA
BIG	maxima
LITTLE	minor
PERENNIAL	media
RABBITRBUSH	CHRYSOTHAMNUS
RUBBER	nauseosus
SMALL	stenophyllus
RAPE (*winter rape*)	BRASSICA napus
Hort. var. DWARF ESSEX	
RATANY	KRAMERIA
rattle-box (CROTALARIA)	CROTALARIA
redroot (JERSEYTEA CEANOTHUS)	CEANOTHUS americanus
REDTOP	AGROSTIS alba
REED, COMMON	PHRAGMITES communis
REEDGRASS	CALAMAGROSTIS
BLUEJOINT	canadensis
reedgrass, giant (BIG SANDREED)	CALAMOVILFA gigantea
reedgrass, prairie (PRAIRIE SANDREED)	CALAMOVILFA longifolia
RESCUEGRASS	BROMUS catharticus
RHODESGRASS	CHLORIS gayana
RHODODENDRON	RHODODENDRON
RICEGRASS	ORYZOPSIS
RICEGRASS, BLOOMER	ORYZOPSIS bloomeri
RICEGRASS, INDIAN	ORYZOPSIS hymenoides
ricegrass (TOWNSEND CORDGRASS)	SPARTINA townsendi
ringgrass (RING MUHLY)	MUHLENBERGIA torreyi
ROUGHPEA	LATHYRUS hirsutus

SCIENTIFIC NAMES

COMMON NAMES	SCIENTIFIC NAMES
ROUGHBARK LIGNUMVITAE; GUAYACAN BLANCO (Spanish name)	GUAIACUM sanctum
rubberweed, Colorado (PINGUE)	ACTINEA richardsoni
RUSH	JUNCUS
BALTIC	balticus
BLACK	roemerianus
NEEDLEGRASS	roemerianus
rushgrass, longleaf (TALL DROPSEED)	SPOROBOLUS asper
rushgrass, rough (TALL DROPSEED)	SPOROBOLUS asper
rushgrass, West Indian; MATAJO (Sp.)	SPOROBOLUS indicus
RUSSIAN-THISTLE	SALSOLA kali var. tenuifolia
RYE	SECALE cereale
Hort. vars. of rye	
ABRUZZI (*Abruzzes*)	
BALBO	
MOUNTAIN	montanum
RYEGRASS	LOLIUM
COMMON	multiflorum
ITALIAN	multiflorum
PERENNIAL	perenne
WIMMERA	rigidum
ryegrass (WILD-RYE)	ELYMUS
SACATON	SPOROBOLUS wrightii
ALKALI	airoides
SAINFOIN; COMMON SAINFOIN	ONOBRYCHIS viciaefolia
SAGE	SALVIA
sage, silver (FRINGED SAGEBRUSH)	ARTEMISIA frigida
SAGEBRUSH	ARTEMISIA
BIG	tridentata
BLACK	nova
BUD	spinescens
CUDWEED	gnaphalodes
FALSE-TARRAGON	dracunculoides
FRINGED	frigida
green (FALSE-TARRAGON)	dracunculoides
SAND	filifolia
SILVER	cana
THREETIP	tripartita
SALAL	GAULTHERIA shallon
SALMONBERRY	RUBUS spectabilis
SALTBUSH	ATRIPLEX
FOURWING	canescens
SHADSCALE (*shadscale*)	confertifolia
SAW-PALMETTO	SERENOA
SALTGRASS	DISTICHLIS
INLAND (*desert*)	stricta
SANDBUR	CENCHRUS
SANDREED	CALAMOVILFA
BIG	gigantea
PRAIRIE	longifolia
SANDGRASS, PURPLE	TRIPLASIS purpurea
sandgrass, prairie (PRAIRIE SANDREED)	CALAMOVILFA longifolia
SATINTAIL, COGON	IMPERATA cylindrica
SAWGRASS	MARISCUS
scoke (COMMON POKEBERRY)	PHYTOLACCA americana (*P. decanda*)
SEA-OATS	UNIOLA paniculata
SEDGE	CAREX
THREADLEAF	filifolia
SEEPWEED	SUAEDA
SEMAPHOREGRASS	PLEUROPOGON
SENSITIVEBRIER, PUERTO RICO; ZARZARILLA (Spanish name)	SCHRANKIA portoricensis (*Leptoglottis portoricensis*)
SENSITIVEPLANT	MIMOSA pudica
SENNA, SICKLE	CASSIA tora
SERRADELLA	ORNITHOPUS sativus

COMMON NAMES	SCIENTIFIC NAMES
SERVICEBERRY	AMELANCHIER
SESBANIA, HEMP	SESBANIA exaltata
shadscale (SHADSCALE SALTBUSH)	ATRIPLEX confertifolia
SIGNALGRASS, PERENNIAL	BRACHIARIA ciliatissima
SILVERGRASS, CHINESE	MISCANTHUS sinensis
SKUNKBUSH (SKUNKBUSH SUMAC)	RHUS trilobata
skunkbush (MENZIESIA)	MENZIESIA
SLOUGHGRASS, AMERICAN	BECKMANNIA syzigachne
sloughgrass (PRAIRIE CORDGRASS)	SPARTINA pectinata
SMILOGRASS	ORYZOPSIS miliacea
SMUTGRASS, WEST INDIES (*West Indian rushgrass*)	SPOROBOLUS indicus
snailclover (SNAIL MEDIC)	MEDICAGO scutellata
SNAKEROOT, WHITE	EUPATORIUM rugosum (*E. urticaefolium*)
SNAKEWEED	GUTIERREZIA
BROOM (*snakeweed*)	sarothrae
TARRAGON	dracunculoides
SNEEZEWEED	HELENIUM
COMMON	autumnale
bitter (BITTERWEED)	tenuifolium
ORANGE (*western*)	hoopesii
SNOWBERRY	SYMPHORICARPOS
SOAPWEED, SMALL	YUCCA glauca
SORGHUM	SORGHUM vulgare
Hort. vars. of sorghum	
ATLAS	
AXTELL	
BLACK AMBER	
DAKOTA AMBER	
FREMONT	
LEOTI	
RANCHER	
ROX	
SOURCLOVER	MELILOTUS indica
SOWTHISTLE, COMMON	SONCHUS oleraceus
SOYBEAN	GLYCINE max (*Glycine soja; Soja max*)
SPANISH-CLOVER	DESMODIUM uninatum
SPANISHMOSS	TILLANDSIA usneoides
SPRUCE, ENGELMANN	PICEA engelmanni
spurge, flowering (FLOWERING EUPHORBIA)	EUPHORBIA corollata
spurge, leafy (LEAFY EUPHORBIA)	EUPHORBIA esula
SPURGES	EUPHORBIACEAE, especially the type genus EUPHORBIA
SQUIRRELTAIL	SITANION
BIG	jubatum
BOTTLEBRUSH	hystrix
STAR-OF-BETHLEHEM	ORNITHOGALUM
STARTHISTLE	CENTAUREA solstitialis
ST. AUGUSTINEGRASS	STENOTAPHRUM secundatum
STICKSEED, WESTERN	LAPPULA redowskii (*L. occidentalis*)
stipa (NEEDLEGRASS)	STIPA
ST. JOHNSWORT, COMMON	HYPERICUM perforatum
stonecrop, biting (GOLDMOSS STONECROP)	SEDUM acre
STONECROP, GOLDMOSS	SEDUM acre
SUDANGRASS	SORGHUM vulgare var. sudanense
Hort. vars. of Sudangrass	
NO. 23	
SWEET	
TIFT	
SUGARCANE	SACCHARUM officinarum
Suiter's grass (TALL FESCUE)	FESTUCA elatior var. arundinacea
SULLA; SULLA SWEETVETCH	HEDYSARUM coronarium
sumac, lemonade (SKUNKBUSH SUMAC)	RHUS trilobata
SUMAC, SKUNKBUSH	RHUS trilobata
SUNFLOWER	HELIANTHUS

COMMON NAMES	SCIENTIFIC NAMES
COMMON	annuus
SWAMP	angustifolius
SWEET-ANISE	OSMORHIZA occidentalis
SWEETCLOVER	MELILOTUS
annual yellow (SOURCLOVER)	indica
BANAT	dentata
DAGHESTAN	suaveolens
sour (SOURCLOVER)	indica
WHITE	alba
Hort. vars. of white sweetclover	
EMERALD	
EVERGREEN	
HUBAM	
SANGAMON	
SPANISH	
WILLAMETTE	
YELLOW	officinalis
Hort. vars. of yellow sweetclover	
ERECTOR	
MADRID	
SWEETPOTATO	IPOMOEA batatas
SWEETVETCH	HEDYSARUM
NORTHERN	boreale
SULLA; SULLA	coronarium
SWITCHGRASS	PANICUM virgatum
Hort. var. BLACKWELL	
swordgrass (CHINESE SILVERGRASS)	MISCANTHUS sinensis
TARBUSH	FLOURENSIA cernua
TARWEED	MADIA
CLUSTER	glomerata
TEOSINTE	EUCHLAENA mexicana
THREE-AWN	ARISTIDA
PINELAND	stricta
PURPLE	purpurea
RED	longiseta
THYME	THYMUS
COMMON	vulgaris
TICKBEAN	VICIA faba var. equina
TICKCLOVER	DESMODIUM
SAND	arenicola
TALL	purpureum
ticklegrass (WINTER BENT)	AGROSTIS hiemalis
TIMOTHY	PHLEUM; P. pratense
Hort. vars. of timothy	
ITASCA	
LORAIN	
MARIETTA	
ALPINE	alpinum
TOBOSA	HILARIA mutica
TORPEDOGRASS	PANICUM repens
TREFOIL	LOTUS
BIG	uliginosus (L. major)
BIRDSFOOT	corniculatus
BROADLEAF BIRDSFOOT	corniculatus var. arvensis
marsh birdsfoot (BIG)	uliginosus (L. major)
NARROWLEAF BIRDSFOOT	corniculatus var. tenuifolius
yellow (BLACK MEDIC)	MEDICAGO lupulina
TRIDENS, HAIRY	TRIDENS pilosus
TRIGONELLA, FENUGREEK	TRIGONELLA foenum-graecum
triodia, hairy (HAIRY TRIDENS)	TRIDENS pilosus
TRISETUM, YELLOW	TRISETUM flavescens
TUMBLEMUSTARD	SISYMBRIUM altissimum
turkeyfoot (SAND BLUESTEM)	ANDROPOGON hallii

COMMON NAMES	SCIENTIFIC NAMES
UMBELLIFERS	UMBELLIFERAE: The carrot-parsnip family
UNIOLA, BROADLEAF	UNIOLA latifolia
UVAGRASS	GYNERIUM sagittatum
VASEYGRASS	PASPALUM urvillei
VELVETBEAN	STIZOLOBIUM
DEERING	deeringianum
VELVETGRASS	HOLCUS
COMMON	lanatus
GERMAN	mollis
vernal, sweet (SWEET VERNALGRASS)	ANTHOXANTHUM odoratum
VETCH	VICIA
BIGFLOWER	grandiflora
BIRD	cracca
COMMON	sativa
GRANDIFLORA	grandiflora
HAIRY	villosa
HUNGARIAN	pannonica
MONANTHA	articulata
NARROWLEAF	angustifolia
one-flower (MONANTHA)	articulata
PURPLE	atropurpurea
SHOWY	grandiflora
WOOLLYPOD	dasycarpa
VINE-MESQUITE	PANICUM obtusum
WATERHEMLOCK	CICUTA
DOUGLAS	douglasii (*C. occidentalis*)
SPOTTED	maculata
WHEAT	TRITICUM aestivum
WHEATGRASS	AGROPYRON
BEARDED	subsecundum
BEARDED BLUEBUNCH	spicatum
BEARDLESS	inerme
BLUEBUNCH	spicatum
BLUESTEM	smithii
CRESTED	cristatum
Hort. var. FAIRWAY	
DESERT	desertorum
DROOPING	semicostatum
INTERMEDIATE	intermedium
SAUNDERS	saundersii
SIBERIAN	sibiricum
SLENDER	trachycaulum (*A. pauciflorum*)
STIFFHAIR (*pubescent*)	trichophorum
STREAMBANK	riparium
TALL	elongatum
THICKSPIKE	dasystachyum
WESTERN	smithii
WILDBEAN, TRAILING	STROPHOSTYLES helvola
WILDRICE, ANNUAL	ZIZANIA aquatica
WILD-RYE	ELYMUS
beach (COMMON DUNE WILD-RYE)	mollis
BEARDLESS	triticoides
BLUE	glaucus
CANADA	canadensis
Hort. var. MANDAN	
CHINESE	chinensis (*E. pseudoagropyron*)
CREEPING	triticoides
DUNE, COMMON	mollis
GIANT	condensatus
mammoth (SIBERIAN)	giganteus
MACOUN	macounii
RUSSIAN	junceus
SIBERIAN	giganteus

COMMON NAMES	SCIENTIFIC NAMES
VIRGINIA	virginicus
YELLOW	flavescens
WINTERFAT	EUROTIA
WINTERFAT, COMMON (*winterfat*)	lanata
wiregrass (BERMUDA-GRASS)	CYNODON dactylon
wiregrass (THREE-AWN)	ARISTIDA
WITCHGRASS, FALL	LEPTOLOMA cognatum
WOOLLYFINGER	DIGITARIA stolonifera
woollyfinger (PENTZ FINGERGRASS)	DIGITARIA pentzii
WORMSEED	CHENOPODIUM ambrosioides
YERBA GUATEMALA (Spanish name); GUATE-MALA GAMAGRASS	TRIPSACUM laxum
Yorkshire fog (COMMON VELVETGRASS)	HOLCUS lanatus
YUCCA	YUCCA
ZARZARILLA (Spanish name); PUERTO RICO SENSITIVEBRIER	SCHRANKIA portoricensis (*Leptoglottis portoricensis*)

For Further Reference

OUR AIM: AN INTRODUCTION
(Page 1)

Cardon, P. V.: *Toward a Grassland Agriculture,* Journal of the American Society of Agronomy, volume 31, pages 229–231. 1939.

Salter, R. M., Lewis, R. D., and Slipher, J. A.: *Our Heritage—The Soil,* Ohio Agricultural College Extension Bulletin 175. 1936. (Revised 1938.)

Truog, Emil: *The Soil—A Dependable Bank and Banker,* Fertilizer Review, volume 22, pages 10–13. 1947.

SETTLEMENT OF GRASSLANDS
(Page 16)

Bidwell, Percy Wells, and Falconer, John I.: *History of Agriculture in the Northern United States, 1620–1860,* Carnegie Institution of Washington Publication 358, Washington, D. C. 1925.

Gray, Lewis Cecil: *History of Agriculture in the Southern United States to 1860,* Carnegie Institution of Washington Publication 430, 2 volumes, Washington, D. C. 1933.

Malin, James C.: *The Grassland of North America; Prolegomena to Its History,* published by the author, Lawrence, Kans. 1947.

Oliphant, J. Orin: *The Eastward Movement of Cattle from the Oregon Country,* Agricultural History, volume 20, pages 19–43. 1946.

Robbins, Roy M.: *Our Landed Heritage; The Public Domain, 1776–1936,* Princeton University Press, Princeton, N. J. 1942.

United States Great Plains Committee: *The Future of the Great Plains,* United States Government Printing Office, Washington, D. C. 1936.

Webb, Walter Prescott: *The Great Plains,* Ginn and Company, Boston. 1931.

A BILLION ACRES
(Page 25)

Aamodt, O. S.: *Climate and Forage Crops,* Yearbook of Agriculture 1941 (Climate and Man), pages 439–458.

Baker, O. E.: *A Graphic Summary of Physical Features and Land Utilization in the United States,* U.S.D.A. Miscellaneous Publication 260. 1937.

Biswell, H. H., and Foster, J. E.: *Forest Grazing and Beef Cattle Production in the Coastal Plain of North Carolina,* North Carolina Agricultural Experiment Station Bulletin 334. 1942.

Burmeister, Charles A., Conway, Herman M., and Brodell, Albert P.: *Economic Factors Affecting the Beef-Cattle Industry of Virginia,* U.S.D.A. Technical Bulletin 237. 1931.

Culley, Matt J.: *An Economic Study of Cattle Business on a Southwestern Semidesert Range,* U.S.D.A. Circular 448. 1937.

Hockmuth, H. R., Franklin, Earl R., and Clawson, Marion: *Sheep Migration in the Intermountain Region,* U.S.D.A. Circular 624. 1942.

Jennings, R. D.: *Feed Consumption by Livestock, 1910–41,* U.S.D.A. Circular 670. 1943.

North Great Plains Agricultural Council, Tenure Committee: *Improving Farm and Ranch Tenure in the Northern Plains,* Montana Agricultural Experiment Station Bulletin 436. 1946.

Saunderson, Mont H.: *Ranch Country,* American Cattle Producer, volume 28, No. 2, pages 11–13, 24–27. 1946.

Semple, A. T., Vinall, H. N., Enlow, C. R., and Woodward, T. E.: *A Pasture Handbook,* U.S.D.A. Miscellaneous Publication 194. 1934. (Revised 1942.)

Wilcox, Walter W.: *Livestock Production in Iowa as Related to Hay and Pasture,* Iowa Agricultural Experiment Station Bulletin 361. 1937.

SOILS DEVELOP UNDER GRASS
(Page 55)

Baldwin, Mark; Kellogg, Charles E., and Thorp, James: *Soil classification,* Yearbook of Agriculture 1938 (Soils and Men), pages 979–1001.

Condra, G. E., Reed, E. C., and Gordon, E. D.: *Correlation of the Pleistocene of Nebraska,* Nebraska Geological Survey Bulletin 15. 1947.

Ellis, J. H., and Shafer, W. H.: *Report of Reconnaissance Soil Survey of South-Central Manitoba,* Manitoba Soils Survey Soils Report 4. 1943.

Jenny, Hans: *A Study on the Influence of Climate Upon the Nitrogen and Organic Matter Content of the Soil,* Missouri Agricultural Experiment Station Research Bulletin 152. 1930.

Marbut, C. F.: *Soils of the United States,* U.S.D.A. Atlas of American Agriculture, Part 3. 1936.

Mitchell, J., Moss, H. C., and Clayton, J. S.: *Soil Survey of Southern Saskatchewan from Township 1 to 48, Inclusive,* Soil Survey Report 12, Saskatchewan University, College of Agriculture, Saskatoon. 1944.

Nikiforoff, Constantin C.: *Soil Organic Matter and Soil Productivity,* Yearbook of Agriculture 1938 (Soils and Men), page 938 .

Templin, E. H., and Huckabee, J. W., Jr.: *Soil Survey, Kaufman County, Texas,* Bureau of Plant Industry, Series 1936, No. 3. 1940.

Thornthwaite, C. W.: *Atlas of Climatic Types in the United States, 1900–1939,* U.S.D.A. Miscellaneous Publication 421. 1941.

Weaver, J. E.: *Competition of Western Wheat Grass with Relict Vegetation of Prairie,* American Journal of Botany, volume 29, pages 366–372. 1942.

Weaver, J. E., and Albertson, F. W.: *Nature and Degree of Recovery of Grassland from the Great Drought of 1933 to 1940,* Ecological Monographs 14, pages 393–479. 1944.

Weaver, J. E., Hougen, V. H., and Weldon, M. D.: *Relation of Root Distribution to Organic Matter in Prairie Soil,* The Botanical Gazette, volume 96, pages 389–420. 1935.

TOOLS OF FLOOD CONTROL
(Page 66)

Ellison, W. D.: *Soil Erosion Studies,* Agricultural Engineering, volume 28, pages 145–146, 197–201, 245–248, 297–300. 1947.

Flory, Evan L., and Marshall, Charles G.: *Regrassing for Soil Protection in the Southwest,* U.S.D.A. Farmers' Bulletin 1913. 1942.

Hoover, Max M., Smith, James E., Jr., Ferber, A. E., and Cornelius, D. R.: *Seed for Regrassing Great Plains Areas.* U.S.D.A. Farmers' Bulletin 1985. 1947.

Lowdermilk, W. C.: *Influence of Forest Litter on Run-off, Percolation, and Erosion,* Journal of Forestry, volume 28, pages 474–491. 1930.

Uhland, R. E.: *Rotations in Conservation,* Yearbook of Agriculture 1943–1947 (Science in Farming), pages 527–536. 1947.

FIXATION OF SAND DUNES
(Page 70)

Altpeter, L. Stanford: *Reforestation of Sandblows in Northern Vermont,* Journal of Forestry, volume 30, pages 705–709. 1941.

Lamson - Scribner, F.: *Sand - binding Grasses,* Yearbook of Agriculture 1898, pages 405–420.

Lowdermilk, W. C.: *Les Landes, France Transforms Vast Mobile Sand Dunes into Rich Productive Areas,* American Forests. August 1944.

McLaughlin, Willard T., and Brown, Robert L.: *Controlling Coastal Sand Dunes in the Pacific Northwest,* U.S.D.A. Circular 660. 1942.

Whitfield, Charles J., and Perrin, John A.: *Sand-Dune Reclamation in the Southern Great Plains,* U.S.D.A. Farmers' Bulletin 1825. 1939.

PLUS AND MINUS
(Page 75)

Beeson, Kenneth C., Gray, Louise, and Adams, Mary B.: *The Absorption of Mineral Elements by Forage Plants: 1. The Phosphorus, Cobalt, Manganese, and Copper Content of Some Common Grasses,* Journal of the American Society of Agronomy, volume 39, pages 356–362. 1947.

Biswell, H. H., Shepherd, W. O., Southwell, B. L., and Boggess, T. S., Jr.: *Native Forage Plants of Cut-over Forest Lands in the Coastal Plain of Georgia,* Georgia Coastal Plain Experiment Station Bulletin 37. 1943.

Black, W. H., Tash, L. H., Jones, J. M., and Kleberg, R. J., Jr.: *Effects of Phosphorus Supplements on Cattle Grazing on Range Deficient in this Mineral,* U.S.D.A. Technical Bulletin 856. 1943.

Crampton, E. W., and Jackson, I. R. C.: *Seasonal Variation in Chemical Composition of Pasture Herbage and the Relation to Its Digestibility by Steers and Sheep. Pasture Studies—26,* Journal of Animal Science, volume 3, pages 333–339. 1944.

Ellis, N. R.: *New Ideas in Feeding,* Yearbook of Agriculture 1943–1947 (Science in Farming), pages 95–106.

Neal, W. M.: *Present Knowledge of the Nutritional Value of Grassland Herbage,* Journal of the American Society of Agronomy, volume 33, pages 666–670. 1941.

Russell, F. C.: *Minerals in Pasture Deficiencies and Excesses in Relation to Animal Health,* Imperial Bureau of Animal Nutrition Technical Communication 15, Aberdeen, Scotland. 1944.

Schneider, Burch Hart: *Feeds of the World; Their Digestibility and Composition,* Jarrett Printing Co., Charleston, W. Va. 1947.

SOILS, CROPS, MINERALS
(Page 81)
Beeson, Kenneth C.: *The Effect of Mineral Supply on the Mineral Concentration and Nutritional Quality of Plants,* Botanical Review, volume 12, pages 424–455. 1946.

Bowstead, J. E., Sackville, J. P., and Sinclair, R. D.: *The Development of Cobalt Deficiency in Sheep,* Scientific Agriculture, volume 22, pages 314–325. 1942.

Britton, J. W., and Goss, H.: *Chronic Molybdenum Poisoning in Cattle,* Journal of the American Veterinary Medical Association, volume 108, pages 176–178. 1946.

Cunningham, I. J.: *Copper Deficiency in Cattle and Sheep, Occurrence and Control in New Zealand,* New Zealand Journal of Agriculture, volume 69, pages 559–569. 1944.

Eden, A., Hunter, A. H., and Green, H. H.: *Contributions to the Study of Swayback in Lambs. II. Blood Copper Investigations,* The Journal of Comparative Pathology and Therapeutics, volume 55, pages 29–40. 1945.

Ferguson, W. S., Lewis, A. H, and Watson, S. J.: *The Teart Pastures of Somerset. I. The Cause and Cure of Teartness,* Journal of Agricultural Science (England), volume 33, pages 44–51. 1943.

Huffman, C. F.: *The Role of Minerals in the Dairy Ration,* Michigan Agricultural Experiment Station Circular 207. 1947.

Kalkus, J. W.: *A Study of Goitre and Associated Conditions in Domestic Animals,* Washington Agricultural Experiment Station Bulletin 156. 1920.

Moxon, A. L.: *Alkali Disease or Selenium Poisoning,* South Dakota Agricultural Experiment Station Bulletin 311. 1937.

Neal, W. M., and Ahmann, C. F.: *The Essentiality of Cobalt in Bovine Nutrition,* Journal of Dairy Science, volume 20, pages 741–753. 1937.

FEED FOR HORSES
(Page 86)
Dawson, W. M., Phillips, R. W., and Speelman, S. R.: *Growth of Horses Under Western Range Conditions,* Journal of Animal Science, volume 4, pages 47–54. 1945.

Guilbert, H. R., Howell, C. E., and Hart, G. H.: *Minimum Vitamin A and Carotene Requirements of Mammalian Species,* The Journal of Nutrition, volume 19, pages 91–103. 1940.

Hudson, R. S.: *Liberal vs. Limited Rations for Draft Colts in Michigan,* Michigan Agricultural Experiment Station Special Bulletin 253. 1934.

Jones, T. C., Roby, Thomas O., and Maurer, Fred D.: *The Relation of Riboflavin to Equine Periodic Ophthalmia,* American Journal of Veterinary Research, volume 7, pages 403–416. 1946.

Pearson, P. B., Sheybani, M. K., and Schmidt, H.: *The B Vitamin Requirements of the Horse,* Journal of Animal Science, volume 3, pages 166–174. 1944.

Trowbridge, E. A., and Chittenden, D. W.: *Horses Grown on Limited Grain Rations,* Missouri Agricultural Experiment Station Bulletin 316. 1932.

THE VITAL 10 PERCENT FOR POULTRY
(Page 90)
Heuser, G. F., Norris, L. C., and Bruckner, J. H.: *Pasture Experiments with Growing Pullets,* New York (Cornell) Agricultural Experiment Station Bulletin 823. 1945.

Hoffman, Edmund: *Poultry Pasture,* Delaware Agricultural Experiment Station Bulletin 254. 1945.

Kennard, D. C., Thatcher, L. E., and Chamberlin, V. D.: *Feeding for Growth of Chickens on Pasturage,* Ohio Agricultural Experiment Station Bimonthly Bulletin 244, volume 32, pages 22–27. 1947.

Payne, Loyal F., and Gish, Clarence L.: *Grass and Alfalfa as Silage, Forage, and Meal for Poultry,* Kansas Agricultural Experiment Station Bulletin 320. 1943.

Stephenson, Alfred B., and Bryant, Reece L.: *The Value of a Sod Range for Starting Chicks, Growing Pullets, and Laying Hens,* Virginia Agricultural Experiment Station Bulletin 362. 1944.

Taylor, M. W., Russell, W. C., and Platt, C. S.: *The Value of Grass Clippings Silage for the Growing Chick,* Poultry Science, volume 23, pages 213–216. 1944.

SHEEP AND GOATS
(Page 94)

Doran, C. W., and Cassady, J. T.: *Management of Sheep on Range Infested with Orange Sneezeweed,* U.S.D.A. Circular 691. 1944.

Hochmuth, H. R., Franklin, Earl R., and Clawson, Marion: *Sheep Migration in the Intermountain Region,* U.S.D.A. Circular 624. 1942.

Marshall, F. R., Millin, R. B., Spencer, D. A., and Potts, C. G.: *Farm Sheep Raising for Beginners,* U.S.D.A. Farmers' Bulletin 840. (Revised 1944.)

Nelson, Oran M.: *The Angora Goat Industry of Oregon,* Oregon State Agricultural Experiment Station Bulletin 289. 1931.

Shaw, Edward L.: *Milk Goats,* U.S.D.A. Farmers' Bulletin 920. 1918. (Revised by C. G. Potts and V. L. Simmons, 1946.)

Willingmyre, G. T., Window, J. J., Spencer, Damon A., and others: *The Angora Goat and Mohair Industry,* U.S.D.A. Miscellaneous Circular 50. 1929.

FORAGE IN FEEDING HOGS
(Page 99)

Ellis, N. R., Zeller, J. H., and King, J. X.: *The Value of Legume Hays in the Rations of Fall Farrowed Pigs,* Journal of Animal Science, volume 1, page 358. 1942.

Headley, F. B.: *Protein Supplements in Pig Rations,* Nevada Agricultural Experiment Station Bulletin 175. 1945.

Keith, T. B., Miller, R. C., and McCarty, M. A.: *Levels of Supplementary Protein for Pigs on Pasture,* Pennsylvania Agricultural Experiment Station Bulletin 407. 1941.

Pennsylvania Agricultural Experiment Station: *Ladino Clover Pasture Valuable for Pigs,* Bulletin 480. 1946.

Robbins, E. T., Walker, E. D., and Nevens, W. B.: *Making Better Use of Legumes and Grasses,* Illinois Agricultural College Extension Service, AG–860. 1940.

Southwell, Byron L., and Treanor, Kenneth: *Hogging-Off Crops in the Coastal Plain,* Georgia Coastal Plain Experiment Station Bulletin 41. 1945.

Wisconsin Agricultural Experiment Station: *Alfalfa Boosts the B Vitamins in Swine Rations,* Wisconsin Agricultural Experiment Station Annual Report 59, Part 1, Bulletin 456, pages 62–63. 1942.

GRASS FOR BEEF
(Page 103)

Anderson, Kling L.: *Deferred Grazing of Bluestem Pasture,* Kansas Agricultural Experiment Station Bulletin 291. 1940.

Anderson, Kling L.: *Korean Lespedeza in Kansas,* Kansas Agricultural Experiment Station Circular 210. 1941.

Baker, Marvel L., Arthaud, V. H., Conard, E. C., and Newell, L. C.: *Effects of Time of Cutting on Yields and Feeding Value of Prairie Hay; A Progress Report for 1945–1946,* Nebraska Agricultural Experiment Station Bulletin 385. 1947.

Black, W. H., Hiner, R. L., Burk, L. B., and others: *Beef Production and Quality as Affected by Method of Feeding Supplements to Steers on Grass in the Appalachian Region,* U.S.D.A. Technical Bulletin 717. 1940.

Brouse, E. M.: *Wintering Steer Calves in the Nebraska Sandhills,* Nebraska Agricultural Experiment Station Bulletin 357. 1944.

Clarke, S. E., Tisdale, E. W., and Skoglund, N. A.: *The Effects of Climate and Grazing Practices on Short-Grass Prairie Vegetation in Southern Alberta and Southwestern Saskatchewan,* Canadian Ministry of Agriculture (Publication 747) Technical Bulletin 46. 1943.

Ensminger, M. E., McDowell, H. G., Law, A. G., and others: *Grass and Grass-Alfalfa Mixtures for Beef Production in Eastern Washington,* Washington Agricultural Experiment Station Bulletin 444. 1944.

Oklahoma Agricultural Experiment Station: *Feeding Tests with Sheep, Swine, and Beef Cattle, 1945–46,* Oklahoma Agricultural Experiment Station Bulletin 296. 1946.

Rhoad, A. O., and Carr, R. B.: *Measuring Productive Capacity of Pastures Through Maintenance Studies with Mature Steers,* U.S.D.A. Technical Bulletin 890. 1945.

Rogler, George A.: *Summer Gains of Yearling Hereford Steers on Native and Cultivated Pastures,* North Dakota Agricultural Experiment Station Bimonthly Bulletin, volume 6, No. 6, pages 20–27. (July–August) 1944.

Savage, D. A., and Heller, V. G.: *Nutritional Qualities of Range Forage Plants in Relation to Grazing with Beef Cattle on the Southern Plains Experimental Range,* U.S.D.A. Technical Bulletin 943. 1947.

Stephens, J. L.: *Pastures for the Coastal Plain of Georgia*, Georgia Coastal Plain Experiment Station Bulletin 27. 1942.

Williams, Ralph M., and Post, A. H.: *Dry Land Pasture Experiments at the Central Montana Branch Station, Moccasin, Montana*, Montana Agricultural Experiment Station Bulletin 431. 1945.

MANAGEMENT OF GRAZING
(Page 135)

Ahlgren, H. L., and Burcalow, F. V.: *Bromegrass and Alfalfa for Hay, Pasture, or Silage*, Wisconsin Agricultural College Extension Circular 344. 1944.

Ahlgren, H. L., and Burcalow, F. V.: *Ladino Clover—a Promising Pasture Crop*, Wisconsin Agricultural College Extension Circular 367. 1946.

Ahlgren, H. L., Rupel, I. W., Bohstedt, G., and Graul, E. J.: *Eight Years' Results on the Effectiveness of Fertilization and Management in Increasing the Production of Permanent Pastures*, Journal of the American Society of Agronomy, volume 36, pages 301–315. 1944.

Ahlgren, H. L., Wall, M. L., Muckenhirn, R. J., and Burcalow, F. V.: *Effectiveness of Renovation in Increasing Yields of Permanent Pastures in Southern Wisconsin*, Journal of the American Society of Agronomy, volume 36, pages 121–131. 1944.

Brown, E. Marion.: *Seasonal Variations in the Growth and Chemical Composition of Kentucky Bluegrass*, Missouri Agricultural Experiment Station Research Bulletin 360. 1943.

Brown, E. Marion: *Improve Permanent Pastures with Lespedeza, Phosphate, Lime, and Supplementary Grazing*, Missouri Agricultural Experiment Station Circular 285. 1944.

Fink, D. S.: *Grassland Experiments*, Maine Agricultural Experiment Station Bulletin 415. 1943.

Hilton, J. H., Wilbur, J. W., and Mott, G. O.: *Alfalfa-Bromegrass Makes Good Pasture*, Indiana Agricultural Experiment Station Circular 290. 1944.

Killinger, G. B., Glasscock, R. S., and Stokes, W. E.: *Winter Oats as Grazing for Beef Cattle*, Florida Agricultural Experiment Station Press Bulletin 627. 1946.

Mott, G. O.: *Effectiveness of Fertilization and Management in Increasing Yields of Pastures in Indiana*, Soil Science Society of America Proceedings, volume 8, pages 276–281. 1943.

Odland, T. E., Cox, T. R., and Moran, C. H.: *Adaptation of Various Crops for Supplementary Pasture*, Journal of the American Society of Agronomy, volume 34, pages 229–237. 1942.

Rather, H. C., and Harrison, C. M.: *Alfalfa and Smooth Bromegrass for Pasture and Hay*, Michigan Agricultural Experiment Station Bulletin 189. 1944.

Robinson, R. R., and Sprague, V. G.: *The Clover Populations and Yields of a Kentucky Bluegrass Sod as Affected by Nitrogen Fertilization, Clipping Treatments, and Irrigation*, Journal of the American Society of Agronomy, volume 39, pages 107–116. 1947.

Stansel, R. H., Dunkel, P. B., and Jones, D. L.: *Small Grain and Rye Grass for Winter Pastures*, Texas Agricultural Experiment Station Bulletin 539. 1937.

Stephens, J. L.: *Pastures for the Coastal Plain of Georgia*, Georgia Coastal Plain Experiment Station Bulletin 27. 1942.

Sotola, Jerry: *The Chemical Composition and Apparent Digestibility of Nutrients in Smooth Bromegrass Harvested in Three Stages of Maturity*, Journal of Agricultural Research, volume 63, pages 427–432. 1941.

Wilsie, C. P., Peterson, M. L., and Hughes, H. D.: *Bromegrass in Iowa*, Iowa Agricultural Experiment Station Extension Bulletin P–75. 1945.

Woodhouse, W. W., and Lovvorn, R. L.: *Establishing and Improving Permanent Pastures in North Carolina*, North Carolina Agricultural Experiment Station Bulletin 338. 1942.

NATURAL FORESTED AREAS
(Page 144)

Bizzell, J. A., and Lyon, T. L.: *Composition of Drainage Waters from Lysimeters at Cornell University*, First International Congress of Soil Science, 1927, Proceedings and Papers, volume 2, pages 342–349. 1928.

Pierre, W. H., Longwell, J. H., Robinson, R. R., and others: *West Virginia Pastures: Type of Vegetation, Carrying Capacity, and Soil Properties*, West Virginia Agricultural Experiment Station Bulletin 280. 1937.

Stapledon, R. G.: *The Manuring of Permanent and Temporary Grass*. In Profit from Fertilizers, pages [53]-66, Charles Lockwood and Sons, Ltd., London. 1936. (Edition 2, revised, pages [46]–57. 1945.)

PRINCIPLES OF MAKING HAY
(Page 161)

Camburn, O. M., Ellenberger, H. B., Jones, C. H., and Crooks, G. C.: *The Conservation of Alfalfa and Timothy Nutrients as Silages and as Hays. III*, Vermont Agricultural Experiment Station Bulletin 509. 1944.

Dawson, J. R., Kopland, D. V., and Graves, R. R.: *Yield, Chemical Composition, and Feeding Value for Milk Production of Alfalfa Hay Cut at Three Stages of Maturity,* U.S.D.A. Technical Bulletin 739. 1940.

Henson, Edwin R.: *Curing and Storage of Alfalfa Hay,* Iowa Agricultural Experiment Station Research Bulletin 251. 1939.

Hodgson, R. E., and Knott, J. C.: *The Feeding Value of Alfalfa Hay Compared with Mixed Hay and Grass Silage as a Ration for Dairy Cattle,* Washington Agricultural Experiment Station Bulletin 386. 1940.

Huffman, C. F.: *Roughage Quality and Quantity in the Dairy Ration, A Review,* Journal of Dairy Science, volume 22, pages 889–980. 1939.

Jones, T. N., Leonard, O. A., and Hamblin, I. E.: *Methods of Field Curing Hay,* Mississippi Agricultural Experiment Station Technical Bulletin 27. 1941.

LeClerc, J. A.: *Losses in Making Hay and Silage,* Yearbook of Agriculture 1939 (Food and Life), pages 992–1016.

Shepherd, J. B., and Woodward, T. E.: *Further Investigations in Chopping Hay at the Time of Storage,* Journal of Dairy Science, volume 21, pages 89–96. 1938.

Terry, C. W.: *Relation of Time and Operating Schedule to Hay Quality, Mold Development, and Economy of Operation,* Agricultural Engineering, volume 28, pages 141–144. 1947.

Wiseman, Herbert G., Kane, Edward G., Shinn, Leo A., and Cary, C. A.: *The Carotene Content of Market Hays and Corn Silage,* Journal of Agricultural Research, volume 57, pages 635–669. 1938.

GRASS AND YIELDS OF CROPS
(Page 191)

Smith, G. E.: *Sanborn Field: Fifty Years of Field Experiments with Crop Rotations, Manure and Fertilizers,* Missouri Agricultural Experiment Station Bulletin 458. 1942.

Uhland, R. E., and Hendrickson, B. H.: *Evaluation of Cropping Systems for Soil and Water Conservation in the Southeast,* Soil Science Society of America Proceedings, volume 11, pages 527–531. 1946.

Wiancko, A. T., Mulvey, R. R., and Miles, S. R.: *Progress Report of the Soils and Crops Experiment Farm from 1915–1940,* Indiana Agricultural Experiment Station Circular 242. 1941.

Wilson, H. A., and Browning, G. M.: *Soil Aggregation, Yields, Runoff, and Erosion as Affected by Cropping Systems,* Soil Science Society of America Proceedings, volume 10, pages 51–57. 1945.

PROBLEM FIELDS
(Page 195)

Borst, Harold L., McCall, A. G., and Bell, F. G.: *Investigations in Erosion Control and the Reclamation of Eroded Land at the Northwest Appalachian Conservation Experiment Station, Zanesville, Ohio, 1934–42,* U.S.D.A. Technical Bulletin 888. 1945.

FERTILIZERS FOR GRASS ROTATIONS
(Page 199)

Ahlgren, Gilbert Howard; Sprague, H. B., and Bear, Firman E.: *Growing Alfalfa in New Jersey,* New Jersey Agricultural Experiment Station Bulletin 718. 1945.

Bachtell, Myron A., Willard, C. J., and Livezey, Walter: *Dairy Farming Based on the Liberal Use of Meadow Crops, Part I. Producing Meadow Crops for Dairy Feed,* Ohio Agricultural Experiment Station Bulletin 662. 1946.

Bear, F. E.: *Alfalfa—The Aristocrat,* Better Crops with Plant Food, volume 29, No. 5, pages 6–10, 43–44. 1945.

Cook, R. L., and Millar, C. E.: *Fertilizers for Legumes,* Michigan Agricultural Experiment Station Special Bulletin 328. 1944.

Hansen, Dan, and Post, A. H.: *Irrigated Crop Rotations, Huntley Branch Station, Huntley, Montana,* Montana Agricultural Experiment Station Bulletin 414. 1943.

Jones, G. D., Smith, T. J., and McVickar, M. H.: *Nitrogen on Orchard Grass Pays,* Virginia Agricultural Experiment Station Bulletin 404. 1947.

Norman, A. G.: *Soybeans and the Fertility Level,* Soybean Digest, volume 6, No. 11, pages 35–37. 1947.

Stephenson, R. E.: *The Fertilizer Rate Problem,* Better Crops with Plant Food, volume 30, No. 1, pages 16–18, 40. 1946.

Whyte, R. O., Jacks, G. W., Nichols, J. E., and others: *Alternate Husbandry,* Imperial Agricultural Bureaux (Great Britain) Joint Publication 6. 1944.

Worzella, W. W., and Puhr, L. F.: *Field Trials With Fertilizers in South Dakota,* Better Crops with Plant Food, volume 30, No. 3, pages 14–18, 41–42. 1946.

HOW RANGE FORAGE GROWS
(Page 203)

Costello, David F., and Price, Raymond: *Weather and Plant-Development Data as Determinants of Grazing Periods on Mountain Range,* U.S.D.A. Technical Bulletin 686. 1939.

McCarty, Edward J., and Price, Raymond: *Growth and Carbohydrate Content of Important Mountain Forage Plants in Central Utah as Affected by Clipping and Grazing,* U.S.D.A. Technical Bulletin 818. 1942.

Miller, Edwin Cyrus: *Plant Physiology, With Reference to the Green Plant,* edition 2, McGraw-Hill Book Co., Inc., New York. 1938.

Weaver, John E., and Clements, Frederic E.: *Plant Ecology,* McGraw-Hill Book Co., Inc., New York. 1938.

MAJOR RANGE TYPES
(Page 205)

Allred, B. W.: *Some Conditions and Influences Pertaining to the Native Forage Crop of the Northern Mixed Prairie,* Journal of the American Society of Agronomy, volume 37, pages 876–887. 1945.

Darrow, Robert A.: *Arizona Range Resources and Their Utilization. I. Cochise County,* Arizona Agricultural Experiment Station Technical Bulletin 103, pages 311–366. 1944.

Dayton, William A.: *Important Western Browse Plants,* U.S.D.A. Miscellaneous Publication 101. 1931.

McArdle, Richard E., and Costello, David F.: *The Virgin Range.* In United States Forest Service, The Western Range, 74th Cong., 2d sess., Senate Document 199, pages 71–80. 1936.

Shantz, H. L., and Zon, Raphael: *The Natural Vegetation of the United States.* In U.S.D.A. Atlas of American Agriculture: The Physical Basis of Agriculture. 1924.

United States Forest Service: *Range Plant Handbook,* U.S.D.A. Washington, D. C. 1937.

GRAZING RANGE LANDS
(Page 212)

Campbell, R. S., and Biswell, H. H.: *Better Management on Southern Coastal Forest Ranges,* U.S.D.A. AIS–17. 1945.

Hamilton, C. L., and Jepson, Hans G.: *Stock-Water Developments: Wells, Springs, and Ponds,* U.S.D.A. Farmers' Bulletin 1859. 1940.

Hormay, August L.: *Moderate Grazing Pays on California Annual-Type Ranges,* U.S.D.A. Leaflet 239. 1944.

Parker, Kenneth W.: *Southwestern Stockman—Play to Win!* U.S.D.A. AWI–74. 1943.

Sarvis, J. T.: *Grazing Investigations on the Northern Great Plains,* North Dakota Agricultural Experiment Station Bulletin 308. 1941.

PLANNING RANGE CONSERVATION
(Page 217)

Allred, B. W.: *Some Conditions and Influences Pertaining to the Native Forage Crop of the Northern Mixed Prairie,* Journal of the American Society of Agronomy, volume 37, pages 876–887. 1945.

Chapline, W. R., and Cooperrider, C. D.: *Climate and Grazing,* Yearbook of Agriculture 1941 (Climate and Man), pages 459–476.

Chapline, W. R., Renner, F. G., and Price, Raymond: *The New Range Outlook,* Yearbook of Agriculture 1940 (Farmers in a Changing World), pages 441–457.

Johnson, Neil W.: *Planning the Farm for Profit and Stability,* U.S.D.A. Farmers' Bulletin 1965. 1945.

Lantow, J. L., and Flory, E. L.: *Fluctuating Forage Production; Its Significance in Proper Range and Livestock Management on Southwestern Ranges,* U. S. Soil Conservation Service, Soil Conservation, volume 6, pages 137–144. 1940.

Renner, F. G., and Johnson, E. A.: *Improving Range Conditions for Wartime Livestock Production,* U.S.D.A. Farmers' Bulletin 1921. 1942.

Weaver, J. E., and Hansen, W. W.: *Native Midwestern Pastures; Their Origin, Composition, and Degeneration,* Nebraska Conservation Bulletin 22. 1941.

White, W. T.: *Profit in Range Conservation,* The National Woolgrower, volume 35, No. 11, pages 16–18. 1945.

White, W. T.: *Take Care of the Range and the Profits Take Care of Themselves,* U. S. Soil Conservation Service, Soil Conservation, volume 10, pages 168–171, 175. 1945.

White, W. T., Frandsen, W. R., Humphrey, R. R., and Nelson, N. T.: *Food for Freedom by Better Range-Conservation Practices in the Pacific Northwest,* U.S.D.A. Miscellaneous Publication 514. 1943.

TO RESTORE THE RANGE
(Page 221)

Costello, David F., and Turner, George T.: *Judging Condition and Utilization of Short-grass Ranges on the Central Great Plains,* U.S.D.A. Farmers' Bulletin 1949. 1944.

Parker, Kenneth W., and Woodhead, P. V.: *What's Your Range Condition?* American Cattle Producer, volume 26, No. 6, pages 8–11. 1944.

Reid, Elbert H., and Pickford, G. D.: *Judging Mountain Meadow Range Condition in Eastern Oregon and Eastern Washington,* U.S.D.A. Circular 748. 1946.

Renner, F. G., and Johnson, E. A.: *Improving Range Conditions for Wartime Livestock Production,* U.S.D.A. Farmers' Bulletin 1921. 1942.

Rowalt, E. M.: *Soil Defense of Range and Farm Lands in the Southwest,* U.S.D.A. Miscellaneous Publication 338. 1939.

RESTORING BY RESEEDING
(Page 227)

Bridges, J. O.: *Reseeding Trials on Arid Range Lands,* New Mexico Agricultural Experiment Station Bulletin 278. 1941.

Flory, Evan L., and Marshall, Charles G.: *Regrassing for Soil Protection in the Southwest,* U.S.D.A. Farmers' Bulletin 1913. 1942.

Hull, A. C., Jr.: *Regrassing Southern Idaho Range Lands,* Idaho College of Agriculture Extension Bulletin 146. 1944.

Pearse, C. Kenneth: *Regrassing the Range,* Yearbook of Agriculture 1943–1947 (Science in Farming), pages 897–904.

Pechanec, Joseph F., and Stewart, George: *Sagebrush Burning—Good and Bad,* U.S.D.A. Farmers' Bulletin 1948. 1944.

Pickford, G. D., and Jackman, E. R.: *Reseeding Eastern Oregon Summer Ranges,* Oregon Agricultural Experiment Station Circular 159. 1944.

Short, L. R.: *Reseeding to Increase the Yield of Montana Range Lands,* U.S.D.A. Farmers' Bulletin 1924. 1943.

SPACING WATER HOLES
(Page 236)

Allred, B. W.: *Range Conservation Practices for the Great Plains,* U.S.D.A. Miscellaneous Publication 410. 1940.

Hamilton, C. L., and Jepson, H. G.: *Stock-Water Developments: Wells, Springs, and Ponds,* U.S.D.A. Farmers' Bulletin 1859. 1940.

Heller, V. G.: *The Effect of Saline and Alkaline Waters on Domestic Animals,* Oklahoma Agricultural Experiment Station Bulletin 217. 1933.

Smith, G. E. P.: *The Physiography of Arizona Valleys and the Occurrence of Groundwater,* Arizona Agricultural Experiment Station Technical Bulletin 77. 1938.

GRASS AND WATER AND TREES
(Page 239)

Bailey, Reed W., Forsling, C. L., and Becroft, R. J.: *Floods and Accelerated Erosion in Northern Utah,* U.S.D.A. Miscellaneous Publication 196. 1934.

Chapline, W. R., and Campbell, R. S.: *Forest Ranges* and *A Forest Range Program.* In A National Plan for American Forestry, 73d Cong., 1st sess., Senate Document 12 (in 2 volumes), volume 1, pages 527–562; volume 2, pages 1537–1541. 1934.

Cooperrider, Charles K., and Hendricks, Barnard A.: *Soil Erosion and Stream Flow on Range and Forest Lands of the Upper Rio Grande Watershed in Relation to Land Resources and Human Welfare,* U.S.D.A. Technical Bulletin 567. 1937.

Craddock, George W., and Pearse, C. Kenneth: *Surface Run-off and Erosion on Granitic Mountain Soils of Idaho as Influenced by Range Cover, Soil Disturbance, Slope, and Precipitation Intensity,* U.S.D.A. Circular 482. 1938.

Forsling, C. L.: *A Study of the Influence of Herbaceous Plant Cover on Surface Run-off and Soil Erosion in Relation to Grazing on the Wasatch Plateau in Utah,* U.S.D.A. Technical Bulletin 220. 1931.

WILDLIFE, A RESOURCE
(Page 243)

Graham, Edward H.: *Natural Principles of Land Use,* Oxford University Press, New York. 1944.

Graham, Edward H.: *The Land and Wildlife,* Oxford University Press, New York. 1947.

Sperry, Charles Carlisle: *Food Habits of the Coyote,* U. S. Department of the Interior, Fish and Wildlife Service, Wildlife Research Bulletin 4. 1941.

Stoddart, L. A., and Rasmussen, D. I.: *Deer Management and Range Livestock Production,* Utah Agricultural Experiment Station Circular 121. 1945.

Stoddart, L. A., and Smith, A. D.: *Range Management,* McGraw-Hill Book Co., Inc., New York. 1943.

RODENTS, RABBITS, AND GRASS
(Page 248)

Ellison, Lincoln: *The Pocket Gopher in Relation to Soil Erosion on Mountain Range,* Ecology, volume 27, pages 101–114. 1946.

Hawbecker, Albert C.: *The Giant Kangaroo Rat and Sheep Forage,* Journal of Wildlife Management, volume 8, pages 161–165. 1944.

Horn, E. E., and Fitch, H. S.: *Interrelations of Rodents and Other Wildlife on the Range . . .,* California Agricultural Experiment Station, Bulletin 663, pages 96–129. 1942.

Kelso, Leon H.: *Food Habits of Prairie Dogs,* U.S.D.A. Circular 529. 1939.

Linsdale, Jean M.: *The California Ground Squirrel: A Record of Observations. . . .* University of California Press, Berkeley and Los Angeles. 1946.

Piemeisel, R. L.: *Natural Replacement of Weed Hosts of the Beet Leafhopper as Affected by Rodents,* U.S.D.A. Circular 739. 1945.

Tappe, Donald T.: *Natural History of the Tulare Kangaroo Rat,* Journal of Mammalogy, volume 22, pages 117–148. 1941.

Taylor, Walter P.: *Methods of Determining Rodent Pressure on the Range,* Ecology, volume 11, pages 523–542. 1940.

Vorhies, Charles T.: *Water Requirements of Desert Animals in the Southwest,* Arizona Agricultural Experiment Station Technical Bulletin 107. 1945.

Vorhies, Charles T., and Taylor, Walter P.: *Life History and Ecology of the Whitethroated Wood Rat, Neotoma albigula albigula Hartley, in Relation to Grazing in Arizona,* Arizona Agricultural Experiment Station Technical Bulletin 86. 1940.

CONTROLLING NOXIOUS PLANTS
(Page 256)

Costello, David F.: *Pricklypear Control on Short-grass Range in the Central Great Plains,* U.S.D.A. Leaflet 210. 1941.

Doran, G. W., and Cassady, J. T.: *Management of Sheep on Range Infested With Orange Sneezeweed,* U.S.D.A. Circular 691. 1944.

Fisher, C. E., and Fults, Jess L.: *Principles and Methods of Eradicating Mesquite,* The Cattleman, volume 31 (12), pages 20–21, 80, 81. May 1945.

Fisher, C. E., Fults, Jess L., and Hopp, Henry: *Factors Affecting Action of Oils and Water-soluble Chemicals in Mesquite Eradication,* Ecological Monographs, volume 16, pages [109]–126. April 1946.

Marsh, C. Dwight; Clawson, A. B., and Marsh, Hadleigh: *Larkspur, or "Poison Weed,"* U.S.D.A. Farmers' Bulletin 988. 1918. (Revised, 1934.)

Parker, Kenneth W.: *Juniper Comes to the Grasslands, . . . its Control,* American Cattle Producer, volume 27, pages 12–14, 30–32. November 1945.

Platt, Kenneth, and Jackman, E. R.: *The Cheatgrass Problem in Oregon,* Oregon State College Extension Bulletin 668. 1946.

Robbins, Wilfred W., Crafts, Alden S., and Raynor, Richard N.: *Weed Control,* McGraw-Hill Book Company, Inc., New York. 1942.

Savage, D. A.: *Twice the Beef—for $1.50 an Acre,* The Country Gentleman, volume 114, pages 22, 66, 67. May 1944.

DISEASES OF FORAGE GRASSES
(Page 261)

Allison, J. Lewis, and Chamberlain, Donald W.: *Distinguishing Characteristics of Some Forage-Grass Diseases Prevalent in the North Central States,* U.S.D.A. Circular 747. 1946.

Burton, Glenn W.: *Tift Sudan,* Georgia Coastal Plain Experiment Station Circular 11. 1943.

Chamberlain, Donald W., and Allison, J. Lewis: *The Brown Leaf Spot on Bromus inermis Caused by Pyrenophora bromi,* Phytopathology, volume 35, pages 241–248. 1945.

Fischer, George W.: *The Blind Seed Disease of Ryegrass (Lolium spp.) in Oregon,* (Abstract) Phytopathology, volume 34, pages 934–935. 1944.

Hardison, J. R.: *Specialization of Pathogenicity in Erysiphe graminis on Wild and Cultivated Grasses,* Phytopathology, volume 34, pages 1–20. 1944.

Hayes, H. K., and Schimid, A. R.: *Selection in Self-Pollinated Lines of Bromus inermis Leyss., Festuca elatior L., and Dactylis glomerata L.,* Journal of the American Society of Agronomy, volume 35, pages 934–943. 1943.

Leach, J. G., Lowther, C. V., and Ryan, Mary A.: *Stripe Smut (Ustilago striaeformis) in Relation to Bluegrass Improvement,* Phytopathology, volume 36, pages 57–72. 1946.

Tsiang, Y. S.: *Variation and Inheritance of Certain Characters of Brome Grass, Bromus inermis Leyss.,* Journal of the American Society of Agronomy, volume 36, pages 508–522. 1944.

Weiss, Freeman: *Check List of Diseases of Economic Plants in United States,* U. S. Bureau of Plant Industry, Plant Disease Reporter, volume 28, Nos. 28–29, 1944; and volume 29, Nos. 1–24, 1945.

DISEASES OF FORAGE LEGUMES
(Page 267)

Allington, William B.: *Wildfire Disease of Soybeans,* Phytopathology, volume 35, pages 857–869. 1945.

Allington, William B.: *Bud Blight of Soybean Caused by the Tobacco Ring-Spot Virus,* Phytopathology, volume 36, pages 319–322. 1946.

Cormack, M. W.: *Studies on Ascochyta imperfecta, A Seed- and Soil-Borne Parasite of Alfalfa,* Phytopathology, volume 35, pages 838–855. 1945.

Cormack, M. W.: *Sclerotinia sativa, and Related Species, as Root Parasites of Alfalfa and Sweet Clover in Alberta,* Scientific Agriculture, volume 26, pages 448–459. 1946.

Grandfield, C. O.: *Buffalo Alfalfa,* Kansas Agricultural Experiment Station Circular 226. 1945.

Hollowell, E. A.: *Registration of Varieties and Strains of Red Clover, I.* Journal of the American Society of Agronomy, volume 35, pages 830–833. 1943.

Horsfall, James G.: *A Study of Meadow-Crop Diseases in New York,* New York (Cornell) Agricultural Experiment Station Memoir 130. 1930.

Johnson, H. W., Lefebvre, C. L., and Ayers, T. T.: *Powdery Mildew of Lespedeza,* (Phytopath. Note) Phytopathology, volume 30, pages 620–621. 1940.

Johnson, Howard, W., and Koehler, Benjamin: *Soybean Diseases and Their Control,* U.S.D.A. Farmers' Bulletin 1937. 1943.

Jones, Fred Reuel: *Life History of Cercospora on Sweetclover,* Mycologia, volume 36, pages 518–525. 1944.

Menzies, J. D.: *Witches' Broom of Alfalfa in North America,* Phytopathology, volume 36, pages 762–774. 1946.

Peterson, Maurice L., and Melchers, L. E.: *Studies on Black Stem of Alfalfa Caused by Ascochyta imperfecta,* Phytopathology, volume 32, pages 590–597. 1942.

Sampson, Kathleen, and Western, J. H.: *Diseases of British Grasses and Herbage Legumes,* Cambridge University Press, Cambridge, England. 1941.

Smith, Oliver F.: *Stemphylium Leaf Spot of Red Clover and Alfalfa,* Journal of Agricultural Research, volume 61, pages 831–846. 1940.

Sullivan, J. T., and Chilton, S. J. P.: *The Effect of Leaf Rust on the Carotene Content of White Clover,* Phytopathology, volume 31, pages 554–557. 1941.

Westover, H. L.: *Alfalfa Varieties in the United States,* U.S.D.A. Farmers' Bulletin 1731. 1934. (Revised by H. M. Tysdal, 1946.)

SOME OF THE INSECTS
(Page 273)

Batten, E. T., and Poos, F. W.: *Spraying and Dusting to Control the Potato Leafhopper on Peanuts in Virginia,* Virginia Agricultural Experiment Station Bulletin 316. 1938.

Bohart, Richard M.: *Sod Webworms and Other Lawn Pests in California,* U.S.D.A. Technical Bulletin 741. 1940.

Cowan, F. T., Shipman, H. J., and Wakeland, Claude: *Mormon Crickets and Their Control,* U.S.D.A. Farmers' Bulletin 1928. 1943.

Hamlin, J. C., McDuffie, W. C., Lieberman, F. V., and Bunn, R. W.: *Prevention and Control of Alfalfa Weevil Damage,* U.S.D.A. Farmers' Bulletin 1930. 1943.

Luginbill, Philip: *Control of Common White Grubs in Cereal and Forage Crops,* U.S.D.A. Farmers' Bulletin 1798. 1938.

Osborn, Herbert: *Meadow and Pasture Insects,* The Educators' Press, Columbus, Ohio. 1939.

Packard, C. M., and Benton, Curtis: *How to Fight the Chinch Bug,* U.S.D.A. Farmers' Bulletin 1780. 1937.

Parker, J. R.: *Grasshoppers and Their Control,* U.S.D.A. Farmers' Bulletin 1828. 1939.

Poos, F. W.: *The Potato Leafhopper, a Pest of Alfalfa in the Eastern States,* U.S.D.A. Leaflet 229. 1942.

Stitt, Loyd L.: *Three Species of the Genus Lygus and Their Relation to Alfalfa Seed Production in Southern Arizona and California,* U.S.D.A. Technical Bulletin 741. 1940.

Walter, E. V., Seaton, Lee, and Mathewson, A. A.: *The Texas Leaf-cutting Ant and Its Control,* U.S.D.A. Circular 494. 1938.

Walton, W. R., and Packard, C. M.: *The Armyworm and Its Control,* U.S.D.A. Farmers' Bulletin 1850. 1940.

Wildermuth, V. L.: *The Alfalfa Caterpillar,* U.S.D.A. Farmers' Bulletin 1094. 1920. (Revised 1922.)

WHAT IS NUTRITIOUS FORAGE?
(Page 285)

Brown, B. A., and Hollowell, E. A.: *The Chemical Composition of Some Pasture and Hay Plants as Affected by Soils and Fertilizers,* Soil Science Society of America Proceedings, volume 5, pages 131–139. 1940.

Vandecaveye, S. C., and Baker, G. O.: *Chemical Composition of Certain Forage Crops as Affected by Fertilizers and Soil Types,* Journal of Agricultural Research, volume 68, pages 191–220. 1944.

SOD IS IDEAL
(Page 297)

Davis, Fanny-Fern: *Turf Weed Control With 2,4–D,* United States National Park Service. 1947.

Monteith, John, Jr.: *Better Turf for Playgrounds and Playfields,* Recreation, volume 35, pages 105–107, 128. 1941.

Noer, O. J.: *The Effect of Acidity on Turf and the Chemistry of Acid Soils,* Golfdom, volume 20, No. 6, pages 41, 44, 56. 1946.

Noer, O. J.: *Practical Aspects of Lime Usage on Turf Grasses,* Golfdom, volume 20, No. 9, pages 15–16, 18, 58. 1946.

Rampton, H. H.: *Alta Fescue Production in Oregon,* Oregon Agricultural Experiment Station Bulletin 427. 1945.

POINTS ON MAKING LAWNS
(Page 302)

Ahlgren, Gilbert H.: *Planting and Caring for the Lawn,* New Jersey Agricultural Experiment Station Bulletin 724. 1946.

Cornman, John F.: *The Home Lawn,* New York Agricultural College (Cornell) Extension Bulletin 469. 1941. (Revised 1946.)

Davis, Fanny-Fern: *Better Lawns for Schools and Colleges,* American School and University, volume 15, pages 130–138. 1943.

Sturkie, D. G., and Fisher, Homer S.: *The Planting and Maintenance of Lawns,* Alabama Agricultural Experiment Station Circular 85. 1942.

GREENSWARDS IN COOL REGIONS
(Page 307)

Conner, S. D., and Fisher, M. L.: *How to Make and Maintain a Lawn,* Purdue Agricultural Extension Leaflet 41. 1931. (Revised.)

Lapp, Walter S.: *A Study of Factors Affecting the Growth of Lawn Grasses,* Pennsylvania Academy of Sciences Proceedings, volume 17, pages 117–148. 1943.

Robbins, Wilfred W., Crafts, Alden S., and Raynor, Richard N.: *Weed Control,* McGraw-Hill Book Company, Inc., New York. 1942.

Sprague, Howard B.: *Better Lawns . . .,* McGraw-Hill Book Company, Inc., New York. 1940.

GREENSWARDS IN WARM REGIONS
(Page 311)

Enlow, C. R., and Stokes, W. E.: *Lawns in Florida,* Florida Agricultural Experiment Station Bulletin 209. 1929.

SAFETY AND BEAUTY FOR HIGHWAYS
(Page 315)

Highway Research Board: *Report of Committee on Roadside Development,* Twenty-fourth Annual Meeting Proceedings, pages 157–166. 1944. Twenty-fifth Annual Meeting Proceedings, pages 104–116. 1945.

Mott, G. O.: *Turf on Stabilized Granular Materials,* American Association of State Highway Officials, Group Meeting Book, 1944.

U. S. Engineer Office: *Report on Stabilized Soil and Turfing,* Jacksonville, Fla. August 1944.

BREEDER'S WAYS AND MEANS
(Page 331)

Ahlgren, H. L.: *A Comparison of Methods Used in Evaluating the Results of Pasture Research,* Journal of the American Society of Agronomy, volume 39, pages 240–259. 1947.

Andrews, E. A.: *Seedling Blight and Root Rot of Grasses in Minnesota,* Phytopathology, volume 33, pages 234–239. 1943.

Armstrong, J. M.: *Investigations in Triticum-Agropyron Hybridization,* Empire Journal of Experimental Agriculture, volume 13, pages 41–53. 1945.

Atwood, S. S., and MacDonald, H. A.: *Selecting Plants of Bromegrass for Ability to Grow at Controlled High Temperature,* Journal of the American Society of Agronomy, volume 38, pages 824–832. 1946.

Blanchard, Ralph A.: *Insect Resistance in Forage Plants,* Journal of the American Society of Agronomy, volume 35, pages 716–724. 1943.

Brink, R. A. et al.: *A Hybrid Between Hordeum jubatum and Secale cereale, . . .* Journal of Heredity, volume 35, pages 67–75. 1944.

Brittingham, W. H.: *An Artificial Hybrid Between Canadian Bluegrass and Kentucky Bluegrass,* Journal of Heredity, volume 32, pages 57–63. 1941.

Burton, Glenn W.: *Hybrids between Napier Grass and Cattail Millet,* Journal of Heredity, volume 35, pages 227–232. 1944.

Burton, Glenn W.: *Dallas Grass Seed Sources,* Journal of the American Society of Agronomy, volume 37, pages 458–468. 1945.

Burton, Glenn W.: *Bahia Grass Types,* Journal of the American Society of Agronomy, volume 38, pages 273–281. 1946.

Burton, Glenn W., McBeth, C. W., and Stephens, J. L.: *The Growth of Kobe Lespedeza as Influenced by the Root Knot Nematode Resistance of the Bermuda Grass Strain With Which it is Associated,* Journal of the American Society of Agronomy, volume 38, pages 651–656. 1946.

Carroll, J. C.: *Effects of Drought, Temperature and Nitrogen on Turf Grasses,* Plant Physiology, volume 18, pages 19–36. 1943.

Cheng, Chung-Fu: *Self-Fertility Studies in Three Species of Commercial Grasses,* Journal of the American Society of Agronomy, volume 38, pages 873–881. 1946.

Clark, John W.: *The Effect of Some Environmental Influences in Bulk Hybridization of Grass,* Journal of the American Society of Agronomy, volume 36, pages 132–140. 1944.

Cook, C. W.: *A Study of the Roots of Bromus inermis in Relation to Drought Resistance,* Ecology, volume 24, pages 169–182. 1943.

Cooper, D. C., and Brink, R. A.: *Collapse of the Seed Following the Mating of Hordeum jubatum × Secale cereale,* Genetics, volume 29, pages 370–390. 1944.

DeFrance, J. A.: *A Comparison of Bent Turf from Self- and Open-Pollinated Seed and from Stolons,* Turf Culture, volume 2, pages 169–177. 1941.

Dermen, H.: *Colchicine Polyploidy and Technique,* Botanical Review, volume 6, pages 599–635. 1940.

Dillman, A. C.: *The Beginnings of Crested Wheatgrass in North America,* Journal of the American Society of Agronomy, volume 38, pages 237–250. 1946.

Domingo, Wayne E.: *Bulk Emasculation and Pollination of Smooth Bromegrass, Bromus inermis,* Journal of the American Society of Agronomy, volume 33, pages 993–1002. 1941.

Edgecombe, S. W.: *Report of Fine Turf Research at Iowa State College,* Iowa State Horticultural Society Transactions, volume 75, pages 320–329. 1940.

Evans, Marshall, and Wilsie, C. P.: *Flowering of Bromegrass, Bromus inermis, in the Greenhouse as Influenced by Length of Day, Temperature, and Level of Fertility,* Journal of the American Society of Agronomy, volume 38, pages 923–932. 1946.

Evans, Morgan W.: *Selection of Open-Pollinated Timothy,* Journal of the American Society of Agronomy, volume 28, pages 389–394. 1936.

Fischer, G. W., and Levine, M. N.: *Summary of the Recorded Data on the Reaction of Wild and Cultivated Grasses to Stem Rust (Puccinia graminis), Leaf Rust (P. rubigo-vera), Stripe Rust (P. glumarum), and Crown Rust (P. coronata) in the United States and Canada,* U.S.D.A. Plant Disease Reporter, Supplement 130. 1941.

Franzke, C. J.: *Rancher Sorghum, A Low Hydrocyanic Acid Forage,* South Dakota Agricultural Experiment Station Circular 57. 1945.

Franzke, C. J.: *Ree Wheatgrass; Its Culture and Use,* South Dakota Agricultural Experiment Station Circular 58. 1945.

Hayes, Wm. P., and Johnston, C. O.: *The Reaction of Certain Grasses to Chinch-Bug Attack,* Journal of Agricultural Research, volume 31, pages 575–583. 1925.

Hogg, Peter G., and Ahlgren, H. L.: *Environmental, Breeding, and Inheritance Studies of Hydrocyanic Acid in Sorghum vulgare var. sudanense,* Journal of Agricultural Research, volume 67, pages 195–210. 1943.

Hopkins, Harold: *Variations in the Growth of Side-Oats Grama Grass at Hays, Kansas, from Seed Produced in Various Parts of the Great Plains Region,* Transactions of Kansas Academy of Science, volume 44, pages 86–95. 1941.

Imperial Agricultural Bureaux: *The Breeding of Herbage Plants in Scandinavia and Finland,* Imperial Agricultural Bureaux (Great Britain) Joint Publication 3. 1940.

International Crop Improvement Association: *Minimum Seed Certification Standards,* International Crop Improvement Association Publication 16. 1946.

Johnson, B. Lennart: *Natural Hybrids Between Oryzopsis hymenoides and Several Species of Stipa,* American Journal of Botany, volume 32, pages 599–608. 1945.

Johnson, B. Lennart, and Rogler, George A.: *A Cyto-taxonomic Study of an Intergeneric Hybrid between Oryzopsis hymenoides and Stipa viridula,* American Journal of Botany, volume 30, pages 49–56. 1943.

Keller, Wesley: *Designs and Technic for the Adaptation of Controlled Competition to Forage Plant Breeding,* Journal of the American Society of Agronomy, volume 38, pages 580–588. 1946.

Knobloch, Irving William: *Development and Structure of Bromus inermis Leyss.,* Iowa State College Journal of Science, volume 19, pages 67–98. 1944.

Knowles, P. F.: *Improving an Annual Brome Grass, Bromus mollis L., for Range Purposes,* Journal of the American Society of Agronomy, volume 35, pages 584–594. 1943.

Knowles, R. P., and Horner, W. H.: *Methods of Selfing and Crossing Crested Wheatgrass, Agropyron cristatum (L.) Beauv.,* Scientific Agriculture, volume 23, pages 598–611. 1943.

Kreitlow, K. W., and Myers, W. M.: *Prevalence and Distribution of Stripe Smut of Poa pratensis in Some Pastures of Pennsylvania,* Phytopathology, volume 34, pages 411–415. 1944.

Law, Alvin G., and Anderson, Kling L.: *The Effect of Selection and Inbreeding on the Growth of Big Bluestem (Andropogon furcatus, Muhl.),* Journal of the American Society of Agronomy, volume 32, pages 931–943. 1940.

McAllister, Dean F.: *Determination of Soil Drought Resistance in Grass Seedlings,* Journal of the American Society of Agronomy, volume 36, pages 324–336. 1944.

Myers, W. M.: *Heritable Variations in Seed Set Under Bag Among Plants of Orchard Grass, Dactylis glomerata L.,* Journal of the American Society of Agronomy, volume 34, pages 1042–1051. 1942.

Myers, W. M.: *Analysis of Non-Heritable Variations in Seed Set Under Bag Among Plants of Orchard Grass, Dactylis glomerata L.,* Journal of the American Society of Agronomy, volume 34, pages 1114–1124. 1942.

Myers, W. M.: *Effects of Cytoplasm and Gene Dosage on Expression of Male-Sterility in Dactylis glomerata,* Genetics, volume 31, pages 225–226. 1946.

Myers, W. M., and Garber, R. J.: *The Evaluation of Individual Plants of Pasture Grasses in Association with White Clover,* Journal of the American Society of Agronomy, volume 34, pages 7–15. 1943.

Newell, L. C., and Tysdal, H. M.: *Numbering and Note-Taking Systems for Use in the Improvement of Forage Crops,* Journal of the American Society of Agronomy, volume 37, pages 736–749. 1945.

Nielsen, E. L.: *An Analysis of Variation in Panicum virgatum,* Journal of Agricultural Research, volume 69, pages 327–353. 1944.

Nielsen, Etlar L.: *Cytology and Breeding Behavior of Selected Plants of Poa pratensis,* Botanical Gazette, volume 106, pages 357–382. 1945.

Olmsted, Charles E.: *Growth and Development in Range Grasses. V. Photoperiodic Responses of Clonal Divisions of Three Latitudinal Strains of Side-Oats Grama,* Botanical Gazette, volume 106, pages 383–401. 1945.

Reitz, L. P., and others: *New Combinations of Genes in Wheat × Wheatgrass Hybrids,* Kansas Academy of Science Transactions, volume 48, pages 151–159. 1945.

Schoth, H. A., and Hein, M. A.: *The Ryegrasses,* U.S.D.A. Leaflet 196. 1940.

Schultz, H. K.: *A study of Methods of Breeding Orchard Grass (Dactylis glomerata L.),* Journal of the American Society of Agronomy, volume 33, pages 546–558. 1941.

Skirm, G. W.: *Embryo Culturing as an Aid to Plant Breeding,* Journal of Heredity, volume 33, pages 211–215. 1942.

Smith, D. C., Nielsen, E. L., and Ahlgren, H. L.: *Variation in Ecotypes of Poa pratensis,* Botanical Gazette, volume 108, pages 143–166. 1946.

Smith, D. C., and Nielsen, E. L.: *Morphological Variation in Poa pratensis L. as Related to Subsequent Breeding Behavior,* Journal of American Society of Agronomy, volume 37, pages 1033–1040. 1945.

Sprague, V. G., and Myers, W. M.: *A Comparative Study of Methods for Determining Yields of Kentucky Bluegrass and White Clover, When Grown in Association,* Journal of the American Society of Agronomy, volume 37, pages 370–377. 1945.

Stebbins, G. L.: *Artificial and Natural Hybrids in the Gramineae, Tribe Hordeae. II. Agropyron, Elymus, and Hordeum,* American Journal of Botany, volume 33, pages 579–586. 1946.

Stephens, J. L.: *Tift Bermudagrass, Cynodon dactylon (L.) Pers.,* Journal of the American Society of Agronomy, volume 33, pages 942–943. 1941.

Stuckey, Irene H., and Banfield, William G.: *The Morphological Variations and the Occurrence of Aneuploids in Some Species of Agrostis in Rhode Island,* American Journal of Botany, volume 33, pages 185–190. 1946.

Sullivan, J. T., and Garber, R. J.: *The Nitrogen Content of Poa pratensis: Its Range and Relation to Flowering Date,* Journal of the American Society of Agronomy, volume 33, pages 933–937. 1941.

Suneson, C. A., and Pope, W. K.: *Progress with Triticum × Agropyron Crosses in California,* Journal of the American Society of Agronomy, volume 38, pages 956–963. 1946.

Thomas, H. L., and Hayes, H. K.: *A Selection Experiment with Kentucky Bluegrass,* Journal of the American Society of Agronomy, volume 39, pages 192–197. 1947.

Tinney, F. W.: *Cytology of Parthenogenesis in Poa pratensis,* Journal of Agricultural Research, volume 60, pages 351–360. 1940.

Vanterpool, T. C.: *Pythium Root Rot of Grasses,* Scientific Agriculture, volume 22, pages 674–687. 1942.

Wallin, J. R.: *Parasitism of Xanthomonas translucens (J. J. and R.) Dowson on Grasses and Cereals,* Iowa State College Journal of Science, volume 20, pages 171–193. 1946.

Wenger, L. E: *Improvement of Buffalo Grass in Kansas,* Biennial Report of the Kansas State Board of Agriculture, pages 211–224. 1941.

White, W. J.: *Intergeneric Crosses Between Triticum and Agropyron,* Scientific Agriculture, volume 21, pages 198–232. 1940.

PARAGON FOR THE RANGE
(Page 347)

Clausen, Jens; Keck, David D., and Hiesey, William M.: *Experimental Taxonomy,* Carnegie Institution of Washington Yearbook No. 44, 1944–1945, pages 71–83. 1945.

Johnson, B. Lennart: *Cyto-taxonomic Studies in Oryzopsis,* Botanical Gazette, volume 107, pages 1–32. 1945.

Knowles, P. F.: *Interspecific Hybridizations of Bromus,* Genetics, volume 29, pages 128–140. 1944.

Love, R. Merton: *Interspecific Hybridization in Stipa L., I. Natural Hybrids,* American Naturalist, volume 80, pages 189–192. February 1946.

McCall, R., Clark, R. T., and Patton, A. R.: *The Apparent Digestibility and Nutritive Value of Several Native and Introduced Grasses,* Montana Agricultural Experiment Station Technical Bulletin 418. 1943.

Murphy, R. P.: *Methods of Breeding Crested Wheatgrass, Agropyron cristatum (L) Beauv.,* Journal of the American Society of Agronomy, volume 34, pages 553–565. 1942.

Newell, L. C., and Keim, F. D.: *Field Performance of Bromegrass Strains from Different Regional Seed Sources,* Journal of the American Society of Agronomy, volume 35, pages 420–434. 1943.

Rogler, George A.: *Russian Wild-rye, Elymus junceus, Fisch.,* (Note) Journal of the American Society of Agronomy, volume 33, pages 266–268. 1941.

Smith, D. C.: *Pollination and Seed Formation in Grasses,* Journal of Agricultural Research, volume 68, pages 79–95. 1944.

Smith, D. C.: *Intergeneric Hybridization of Cereals and Other Grasses,* Journal of Agricultural Research, volume 64, pages 33–47. 1942.

Stebbins, G. L., Jr., and Love, R. M.: *A Cytological Study of California Forage Grasses,* American Journal of Botany, volume 28, pages 371–382. 1941.

Watkins, W. E.: *Composition of Range Grasses and Browse at Varying Stages of Maturity,* New Mexico Agricultural Experiment Station Bulletin 311 (Technical), page 43. 1943.

DOMESTICATED GRASS
(Page 354)

Crider, Franklin J.: *Three Introduced Lovegrasses for Soil Conservation,* U.S.D.A. Circular 730. 1945.

Hockensmith, R. D., and Steele, J. G.: *Classifying Land for Conservation Farming,* U.S.D.A. Farmers' Bulletin 1853. 1943.

Richards, D. E., and Hawk, Virgil B.: *Palatability for Sheep and Yield of Hay and Pasture Grasses,* Oregon Agricultural Experiment Station Bulletin 431. 1945.

Stark, R. H., Toevs, J. L., and Hafenrichter, A. L.: *Grasses and Cultural Methods for Reseeding Abandoned Farm Lands in Southern Idaho,* Idaho Agricultural Experiment Station Bulletin 267. 1946.

Weber, G. L.: *A Method of Preparing Some Native Grass Seeds For Handling and Seeding,* Journal of the American Society of Agronomy, volume 31, pages 729–733. 1939.

GRASSES FOR SPECIAL USES
(Page 367)

Åkerberg, Erik: *Cytogenetic Studies in Poa pratensis and its Hybrid with Poa alpina,* Hereditas, volume 28, pages 1–126. 1942.

Ahlgren, H. L., Smith, D. C., and Nielsen, E. L.: *Behavior of Various Selections of Kentucky Bluegrass, Poa pratensis L., When Grown as Spaced Plants and in Mass Seedings,* Journal of the American Society of Agronomy, volume 37, pages 268–281. 1945.

Armstrong, J. M. A.: *A Cytological Study of the Genus Poa,* Canadian Journal of Research, Section C, volume 15, pages 281–287. 1937.

Brittingham, W. H.: *Types of Seed Formation as Indicated by the Nature and Extent of Variation in Kentucky Bluegrass, and its Practical Implications,* Journal of Agricultural Research, volume 67, pages 225–264. 1943.

Kramer, Herbert H.: *Morphologic and Agronomic Variation in Poa pratensis L. in Relation to Chromosome Numbers,* Journal of the American Society of Agronomy, volume 39, pages 181–191. 1947.

Stebbins, G. L., and Love, R. M.: *A Cytological Study of California Forage Grasses,* American Journal of Botany, volume 28, pages 371–382. 1941.

Stebbins, G. L., Valencia, Juan I., and Valencia, R. Marie: *Artificial and Natural Hybrids in the Gramineae, tribe Hordeae, I. Elymus, Sitanion, and Agropyron,* American Journal of Botany, volume 33, pages 338–351. 1946.

ADJUSTMENTS NECESSARY
(Page 383)

U.S.D.A., Interbureau Committee on Postwar Programs: *Peacetime Adjustments in Farming; Possibilities under Prosperity Conditions,* U.S.D.A. Miscellaneous Publication 595. 1945.

[U. S.] House Committee on Agriculture: *Long-Range Agricultural Policy and Programs,* Hearings before House Congressional Committee on Agriculture, 80th Cong., 1st sess. (Parts 1–5), April 21 through October 10, 1947.

THE NORTHEASTERN STATES
(Page 391)

Alderfer, R. B., and Robinson, R. R.: *Runoff from Pastures in Relation to Grazing Intensity and Soil Compaction,* Journal of the American Society of Agronomy, volume 39, pages 948–958. 1947.

Carncross, John W., and Hauck, Joseph F.: *Roughage Makes Milk Profits*, New Jersey Agricultural Experiment Station Circular 505. 1947.

Colby, William G.: *Pasture Culture in Massachusetts*, Massachusetts Agricultural Experiment Station Bulletin 380. 1941.

Free, G. R., Carleton, E. A., Lamb, John Jr., and Gustafson, A. F.: *Experiments in the Control of Soil Erosion in Central New York*, N. Y. (Cornell) Agricultural Experiment Station Bulletin 831. 1946.

Garber, R. J., Myers, W. M., and Sprague, V. G.: *Pastures and Pasture Problems in Northeastern States*, Pennsylvania Agricultural Experiment Station Bulletin 485. 1946.

Haynes, J. L., and Neal, O. R.: *The Effect of Certain Pasture Practices on Runoff and Production of Protective Cover*, Journal of the American Society of Agronomy, volume 35, pages 205–211. 1943.

McDonald, Angus: *Early American Soil Conservationists*, U.S.D.A. Miscellaneous Publication 449. 1941.

Sprague, H. B., Blaser, R. E., and Boyce, J. H.: *A Comparison of Treatments on Permanent Pastures*, New Jersey Agricultural Experiment Station Bulletin 673. 1940.

Sprague, V. G., Robinson, R. R., and Clyde, A. W.: *Pasture Renovation: I. Seedbed Preparation, Seedling Establishment, and Subsequent Yields*, Journal of the American Society of Agronomy, volume 39, pages 12–25. 1947.

CORN BELT AND LAKE STATES
(Page 423)

Ahlgren, H. L.: *The Establishment and Early Management of Sown Pastures: United States of America, North-Central Region*, Imperial Bureau of Pastures and Forage Crops Bulletin 34, pages 139–160. 1945.

Ahlgren, H. L., and Burcalow, F. V.: *Bromegrass and Alfalfa for Hay, Pasture, or Silage*, Wisconsin Agricultural College Extension Circular 344. 1944.

Ahlgren, H. L., Rupel, I. W., Bohstedt, G., and Graul, E. J.: *Eight Years' Results on the Effectiveness of Fertilization and Management in Increasing the Production of Permanent Pastures*, Journal of the American Society of Agronomy, volume 36, pages 301–315. 1944.

Ahlgren, H. L., Wall, M. L., Muckenhirn, R. J., and Burcalow, F. V.: *Effectiveness of Renovation in Increasing Yields of Permanent Pastures in Southern Wisconsin*, Journal of the American Society of Agronomy, volume 36, pages 121–131. 1944.

Beck, F. V.: *The Field Seed Industry in the United States, an analysis of the Production, Consumption and Prices of Leguminous and Grass Seeds*, The University of Wisconsin Press. Madison, Wis. 1944.

Bohstedt, G.: *Nutritional Values of Hay and Silage as Affected by Harvesting, Processing, and Storage*, Agricultural Engineering, volume 25, pages 337–340, 388, 390, 392. 1944.

Boyd, F. T., Aamodt, O. S., Bohstedt, G., and Truog, E.: *Sudan Grass Management for Control of Cyanide Poisoning*, Journal of the American Society of Agronomy, volume 30, pages 569–582. 1938.

Brown, E. Marion.: *Orchard Grass in Missouri*, Missouri Agricultural College Extension Circular 431. 1941.

Churchill, B. R.: *Smooth Bromegrass Seed Production in Michigan*, Michigan Agricultural Experiment Station Circular Bulletin 192. 1944.

Coleman, O. T., and Klemme, A. W.: *Soils and Soil Fertility for Alfalfa*, Missouri Agricultural College Extension Circular 493. 1943.

Crim, Ralph F., and Burson, Paul M.: *Well-managed Pastures*, Minnesota University Agricultural Extension Bulletin 241. 1944.

DenUyl, D.: *Farm Woodlands Should Not Be Grazed*, Journal of Forestry, volume 43, pages 729–732. 1945.

DenUyl, Daniel, Diller, Oliver D., and Day, Ralph K.: *The Development of Natural Reproduction in Previously Grazed Farmwoods*, Indiana Agricultural Experiment Station Bulletin 431. 1938.

Dickson, J. G.: *Diseases of Field Crops*, McGraw-Hill Book Company, Inc. 1947.

Dodd, D. R.: *Some Factors Affecting the Content, Fluctuation, and Distribution of White Clover in Permanent Sod Areas in Ohio*, Soil Science Society of America Proceedings, volume 6, pages 288–297. 1941.

Dodd, D. R., and Salter, R. M.: *Better Pastures For Ohio Livestock*, Ohio Agricultural Experiment Station Bulletin 154. 1934. (Revised 1941.)

Fuelleman, R. F., Burlison, W. L., and Kammlade, W. G.: *A Comparison of Bromegrass and Orchard Grass Pastures*, Journal of the American Society of Agronomy, volume 36, pages 849–858. 1944.

Graber, L. F., and Ahlgren, H. L.: *Agronomy, Principles and Practices*. William C. Brown Company. 1946.

Hogg, Peter G., and Ahlgren, H. L.: *Environmental, Breeding and Inheritance Studies of Hydrocyanic Acid in Sorghum Vulgare var. sudanense*, Journal of Agricultural Research, volume 67, pages 195–210. 1943.

Hughes, H. D., and Peterson, M. L.: *Building Better Pastures,* Farm Science Reporter, volume 7, pages 14–18. 1946.

Megee, C. R., Frakes, M. G., and Larsen, I. T.: *The Influence of Clipping Treatment and Rolling on the Yield of Clover Seed,* Journal of American Society of Agronomy, volume 34, pages 841–843. 1942.

Nevens, W. B.: *Improving Bluegrass Pastures,* Illinois Agricultural Experiment Station Bulletin 504. 1944.

Perkins, A. E.: *Dry Matter Content of Crops in Relation to Hay and Silage Making,* Ohio Agricultural Experiment Station Bimonthly Bulletin 208, volume 26, pages 6–10. 1941.

Peterson, Maurice L.: *Effect of Method of Grazing Unimproved Kentucky Bluegrass on Beef Production, Botanical Composition, and Herbage Yields,* Journal of American Society of Agronomy, volume 39, pages 412–422. 1947.

Rather, H. C., and Harrison, C. M.: *Alfalfa and Smooth Bromegrass for Pasture and Hay,* Michigan Agricultural Experiment Station Circular Bulletin 189. 1944.

Smith, D. W.: *The Influence of Top Growth Removals on the Root and Vegetative Development of Sweet Clover,* Doctorate Thesis, Wisconsin Agricultural Experiment Station. 1947.

Sprague, M. A., and Graber, L. F.: *Ice Sheet Injury to Alfalfa,* Journal of the American Society of Agronomy, volume 35, pages 881–894. 1943.

Vander Meulen, E.: *Curing Early Cut Hay on Tripods,* Michigan Agricultural Experiment Station, Quarterly Bulletin, volume 25, pages 336–341. 1943.

Weaver, Dee Lee: *Wildland Grazing in Northern Michigan,* Michigan Agricultural Experiment Station Quarterly Bulletin, volume 25, pages [83]–93. 1942.

Wilsie, C. P.: *Better Alfalfa Coming,* Farm Science Reporter, volume 6, No. 3, pages [14]–[16]. 1945.

Wilsie, C. P., Peterson, M. L., and Hughes, H. D.: *Bromegrass in Iowa,* Iowa Agricultural Experiment Station Extension pages [14]–[16]. 1945.

A WIDE EMPIRE
(Page 455)

Bennett, H. H.: *The Soils and Agriculture of the Southern States,* The Macmillan Company, New York. 1921.

Cummings, Ralph, W.: *Principles Determining Where Fertilizer Should Be Placed for Greatest Efficiency,* National Fertilizer Association, Nineteenth Annual Meeting of the National Joint Committee on Fertilizer Application, pages 27–32. [1944.]

Odum, Howard W.: *Southern Regions of the United States,* The University of North Carolina Press, Chapel Hill, N. C. 1936.

MAINTAINING PASTURES
(Page 458)

Bailey, R. Y.: *Kudzu for Erosion Control in the Southeast,* U.S.D.A. Farmers' Bulletin 1840. 1939.

Blaser, R. E., and Stokes, W. E.: *Effect of Fertilizer on Growth and Composition of Carpet and Other Grasses,* Florida Agricultural Experiment Station Technical Bulletin 390. 1943.

Blaser, R. E., Stokes, W. E., Warner, J. D., and others: *Pastures for Florida,* Florida Agricultural Experiment Station Bulletin 409. 1945.

Bledsoe, R. P., and Sell, O. E.: *Permanent Pastures,* Georgia Agricultural Experiment Station Bulletin 207. 1940.

Carr, R. B., and Rhoad, O. A.: *Influence of Lime and Fertilizers on Pasture Establishment and Production at Jeanerette, La., 1932 to 1938,* U.S.D.A. Circular 666. 1943.

Edens, W. J.: *Problems in Farm Management and Production Costs on 40 Farms in Northeast Mississippi,* Mississippi Agricultural Experiment Station Bulletin 431. 1946.

Hutcheson, T. B.: *Experiments and Observations on Pasture Management in Appomattox County,* Virginia Agricultural Experiment Station Bulletin 333. 1941.

Kik, M. C.: *Nutritive Studies of Forage Plants,* Arkansas Agricultural Experiment Station Bulletin 434. 1943.

Kinney, E. J., Kenney, Ralph, and Fergus, E. N.: *Seeding Meadow and Pasture Crops,* Kentucky Agricultural Extension Service Circular 402. 1944.

Lovvorn, R. L.: *The Effects of Fertilization, Species Competition, and Cutting Treatments on the Behavior of Dallis Grass, Paspalum dilatatum Poir., and Carpet Grass, Axonopus affinis Chase,* Journal of the American Society of Agronomy, volume 36, pages 590–600. 1944.

Lowry, S. J., and Caldwell, L. M.: *Grass Farming for Improving Depleted Soils,* Kentucky Agricultural Experiment Station Circular 52. 1942.

Massey, Z. A., and Fisher, S. W.: *Preliminary Report of Green Grazing Versus Hays for Fattening Swine,* Georgia Agricultural Experiment Station Circular 152. 1946.

Means, Ray H., Coleman, Russell, and Bennett, H. W.: *Grazing Beef Cattle on Winter Growing Crops,* Mississippi Agricultural Experiment Station Circular 125. 1946.

Mooers, C. A., and Hazlewood, B. P.: *Sericea as a Soil Improving Crop for Corn,* Tennessee Agricultural Experiment Station Bulletin 197. 1945.

Moore, J. S., and Cowsert, W. C.: *The Relation of Feed of the Dairy Cow to Production,* Mississippi Agricultural Experiment Station Bulletin 383. 1943.

McClendon, J. W., and Mayton, E. L.: *The Effect of Lime and Fertilizer on the Composition and Yield of Pasture Herbage in Alabama,* Soil Science Society of America Proceedings, volume 6, pages 285–287. 1941.

McKee, Roland, and Stephens, J. L.: *Kudzu as a Farm Crop,* U.S.D.A. Farmers' Bulletin 1923. 1943.

Neel, L. R.: *Control of Broom Sedge,* Tennessee Agricultural Experiment Station Circular 57. 1936.

Nielsen, Etlar L.: *Adaptability of Grass Species to Arkansas,* Arkansas Agricultural Experiment Station Bulletin 408. 1941.

Neller, J. R.: *Factors Affecting Composition of Everglades Grasses and Legumes With Special Reference to Proteins and Minerals,* Florida Agricultural Experiment Station Bulletin 403. 1944.

O'Brien, R. E., and Obenshain, S. S.: *The Effect of Different Phosphatic Fertilizers on the Yield, Plant Population, and Chemical Composition of Pasture Herbage on Dunmore and Emory Soils,* Virginia Agricultural Experiment Station Technical Bulletin 80. 1942.

O'Leary, W. G.: *Organization and Operation of Farms in Black Prairie Area, Mississippi,* Mississippi Agricultural Experiment Station Bulletin 404. 1944.

Perkins, W. R., Grizzard, A. L., and Hutcheson, T. B.: *Lime and Fertilizers Improve Pastures,* Virginia Agricultural Experiment Station Bulletin 330. 1941.

Price, N. D., Ellett, W. B., and Hill, H. H.: *Pasture Production as Affected by Type and Chemical Composition of the Soil,* Virginia Agricultural Experiment Station Technical Bulletin 78. 1941.

Price, N. D., Linkous, W. N., and Hill, H. H.: *Mineral Constituents and Protein Content of Certain Grasses and Legumes Grown in Pure Stands on Three Soil Types,* Virginia Agricultural Experiment Station Technical Bulletin 102. 1946.

Roberts, John B.: *Feed for Kentucky Livestock; amounts of livestock and feed produced, and sources of purchased feed,* Kentucky Agricultural Experiment Station Bulletin 480. 1945.

Seath, D. M.: *Profitable Permanent Pastures for Dairy Cattle,* Louisiana Agricultural Experiment Station Bulletin 341. 1942.

Semple, A. T., and Hein, M. A.: *Pastures to Hold and Enrich the Soil,* U.S.D.A. Farmers' Bulletin 1900. 1942.

Semple, A. T., and Hein, M. A.: *Good Pastures,* U.S.D.A. Farmers' Bulletin 1942. 1943.

Skelton, D. W.: *Improving Pastures in Mississippi,* Mississippi Agricultural Experiment Station Bulletin 419. 1945.

Stephens, J. L.: *Pastures for the Coastal Plain of Georgia,* Georgia Coastal Plain Experiment Station Bulletin 27. 1942.

Stewart, Fred, and Boseck, J. K.: *Feed and Forage Cropping Systems for Process Milk Production in the Alabama-Tennessee Valley,* Alabama Agricultural Experiment Station, Mimeograph Series, No. 9. 1944.

IMPORTANCE OF PASTURES
(Page 465)

Elting, E. C., LaMaster, J. P., and Mitchell, J. H.: *Permanent Pasture Studies,* South Carolina Agricultural Experiment Station Bulletin 308. 1937.

Tucker, Elbridge A., Welch, Frank J., and Downing, James C.: *Farm Organization and Adjustment Problems in the Shortleaf Pine Area of Mississippi,* Mississippi Agricultural Experiment Station Bulletin 405. 1944.

Woodhouse, W. W., Jr. and Lovvorn, R. L.: *Establishing and Improving Permanent Pastures in North Carolina,* North Carolina Agricultural Experiment Station Bulletin 338. 1942.

GRAZING ON FORESTED LANDS
(Page 468)

Biswell, H. H., Collins, R. W., Foster, J. E., and Boggess, T. S., Jr.: *Native Forage Plants: Species Utilized by Beef Cattle on Forage Range in the North Carolina Coastal Plain,* North Carolina Agricultural Experiment Station Bulletin 353. 1945.

Biswell, H. H., Southwell, B. L., Stevenson, J. W., and Shepherd, W. O.: *Forest Grazing and Beef Cattle Production in the Coastal Plain of Georgia,* Georgia Coastal Plain Experiment Station Circular 8. 1942.

Campbell, R. S.: *Determination of Grazing Values of Native Vegetation on Southern Pine Forest Ranges,* Ecology, volume 27, pages 195–204. 1946.

Campbell, Robert S., and Rhodes, Robert R.: *Forest Grazing in Relation to Beef Cattle Production in Louisiana,* Louisiana Agricultural Experiment Station Bulletin 380. 1944.

Georgia Coastal Plain Experiment Station: *Silver Anniversary (twenty-fifth) Annual Report 1944–1945,* Georgia Coastal Plain Experiment Station Bulletin 42. 1945.

Kelsey, Harlan P., and Dayton, William A.: *Standardized Plant Names,* 2d edition, J. Horace McFarland Co., Harrisburg, Pa. 1942.

Lewis, L. H.: *Beef Cattle in Florida* (Revised), Florida Department of Agriculture Bulletin 28 (new series). 1944.

Oosting, Henry J.: *An Ecological Analysis of the Plant Communities of Piedmont, North Carolina,* American Midland Naturalist, volume 28, pages 1–126. 1942.

Penfound, Wm. R., and Hathaway, Edward S.: *Plant Communities in the Marshlands of Southeastern Louisiana,* Ecological Monographs, volume 8, pages [1]–56. 1938.

UNFINISHED BUSINESS
(Page 472)

Bear, Firman E., Prince, Arthur L., and Malcolm, John L.: *The Potassium Supplying Powers of 20 New Jersey Soils,* Soil Science, volume 58, pages 139–149. 1944.

Jenny, Hans: *Factors of Soil Formation,* McGraw-Hill Book Company, Inc., New York and London. 1941.

Jones, Randall J.: *Nitrogen Losses from Alabama Soils in Lysimeters as Influenced by Various Systems of Green Manure Crop Management,* Journal of the American Society of Agronomy, volume 34, pages 574–585. 1942.

Pohlman, G. G.: *Effect of Liming Different Soil Layers on Yield of Alfalfa and on Root Development and Nodulation,* Soil Science, volume 62, pages 255–266. 1946.

RANGE MANAGEMENT
(Page 486)

Hurtt, Leon C.: *Crested Wheatgrass Builds Beef,* American Hereford Journal, volume 33, No. 12, pages 14–15, 102. Oct. 15, 1942.

National Resources Planning Board: *Public Works and Rural Land Use.* 1942.

Renne, R. R., and Brownlee, O. H.: *Uncollected Property Taxes in Montana,* Montana Agricultural Experiment Station Bulletin 382. 1940.

Weaver, J. E., and Albertson, F. W.: *Deterioration of Midwest Ranges,* Ecology, volume 21, pages 216–236. 1940.

Whitman, Warren; Hanson, Herbert C., and Peterson, Ronald: *Relation of Drought and Grazing to North Dakota Range Lands,* North Dakota Agricultural Experiment Station Bulletin 320. 1943.

Williams, Ralph M., and Post, A. H.: *Dry Land Pasture Experiments . . .,* Montana Agricultural Experiment Station Bulletin 431. 1945.

SEEDED PASTURES
(Page 495)

Franzke, C. J., and Hume, A. N.: *Regrassing Areas in South Dakota,* South Dakota Agricultural Experiment Station Bulletin 361. 1942.

Frolik, A. L., and Newell, L. C.: *Bromegrass Production in Nebraska,* Nebraska Agricultural Experiment Station Circular 68. 1941.

Fults, Jess L.: *Some Factors Affecting the Establishment of Perennial Grass for Erosion Control in Eastern Colorado,* Journal of the American Society of Agronomy, volume 36, pages 615–625. 1944.

Garver, S., Slatensek, J. M., and Kieselbach, T. A.: *Sweetclover in Nebraska,* Nebraska Agricultural Experiment Station Bulletin 352. 1943.

Newell, L. C., and Keim, F. D.: *Field Performance of Bromegrass Strains From Different Regional Seed Sources,* Journal of the American Society of Agronomy, volume 35, pages 420–434. 1943.

Rogler, George A.: *Relative Palatabilities of Grasses Under Cultivation on the Northern Great Plains,* Journal of the American Society of Agronomy, volume 36, pages 487–496. 1944.

Walster, H. L.: *Grass—The Stockmen's Greatest Asset,* North Dakota Agricultural Experiment Station Bimonthly Bulletin, volume 5, No. 2, pages 2–6. 1942.

Whitman, Warren; Stoa, T. E., and Hanson, Herbert C.: *Grasses and Legumes for Pasture and Hay,* North Dakota Agricultural Experiment Station Circular 64. 1939.

HAY, FODDER, SILAGE CROPS
(Page 497)

Christensen, F. W., and Hopper, T. H.: *Effect of Weathering and Stage of Maturity on the Palatability and Nutritive Value of Prairie Hay,* North Dakota Agricultural Experiment Station Bulletin 260. 1932.

Cushing, R. L., Kiesselbach, T. A., and Webster, O. J.: *Sorghum Production in Nebraska,* Nebraska Agricultural Experiment Station Bulletin 329. 1940.

Franzke, C. J.: *Rancher, A Low Hydrocyanic Acid Forage,* South Dakota Agricultural Experiment Station Circular 57. 1945.

Garver, Samuel: *Alfalfa in South Dakota, Twenty-One Years Research at the Redfield Station,* South Dakota Agricultural Experiment Station Bulletin 383. 1946.

Hathaway, I. L., Davis, H. P., and Keim, F. D.: *Carotene Content of Nebraska Grasses,* Nebraska Agricultural Experiment Station Research Bulletin 140. 1945.

Hume, A. N., and Franzke, Clifford: *Sorghums for Forage and Grain in South Dakota,* South Dakota Agricultural Experiment Station Bulletin 285. 1934.

Newell, L. C.: *The Nebraska Grass Improvement and Testing Program,* Thirty-Seventh Annual Report of the Nebraska Crop Improvement Association. 1947.

Newell, L. C., and Keim, F. D.: *Effects of Mowing Frequency on the Yield and Protein Content of Several Grasses Grown in Pure Stands,* Nebraska Agricultural Experiment Station Research Bulletin 150. 1947.

Tysdal, H. M., and Kiesselbach, T. A.: *Alfalfa in Nebraska,* Nebraska Agricultural Experiment Station Bulletin 331. 1941.

Williams, Ralph M., Clark, R. T., and Patton, A. R.: *Wintering Steers on Crested Wheatgrass,* Montana Agricultural Experiment Station Bulletin 407. 1942.

SOUTHERN GREAT PLAINS
(Page 503)

Brandon, J. F., Curtis, J. J., and Robertson, D. W.: *Sorghums in Colorado,* Colorado Agricultural Experiment Station Bulletin 449. 1938.

Bridges, J. O.: *Reseeding Practices for New Mexico Ranges,* New Mexico Agricultural Experiment Station Bulletin 291. 1942.

Caird, Ralph W.: *Eradicating Mesquite,* The Cattleman, volume 33, No. 8 (January), pages 23–26, 85. 1947.

Costello, David F.: *Tune Up Now for Increased Production,* American Hereford Journal, volume 33, No. 17 (January 1), pages 19, 116–118. 1943.

Costello, David F.: *Important Species of the Major Forage Types in Colorado and Wyoming,* Ecological Monographs 14, pages 107–134. 1944.

Costello, David F., and Turner, George T.: *Judging Condition and Utilization of Short-Grass Ranges on the Central Great Plains,* U.S.D.A. Farmers' Bulletin 1949. 1944.

Cox, Maurice B.: *Small Machines for Removing Trees and Brush,* Agricultural Engineering, volume 27, pages 305–306. 1946.

Crider, Franklin J.: *Three Introduced Lovegrasses for Soil Conservation,* U.S.D.A. Circular 730. 1945.

Daniel, Harley A., Elwell, Harry M., and Murphy, H. F.: *Conservation and Better Land Use for Oklahoma,* Oklahoma Agricultural Experiment Station Bulletin B-257. 1942.

Elwell, Harry M.: *Seed Hay for Regrassing Eroded Land,* Oklahoma Academy of Science Proceedings, volume 25, pages 43–45. 1945.

Fisher, C. E.: *Present Information on the Mesquite Problem,* Texas Agricultural Experiment Station Progress Report 1056. 1947.

Fisher, C. E., Fults, Jess L., and Hopp, Henry: *Factors Affecting Action of Oils and Water-Soluble Chemicals in Mesquite Eradication,* Ecological Monographs, volume 16, pages [109]–126. 1946.

Fudge, J. F., and Fraps, G. S.: *The Chemical Composition of Grasses of Northwest Texas as Related to Soils and to Requirements for Range Cattle,* Texas Agricultural Experiment Station Bulletin 669. 1945.

Hamilton, J. G., Brown, Grover B., Tower, Harold E., and Collins, Wilkie, Jr.: *Irrigated Pastures for Forage Production and Soil Conservation.* U.S.D.A. Farmers' Bulletin 1973. 1945.

Hoover, M. M., Smith, James E., Jr., Ferber, A. E., and Cornelius, D. R.: *Seed for Regrassing Great Plains Areas,* U.S.D.A. Farmers' Bulletin 1985. 1947.

Johnson, W. M.: *3 Main Pasture Types Require Different Use,* Colorado Agricultural College News, volume 1, No. 1, page 6. 1946.

Knox, J. H., and Watkins, W. E.: *The Use of Phosphorus and Calcium Supplements for Range Livestock in New Mexico,* New Mexico Agricultural Experiment Station Bulletin 287. 1942.

McDowell, C. H.: *Panorama of Agricultural Research,* Texas Agricultural Experiment Station Fifty-Eighth Annual Report. 1945.

McMillen, Warren N., and Williams, Quentin: *Range and Pasture Studies and Grazing Recommendations for the Southern Great Plains,* [Oklahoma] Panhandle Agricultural Experiment Station, Panhandle Bulletin 67. 1944.

Martin, J. H., Cole, J. S., and Semple, A. T.: *Growing and Feeding Grain Sorghums,* U.S.D.A. Farmers' Bulletin 1764. 1936. (Revised 1946.)

Nelson, E. W., and Shepherd, W. O.: *Restoring Colorado's Range and Abandoned Croplands,* Colorado Agricultural Experiment Station Bulletin 459. 1940.

Oklahoma Agricultural Experiment Station: *Progress Reports: Feeding Tests with Sheep, Swine, and Beef Cattle, 1945–1946,* Oklahoma Agricultural Experiment Station Bulletin 296. 1946.

Renner, F. G., and Johnson, E. A.: *Improving Range Conditions for Wartime Livestock Production,* U.S.D.A. Farmers' Bulletin 1921. 1942.

Robertson, D. W., Weihing, R. M., and Stewart, T. G.: *Pasture and Forage Crops for Irrigated Areas in Colorado,* Colorado Agricultural Experiment Station Bulletin 469. 1942.

Riegel, Andrew: *A Comparative Study of Natural and Artificial Revegetation of Land Retired From Cultivation at Hays, Kansas,* Transactions of the Kansas Academy of Science, volume 47, pages 195–213. 1944.

Savage, D. A.: *The Establishment and Early Management of Sown Pastures in the Central and Southern Great Plains,* Imperial Bureau of Pastures and Forage Crops, Great Britain, Bulletin 34, pages 161–168. 1945.

Savage, D. A.: *Results of Sagebrush Control Studies at Woodward, Okla.,* Oklahoma Agricultural Experiment Station Bulletin B–295, pages 68–70. 1946.

Savage, D. A., and Heller, V. G.: *Nutritional Qualities of Range Forage Plants in Relation to Grazing With Beef Cattle on the Southern Plains Experimental Range,* U.S.D.A. Technical Bulletin 943. 1947.

Smith, Harry H.: *Beef Production in Colorado,* Colorado Agricultural College Extension Bulletin 389–A. 1946.

Staten, Hi W.: *Crop Calendars for a Year-Round Pasture Program,* Oklahoma Agricultural Experiment Station Circular C–116. 1944.

Staten, Hi W., and Elwell, Harry M.: *Weeping Lovegrass in Oklahoma,* Oklahoma Agricultural Experiment Station Bulletin 281. 1944.

Turner, George T., and Costello, David F.: *Ecological Aspects of the Pricklypear Problem in Eastern Colorado and Wyoming,* Ecology, volume 23, pages 419–426. 1942.

Wasser, C. H.: *Reseed Range Land to Increase Grazing Capacity and Produce More Beef per Acre,* Colorado Farm Bulletin volume 6, No. 5, pages 12–14. 1944.

Watkins, W. E.: *Composition of Range Grasses and Browse at Varying Stages of Maturity,* New Mexico Agricultural Experiment Station Bulletin 311. 1943.

Wenger, Leon E.: *Re-establishing Native Grasses by the Hay Method,* Kansas Agricultural Experiment Station Circular 208. 1941.

GRASS AND WATER, THE KEYS
(Page 541)

Bailey, Reed W.: *Climate and Settlement in the Arid Region,* Yearbook of Agriculture 1941 (Climate and Man), pages 188–196.

Smith, Joseph Russell: *North America,* Harcourt, Brace and Company. 1925. (See pages 436–522.)

Stewart, George: *History of Range Use,* In United States Forest Service, The Western Range, 74th Cong., 2d sess., Senate Document 199, pages 119–133. 1936.

PASTURES AND MEADOWS
(Page 543)

Bracken, A. F., and Evans, R. J.: *Pastures,* Utah Agricultural Extension Service, N. S. 120. 1943.

Fleming, C. E., and Brennen, C. A.: *Possibilities and Limitations in the Use of Irrigated Land for Forage Production in Northeastern Nevada,* Nevada Agricultural Experiment Station Bulletin 154. 1940.

Hamilton, J. G., Brown, Grover F., Tower, Harold E., and Collins, Wilkie, Jr.: *Irrigated Pastures for Forage Production and Soil Conservation,* U.S.D.A. Farmers' Bulletin 1973. 1945.

Jones, Burle J., and Brown, J. B.: *Irrigated Pastures in California,* California Agricultural Extension Circular 125. 1942.

Keller, Wesley; Bateman, George Q., and Packer, J. Elmo: *More Productive Grass and Legume Pastures for Dairy Cattle on Irrigated Lands,* Utah Agricultural Experiment Station Farm and Home Science, volume 8, No. 1, pages 6, 7, 14. 1947.

Koonce, Dwight: *High Altitude Studies of Dry-land Grasses and Clovers,* Colorado Agricultural Experiment Station Bulletin 439. 1937.

Law, A. G., Singleton, H. P., and Ingham, I. M.: *Irrigated Pastures for Central Washington,* Washington State College Experiment Station Bulletin 319. 1945.

Orr, J. B.: *Minerals in Pastures and Their Relation to Animal Nutrition,* H. K. Lewis and Co., Ltd., London. 1929.

Piper, Charles V.: *Forage Plants and Their Culture,* The Macmillan Company. 1914.

Post, A. H., and Tretsven, J. O.: *Irrigated Pastures in Montana,* Montana Agricultural Extension Bulletin 174. 1939.

Richards, D. E., and Hawk, Virgil B.: *Palatabilities for Sheep and Yield of Hay and Pasture Grasses at Union, Oregon,* Oregon Agricultural Experiment Station Bulletin 431. 1945.

Stewart, George, and Clark, Ira: *Effect of Prolonged Spring Grazing on the Yield and Quality of Forage from Wild-Hay Meadows,* Journal of the American Society of Agronomy, volume 36, pages 238–248. 1944.

Stroud, Rufus: *Irrigated Pastures for the Middle Rio Grande Area,* New Mexico Agricultural Experiment Station Press Bulletin 959. 1943.

Thomas, H. L., Kuhlman, G. W., and Mumford, D. Curtis: *Cost of Production and Utilization of Crested Wheatgrass on Eastern Oregon Wheat Farms,* Oregon Agricultural Experiment Station Circular 167. 1945.

CULTIVATED FORAGE CROPS
(Page 548)

Boyd, George W.: *Produce High Quality Hay,* Wyoming Agricultural Extension Service, Circular 85. 1945.

Fluharty, L. W., and Hays, J. C.: *Wild-Hay Management Practices in Modoc County,* California Agricultural Experiment Station Bulletin 679. 1943.

Hayward, H. E., and Magistad, O. C.: *The Salt Problem in Irrigation Agriculture,* U.S.D.A. Miscellaneous Publication 607. 1946.

Koonce, Dwight: *High Altitude Forage Investigations in Southwestern Colorado,* Colorado Agricultural Experiment Station Bulletin 490. 1946.

Kreizinger, E. J., and Law, Alvin G.: *Alfalfa in Eastern Washington,* Washington Agricultural Experiment Station Bulletin 462. 1945.

Staten, Glen, Stroud, R. S., and Carter, John Jr.: *Alfalfa Production Investigations in New Mexico,* New Mexico Agricultural Experiment Station Bulletin 323. 1945.

Weihing, R. M., Robertson, D. W., Coleman, O. H., and Gardner, C.: *Growing Alfalfa in Colorado,* Colorado Agricultural Experiment Station Bulletin 480. 1943.

FOUNDATION OF THE RANGE
(Page 553)

Darrow, Robert A.: *Arizona Range Resources and Their Utilization, I. Cochise County,* University of Arizona Technical Bulletin 103, pages 311–366. 1944.

McArdle, Richard E., Costello, David F., Birkmaier, E. E., and others: *III. The White Man's Toll,* In United States Forest Service, The Western Range, 74th Cong., 2d sess., Senate Document 199, pages 81–116. 1936.

PRACTICES AND PROBLEMS
(Page 557)

Carpenter, Alvin G., Clawson, Marion, and Fleming, C. E.: *Ranch Organization and Operation in Northeastern Nevada,* Nevada Agricultural Experiment Station Bulletin 156. 1941.

Cockerill, P. W., Hunter, Byron, and Pingrey, H. B.: *Type of Farming and Ranching Areas in New Mexico, Part II,* New Mexico Agricultural Experiment Station Bulletin 267. 1939.

Hunter, Byron; Cockerill, P. W., and Pingrey, H. B.: *Type of Farming and Ranching Areas in New Mexico, Part I,* New Mexico Agricultural Experiment Station Bulletin 261. 1939.

A SAVINGS ACCOUNT
(Page 560)

Doran, C. W., and Cassady, J. T.: *Management of Sheep on Range Infested with Orange Sneezeweed,* U.S.D.A. Circular 691. 1944.

Knox, J. H., and Watkins, W. E.: *The Use of Phosphorus and Calcium Supplements for Range Livestock in New Mexico,* New Mexico Agricultural Experiment Station Bulletin 287. 1942.

McCampbell, Sam C.: *Improve Your Range by Rodent Control,* Colorado State College Extension Service Circular 121–A. 1937. (Revised by J. L. Hoerner, 1945.)

McCarty, Edward C., and Price, Raymond: *Growth and Carbohydrate Content of Important Mountain Forage Plants in Central Utah as Affected by Clipping and Grazing,* U.S.D.A. Technical Bulletin 818. 1942.

Parker, Kenneth W.: *Control of Mesquite on Southwestern Ranges,* U.S.D.A. Leaflet 234. 1943.

Parker, Kenneth W.: *Southwestern Stockman—Play to Win!* U.S.D.A. AWI–74. 1943.

Pechanec, Joseph F., and Stewart, George: *Sagebrush Burning—Good and Bad,* U.S.D.A. Farmers' Bulletin 1948. 1944.

Reid, Elbert H., and Pickford, G. D.: *Judging Mountain Meadow Range Condition in Eastern Oregon and Eastern Washington,* U.S.D.A. Circular 748. 1946.

Stoddart, L. A., and Rasmussen, D. I.: *Deer Management and Range Livestock Production,* Utah Agricultural Experiment Station Circular 121. 1945.

U.S.D.A., U. S. Department of the Interior, New Mexico College of Agriculture and Mechanic Arts, and the University of Arizona: *Range and Livestock Production Practices in the Southwest,* U.S.D.A. Miscellaneous Publication 529. 1943.

Watkins, W. E.: *Composition of Range Grasses and Browse at Varying Stages of Maturity,* New Mexico Agricultural Experiment Station Bulletin 311. 1943.

Young, V. A., Doll, G. B., Harris, G. A., and Blaisdell, J. P.: *The Influence of Sheep Grazing on Coniferous Reproduction and Forage on Cut-Over Western White Pine Areas in Northern Idaho,* University of Idaho Bulletin, volume 37, No. 6. 1942.

IMPROVEMENT BY RESEEDING
(Page 564)

Bridges, J. O.: *Reseeding Practices for New Mexico Ranges,* New Mexico Agricultural Experiment Station Bulletin 291. 1942.

Glendening, George E.: *Germination and Emergence of Some Native Grasses in Relation to Litter Cover and Soil Moisture,* Journal American Society of Agronomy, volume 34, pages 797–804. 1942.

Hull, A. C., Jr., and Pearse, C. Kenneth: *How to Reseed Southern Idaho Range Lands,* Intermountain Forest and Range Experiment Station Research Paper 2. 1943.

Pickford, G. D., and Jackman, E. R.: *Reseeding Eastern Oregon Summer Ranges,* Oregon Agricultural Experiment Station Circular 159. 1944.

Plummer, A. Perry; Hurd, Richard M., and Pearse, C. Kenneth: *How to Reseed Utah Range Lands,* Intermountain Forest and Range Experiment Station Research Paper 1. 1943.

Robertson, Joseph H., and Pearse, C. Kenneth: *How to Reseed Nevada Range Lands,* Intermountain Forest and Range Experiment Station Research Paper 3. 1943.

Stark, R. H., Toevs, J. L., and Hafenrichter, A. L.: *Grasses and Cultural Methods for Reseeding Abandoned Farm Lands in Southern Idaho,* Idaho Agricultural Experiment Station Bulletin 267. 1946.

Stoddart, L. A.: *Seeding Arid Ranges to Grass with Special Reference to Precipitation,* Utah Agricultural Experiment Station Circular 122. 1946.

THE RANGE IN CALIFORNIA
(Page 575)

Adams, Frank: *The Historical Background of California Agriculture,* California Agriculture, University of California Press, Berkeley, pages 1–50. 1946.

Adams, Frank; Ewing, Paul A., and Huberty, Martin R.: *Hydrologic Aspects of Burning Brush and Woodland-Grass Ranges in California,* California Division of Forestry. 1947.

Beeson, R. W., Cronemiller, F. P., and others: *Handbook for Range Managers,* U.S.D.A., Forest Service. 1940.

Beetle, Alan A.: *Distribution of the Native Grasses of California,* Hilgardia, volume 17, No. 9, pages [309]–357. 1947.

Bentley, J. R., and Talbot, M. W.: *How Many Head? Moderate Grazing Best Range Practice for Plant Life,* Western Livestock Journal, volume 23, No. 43, pages 21, 40, 42–43. 1945.

Bidwell, General John: *Annual Address Delivered at the Annual Fair of the Agricultural Society of the Northern District of California,* Transactions of the California State Agricultural Society, 1864 and 1865, pages 202–213. O. M. Clayes, State Printer, Sacramento. 1866.

California Forestry Study Committee: *The Forest Situation in California,* Report to the Legislature, volume 2, California State Printing Office, Sacramento, pages 46–50. 1947.

California Forestry Study Committee: *The Range Livestock Industry and Forestry, The Forest Situation in California,* Report to the Legislature, California State Printing Office, Sacramento, pages 98–100. 1945.

Grover, D. I.: *Range Condition, A Classification of the Annual Forage Type in the Corning Soil Conservation District,* Soil Conservation Service, Pacific Coast Region, Portland, Oreg. 1945.

Guilbert, H. R., and Hart, G. H.: *California Beef Production,* California Agricultural College Extension Service Circular 131. 1946.

Guilbert, H. R., Hart, G. H., Wagnon, K. A., and Goss, H.: *The Importance of Continuous Growth in Beef Cattle,* California Agricultural Experiment Station Bulletin 688. 1944.

Hart, George: *Wealth Pyramiding in the Production of Livestock,* California Agriculture, University of California Press, Berkeley. 1946. (See pages 51–112).

Hormay, A. L.: *Moderate Grazing Pays on California Annual-Type Ranges,* U.S.D.A. Leaflet 239. 1944.

Horn, E. E., and Fitch, H. S.: *Interrelations of Rodents and Other Wildlife on the Range . . .,* California Agricultural Experiment Station Bulletin 663, pages 96–129. 1942.

Jones, Burle J., and Love, R. M.: *Improving California Ranges,* California College of Agriculture, Agricultural Extension Service, Circular 129. 1945.

McNutt, W. P.: *Range Condition, A Classification of the Annual Forage Type in the Pajaro Soil Conservation District,* U.S.D.A. Soil Conservation Service, Pacific Coast Region. 1945.

Reynolds, H. G., and Sampson, A. W.: *Chaparral Crown Sprouts as Browse for Deer,* Journal of Wildlife Management, volume 7, pages 119–122. 1943.

Rowe, P. B.: *Some Factors of the Hydrology of the Sierra Nevada Foothills,* American Geophysical Union Transactions of 1941, Part 1, pages 90–100. July 1941.

Sampson, Arthur W.: *Plant Succession on Burned Chaparral Lands in Northern California,* California Agricultural Experiment Station Bulletin 685. 1944.

Sampson, Arthur W.: *Effect of Chaparral Burning on Soil Erosion and on Soil-Moisture Relations,* Ecology, volume 25, pages 171–191. 1944.

Shantz, H. L.: *The Use of Fire as a Tool in the Management of the Brush Ranges of California,* California Division of Forestry. 1947.

Sprague, Malcolm: *Climate of California,* Yearbook of Agriculture 1941 (Climate and Man), pages 783–797.

Talbot, M. W., and Biswell, H. H.: *The Forage Crop and Its Management,* California Agricultural Experiment Station Bulletin 663, pages 13–49. 1942.

U. S. Forest Service: *Statistical Supplement, Report of the Chief of the Forest Service,* Washington, D. C. 1946.

Veihmeyer, F. J., and Johnson, C. H.: *Soil-Moisture Records from Burned and Unburned Plots in Certain Grazing Areas of California,* National Research Council American Geophysical Union, Transactions, Part I, pages 72–84. 1944.

Wieslander, A. E., and Jensen, Herbert A.: *Forest Areas, Timber Volumes and Vegetation Types in California,* U. S. Forest Service, California Forest and Range Experiment Station, Forest Survey Release No. 4. 1946.

Young, V. A.: *Range Condition, A Classification of the Annual Type Vegetation Found Within the Soil Conservation Districts in San Diego County, California,* Soil Conservation Service, Pacific Coast Region, Portland, Oreg. 1945.

TREES, GRASS, AND WATER
(Page 586)

Andrews, H. J., and Cowlin, R. W.: *Forest Resources of the Douglas-Fir Region,* U.S.D.A. Miscellaneous Publication 389. 1940.

Daniel, T. W., and Ensminger, M. E.: *Grazing on the Cutover Lands of Western Washington,* Washington Agricultural Experiment Station, Popular Bulletin 179. 1945.

Heisig, Carl P.: *Settlement Experience and Opportunities on Cut-Over Lands of Western Washington,* Washington Agricultural Experiment Station Bulletin 399. 1941.

Hochmuth, Harold R., and Gorton, William W.: *Ranch Organization and Range Land Use in Coos and Curry Counties, Oregon,* Oregon Agricultural Experiment Station Bulletin 381. 1940.

Ingram, Douglas C.: *Vegetative Changes and Grazing Use on Douglas Fir Cut-Over Land,* Journal Agricultural Research 43, pages 387–417. 1931.

Isaac, Leo A.: *Vegetative Succession Following Logging in the Douglas-Fir Region with Special Reference to Fires,* Journal of Forestry volume 38, pages 716–721. 1940.

Reid, Elbert H., Isaac, Leo A., and Pickford, G. D.: *Plant Succession on a Cut-Over, Burned, and Grazed Douglas-Fir Area,* Pacific Northwest Forest and Range Experiment Station, Forest Research Note 26. 1938.

WESTERN WASHINGTON
(Page 589)

Archibald, J. G., and Parsons, C. H.: *Grass Silage,* Massachusetts Agricultural Experiment Station Bulletin 425. 1945.

Forage Committee of the State College of Washington: *Clovers for Greater Production in Washington,* Washington Agricultural Extension Circular 83, revised. 1946.

Forage Committee of the State College of Washington: *Grasses for Greater Production in Washington,* Washington Agricultural Extension Circular 104. 1946.

Hegnauer, Leonard: *Alfalfa in Western Washington,* Washington Agricultural Extension Circular 18. 1932. (Revised 1941.)

Hodgson, R. E., Knott, J. C., Miller, V. L., and Wolberg, F. B.: *Measuring the Yield of Nutrients of Experimental Pastures,* Washington Agricultural Experiment Station Bulletin 411. 1942.

Law, Alvin G., and Ingham, I. M.: *Grasses for Greater Production in Western Washington—Perennial and Common (Italian or domestic) Ryegrasses,* Washington State College Extension Service Circular 80. 1944.

Law, Alvin G., and Ingham, I. M.: *Grasses for Greater Production in Western Washington—Meadow Foxtail,* Washington College of Agriculture Agricultural Extension Circular 82. 1944.

Shepherd, J. B.: *How to Put Up Wilted Grass Silage,* Guernsey Breeders Journal, pages 1117–1118. 1946.

Vandecaveye, S. C., and others: *Fertilizer Recommendations for Washington,* Washington State College Extension Service Bulletin 338, page 18. 1946.

ALASKA
(Page 607)

Alaska Agricultural Experiment Station: *Progress Report[s].* 1932–1948.

Lambert, W. V., and Aamodt, O. S.: *Agricultural Research Needed in Alaska,* Hearings before the Subcommittee of the Committee on Appropriations, House of Representatives, 80th Congress, 1st session, [U. S.] Department of Agriculture Appropriation Bill for 1948, pages 1824–1869. 1947.

Rockie, W. A.: *Physical Land Conditions in Matanuska Valley, Alaska,* U.S.D.A. Soil Conservation Service. 1946.

Sundberg, George: *Opportunity in Alaska,* The MacMillan Company, New York. 1945.

United States Department of the Interior, Division of Territories and Island Possessions: *Alaska,* Washington, D. C. 1946.

HAWAII
(Page 617)

Coulter, John W.: *Agricultural Land-Use Planning in the Territory of Hawaii, 1940,* Agricultural Extension Service, University of Hawaii, Extension Bulletin 36. 1940.

Hawaii Agricultural Extension Service: *1946 Statistics of Diversified Agriculture in Hawaii,* Hawaii University Agricultural Extension Service, Extension Circular 217. 1947.

Henke, L. A.: *A Survey of Livestock in Hawaii,* Hawaii University Research Publication 5. 1929.

Henke, L. A.: *Roughages for Dairy Cattle in Hawaii,* Hawaii Agricultural Experiment Station Bulletin 92. 1943.

Henke, L. A., Work, S. H., and Burt, W. A.: *Beef Cattle Feeding Trials in Hawaii,* Hawaii Agricultural Experiment Station Bulletin 85. 1940.

Hosaka, E. Y., and Ripperton, J. C.: *Legumes of the Hawaiian Ranges,* Hawaii Agricultural Experiment Station Bulletin 93. 1944.

Kunesh, Joseph H.: *An Historic Inventory of the Physical, Social, Economic and Industrial Resources of the Territory of Hawaii,* Hawaii Territorial Planning Board, Progress Report 1. 1939.

Parris, G. K.: *Eye-spot of Napier Grass in Hawaii, Caused by Helminthosporium sacchari,* Phytopathology volume 32, pages 46–63. 1942.

Ripperton, J. C., and Hosaka, E. Y.: *Vegetation Zones of Hawaii,* Hawaii Agricultural Experiment Station Bulletin 89. 1942.

Wilsie, C. P., Akamine, E. K., and Takahashi, M.: *Effects of Frequency of Cutting on the Growth, Yield, and Composition of Napier Grass,* Journal of the American Society of Agronomy, volume 32, pages 266–273. 1940.

Yoshida, Ruth: *A Chemical and Physiological Study of the Nature and Properties of Leucaena glauca (Koa Haole),* Proceedings of the Hawaiian Academy of Science Nineteenth and Twentieth Annual Meetings, 1943–1945. 1945. (See page 5.)

PUERTO RICO
(Page 629)

Fernandez Garcia, E., Astol, Eugenio, and Hoadley, Francis W.: *El Libro de Puerto Rico* (The Book of Puerto Rico). San Juan, P. R. 1923.

Roberts, R. C., and party: *Soil Survey of Puerto Rico,* U. S. Bureau of Plant Industry, Soil Survey, Series 1936, No. 8. 1942.

GRASS: GREEN
(Page 637)

Chase, Agnes: *First Book of Grasses,* The Macmillan Co., New York. 1922.

Dayton, W. A.: *Some Outstanding Forage Grasses of Western Cattle Ranges,* The Producer, volume 9, No. 10, pages 3–7. 1928.

Hitchcock, A. S.: *Manual of the Grasses of the United States,* U.S.D.A. Miscellaneous Publication 200. 1935.

Sampson, Arthur W.: *Native American Forage Plants,* John Wiley and Sons, Inc., New York. 1924.

WEEDS
(Page 727)

Beal, W. J.: *Michigan Weeds,* Michigan Agricultural Experiment Station Bulletin 267. 1911. (Revised by E. A. Bessey, 1915.)

Gates, Frank C.: *Weeds in Kansas,* Kansas State Board of Agriculture Report, volume 60, number 243. Topeka, Kans. 1941.

Georgia, Ada E.: *A Manual of Weeds,* The Macmillan Co., New York. 1935.

Pammel, L. H.: *Weeds of the Farm and Garden,* Orange Judd Co., New York. 1911.

Pammel, L. H.: *The Weed Flora of Iowa,* Iowa Geological Survey Bulletin 4, revised edition. 1926.

Pieters, A. J.: *What is a Weed?* Journal of the American Society of Agronomy, volume 27, pages 781–783. 1935.

Robbins, W. W., Bellue, Margaret K., and Ball, Walter S.: *Weeds of California,* State Department of Agriculture, Sacramento, Calif. [1941.]

Robbins, Wilfred W., Crafts, Alden S., and Raynor, Richard N.: *Weed Control, a Textbook and Manual,* McGraw-Hill Book Company, Inc., New York. 1942.

Sampson, Arthur W.: *Native American Forage Plants,* John Wiley & Sons, Inc., New York. 1924.

BAMBOO
(Page 735)

Anonymous: *Bamboo Pulp; Its Possibilities for Rayon Manufacture,* Fibres, volume 8, pages 82–84. March 1947.

Josephson, H. R.: *Pulpwood Stands, Procurement, and Utilization: VII. Pulpwood Supplies of the United States,* Technical Association of the Pulp and Paper Industry, TAPPI Monograph Series, No. 4. New York. 1947.

Young, Robert A.: *Bamboos for American Horticulture,* National Horticultural Magazine, volumes 24 and 25. 1945–46.

NOTE.—Index by MABEL H. DOYLE, Chief, L. LOUISE CROUSE, and LAURA B. LANE, Indexing Section, Office of Information.